THE ENGLISH NOVEL
1740-1850

THE ENGLISH NOVEL

1740-1850

A CATALOGUE INCLUDING PROSE ROMANCES, SHORT STORIES, AND TRANSLATIONS OF FOREIGN FICTION

by

ANDREW BLOCK

With introductions by

JOHN CROW, M.A.

Lecturer in English at University of London, King's College

AND

ERNEST A. BAKER, M.A., D.LIT.

1961

DAWSONS OF PALL MALL

London

First published 1939.

New and revised edition 1961.

PRINTED IN GREAT BRITAIN BY ROBERT STOCKWELL LTD., LONDON, ENGLAND.

INTRODUCTION TO THE
SECOND EDITION

WE know the party-line well enough. " Life is short and there's so much art about that we have no time for the second-rate. Out of the window with your Priestley, your Wilkie Collins, your *Diary of a Nobody*; buckle down to *Pudd'nhead Wilson* and *Hard Times.*

> You will not obtain employment
> From *our* County Education
> If you talk about *enjoyment;*
> What we want's evaluation.

Don't let me catch you *enjoying* books again." It's splendidly arid and splendidly priggish. But the great writer is the abnormal, and it might be argued that you'll learn more from the study of the typical than from the study of the eccentric. If you pore over the works of Shakespeare, you can learn much about the workings of the great artistic mind; if you wish to be better informed about the " spirit of the age," you turn to the minors, to the Grub-street hack, to the garret-boy who can yark up a pamphlet in a couple of hours and can get together with four others of his kind to knock out a quickie topical play about the latest scandal or murder. Probing into the abnormal psychology of a genius brings its reward; but the other task of learning the history of taste can't be despised as an inferior discipline.

Andrew Block's agreeable check-list appeals to many kinds of reader. It is right, one supposes, to say first that it is an indispensable tool in the hand of the book-collector, the librarian, the bookseller, the research student and the supervisor of research students. That needs no discussion: the proof lies in the way that the first edition of the pudding was received. It was published, it was bought, it ran out of print, its secondhand price soared almost uncontrollably, it insisted on being reprinted. As a work of reference, Block's book needs to hire no trumpeter.

You can use the book for much more than the rapid finding of the wanted fact. It deserves a reading for its own sake. The world of fiction is the world of dream; with Block as guide we may walk through a section that seems at times to be the world

v

of nightmare. There is a signpost in the book's first entry: *The Abbess of St. Hilda. A Dismal, Dreadful, Horrid Story.* An inch or two lower we have the *Moral Tales and Histories* of the Reverend John Adams. Later in the book, *The Juvenile Adventures of Miss Kitty F . . . r* rubs slimy shoulders with Henrietta Louisa Farrer's *Baby's Baptism.*

When we stare at Block's list, we transport ourselves by some Wellsian machine into another century, into another world. Here are the monks and the baronets and the horrid castles. We may read of *The Affecting History of Louise, The Wandering Maniac. A Real Tale of Woe.* Of *Almager & Claude, or Monastic Murder.* Of *The Bleeding Nun, or, Raymond and Agnes* (would he be the same person as the one in *Nobility Run Mad, or, Raymond and His Three Wives?*). Or *The Female Pilgrim, or Deserted Wife. By the author of The Midnight Horrors, Spectre Mother, &c.* And who would not be allured by the book that gives " a Curious and Voluptuous History " of " luscious intrigues of Sir Edward Walford . . . with some Ticklish Songs "? Will not the readers of Conan Doyle rejoice in such Holmesian titles as *The Deformed Mendicant, The Observant Pedestrian, The Idiot Heiress* and *The Birmingham Counterfeit?*

A different taste must have been catered for by the authors of such books as *In What Manner Little Henry came to the Knowledge of God;* as *Frederick, or, Incidents Illustrative of the Beauties and Graces of Vital Piety in the Domestic Circle.* Or something so nakedly didactic as *Ashford Rectory, or, The Spoiled Child Reformed, with a short introduction to the science of Architecture and Heraldry.*

The entries which disturb me most and delight me most are those which seem to defy explanation. What *can* we expect to find in *Gustavus, or, The Macaw?* In *The Mental Novelist and Amusing Companion;* in *Jane Hudson, the American Girl, or, Exert Yourself;* in *The Observant Pedestrian, or, A Donkey Tour to Brighton;* in *Lucy, or, " I will not be naughty again, Papa ";* in *Says She to Her Neighbour, What? By an Old-fashioned Englishman;* in *Memoirs of a Social Monster, or, The History of Charles Price;* or in *The Sailor Boy, or, The Admiral and His Protegee?*

We are given a Pisgah-sight of the strangest world. Even if we wish not to enter it for a serious visit, we can be happy in studying it in the pages of Block's alluring Baedeker.

We are accustomed to think back, sighing, to the great good old days of English fiction. We muse on the giants of a former age. We forget that the mighty mountains—Austen, Scott, the Brontes, Dickens, Thackeray—soared out of the dismal swampy plain of the innumerable military novels, naval novels, Irish novels, dirty novels, horrid novels of the Block list. And, nastiest of all surely, the Grub-street fictional journalism that wore the mask of piety. The good old days were little better than our own bad modern days. Then, as now, some tolerable work was published. Then, as now, the great bulk of published fiction was the utterest trash. We can perhaps find cause for rejoicing that it was actually out of this swampy plain that the mountains did soar—and nourish the hope that, out of our plain, new mountains may soar to-morrow.

Block's list, rightly looked at, gives us the *data* for a chapter in the history of taste. Those were the books our forefathers were given; those, we must assume, were the books which our forefathers demanded. We cannot sneer at them; and they can hardly sneer at us. Our taste is not their taste and we think that their taste was bad. It was no more than the product of a fashion. It is good that we should be given the opportunity of musing that our taste too must prove a passing thing, that the " great books " of to-day will be forgotten items in the check-lists of to-morrow. And that the " final judgements " of to-day's puritanical critical pontiffs will melt into air when the fashions change.

But I do not want to start a course of sermons on Block's book. May I sum up by saying that it seems to me to be a useful work of reference for the shelves of many different kinds of people; that it is a valuable guide when it leads us to the libraries where lie the books it lists; that it is also something which, because of the entertainment and instruction which it provides, deserves to be read for its own sake?

JOHN CROW.

INTRODUCTION TO THE
FIRST EDITION

MR. BLOCK has achieved, not a thankless task, for he has deserved and will have the applause of those living and to come, whose gratitude he will consider an ample recompense for his years of labour. But the task he has now brought to a conclusion is one that only an unselfish and devoted worker, who asks for no other return than the joy of labouring for a chosen army of fellow-toilers, would ever have taken in hand. For many years it has been borne in upon me how urgently such a catalogue as this is needed. Personally, I have wanted it badly; and innumerable inquiries from all parts of the world have had to go meagrely or entirely unanswered through its non-existence. But now, with Esdaile's invaluable bibliography coming down from the beginnings to the eve of *Pamela*, the day when literature was in labour of the modern novel, and this worthy supplement going on to the period which is still our own, we shall be fully equipped, and no reasonable or indeed unreasonable question will be left unanswerable. My own gratitude to Mr. Block and my warmest congratulations are only an earnest of what he will doubtless receive, or be sure that though unspoken they are felt and transmitted in the spirit, from countless students and scholars whom he has made his staunch friends.

ERNEST A. BAKER, 1939.

$\sqrt{}$ PREFACE

In this compilation each title-page is transcribed from the earliest edition I have been able to trace: in cases where it is known to be other than a first edition the fact is mentioned.

All translations are listed under the original author, where known: when the author's name is not available the book will be found under the name of the translator, or, if that also in unknown, under the title.

The arrangement throughout is strictly alphabetical. Where the author's Christian names or initials are unknown the entry is inserted (whether with or without a prefix) *before* the same surname with initials; e.g. Ffoulkes, Mr., would precede Ffoulkes, Araminta. Books by anonymous or pseudonymous authors are listed under their title in due order, sub-title being included in the alphabetical arrangement, which takes account of all words except the articles *a, an,* and *the:* where the title is in a foreign language, however, it has been found more convenient to include the articles also in the alphabetical arrangement.

Frontispieces and other illustrations are mentioned where they occur, but it has been considered inadvisable to state specifically when they are coloured since it is in many cases difficult to determine whether they were originally issued in colour or coloured by hand after publication.

If any difficulty is found in tracing a book in the main text application should be made to the Index of Titles.

I wish to make grateful acknowledgments to the following for the assistance they have given me in my researches:

The American Antiquarian Society; Mr. Algar; Dr. E. A. Baker; Miss D. Blakey; Mr. John Bligh; *The Book Trade Journal;* the British Museum; Mr. F. J. Brown; Dr. P. L. Carver; *The Clique,* Ltd.; The Court Book Shop; Mr. Herbert Cutner; Mr. A. I. Ellis; Mrs. M. L. G. Ewen-Munden; Mr. Hugh W. Fennell; Dr. F. S. Ferguson; Mr. A. Filcek; Mr. H. M. Fletcher; Mr. Maurice Buxton Forman; Mr. John Gawsworth; Mr. James Glaisher; Mr. E. W. Goepel; Miss Mollie Green; Peter Murray Hill Ltd.; the Huntington Library; Mr. Roger Ingpen; Mrs. W. H. Ingram; Mr. Raphael King; Mr. E. J. E. Law; Messrs.

McLeish & Sons; Mr. Martin A. McGoff; Mr. Ernest Maggs; Mr. A. Margery; Mr. W. A. Marsden; Mr. G. Meredith; *The Observer;* Mr. Barry Ono; Mr. E. A. Osborne; Mr. R. A. Peddie; *The Publisher's Weekly;* Bernard Quaritch, Ltd.; Mr. Arthur Rogers; Messrs. W. T. Spencer; Mr. C. A. Stonehill; Mr. R. Stotesbury; the University of London Library; Mr. R. W. G. Vail; Mrs. Elizabeth Villiers; Mr. George Ward; and Mr. Lyle H. Wright.

ANDREW BLOCK.

LONDON,
January, 1939-1960.

LIST OF SOURCES, IN THE FORM USED IN THE TEXT

Algar. (Bookseller.)
Allibone. (*A Critical Dictionary of English Literature*, by S. A. Allibone.)
American Art Association.
Anderson Galleries. (New York.)
Ashbee Collection. (British Museum.)
Ashley Lib. (Ashley Library.)

B. M. (British Museum.)
Backus, E. (Booksellers.)
Bailey Bros. (Booksellers.)
Baker, Dr. E. A.
Baker's Bookshop.
Barnard, P. M.
Bates, Geo.
Bates, H.
Berry's "Journal," Miss.
Bibliot. Brit. (Bibliotheca Britannica.)
Bibliothèque de l'Enfer. (Bibliothèque des Curieux.)
Biographical Dict. Eng. Lit.
Birrell and Garnett. (Booksellers.)
Blackwell. (Booksellers.)
" Blackwood's Edin. Mag."
" Blackwood's Mag."
Blakey. (Dorothy Blakey's *Minerva Press*.)
Bligh, John.
Block, Andrew.
Bod. Lib. (Bodleian Library.)
" Bookworm."
Borrow Head Bookshop.
Broadbent, Noel. (Bookseller.)
Brough. (Bookseller.)
Brown, F. J.
Brown, W. (Bookseller.)
Brown's " Godwin," F. K.
Brussel, I. R. (Bookseller.)
Bumpus Exhibition.
Burl, R. W. (Bookseller.)
Burton's Arab. Nts. (Burton's *Arabian Nights.*)
Butland. (Bookseller.)

Camb. Hist. Eng. Lit. (*Cambridge History of English Literature.*)
Carter, John.
Carver, Dr. P. L.
Carver and Staniforth. (Booksellers.)
Cat. Lib. Prohib. (*Catalogus Librorum Prohibitorum.*)
Chambers' Cyclop. Eng. Lit. (*Cyclopædia of English Literature.*)

Chambers, F.
Chave, Mr.
Clarke-Hall. (Bookseller.)
Cleverdon, D. (Bookseller.)
Cohn. (*Cruikshank.*)
Colbeck. (Bookseller.)
Colvin, Ian.
Combridges. (Booksellers, Hove.)
Commin, J. G. (Booksellers.)
Cooper, Ernest. (Bookseller.)
Copinger, H. B. (Bookseller.)
Court Book Shop.
Cremen.
" Critic."
Cross, Wm.
Crowe. (Bookseller.)
Cuttelle, P. C. (Bookseller.)

D.N.B. (Dictionary of National Biography.)
Dahl, Dr. F.
Danielson. (Bookseller.)
Davey, H. and J. (Booksellers.)
David, G. (Bookseller.)
Davies, H. W.
Dawson, A. H.
" Denmark in Eng. and Amer. Lit."
Dobell. (Bookseller.)
Dulau. (Booksellers.)

" Edin. Mag." (Edinburgh Magazine.)
Edwards, Francis. (Booksellers.)
Ellis. (Booksellers.)
"Eng. Cat." (*English Catalogue* or *London Catalogue.*)
Eng. Lit. in Germany. (*The Publication of English Literature in Germany in the Eighteenth Century.*)
" European Mag."
Evans, E. J. (Bookseller.)
Ewen-Munden, Mrs. M. L. G.

Fennell, H. W. (Bookseller.)
Filcek, A.
Fletcher, H. M. (Bookseller.)
Fletcher, Kyrle. (Bookseller.)
Fletcher, W. (Bookseller.)
Forman, M. Buxton.
Foyle. (Booksellers.)
Frampton, R. S. (Bookseller.)

Galloway. (Bookseller.)
" Gentleman's Mag."
George's Sons. (Booksellers.)

Start, Henry. (Booksellers.)
Stonehill. (Booksellers.)
Storey. (Booksellers.)
Stotesbury, R.
" Sweden Year Book."

" Tait's Edin. Mag." (*Edinburgh Magazine.*)
Thorp, T. (Booksellers.)
" Times " and " Times Literary Supplement."
" Town and Country Mag."
Tregaskis. (Booksellers.)
Turner, A. V.

" Univ. Mag." (*Universal Magazine.*)

Vail, R. W. G. (Librarian.)
Varda. (Booksellers.)
Victorius. (Bookseller.)
Villiers, Mrs. Elizabeth.

Ward, Geo.
Webster, T. D. (Bookseller.)
" Westminster Mag."
Wheatley, H. B.
Whyte, Bernard. (Bookseller.)
Williams, Iolo.
Woore. (Bookseller.)
Worthington, G.
Wright, Lyle H. (Librarian.)

Young, Henry. (Booksellers.)

Abbess of St. Hilda (The). A Dismal, Dreadful, Horrid Story. Frontispiece. London N.D. [Murray Hill.]

Abbess of Shaftesbury (The) ; or, The Days of John of Gaunt. London, Rivington, 1846. [B.M. : *Eng. Cat.*]

Abbey of Weyhill. 2 vols., London, A. K. Newman [1804] [Publisher's advert. : Blakey.]

Abbotsmere ; or, illustrations of home education, by Mary Gertrude, author of " Philip Randolph, a tale of Virginia." London, Whittaker, 1846. [B.M. : *Eng. Cat.*]

Abdiel : A Tale of Ammon. With a woodcut frontispiece and vignette. London, James Burns, 1842. [B.M.]

Abduction (The) ; or, The Adventures of Major Sarney ; A Story of the Times of Charles the Second. 3 vols., London, Charles Knight, 1825. [B.M. : Publisher's advert.]

A'Beckett, Gilbert Abbott, [Edited by]. The Table Book. With 12 etchings and 100 woodcuts by George Cruikshank. London, Punch Office, 1845. [Sotheran.]

Abel-Remusat, M. Iu-Kiao-Li : or, the Two Fair Cousins. A Chinese Novel. From the French Version of M. Abel-Remusat. 2 vols., London, Hunt and Clarke, 1827. [B.M. : Ingpen : Publisher's advert.]

Abou Ali, Mohammed, Ben Ali, Ben Hassan Ebn Moclah. Al Kalomeric, The Son of Maugraby : An Arabian Tale. Now first faithfully Translated from the Original MSS. Discovered since the taking of Paris by the Allied Powers of Europe, and replete with Marvellous Coincidences ! London, J. Ginger, 1814. [B.M. : *European Mag.* : *Quarterly Review.*]

Absent Man (The), A Narrative, Edited by Sir Peter Plastic, Knight of the Order of the Tower and Sword. London, Baldwin, Cradock, and Joy, 1817. [B.M. : *New Monthly Mag.*]

Abstract (The), a Character from Life. 3 vols., 1796. [*New Ann. Reg.*]

Academy (The) ; or, A Picture of Youth. With a frontispiece. London, J. Harris ; and Darton and Harvey ; and W. Berry, Edinburgh, 1808. [B.M.]

Acceptance (The). 3 vols., 1810. [*Monthly Mag.*]

Accomplished Hypocrite (The) ; or Brass glitters more than Gold. A Moral Tale, Founded on Facts. By A. D. 2

vols., London, A. K. Newman, 1882 [B.M.]

Account of Barbarossa (An), the Usurper of Algiers, being the Story on which the tragedy [by J. Brown] is founded, now in rehearsal at Drury Lane. London, 1755. [B.M.]

Ackfield, Emma. The Intellectual Family. A Tale. With a frontispiece. Colchester, J. Brackett ; London, Simpkin Marshall, 1847. [B.M.]

Acton, Eugenia de. The Discarded Daughter. 4 vols., London, Minerva Press, 1810. [*Bibliot. Brit.* : Blakey.]

—— The Nuns of the Desert ; or, The Woodland Witches. 2 vols., London, Minerva Press, 1805. [*Bibliot. Brit.* : Stonehill.]

—— A Tale without a Title : Give it what you Please. With a frontispiece. 3 vols., London, Minerva Press, 1804. [*Bibliot. Brit.* : Stonehill.]

Actress of the Present Day (The). 3 vols., London, James Harper, 1817. [B.M. : *New Monthly Mag.*]

Adams, Ann. Convent Tales, During the Reigns of Henry the Eighth of England, Louis the Sixteenth of France, Napoleon Buonaparte, &c. &c., Interspersed with Notices from History. By a Protestant Lady. With a frontispiece. London, F. C. Westley, 1838. [B.M.]

Adams, C. P. Cressingham ; Or, The Missionary. London, Joseph Masters, 1846. [B.M.]

Adams, Charlotte. The Child of the Atlantic. With a frontispiece and vignette. London, John W. Parker, 1839. [B.M.]

—— The Etonian, And Geoffrey Selwood. With a frontispiece. London, L. Booth, 1841. [B.M.]

—— William Woodland. With a frontispiece. London, Society for Promoting Christian Knowledge, 1845. [B.M.]

Adams, Rev. John. Moral Tales and Histories. London, 1791. [*Bibliot. Brit.*]

—— Popular Moral Tales. London, 1808. [*Bibliot. Brit.*]

Adams, Rev. William. The Distant Hills. With a woodcut border to each page. London, Rivington, 1844. [B.M.]

—— The Shadow of The Cross. With a woodcut border to each page. London, Society for Promoting Christian Knowledge, 1842. [B.M.]

Addison, Julia. The Curate of Wildmere. A Novel. 3 vols., London, Thomas Cautley Newby, 1847. [B.M.]

Adelaide ; or, Conjugal affection. From the French. [W. Lane, 1785.] [Blakey.]

Adelaide de Narbonne. With Memoirs of Charlotte de Cordet. A tale. By the author of Henry of Northumberland. [Helen Craik]. 4 vols., London, Minerva Press, 1800. [Stonehill : Blakey : *Minerva Press Catalogue.*]

Adelfrida. 4 vols., 1792. [*New Ann. Reg.*]

Adeline, or, the Grave of the Forsaken. London, Lloyd [c. 1840]. [J. Glaisher : Hollings : B. Ono.]

Adeline ; or the Orphan. A novel. 3 vols., London, W. Lane, 1790. [Ingpen.]

Adkins, W. The Hortorian Miscellany, being a Collection of Original Poems, Tales. 1768. [*Bibliot. Brit.*]

Adlerjung. A Series of Tales from a Preceptor to his Pupils, written for the Instruction of Youth of both Sexes, from the German, by William Wennington, 1811. [Allibone : *Bibliot. Brit.*]

Adonia. A Desultory Story. Inscribed, by permission to Her Grace the Duchess of Buccleugh. 4 vols., London, A. and J. Black and H. Parry ; and Bell and Bradfute, Edinburgh, 1801. [B.M. : Ingpen.]

Adultress (The), or Anecdotes of Two Noble Families. A Tale by an Englishwoman. 4 vols., London, Printed for the Author, 1810. [Ingpen : *Monthly Mag.*]

Adventure of the Hunch Back (The), and the Stories connected with it. With 17 engravings by W. Daniell after R. Smirke. London, Hurst, 1814.

Adventurers (The) ; or, Scenes in Ireland, in The Reign of Elizabeth. 3 vols., London, Longman, Hurst, Rees, Orme, Brown, and Green, 1825. [B.M. : *Edin. Mag.* : *I. in F.*]

Adventures in Borneo. A Tale of Shipwreck. London, Colburn, 1849. [*Eng. Cat.* : Lond. Lib.]

Adventures in the Moon and Other Worlds. London, Longman, Rees, Orme, Brown, Green and Longman, 1836. [B.M. : Ingpen.]

Adventures, Intrigues, and Amours of a Lady's Maid ; Written by herself. Never before published. With illustrations. London, J. Ryder, 1822. [*Cat. Lib. Prohib.*]

Adventures of Alonzo : containing some Striking Anecdotes of the present Prime Minister of Portugal. 2 vols., London, J. Bew, 1775. [Ingpen.]

Adventures of an Author (The). Written by Himself and a Friend. 2 vols., London, Robinson and Roberts, 1767. [H. W. Davies.]

Adventures of a Black Coat (The), containing a Series of Remarkable Occurences and Entertaining Incidents that it was a Witness to in its Peregrinations through the Cities of London and Westminster. London, J. Williams and J. Burd, 1760. [W. Brown : Pickering : Murray Hill.]

Adventures of the Celebrated Little Thomas Dellow (The), Who was Stolen from his Parents on the 18th of November, 1811, & Restored to Them on the 3rd of January, 1812. With 8 copper plates, a woodcut, and a vignette. London, William Darton, 1812. [Mollie Green.]

Adventures of Charles Villars, an Unfortunate Court Dependent. 2 vols., 1766. [W. Brown : *Eng. Lit. in Germany.*]

Adventures of a Colonist ; or Godfrey Arabin The Settler. London, John and A. Darling, [1845 ?] [B.M.]

Adventures of Congo in Search of His Master (The). A Tale, containing a True Account of a Shipwreck. London, Harris, 1832. [*Eng. Cat.* : Arthur Rogers.]

Adventures of a Cork-screw (The) ; In which, Under the pleasing method of a Romance, The Vices, Follies and Manners Of the Present Age are exhibited and satirically delineated. Interpersed with Striking Anecdotes, Characters and Actions Of Persons in Real Life ; All drawn to promote Virtue, expose Vice, and Laugh Folly out of Countenance, London, T. Bell, 1775. [B.M. : W. Brown : Ingpen.]

Adventures of Dick Hazard (The). London, W. Reeve, 1755. [B.M. : Pickering.]

Adventures of Emmera (The) ; Or, the Fair American. Exemplifying the peculiar advantages of society and retirement. 2 vols., London, 1767. [W. Brown.]

Adventures of a Fly (The). With a frontispiece. London, James Burns, 1847. [B.M.]

Adventures of Frank Hammond. 1754. [W. Brown.]

Adventures of Gabriel Tangent (The). 3 vols., London, J. F. Hughes. [Publisher's advert., 1806.]

Adventures of George Maitland, Esq. (The). 3 vols., London, J. Murray, 1786. [B.M.]

Adventures of a Gold-finder. Written by himself. 3 vols., London, Henry Colburn, 1850. [B.M.]

Adventures of a Gold-Headed Cane. 2 vols., 1783. [W. Brown.]

Adventures of Grimmalkin (The), the eldest Son of Dame Trot's cat. With 10 engravings. London, Tabart, 1808. [Gumuchian.]

Adventures of a Halfpenny (The) ; Commonly called a Birmingham Halfpenny, or Counterfeit ; As related by itself. With woodcuts. Banbury, J. G. Rusher, [1835]. [B.M.]

Adventures of Henry Fitzherbert, Gentleman (The). London, 1794. [B.M.]

Adventures of Jack Smart (The). London, S. Crowder and H. Woodgate, 1756. [Pickering.]

Adventures of a Kidnapped Orphan (The). London, M. Thrush, 1747. [B.M.: W. Fletcher : Stonehill.]

Adventures of the Little Girl in the Wood (The). With woodcuts. London, J. Harris, 1808. [B.M. : Dobell.]

Adventures of Madiboo (The), a native of the Pellew Islands. London, 1809. [B.M.]

Adventures of Marmaduke Midge (The), The Pickwickian Legatee. With woodcuts. London, Vickers, N.D. [Stonehill.]

Adventures of Master Headstrong and Miss Patient (The), in their Journey towards the Land of Happiness. London, Harris. [Guardian of Education.]

Adventures of Michailow, a Russian Captive, among the Kalmucs, Kirghiz, and Kievenses. Written by Himself. London, Sir Richard Phillips, 1822. [Elkin Mathews.]

Adventures of Miss Beverly (The). Interspersed with genuine memoirs of a Northern Lady of Quality. 2 vols., London, S. Bladon, 1768. [B.M.]

Adventures of Miss Lucy Watson (The). A novel. London, 1768. [B.M.]

Adventures of Monsieur Provence (The), Being a Supplement to the Englishman's Fortnight at Paris. Translated from the French. 2 vols., London, G. Kearsley, 1787. [W. Brown : Lyle H. Wright.]

Adventures of Mr. Loveill (The), Interspers'd with many Real Amours of the Modern Polite World. 2 vols., London, M. Cooper, 1750 . [W. Brown : Arthur Rogers.]

Adventures of Musul ; or, the three gifts. With other tales. By M. J. Horne. London, J. Bonsor, 1800. [B.M.]

Adventures of Naufragus. Written by Himself. London, Smith, Elder, 1827. [Ingpen.]

Adventures of an Ostrich Feather of Quality (The). London, Sherwood, Neely, and Jones, 1812. [B.M. : Dobell : Pickering.]

Adventures of Patrick O'Donnell (The). In his Travels through England and Ireland. Written by Himself. London, J. Williams, 1763. [Pickering (2nd edn.)]

Adventures of Philip Quarll (The), The English Hermit; Who was discovered by Mr. Dorrington On an Uninhabited Island, Where he had lived Upwards of Fifty year. With a folding frontispiece by George Cruikshank. London, Hodgson, [1823]. [B.M. : Huntington.]

Adventures of a Poor Beggar (The) ; Or The Vicissitudes of Life. With woodcuts. London, T. Bell, [1820]. [B.M.]

Adventures of a Post Captain (The). London. Johnston, 1817. [Eng. Cat. : New Monthly Mag.]

Adventures of a Schoolboy (The). With a frontispiece. London, William Jackson, 1826. [B.M.]

Adventures of a Sergeant in the French Army. Written by Himself. London, Henry Colburn, 1826. [Publisher's advt.]

Adventures of a Silver Penny. Including many Secret Anecdotes of Little Misses and Masters both Good and Naughty. London, Newbery. [1787]. [Guardian of Education : Nat. Mag. Co.]

Adventures of a Silver Three-Pence (The). Written by Mr. Truelove. With woodcuts. London, J. Harris, [1800 ?]. [B.M.]

Adventures of A Soldier (The) ; or, Memoirs of Edmond Costello. London, 1841. [B.M.]

Adventures of Sylvia Hughes, Written by herself. London, 1761. [B.M.]

Adventures of Thomas Eustace (The). By a Clergyman. London, Hatchard, 1820. [B.M.]

Adventures of a Turk (The). Translated from the French. 2 vols., London, J. Coote, 1758. [J. C. Hardy.]

Adventures of a Vagabond (The). A Romance. With woodcuts. London, Lloyd, [c. 1848]. [B.M. : Stonehill.]

Adventures of a Valet (The). Written by Himself. 2 vols., London, J. Robinson, 1752. [Court Bookshop.]

Adventures of a Watch (The) ! London, G. Kearsley, 1788. [W. Brown : Norman : Pickering.]

Adventures of a Whipping-Top (The). Illustrated With Stories of many Bad Boys, who themselves deserve Whipping, And Of some Good Boys, who deserve Plum-cakes. Written by Itself. With woodcuts. London. [John Marshall, 1780 ?]. [B.M.]

Adventures of a Young Rifleman, In the French and English Armies, during the War in Spain and Portugal from 1806 to 1816. Written by Himself. London, Henry Colburn, 1826. [Bailey Bros. : B.M. : Ingpen.]

Aesop. Æsop's Fables : A New Version, Chiefly from Original Sources. By The Rev. Thomas Jeans. With illustrations by John Tenniel. London, John Murray, 1848. [B.M.]

Affecting History of the Duchess of C * * * *, who was confined nine years in a horrid dungeon. With a frontispiece. London, [1820 ?]. [B.M.]

Affecting History of an Inn-keeper in Normandy (An). Together with a tragical story, on the unhappy consequences of an immoderate attachment to riches. London, [1780 ?]. [B.M.]

Affecting History of Louisa (The), The Wandering Maniac. A Real Tale of Woe. With a frontispiece. 1804. [Arthur Rogers.]

Affecting History of Tom Bragwell (The), wherein are strikingly delineated the rise, progress, and fatal termination of juvenile delinquency. Haddington, 1821. [B.M.]

Affecting History of Two Young Gentlewomen (The), who were ruined by their excessive attachment to the amusements of the town. To which are added many practical notes, by Dr. Typo, P.T.M. London, 1780. [B.M.]

Affecting Narrative of Peggy and Patty Summers ... Lord Racket, etc. Frontispiece. London, N.D. [Murray Hill.]

Affectionate Orphans (The). London, [1797]. [B.M.]

Agatha ; Or, A Narrative Of Recent Events. A Novel. With Vignette Titles by Stothard. 3 vols., London, Printed for the Author, 1796. [B.M. : Ingpen : *New Ann. Reg.*]

Age We Live In (The). A Fragment. Dedicated to Every Young Lady of Fashion. London, Lackington, Allen, 1813. [*Quarterly Review.*]

Agent and His Natural Son (The). A New and True Story with important strictures on the Commander in Chief ; Relative to his Duties and his Confidants, by an Inhabitant of Craig's Court. London, Hughes, 1808. [G. Worthington.]

Agg, John. Edwy and Elgiva, An Historical Romance Of The Tenth Century. 4 vols., London, C. Chapple, 1811. [*Bibliot. Brit.* : B.M. : *Quarterly Review.*]

—— Eighteen Hundred and Fifteen : A Satirical Novel. By Humphry Hedgehog, Esq. Author of " A Month in Town "—" The General Post Bag," " Rejected Odes, &c., &c." 3 vols., London, James Johnston, 1816. [Block : B.M. : *New Monthly Mag.*]

—— Macdermot, a Novel. 3 vols., 1810 [*Bibliot. Brit.*]

—— A Month At Brussels, A Satirical Novel. By the Author of " A Month in Town," " Rejected Odes," " General Post Bag," &c. &c. 3 vols., London, M. Iley, 1815. [B.M. : Marks : Stonehill.]

—— A Month in Town. A Satirical Novel, by Humphry Hedgehog, Esq. Author of " The General-Post Bag," " Rejected Odes," &c. &c. &c. London, J. Johnston, 1815. [Block : B.M. : Ingpen.]

—— The Pavilion ; or, a Month in Brighton. A satirical novel. 3 vols., London, 1817. [B.M.]

—— The Royal Sufferer ; Or, Intrigues At the Close of the Eighteenth Century. A Fashionable Novel. Interspersed with Anecdotes, Connected with The British Court. 3 vols., London, Printed by E. Thomas, for George Hughes, 1810. [*Bibliot. Brit.* : B.M. : *Quarterly Review.*]

Agg, John. Secret Memoirs of an Illustrious Princess. 3 vols., London, 1813. [*Bibliot. Brit.*]

Agitation ; Or, Memoirs Of George Woodford and Lady Emma Melvill. A Novel. By the Author of the Ring, and the False Friends. 3 vols., London, J. Barker, 1788. [Fletcher.]

Agnes Morton ; or, the Idolatry of the Heart. By the author of " The Bread of Deceit." London, 1847. [B.M.]

Agnes. A novel. By the author of Frederica Risberg. 3 vols. [W. Lane, 1801]. [Blakey : T. D. Webster.]

Agnes, a tale founded on facts. By a Lady. London, Chatfield and Wild, 1829. [B.M.]

Agnew, Eleanor C. Geraldine : A Tale of Conscience. By E. C. A. 3 vols., London, Booker and Dolman, 1837. [B.M. : Martin A. McGoff.]

—— Rome and the Abbey : The Sequel to, and by the Author Of Geraldine : A Tale of Conscience. London, James Burns, 1849. [B.M.]

—— Tales Explanatory of The Sacraments. By the Authoress of Geraldine, A Tale of Conscience, And, the Young Communicants. 2 vols., London, C, Dolman, 1846. [B.M. : Lond. Lib.]

Aguilar, Grace. The Days of Bruce. A Story. London, Groombridge, 1834. [*Eng. Cat.* : *Guide to Best Fiction.*]

—— Home Influence ; A Tale for Mothers and Daughters. 2 vols., London, R. Groombridge, 1847. [B.M.]

—— A Mother's Recompense, a Tale. London, Groombridge, 1850. [*Biographical Dict. Eng. Lit.* : *Eng. Cat.*]

—— Records of Israel. London, John Mortimer, 1844. [B.M.]

—— The Vale of Cedars ; Or, The Martyr. A Story of Spain in the Fifteenth Century. With a frontispiece. London, Groombridge, 1850. [B.M. *Guide to Best Fiction.*]

—— Woman's Friendship ; A Story Of Domestic Life. With a frontispiece. London, Groombridge, 1850. [B.M.]

Aiken, Miss. Lorimer, A Tale. London, Henry Colburn, 1814. [B.M. : Publisher's advert.]

Aikin, Dr. John, and **Barbauld,** Mrs. Evenings at Home ; or the Juvenile Budget Opened : Consisting of A Variety of Miscellaneous Pieces for the Instruction and Amusement of Young Persons. With 32 engravings. London, J. F. Dove, N.D. [Block (New edn.)]

Ailzie Grierson : or, a Tale of a Prisoner. By a Lady. Edinburgh, 1846. [B.M.]

Aimwell, Miss. Good-Nature : or, Sensibility : and other Tales. 3 vols., London, A. K. Newman, 1822. [B.M.]

Ainslie, John. Antipathy, Or The Confessions of a Cat-Hater. 3 vols., London, John Macrone, 1836. [B.M.]

4

Ainslie, John. Aurungzebe ; Or, A Tale of Alraschid. 3 vols. London, Cochrane and McCrone, 1833. [B.M.]

—— Ernest Campbell. 3 vols., London, James Cochrane, 1835. [B.M. : G. Worthington.]

Ainsworth, William Harrison. Auriol. Fragment of a Romance. 1850. [Arthur Rogers.]

—— Crichton. 3 vols., London, Richard Bentley, 1837. [Block : B.M. : Ingpen.]

—— December Tales. London, G. and B. Whittaker, 1823. [Block : B.M. : Locke.]

—— Guy Fawkes ; Or, The Gunpowder Treason. An Historical Romance. With 22 etchings by George Cruikshank. 3 vols., London, Richard Bentley, 1841. [B.M. : F. Harvey : Locke.]

—— Jack Sheppard. A Romance. With a portrait and 27 plates by George Cruikshank. 3 vols., London, Richard Bentley, 1839. [B.M. : Maggs : Marks.]

—— James the Second ; Or, The Revolution of 1688. An Historical Romance. Edited [or rather written] by W. Harrison Ainsworth. With frontispieces by R. W. Buss. 3 vols., London, Henry Colburn, 1848. [B.M. : Dobell : Publisher's advert.]

—— The Lancashire Witches. A Novel. London, Printed for Private Circulation only, 1849. [B.M. : W. Fletcher : Maggs.]

—— The Miser's Daughter : A Tale. With 20 etchings by George Cruikshank. 3 vols., London, Cunningham and Mortimer, 1842. [B.M. : Locke : T. Thorp.]

—— Old Saint Paul's : A Tale of The Plague and the Fire. With 20 illustrations by John Franklin. 3 vols., London, Hugh Cunningham, 1841. [B.M. : King : Locke.]

—— Rookwood : A Romance. 3 vols., London, Richard Bentley, 1834. [B.M. : Locke.]

—— Saint James's : Or, The Court of Queen Anne. An Historical Romance. With 9 etchings by George Cruikshank. 3 vols., London, John Mortimer, 1844. [B.M. : Locke.]

—— Sir John Chiverton. A Romance. London, John Ebers, 1826. [B.M. : F. Harvey : *Quarterly Review.*]

—— The Tower of London, A Historical Romance. With 40 etchings and 58 woodcuts by George Cruikshank. London, Richard Bentley, 1840. [B.M. : Maggs : Marks.]

—— Windsor Castle : An Historical Romance. With frontispieces by George Cruikshank. 3 vols., London, Henry Colburn, 1843. [B.M. : Noel Broadbent : Locke.]

Aird, Thomas. The Old Bachelor In The Old Scottish Village. Edinburgh, 1845. [Arthur Rogers.]

Akerman, John Yonge. London Legends. By Paul Pindar, Gent. 2 vols., London, Richard Bentley, 1842. [B.M.]

—— Tales of Other Days. By J. Y. A. With illustrations by George Cruikshank. Engraved by J. Thompson and S. and T. Williams. London, Effingham Wilson, 1830. [B.M. : Marks : A. V. Turner.]

Aladdin ; Or, The Wonderful Lamp. A New and Correct Edition With 4 plates. London, Printed for the Booksellers, 1816. New Juvenile Library. [B.M.]

Aladdin ; Or, the Wonderful Lamp. An Eastern Tale. A New Edition. Corrected, and adapted for Juvenile Readers of the present time. By a Lady. With a folding frontispiece. London, Dean and Munday ; and A. K. Newman, [1840 ?] [B.M.]

Alan Gilbert's Last Birthday. By the Author of " The Boy's Week-day Book." London, Thomas Ward, 1837. [Publisher's advert.]

Albani ; Or The Murderer of his Child. Containing the Different Views of his Character, As a Libertine in Palermo, An Officer in the Spanish Service, A Planter in the Island of Cuba, And an Independent Gentleman, On his return to Italy. London, Tegg and Castleman ; T. Hurst ; T. Brown, Edinburgh ; and B. Dugdale, Dublin, [1803]. [B.M. : Stonehill.]

Albany. A Novel. By the Author of Beau Monde, &c. &c. &c. 3 vols., London, Printed at the Minerva Press, for A. K. Newman, 1819. [B.M.]

Albert de Nordenshild : or, The Modern Alcibiades. A Novel. Translated from the German. 2 vols., London, Robinson, 1796, [Ingpen.]

Albina. A novel. In a series of letters. 2 vols. [W. Lane, 1786]. [Blakey.]

Alcoforado, Marianna. Letters From a Portuguese Nun To An Officer In the French Army. Translated by W. R. Bowles. With a frontispiece. London, S. A. and H. Oddy ; and C. La Grange, 1808. [B.M.]

Alderman and Peer, or Ancient Castle and Modern Villa. 3 vols. 1809. [Cawthorn's Catalogue.]

Alemán, Mateo. The Life and Adventures of Guzman D'Alfarache Or The Spanish Rogue. Translated from the excellent French Edition of Mons. Le Sage. By John Henry Brady. 2 vols., London, Printed by P. Pigott, for the Translator, 1821. [B.M.]

—— Pleasant Adventures of Gusman, Of Alfarache. Taken from the History of his Life, And Translated from the Spanish into French, By M. Le Sage, Translated from the French, By A. O'Conner. 3 vols., London, Allen, 1812. [B.M.]

Alemán, Mateo. The Spanish Rogue, Or, The Life of Guzman de Alfarache. Giving an Exact Account of all his Witty and Unparalel'd Rogueries. In two Parts. London, Thomas Smith, [1790]. [B.M.]

Alexander, Mrs. Cecil Francis,—The Baron's Little Daughter, and other Tales in Prose and Verse, By the Author of "The Lord of the Forest and his Vassals." Edited by William Gresley. With 3 illustrations. London, J. Masters, 1848. [B.M.: Sotheran.]

Alexander, Gabriel. The Bottle; or, The Drunkard's Career. With woodcuts, London, Dicks, [1848.] [Publisher's advert.: Stonehill.]

—— The Fair Maid of Wyoming. A Tale of the War of Independence. London, James Steward, 1846. [B.M.]

—— Lilias, The Milliner's Apprentice. With woodcuts by W. H. Thwaits. London, Dicks, [c. 1850]. [Stonehill.]

—— Robert Bruce, The Hero-King of Scotland. With woodcuts by W. H. Thwaits. London, Dicks [c. 1840]. [Stonehill.]

—— Wallace: The Hero of Scotland. With 36 illustrations. London, Dicks, 1848. [Publisher's advert.]

Alexander, James. The Witty Parson And the Twelve Highwaymen: A Narrative Moral and Entertaining; In which are introduced Two seasonably witty and uncommonly well-applied Sermons, Delivered to the Banditti with strange effect, By the Rev. and facetious Mr. Dodd of Dedham. The whole expanded and improved. To which is added A Remarkable Story Of Three Penitent Criminals. By the Author of "The Orthographic English 'Ladder'," a Spelling-book on an improved Construction, just published, &c. &c. With a frontispiece. Cork, Henry Denmead, 1811. [B.M.]

Alexander, Judith. The Young Lady of Fortune, Or her Lover Gained by Stratagem. A Novel. 2 vols., London, Printed for the Author by L. Alexander, 1789. [B.M.]

Alexander, William. The Juvenile Gleaner: Or, Anecdotes and Miscellaneous Pieces; Designed for Amusement & Instruction. By the Author of A Brief Historical Catechism of the Holy Scriptures; &c. &c. York, W. Alexander, 1825. [B.M.]

Alexandrians (The); An Egyptian Tale Of the Fourth Century. 2 vols., London, Whittaker, Treacher, 1830. [B.M.: *New Monthly Mag.*]

Alexena ; or, The Castle of Santa Marco. Illustrated. London, A. K. Newman, 1817. [Blakey.]

Alexis, The Tyrant of the East. A Persian Tale. London, Henry Colburn, 1812. [Pickering: *Quarterly Review.*]

Alfred and Cassandra. A romantic tale. By the author of The School of Virtue. 2 vols. [W. Lane, 1788]. [Blakey.]

Alfred Dudley ; Or, The Australian Settlers. With plates. London, Harvey and Darton, 1830. [B.M.: E. Hector.]

Alfred; Or, The Effects of True Repentance. By the Author of "The Better Part." London, Simpkin, Marshall, 1837. [B.M.]

Alice Grant, the Two Cousins, and the Fair Day. London, Harvey, 1835. [B.M.]

Alice Home ; or, the revenge of the blighted one. A romance. London, [1848]. [B.M.]

Alice Leighton ; or, The Murder at the Druid's Stones. With woodcuts. London, Caffyn, [c. 1850]. [Stonehill.]

Alicia and her Aunt, or Think before you speak. A Tale for Young Persons. With a frontispiece and an engraved title-page. London, A. K. Newman, 1822, [Gumuchian.]

Alidia and Cloridan ; Or, the Offspring of Bertha. A Romance of former Times. 2 vols., London, N. L. Pannier, 1811. [B.M.]

Alithea Woodley, or the advantages of an early friendship founded on virtue. Bath, [1820 ?]. [B.M.]

All for Love, or The World Well Lost. A New Romance, founded entirely on Fiction. London, R. Freeman, 1762. [Ingpen.]

"All is not Fable "; a tale, novel, grave dissertation, or romance, as it is at each reader's option to consider it. [London ?] [1830 ?]. [B.M.]

Allan, John Hay, and **Stuart,** Charles. Tales of the Century Or Sketches of the Romance of History Between the years 1746 and 1846. By John Sobieski and Charles Edward Stuart. With a frontispiece. Edinburgh, James Marshall; London, Charles Dolman, 1847. [B.M.]

Allan, William. Haslan Gheray: A Narrative Illustrative of the Subject of a Painting. With a frontispiece. Edinburgh, John Robertson, 1817. [B.M.]

Allan McDougal, Or, Scenes in the Peninsula. A Tale. By a Military Officer. 3 vols., London, A. K. Newman, 1831. [B.M.]

Allen, Rev. J. The Widow's Daughter. A Narrative. London, Barr; W. F. Pratt, Howden, 1842. [B.M.]

Almagro & Claude ; Or Monastic Murder; Exemplified In the Dreadful Doom Of an Unfortunate Nun. London, Tegg and Castleman; T. Hurst; T. Brown, Edinburgh; and B. Dugdale, Dublin, [1810 ?]. [B.M.]

Almira ; Or, the History Of a French Lady of Distinction. Interspersed with the Histories of the Marquis de Montalvan; Isabella: Lindamira, Or, the Belle Espagnol, &c. &c. In Four Books. London, Ann and Charles Corbett, 1758. [B.M.]

Almoner (The) ; or Sketches of Scottish Poor. Edinburgh, William Oliphant, 1825. [Block.]

Alphonso and Elinor, Or the Mysterious Discovery. With a frontispiece. London, J. Ker, 1800. [B.M. (This copy has no frontispiece) : Stonehill.]

Alpine Tale (An) : Suggested by Circumstances which Occurred towards the Commencement of the Present Century. By the Author of " Tales from Switzerland." 2 vols., London, Francis Westley and L. B. Seely, 1823. [B.M. : *New Monthly Mag.*]

Altoban : a minor tale. By Omicron. London, 1828. [B.M.]

Alve ; or Infidelity. A Tale of the World. 5 vols., 1822. [*European Mag.*]

Always Happy ! ! ! Or, Anecdotes of Felix and his sister Serena. A Tale. Written for her children, by a Mother. With a frontispiece. London, John Harris, 1814. [B.M. : *Eng. Cat.*]

Ambrose Ward ; or, the Dissenter reclaimed. A tale for the times. London, Cleaver, 1844. [B.M. : *Eng. Cat.*]

Amelia, or, The Distress'd Wife : A History Founded on Real Circumstances. By a Private Gentlewoman. London, Printed for the Authoress, 1751. [B.M.]

Ames, I., The Tragical History Of Walwyn and Avreola ; Containing in it A Rare Example of True Constancy. London, Houlston and Stoneman, 1839. [B.M.]

Amicable Quixote (The), or the Enthusiasm of Friendship. 4 vols., London, 1788. [B.M. : John Orr : Tompkins.]

Ammorvin and Zallida, a Novel. [By Mary Charlton]. [W. Lane]. 1798. [*Eng. Lit. in Germany* : Blakey.]

Amorous Intrigues and Adventures of Don Ferdinand and Donna Marie (The). Ferdinand's Intrigue with the Innkeeper's Wife. Catalien's Amour with Ferdinand. Donna Marie's Intrigue. Curious Adventures of the Duke and Duchess of Storza. London, Printed for the Booksellers, [1820]. [*Cat. Lib. Prohib.*]

Amorous Letters between Miss Loveman and Miss Longfart. 3 Parts in 1 volume. With 6 plates. Paris [London], 1789. [*Cat. Lib. Prohib.*]

Amorous Quaker (The). Or Cupids Miscellany. Printed for Lovers of Venus. With 6 illustrations. London, N.D. [*Cat. Lib. Prohib.*]

Amory, Thomas. The Life of John Buncle, Esq ; Containing Various Observations and Reflections, Made in Several Parts of the World ; And Many extraordinary Relations. 2 vols., London, [Vol. I] J. Noon, 1756. [Vol. II] J. Johnson and B. Davenport, 1766. [B.M. : Ingpen : Arthur Rogers.]
—— Memoirs : Containing the Lives of several Ladies of Great Britain. A History of Antiquities, Productions of Nature, and Monuments of Art . . . In Several Letters. Volume 1 [all published] London, 1755. [T. D. Webster.]

Amours and Adventures of Charles Careless, Esq. Interspersed with a Variety of Curious and entertaining Anecdotes drawn from real life. Written by himself. 2 vols., 1764. [Backus.]

Amours and Adventures of Miss Kitty N——, London, Noble's Library, [1760].

Amours of Lais ; or the Misfortunes of Love. London, M. Folingsby, 1766. [B.M.]

Amphlett, J. Ned Bentley, a Novel. 3 vols., Stafford, J. Drewry, 1808. [Murray Hill.]

Amram, A Tale of Bagdad. London, John Richardson, 1837. [B.M.]

Amurath, Prince of Persia. An Arabian Tale. With a frontispiece. London, G. Walker, 1815. [B.M. : *New Monthly Mag.*]

Amusement in High Life. London, G. and A. Greenland, 1840. [B.M.]

Amusements in High Life ; Or, Conjugal Infidelities in 1786. In a Series of Confidential Letters, Between Ladies who have distinguished themselves by the Multiplicity and Singularity Of their Amours. London, G. Lister, 1786. [B.M.]

Amusing Stories : a collection of histories, adventures, and anecdotes. Dublin, 1824. [B.M.]

Amy : Or, Love and Madness. A Romance. With woodcuts. London, E. Lloyd, 1847. [B.M. : Stonehill.]

Amy Ray. By the author of " Hours of Childhood." London, 1848. [B.M.]

Amyotts' Home (The) ; Or, Life in Childhood. By the Author of " Life's Lessons," " Tales that might be true," etc. London, Groombridge, 1850. [B.M.]

Ancient Highland Story of the Robbers of the Forest (The). Stirling, [1820?]. [B.M.]

Andersen, Hans Christian. A Christmas Greeting To my English Friends. London, Richard Bentley, 1847. [B.M. : Marks : E. A. Osborne.]
—— Danish Fairy Legends And Tales. [Translated by Caroline Peachey.] London, William Pickering, 1846. [B.M. : E. A. Osborne : Arthur Rogers.]
—— A Danish Story-Book. Translated by Charles Boner. With illustrations by Count Pocci. London, Joseph Cundall, 1846. [B.M. : *Denmark in Eng. and Amer. Lit.* : R. Hall.]
—— The Dream Of Little Tuk, And other Tales. Translated by Charles Boner. With 4 illustrations by Count Pocci. London, Grant and Griffith, 1848. [B.M. : *Denmark in Eng. and Amer. Lit.*]
—— The Improvisatore, or Life in Italy, From the Danish of Hans Christian Andersen. Translated by Mary Howitt.

2 vols., London, Richard Bentley, 1845. [Colbeck : *Quarterly Review* : Arthur Rogers.]

Andersen, Hans Christian. The Nightingale and other Tales. Translated by Charles Boner. With illustrations by Count Pocci. London, Joseph Cundall, 1846. [B.M. : *Denmark in Eng. and Amer. Lit.*]

—— Only a Fiddler. Translated from the Danish. 2 vols., London, H. G. Clarke, 1845. [G. Worthington.]

—— The Shoes of Fortune, And other tales. With illustrations by Otto Speckter. London, Chapman and Hall, 1847. [B.M.]

—— Tales for the Young. A New Translation. With illustrations. London, James Burns, 1847. [B.M.]

—— Tales from Denmark, Translated by Charles Boner. With 50 illustrations by Count Pocci. Grant, 1847. [*Eng. Cat.* : Pickering.]

—— Two Baronesses. A Romance. 2 vols., London, Bentley, 1848. [*Eng. Cat.* : Lond. Lib. : Arthur Rogers.]

—— Wonderful Stories For Children. By Hans Christian Anderson. Translated from the Danish by Mary Howitt. With illustrations. London, Chapman and Hall, 1846. [B.M. : *Camb. Hist. Eng. Lit.* : *Denmark in Eng. and Amer. Lit.*]

Anderson, Andreas. Mental Recreations, Four Danish and German Tales. London, 1807. [*Bibliot. Brit.*]

Anderson, John. Chronicles of the Kirk ; or Scenes and Stories from the History of the Church of Scotland from the Earliest Period to the Second Reformation. London, Houlston. [Allibone : *Eng. Cat.*]

Anderson, Walter. History of Croesus, King of Lydia. Edinburgh, 1755. [W. Brown.]

Anderson, William. Odd Sketches, By the Author of " Poetical Aspirations." Edinburgh, Joseph Skeaf, 1831. [B.M.]

Andrews, Dr. Augusta ; or, The female travellers. A novel. 3 vols. [W. Lane, 1788]. *Minerva Press Catalogue* : Blakey.]

Anecdotes for Good Children, being Select Pieces intended to Amuse and Instruct them. With woodcuts. Banbury, [1810]. [King.]

Anecdotes of a Convent. By the Author of Memoirs of Mrs. Williams. 3 vols., London, T. Becket and P. A. de Hondt, 1771. [B.M. : Francis Edwards : Tregaskis.]

Anecdotes of a Croat. London, Sherwood, Neely, and Jones, 1821. [B.M.]

Anecdotes of Kings, selected from history ; or, Gertrude's stories for children. London, John Harris, 1837. B.M.]

Anecdotes of a Little Family, Interspersed with Fables, Stories, and Allegories, Illustrated with Suitable Morals For Children of different Ages, and both Sexes. With plates. London, E. Newbery, [1800 ?]. [B.M.]

Anecdotes of Mary ; or, the Good Governess. By the author of the History of the Davenport Family. London, 1795. [B.M.]

Angelica's Ladies Library ; Or, Parents and Guardians Present. With plates after Angelica Kauffman and H. Bunbury. London, J. Hamilton ; and Mrs. Harlow, 1794. [B.M. : T. Thorp.]

Angelicus and Fergusia, A Tale. London, J. Johnson, 1761. [B.M.]

Angeline ; Or, Sketches from Nature : A Novel. 3 vols., London, Kerby, Lindsell and King, 1794. [B.M. : Ingpen : *New Ann. Reg.*]

Angelo Guicciardini ; or, the Bandit of the Alps. A romance. By Sophia Frances, author of Vivonio. 4 vols., London, H. Colburn, 1809. [B.M.]

Angels' Work ; or the Choristers of St. Mark, and two other tales. London, J. H. Parker, 1848. [B.M. : *Eng. Cat.*]

Anglo-Saxon Version of the Story of Apollonius of Tyre (The), Upon which is founded The play of Pericles, Attributed to Shakespeare ; From a MS. in the Library of C.C.C. Cambridge. With a Literal Translation, &c. By Benjamin Thorpe. London, John and Arthur Arch, 1834. [B.M.]

Animated Skeleton (The). 2 vols., London, William Lane, 1798. [Blakey.]

Anley, Charlotte. Influence ; A Moral Tale For Young People. By a Lady. 2 vols., London, A. J. Valpy, 1822. [B.M. : Arthur Rogers.]

—— Miriam ; Or, The Power of Truth. A Jewish Tale. By the Author of " Influence." London, John Hatchard, 1826. [B.M. : A. Muirhead.]

—— The Prisoners of Australia. A Narrative. By the Author of " Miriam," " Influence." " Essay on Body, Soul, and Spirit," &c. &c. London, J. Hatchard, 1841. [Allibone : B.M.]

Ann and Ellen and the little Kitten. 1832. [B.M.]

Ann Dale, or False Appearances. London, 1848. [B.M.]

Ann Melville. 2 vols. [W. Lane, 1792]. [Blakey.]

Annals of Administration (The). Containing the genuine history of Georgiana, the Queen Mother and Prince Colonius her son. Inscribed to Edmund Burke. London, 1775. [B.M.]

Annals of Humble Life. London, John Miland, 1840. [B.M.]

Annals of Orlingbury. 2 vols., London, 1815. [*New Monthly Mag.*]

Anne of Brittany ; an Historical Romance. 3 vols., 1810. [*Monthly Mag.* : *Quarterly Review.*]

Annesley, James. Memoirs of an Unfortunate Young Nobleman, Return'd from a Thirteen Years' Slavery in America. Where he had been sent by the Wicked Contrivances of his Cruel Uncle. A Story founded on Truth, and address'd equally to the Head and Heart. 3 vols., London, J. Freeman, 1743-1747. [Block : Ingpen : Pickering.]

Annette. London, The Religious Tract Society, [1847]. [B.M.]

Annie Sherwood ; or Scenes at School. London, [1847]. [B.M.]

Annie Walton. A tale from real life. London, 1850. [B.M.]

Anonymous Letters (The). London, Saunders and Otley, 1839. [B.M.]

Anslijn, Nicolaas. The Good Boy Henry Or The Young Child's Book of Manners. Translated from the Dutch by John Ingram Lockhart. With a frontispiece. London, Groombridge, 1849. [B.M.]

Anti-Pamela : Or, Feign'd Innocence Detected ; In a Series of Syrena's Adventures. A Narrative which has really its Foundation in Truth and Nature ; and at the same time that it entertains, by a vast variety of surprizing Incidents, arms against a partial Credulity, by shewing the Mischiefs that frequently arise from a too sudden Admiration. Published as a necessary Caution to all Young Gentlemen. London, J. Huggonson, 1741. [B.M. : *Eng. Lit. in Germany* : Huntington.]

Ants (The) : A Rhapsody. With a Frontispiece and Illustrations. 2 vols., London, L. Davis and C. Reymers ; T. Davies ; and R. Baldwin, 1767. [B.M. : Ingpen.]

Anwyl, Edward Trevor. Reginald Trevor ; or, the Welsh Loyalists. A Tale of the Seventeenth Century. 3 vols., London, A. K. Newman, 1829. [Blackwell : B.M.]

—— Tales of Welshland and Welsherie. By The Author of Reginald Trevor, Youth of Edward Ellis, &c. 2 vols., London, A. K. Newman, 1831. [B.M. : Ingpen : G. Worthington.]

Apel, A. The Original Legend Of Der Freischütz Or The Free Shot. Translated From the German of A. Apel. London, A. Schloss, 1833. [B.M.]

Apostate's Progress (The), From the Kingdom of Christ, The Path of Righteousness, and the Joys of Religion, To the Dominions of Satan, The Road to Misery, and the Sorrows Of Hell, Under the Similitude of a Dream, And Interspersed with Poetical Remarks. Wisbech, Printed and Sold for the Editor by Henry Leach, 1825. [B.M.]

Apparition (The) : A Romance. With woodcuts. London, Edward Lloyd, 1846. [B.M. : B. Ono : Stonehill.]

Appeal of Madame La T — — — — (The). To The Publick Being a short Account of her Life and Amours Written by Herself. London, T. Paris, 1741. [Block.]

Appearance and Principle ; Or, A Sketch Of Three Young Ladies at School, and In Subsequent Life. With a frontispiece. London. The Religious Tract Society, [1847]. [B.M.]

Appenzeller. Gertrude de Wart ; or, Fidelity until Death. Translated from the Original German of Appenzeller. London, Longman, Rees, Orme, Brown, and Green. 1826. [B.M.]

Appleton, Elizabeth. Edgar : A National Tale. 3 vols., London, Printed for Henry Colburn, 1818. [*Bibliot. Brit.* B.M. : *New Monthly Mag.*]

Appointed Hour (The), a Romance of Venice. London, Lloyd, [1848]. [Noel Broadbent.]

Apprentice Turned Master (The) ; Or, the Second Part of the Two Shoemakers. Shewing How James Stock from a Parish Apprentice became a creditable Tradesman. With a woodcut. London, J. Marshall, and R. White, [1796]. Cheap Repository. [B.M. : Court Bk. Shop.]

Apuleius, Lucius. Cupid and Psyche, a Mythological Tale, from the Golden Asse of Apuleius. [Translated by Hudson Gurney.] London, 1799. [*Bibliot. Brit.* : Marks.]

—— The Fable Of Cupid and Psyche, Translated from the Latin of Apuleius [by Thomas Taylor] : To which are added, A Poetical Paraphrase On the Speech of Diotima, In the Banquet of Plato ; Four Hymns, &c. &c. With an Introduction, In which the Meaning of the Fable is unfolded. London, Printed for the Author, 1795. [*Bibliot. Brit.* : Birrell and Garnett : B.M.]

—— The Loves of Cupid and Psyche : In Verse and Prose. From the French of La Fontaine. To which are prefix'd a Version of the same Story from the Latin of Apuleius. With a new life of La Fontaine, extracted from a Great Variety of Authors. The whole illustrated with Notes. By Mr. Lockman. London, H. Chapelle, 1744. [McLeish : Marks : Arthur Rogers.]

—— The Metamorphosis, Or Golden Ass, And Philosophical Works Of Apuleius. Translated from the Original Latin, By Thomas Taylor. London, Robert Triphook ; and Thomas Rodd, 1822. [Block : B.M. : Francis Edwards.]

Arabian Letters. 1788. [W. Brown.]

Arabian Nights' Entertainments. Selected and Revised for general use. To which are added Other Specimens of Eastern Romance. With woodcuts. 2 vols., London, James Burns, 1847. Select Library Edition. [B.M. : *Critic.*]

Arblay, Madame d' (*see* D'ARBLAY).

Arborleigh : A Fiction, By J. C. S. With a vignette. Reading, John Snare, 1845. [B.M.]

Arbuthnot, Archibald. Memoirs of the remarkable life and suprizing adventures of Miss Jenny Cameron, a Lady, who by her Attachment to the Person and Cause of the Young Pretender, has Render'd herself Famous by her Exploits in his Service. London, R. Walker. 1746. [*Eng. Lit. in Germany* : Norman.]

Archdeacon, Matthew. Connaught, A Tale of 1798. Dublin, Printed for M. Archdeacon, 1830. [B.M. : *I. in F.*]

—— Everard : an Irish Tale of the 19th Century. 2 vols., Dublin, Printed for M. Archdeacon by J. Taafe, 1835. [*I. in F.*]

—— Legends of Connaught, Irish Stories, &c. &c. By the Author of " Connaught in 1798." Dublin, John Cumming, 1839. [B.M.]

—— Shawn Na Soggarth, the Priest Hunter : an Irish Tale of the Penal Times. With a frontispiece. Dublin, James Duffy, 1844. [*I. in F.* : T. Thorp.]

Archer, E. A. Saragossa ; or, The Houses of Castello and De Arno. A Romance. 4 vols., London, A. K. Newman, 1825. [B.M.]

Archer, Thomas. Mems. of America, And Reminiscences At Home and Abroad ; A Series of Tales. Illustrated by Robert Cruikshank. London, J. W. Southgate, [1839]. [B.M.]

—— Richard of England ; or, The Lion King ! With plates. London, F. Hextall, 1842. [B.M. : H. W. Fennell.]

—— Roderick Dhu, Clan-Alpine's Chief ; Or, The Scottish Outlaw. A Romance. With woodcuts. London, Hextall and Wall, 1843. [B.M.]

Aretino, Pietro. The Accomplished Whore. Translated by Mary Wilson. London, [Cannon], 1827. [*Cat. Lib. Prohib.*]

Argentine. An Auto-Biography. London, Smith, Elder, 1839. [B.M.]

Argentum : Or, Adventures Of A Shilling. London, J. Nichols, 1794. [B.M.]

Argus, Arabella. The Adventures Of A Donkey. With a frontispiece. London, William Darton, Jun., 1815. [B.M. : Gumuchian : Arthur Rogers.]

—— Further Adventures Of Jemmy Donkey ; Interspersed with Biographical Sketches Of The Horse. With a frontispiece and vignette. London, William Darton, 1821. [B.M. : Gumuchian.]

—— The Juvenile Spectator ; Being Observations On the Tempers, Manners, and Foibles of Various Young Persons, Interspersed With such lively Matter, as it is presumed will amuse as well as instruct. With plates. London, W. and T. Darton, 1810. [B.M. : Dobell : Arthur Rogers.]

—— Ostentation and Liberality. A Tale. With plates. 2 vols., London, William Darton, 1821. [B.M.]

Argus : The House-Dog at Eadlip. Memoirs In a Family Correspondence. By the Author of Constance and The Pharos. 3 vols., London, T. Hookham, 1789. [B.M. : Ingpen : Stonehill.]

Ariel, or the Invisible Monitor. [By Mrs. Isaacs]. 4 vols., London, Minerva Press, 1801. [*Eng. Lit. in Germany* : Arthur Rogers : Blakey.]

Aristrocrat (The), a Novel. 2 vols., 1799. [*New Ann. Reg.*]

Aristomenes : A Grecian Tale. With frontispieces. 2 vols., London, Robert Tyas, 1838. [B.M.]

Arley ; or the Faithless Wife. A Novel. 2 vols., London, 1790. [B.M.]

Arlincourt (*see* D'ARLINCOURT.)

Armitage, Robert. Doctor Hookwell ; Or the Anglo-Catholic Family. 3 vols., London, Richard Bentley, 1842. [B.M. : *Critic* : Elkin Mathews.]

—— Ernest Singleton. By the Author of " Dr. Hookwell." 3 vols., London, Richard Bentley, 1848. [B.M.]

—— Penscellwood Papers. 2 vols., 1846. [Lond. Lib.]

Armourer's Daughter (The). Or, the Border Riders. A Novel. 3 vols., London, Thomas Cautley Newby, 1850. [B.M.]

Armstrong, James Leslie. Pretty Tales For Pretty People ; Or, Pictures of Life. Designed chiefly for The Perusal of Young Persons. With a frontispiece. Halifax, William Milner, 1848. [B.M.]

—— Scenes in Craven ; in A Series of Letters. York, 1835. [B.M.]

Armstrong, Leslie. The Anglo-Saxons ; Or, The Court of Ethelwulph. A Romance. 4 vols., London, Printed at the Minerva Press, for Lane, Newman, 1806. [*Bibliot. Brit.* : B.M.]

Arnaud, Baculard d' (*see* D'ARNAUD).

Arnold, Lieut. The Irishmen ; a military-political novel, wherein the idiom of each character is carefully preserved, and the utmost precaution constantly taken to render the ebullitionary phrases, peculiar to the sons of Erin, inoffensive as well as entertaining. By a native officer. 2 vols., London, Minerva Press, 1810. [Blakey.]

—— Lucky Escapes ; or, Systematic Villany. A novel. By the author of The British Admiral, &c. London, Printed at the Minerva-Press, for Lane, Newman, and Co., 1809. [Blakey : Cawthorn's Catalogue.]

Arnold, Samuel James. The Creole ; or, The Haunted Island. 3 vols., London, Whittingham, 1796. [*Bibliot. Brit.* : B.M. : Stonehill.]

Arnold, Thomas. Dramatic Stories. 3 vols., London, Henry Colburn and Richard Bentley, 1832. [B.M. : Ingpen.]

Arnold, or a Trait and its Consequences of Civil War, a Novel. 2 vols., 1809. [Cawthorn's Catalogue.]

Arnold Zulig : A Swiss Story. By the Author of Constance, Pharos, and Argus. Dublin, 1790. [D. Webster.]

Arouet de Voltaire (see VOLTAIRE).

Arpasia ; or, The wanderer. A novel. By the author of The Nabob. 3 vols., London, William Lane, 1786. [Blakey.]

Arthur Benson ; or, the Five Senses. London, 1849. [B.M.]

Arthur Frankland : or, the Experiences of a tragic poet. A tale. London, Saunders and Otley, 1848. [B.M. : Eng. Cat.]

Arthur Seymour. 2 vols., London, Longman, Hurst, Rees, Orme, Brown, and Green, 1824. [B.M. : Ingpen.]

Artless Lovers, a Novel in a Series of Letters from Miss Lucy Wheatley in town to Miss Annabel Grierson in the Country. 1769. [Eng. Lit. in Germany.]

Arulia ; or, The victim of sensibility. A novel. By a young lady. 2 vols. [W. Lane, 1790.] [Blakey.]

Arvendel, or Sketches in Italy and Switzerland. London, Nisbet, 1826. [Eng. Cat. : Quarterly Review.]

Arville Castle. An Historical Romance. 2 vols., London, R. Crosby ; and T. White, 1795. [B.M. : D. Webster.]

Ashby, Edward. Annette of Yverdon ; or, Modern Switzerland, and other poems, with tales in prose. London, 1829. [B.M.]

Ashe, Captain Thomas. The Liberal Critic, or, Memoirs of Henry Percy, conveying a correct estimate of the manners and principles of the present times. 3 vols., London, 1812. [Bibliot. Brit. : Quarterly Review.]

—— The Soldier of Fortune ; an historical and political romance. 2 vols., London, Sherwood, 1816. [B.M. : Eng. Cat. : New Monthly Mag.]

—— The Spirit of " The Book " ; Or, Memoirs of Caroline, Princess of Hasburgh. A Political and Amatory Romance. Edited by Thomas Ashe. 3 vols., London.—Allen, 1811. [B.M. : Ingpen : A. Margery.]

Ashe, Trevor Lloyd. The Attorney ; or, The Contrast. With a frontispiece. London, Ackerman, 1844. [I. in F.]

Ashworth, Rev. John Harvey. Hurstwood : A Tale of the Year 1715. 3 vols., London, Longman, Hurst, Rees, Orme, Brown, and Green, 1823. [B.M.]

Aspasia ; Or, The Dangers of Vanity : A French Story, Taken from real life. 2 vols., London, J. Bew, 1791. [B.M. : McLeish.]

Assembly of Birds (The). An Instructive Fable, for Little Boys and Girls ; to which is added an amusing dialogue. With 10 woodcuts. Chelmsford, I. Marsden, [1815]. Gumuchian.]

Asteria and Tamerlain ; or, The Distressed Lovers. [D. Webster.]

Astolfo's Journey to the Kingdom of the Moon. The History of Prince Fatal, etc. [1825 ?] [B.M.]

Astonishing History (The) and Adventures of Betsey Warwick, the Female Rambler. A Tale, founded on Fact. With a frontispiece. Birmingham, Martin and Hunter, N.D. [Court Booksop.]

Astrologer (The) : A Legend of the Black Forest. By a lady. 2 vols., London, Saunders and Otley, 1846. [B.M. : Critic.]

Atherstone, Edwin. The Sea-Kings in England. An Historical Romance of the Time of Alfred. By The Author of " The Fall of Nineveh." 3 vols., Edinburgh, Robert Cadell ; and Whittaker, Treacher, and Arnot, London, 1830. [B.M.]

Atkins (?), Lady. The Hermit, a Novel By a Lady. 1769. [Eng. Lit. in Germany.]

Atkins, Sarah. Grove Cottage ; and the India cabinet opened. By the author of " Fruits of Enterprise." London, J. Harris, 1838. [B.M. (new edn.)]

Atkinson, Charles. The Life and Adventures Of An Eccentric Traveller. With Engravings. York, Printed for the Author by M. W. Carrall, 1818. [B.M. : Huntington : Arthur Rogers.]

Atkinson, James. The Aubid : an Eastern Tale. 1820. [New Monthly Mag.]

Atrocities of a Convent, or, the Necessity of Thinking for Ourselves, exemplified in the History of a Nun. 3 vols., London, Clio Rickman, 1808. [W. T. Spencer.]

Aublay, Madame. The Young Child's Moralist ; or, The Two Little Brothers, With 2 Plates. London, Printed for J. Nunn by B. McMillan, 1827. [B.M.]

Auction (The) : A Modern Novel. 2 vols., London, T. Lownds, 1760. [Baker's Bookshop.]

Auerbach, Berthold. Village Tales From The Black Forest. Translated from the German by Meta Taylor. With 4 illustrations by John Absolon. London, David Bogue, 1847. [Allibone : B.M. (This copy has a general title dated 1846) : Publisher's advert.]

Augusta Denbeigh ; A Novel. 3 vols., London, William Lane, 1795. [Blakey.]

Augusta Fitzherbert, or Anecdotes of Real Characters. 2 vols., 1796. [New Ann. Reg.]

Augusta ; Or, The Dependent Niece : In Letters. 2 vols., London, T. Vernor, 1788. [B.M.]

Augustus Fitz-George, a Romance of Yesterday. 3 vols., 1832. [Metropolitan Mag.]

Augustus ; Or, The Ambitious Student. London, Baldwin, Cradock, and Joy, 1820. [B.M.]

Aulnois (see D'ALUNOIS).

Aulnoy (see D'AULNOIS).

Aunt and Niece. A novel. 2 vols., London, Lane, Newman, 1804. [Blakey.]

Aunt Harding's Keepsake ; or the Two Bibles. London, [1848]. [B.M.]

Aunt Henry's Stories. London, [1849] [B.M.]

Aunt Martha Or The Spinster. London, Saunders and Otley, 1843. [B.M.]

Austen, Jane. Emma : A Novel. By the author of " Pride and Prejudice," &c. &c. 3 vols., London, John Murray, 1816. [B.M. : Huntington : Arthur Rogers.]

—— Mansfield Park : A Novel. By the Author of " Sense and Sensibility," and " Pride and Prejudice." 3 vols., London, T. Egerton, 1814. [Huntington : Lib. of Congress : Maggs].

—— Northanger Abbey : And Persuasion. By the Author of " Pride and Prejudice," " Mansfield-Park," &c. With Biographical Notice of the Author. 4 vols., London, John Murray, 1818. [B.M. : Huntington : Lib. of Congress.]

—— Pride and Prejudice : A Novel. By the Author of " Sense and Sensibility." 3 vols., London, T. Egerton, 1813. [Huntington : Lib. of Congress : Arthur Rogers.]

—— Sense and Sensibility : A Novel. By a Lady. 3 vols., London, Printed for the Author, by C. Roworth, 1811. [B.M. : Huntington : King.]

Austenburn Castle. By an unpatronized female. 2 vols. [London, W. Lane]. 1796. [New Ann. Reg. : Blakey.]

Austin, Mrs. The Noble Family. A novel, in a series of letters. London, 1771. [Baker's Bookshop.]

Authentic and Interesting Memoirs of Miss Ann Sheldon ; (Now Mrs. Archer :) A Lady who figured, during several Years, in the highest Line of public Life, and in whose History will be found, all the Vicissitudes, which so constantly attend on Women of her Description. Written by Herself. 4 vols., For the Authoress, 1787. [Pickering.]

Authentic and Interesting History of Miss Moreton (The) ; and the Faithful Cottager. 2 vols., Manchester, W. Shelmerdine, 1798. [Lancs.]

Authentic Memoirs of the Little Man and the Little Maid : with some interesting particulars of their Lives. With 12 plates. London, 1808. [Camb. Hist. Eng. Lit. : Maggs.]

Authoress (The). A Tale. By The Author of " Rachel." With a frontispiece. London, Taylor and Hessey, 1819. [B.M. : Quarterly Review.]

Autobiography of A Footman (The). 1835. [Cat. Lib. Prohib.]

Autobiography of an Irish Traveller. 3 vols. London, Longman, Rees, Orme, Brown, Green and Longman, 1835. [B.M.]

Autobiography of Rose Allen (The). Edited by a Lady. London, Longman, Brown, Green, and Longmans, 1847. [B.M.]

Avellaneda (see FERNANDEZ DE AVELLANEDA).

Avenger (The) ; or The Sicilian Vespers. A Romance of the 13th Century. 3 vols., London, Stockdale, 1810. [Fletcher.]

Azalais and Aimar, a Provençal History of the thirteenth Century, from an ancient Manuscript. 3 vols. [W. Lane]. 1799. [New Ann. Reg. : Blakey.]

Babay. A True Story of a good Negro Woman. With a frontispiece. London, J. Marshall. Cheap Repository. [Block.]

Babington, Benjamin Guy. The Vedàla Cadai, being the Tamul version of a collection of ancient tales in Sanscrit entitled The Vetàla Panchavinsati. Translated by B. G. Babington. London, Oriental Translation Fund, 1831. [B.M.]

Babylon the Great. By the Author of the Modern Athens. 2 vols., London, Henry Colburn, 1825. [Edin. Mag.]

Bachelor, Charity, The Captive's Vow ; or, the Bashaw. A moral tale. London, Simpkin, Marshall, [1840]. [B.M.]

Bachelor's Miseries. By an Old Maid of Distinction. 4 vols., London, Printed at the Minerva Press, for A. K. Newman, 1814. [Eng. Cat. : Publisher's Advert. : Quarterly Review.]

Backslider (The). London, Simpkin, Marshall, 1836. [B.M.]

Bacon, Thomas. The Orientalist ; containing a series of tales, legends, and historical romances. With engravings by W. and E. Finden. London, 1843. [B.M. : New Monthly Mag.]

Baculard D'Arnaud (see D'ARNAUD).

Bad Boy Reformed by Kindness (The) ; To which is added, The Little Miser. With 14 woodcuts. London, Whitrow, [1820 ?]. [B.M.]

Bage, Robert. Barham Downs. A Novel. By the Author of Mount Henneth, 2 vols., London, G. Wilkie, 1784. [B.M. : W. Brown : Stonehill.]

—— The Fair Syrian. A Novel. By the Author of Mount Henneth and Barham Downs. 2 vols., London, Printed for J. Walter ; J. Bew ; and P. Sandford, 1787. [Bibliot. Brit. : Stonehill.]

—— Hermsprong ; Or, Man As He Is Not. A Novel. By the Author of Man as He Is. 3 vols., London, Printed by the Minerva Press for William Lane, 1796. [B.M. : Huntington : King.]

—— James Wallace. A novel. By the author of Mount Henneth, Barham Downs, and The fair Syrian. London, W. Lane, 1788. [Bibliot. Brit. : Camb. Hist. Eng. Lit. : Blakey.]

Bage, Robert. Man as he is. A Novel. 4 vols., London, Printed for William Lane at the Minerva Press, 1792. [B.M. : *New Ann. Reg.* : Stonehill.]

—— Mount Henneth. A Novel. 2 vols., London, T. Lowndes, 1782. [Arthur Rogers : Stonehill.]

Bagnio Miscellany (The). Containing Three Interesting Dialogues between a Jew and a Female Christian. The Adventures of Miss Lais Lovecock, at Miss Twigg's Boarding School. The Force of Instinct, a droll Story, developing an old contrivance to facilitate the growth of the " Lanugo " on the " Labia " of a Young Lady. Erotic Anecdotes : Maria Antoinette, Queen of France—The Widow and the Parson's Bull, or the Benefit of Flagellation. With 8 illustrations. London, John Jones [Cannon], 1792 [1830]. [*Cat. Lib. Prohib.*]

Bailey, Caroline Conway. Charity. A Moral Tale. London, 1814. [McLeish.]

Bailly, A. Mysteries of the old castles of France ; or, secret intrigues of the Kings and Queens, Princes and Princesses, and other great personages of the times. By a society of arch-seers, under the direction of A. B. Le Francois. Translated by W. T. Haley. London, Strange, 1848. [Lib. of Congress : Publisher's advert.]

Bainbridge, Marie. Rose of Woodlee. A Tale. 3 vols., London, Edward Bull, 1843. [B.M. : James Glaisher : McLeish.]

Baker, M. Emily and her Cousins. A Tale of real life for little girls. With a frontispiece by James Mitchell after R. Westall. London, Dean and Munday, 1828. [Gumuchian.]

Balfour, Alexander. Campbell ; Or, the Scottish Probationer. A Novel. 3 vols., Edinburgh, Oliver and Boyd ; G. and W. B. Whittaker, London ; W. Turnbull, Glasgow ; and Johnston and Deas, Dublin, 1819. [B.M.]

—— The Farmers' Three Daughters. A Novel. 4 vols., London, A. K. Newman, 1822. [B.M.]

—— The Foundling of Glenthorn ; or, The Smugglers' Cave. A Novel. By the Author of the Farmer's Three Daughters. 4 vols., London, A. K. Newman, 1823. [B.M. : *Quarterly Review.*]

—— Highland Mary. A Novel. By the Author of the Foundling of Glenthorn, Farmer's Three Daughters, &c. &c. 4 vols., London, A. K. Newman, 1826. [B.M. : *New Monthly Mag.*]

Ball, Edward. The Black Robber ; A Romance. 3 vols., London, A. K. Newman, 1819. [B.M. : *Quarterly Review.*]

—— The Sibyl's Warning, A Novel. 2 vols., London, C. Chapple, 1822. [B.M.]

Ballantyne, John. The Widow's Lodgings. 2 vols., London, Longman. [Allibone : *Eng. Cat.*]

Ballantyne, Mary Howard. Stories about Greece. With illustrations. London, J. H. Jackson, 1849. [B.M.]

Ballin, Rossetta. The Statue Room ; an Historical Tale. 2 vols., London, H. D. Symonds, 1790. [B.M.]

Balloon (The), Or Aerostatic Spy, A Novel, Containing a Series of Adventures of an Aerial Traveller, Including a Variety of Histories and Characters in Real Life. With plates. 2 vols., London, W. Lane, 1786. [B.M. : W. Fletcher : Stonehill.]

Balzac, Honoré de. Mother and Daughter ; or, La Marana. From the French of M. de Balzac. London, J. Clements. 1842. [B.M.]

Bancroft, Edward. The History of Charles Wentworth, Esq. In a Series of Letters. Interspersed With a Variety of Important Reflections, Calculated to improve Morality, and promote the Œconomy of Human Life. 3 vols., London, T. Becket, 1770. [*Bibliot. Brit.* : B.M.]

Bandello, Matthew. Novels. 4 vols., London, 1740. [*Bibliot. Brit.*]

Bandit Chief (The) ; or, Lords of Urvino. A Romance. 4 vols., London, Printed at the Minerva Press, 1818. [B.M. : Stonehill.]

Banditti of Monte Baldo ; Or, The Lass of the Lake. A Romance. With a frontispiece. [1805]. [Ingpen.]

Banim, John. The Anglo-Irish of the Nineteenth Century. A Novel. 3 vols., London, Henry Colburn, 1828. [B.M. : Ingpen : Lib. of Congress.]

—— Bit o' Writin' And Other Tales. By The O'Hara Family. 3 vols., London, Saunders and Otley, 1838. [Baker's Bookshop : B.M. : *I. in F.*]

—— The Celts Paradise, in Four Duans. 1828. [Arthur Rogers.]

—— The Conformists. Dublin, James Duffy, 1829. [*I. in F.*]

—— The Denounced. By the Authors of " Tales by the O'Hara Family." 3 vols., London, Henry Colburn and Richard Bentley, 1830. [B.M. : Ingpen : Publisher's advert.]

—— Father Connell, By The O'Hara Family. 3 vols., London, T. C. Newby ; and T. and W. Boone, 1842. [B.M.]

—— The Fetches. Dublin, James Duffy, 1825. [*I. in F.*]

—— John Doe ; or, The Peep o' Day. 1825. [*I. in F.*]

—— Peter of the Castle. Dublin, James Duffy, 1826. [*I. in F.*]

—— Revelations of The Dead-Alive. With a folding Prophetical chart. London, W. Simpkin and R. Marshall, 1824. [B.M.]

—— The Smuggler ; A Tale. By the Author of " Tales by the O'Hara Family," " The Denounced," &c. 3 vols., London, Henry Colburn and Richard Bentley, 1831. [Block : B.M. : Bernard Whyte.]

13

Banim, John and Michael. The Boyne Water. A Tale. By the O'Hara Family. 3 vols., Dublin, James Duffy, 1826. [*I. in F. : New Monthly Mag. : Quarterly Review.*]

—— The Croppy ; A Tale of 1798. By The Authors of " The O'Hara Tales," " The Nowlans," and " The Boyne Water." 3 vols., London, Henry Colburn, 1828. [B.M. : McLeish : Elkin Matthews.]

—— The Ghost-Hunter and His Family. By The O'Hara Family. London, Smith, Elder, 1833. [B.M. : Ingpen : Arthur Rogers.]

—— The Mayor of Wind-Gap And Canvassing. By the O'Hara Family. 3 vols., London, Saunders and Otley, 1835. [B.M. : Ingpen : Publisher's advert.]

—— Tales, By the O'Hara Family, Containing Crohoore of the Bill-Hook. The Fetches, and John Doe. 3 vols., London, W. Simpkin and R. Marshall, 1825. [B.M. : Clarke-Hall : Arthur Rogers.]

—— Tales by the O'Hara Family. Second Series. Comprising The Nowlans, and Peter of the Castle. 3 vols., London, Henry Colburn, 1826. [*Blackwood's Edin. Mag.* : B.M. : Arthur Rogers.]

Banim, Michael. Crohoore of the Bill-hook. Dublin, James Duffy, 1825. [*I. in F.*]

Banks of the Carron (The) ; or, the Towers of Lothian ; a Scottish legend. By the Author of the " Two Pilgrims." 4 vols., London, 1809. [B.M.]

Bannerman, Anne. Tales of Superstition and Chivalry. London, Printed for Vernor and Hood by James Swan, 1802. [Birrell and Garnett: Pickering.]

Bannockburn ; A Novel. 3 vols., Edinburgh, Printed for John Warren, London ; and William Blackwood, Edinburgh, 1821. [B.M.]

Barbara Markham, or the Profligate Requited, A Novel. 2 vols., London, Printed by the Philanthropic Society, for W. J. and J. Richardson, 1803. [Stonehill.]

Barber, Mrs. Moral Paralysis ; or, the Gambler. London, James Bunn, 1831. [B.M.]

—— Scenes of Life ; or, the Influence of Religion. London, The Author, 1827. [B.M.]

Barber, Agnes Anne. Country Belles ; Or, Gossips Outwitted. 3 vols., London, Longman, Hurst, Rees, Orme, Brown, and Green, 1824. [B.M. : Publisher's advert.]

Barber, Elizabeth. Tales of Modern Days. London, Sherwood, Jones, 1824.

Barber, Mary Ann Serrett. Childhood's Duties ; or, Precepts for Little Emma. London, J. Nisbet, 1842. [B.M.]

—— Missionary Tales, for little listeners. London, J. Nisbet, 1842. [B.M.]

Barclay, John. The Phoenix ; or, the History of Polyarchus and Argenis.

Translated from the Latin, By a Lady [Clara Reeve]. 4 vols., London, John Bell, 1772. [B.M. : W. Brown : Danielson.]

Barham, Richard Harris. The Ingoldsby Legends ; or, Mirth and marvels, by Thomas Ingoldsby, Esquire. With plates by George Cruikshank, John Leech and John Tenniel. 3 vols., London, Richard Bentley, 1840-1847. [Block : B.M. : King.]

—— Some Account of My Cousin Nicholas. By Thomas Ingoldsby, Esq. Author of " The Ingoldsby Legends." To which is added, The Rubber of Life. 3 vols., London, Richard Bentley, 1841. [B.M. : McLeish : Elkin Mathews.]

Barker, B. The Commodore's Daughter. With woodcuts. London, Lloyd, 1847. [Stonehill.]

Barker, David. The Parent's Monitor ; or, Narratives, anecdotes, and observations on religous education and personal piety. London, Richard Baynes, 1827. [B.M.]

Barker, Jane. The Entertaining Novels of Mrs. Jane Barker, of Wilsthorp in Northamptonshire. 2 vols., London, 1736. [Stonehill.]

Barker, Mary. A Welsh Story. 3 vols., London, Hookham and Carpenter, 1798. [B.M. : *New Ann. Reg.* : Stonehill.]

Barker, Matthew Henry. The Fortunes of Frank Fairfield : A Tale of the Sea. With illustrations. London, Orr, 1845. [*Critic* : Arthur Rogers.]

—— Greenwich Hospital : A Series of Naval Sketches, descriptive of the Life of a Man-of-War's Man. By an Old Sailor. With a woodcut on the title-page, plates and woodcuts by George Cruikshank. London, James Robin, 1826. [B.M. : Maggs : Sotheran.]

—— Hamilton King, Or, The Smuggler and the Dwarf. By The Old Sailor, Author of " Tough Yarns," " Stories of Greenwich Hospital," &c. 3 vols., London, Richard Bentley, 1839 [B.M. : James Glaisher.]

—— Jem Bunt. By the Old Sailor. London, Willoughby, [1841]. [B.M. : *Eng. Cat.*]

—— Land and Sea Tales. By the Old Sailor Author of " Tough Yarns," &c. With 2 frontispieces and 2 engraved title-pages by George Cruikshank. London, Effingham Wilson, 1836. [B.M. : Maggs : Marks.]

—— The Naval Club : Or, Reminiscences of Service. 3 vols., London, Henry Colburn, 1843. [B.M.]

—— The Old Sailor's Jolly Boat, laden with Tales, Yarns, Scraps, Fragments, &c. &c. to Please All Hands, pulled by Wit, Fun, Humor and Pathos. Steered by M. H. Barker. With an engraved title and 24 plates by George and Robert Cruikshank, London, W. Strange, 1844. [B.M. : Marks.]

Barker, Matthew Henry. The Quarter-Deck; or, Home and Abroad. By an Old Sailor. London, 1847. [B.M.]

—— Topsail-Sheet Blocks; Or, The Naval Foundling. By "The Old Sailor:" Author of "Tough Yarns;" "Nights at Sea;" "Greenwich Hospital;" &c. &c. With frontispieces by George Cruikshank. 3 vols., London, Richard Bentley, 1838. [B.M.: W. T. Spencer.]

—— Tough Yarns; A Series of Naval Tales and Sketches To Please all Hands, from the Swabs on the Shoulders down to the Swabs in the Head. By the Old Sailor, Author of "Greenwich Hospital," &c. With illustrations by George Cruikshank, London, Effingham Wilson, 1835. [B.M.: Marks: Pickering.]

—— The Victory; Or, The Ward-room Mess. 3 vols., London, Henry Colburn, 1844. [B.M.]

Barlow, F., Junr. A Sequel to Coelebs; or, the Stanley Letters: containing observations on religion and morals, etc. London, M. Jones, 1812. [B.M.: *New Monthly Mag.*: Sotheby's.]

Barnabas Hill, or the Cottage on the Shore. By the Author of The Little Manufacturer. With a frontispiece and a woodcut vignette. London, Francis Westley, 1821. [B.M.]

Barnadiston. A Tale of the Seventeenth Century. 3 vols., London, Saunders and Otley, 1834. [B.M.]

Barnard, Caroline. The Parent's Off-spring; or, Tales for Children. 2 vols., London, M. J. Godwin, 1813. [B.M.]

—— The Prize; or, the Lace-Makers of Missenden. With a frontispiece by Springsguth after Henry Corbould. London, M. J. Godwin, 1817. [B.M.: Gumuchian.]

Barnby, Mrs. The American Savage. 2 vols., 1808. [*Bibliot. Brit.*]

—— Kerwald Castle, Or, Memoirs of The Marquis de Solanges. Translated from the French, By Mrs. Barnby. 2 vols., Maidstone, Printed for the Author, by D. Chalmers, [1803]. [*Bibliot. Brit.*: B.M.: Dobell.]

—— The Rock; Or, Alfred and Anna. A Scottish Tale, By a young lady, Her First Literary Attempt. 2 vols., London, Printed for the Author, 1798. [B.M.: *New Ann. Reg.*]

Baron de Courcy (The); or, Reading Abbey. A legendary tale. 2 vols., London, 1808. [B.M.]

Baron de Falkenheim. A Tale. 2 vols., London, Lane, Newman, 1806. [Publisher's advert.: Blakey.]

Baron of Manstow (The). A novel. From the German. 2 vols., London, William Lane, 1790. [Blakey.]

Baroness de Beaumont (The). A Novel, By a Lady. 2 vols., 1794. [*New Ann. Reg.*]

Baronet (The): a Novel. Founded on Facts. 3 vols., London, 1800. [Mc-Leish.]

Barrell, P. Riches and Poverty: a tale. London, Samuel Tipper; Joseph Robins, 1808. [B.M.]

Barrett, Alfred. The Boatman's Daughter: a narrative for the learned and unleaned. London, John Mason, 1847. [B.M.]

Barrett, C. F. The Black Castle, or The Spectre of the Forest: an Historical Romance; and Tracey Castle, or The Parricide Punished: a Gothic Story. With a frontispiece. 1800. [Dobell.]

—— Mary Queen of Scots, or, the Royal captive of Fotheringay Castle: a Scottish legendary tale, etc. London, Tegg and Castleman, [1810 ?]. [B.M.]

Barrett, Eaton Stannard. The Heroine: or, Adventures of a Fair Romance Reader. 3 vols., London, Henry Colburn, 1813. [Birrell and Garnett: Blackwell: Parker and Son.]

—— The Rising Sun, A Serio-Comic Satiric Romance. By Cervantes Hogg, F.S.M. With folding frontispiece. 2 vols., London, Appleyards, 1807. [B.M.: G. Sexton.]

—— The Metropolis, by Cervantes Hogg. 3 vols., London, A. K. Newman. [Publisher's advert., 1812.]

—— The Miss-led General; a Serio-comic, Satiric, Mock-Heroic romance. By the Author of the Rising Sun. With a Frontispiece. London, H. Oddy, 1808. [B.M.: G. Worthington: T. D. Webster.]

—— Six weeks at Long's. By a Late Resident. 3 vols., London, Printed for the Author, 1817. [B.M.: Lond. Lib.: W. T. Spencer.]

—— The Tarantula; Or, The Dance Of Fools. A Satirical Work. By the Author of the "Rising Sun," &c. 2 vols., With folding frontispieces. London, Printed by Allen, for Holmes and Whitterton, 1809. [B.M.: Huntington: Stonehill.]

Barron, E. The Royal Wanderer; or, Secret Memoirs of Caroline. 3 vols., London, Newman, 1820. [*Eng. Cat.*: Lib. of Congress.]

Barrow, John Henry. Emir Malek, Prince of the Assassins. An Historical Novel of the Thirteenth Century. 3 vols., London, Longman, Rees, Orme, Brown, and Green, 1827. [B.M.: Publisher's advert.]

Barry, Miss. Mabel; or, the Child of the Battle-Field. A romance. London, 1846. [B.M.]

Barry, Mrs. The Amorous Merchant: or, intriguing husband. Being a curious and uncommon process of love and law Founded on facts. Written by Mrs. Graham, now Mrs. Barry, in the manner of Constantia Phillips. London, 1753. [B.M.]

Barth, Rev. Christian Gottlob. The Flight of the Camisards : A Story for the Young. Translated from the German. London, Religious Tract Society, [1850 ?]. [Block.]

—— Gregory Krau ; or, the Window Shutter. Translated by the Rev. Robert Menzies, etc. Edinburgh, Paton and Ritchie, 1850. [B.M.]

—— The Juvenile Artist. From the German. By Samuel Jackson. London, Darton and Clark, [1838 ?]. [B.M.]

—— Mick and Nick ; or, the Power of conscience. Translated by the Rev. Robert Menzies. Edinburgh, Paton and Ritchie, 1849. [B.M.]

—— Poor Henry. Translated from the German. London, William Foster, [1840 ?]. [B.M.]

—— The Raven's Feather : A Story for Children. From the German. London, Religious Tract Society, [1850 ?]. [Block.]

—— Setma, the Turkish girl : and, Woodroof, the Swedish boy, etc. London, Darton and Harvey, 1838. [B.M.]

—— The Swedish Shepherd Boy. Translated from the German. London, Religious Tract Society, [1850 ?]. [Block.]

—— Winter Evening Stories. With 12 illustrations. London, Darton and Clark, [1840]. [Arthur Rogers.]

—— The Young Tyrolese. From the German of the Rev. G. C. Barth. By Samuel Jackson. With plates. London, Darton and Clark, N.D. [Block.]

Barthelemy, L'Abbé Jean Jacques. Carite and Polydorus. To which is prefixed a Treatise on Morals. With the life of the Author. London, Otridge, 1799. [B.M.]

—— Charite and Polydorus. A Romance ; translated from the French. With an abridgement of the Life of the Author, by the Late Duke of Nivernois. London, Charles Dilly, 1799. [B.M.]

Bartholomew Fair ; or, the Adventures of George and Henry. Otley, William Walker, 1815. [B.M.]

Barton, James. Honoria, or the Infatuated. 2 vols., [Minerva Press], 1804. [*Bibliot. Brit.* : Blakey.]

—— The Remorseless Assassin ; or, the Dangers of Enthusiasm. 2 vols., London, J. F. Hughes, 1803. [B.M.]

Barwell, Louisa Mary. Edward, The Crusader's Son. A Tale. Illustrating the History, Manners and Customs of England in the Eleventh Century. With frontispieces. 2 vols., London, Chapman and Hall, 1836. [B.M. : Publisher's advert.]

—— The Novel Adventures of Tom Thumb the Great, showing how he visited the insect world, and learned much wisdom, etc. London, Chapman and Hall, 1838. [B.M.]

Barwell, Louisa Mary. Trials of Strength. A tale, etc. London, Harvey and Darton, 1839. [B.M.]

—— The Value of Money. London, F. Westley and A. H. Davis, 1834. [B.M.]

—— The Value of Time. A tale for children. London, F. Westley and A. H. Davis, 1834. [B.M.]

Base-Born (The). By the Author of " The Cripple of the Railroad," &c. &c. London, Hatchard, 1840. [B.M.]

Basile, Giovanni Battista. The Pentamerone, or the Story of Stories, Fun for the Little Ones. Translated from the Neapolitan by John Edward Taylor. With 6 Plates by George Cruikshank. London, David Bogue, 1848. [B.M. : Gumuchian : Marks.]

Basket Maker (The) ; or, the History of old Sheelah. And the Fisherman and his Dog. London, T. Gardiner, [1820 ?]. [B.M.]

Bastard of Normandy (The). 2 vols., 1793. [*New Ann. Reg.*]

Bastile (The) : or, History of Charles Townly, a Man of the World. 4 vols., London, William Lane, 1789. [Ingpen : G. Worthington : Blakey.]

Batchelor Keeper (The) : or, the effects of a Friend. London, [1750 ?]. [B.M.]

Bateman's Tragedy ; Or the Perjured Bride Justly Rewarded : Being the History of German's Wive, And Young Bateman. With woodcuts. London, Printed and Sold in Aldermary Church Yard, [1750 ?]. [B.M.]

Bath and London ; or, Scenes in each. A Novel. 4 vols., London, Printed at the Minerva Press, for A. K. Newman, 1811. [B.M. : Publisher's advert.]

Baths of Bagnole (The) ; or, the Juvenile Miscellany. With 3 Lithographs. London, Charles Frederick Cock, 1826. [B.M. : *Quarterly Review.*]

Battersby, John. Tell-Tale Sophas. An Eclectic Fable ;—Founded on Anecdotes, Foreign and Domestic. 3 vols., 1814. [*Bibliot. Brit.*: Arthur Rogers: Sotheby's.]

Battle of the Horn-Books : a Romance. Part the First. Shewing the rise and progress of that famous dispute, etc. Dublin, 1774. [B.M.]

Battledore for Miss in her Teens for the Use of Boarding Schools. 1757.

Battleridge, an historical Tale, founded on Fact. By a Lady of Quality. 2 vols., London, 1799. [B.M. : *New Ann. Reg.* : Sanders.]

Baxter, George R. Wythen. Humour and Pathos ; or, essays, sketches, and tales. With Illustrations by Frank Howard. London, Joseph Thomas, 1838. [B.M.]

Bay Wreath (The) : or, Stories of genius and merit. Edinburgh, James Hogg, 1848. [B.M.]

Bayfield, Mrs. Love as it May Be, and Friendship as it ought to Be. 4 vols., London, J. F. Hughes. [Publisher's advert., 1806.]

Bayles, R. B. The Sorrows of Eliza ; a Tale of Misfortune, being the Authentic Memoirs of a Young Lady in the vicinity of London. London, Longman, 1810. [B.M.]

Bayley, Diana. Employment, the true source of happiness ; or, the good uncle and aunt. London, John Harris, 1825. [B.M.]

—— Tales of the Heath for the improvement of the Mind. London, John Harris, 1825. [B.M. : *Edin. Mag.* : Gumuchian.]

Bayley, Frederick William Naylor. Scenes and Stories By a Clergyman in Debt. Written during his confinement In the Debtors' Prisons. 3 vols., London, A. H. Baily, 1835. [B.M. : James Glaisher.]

—— Tales of the Late Revolutions. With A Few Others. With a frontispice and a plan. London, W. H. Dalton, 1831. [B.M.]

Bayly, Nathaniel Thomas Haynes. The Aylmers. A Novel. 3 vols., London, Saunders and Otley, 1827. [Baker's Bookshop : B.M. : Publisher's advert.]

—— Kindness in Women. Tales. 3 vols., London, Richard Bentley, 1837. [B.M. : James Glaisher.]

Beacon Priory ; or Memoirs of the Rockalba Family, including the Melancholy Deaths of the Earl of Rusport, and Sophia, Countess of Rockalba ; also the History of Madeline, daughter of one of the Princes of the House of Stuart. With a frontispiece. London, Langley and Belch, 1810. [Marks : Murray Hill.]

Beaconsfield, Benjamin Disraeli, Earl of. Coningsby ; Or, The New Generation. 3 vols., London, Henry Colburn, 1844. [B.M. : Arthur Rogers : Rosebery.]

—— Contarini Fleming. A Psychological Autobiography. 4 vols., London, John Murray, 1832. [B.M. : Huntington : Ingpen.]

—— Henrietta Temple, A Love Story. By The Author of " Vivian Grey." 3 vols., London, Henry Colburn, 1837. [B.M. : Huntington : Ingpen.]

—— Sybil ; Or, The Two Nations. By B. Disraeli, M.P. 3 vols., London, Henry Colburn, 1845. [B.M. : Huntington : Publisher's advert.]

—— Tancred : Or, The New Crusade. By B. Disraeli, M.P. 3 vols., London, Henry Colburn, 1847. [B.M. : Huntington : T. Thorp.]

—— Venetia. By the Author of " Vivian Grey " and " Henrietta Temple." 3 vols., London, Henry Colburn, 1837. [Birrell and Garnett : B.M. : Publisher's advert.]

—— Vivian Grey. 5 vols., London, Henry Colburn, 1826-1827. [Block : B.M. : Marks.]

—— The Voyage of Captain Popanilla.

By The Author of " Vivian Grey." London, Henry Colburn, 1828. [Block : B.M. : Huntington.]

Beaconsfield, Benjamin Disraeli, Earl of. The Wondrous Tale Of Alroy. The Rise of Iskander. By the Author of " Vivian Grey," " Contarini Fleming," &c. 3 vols., London, Saunders and Otley, 1833. [B.M. : Huntington : Ingpen.]

—— The Young Duke : " A moral Tale, though gay." By the Author of " Vivian Grey." 3 vols., London, Henry Colburn and Richard Bentley, 1831. [B.M. : Ingpen : Arthur Rogers.]

Beale, Anne. Baronet's Family, a Novel. 3 vols., London, Newby. [*Eng. Cat.*]

—— Traits and Stories of the Welsh Peasantry, 1849. [J. D. Miller.]

Beamish, Lieut.-Col. North Ludlow. Peace Campaigns of a Cornet. 3 vols., London, John Ebers, 1829. [B.M. : McLeish : Arthur Rogers.]

Bear Ye One Another's Burthens ; Or, the Valley of Tears : A Vision. With a woodcut. London, J. Marshall ; and R. White, [1796]. Cheap Repository. Sunday Reading. [B.M.]

Beatrice Chesterford. A Novel. 2 vols., London, Thomas Cautley Newby, 1848. [B.M.]

Beatrice ; or, The inconstant. A tragic novel. 2 vols., [W. Lane, 1788.]

Beau Monde (The) ; or, Scenes in Fashionable Life. 3 vols., London, Minerva Press, 1809. [Baker's Bookshop.]

Beauclerc, Amelia. The Deserter. A Novel. 4 vols., London, Printed at the Minerva Press for A. K. Newman, 1817. [B.M. : *New Monthly Mag.*]

—— Disorder and Order. A Novel. 3 vols., London, Printed by the Minerva Press for A. K. Newman, 1820. [B.M. : *Quarterly Review.*]

Beauclerk, Caroline Frederica and Henrietta Mary. Tales of Fashion and Reality. First Series. London, Smith, Elder, 1836. [B.M.]

Beaufort, John (*see* THELWALL, JOHN).

Beaulieu, Madame Mallès de (*see* MALLÈS DE BEAULIEU).

Beaumont, Elie de (*see* DE BEAUMONT).

Beaumont, Jeanne Marie le Prince de. Instructions to young Ladies on their entering into life, their Duties in the Married State, and towards their Children. 4 vols., 1764. [R. Hall.]

—— Letters from Emerance to Lucy. Translated from the French. 2 vols., London, 1766. [B.M.]

—— Moral Tales. Translated from the French. 2 vols., London, 1775. [*Bibliot. Brit.* : B.M. : *Camb. Hist. Eng. Lit.*]

Beau-Philosopher (The) ; or, The History of the Chevalier de Mainvillers. Translated from the French Original. London, Freeman, 1751. [Ingpen : G. Worthington.]

Beautiful Page (The) ; or, Child of Romance, &c. intended as an instructive Lesson for Youth. London, Hurst, 1802. [*Guardian of Education.*]

Beauty and the Beast. A tale. Glasgow, J. Lumsden, [1815 ?]. [B.M.]

Beazley, Samuel. The Oxonians ; A Glance at Society. By the Author of " The Roué." 3 vols., London, Henry Colburn and Richard Bentley, 1830. [B.M. : Pickering : Publisher's advert.]
—— The Roué. 3 vols. London, Henry Colburn, 1828. [B.M. : Holland Bros. : Ingpen.]

Bechuana Girl (The). London, John Snow, 1842. [B.M.]

Beck, William. Don't despair ; an interesting history. With illustrations. London, For the Author, 1817. [B.M.]

Becke, Richard. The Prima Donna. A Tale of To-Day. London, Edward Bull, 1828. [B.M.]

Becker, Wilhelm Adolf. Charicles : or, Illustrations of the Private Life of the Ancient Greeks ; with notes and excursus. Translated by the Rev. Frederick Metcalf. London, J. W. Parker, 1845. [B.M. : *Eng. Cat.* : *Guide to Best Fiction.*]
—— Gallus ; or, Roman Scenes of the Times of Augustus ; with notes and excursus illustrative of the manners and customs of the Romans. Translated from the German by Frederick Metcalfe. London, John W. Parker, 1844. [B.M. : *Eng. Cat.* : *Guide to Best Fiction.*]

Beckford, William. An Arabian Tale, From An Unpublished Manuscript : With Notes Critical and Explanatory [By Samuel Henley]. London, J. Johnson, 1786. [The first edition of " Vathek."] [Block : B.M. : Huntington.]
—— Azemia : A Descriptive and sentimental Novel. By Jacquetta Agneta Mariana Jenks, of Bellegrove Priory in Wales. Dedicated to the Right Honorable Lady Harriet Marlow. 2 vols., London, Sampson Low, 1797. [*Camb. Hist. Eng. Lit.* : *New Ann. Reg.* : Rosebery.]
—— Modern Novel Writing, or the Elegant Enthusiast ; and Interesting Emotions of Arabella Bloomville. A Rhapsodical Romance ; interspersed with poetry. By the Right Hon. Lady Harriet Marlowe. 2 vols., London, G. G. and J. Robinson, 1796. [B.M. : *Eng. Lit. in Germany* : Rosebery.]
—— The Story of Al Raoui. A Tale from the Arabic. London, 1799. [B.M. : *Eng. Lit. in Germany* : John Pearson.]

Beford, Lieut. John Harman. Wanderings of Childe Harolde ; A Romance of Real Life. Interspersed with Memoirs of the English Wife, The Foreign Mistress, and Various other Celebrated Characters. 3 vols., London, Sherwood, Jones, 1825. [Ashley Lib. : B.M. : Ingpen.]

Bedingfield, R. The Peer and The Blacksmith. With illustrations. [1844]. [R. S. Frampton.]

Before and After. 2 vols., London, T. C. Newby, 1849. [B.M.]

Beggarly Box (The). A religious Parable. London, [1795]. Cheap Repository. [B.M.]

Behadur, Rajah Kalee-Krishen. Bytal-Puchisi ; or the Twenty-five Tales of Bytal, Translated from the Brujbhakha into English. By Rajah Kalee-Krishen Behadur. Calcutta, Sobha Bazar Press, 1834. [B.M.]

Belinda, or The Fair Fugitive. A Novel. By Mrs. C—. 2 vols., London, Allen, 1789. [*Eng. Lit. in Germany* : Ingpen.]

Bell, Catherine Douglas. Mary Elliot, or Be ye Kind to One Another. By Cousin Kate. London, Hamilton, 1850. [*Eng. Cat.* : Arthur Rogers.]
—— Set about it at Once, or Cousin Kate's Story. With a frontispiece. Edinburgh, Hamilton, 1847. [B.M. : *Eng. Cat.* : T. Thorp.]

Bell, Henry Glassford. My Old Portfolio ; or, Tales and Sketches. London, Smith, Elder, 1832. [B.M. : *Literary Gazette.*]

Bell, Mrs. Henry Glassford. The History of a Sandalwood Box : Written by Itself, A Tale for Youth. Glasgow, Not Printed for Publication, [1848]. [B.M. : Arthur Rogers.]

Bell, J. T. Joseph Benson ; or, It's only a penny. A tale for children. London, [1845 ?]. [B.M.]
—— Little Jem, the Rag Merchant. A tale of truth and honesty. London, 1848. [B.M.]

Bell, Robert. The Ladder of Gold : an English Story. 3 vols., London, Bentley, 1850. [B.M. : *Eng. Cat.*]

Bellairs, Henry Walford. Tales of the Town. London, Burns, 1843. [B.M. : *Eng. Cat.*]

Bellairs, Nona. Strength and weakness ; or the Letter and the Spirit. A tale. London, 1848. [B.M.]

Bellamy, Thomas. The Beggar Boy : a novel. To which are prefixed Biographical particulars of the author by Mrs. Villa-Real Gooch. 3 vols., London, 1801. [B.M.]
—— Sadaski ; or, The Wandering Penitent. 2 vols., London, 1798. [Allibone : *Bibliot. Brit.* : B.M.]

Bellegarde, The Adopted Indian Boy. A Canadian Tale. 3 vols., London, Saunders and Otley, 1832. [B.M.]

Belleville Lodge, a novel. 2 vols., London, William Lane, [1793]. [Blakey.]

Bellew, Captain F. H. T. The Cockney in Scotland. With illustrations by the Author. London, H. J. Gibbs, 1850. [Publisher's advert.]
—— Memoirs of a Griffin ; or, a Cadet in India. With Plates. 2 vols., London, Allen, 1843. [*Eng. Cat.* : G. H. Last.]

Bellgrove Castle ; or, The Hour of Retribution. With woodcuts. [c. 1840.] [Stonehill.]

Belmont Grove : or, The discovery. A novel, in a series of letters, by a lady. 2 vols., London, W. Lane, 1785. [Blakey.]

Beloe, William. Incidents of youthful life, or the true history of William Langley. London, 1790. [B.M.]

—— Miscellanies, consisting of poems, classical extracts, and Oriental Apologues. London, 1795. [Burton's *Arab. Nts.*]

Belson, Mary (*see* ELLIOTT, Mary).

Ben Bradshawe ; The Man without a head, A Novel. With 9 plates by T. Onwhyn. 3 vols., London, T. C. Newby, 1843. [B.M. : G. H. Last : McLeish.]

Ben Howard ; or the pedlar and the publican. By the author of the Poor Childs friend. London, 1831. [B.M.]

Benedicta. A Novel. 2 vols., London, William Lane, 1741. [B.M. : Blakey.]

Benett, J. T. The Sicilian, A Romance. 2 vols., London, T. C. Newby, 1845. [B.M.]

Benevola ; A Tale : In Two Parts. Part the First—England, Part the Second—Ireland. London, Charles Knight, 1840. [B.M.]

Benevolent Man (The) ; or, The History of Mr. Belville : In Which is Introduced, the Remarkable Adventures of Captain Maclean, the Hermit. Dedicated to the Earl of Dartmouth. 2 vols., London, Lewis, 1775. [Ingpen : Stonehill.]

Benevolent Merchant (The) ; or, the Dealings of God in Providence and Grace. By M. N. Wellington, 1840. [B.M.]

Benevolent Quixote. 4 vols., 1791. [W. Brown.]

Benger, Elizabeth Ogilvy. The Heart and the Fancy, or Valsinore. A Tale. With a map. 2 vols., London, Longman, 1813. [*Bibliot. Brit.* : B.M. : Ingpen.]

Benignity ; or, The Ways of Happiness. A Serious Novel. Selected (with Additional Conversations,) from the Works of Henry Brooke, Esq. By A Lady. Brentford, Printed by P. Norbury, 1818. [B.M. : *New Monthly Mag.*]

Beningbrough Hall : A Tale Of the Eighteenth Century. By the author of " Scenes in Craven." York, Herald-Office ; Simpkin and Marshall, London ; W. Hargrove, York, 1836. [B.M.]

Bennett, Agnes Maria. Agnes de Courci. A Domestic Tale. 4 vols., 1789. [*Bibliot. Brit.*]

—— Anna ; Or Memoirs Of a Welch Heiress. Interspersed with Anecdotes Of a Nabob. 4 vols., London, William Lane, 1785. [*Bibliot. Brit.* : B.M. : Ingpen.]

—— The Beggar Girl and Her Benefactors. By Mrs. Bennett. 7 vols., London, Minerva Press, 1797. [B.M. : Ingpen : Stonehill.]

Bennett, Agnes Maria. De Valcourt. 2 vols., London, Dutton, 1800. [B.M. : McLeish : Stonehill.]

—— Ellen, Countess of Castle Howel, A Novel. 4 vols., London, Minerva Press, 1794. [*Bibliot. Brit.* : B.M. : Stonehill.]

—— Juvenile Indiscretions ; A Novel. By the Author of Anna, or The Welch Heiress. 5 vols., London, W. Lane, 1786. [Martin A. McGoff : Pickering : Stonehill.]

—— Vicissitudes Abroad ; or, the Ghost of my Father. A Novel. 6 vols., London, Lane, Newman, 1806. [Publisher's advert : Blakey.]

Bennett, Elizabeth. Emily, or, The Wife's First Error ; and Beauty & Ugliness, or, The Father's Prayer and the Mother's Prophecy. Two Tales. 4 vols., London, Printed at the Minerva Press for A. K. Newman, 1819. [B.M. : Pickering.]

—— Faith and Fiction, Or Shining Lights In a Dark Generation. A Novel. 5 vols., London, Printed at the Minerva Press, for A. K. Newman, 1816. [B.M. : *New Monthly Mag.*]

Bennett, G. The Empress. A Novel. 2 vols., London, Smith, Elder, 1835. [B.M.]

Bennett, Mary. The Boy's own book of stories from history, etc. London, Nelson, 1850. [B.M. : *Eng. Cat.*]

—— The Broken Heart ; or, The Village Bridal. With illustrations. London. Lofts. [c. 1845]. [Stonehill.]

—— The Cottage Girl ; Or, The Marriage Day, By the Author of " The Gipsey Bride," etc. With woodcuts. [1835]. [Dobell : Lowe.]

Bennett, W. J. E. Tales of Kirkbeck : or, the Parish in the Fells, etc. By the Author of " Aunt Atta." London, Cleaver, 1848. [B.M. : *Eng. Cat.*]

Bennett, William. The Cavalier. A Romance. By Lee Gibbons, Student of Law. 3 vols., London, Longman, Hurst, Rees, Orme, and Brown, 1821. [Baker's Bookshop : B.M. : Publisher's advert.]

—— The King of the Peak. A Romance. By the Author of " The Cavalier," &c. 3 vols., London, Longman, Hurst, Rees, Orme, and Brown, 1823. [B.M. : *New Monthly Mag.* : Publisher's advert.]

—— Malpas ; or, Le Poursuivant D'Amour. A Romance. By the Author of " The Cavalier." 3 vols., London, Longman, Hurst, Rees, Orme, and Brown, 1822. [B.M. : Publisher's advert.]

—— Owain Goch. A Tale of the Revolution. By the Author of " The Cavalier," " King of the Peak," &c. &c. 3 vols., London, Longman, Rees, Orme, Brown, and Green, 1827. [B.M. : Publisher's advert.]

Benson, Maria. The Carriage. With a frontispiece. London, E. Wallis, 1819. [B.M.]

Benson, Maria. System and No System, or the Contrast. London, Hatchard, 1815. [*Eng. Cat.* : *New Monthly Mag.*]
—— The Wife. A Novel. 3 vols., London, Longman, Hurst, Rees, and Orme, 1810. [*Bibliot. Brit.* : B.M. : *Monthly Mag.*]

Benson, Richard. Morni ; an Irish Bardic Story ; and the Pilgrim of Carmel, an Eastern tale. Dublin, 1815. [B.M.]

Benson Powlet ; Or the French in Moscow in 1812. 2 vols., London, A.K. Newman, 1833. [B.M.]

Berens, Edward. Christmas Stories, Containing John Wildgoose the Poacher, The Smuggler, and Good-Nature. or Parish matters. With illustrations by George Cruikshank. Oxford, Printed by W. Baxter for J. Parker and F. C. and J. Rivington, 1823. [B.M. : Pickering.]
—— Robin Goodfellow, who was nobody's enemy but his own. A tale. London, J. Rivington, 1845. [B.M.]
—— The Smuggler. A Tale. Oxford, W. Baxter for Rivington, London ; and Parker, Oxford, 1823. [B.M.]

Beresford, James. The Miseries of Human Life, or the Groans of Timothy Testy, and Samuel Sensitive. With illustrations. 2 vols., London, William Miller, 1806-1807. [Blackwell : B.M. : *Eng. Lit. in Germany.*]
—— More Miseries, by Sir Fretful Murmur. With a folding frontispiece. 1806. [T. Thorp.]

Berington, Joseph. The History of the Lives of Abeillard and Heloisa, comprising a period of 84 years from 1079 to 1163. With their genuine letters, from the collection of Amboise. Birmingham, M. Swinney, 1787. [B.M.]

Berkeley, Hon. George Charles Grantley Fitzhardinge. Berkeley Castle, An Historical Romance. 3 vols., London, Richard Bentley, 1836. [B.M. : Pickering.]
—— Sandron Hall, Or The Days of Queen Anne. 3 vols., London, Henry Colburn, 1840. [B.M. : G. Worthington.]

Berkeley, George Monck. Heloise : Or, the Siege of Rhodes. A Legendary Tale. By the Author of " Maria : or, the Generous Rustic." 2 vols., London, J. Forbes, C. Elliot and T. Kay, 1788. [D. Webster.]
—— The Independent. A Novel. 2 vols., London, T. Cadell ; and C. Elliot, Edinburgh, 1784. [B.M.]
—— Spanish Memoirs ; in a series of original letters. Containing the history of Donna Isabella della Villarea Published by the author of Maria, or the Generous Rustic. 2 vols., London, 1787. [B.M. : W. Brown.]

Berkeley Hall : or, The Pupil of Experience. A Novel. 3 vols., London, Tindal, 1796. [Stonehill.]

Berkenhout, Helina. The History of Victoria Mortimer. 4 vols., London, 1805. [*Bibliot. Brit.*]

Berkley, Theresa. The Favourite of Venus. Or Secrets of my Note Book explained in the Life of a Votary of Pleasure. London, J. Sudbury, 1820. [*Cat. Lib. Prohib.*]

Bernard, Charles de. The Lover and the Husband. The Woman Of a Certain age, &c. Edited by Mrs. Gore. 3 vols., London, Richard Bentley, 1841. [B.M.]

Berquin, Arnaud. The Blossoms of Morality Intended for the Amusement & Instruction of Young Ladies & Gentlemen. By the Editor of The Looking-Glass for the Mind. With a frontispiece and vignette. London, E. Newbery, 1789. [Gumuchian.]
—— Children's Friend, consisting of Apt Tales, Short Dialogues, and Moral Dramas, translated by Rev. Mark A. Meilan from the French of M. Berquin. London, 1786. [T. C. Godfrey.]
—— The Family Book ; Or, Children's Journal ; consisting of Moral and entertaining stories with Instructive Dialogues upon Subjects which generally occur in Familiar Society. Interspersed with poetical pieces, written by the translator, Miss Stockdale. With a frontispiece. London, Vernor and Hood, 1798. [B.M. : Sotheran.]
—— The Garters and Ruffles. Altered from the French of M. Berquin, by J. H. Crozer. Hull, [1830 ?]. [B.M.]
—— The Looking-Glass for the Mind ; Or Intellectual Mirror, Being an elegant collection of the most delightful little stories and interesting tales, chiefly translated from that much admired work L'Ami des Enfans. With 74 woodcuts by J. Bewick. London, J. Crowder for E. Newbery, 1796. [B.M. : Gumuchian : Parker & Son.]
—— Select Stories for the Instruction and Entertainment of Children from the French of M. Berquin. With 3 Plates by Skelton after M. Brown and one by Foot. London, Stockdale, 1787. [Gumuchian.]

Berry [?], Miss. The Correspondents, An Original Novel ; In a Series of Letters. London, T. Becket, 1775. [B.M. : G. Worthington : Lyle H. Wright.]

Bertrand ; or, Memoirs of a Northumbrian Nobleman in the 17th Century, written by himself. [Henry Savile de Starck]. 3 vols. London, Minerva Press, 1808. [Baker's Bookshop : Blakey.]

Beschius, Constantinus Josephus. The Adventures of the Gooroo Paramartan : A Tale in the Tamul language accompanied by a translation and vocabulary, together with an analysis of the first story, by B[enjamin Guy]. Babington. London, J. M. Richardson, 1822. [B.M. : Huntington.]

Bessy Grey. A tale from the Pastor's Journal. By the author of "The Gypsies." [B.M.]

Best, Eliza. St. James's ; Or, A Peep at Delusion. A Novel. 2 vols., London, Printed for the Author, 1830. [B.M. : *New Monthly Mag.*]

Best, John Richard Digby. Isidora Or the Adventures of a Neapolitan. A Novel, By The Old Author, In a New Walk ; Author of " The Pope and the Colonnas," &c. &c. &c. 3 vols., London, Saunders and Otley, 1841. [B.M.]

—— Odious Comparisons ; or, the Cosmopolite in England. 2 vols., London, Saunders and Otley, 1839. [B.M.]

—— The Pope : A Novel. By an old author, In a new walk. 3 vols., London, Saunders and Otley, 1840. [B.M.]

Best, Mrs. M. C. Memoir of Valentine de T—, son of the Baron de T—. London, Religious Tract Society, [1847]. [B.M.]

—— The Mother's Jewels. Berwick, Thomas Melrose, 1833. [B.M.]

Beste, Henry Digby. Poverty and the Baronet's Family : An Irish Catholic Novel. London, Jones, 1845. [*I. in F.*]

Bethune, Alexander. The Scottish Peasant's Fireside : a Series of Tales and Sketches illustrating the Character of the Peasantry of Scotland, Edinburgh, A. and C. Black, 1843. [Allibone : B.M.]

Bethune, Alexander and John. Tales and Sketches of the Scottish Peasantry. Edinburgh, Fraser, 1838. [Allibone : B.M.]

Bethune, John. Allan of Olway ; a Tale of the Eleventh Century. 1815. [*Bibliot. Brit.*]

Betts, Henry John. A Tale of the Jewish captivity. London, J. Bigg, 1848. [B.M.]

Betty Brown, The St. Giles's Orange Girl : With Some Account of Mrs. Sponge, the Money-lender. With a woodcut. London, J. Marshall, [1796]. Cheap Repository. [B.M.]

Betty Gillis ; or honesty rewarded. London, [1796 ?].

Bevan, Samuel. Sand and Canvas ; A Narrative of Adventures in Egypt, with a sojourn among the Artists in Rome. With illustrations. London, Charles Gilpin, 1849. [B.M. : Ingpen : Tregaskis.]

Bianchi, Michael Angelo. Levity and Sorrow ; A German Story, With a Preface by A. von Kotzebue. Translated by Michael Angelo Bianchi. 2 vols., London, Minerva Press, 1809 ; [Blackwell.]

Bicknell, Alexander. Doncaster Races, or the History of Miss Maitland ; a Tale of Truth, in a Series of Letters. Published from the Original, With Interesting Additions. 2 vols., London, 1790. [*Bibliot. Brit.*]

—— The History of Lady Anne Neville, sister to the great Earl of Warwick : In which are interspersed Memoirs of that Nobleman, and the Principal Characters of the Age in which she lived. 2 vols., London, T. Cadell, 1776. [*Bibliot. Brit.* : Birrell & Garnett : Ingpen.]

Bicknell, Alexander. Prince Arthur. An Allegorical Romance ; the Story from Spenser. 2 vols., London, 1779. [Lowndes.]

Bicknell, T. L. Musical Travels through England by the late Joel Collier, Licentiate in Music. London, Kearsley, 1785. [Ingpen.]

Biernatzki, Johann Christoph. The Maid of the Hallig ; or, The Unfortunate Islanders. A narrative founded on fact : by the Rev. Johann Christoph Biernatzki, from the German, by S. Jackson. London, Cradock, 1843. [B.M. : *Denmark in Eng. and Amer. Lit.* : *Eng. Cat.*]

Bigland, John. The Philosophical Wanderers ; or The History of the Roman Tribune and the Priestess of Minerva. 1811. [Arthur Rogers.]

Bigotry ; or, The Warning Voice. A Novel. 4 vols., London, A. K. Newman, 1821. [B.M.]

Bigsby, Robert. Boldon Delaval ; a love story. Also My Cousin's Story ; the Man on the Grey Horse. Derby, 1850. [B.M.]

Bingham, Miss F. L. Hubert, or, the Orphans of St. Madelaine. A Legend of the Vaudois. By a Clergyman's daughter. London, Simpkin, 1845. [B.M. : *Eng. Cat.*]

Bingley, Thomas. Stories About Dogs. With plates by Thomas Landseer. London, Bogue, [1845]. [*Eng. Cat.* : Arthur Rogers.]

—— Stories About Horses, Illustrative of their Intelligence. Fidelity and Docility. With steel engravings. London, Bogue, 1839. [*Eng. Cat.* : R. Hall : Arthur Rogers.]

—— Stories Illustrative of the Instinct of Animals. With engravings after Thomas Landseer. London, Bogue, 1838. [*Eng. Cat.* : Arthur Rogers.]

—— Tales about Travellers, their perils, adventures, and discoveries. London, Bogue, 1840. [B.M. : *Eng. Cat.*]

Biography of a Spaniel. To which is annexed, The Idiot, A Tale. With a frontispiece by Hopwood. London, A. K. Newman, 1816. [Blakey.]

Biondetta, or The Enamoured Spirit. Translated from Le Diable Amoureux de Cazotte. London, 1810. [Bumpus Exhibition : *Monthly Mag.*]

Birch, John Brereton. The Cousins of Schiras, Translated from the French by John Brereton Birch. 2 vols., London, William Lane, 1797. [*Bibliot. Brit.* : B.M. : Ingpen.]

Bird, John. The Castle of Hardayne ; a Romance. 2 vols., 1795. [*Bibliot. Brit.* : *New Ann. Reg.*]

Bird's Nest and other tales ; from the German. London, 1843. [B.M.]

Birmingham Counterfeit (The), Or, Invisible Spectator. A Sentimental Romance. 2 vols., London, S. Bladon, 1772. [B.M. : W. Brown : Stonehill.]

Birth, Life, and Death of John Franks (The), With the Pranks he Played, Though a meer Fool. With woodcuts. London, Printed and Sold in Aldermary Church Yard, [1750 ?]. [B.M.]

Bisset, Robert. Douglas, or, the Highlander. 4 vols., London, T. Crouder. 1800. [Baker's Bookshop : *Bibliot. Brit.* : Murray Hill.]

—— Modern Literature : A Novel. 3 vols., London, T. N. Longman and O. Rees, 1804. [*Bibliot. Brit.* : Huntington : Internatl. Bk. Shop.]

Bitaubé, Paul Jeremiah. Joseph. A Poem [sic]. In Nine Books. Translated from the French by Kenneth Fergusson. 2 vols., 1783. [*Bibliot. Brit.* : W. Brown : Stonehill.]

Black Banner (The) ; Or, The Siege of Clagenfurth. A Romantic tale. By the Author of The Baron de Falkenheim, Mystery upon Mystery, &c. &c. 4 vols., London, Printed at the Minerva Press, for A. K. Newman, 1811. [B.M.]

Black Convent (The) ; Or, A Tale of Feudal Times. 2 vols., London, Printed at the Minerva Press for A. K. Newman, 1819. [B.M. : *Quarterly Review.*]

Black Giles the Poacher ; With some Account of a Family who had rather live by their Wits than their Work. Part I. With 2 woodcuts. London, J. Marshall ; and R. White. [1796]. Cheap Repository. [B.M. : Court Bk. Shop : R. S. Frampton.]

Black Giles the Poacher. With the History of Widow Brown's Apple-Tree. Part II. With a woodcut. London, J. Marshall ; and R. White, [1796]. Cheap Repository. [B.M. : Court Bk. Shop : R. S. Frampton.]

Black Pirate (The) ; or, the Phantom Ship. A Romance. London, [1848]. [B.M.]

Black Vulture (The) ; or, The Rival Brothers. A Romance of Passion. With woodcuts. London, E. Lloyd, [c. 1840]. [Stonehill.]

Black William's Grave. By Minimus Mote. 3 vols., London, T. C. Newby, 1849. [B.M. : *Eng. Cat.*]

Blackbird's Nest (The), a tale for children. London, 1809. [B.M.]

Blackford, Martha. Annals of the Family of McRoy. 3 vols., London, W. Wetton, 1823. [B.M.]

—— Arthur Monteith : a moral tale being a continuation of the " Scottish Orphans." London, Barnet, Hurst, 1822. [B.M. : *Eng. Cat.*]

—— The Orphan of Waterloo, a Tale. London, Cundall, 1844. [*Critic.*]

Blackford, Martha. The Scottish Orphans ; a moral tale, etc. London ; Barnet, Hurst, 1822. [B.M. : *Eng. Cat.*]

—— William Montgomery ; or, The Young Artist. London, Hurst Chance ; Wettons, Egham, Chertsey and Maidenhead, 1829. [B.M.]

—— The Young Artist. With a Frontispiece. London, W. Wetton, 1825. [B.M.]

Blacklegs and Whitefeet ; a tale of the extra super-improved era of Irish tranquillity. Nos. 1, 2 [all published]. Dublin, [1840 ?]. [B.M.]

Black-Rock House, or dear bought Experience. 3 vols. [Cawthorn's Catalogue, 1810.]

Blackwell, Miss. Ellen Braye ; Or, The Fortune-Teller. 2 vols., London, Saunders and Otley, 1841. [B.M. : Victorius.]

—— Ernestine ; Or, The Child of Mystery. By A Lady of Fashion. 3 vols., London, Henry Colburn, 1840. [B.M. : Elkin Mathews.]

Blakiston, ——. Twenty Years in Retirement. By the Author of " Twelve years' military adventure." 2 vols., London, Cochrane, 1835. [B.M. : *Eng. Cat.*]

Blanch and Rosalinda. Manchester, [1840 ?]. [B.M.]

Blanchard, Edward Lytton. The Life of George Barnwell ; or, The London Apprentice of the Last Century. With woodcuts. London, White, 1820. [Stonehill.]

—— The Mysteries of London ; or Lights and Shadows of London Life. Fourth Series. With illustrations. London, Vickers, [c. 1845]. [Stonehill.]

Blanche and Carlos ; Or the Constant Lovers : Including the Adventures of Valville and Adelaide, A Mexican Tale. With a frontispiece. London, 1803. [Murray Hill.]

Blanche Cressingham. By M. E. 2 vols., London, Saunders and Otley, 1844. [B.M.]

Blanche Leslie ; Or the Living Rosary. With a vignette. London, James Burns, [1849]. [B.M.]

Bleeding Nun (The), or Raymond and Agnes, a Romance, containing some Account of the Wandering Jew. With a plate. London, Kemmish, and Stevens, [1820]. [Pickering.]

Blenheim Lodge. A novel. 2 vols. London, W. Lane, 1786. [Blakey.]

Blessington, Charles John Gardiner Earl of. De Vavasour : A Tale Of the Fourteenth Century. 3 vols., London, Henry Colburn, 1826. [B.M. : Ingpen : Publisher's advert.]

Blessington, Marguerite Countess of. The Confessions of an Elderly Gentleman. Illustrated by Six Female Portraits from highly-finished drawings by E. T. Parris. London, Longman, Rees, Orme, Brown, Green and Longman, 1836. [Block : B.M. : Huntington.]

Blessington, Marguerite Countess of. The Confessions of an Elderly Lady. With 8 portraits by E. T. Parris. London, Longman, Orme, Brown, Green, and Longmans, 1838. [Block : B.M. : Huntington.]

—— Country Quarters. A novel. With a memoir by [M. A.] Power. 3 vols., London, Shoberl, 1850. [Allibone : B.M. : *I. in F.*]

—— The Governess. With a frontispiece. 2 vols., London, Longman, Orme, Brown, Green, and Longmans, 1839. [B.M. : Ingpen : John Smith.]

—— The Lottery of Life. 3 vols., London. Henry Colburn, 1842. [B.M. : Lib. of Congress.]

—— The Magic Lantern, or Sketches of Scenes in the Metropolis. London, Longman, 1822. [Baker's Bookshop : *Eng. Cat.* : Pickering.]

—— Marmaduke Herbert ; Or, The Fatal Error. A novel, Founded on fact. 3 vols., London, Richard Bentley, 1847. [B.M. : *Critic* : Lib. of Congress.]

—— The Memoirs Of a Femme de Chambre. A Novel. 3 vols., London, Richard Bentley, 1846. [B.M. : Lib. of Congress.]

—— Meredith. 3 vols., London, Longman, Brown, Green and Longmans, 1843. [B.M. : Lib. of Congress.]

—— The Repealers. A Novel. 3 vols., London, Richard Bentley, 1833. [B.M. : *I. in F.* : Arthur Rogers.]

—— Strathern ; Or, Life at Home and Abroad. A Story of the Present Day. With a portrait. 4 vols., London, Henry Colburn, 1845. [Block : B.M. : Lib. of Congress.]

—— The Two Friends. A Novel. 3 vols., London, Saunders and Otley, 1835. [B.M. : Ingpen : Lib. of Congress.]

—— The Victims of Society. 3 vols., London, Saunders and Otley. 1837. [B.M. : Lib. of Congress.]

Blind Beggar of Bethnal-Green and Pretty Bessy. London, Peirce and Hyde, 1848. [B.M.]

Blind Betsy, or comfort for the afflicted. London, Religious Tract Society, [1830 ?]. [B.M.]

Blind Man and his Son (The) : a Tale for Young People. The Four Friends, a fable. And a Word for the Gipsies. With a frontispiece by Neagle after Hilton. London, Taylor and Hessey, 1816. [B.M. : Gumuchian.]

Blind Soldier (The). An Authentic Narrative. London, The Religious Tract Society, N.D., [Block.]

Blood-Stained Mantle (The) ; or a Sister's Revenge ; a Legendary Tale. With a frontispiece. London, Hodgson, [c. 1824]. [Marks.]

Blossoms of Peace. A Series of Tales and Narratives, in Prose and Verse ; designed as easy lessons for young persons

of either sex. With woodcuts. London, Hodgson, [1820]. [Gumuchian.]

Blower, Elizabeth. Features from Life, or a Summer Visit. 2 vols., London, 1788. [*Times*.]

—— George Bateman : a Novel. 3 vols., London, Dodsley, 1782. [*Bibliot. Brit.* : Stonehill.]

—— Maria. 2 vols., London, 1785. [*Bibliot. Brit.* : B.M. : *Times*.]

—— The Parsonage House. A Novel. By a young Lady. In a Series of Letters. 2 vols., Macgowan, 1780. [*Bibliot. Brit.* : *Times* : *Town and Country Mag.*]

Blue Beard, or Female Curiosity ; an entertaining story. With 9 woodcuts. Warrington, [1820 ?]. [B.M.]

Blue Mountains (The). A West-Indian Tale. By the Author of Romantic Facts, or Which is his Wife : Veronica, or the Mysterious Stranger ; My Old Cousin, &c. 3 vols., London, A. K. Newman, 1822. [B.M.]

Boaden, James. The Doom of Giallo ; Or, The Vision of Judgment. 2 vols., London, John Macrone, 1835. [B.M.]

—— The Man of Two Lives. A Narrative Written by Himself. 2 vols., London, Henry Colburn, 1828. [B.M. : Arthur Rogers.]

Boarding School ; or Familiar Conversations Between a Governess and her Pupils. Written for the Amusement and Instruction of Young Ladies. London, G. and W. B. Whittaker, 1823. [B.M.]

Boccaccio, Giovanni. The Decameron, or Ten Days' Entertainment of Boccace. Translated from the Italian [by Mr. Balguy]. London, R. Dodsley, 1741. [B.M. : G. Worthington.]

—— The Decameron, or Ten Days' Entertainment. Translated from the Italian, with Remarks on the Life and Writings of Boccaccio. By the Author of " Old Nick " [E. Dubois]. With a portrait. 2 vols., 1804. [Marks : Sotheran : T. Thorp.]

—— The Decameron, or Ten Days. Entertainment. Translated from the Italian. A New edition. In which are restored many Passages omitted in former Editions. With a portrait. 4 vols., London, William Sharp, 1822. [Dobell : Marks : Pickering.]

—— The Decameron, or, Ten Days' Entertainment, translated from the Italian, a new edition, corrected and enlarged, to which are prefixed, remarks on the Life and Writings of Boccaccio. With a frontispiece and 10 plates. 2 vols., London, James Griffin, [1822]. [Pickering.]

—— Patient Griselda ; a Tale from the Italian of Boccaccio By Miss Sotheby. 1799. [Allibone.]

Boddington, Mary. The Gossip's Week. By the Author of " Slight Reminiscences." With woodcuts. 2 vols., London, Longman, Rees, Orme, Brown,

Green, and Longman ; and John Rodwell. 1836. [B.M.]

Boddy, J. A. Euston Hall : A Tale. London, Suttaby ; and J. Murray, 1834. [B.M.]

Bolas, T. The English Merchant, or Fatal Effects of Speculation in the Funds. 2 vols., 1795. [*New Ann. Reg.*]

Bolen, C. A. The Mysterious Monk ; or, The Wizard's Tower. An Historical Romance. 3 vols., London, A. K. Newman, 1826. [B.M. : *Quarterly Review.*]

—— Walter the Murderer ; or, The Mysteries of El Dorado. An Historical Romance. 3 vols., London, A. K. Newman, 1827. [B.M. : Publisher's advert.]

Bond, Elizabeth. Letters of a Village Governess : descriptive of rural scenery and manners ; with Anecdotes of Highland Children ; displaying the dawnings of youthful genius, and the methods taken to improve it. 2 vols., London, 1814. [*Bibliot. Brit.* : B.M.]

Bonhote, Elizabeth. Bungay Castle : A Novel. 2 vols., London, Lane, 1796. [B.M. : Stonehill.]

—— Darnley Vale, or, Emelia Fitzroy. A novel. 3 vols., London, W. Lane, 1789. [*Bibliot. Brit.* : Blakey: Publisher's adv.]

—— Ellen Woodley. A novel. 2 vols., London, W. Lane, 1790. [*Bibliot. Brit.* : Blakey.]

—— Fashionable Friend (The). A Novel. London, 1773. [G. Sexton.]

—— Olivia ; or, Deserted bride. By the author of Hortensia, The rambles of Frankly, and The fashionable friend. 3 vols., London, W. Lane, 1787. [Blakey.]

—— The Parental Monitor. 2 vols., London, William Lane, 1788. [B.M. : Blakey.]

—— The Rambles of Mr. Frankly. Published by his Sister. 2 vols., London, 1772. [B.M.]

Book for the Cottage (A) ; or, the history of Mary and her family. By the Author of " The Female Visitor to the Poor." [London], Seeley, 1848. [B.M. : *Eng. Cat.*]

Book of Nursery Tales (The). A keepsake for the young. First [to third] series 3 vols., London, Burns, 1845. [B.M. : *Eng. Cat.*]

Book of Oddities ; or, Agreeable Variety for Town and Country. Containing an Uncommon Collection of the most curious Stories. By Sir Toby Broadgrin, Knt. Dublin, 1790. [B.M.]

Book of Stories for Young People (A). By Mary Howitt, Mrs. S. C. Hall, Mrs. Cowden Clarke, etc. London, Orr, [1847]. [B.M.]

Book (The). Or, Procrastinated Memoirs. An Historical Romance. London, Sherwood, Neely and Jones, 1812. [Ingpen.]

Booth, Miss A. E. Alf Von Deulman, or the History of the Emperor and his Daughters, translated from the German. 2 vols., 1795. [*New Ann. Reg.*]

Booth, David. Eura and Zedepyra ; a Classical Tale, with Poetical Pieces. 1816. [Allibone : *Bibliot. Brit.*]

Boothby, Lady. Leonora : A Love Story. 3 vols., London, Henry Colburn, 1848. [B.M. : Publisher's advert : G. Worthington.]

Borrow, George. Tales of the Wild and the Wonderful. London, Hurst, Robinson ; and A. Constable, Edinburgh, 1825. [B.M. : Tregaskis : Victorius.]

Boswell, Miss H. The Idiot. A Novel. 3 vols., London, 1810. [Allibone : *Bibliot. Brit.*]

Boswell, James. Dorando, A Spanish Tale. London, J. Wilkie, 1767. [B.M. : Huntington.]

Boswell, Thomas Alexander. The Journal of an Exile. 2 vols., London, Saunders and Otley, 1825. [B.M.]

—— Recollections of a Pedestrian. By the Author of " The Journal of an Exile." 3 vols., London, Saunders and Otley, 1826. [B.M.]

Bottens, Jeanne Isabelle (*see* MONTOLIEU).

Bottle (The), or the first step to crime. A romance. London, Lloyd, [1847]. [B.M.]

Bouilly, Jean Nicolas. A Father's Advice to his Daughter ; or instructive narratives from real life. By the author of a Father's Tales to his daughter. With plates. London, Henry Colburn, 1813. [B.M. : *Eng. Cat.* : Publisher's advert.]

—— A Father's Tales to his Daughter. With plates. London, Henry Colburn, 1814. [Publisher's advert. (2nd edn.)]

—— Tales for Mothers. Translated from the French. London, Relfe, 1831. [B.M. : *Eng. Cat.*]

Bounden, J. The Murderer ; or, The Fall of Lecas. 2 vols., London, Minerva Press, 1808. [Blakey.]

Bourne, John George Hamilton. The Picture : And The Prosperous Man. By the Author of " The Exile of Idria." 3 vols., London, James Cochrane, 1835. [B.M.]

Bourne, Mary Anne. Clara and Emma, or the value of minutes ; a tale. Yarmouth, 1835. [B.M.]

—— Exertion or the Children of the Forest : A Tale founded on facts. With a frontispiece by R. Johns. Yarmouth, F. Skill, 1836. [Gumuchian : J. D. Miller.]

—— A Summer At De Courcy Lodge : Interspersed With Anecdotes of Natural History and Science. Coventry, Charles A. N. Rollason, 1845. [B.M.]

—— Tales ; comprising The Garden ; Williams Wishes ; Precepts. Second edition. To which are added : More Precepts : and The Election. Whitehaven, 1830. [B.M.]

—— A Winter at De Courcy Lodge ; or, anecdotes illustrative of natural history. London, Houlston, 1837. [B.M. : *Eng. Cat.*]

Bouverie, Georgina. Georgina, Or, Memoirs of the Bellmour Family. By a young lady. 4 vols., London, Printed for the Author, 1787. [B.M. : Pickering : Arthur Rogers.]

Bouverie, Sophia. St. Justin ; or, The Hour of Trial ; a Romance. 3 vols., London, 1808. [Allibone : *Bibliot Brit.*]

Bowdich, Sarah. The Juvenile Album, or, Tales from far and near. With illustrations by T. Woolnoth. London, 1841. [B.M.]

Bowdler, Mrs. H. M. Pen Tamar ; Or, The History of an old maid. With Aquatint plates. London, Longman, Rees, Orme, Brown, and Green, 1830. [B.M.]

Bowles, Caroline (*see* SOUTHEY, Caroline.)

Bowring, Sir John. Minor Morals For Young People. Illustrated in Tales and Travels. With 12 engravings by George Cruikshank and 8 by William Heath. 3 vols., London, Whittaker, 1834-1839. [B.M. : Ingpen : Marks.]

Boyd, A. The Duchess ; or Woman's Love and Woman's Hate. A romance. 3 vols., London, Bentley, 1850. [B.M. : *Eng. Cat.* : Hodgson.]

Boyle, Charles John. Love's Exchange : A Tale. 3 vols., London, Longman, Orme, Brown, Green, and Longmans, 1839. [B.M.]

Boyle, Hon. Mary Louisa. The Forester : A Tale of 1688. 3 vols., London, Longman, Orme, Brown, Green, and Longmans, 1839. [B.M.]

—— The State Prisoner. A Tale Of The French Regency. 2 vols., London, Saunders and Otley, 1837. [B.M. : Court Bookshop : Ingpen.]

Boys, Mrs. S. The Coalition ; Or Family Anecdotes. 2 vols., London, Logographic Press, 1785. [*Bibliot. Brit.* : Stonehill.]

Bradford, John. Tales of the Moor. By Josias Homely. Containing Reginald Arnolf, Tom Stirlington, Etc. London, Simpkin, Marshall ; Crews, Newton-Abbot, 1841. [B.M.]

Bradley, Edward. College Life. With 24 etchings. Oxford, [1850].

Bradshaw, Hon. Mary Ann Cavendish. Ferdinand and Ordella. A Russian Story, with Authentic Anecdotes of the Russian Court after the Demise of Peter the Great. To which is added a Prefatory Address to the Satirist upon Patron and Dedications, Reformers and Reformations. By Priscilla Parlante. 2 vols., London, Samuel Tipper, 1810. [Allibone : *Bibliot. Brit.* : B.M.]

Brady, John Henry. Little Fables for little folks. London, Van Voorst, 1835. [B.M.]

Brambleton Hall, a Novel, Being a Sequel to the Celebrated Expedition of Humphrey Clinker, By Tobias Smollett. With a frontispiece. London, T. H.

Green ; A. K. Newman & Co., and Sherwood, Neely, and Jones, 1818. [*New Monthly Mag.* : W. T. Spencer : Sotheby's.]

Brandon, Isaac. Fragments : In the Manner Of Sterne. With 3 engravings. London, Printed for the Author, 1797. [B.M.]

Bransby, Miss A. Fernando ; or the Hero of the Times. 2 vols., 1823. [*New Monthly Mag.*]

Bravo of Bohemia (The) ; or, The Black Forest. A Romance. 4 vols., London, Lane, Newman. [Publisher's advert. : Blakey.]

Bray, Anna Eliza. Courtenay Of Walreddon. A Romance of the West. 3 vols., London, Richard Bentley, 1844. [B.M.]

—— De Foix ; or, Sketches of the Manners and Customs of the Fourteenth Century. An Historical Romance. 3 vols., London, Longman, Rees, Orme, Brown, and Green, 1826. [B.M. : Publisher's advert. : Stonehill.]

—— A Father's Curse and a Daughter's Sacrifice. 3 vols., 1849. [James Glaisher.]

—— Fitz of Fitz-Ford ; a Legend of Devon. 3 vols., London, Smith, Elder, 1830. [B.M. : Elkin Mathews.]

—— Henry de Pomeroy ; Or, The Eve of St. John. A Legend of Cornwall and Devon. 3 vols., London, Richard Bentley, 1842. [B.M.]

—— The Protestant ; A Tale of The Reign of Queen Mary. By the Author of ' De Foix,' ' The White Hoods,' &c. 3 vols., London, Henry Colburn, 1828. [B.M. : *Guide to Best Fiction* : Y. Thorp.]

—— The Talba, Or Moor of Portugal. A Romance. 3 vols., London, Longman, Rees, Orme, Brown, and Green, 1830. [B.M.]

—— Traditions, Legends, Superstitions, and Sketches of Devonshire, on the Borders of the Tamar and the Tavy. In a Series of Letters from Mrs. Bray to Robert Southey, Esq. 3 vols., 1838. [Allibone.]

—— Trelawney of Trelawne ; Or, The Prophecy : A Legend of Cornwall. 3 vols., London, Longman, Orme, Brown, Green, and Longmans, 1837. [B.M.]

—— Trials of Domestic Life. 3 vols., London, Henry Colburn, 1848. [Allibone : B.M. : *Eng. Cat.*]

—— Trials Of The Heart. 3 vols., London, Longman, Orme, Brown, Green, and Longmans, 1839. [B.M.]

—— Warleigh ; Or, The Fatal Oak. A Legend of Devon. 3 vols., London, Longman, Rees, Orme, Brown, Green, and Longman, 1834. [B.M.]

—— The White Hoods ; An Historical Romance. 3 vols., London, Longman, Rees, Orme, Brown, and Green, 1828. [B.M. : Pickering : Sanders.]

Bréhier (*see* LAFAYE-BRÉHIER).

Bremer, Frederika. The Bondmaid. To which is added Axel and Anna ; or, a correspondence between two stories of the same house. Translated from the Swedish by M. L. Putnam. London, 1844. [B.M. : Lib. of Congress.]

—— Brothers and Sisters : a tale of domestic life. Translated from the original unpublished manuscript by M. Howitt. 3 vols., London, Colburn, 1848. [B.M. : Lib. of Congress : Lond. Lib.]

—— Christmas Eve and Christmas Matins. A scene in Swedish peasant life. London, [1849]. [B.M. : Sweden Year-Book.]

—— The Diary. and Strife, and Peace. Translated by M. Howitt. 2 vols., London, Longman, 1844. [*Eng. Cat.* : Lib. of Congress.]

—— The Easter Offering. Tales. Translated by M. Howitt. London, Colburn, 1850. [*Eng. Cat.* : Lib. of Congress : Lond. Lib.]

—— The H —— Family : Tralinnan ; Axel and Anna ; and other Tales. Translated by Mary Howitt. With a portrait. 2 vols., London, Longman, Brown, Green, and Longmans, 1843. [B.M. : Publisher's advert.]

—— Home ; or Family cares and Family Joys. Translated by Mary Howitt. 2 vols., London, Longman, 1843. [B.M. : H. H. Langley : Sweden Year-Book.]

—— The Home ; or Family Cares and Family Joys. Translated from the Swedish, by E. A. Friedlænder. 2 vols., London, H. G. Clarke, 1844. [Block.]

—— Life in Dalecarlia : the Parsonage of Mora. Translated by W. Howitt. London, Chapman and Hall, 1845. [B.M. : *Eng. Cat.*]

—— The Midnight Sun. Translated by M. Howitt. London, Colburn, 1848. [*Eng. Cat.* : Lib. of Congress.]

—— The Neighbours : A Story of Every-day Life. Translated by Mary Howitt. 3 vols., London, Longman, 1842. [B.M. : Francis Edwards : Lond. Lib.]

—— The Neighbours. Translated from the Swedish by E. A. Friedlaender, etc. 2 vols., London, Tegg, 1844. [B.M. : *Eng. Cat.*]

—— New Sketches of Every-day Life : a Diary ; together with Strife and Peace, translated by Mary Howitt. 2 vols., London, Longman, 1844. [B.M. : Stonehill : Sweden Year-Book.]

—— Nina. Translated from the Swedish. By E. A. Friedlænder. 2 vols., London, H. G. Clarke, 1844. [Block.]

—— The President's Daughter : including Nina. Translated by Mary Howitt. 3 vols., London, Longman, Brown, Green, and Longmans, 1843. [B.M. : Lib. of Congress : John Smith.]

—— Strife and Peace : or, Scenes in Norway. Translated from the Swedish. London, 1843. [B.M. : Sweden Year-Book.]

Brendlah, Madame. Tales of a Jewess : Illustrating The Domestic Manners And Customs of the Jews. Interspersed with Original Anecdotes of Napoleon. First Series. London, Simpkin, Marshall, 1838. [B.M. : Lib. of Congress.]

Brent, John. The Battle Cross : A Romance of the Fourteenth Century. 3 vols., London, T. C. Newby, 1845. [B.M.]

—— Ellie Forestere, a novel. 3 vols., London, T. C. Newby, 1850. [B.M. : *Eng. Cat.*]

—— The Sea-Wolf, A Romance of " The Free Traders." London, Smith and Elder, 1834. [Allibone : P. C. Cuttelle : *Eng. Cat.*]

Brentano, Clemens. Honor ; Or, the Story of The Brave Caspar and the Fair Annerl. With an Introduction and a Biographical Notice of The Author, By T. W. Appell. Translated from the German, London, John Chapman, 1847. [B.M.]

Brereton, Mrs. Woman's Influence. 3 vols., London, T. C. Newby, 1845. [B.M.]

Brerewood, Thomas. Galfred and Juletta, or the Road of Nature. A Tale. 3 vols., London, 1772. [Allibone : *Bibliot. Brit.*]

Breton, Marianne. The Wife of Fitzalice, And the Caledonian Siren. A Romance. With Historical Notes. 5 vols., London, Printed at the Minerva Press, for A. K. Newman, 1817. [B.M. : *New Monthly Mag.* : *Quarterly Review.*]

Breues, John. The Fortunate Lovers ; or the most successful Arts used in honourable Courtship, set forth in the history of persons of different characters and stations. 1754. [*Bibliot. Brit.*]

Brewer, George. The History of Tom Weston. A Novel, after the manner of Tom Jones. 2 vols., London, 1791. [*Bibliot. Brit.* : Sotheby's.]

—— The Motto : or History of Bill Woodcock. 2 vols., London, 1795. [*Bibliot. Brit.* : B.M. : *New Ann. Reg.*]

—— The Witch of Ravensworth : a romance. 2 vols., London, 1808. [B.M.]

Brewer, James Norris. The Fitzwalters, Barons of Chesterton ; or, Ancient Times in England. By the Author of A Winter's Tale, Secrets Made Public, Sir Ferdinand of England, Sir Gilbert Easterling, Old Family Legend, &c. &c. 4 vols., London, A. K. Newman, 1829. [B.M.]

—— An Old Family Legend ; or, One Husband and Two Marriages. A Romance. 4 vols., London, Printed at the Minerva Press, for A. K. Newman, 1811. [Allibone : Publisher's advert. : Blakey.]

—— Secrets Made Public. A novel. 4 vols., London, Lane, Newman, 1808. [Blakey.]

26

Brewer, James Norris. Sir Ferdinand of England. A Romance. 4 vols., London, Printed at the Minerva Press, for A. K. Newman, 1813. [B.M. : *Eng. Cat.* : Blakey.]
—— Sir Gilbert Easterling. A Romance. 4 vols., London, Printed at the Minerva Press, for A. K. Newman, 1813. [*Bibliot. Brit.* : *Eng. Cat.* : Publisher's advert.]
—— A Winter's Tale ; a Romance. With frontispieces. 3 vols., London, Minerva Press, 1799. [*Bibliot. Brit.* : Ingpen : Publisher's advert.]
Bride, Arthur Stanley. Edrick the Saxon. A Tale Of The Eleventh Century. 2 vols., London, John Macrone, 1836. [B.M. : C. Howes.]
Bride of Obeyda (The) ; And other Tales. By the Author of Montville, or the Dark Heir of the Castle. 3 vols., London, A. K. Newman, 1827. [B.M.]
Bridges, Thomas. The Adventures of a Bank-Note. 4 vols., London, T. Davies, 1770. [B.M. : Francis Edwards : Ingpen.]
Bridget, Mrs. The Baron of Falconberg ; Or, Childe Harolde in Prose. By Bridget Bluemantle. 3 vols., London, Printed at the Minerva Press, for A. K. Newman, 1815. [*Bibliot. Brit.* : B.M. : Publisher's advert.]
—— Claudine ; Or Pertinacity. A Novel. By Mrs. Bridget Bluemantle. 3 vols., London, Printed at the Minerva Press for A. K. Newman, 1817. [B.M. : *New Monthly Mag.* : *Quarterly Review.*]
—— Monte Video ; or, The Officer's Wife & her Sister. A novel. By Bridget Bluemantle. 4 vols., London, Minerva Press, 1809. [Baker's Bookshop : Blakey.]
—— Mortimer Hall, or the Labourers Hire, by Bridget Bluemantle. 4 vols., London, Printed at the Minerva Press, for A. K. Newman, 1811. [*Bibliot. Brit.* : Publisher's advert.]
—— The Prison-House ; Or, The world we live in. A Novel. By Mrs. Bridget Bluemantle. 4 vols., London, Printed at the Minerva Press, 1814. [B.M. : Publisher's advert : *Quarterly Review.*]
—— The Vindictive Spirit. A Novel. By Bridget Bluemantle. 4 vols., London, Printed at the Minerva Press, for A. K. Newman, 1812. [*New Monthly Mag.* : Publisher's advert. : *Quarterly Review.*]
Brief Account of Little William (A) : As an Encouragement to Parents to train up, from Infancy, their Children in the Fear of God. Founded on Fact. With a woodcut. London, Houlston, N.D. No. 15 of Houlston's Series of Tracts. [Block.]
Briggs, John. The History of Jim Crow. London, Smallfield, 1839. [B.M.]
Briggs, Sophia. The Gitana. A Tale. 3 vols., London, Saunders and Otley, 1845. [B.M. : McLeish : Elkin Mathews.]

Briscoe, C. W. Clerimont, or Memoirs of the life and adventures of Mr. B * * * * * *. Written by himself. Liverpool, Charles Wosencroft, 1786. [B.M. : *Lancs.*]
Briscoe, Sophia. The Fine Lady. A Novel. By the Author of Miss Melmoth. 2 vols., London, T. Lowndes, 1772. [B.M. : Pickering : Stonehill.]
—— Miss Melmoth or The New Clarissa. 1771. [*Eng. Lit. in Germany.*]
Bristed, Rev. John. Edward and Anna ; or A Picture of Human Life. 2 vols., Lane, Newman, 1805. [Allibone.]
Bristow, Amelia. Emma de Lissau ; A Narrative of Striking Vicissitudes, and Peculiar Trials ; With explanatory Notes, Illustrative of the Manners and Customs of the Jews. By the Author of " Sophia de Lissau," " Elizabeth Allen," &c. &c. 2 vols., London, T. Gardiner, 1828. [B.M.]
—— Miriam and Rosette ; or, The Twin Sisters : a Jewish Narrative of the XVIIIth Century. By the Author of " Emma de Lissau." With illustrations by Gilbert. London, David Bogue, 1846. [Publisher's advert.]
—— The Orphans of Lissau, And other Interesting Narratives, Immediately connected with Jewish Customs, Domestic and Religious, With Explanatory Notes. By the Author of " Sophia de Lissau," " Emma de Lissau," &c. 2 vols., London, T. Gardiner : and the Author, Blackheath, 1830. [B.M.]
—— Sophia de Lissau. By the author of " Elizabeth Allen or the faithful servant." Gardiner, 1826. [B.M. : *Eng. Cat.*] *See also under* VILLAGE WALKS.
British Admiral (The). A Novel. By A Naval Officer [Lieut. Arnold]. 3 vols., London, Minerva Press, 1808. [H. H. Langley : Blakey.]
British Oak ; or, a Soldier's Benevolence. A Pathetic Tale. To which is added, The Water Carrier. An Eastern Tale. With a frontispiece. London, Printed by T. Maiden, For Ann Lemoine, and J. Roe, [1804]. [Block : Stonehill.]
British Knight Errant (The). A Tale of Chivalry. 2 vols., [W. Lane, 1790]. [Blakey.]
Brittaine, Rev. George. The Confessions of Honor Delany. By the author of " Hyacinth O'Gara." Dublin, Richard Moore Tims, 1830. [B.M. : *I. in F.*]
—— The Election. By the Author of " Recollections of Hyacinth O'Hara." Dublin, Richard Moore Tims, 1840. [B.M. : *I. in F.*]
—— Irish Priests and English Landlords. By the author of Hyacinth O'Gara. Dublin, Richard Moore Tims, 1830. [B.M. : *I. in F.*]
—— Irishmen and Irishwomen. By the author of " Hyacinth O'Gara." Dublin, Richard Moore Tims, 1831. [B.M. (2nd edn.)]

27

Brittaine, Rev. George. Johnny Derrivan's Travels. Dublin, Richard Moore Tims, 1833. [*I. in F.*]

—— Mothers and Sons. By the author of " Hyacinth O'Gara." Dublin, Richard Moore Tims, 1833. [B.M. : *I. in F.*]

—— Nurse M'Vourneen. Dublin, Richard Moore Tims, [1839]. [*I. in F.* (2nd edn.)]

—— Recollections of Hyacinth O'Gara. Dublin, Richard Moore Tims, 1828. [B.M.]

Broderick, Miss. The Cumberland Cottager. A Story, Founded on Facts. 3 vols., London, Printed at the Minerva Press for A. K. Newman, 1818. [B.M. : *New Monthly Mag.* : Blakey.]

Brodie, Alexander. The Prophetess : A Tale of the Last Century, In Italy. 3 vols., Edinburgh, Thomas Clark ; and Longman, Rees, Orme, Brown and Green, 1826. [B.M. : Ingpen : *New Monthly Mag.*]

Broken Heart (The) ; A Tale of the Rebellion of 1745. Glasgow, William Inglis, [1825 ?]. [B.M.]

Bromley, Eliza. The Cave of Consenza ; a Romance, altered from the Italian. 2 vols., 1803. [*Bibliot. Brit.*]

Bronikowski, Alexander. The Court of Sigismund Augustus, Or Poland In The Sixteenth Century. By Alexander Bronikowski : Done into English By a Polish Refugee. 3 vols., London, Longman, Rees, Orme, Brown, Green, and Longman, 1834. [B.M.]

Brontë, Anne. The Tenant of Wildfell Hall. By Acton Bell. 3 vols., London, T. C. Newby, 1848. [Ashley Lib. : Arthur Rogers.]

Brontë, Charlotte. Jane Eyre. An Autobiography. Edited by Currer Bell. 3 vols., London, Smith, Elder, 1847. [B.M. : Arthur Rogers : Varda.]

—— Shirley, a Tale, by Currer Bell, Author of ' Jane Eyre.' 3 vols., London, Smith, Elder, 1849. [B.M. : Gregory : Varda.]

Brontë, Emily and Anne. Wuthering Heights. A Novel by Ellis Bell. 3 vols., London, Thomas Cautley Newby, 1847. [Vols. I and II : Wuthering Heights, by Emily Brontë ; Vol. III : Agnes Grey, by Anne Brontë.] [Ashley Lib. : B.M. : King.]

Brontë, Rev. Patrick. The Maid of Killarney ; Or, Albion and Flora : A Modern Tale ; In which are interwoven some cursory remarks On Religion and Politics. London, Baldwin, Cradock, and Joy, 1818. [*Ashley Lib.* : B.M. : *I. in F.*]

Brooke, Charlotte. Emma, or the Foundling of the Wood. A Novel. 1803. [Allibone : *Bibliot. Brit.*]

—— The Excursion. 2 vols., London, T. Cadell, 1777. [B.M. : W. Brown : G. Worthington.]

Brooke, Frances (*see* MOORE, FRANCES).

Brooke, Henry. The Fool of Quality ; or, the History of Henry Earl of Moreland. 5 vols., London, W. Johnston, 1766-1770. [B.M. : Marks : Arthur Rogers.]

—— History of Henry Earl of Moreland. 2 vols., London, 1781. (Abridgement of " Fool of Quality," by John Wesley). [Howard S. Mott.]

—— Juliet Granville ; or, the history of the human heart. 3 vols., London, 1774. [Allibone : B.M. : *Camb. Hist. Eng. Lit.*]

—— A new Collection of Fairy Tales, none of which were ever before printed ; containing many useful Lessons, moral Sentiments, surprising Incidents, &c. 2 vols., 1750. [Allibone : *Bibliot. Brit.*]

Brooke, Indiana. Eliza Beaumont and Harriet Osborne : or, The Child of Doubt. 2 vols., London, 1789. [D. Webster.]

Brooks, Maria. Zophiël ; or, the Bride of Seven. By Maria del Occidente. London, 1833. [B.M.]

Broster, John. The Castle of Beeston, or, Randolf, Earl of Chester. An Historical Romance. 2 vols., London, 1798. [*New Ann. Reg.* : T. D. Webster.]

Brother (The). A Novel. By a Lady. London, 1771. [T. D. Webster].

Brothers (The). By the Author of The Stage-Coach and Lucy Wellers. 2 vols., London, Dodsley, 1758. [B.M. : Arthur Rogers.]

Brothers (The) ; a novel for children. Henley, G. Norton, 1794. [*Camb. Hist. Eng. Lit.*]

Brothers (The) ; or, Consequences. A story with a short account of saving banks, and other essays. Dublin, Cock, 1820. [B.M. : *Eng. Cat.*]

Brougham and Vaux, Henry, Baron. Albert Lunel, or, The Château of Languedoc. A Novel. 3 vols., London, Charles Knight, 1844. [B.M. : Ingpen : Arthur Rogers.]

Brown, A. The Alpine Wanderers ; Or, the Vindictive Relative. Frontispiece. London. N.D. [Murray Hill.]

Brown, Elizabeth Cullen. Passion and Reason ; Or, The Modern Quintilian Brothers. A Novel. 4 vols., London, T. Hookham, 1832. [B.M. : G. Worthington.]

—— The Sisters of St. Gothard. A Tale. 2 vols., London, Printed at the Minerva Press, 1819. [B.M.]

Brown, Thomas. Brighton, or, The Steyne. A Satirical Novel. 3 vols., London, Sherwood, Neely, and Jones, 1818. [B.M. : *New Monthly Mag.* : Pickering.]

Brown, Thomas, the Elder. Bath, a Satirical Novel. With Portraits. 3 vols., Printed for the Author, 1818. [Backus : Marks : *New Monthly Mag.*]

Browning, William Shergold. Hoel Morvan ; Or, The Court and Camp of Henry V. 3 vols., London, T. C. Newby, 1844. [B.M. : Ingpen : *Tait's Edin. Mag.*]

—— Provost of Paris. A Tale. 3 vols.. London, Smith Elder. [Allibone : *Eng, Cat.*]

Brownlow, John. Hans Sloane. A Tale. Illustrating the History of the Foundling Hospital in London. London, F. Warr, 1831. [B.M.]

Bruce, Carlton (*see* MOGRIDGE, George).

Bruce's Voyage. The Discovery of the Central World ; With the Laws, Customs and Manners of the Nation Described. With a frontispiece. London, S. Fisher, 1802. [Victorius.]

Brunton, Mary. Discipline : A Novel. By the Author of " Self-Control." 3 vols., Edinburgh, Printed by George Ramsay for Manners and Miller ; and Longman, Hurst, Rees, Orme, and Brown, 1814. [Backus : Dr. E. A. Baker : B.M.]

—— Emmeline. With Some Other Pieces. To which is Prefixed A Memoir of Her Life, Including some extracts from Her Correspondence. With a Portrait. Edinburgh, Manners and Miller, 1819. [Ingpen : McLeish : Arthur Rogers.]

—— Self-Control : A Novel. 2 vols., Edinburgh, Manners and Miller, 1811. [Holland Bros. : Pickering : Publisher's advert.]

Brydges, Sir Samuel Egerton. Arthur Fitz-Albini ; A Novel. 2 vols., 1798. [*Bibliot. Brit.* : B.M. : *Times Literary Supplement.*]

—— Coningsby, A Tragic Tale. Paris, Geneve, London, J. J. Paschoud, 1819. [B.M. : Dobell : Pickering.]

—— The Hall of Hellingsley : A Tale. 3 vols., London, Longman, Hurst, Rees, Orme, and Brown, 1821. [Birrell and Garnett : B.M. : Pickering.]

—— Imaginary Biography. 2 vols., London, Saunders and Otley, 1834. [Allibone : *Eng. Cat.*]

—— Le Forester : a novel. By the Author of Arthur Fitz Albini. 3 vols., 1802. [Allibone : B.M.]

—— Lord Brokenhurst, or a Fragment of Winter Leaves, a tragic tale by the author of Mary de Clifford. Geneva, 1819. [B.M.]

—— Mary de Clifford, A Novel. 1792. [Allibone : *Bibliot. Brit.*]

—— Sir Ralph Willoughby. An Historical Tale of the Sixteenth Century. In which are inserted the Dedicatory Sonnets of Edmund Spenser, with Sketches of Character. By the Author of " Coningsby." Florence, F. Magheri, 1820. [B.M. : Ingpen : Elkin Mathews.]

Bulgárin, Thaddeus. Ivan Vejeeghen ; or Life in Russia. 2 vols., London, Whittaker, 1831. [*Eng. Cat.* : Arthur Rogers.]

Bulkeley, James. La Hougue Bie de Hambie, A Tradition of Jersey ; With Historical, Genealogical, and Topographical Notes. With frontispieces. 2 vols., London, Whittaker, 1837. [Bailey Bros. : B.M.]

Bullock, Mrs. Susanna ; or, Traits of a Modern Miss. 4 vols., London, Minerva Press, 1795. [*New Ann. Reg.* : Stonehill : Blakey.]

Bunbury, H. W. Tales of the Devil, from the Original Gibberish of Professor Lumpwitz, S.U.S. and C.A.C. in the University of Snorinberg. With 4 plates. Bury St. Edmunds, 1801. [Marks.]

Bunbury, Selina. The Abbey of Innismoyle : A story of another Century. By the Author of " Early Recollections." With a frontispiece. Dublin, William Curry, 1829. [*I. in F.*]

—— The Blind Clergyman and his little Guide. London, 1850. [B.M.]

—— Cabin Conversations and Castle Scenes. London, Nisbet, 1827. [B.M. : *I. in F.*]

—— The Castle and Hovel ; or, the two sceptics. London, 1844. [B.M.]

—— Coombe Abbey ; An Historical Tale of the Reign of James the First. With a frontispiece and illustrations. Dublin, Curry, 1843. [Block.]

—— Eleanor. By the Author of " A Visit to my Birthplace." Dublin, 1830. [B.M.]

—— Evelyn ; or a Journey from Stockholm to Rome in 1847-48. 2 vols., London, Richard Bentley, 1849. [Allibone : B.M. : *Eng. Cat.*]

—— Evenings in the Pyrenees ; comprising the stories of wanderers from many lands. London, Masters, 1845. [B.M. : *Eng. Cat.*]

—— My Foster Brother. Dublin, Tims, 1827. [*I. in F.*]

—— Retrospections ; a Soldier's Story. By the author of " A Visit to my Birthplace." Dublin, 1829. [B.M.]

—— The Star of the Court ; or, the Maid of Honour and Queen of England, Anne Boleyn. London, Grant, 1844. [B.M. : *Eng. Cat.* : *Spectator.*]

—— Tales Of My Country. By the author of " Early Recollections," " A Visit to my Birth Place," " The Abbey of Innismoyle," &c. &c. Dublin, William Curry, Jun. ; Simpkin and Marshall, London, 1833. [B.M. : *I. in F.*]

—— The Triumph of Truth, or Henry and his Sister. London, Tract Society, [1847 ?]. [B.M. : *Eng. Cat.*]

Buonaparte, Louis. Maria ; Or, The Hollanders. 3 vols., London, Printed by J. Gillet, for H. Colburn, and Longman, Hurst, Rees, Orme, and Brown, 1815. [B.M. : Kyrle Fletcher : *New Monthly Mag.*]

Burbury, E. J. Seven Tales by Seven Authors, etc. Hoby, 1849. [B.M. : *Eng. Cat.*]

Burdett, Mrs. C. D. At Home. A Novel. By the Author of English Fashionables Abroad. 3 vols., London, Henry Colburn, 1828. [B.M. : Elkin Mathews.]

—— English Fashionables Abroad. A Novel. 3 vols., London, Henry Colburn, 1827. [B.M. : *Literary Gazette* : A. Margery.]

—— Walter Hamilton. A Novel. 3 vols., London, Thomas Cautley Newby, 1846. [B.M. : McLeish.]

Burdon, Hannah D. All Classes, a Novel. 3 vols., London, T. C. Newby, 1847. [Allibone : *Critic* : *Eng. Cat.*]

—— The Forester's Daughter : A Tale of the Reformation. By the Authoress of " Seymour of Sudley," " Thirst for Gold," " The Pope and the Actor," &c. 3 vols., London, T. C. Newby, 1844. [B.M.]

—— The Friends of Fontainbleu. 3 vols., London, Saunders and Otley, 1839. [B.M.]

—— The Lost Evidence. 3 vols., London, Saunders and Otley, 1838. [B.M.]

—— The Pope And the Actor, An Historical Novel. 3 vols., London, T. C. Newby ; and T. and W. Boone, 1842. [B.M.]

—— Seymour of Sudley ; Or, The Last of the Franciscans. 3 vols., London, Richard Bentley, 1836. [B.M.]

—— The Thirst for Gold. 3 vols., London, T. and W. Boone, 1841. [B.M.]

—— The Three Baskets or how Henry, Richard and Charles were occupied while papa was away. With 7 woodcuts. London, Dean and Munday, [1840 ?]. [B.M. : Gumuchian.]

—— Ward of the Crown. 3 vols., London, T. C. Newby. [Allibone : *Eng. Cat.*]

Burges, Mary Ann. The Progress of the Pilgrim Good-Intent, in Jacobinical Times. London, Hatchard, 1800. [B.M.]

Burke, Mrs. Adela Northington, A Novel. 3 vols., London, W. Cawthorne, 1796. [*Bibliot. Brit.* : B.M. : *New Ann. Reg.*]

—— Ela, or the Delusions of the Heart ; A Tale, founded on facts. London, 1787. [Allibone : *Bibliot. Brit.* : D. Webster.]

—— Elliott, or Vicissitudes of Early Life ; A Novel. 2 vols., 1800. [Allibone : *Bibliot. Brit.* : *Monthly Review.*]

—— The Secret of the Cavern, A Novel. 2 vols., London, Minerva Press, 1805. [*Bibliot. Brit.* : Stonehill.]

—— The Sorrows of Edith, or the Hermitage of the Cliffs ; a Tale. 2 vols., 1797. [*New Ann. Reg.*]

Burman Slave Girl (The). London, Religious Tract Society, [1830 ?]. [B.M.]

Burne, James. The Man of Nature. Translated from the French by James Burne. With frontispieces. 2 vols.,

London, T. Cadell, 1773. [B.M. : Colbeck : Ingpen.]

Burney, Caroline. Seraphina, or A Winter in Town. A Modern Novel. 3 vols., London, Hughes, 1809. [*Bibliot. Brit.* : Ingpen.]

Burney, Fanny, or Frances (*see* D'ARBLAY).

Burney, Sarah Harriet. Clarentine. A Novel. 3 vols., London, G. G. and J. Robinson, 1796. [B.M. : Ingpen : Pickering.]

—— Country Neighbours, being a Continuation of the Tales of Fancy. 2 vols., London, Henry Colburn, 1820. [*Eng. Cat.* : *Monthly Mag.* : *Quarterly Review.*]

—— Geraldine Fauconberg. By the Author of Clarentine. 3 vols., London, G. Wilkie and J. Robinson, 1808. [B.M. : Dobell : Francis Edwards.]

—— The Romance of Private Life. 3 vols., London, Henry Colburn, 1839. [B.M. : Huntington : Lib. of Congress.]

—— Tales of Fancy : 3 vols., London, Henry Colburn, 1816-1820. [B.M. : Francis Edwards : McLeish.]

—— Traits of Nature. By Miss Burney, Author of Clarentine. 5 vols., London, Henry Colburn, 1813. [Birrell and Garnett : Ingpen : Stonehill.]

Burrows, J. Life in St. George's Fields : or, the Rambles and Adventures of Disconsolate William, Esq. (from St. James's) and his accomplished Surrey Friend, the Hon. Flash Dick ; exhibiting a true picture of the Day and Night Scenes of that Region of Pleasure which for Real Life stands unrivalled. Containing Original Songs and a Slang Dictionary. With a folding view. London, J. Smith, 1821. [Block.]

Burton, Anne. Laura, or the Orphan ; A Novel. 2 vols., 1798. [*New Ann. Reg.*]

Bury, Lady Charlotte Susan Maria. " Alla Giornata ; " or, To the Day. 3 vols., London, Saunders and Otley. 1826. [B.M. : Ingpen : *Quarterly Review.*]

—— Conduct is Fate. 3 vols., Edinburgh, Wm. Blackwood ; and T. Cadell, London, 1822. [Backus : B.M. : Ingpen.]

—— The Devoted. By the Authoress of " The Disinherited," " Flirtation," &c. 3 vols., London, Richard Bentley, 1836. [B.M.]

—— The Disinherited. And The Ensnared. By the Authoress of " Flirtation." 3 vols., London, Richard Bentley, 1834. [B.M. : Kyrle Fletcher.]

—— The Divorced. 2 vols., London, Henry Colburn, 1837. [B.M. : James Glaisher : Publisher's advert.]

—— The Exclusives. 3 vols., London, Henry Colburn and Richard Bentley, 1830. [P. C. Cuttelle : Grafton : Ingpen.]

Bury, Lady Charlotte Susan Maria. Family Records ; Or The Two Sisters. 3 vols., London, Saunders and Otley, 1841. [B.M.]

—— Flirtation. A Novel. 3 vols., London, Henry Colburn, 1827. [Clarke-Hall : A. Margery : J. Richardson.]

—— The History of a Flirt. Related by Herself. 3 vols., London, Henry Colburn, 1840. [B.M.]

—— Journal of the Heart. Edited by The Authoress of " Flirtation." London, Henry Colburn and Richard Bentley, 1830. [B.M. : Publisher's advert. : T. D. Webster.]

—— Journal of the Heart. Edited by The Authoress of " Flirtation." Second Scries. London, James Cochrane, 1835. [B.M. : *New Monthly Mag.*]

—— Love. By the Authoress of " Flirtation," " The Divorced," &c. 3 vols., London, Henry Colburn, 1837. [B.M.]

—— The Manœuvring Mother. By the Author of " The History of a Flirt." 3 vols., London, Henry Colburn, 1842. [B.M.]

—— The Separation. A Novel. By the Authoress of " Flirtation." 3 vols., London, Henry Colburn and Richard Bentley, 1830. [Birrell and Garnett : B.M. : James Glaisher.]

Busk, Mrs. Tales of Fault and Feeling. By the Author of Zeal and Experience. 3 vols., London, T. Hookham, 1825. [B.M.]

Bussey, George Moir. The Arabian Nights' Entertainments revised and corrected, with an explanatory and historical introduction by George Moir Bussey. 1839. [B.M.]

Buston, G. The Political Quixote, Or The Adventures of the Renowned Don Blackibo Dwarfino and his Trusty Squire Seditiono, A Romance, In which are introduced many Popular and Celebrated Political Characters of the Present Day. With 3 woodcuts by George Cruikshank. London, 1820. [Chas. Hutt : Marks.]

Busy-Body. A Novel. 3 vols., London, Richard Bentley, 1843. [B.M.]

But How to Spend the Evening ? London, Cock, 1833. [B.M. : *Eng. Cat.*]

Butler, Alfred. Elphinstone. 3 vols., London, Richard Bentley, 1841. [B.M. : McLeish.]

—— The Herberts. By The Author of " Elphinstone." 3 vols., London, Saunders and Otley, 1842. [B.M. : McLeish.]

Butler, Harriet. Count Eugenio ; a Novel. 2 vols., 1807. [*Bibliot. Brit.*]

—— Versenshon ; or, Love's Mazes. A Novel. 3 vols., London, 1806. [B.M.]

Butler's Diary (A) ; or, The history of Miss Eggerton. A novel. 2 vols., London, William Lane, 1792. [Blakey.]

Butt, Rev. George. The Spanish Daughter. By The Rev. George Butt, late Chaplain in Ordinary to His Majesty ; Revised and Corrected by his Daughter, Mrs. Sherwood. 2 vols., London, Knight and Lacey ; and M. A. Nattali, 1824. [B.M.]

Butt, Isaac. The Gap of Barnesmore : A tale of the Irish Highlands, and The Revolution of 1688. 3 vols., London, Smith, Elder, 1848. [B.M. : *I. in F.*]

—— Irish Life : In The Castle, the Courts, and the Country. 3 vols., London, How and Parsons, 1840. [B.M. : *I. in F.*]

Butter, Alfred. Midsummer Eve : A Tale. 3 vols., London, Saunders and Otley, 1842. [B.M.]

Buxton Diamonds, or, Grateful Ellen. London, [1830 ?]. [B.M.]

Byerley, John Scott. The Conscript, a Serio Comic Romance [founded on M. Le Maires's tale of " Le Conscrit, ou les billets de logements "]. 2 vols., London, 1807. [B.M.]

Byrne, Mrs. The Passions. By Rosa Matilda. London, T. Cadell and W. Davies, 1811. [B.M. : *New Monthly Mag.*]

Byron, Mrs. Anti-Delphine. A Novel. 2 vols., 1806. [Allibone : *Bibliot. Brit.*]

—— The Borderers. An Historical Romance, illustrative of the manners of the fourteenth century. 3 vols., London, Printed at the Minerva Press, for A. K. Newman, 1812. [B.M. : Publisher's advert. : *Quarterly Review.*]

—— Drelincourt and Rodalvi, Or Memoirs of two Noble Families. 3 vols., 1807. [Allibone : *Bibliot. Brit.*]

Byron, Medora Gordon. The Bachelor's Journal, Inscribed (Without Permission) To the Girls of England. Edited by Miss Byron. 2 vols., London, Printed at the Minerva Press, for A. K. Newman, 1815. [B.M. : Dobell : Publisher's advert.]

—— Celia in Search of a Husband. By A Modern Antique. 2 vols., London, Printed at the Minerva Press, 1809. [B.M. : Dobell : Stonehill.]

—— The English Exposé ; or, Men and Women " Abroad " and " at Home." By a Modern Antique, author of " Celia in search of a Husband." 4 vols., London, Printed at the Minerva Press, for A. K. Newman, 1814. [B.M. : *Eng. Cat.* : Publisher's advert.]

—— The Englishman. A Novel. 6 vols., London, Minerva Press for A. K. Newman, 1812. [Birrell and Garnett : *Quarterly Review* : Stonehill.]

—— The Englishwoman ; A Novel. 5 vols., London, Minerva Press, 1808. [Blakey.]

—— Hours of Affluence, And Days of Indigence. A Novel. 4 vols., London, Printed at the Minerva Press for Lane, Newman, 1809. [*Bibliot. Brit.* : B.M.]

—— The Modern Villa and Ancient Castle ; or, the Peer and the Alderman. 3 vols., London, Printed at the Minerva

Press, for A. K. Newman, 1810. [Allibone : *Bibliot. Brit.* : Publisher's advert.]

Byron, Medora Gordon. The Spinster's Journal. By a Modern Antique, Author of Celia in Search of a Husband, English Exposé, &c. 3 vols., London, Printed at the Minerva Press for A. K. Newman, 1816. [B.M. : Dobell : *New Monthly Mag.*]

Cabal (The). A Tale of the Reign of William the Fourth. 2 vols., London, James Cochrane, 1831. [*Metropolitan Mag.* : Pickering.]

Cabinet of Amorous Curiosities (The). In Three Tales. Highly calculated to please the Votaries of Venus. Tale I. The Village Bull. Tale II. The Memoirs of a Feather Bed. Tale III. Adventures of a Droll One, or the Broke Open Casket. London, R. Borewell, 1786. [*Cat. Lib. Prohib.*]

Cabinet of Instruction and Amusement (The). With woodcuts. 12 volumes in a miniature bookcase. London, J. Fairburn, 1802. [B. Halliday.]

Cabinet of Lilliput : Instructive Stories. 12 volumes in a box. [The title on the lid reads *The Cabinet of Lilliput : Stories with Instruction and Delight.*] With engraved frontispieces. London, J. Harris, 1802. [B. Halliday : Arthur Rogers.]

Cabinet of Momus (The), and Caledonian Humorist ; being a collection of the most entertaining English and Scotch stories, selected from the best authors, in prose and verse. London, 1786. [B.M.]

Cabronazos (The), or a Spaniard in London. By a Graduate of the University of Cambridge. 2 vols., London, Sherwood, 1814. [*New Monthly Mag.*]

Caddick, Mrs. Tales of the Affections : Being Sketches from Real Life. London, Longman, Rees, Orme, Brown, and Green ; and T. Sowler, Manchester, [1828.] [B.M. : *Quarterly Review.*]

Cadell, Cecilia Mary. Massenburg. A Tale. 3 vols., London, T. Cadell ; and William Blackwood, Edinburgh, 1825. [B.M. : *Edin. Mag.*]

—— The Reformer. By the Author of " Massenburg." 3 vols., London, Effingham Wilson, 1832. [B.M.]

Calabrella, Baroness de. Double Oath ; A Novel. 3 vols., London, Bentley. [Allibone : *Eng. Cat.*]

—— Evenings At Haddon-Hall. Edited by The Baroness de Calabrella. With illustrations by George Cattermole. London, Henry Colburn, 1846. [Block : B.M.]

—— The Tempter and the Tempted. 3 vols., London, Thomas Miller, 1842. [B.M. : Ingpen.]

Callcott, Maria Hutchins. Home among Strangers. A Tale. 2 vols., London, Longman, 1848. [*Eng. Cat.*]

—— The Little Bracken-Burners, A Tale ; And, Little Mary's Four Saturdays. With a frontispiece. 1841. [Arthur Rogers.]

Callistus and Sophronius, Three Dialogues between a Man of Fashion and a Country Gentleman. 1768. [W. Brown.]

Callou, ——. Angelina. Interspersed with the Histories of Dona Vittorina, Dom. Matheo, And the Chevalier de Riva Franca. Translated from the French. London, J. Hinton, 1753. [B.M.]

Cambon, Maria Geertruida de. Clementine Bedford. A Novel—in Letters and Narrative. London, 1796. [*Bibliot. Brit.* : D. Webster.]

—— Young Grandison. A Series of Letters from Young Persons to their Friends. Translated [by J. Hall] from the Dutch of Madame de Cambon, with Alterations and Improvements. 2 vols., London, 1790. [*Bibliot. Brit.* : B.M. : Holland.]

Cambridge, Richard Owen. The Fakeer : A Tale. London, R. and J. Dodsley, 1756. [*Bibliot. Brit.* : Birrell and Garnett.]

Cameron, Lucy Lyttelton. The Berkshire Shepherd. London, Houlston, N.D., [B.M. (6th edn.)]

—— The Caskets. London, [1815 ?]. [B.M.]

—— Crooked Paths ; or, The Gains of Dishonesty. With a woodcut. London, Houlston, N.D. No. 25 of Houlston's Series of Tracts. [Block.]

—— The Evening Visit. By the Author of " Margaret Whyte," " Emma and her Nurse," " Two Lambs," " Village Nurse," " Oaken Gates Wake," &c. &c. With a woodcut. London, Printed for W. Whittemore, By John Hill, 1824. [Block.]

—— The Farmer's Daughter. London, Houlston, 1843. [Allibone : *Eng. Cat.*]

—— Forms of Pride ; Or, The Midsummer Visit. With a woodcut frontispiece. London, Houlston, 1829. [B.M.]

—— The Fruits of Education ; or, The Two Guardians. Wellington, Salop : Houlston, 1827. [B.M.]

—— The History of Margaret Whyte. [Pre 1805]. [Algar : *Camb. Hist. Eng. Lit.*]

—— The History of Samuel Thomson. With a woodcut. London, Houlston, N.D. No. 84 of Houlston's Series of Tracts. [Block.]

—— An Honest Penny Is worth a Silver Shilling. With a woodcut. London, Houlston, N.D. No. 10 of Houlston's Series of Tracts. [Block.]

—— Marten and his Scholars. London, Houlston. [Allibone : *Eng. Cat.*]

—— Memoirs of Emma and her Nurse, or, the History of Lady Harewood. By the Author of " The History of Margaret Whyte." Wellington, Houlston, 1821. [B.M. (2nd edn.)].

Cameron. Lucy Littleton. My Bible and my Calling. With 2 woodcuts. London, Houlston, N.D. Nos. 53 and 54 of Houlson's Series of Tracts. [Block.]

—— The Novice. With 2 woodcuts. London, Houlston, N.D. Nos. 43 and 44 of Houlston's Series of Tracts. [Block.]

—— The Pink Tippet. By the Author of Margaret White, Oaken Gates Wake &c. &c. With 3 woodcuts. 4 parts. London, W. Whittemore : Wightman and Cramp, [1820 ?]. [Block.]

—— Proper Spirit. With a woodcut. London, Houlston, [1830 ?] No. 9 of Houlston's Series of Tracts. [Block.]

—— The Raven and the Dove. By the author of " The Two Lambs." Wellington, Houlston, 1817. [B.M.]

—— The Self-Seeker. With a woodcut. London, Houlston, N.D. No. 83 of Houlston's Series of Tracts. [Block.]

—— The Sunday-School Teachers. With a woodcut. London, Houlston, N.D. No. 6 of Houlston's Series of Tracts. [Block.]

—— The Two Death-Beds. By the Author of " Margaret Whyte," &c. With a woodcut. London, W. Whittemore : Wightman and Cramp, [1820 ?] [Block.]

—— The Two Lambs. 1821. [*Camb. Hist. Eng. Lit.*]

—— The Two Mothers, or Memoirs of the Last Century. By the Author of " Emma and her Nurse," " Margaret Whyte," &c. 1824. [Arthur Rogers.]

—— Vain Wishes. By the Author of Margaret Whyte, &c. &c. With a woodcut. London, W. Whittemore : Wightman and Cramp, [1820 ?]. [Block.]

—— What is Liberty ? or, the Easy Yoke and the Heavy One. With 2 woodcuts. London, Houlston, N.D. Nos. 63 & 64 of Houlston's Series of Tracts. [Block.]

Cameron. A Novel. 3 vols., London, Edward Bull, 1832. [B.M. : Elkin Mathews.]

Camillo. A Novel. Written by R. H. A[rtium] B[accalaureus] T[rinity] C[ollege] D[ublin] Cork, [1745 ?] [B.M.]

Campbell, Mrs. Tales About Wales. Edinburgh, Robert Cadell. [Publisher's advert.]

Campbell, Alexander. Perkin Warbeck ; or, The Court Of James the Fourth of Scotland. An Historical Romance. 3 vols., London, A. K. Newman, 1830. [B.M.]

Campbell, Calder. Rough Recollections Of Rambles, Abroad and at home. 3 vols., London, Thomas Cautley Newby, 1847. [B.M.]

Campell, Calder. Winter Nights ; 3 vols., London, T. C. Newby, 1850. [B.M. : *Eng. Cat.* : James Glaisher.]

Campbell, Lady Charlotte. Self-Indulgence ; a Tale of the Nineteenth Century. 2 vols., Edinburgh, 1812. [B.M. : Ingpen : McLeish.]

Campbell, Miss D. P. Harley Radington. A Tale. 2 vols., London, A. K. Newman, 1821. [B.M. : Arthur Rogers.]

Campbell, Harriette. The Cardinal Virtues ; or, Morals and Manners connected. 2 vols., London, Parker, 1841. [B.M. : *Eng. Cat.*]

—— The Only Daughter. A Domestic Story. Edited by The Author of " The Subaltern," " The Hussar," &c. [George Robert Gleig]. 3 vols., London, Henry Colburn, 1839. [B.M. : James Glaisher : Holland.]

—— Self-Devotion ; Or, The History of Katherine Randolph. By the Author of " The Only Daughter." Edited by the Author of " The Subaltern," &c. [George Robert Gleig]. 3 vols., London, Henry Colburn. 1842. [B.M.]

Campbell, Rev. John. Alfred and Galba, or, the History of Two Brothers, supposed to be written by themselves. For the use of young people. London, 1805. [B.M.]

—— Voyages and travels of a Bible. London, 1815. [B.M. (5th edn.)]

Campbell, Margaret. The Midnight Wanderer : Or, A Legend of the Houses of Altenburg and Lindendorf. A Romance. 4 vols., London, A. K. Newman, 1821. [B.M.]

Campe, Joachim Heinrich. Columbus : or, The Discovery of America. As related by a Father to his Children. Translated by Elizabeth Helme. London, Sampson Low, 1799. [Pickering.]

—— The New Robinson Crusoe ; An Instructive and Entertaining History For the Use of Children of Both Sexes. Translated from the French. With 36 woodcuts by John Bewick. 4 vols., London, John Stockdale, 1788. [B.M. : Gumuchian : King.]

—— Pizarro ; Or, The Conquest of Peru : As related by a Father to his Children, and designed for the Instruction of Youth. Translated from the German of J. H. Campe [by Elizabeth Helme]. With a folding map. 2 vols., London, Low, 1799. [Ingpen.]

Camus, A. Le. Abdeker : Or, The Art of Preserving Beauty. Translated from an Ancient Arabic Manuscript. London, A. Millar, 1754. [B.M. : Ingpen : Arthur Rogers.]

Camus, Jean Pierre. Triumphs of Love. Glasgow, 1750. [Ingpen.]

Canadian Girl (The) ; or Pirate of the Lakes. A Story of the Affections. By the Author of Jane Shore, etc. With frontispieces. 3 vols. London, William Bennett, 1845. [Block.]

Cannon, C. J. Father Felix, a Tale. By the author of " Mora Carmody." London, 1850. [B.M.]

Canterbury Tales. Composed for the Entertainment of all Ingenious Young Men and Maids. At their Merry Meetings at Christmas, Easter, Whitsuntide, or any other Time, especially on the long winter Evening, to keep Wits, pleasant Stories, witty Jests, and delightful Songs, very proper for either City, Town or Country. By J. Chaucer, Junior. With woodcuts. London, Printed and sold in Aldermary Church Yard, [1750 ?]. [B.M.]

Canton, John. Alvar and Seraphina ; or the Troubles of Murcia ; A Novel. 2 vols., London, 1803. [Allibone : *Bibliot. Brit.*]

—— The English Gil Blas ; Or, the Adventures of Gabriel Tangent. 3 vols., London, 1807. [B.M.]

Capern, Edward. The Pryings of a Postman. London, Saunders and Otley, 1845. [Ingpen.]

Caprice : or Anecdotes of The Listowel Family. An Irish Novel. By an Unknown. 3 vols. London, Sherwood, Jones, 1824. [B.M. : *I. in F.*]

Capricious Father or The History of Mr. Mutable and his Family. 1775. [*Eng. Lit. in Germany.*]

Capricious Mother (The) ; or Accidents and Chances. 3 vols., 1812. [*Quarterly Review.*]

Captive Fair (The), And Enchanted Rock ; or, the Legend of St. Altram. A Romance. Translated from an Ancient British Manuscript. With a frontispiece. London, Hughes, [c. 1810]. [Stonehill..]

Captive Maiden (The), a tale of the third century. London, Mozley, 1846. [B.M.]

Captive of Valence (The), Or the Last Moments of Pius VI. 2 vols., 1804] [Blackwell.]

Captive (The) : or, the history of Mr. Clifford. Translated from the French. 2 vols., London, 1771. [B.M.]

Captive (The). A Tale of the War of Guienne. By the Author of "The Pilgrim Brothers." 3 vols., London, Edward Churton, 1835. [B.M.]

Captives (The) : or, the History of Charles Arlington, Esq. ; and Miss Louisa Somerville. 3 vols., London, T. Vernor, 1771. [Maggs.]

Caraccioli, Charles. Chiron ; or, The Mental Optician. 2 vols., London, J. Robinson, 1758. [Birrell & Garnett : Pickering : D. Webster.]

Card, Henry. Beauford ; or, a Picture of High Life. 2 vols., London, Rivington, 1811. [*Eng. Cat.* : R. Hall : *Quarterly Review.*]

Cardonne, Denis Dominique. A Miscellany of Eastern Learning. Translated from Turkish, Arabian, and Persian Manuscripts. In the Library of the King

of France. Translated into English. 2 vols., London, Wilkie, 1771. [Ingpen.]

Cards Spiritualized ; Or the Soldier's Almanack, Bible and Prayer Book. With woodcut illustrations. A single Folio Leaf. York, Carrall, [181-]. [B.M. : Court Bookshop.]

Carew, Charlton. The Poacher's Wife : A Story of the Times. 2 vols., London, Charles Ollier, 1847. [B.M.]

Carey, Agnes. Anne Groves ; or, Barnet Fair. London, A. K. Newman, 1821. [B.M.]

Carey, David. Frederick Morland ; By the Author of " Lochiel ; or, The Field of Culloden," &c. &c. 2 vols., London, G. and W. B. Whittaker, 1824. [Backus : B.M. : Arthur Rogers.]

—— A Legend of Argyle ; Or, 'Tis a Hundred Years Since. 3 vols., London, G. and W. B. Whittaker, 1821. [Blackwell : B.M. : Stonehill.]

—— Life in Paris. Comprising The Rambles, Sprees, and Amours, of Dick Wildfire, of Corinthian Celebrity, and his Bang-up Companion, Squire Jenkins and Captain O'Shuffleton ; With the Whimsical Adventures of the Halibut Family, including Sketches of a Variety of other Eccentric Characters in the French Metropolis. With 21 plates by George Cruikshank. London, John Fairburn, 1822. [E. Hector : Chas. Hutt : Maggs.]

—— Lochiel ; Or, the Field of Culloden. 3 vols., London, G. and W. B. Whittaker, 1820. [B.M. : Marks : *New Monthly Mag.*]

—— Secrets of the Castle ; a Novel. 2 vols., London, J. Swan, 1806. [*Bibliot. Brit.* : Murray Hill.]

Carey, Joanna. Lasting Impressions : A Novel. 3 vols., London, Longman, Hurst, Rees, Orme, Brown, and Green, 1824. [B.M. : Publisher's advert.]

—— Learning Better than House and Land, as exemplified in the History of Harry Johnson and Dick Hobson. 1824. [*Camb. Hist. Eng. Lit.*]

Carlén, Emilie. Marie Louise ; or, the Opposite Neighbours. A Novel. London, Ingram, 1833. [B.M. : *Eng. Cat.* : *Sweden Year-Book.*]

—— The Rose of Tistelön : A Tale of the Swedish Coast. Translated from the original Swedish [By Mary Howitt]. 2 vols., London, Longman, Brown, Green, and Longmans, 1844. [There is another translation the same year.] [B.M. : Salkeld : *Sweden Year-Book.*]

—— The Temptation of Wealth. A Romance. London, [1847.] [B.M. : *Sweden Year-Book.*]

Carleton, William. Art Maguire ; or, The Broken Pledge. Dublin, James Duffy, 1841. [Lib. of Congress.]

—— The Black Prophet : A Tale of the Irish Famine. Belfast, Simms and

McIntyre. 1847. [C. J. Cremen : Lib. of Congress : *Times Literary Supplement.*]

Carleton, William. The Emigrants of Ahadarra. Belfast : Simms and McIntyre, 1848. [*Guide to Best Fiction : I. in F. : Times Literary Supplement.*]

—— Fardorougha the Miser, Or The Convicts of Lisnamona. Dublin, Curry, 1839. [*I. in F.* : Arthur Rogers : G. Worthington.]

—— Father Butler and the Lough Derg Pilgrim : Sketches of Irish Manners, Dublin, William Curry, 1829. [*I. in F.*]

—— The Fawn of Spring-Vale, The Clarionet, And other Tales. 3 vols., Dublin, William Curry, Jun. ; and Longman, Orme, 1841. [B.M. : Ingpen.]

—— Hyde Marston ; Or, A Sportsman's Life. By Craven. 3 vols., London, Henry Colburn, 1844. [B.M. : F. J. Brown.]

—— The Misfortunes of Barney Branagan. 1841. [*Chambers' Cyclop. Eng. Lit.*]

—— Paddy-go-Easy and his Wife Nancy. Dublin, James Duffy, 1845. [*Guide to Best Fiction : I. in F.*]

—— Rody the Rover. Dublin, James Duffy, 1845. [*Guide to Best Fiction : I. in F.*]

—— Tales and Sketches, illustrating the Character, Usages, Traditions, Sports and Pastimes of the Irish Peasantry. With illustrations by " Phiz " [Hablot K. Browne]. Dublin, 1845. [Block.]

—— Tales of Ireland. By the Author of " Traits and Stories of the Irish Peasantry." With etchings by W. H. Brooke. Dublin, William Curry, Jun. ; Simpkin and Marshall, London, 1834. [B.M. : *I. in F.* : G. Worthington.]

Carleton, William. The Tithe-Proctor. A Novel, being a tale of the Tithe Rebellion in Ireland. Belfast, Simms and M'Intyre, 1849. [*I. in F.* : Blakey.]

—— Traits and Stories Of the Irish Peasantry. With illustrations by W. H. Brooke. 2 vols., Dublin William Curry, Jun., 1830. [B.M. :, *Guide to Best Fiction* : Marks.]

——Traits and Stories Of the Irish Peasantry. Second Series. 3 vols., William Frederick Wakeman, 1833. [B.M. : *Guide to Best Fiction* : Pickering.]

—— Valentine M'Clutchy, The Irish Agent ; Or, Chronicles of the Castle Cumber Property. 3 vols., Dublin, James Duffy ; Chapman and Hall, London ; Oliver and Boyd, Edinburgh, 1845. [B.M. : *Critic* : *I. in F*.]

Carlyle, Thomas. German Romance : Specimens of its chief authors ; with Biographical and Critical Notices. By the Translator of Wilhelm Meister, and Author of the Life of Schiller. With engraved title-pages. 4 vols., Edinburgh, William Tait ; and Charles Tait, London, 1827. [B.M. : Colbeck : Ingpen.]

Carmichael, Mrs. A. C. Tales Of a Grandmother. London, Richard Bentley, 1841. [B.M.]

Carnan, T. (?), [Edited by]—Six Pennyworth of Wit ; or, Little stories for little folks of all denominations. With woodcuts. London, [1780 ?]. [B.M.]

Carne, John. The Exiles of Palestine. A Tale of The Holy Land. By the Author of " Letters from the East," &c. 3 vols., London, Saunders and Otley, 1831. [B.M. : Lib. of Congress.]

—— Stratton Hill, A Tale of The Civil Wars. By the Author of " Letters from the East," " Tales of the West of England," &c. &c. 3 vols., London, Henry Colburn, 1829. [B.M. : Sotheran.]

—— Tales of the West. By the Author of Letters from the East. 2 vols., London, Henry Colburn, 1828. [B.M. : Ingpen : McLeish.]

Caroline, by a Lady. 3 vols., 1798. [B.M. : *New Ann. Reg.*]

Caroline de Montmorenci : a tale, founded in fact. By La Marquise de * * * * *. London, T. N. Longman, 1794. [B.M. : *New Ann. Reg.*]

Caroline Merton, a Novel Founded on Facts, By a Lady. 2 vols., London, 1794. [*Eng. Lit. in Germany : New Ann. Reg.* : W. T. Spencer.]

Caroline Ormsby, or the Advantage of Education. London, Printed at the Minerva Press, for A. K. Newman, 1809. [*Monthly Mag.*]

Carové, Friedrich Wilhelm. The Story without an End. From the German of Friedrich Wilhelm Carové. By Sarah Austin. With 17 woodcuts by Harvey. London, Effingham Wilson, 1834. [*Camb. Hist. Eng. Lit.* : J. G. Commin : Publisher's advert.]

Carpenter's Daughter, of Derham-Down (The) ; or Sketches on the Banks of Windermere. 2 vols., London, William Lane, Minerva Press, 1791. [B.M. : Pickering : Stonehill.]

Carr, E. D. Fears and Cares. A Novel. 3 vols., London, A. K. Newman, 1821. [B.M.]

Carr, Frances Susanna. Genevive : A Tale. Isabella : An Historical Sketch. London, Cowie, Low. 1826. [B.M.]

Carr, John. The Life and Opinions of Tristram Shandy, Gentleman. Volume III. London, Scott, 1760. [B.M. : Lowndes.]

Carr, R. Blighted Ambition ; Or, The Rise and Fall of The Earl of Somerset. A Romance. 3 vols., London, G. and W. B. Whittaker, 1822. [B.M. : P. C. Cuttelle : Pickering.]

Carrington, E. Confessions of An Old Bachelor. London, Henry Colburn, 1827. [*Blackwood's Edin. Mag.* : B.M. : Ingpen.]

—— Confessions of an Old Maid. 3 vols., London, Henry Colburn, 1828. [B.M. : McLeish : T. Thorp.]

Carter, John. The Scotch Parents ; or, the remarkable case of John Ramble, written by himself. With 2 plates, London, 1773. [B.M.]

Cartwright, Mrs. H. The Duped Guardian : or, the Amant Malade. A novel. In a series of letters. 2 vols., London, 1785. [*Bibliot. Brit.* : B.M.]

—— The Generous Sister. In a Series of Letters. 2 vols., 1780. [*Bibliot. Brit.*]

—— Memoirs of Lady Eliza Audley. 2 vols., 1779. [*Bibliot. Brit.* : *Eng. Lit. in Germany*].

—— The Platonic Marriage : a Novel, in a Series of Letters. 2 vols. Dublin, 1787. [T. D. Webster.]

—— Retaliation ; or, the History of Sir Edward Oswald, and Lady Francis Seymour. A Novel. In a Series of Letters. 4 vols., London, F. Noble, 1787. [*Bibliot. Brit.* : Block.]

Cartwright, Mrs. Robert. Lamia : A Confession. 2 vols., London, Henry Colburn, 1850. [Kyrle Fletcher : Arthur Rogers : Geo. Ward.]

Carver, Mrs. Elizabeth. A novel. 3 vols., London, William Lane, 1797. [Blakey.]

—— The Old Woman. A novel By the author of The Horrors of Oakendale Abbey. London, Author, 1800. [*Minerva Press Catalogue* : Blakey.]

Casket (The), or, the Orphan's Portion. With 3 plates. London, J. Harris, 1808. [Dobell.]

Castle de Albani (The) ; Or, The Usurper Punished : Including The Memoirs of The Countess St. Alva, And her Daughter Isabella. An Original Romance. With an engraving and a woodcut. London, John Arliss, N.D. [Court Bk. Shop.]

Castle Fiend (The) ; or, the Fate of the loved and the lost. An old English romance. London, [1847]. [B.M.]

Castle Martyr ; Or, A Tale of Old Ireland. 2 vols., London, Cunningham & Mortimer, 1839. [Publisher's advert. : T. D. Webster.]

Castle of Bucktholme (The). 3 vols., 1797. [*New Ann. Reg.*]

Castle of Caithness. A romance of the thirteenth century. By F. H. P. 2 vols., London, Printed at the Minerva Press, for Lane & Newman, 1802. [Blakey.]

Castle of Probation (The), or Perceptive Romances ; chiefly taken from life. By a Clergyman. 2 vols., London, 1802. [B.M.]

Castle of the Pyrenees (The) ; or, the Wanderer of the Alps. An historic tale. London, A. Lemoine, [1803]. [B.M.]

Castle of St. Bernard ; or, the Captive of the Watch Tower. In which is Illustrated the Fatal Effects of Misplaced Love, and the Errors of Credulity. To which is added, the Twin Brothers of Mezzorania. With a frontispiece. London, Langley and Belch, 1810. [Stonehill.]

Castle of St. Caranza (The). A romance. 2 vol. [Minerva Press, 1803]. [Blakey.]

Castle of St. Donats (The), or, The History of Jack Smith By Charles Lucas. 3 vols., London, William Lane, 1798. [*New Ann. Reg.* : Blakey.]

Castle of Santa Fe, a novel By a Clergyman's Daughter, author of Jealousy, or The Dreadful Mistake. With a frontispiece. 4 vols., London, Lane, Newman, and Co., 1805. [Publisher's advert. : Blakey.]

Castle of St. Vallery (The), an Ancient Story. 1792. [*Eng. Lit. in Germany* : *New Ann. Reg.*]

Castle of Tariffa (The) ; or, the Self-banished Man. A novel. By the author of " The Fugitive Daughter, or Eva of Cambria, etc. 4 vols., London, B. Crosby, 1812. [B.M. : *Quarterly Review.*]

Castle of Villa-Flora (The). A Portuguese Tale, From a Manuscript lately found by a British Officer of Rank in an Old Mansion in Portugal. 3 vols., London, Printed at the Minerva Press for A. K. Newman, 1819. [B.M. : *Quarterly Review.*]

Castle on the Rock (The), or Memoirs of the Elderland Family. 3 vols., 1798. [*New Ann. Reg.*]

Castle Zittaw : a German Tale. By C. R. 3 vols., London, William Lane, 1794. [Blakey.]

Castle-Builders (The) : or the History of William Stephens of the Isle of Wight, Esq. A Political Novel. London, 1759. [Parker & Son.]

Castles in the Air ; Or, the Whims of my aunt. A Novel By the Authoress of " Dunethvin ; or, a Visit to Paris." 3 vols., London, Baldwin, Cradock, and Joy, 1818. [B.M. : *New Monthly Mag.*]

Castles of Marsange and Nuger ; Or The Novitiate de Ronsillon. A Tale altered from the French by a Lady. In which is introduced the History of Paulina and Isabella by the Translator. 3 vols., Faversham, Warren, 1809. [Ingpen.]

Castles of Montreuil and Barre (The) ; or, the Histories of the Marquis La Brun and the Baron La Marche, the late Inhabitants and Proprietors of the Two Castles. A Gothic Story. With a frontispiece. London, Fisher, 1799. [Stonehill.]

Castles of Wolfnorth and Mont Eagle. 4 vols., London, Hookham, 1812. [*Eng. Cat.* : *Quarterly Review.*]

Castro, Adolphe de. El Buscapié ; or, the serpent. From the Spanish, by J. Ross. London, 1849. [Lib. of Congress.]

Catharine Howell, or, the little burnt girl. London, [1847]. [B.M.]

Cathcart, Miss. Adelaide ; A Story of Modern Life. 3 vols., London, Longman, Rees, Orme, Brown, Green and Longman ; Richard Nichols, Wakefield, 1833. [B.M.]

Cathcart, Miss. The Heir of Mordaunt. By the author of " Adelaide." 3 vols., London, Richard Bentley, 1835. [B.M.]

Catherine II. Empress of Russia. Ivan Clarowitz, Or The Rose without Prickles that Stings not. A Tale. Written by Her Imperial Majesty. Translated from the Russian Language. With a vignette title. London, Robinson ; G. Edwards ; T. Kay ; and T. Chapman, 1793. [B.M.]

Catherine de Medicis, Or The Rival Faiths. London, Smith, Elder, 1834. [B.M.]

Catherine Howard ; or, Trials and Triumphs. By the author of " Look up." London, Religious Tract Society, [1848]. [B.M. : *Eng. Cat.*]

Catherine Waters : A Tale, Founded on Facts, Addressed to Young Women, on Their Entering into Service. By the Author of " Hannah Lancaster." London, Harvey and Darton, 1826. [B.M.]

Cathluna, a Tale, in Five Parts. London, 1820. [*Quarterly Review.*]

Cato, or interesting adventures of a dog of sentiment : interspersed with anecdotes. By a Lady. London, J. Harris, 1816. [B.M.]

Caunter, John Hobart. The Fellow Commoner. 3 vols., London, Edward Churton, 1836. [B.M.]

—— Posthumous Records of a London Clergyman. London, Parker, 1835. [*Eng. Cat.* : Lib. of Congress.]

—— The Romance of History : India. 3 vols., London, Edward Churton, 1836. [B.M.]

Cave of St. Sidwell (The) ; or the Hermit of the Forest, History and Interesting Adventures of Reginald, Count of St. Osbert and his daughter Rosa, Crimes and Intrigues of the Countess, Their Escape from Banditti. With a folding frontispiece. London, Dean and Munday, [183-]. [R. S. Frampton.]

Cavern in the Wicklow Mountains (The) ; or, Fate of the O'Brien Family. 2 vols., Dublin, Printed for the Author, 1821. [*I. in F.*]

Cavern of Astolpho (The). 2 vols., London, Simpkin, 1815. [*Eng. Cat.* : *New Monthly Mag.*]

Cavern of Death (The). A moral tale. London, 1794. [B.M. (2nd edn.)]

Cavern of Horrors (The) ; or, Miseries of Miranda : a Neapolitan Tale. With a frontispiece. London, Hurst, 1802. [*Eng. Lit. in Germany* : Stonehill.]

Cavern of Strozzi (The). A Venetian tale. [W. Lane, 1800]. [Blakey.]

Cazotte, Jacques. The Devil in Love, from the French of Cazotte. 1793. [*New Ann. Reg.*]

—— The Enamoured Spirit. A novel. Translated from the French. London, 1798. [B.M.]

Cecil, Mrs. Charles. New Juvenile Scrapbook : a collection of most interesting tales for the instruction of young people. Edited by Mrs. Charles Cecil. London, [1830 ?] [B.M.]

Cecil, Henry Montague. The Mysterious Visitor, Or May, the Rose of Cumberland. A Novel. 2 vols., London, 1805. [Allibone : *Bibliot. Brit.*]

Cecilia : or the Eastern Lovers. A Novel. Translated from the French. London, Printed for the Author, 1773. [J. C. Hardy.]

Cecily Fitz-Owen ; Or, a Sketch of Modern Manners. 2 vols., London, Printed for Vernor and Hood ; By W. Blackader, 1805. [B.M.]

Celensis ; or, The History of Hyempsal, King of Numidia. [T. D. Webster.]

Celia Suited, or the Rival Heiresses ; comprising new sketches of modern female habits and manners. 2 vols., London, 1810. [B.M. : *Monthly Mag.*]

Cephas ; or, the Shipwrecked Sailor. By his Father. A warning to the young, and an incentive to the faith of pious but discouraged parents. London, Thomas Ward, 1837. [*Publisher's advert.*]

Cervantes, Miguel de. A Dialogue between Scipio and Bergansa, two Dogs belonging to Toledo. To which is annexed the History of Rincon and Cortado. Now first translated from the Spanish. London, 1767. [B.M.]

—— Exemplary Novels. [Translated by Miss Moore.] 2 vols., London, Cadell, 1824. [Allibone : *Eng. Cat.*]

—— The Exploits of Don Quixote, de la Mancha, with the humorous conceits of his facetious squire Sancho Panca. Abridged. With a frontispiece and 6 plates. London, J. Harris, 1806. [Gumuchian. " The first edition of this adaptation for children."]

—— The Force of Blood. A novel. Translated from the Spanish of Miguel de Cervantes. London, 1800. [B.M.]

—— The History and Adventures of the Renowned Don Quixote. Translated From the Spanish of Miguel de Cervantes Saavedra. To which is prefixed Some Account of the Author's Life. By T[obias]. Smollett, M.D. With 28 plates after Hayman. 2 vols., London, A. Millar, T. Osborn, T. and T. Longman, 1755. [B.M. : Maggs : Marks.]

—— The History of Don Quixote de la Mancha. A new edition divested of cumbrous matter and revised for general reading. To which is prefixed a sketch of the life and writings of the author. London, 1847. [B.M.]

—— The History of the ingenious gentleman, Don Quixote de la Mancha. A new edition, with copious notes ; and an essay on the life and writings of Cervantes [by John Gibson Lockhart]. 5 vols., Edinburgh, 1822. [B.M.]

—— The History of the renowned Don Quixote de la Mancha Translated into English by G. Kelly, Esq. To which are added notes. With plates. 4 vols., London, E. Carpenter and A. Bridgman, 1769. [B.M.]

Cervantes, Miguel de. Instructive and entertaining novels. Translated from the original Spanish By T. Shelton. With an account of the work, by a gentleman of the Middle Temple. London, 1742. [B.M.]

—— Life and Exploits of the Ingenious gentleman, Don Quixote de la Mancha. From the Spanish, by Mary Smirke. With illustrations by Robert Smirke. 4 vols., London, Cadell and Davies, 1818. [B.M. : Lib. of Congress : Marks.]

—— The Life and exploits of the ingenious gentleman Don Quixote de la Mancha. Now carefully revised and corrected ; with a new translation of the Spanish Poetry : To which is prefixed a new life of Cervantes ; including a critique on the Quixote : also a chronological plan of the work. With engravings and a map. 4 vols., London, 1801. [B.M.]

—— The Life and Exploits of the Ingenious Gentleman Don Quixote de la Mancha, with the Humorous Conceits of his Facetious Squire Sancho Panca. Abridged. With a frontispiece. London, F. Newbery, 1778. [Arthur Rogers.]

—— Persiles and Sigismunda, A Celebrated Novel, Intermix'd with a great Variety of Delightful Histories and Entertaining Adventures, Translated from the Spanish. With a portrait. 2 vols., London, 1741. [McLeish.]

Chadwick, Mrs. Novels of Nature. London, Longman, Rees, Orme, Brown, Green and Longman ; George Davey, Bristol, 1837. [B.M.]

Chaigneau, William. The History of Jack Connor. 2 vols., London, W. Johnston, 1752. [Vol. II is entitled " The History of Jack Connor, now Conyers."] [B.M. : Ingpen : W. T. Spencer.]

Chamber of Death (The) ; or, The Fate of Rosario. An Historical Romance of the Sixteenth Century. By Orlando. 2 vols., London, Minerva Press, 1809. [*Monthly Mag.* : Stonehill.]

Chambers, Marianne. He Deceives Himself ; A Domestic Tale. 3 vols., 1799. [Allibone : *Bibliot. Brit.* : *New Ann. Reg.*]

Chambers, William. Truth and Trust. 1848. [B.M.]

Chamerovzow, Louis Alexis. The Yule Log, for Everybody's Hearth. Showing where it grew, how it was cut and brought home, and how it was burnt. By the author of " Chronicles of the Bastile." With illustrations by George Cruikshank. London, J. & D. A. Darling, 1847. [Cleverdon : Publishers; advert.]

Chamerovzow, Louis Alexis. Chronicles of the Bastile. First Series. The Bertaudière. An historical romance. (The Iron Mask. An episode. 1697-1703.) With plates by I. R. Cruikshank. London, T. C. Newby, 1845. [B.M.]

—— The Embassy ; or, the Key to a Mystery. Being the second series of the Chronicles of the Bastille. London, T. C. Newby, 1846. [B.M.]

Chamier, Frederick. The Arethusa. A Naval Story. 3 vols., London, Richard Bentley, 1837. [B.M. : T. Thorp.]

—— Ben Brace, The Last of Nelson's Agamemnons. 3 vols., London, Richard Bentley, 1836. [B.M.]

—— Count Königsmark : An Historical Novel. 3 vols., London, Henry Colburn, 1845. [B.M. : Publisher's advert. : G. Worthington.]

—— Jack Adams, The Mutineer. 3 vols., London, Henry Colburn, 1838. [B.M. : Pickering.]

—— The Life of a Sailor. By A Captain in the Navy. 3 vols., London, Richard Bentley, 1832. [B.M. : E. J. Evans Stonehill.]

—— Passion and Principle. A Novel. Edited by Captain Frederick Chamier, R.N. 3 vols., London, Henry Colburn, 1842. [B.M.]

—— The Peril of Beauty. 3 vols., London, Henry Colburn, 1843. [B.M.]

—— The Spitfire. A Tale of the Sea. 3 vols., London, Henry Colburn, 1840. [B.M. : Ingpen.]

—— Tom Bowling : A Tale of the Sea. 3 vols., London, Henry Colburn, 1841. [B.M. : T. Thorp.]

—— The Unfortunate Man. 3 vols., London, Richard Bentley, 1835. [B.M. : Marks : G. Worthington.]

—— Walsingham, The Gamester. 3 vols., London, Richard Bentley, 1837. [B.M.]

Chamisso, Adelbert von. Peter Schlemihl, The Shadowless Man, From the German of Adelbert Von Chamisso, By Sir John Bowring. With plates by George Cruikshank. London, Whittaker, 1824. [*Eng. Cat.* : Chas. Hutt.]

—— The Wonderful History of Peter Schlemihl. Translated by William Howitt. With 6 illustrations. London, Longman, Brown, Green and Longman, 1843. [Pickering.]

Chances (The), or Nothing of the New School. A Novel. By a disciple of the Old School. 3 vols., London, Cuthell, 1803. [Baker's Bookshop : Ingpen.]

Chantilly. 3 vols., London, Edward Bull, 1832. [B.M. : Elkin Mathews : G. Worthington.]

Characters and Opinions : or the Blue Book. London, Saunders, 1825. [*Edin. Mag.* : *Eng. Cat.*]

Chariton of Aphrodisias. The Loves of Chaereas and Callirrhöe. Written originally in Greek, by Chariton of Aphrodisios. Now first translated into English.

2 vols., London, T. Becket, 1764. [*Bibliot. Brit.* : *Guide to Best Fiction* : Pickering.]

Charles, Mrs. E. Tales and Sketches of Christian Life in different lands and ages. London, Nisbet, 1850. [B.M. : *Eng. Cat.*]

Charles and Charlotte. 2 vols., London, William Lane, 1777. [Blakey. *Eng. Lit. in Germany.*]

Charles Mowbray ; or, Duelling. A tale founded on fact. By the author of " The Widow O'Leary." Cork, 1847. [B.M. : *I. in F.*]

Charles Ross ; or, Truth and Fiction. By the author of " The New Estate." London, Harvey, 1835. [B.M. : *Eng. Cat.*]

Charley Chalk, or the Career of an Artist, being Sketches from Real Life. With vignette title and 19 illustrations by Jacob Parallel. Berger, [1840]. [*Eng. Cat.* : Marks.]

Charlie Seymour, Or the Good Aunt, and the Bad Aunt. London, Whittaker, Treacher, 1832. [Publisher's Advert.]

Charlton, Mary. Andronica ; or the Fugitive Bride. A novel. 2 vols., 1797. [*Bibliot. Brit.* : Blakey.]

—— Grandeur and Meanness ; Or, Domestic Persecution. A Novel. 3 vols., London, A. K. Newman, 1824. [*Eng. Cat.*]

—— The Homicide. A Novel. Taken from the Comedie di Goldoni. 2 vols., London, Printed at the Minerva Press for Lane, Newman & Co., 1805. [*Bibliot. Brit.* : Ingpen : Blakey.]

—— The Parisian ; or, genuine anecdotes of distinguished and noble characters. 2 vols., London, William Lane, 1794. [B.M. : *New Ann. Reg.* : Publisher's advert.]

—— Past Events ; An Historical Novel, Of the Eighteenth Century, By the Author of " The Wife & the Mistress," " The Pirate of Naples," " Rosella," Andronica," &c. &c. 3 vols., London, R. P. Moore. 1824. [B.M.]

—— Phedora ; Or, The Forest of Minski. A Novel. With a frontispiece. 4 vols., London, Printed at the Minerva Press, for William Lane, 1798. [*Bibliot. Brit.* : B.M. : Blakey.]

—— The Philosophic Kidnapper. A Novel. Altered from the French by the Author of The Wife and The Mistress. 3 vols., London, Printed at the Minerva Press, 1803. [Arthur Rogers : Blakey.]

—— Pirate of Naples (The). A Novel. 3 vols., London, William Lane, 1801. [*Eng. Lit. in Germany* : Blakey.]

—— Rosaura di Viralva ; or, The Homicide. A Novel. 2 vols., London, Printed at the Minerva Press, for A. K. Newman, 1813. [Publisher's advert. (2nd edn.) : Stonehill (2nd edn.).]

—— Rosella, Or Modern Occurrences. A Novel. 4 vols., London, William Lane, 1799. [Ingpen : Blakey.]

Charlton, Mary. The Wife And the Mistress. A Novel. 4 vols., London, Printed at the Minerva Press for Lane & Newman, 1802. [Birrell and Garnett : B.M. : Stonehill.]

Charriere, Madame de. Honorine d' Userchi, St. Anne, and the Ruins of Yedburg. 3 vols., London, 1808. [*Bibliot. Brit.*]

Chateau de Myrell. A Novel. London, T. Hookham and J. Carpenter. [Publisher's advert., 1791.]

Chateau of Leaspach ; or, the Stranger in Switzerland. A Tale. 3 vols., London, A. K. Newman, 1827. [B.M.]

Chateaubriand, François René, Vicomte de. Aben-Hamet, The Last of The Abencerages ; A Romance, By the Viscount de Chateaubriand. Translated from the French. With a portrait, vignette and a page of music. London, Treuttel and Würtz, Treuttel, Jun., and Richter, 1826. [B.M.: Lib. of Congress : *Quarterly Review.*]

—— Atala ; or, The Amours of Two Indians in the wilds of America. London, 1802. [*Bibliot. Brit.* : Lib. of Congress : *Quarterly Review.*]

—— The Natchez ; An Indian Tale. 3 vols., London, Henry Colburn, 1827. [*Blackwood's Edin. Mag.* : B.M. : Lib. of Congress.]

—— René : a Tale from the French. 1813. [*Guide to best Fiction.*]

—— The Two Martyrs : a Moral Tale. 1819. [*Guide to Best Fiction.*]

Chatelain, Madame de. The Silver Swan. A Fairy Tale. With illustrations by John Leech. London, Grant and Griffith, 1848. [Publisher's advert.]

Chater, John. History of Tom Rigby. 1773. [*Eng. Lit. in Germany.*]

Chatterton, Lady Georgiana. Allanston ; or, The Infidel. Edited by Lady Chatterton. 3 vols., London, T. C. Newby, 1844. [*Tait's Edin. Mag.*]

—— Aunt Dorothy's Tale ; Or, Geraldine Morton. A Novel. 2 vols., London, Richard Bentley, 1837. [B.M.: Pickering.]

—— A Good Match, The Heiress of Drosberg, And the Cathedral Chorister. 3 vols., London, Richard Bentley, 1840. [B.M.]

—— Lost Happiness, or the Effects of a Lie. London, James Burns, 1845. [Allibone : *Eng. Cat.*]

Chavis, Dom, and **Cazotte,** Jacques. Arabian Tales : or, a continuation of the Arabian Nights Entertainments. Consisting of Stories related by the Sultana of the Indies, To divert her Husband from the Performance of a rash Vow. Exhibiting A most interesting View of the Religion, Laws, Manners, Customs, Arts, and Literature, of the Nations of the East ; and Affording a rich Fund of the most pleasing Amusement, which Fictitious Writings can supply. Newly translated from the Original Arabic into French, By Dom Chavis, a native Arab, and Mr. Cazotte, Member of the Academy of Dijon. And translated from the French into English, By Robert Heron. 4 vols. Edinburgh, Bell & Bradfute, J. Dickson, E. Balfour, and P. Hill, Edinburgh; And G. G. J. & J. Robinson, London, 1792. [Block : Marks : *New Ann. Reg.*]

Cheney, Edward. Malvagna. A Romance of the Nineteenth Century. 3 vols., London, Richard Bentley, 1835. [B.M.]

Cherries (The). From the German. With a vignette. London, James Burns, [1849]. [B.M.]

Chetwood, W. R. Adrastus and Olinda ; or Love's Champion. [P. L. Carver.

—— The Inhuman Uncle ; or, the Repentant Villains. [P. L. Carver.]

—— The Stepmother ; or Good Luck at Last. [P. L. Carver.]

—— The Twins ; or, the Female Traveller. A novel. Written by Mr. C——d, etc. 1742. [B.M. : P. L. Carver.]

—— The Virgin Widow. [P. L. Carver.]

Chiari, Abbé Pietro. The Generous Lover : or The Adventures of the Marchioness de Brainville. Translated from the original Italian of the Abbé Pietro Chiari. 3 vols., London, D. Steel, 1771. [Pickering.]

—— A Prize in the Lottery ; or, the Adeventures of a Young Lady, written by herself. From the Italian of l'Abbate Chiari. Translated by Thomas Evanson White, with an introduction and notes. 2 vols., London, Sherwood, Neely and Jones, 1817. [B.M. : *New Monthly Mag. : Quarterly Review.*]

—— Rosara ; or, the Adventures of an Actress. A Story from Real Life. Translated from the Italian. 3 vols., London, 1771. [*Bibliot. Brit.*]

Chicken, Edward. The comical history of the collier's wedding at Benwell near Newcastle upon Tyne. [London ?] [1815 ?] [B.M.]

Child and the Hermit (The) ; or, a sequel to the Story without an End ; by C. M. London, Darton, [1840 ?] [B.M.]

Child of Disobedience (The) ; or, the Broken Heart. A tale for youth, founded on fact. Dublin, 1830. [B.M.]

Child of Providence (The) ; a novel. 4 vols. London, William Lane, 1792. [Blakey.]

Child of Two Fathers (The) ; or, The Mysteries of the Days of Old. A Romance of Deep Interest. With wood-cuts. London, E. Lloyd, [1850 ?] [B. Ono.]

Childe, Miss A. F. Good out of Evil ; or, the History of Adjai, the African Slave-boy ; by a Lady. With an intro-ductory notice, by C. F. Childe. London, Wertheim, 1850. [B.M. : *Eng. Cat.*]

Children as They Are ; Or, Tales and Dialogues, For Young Readers From Seven to Twelve Years of Age. By the Author of " The Transformation of a Beech-Tree." With plates. London, Harvey and Darton, 1830. [B.M.]

Child's Vision (The) : or the Angel and the Oak. By the author of " The Priestess." London, Hatchard, 1846. [B.M. : *Eng. Cat.*]

Chilton, John. The History of Arden of Faversham. A Tragic Fact, of 1550. To which is added, The White Tower. An Historic Tale. With a frontispiece. London, Printed by T. Maiden for Ann Lemoine ; and J. Roe, [1804]. [B.M.]

Chit-Chat : or Natural Characters ; and the Manners of Real Life, Represented in a series of Interesting Adventures. 2 vols., London, R. and J. Dodsley, 1754. [B.M.]

Chit-Chat, Or Short Tales in Short Words. By the Author of " Always Happy," &c. With plates. London, John Harris, 1831. [Court Bk. Shop (2nd edn.).]

Choice Gift (The) ; containing the Art of Talking with the Fingers, and the enter-taining stories of Sally Bark and Harry Jones. London, 1821. [B.M.]

Choice Tales. For the instruction and amusement of young persons. London, Vernor & Hood, 1799. [B.M.]

Choiseul, Comtesse de. The Return of the Fairies, from the French. [Trans-lated by Charlotte Herdman.] With plates. Dublin, John Cumming, [1827]. [Pickering ; *Nat. Mag. Co.*]

Chorley, Henry Fothergill. Conti the Discarded ; With Other Tales and Fancies. 3 vols., London, Saunders and Otley, 1835. [B.M.]

—— The Lion ; A Tale of the Coteries. 3 vols., London, Henry Colburn, 1839. [B.M.]

—— Pomfret ; Or, Public Opinion and Private Judgment. 3 vols., London, Henry Colburn, 1845. [B.M. : *Critic.*]

—— Sketches Of a Sea Port Town. 3 Vols., London, Richard Bentley, 1834. [B.M.]

Choudard-Desforges. Eugène and Eugenia ; or, One night's error. Altered from the French of Choudard-Desforges. 3 vols. [Minerva Press, 1805.] [Blakey : Publisher's advert.]

Christian Drummer (The) ; a true story. Gainsborough, [1825 ?] [B.M.]

Christian Trials. A narrative from real life. By the Author of " The Week." London, Seeley, 1837. [B.M. : *Eng. Cat.*]

Christmas, Jane. Glendearg Cottage. A tale concerning Church principles. With a preface by H. Christmas. London, Smith, Elder, 1846. [B.M.]

Christmas Box (The), or New Year's Gift. With illustrations. London, Religious Tract Society, [1820 ?]. [B.M.]

Christmas Dinner (The). With a woodcut. London, Houlston, N.D. No. 57 of Houlston's Series of Tracts. [Block.]

Christmas Holidays or the Young Visitants ; A Tale in which many pleasant descriptions of that festive season, both in Town and Country, are given, for the benefit of the Rising Generation. With 4 plates. London, J. Harris, 1806. [Gumuchian.]

Christmas Log (The). A tale Of a fireside that had a good genius and A bad one. London, E. Lloyd, [1846]. [Block : B.M. : B. Ono.]

Christmas Shadows. A tale of the times. London published, Woking printed, [1850]. [B.M.]

Christmas Tales. London, R. Ackermann, 1825. [Ingpen : *Quarterly Review* : Arthur Rogers.]

Christmas Tales. Containing the following interesting Stories : Time Lost and Afterwards Regained. 1799. [Arthur Rogers.]

Christmas Tales for the Amusement and Instruction of Young Ladies and Gentlemen in Winter Evenings. By Solmon Sobersides. With a frontispiece and 44 woodcuts. Gainsborough, Mozley, 1795. [F. Hollings.]

Christmas Week in the Country. London, J. Hatchard, 1826. [B.M.]

Chronicle of Abomilech (The), King of the Isles, translated from a Latin manuscript written in the year 1820. By William of Salisbury. London, 1820. [B.M.]

Chronicle of the Cid. 1808. [*Guide to Best Fiction.*]

Chronicle of the City of the Seven Hills : Translated from An Ancient Manuscript, Found in an Old Chest, while searching for the Keys of the City, which were supposed to have been pawned during its Bankruptcy. As it appeared in the Observer of Friday, Sept. 9, 1842. Edinburgh, W. & H. Robinson, 1842. [B.M.]

Cicely and Agnes. London, 1848. [B.M.]

Cicely, or, the Power of Honesty. London, [1797 ?] Cheap Repository. [B.M.]

Citizen's Daughter (The) ; or, What might be. London, 1804. [B.M.]

City Cousins. By the author of Annie Sherwood. London, Religious Tract Society, [1847]. [B.M.]

City Jilt (The) : Or, the Alderman turn'd Beau. A Secret History. London, T. Bailey, [1740 ?] [B.M.]

City Nobility ; or, a Summer at Margate : a novel. By the author of two popular novels. 3 vols., London, 1808. [B.M.]

Clara, a Tale. 2 vols., London, G. Kearsley, 1801. [B.M. : Ingpen.]

Clara Webster ; a tale. By Nero. London, Piper, 1850. [B.M. : *Eng. Cat.*]

Clarinda, Or a Genuine Narrative of all that befell a Lady, her escapes from her many lovers, and the method used by a Jesuit Priest to obtain her good graces, with the manner of his putting her to death. London, Printed for the Author, 1751. [Dobell.]

Clarisse ; or The Merchant's Daughter. A Romance. With woodcuts. London, E. Lloyd, 1847. [B.M. : Stonehill : Hollings.]

Clark, John. The Works Of the Caledonian Bards, Translated from the Galic [mostly in prose], By John Clark. Edinburgh, Printed for T. Cadell, London, and C. Elliot, Edinburgh, 1783. [Block (2nd edn.).]

Clarke, Charles Cowden. Adam, the Gardener. London, Effingham Wilson, 1834. [B.M.]

—— Perseverance ; Or God Helps Them who Help Themselves. A Tale. With illustrations by John Absolon. London, Wm. S. Orr, 1844. [B.M.]

—— The Princess Narina, And Her Silver-Feathered Shoes. A Tale. Illustrated by John Absolon. London, Wm. S. Orr, 1844. [B.M.]

—— Tales from Chaucer, In Prose : Designed chiefly for the Use of Young Persons. With 14 woodcuts by Samuel Williams. London, Effingham Wilson, 1833. [Elkin Mathews : Publisher's advert.]

Clarke, Eliza. The Advertisement ; Or, Twenty Years Ago. A Novel. 3 vols., London, Longman, Hurst, Rees, Orme and Brown ; and Barratt, Bath, 1818. [B.M. : *New Monthly Mag.*]

—— The Sword ; Or Father Bertrand's History of his own Times from the Original MS. 2 vols., Liverpool, Printed for the Author, 1791. [Stonehill.]

Clarke, Emily. The Banks of the Douro ; or the Maid of Portugal. 3 vols., Minerva Press, 1805. [*Bibliot. Brit.*]

—— Ermina Montrose, or the Cottage of the Vale ; with Characters from Life. 3 vols., London, 1800. [*Bibliot. Brit.* : B.M.]

—— The Esquimaux ; Or, Fidelity. A Tale. 3 vols., London, Printed at the Minerva Press for A. K. Newman, 1819. [B.M.]

—— Ianthé ; or the Flower of Caernarvon. A novel. 2 vols., London, 1798. [*Bibliot. Brit.* : B.M. : *New Ann. Reg.*]

—— Tales At The Fire Side ; Or, A Father and Mother's Stories. Dedicated by Permission to Colonel M'Mahon. 3 vols., Brentford, P. Norbury, 1817. [B.M.]

Clarke, Hewson. Felician Alphery ; or, The Fortunes of the Raleigh Family. By the Author of " Herwald De Wake."

41

3 vols., London, A. K. Newman, 1828'
[B.M.]

Clarke, Hewson. Herwald De Wake ;
Or, The Two Apostates. A Romance.
3 vols., London, G. and W. B.
Whittaker, 1823. [B.M. : Pickering.]

Clarke, Mary Cowden. Kit Bam's Ad-
ventures ; Or, The Yarns of an Old
Mariner. With illustrations by George
Cruikshank. London, Grant and
Griffith, 1849. [B.M. : Clarke-Hall :
Maggs.]

Clarke, William. The Cigar ; by Ebene-
zer Cullchickweed. With woodcuts by
George Cruikshank. 2 vols., 1825.
[Sotheran.]

—— Three Courses and a Dessert. With
51 illustrations by George Cruikshank.
London, Vizetelly, Branston, 1830.
[Cohn : Publisher's advert.]

Claudine . . . A Swiss Tale by the
Author of Always Happy, Nina, etc.
London, J. Harris, 1822. [Gumuchian.[

Clauren, Heinrich (*see* HEUN).

Clavis de Florian (*see* FLORIAN).

Clayton, W. The Invisible Hand. A
tale. London, Cadell, 1815. [B.M. :
Eng. Cat.]

Cleland, John. Memoirs of a * * * * *
[Woman] ** [of] ******** [Pleasure].
2 vols., London, G. Fenton, [1747 or
1748]. [This is the first edition of
Fanny Hill.] [Bibliothèque de l'Enfer :
I. R. Brussel : *Monthly Review.*]

—— The Memoirs of a Coxcomb. With
a vignette title. London, R. Griffiths,
1751. [Birrell & Garnett : *Cat. Lib.
Prohib. :* Lib. of Congress.]

—— Surprises of Love. London, Lownds,
1765.

Clematis Cottage : a Narrative of the
Afflictions of Mrs. W——, by the
Profligate Life of her Son, with an
account of his conversion. London,
Thomas Ward, 1837. [Publisher's
advert.]

Cliffe, Leigh (*see* JONES, George).

Clifford, Francis. Ruins of Tivoli ; a
Romance. 4 vols., 1804. [*Bibliot. Brit.*]

Clio : Or a Secret History of the Life
and Amours of the late celebrated
Mrs. S—m—n Written by herself in a
letter to Hilarius. London, M. Cooper,
1752. [B.M. : *Cat. Lib. Prohib. :*
Tregaskis.]

Clive, Caroline. Paul Ferrol. A Tale.
By the Author of " IX Poems by V."
London, Saunders & Otley. [*Camb.
Hist. Eng. Lit. : Eng. Cat.*]

Clos, Du. Course of Gallantries. 2 vols.,
1775. [W. Brown.]

Close, John. The Old Farm House. A
tale of the Olden Times, founded upon
the records of " The Book of the
Chronicles of Little Town." And other
pieces in prose and verse. London,
Appleby, 1841. [B.M.]

Coates, H. J. Lucius Carey ; Or the
Mysterious Female of Mora's Dell. An
Historical Tale. By the Author of " The
Weird Woman." 4 vols., London, A. K.
Newman, 1831. [B.M. : *I. in F.*]

—— The Water Queen, Or, the Mermaid
of Loch Lene. And other tales. 3 vols.,
London, A. K. Newman, 1832. [B.M. :
I. in F. : Metropolitan Mag.]

—— The Weird Woman Of the Wraagh ;
or, Burton and le Moore. An Historical
Tale. 4 vols., London, A. K. Newman,
1830. [B.M. : *I. in F.*]

Coates, Henry. The British Don Juan ;
Being a Narrative of the Singular
Amours, Entertaining Adventures,
Remarkable Travels, &c. of the Hon.
Edward W. Montague, Son of the
celebrated Lady Mary Wortly Montague.
With plates. London, James Grffin,
1823. [J. C. Hardy.]

Cobbler ! Stick to your Last ; or, The
Adventures of Joe Dobson. 1807.
[*Camb. Hist. Eng. Lit.*]

Cobbold, Rev. Richard. Freston Tower ;
or, the early days of Cardinal Wolsey.
3 vols., London, 1850. [B.M.]

—— The History of Margaret Catchpole,
a Suffolk Girl. With illustrations. 3
vols., London, Henry Colburn, 1845.
[B.M. : Dobell : E. Hector.]

—— Mary Anne Wellington, The Sol-
dier's Daughter, Wife, and Widov
With 8 Engravings. 3 vols., London,
Henry Colburn, 1846. [B.M. :
McLeish : T. Thorp.]

—— The Young Man's Home ; or, the
Penitent returned. A narrative of the
present day. London, Saunders & Otley,
1848. [B.M.]

—— Zenon, The Martyr ; A Record of
the Piety, Patience, and Persecution Of
the Early Christian Nobles. 3 vols.,
London, Henry Colburn, 1847. [Baker's
Bookshop : B.M. : Elkin Mathews.]

Cochrane, Alexander Baillie. Lucille
Beaumont. A Novel. 3 vols., London,
1849. [B.M. : McLeish.]

Cock-Fighter (The) ; a true history.
Bath, [1820 ?] [B.M.]

Cockle, Mrs. E. The Juvenile Journal ;
or, Tales of Truth. London, Chapple.
1807. [*Bibliot Brit. :* B.M. : *Eng. Cat*].

Cockton, Henry. George St. George
Julian, The Prince. With plates by T.
Onwhyn and a portrait. London,
Grattan and Gilbert, 1841. [Block :
B.M. : G. H. Last.]

—— The Life and Adventures of
Valentine Vox, the Ventriloquist. With
60 plates by T. Onwhyn. London,
Robert Tyas, 1840. [B.M. : Brough :
Arthur Rogers.]

—— The Love Match, designed to illustrate the various conflicting influences
which sprang from the Union of Mr.
and Mrs. Todd. With illustrations.
London, W. M. Clark, 1845. [B.M. :
Mudie's.]

Cockton, Henry. Stanley Thorn. With plates by George Cruikshank. 3 vols., London, Richard Bentley, 1841. [B.M.]
—— The Steward. A Romance of Real Life. With steel engravings by T. Onwhyn. London, W. M. Clark, 1850. [B.M. : *Eng. Cat. :* Stonehill.]
—— Sylvester Sound, The Somnambulist. With illustrations by Onwhyn. London, W. M. Clark, 1844. [B.M. : *Eng. Cat. : Guide to Best Fiction.*]
Cœlebs in Search of a Mistress. 2 vols. 1810. [Sotheby's.]
—— **Married.** Being intended as a Continuation of Cœlebs in Search of a Wife. London, Walker, 1814. [Dobell : Ingpen : *New Monthly Mag.*]
Cogan, Thomas. John Buncle, Junior, Gentleman. 2 vols., London, J. Johnson, 1776. [Birrell & Garnett : *Eng. Lit. in Germany :* Ingpen.]
Cole, Benjamin. Select Tales and Fables, with Prudential Maxims and other Little Lessons of Morality, in Prose and Verse. With engravings. 2 vols., 1746. [Arthur Rogers.]
Cole, Rev. William. The Contradiction. London, T. Cadell and W. Davies, 1796. [B.M. : McLeish : *New Ann. Reg.*]
Coleridge, Sara. Phantasmion. London, William Pickering, 1837. [B.M. : Ingpen.]
Collard, N. The Life and Extraordinary Adventures of James Molesworth Hobart. By N. Dralloc. London, G. Sael, 1794. [Murray Hill.]
College Recollections. London, Longman, 1825. [*Edin. Mag.*]
Collin St. Clyde. 3 vols., London, 1816. [*New Monthly Mag.*]
Collingridge, Augustus. The Lieutenant, And the Crooked Midshipman. A Tale of the Ocean. By a Naval Officer, Author of " Cutting out ashore," " Rough sketches afloat," etc. 2 vols., London, A. K. Newman, 1844. [B.M.]
—— A Night Near Windsor Or Port Royal Annals ; And A Tale of the Turf. London, James Fraser, 1838. [B.M.]
Collins, W., and **Sears,** A. The Young French Emigrants. Or, The Orphans of Montmorency, A Tale for the Moral Instruction and Amusement of Youth of Both Sexes. With a frontispiece. 2 vols., London, J. Souter, and N. Hailes, 1823. [B.M.]
Collins, William. Memoirs Of a Picture : Containing The Adventures of many conspicuous characters, And interspersed with a variety Of amusing anecdotes of several very extraordinary Personages connected with the arts ; Including A genuine Biographical Sketch of that celebrated original and eccentric Genius, The late Mr. George Morland. Drawn from the tolerably authentic source of more than twenty years' intimate acquaintance with him, his family, and connections. To which

is added, A Copious Appendix, Embracing every interesting subject relative to our justly admired English Painter, and his most valuable works. 3 vols., London, Printed by C. Stower, for H. D. Symonds, Bell, Ginger, 1805. [B.M.]
Collins, William Wilkie. Antonina : Or, The Fall of Rome. A Romance of the Fifth Century. 3 vols., London, Richard Bentley, 1850. [R. Hall : King : T. Thorp.]
Collyer, Mary. The Death of Cain, In Five Books ; After the Manner of The Death of Abel. By a Lady. London, B. Crosby, 1789. [B.M. (2nd. edn.).]
—— Felicia to Charlotte : Being Letters from a Young Lady in the Country to Her Friend in Town. 2 vols., London, Jacob Robinson, 1744. [G. Worthington : Murray Hill.]
Colman, George (?) Love and Satire. Containing the Sarcastic Correspondence of Julius & Eliza. To which is prefixed a few brief Memoirs of an Unfortunate Lover. London, M. Allen, 1805. [Baker's Bookshop.]
Colman, George, The Younger. The History of Elsmere and Rosa : An Episode. The Merry Matter written by John Mathers ; The Grave, by a solid gentleman. 2 vols., London, Baldwin, Cradock, and Joy, 1817. [B.M. : Ingpen : Stonehill.]
—— The History of Mr. John De Castro And his Brother Bat, Commonly called Old Crab. The Merry Matter written by John Mathers ; The Grave by a Solid Gentleman. 4 vols., London, T. Egerton, 1815. [B.M. : Ingpen : Arthur Rogers.]
Colombo, M., [attributed to]. Tales of the Cordelier Metamorphosed, as narrated in a manuscript from the Borromeo collection ; and in the Cordelier Cheval of M. Piron. With translations [by G. Hibbert]. With illustrations by I. R. Cruikshank. London, Privately Printed, 1821. [B.M.]
Colonel Berkley and His Friends ; containing sketches of life south of the Potomac ; a tale. 3 vols., London, A. K. Newman, 1825. [B.M. : *Eng. Cat.*]
Colonel Ormsby ; or the Genuine History of an Irish Nobleman in the French Service. 2 vols., Dublin, 1781. [B.M. : *I. in F.*]
Colpoys, Mrs. The Irish Excursion, or I Fear to Tell You. A Novel. 4 vols., London, Printed at the Minerva Press, for William Lane, 1801. [B.M. : Ingpen : *I. in F.*]
Colquhoun, Mrs. Maurice, The Elector of Saxony. An Historical Romance of the Sixteenth Century. Dedicated, by Permission, To His Majesty the King of Saxony. 3 vols., London, T. C. Newby, 1844. [B.M. : *Tait's Edin. Mag. :* T. D. Webster.]

Colquhoun, John Campbell. Zoë : an Athenian Tale. Edinburgh, Archibald Constable, and Hurst, Robinson, 1824. [B.M. : Dobell : Elkin Mathews.]

Colthurst, Miss E. Irrelagh ; or, The Last of the Chiefs. London, Houlston & Stoneman, 1849. [*I. in F.*]

Combe, William. The Devil upon two Sticks In England. Being A continuation of Le Diable Boiteux Of Le Sage. 6 vols., London, Printed at the Logographic Press, 1790–1791. [B.M. : Marks : Stonehill.]

—— Letters Between Amelia in London and her Mother in the Country. With a frontispiece by Corbould. London, R. Ackermann, 1824. [B.M. : Publisher's advert. : Arthur Rogers.]

—— Letters Between Two Lovers and Their Friends. By the Author of " Letters Supposed to have been Written by Yorick and Eliza." London, J. Bew, 1781. [*Eng. Lit. in Germany :* J. C. Hardy.]

—— Letters Supposed to Have Been Written by Yorick and Eliza. 1779. [B.M. : *Eng. Lit. in Germany.*]

Comforts of Arabella (The), The Daughter of Amanda. Printed for the Author by J. Brown, [1800]. [B.M.]

Comic Novel (The) : or, Downing Street and the Days of Victoria. By Lynx. With illustrations. London, H. Bailliere, 1840. [B.M. : Publisher's advert.]

Comical Adventures (The), at sea and on shore of Jacko the baboon. By an Eye-Witness. With engravings. London, [1830 ?] [B.M.]

Comical Adventures of Beau Ogleby (The). London, Tilt and Bogue, [1840]. [Gumuchian.]

Comical and Diverting Courtship, which lately happened between an old woman of fourscore and fifteen and a youth about nineteen, with which she was married. [1750 ?] [B.M.]

Comical Courtship between a Leith Carter and a Fish Woman (A). [Edinburgh ?] [1820 ?]

Comical Fellow (The) ; or, Wit and Humour for Town and Country, containing the Newest, Drollest, Laughable Collections of Pleasant Adventures, Wholesome Stories, Humourous Sayings, Entertaining Tales, Agreeable Humbugs, Merry Waggaries, Smart Repartees, Good Quibbles, Keen Replies, Diverting Jests, Funny Jokes, Lively Bon Mots, Excellent Puns, Curious Bulls, and other Flashes of Merriment ; the Whole being freed from the old, stale, and insipid Jests which are in most other Collections, and contain more Wit and Fun than any thing of the kind ever yet published, though at more than treble the price, by Tim.Gape, Grin-Master General. With a frontispiece. London, W. Lane, 1791. [Pickering.]

Comical History of Simple John and His Twelve Misfortunes. Edinburgh, 1785. [B.M.]

Commodore And his Daughter (The). A Novel. By the Author of The Soldier Boy, Sailor Boy, &c. 3 vols., London, A. K. Newman, 1838. [B.M.]

Common Life. An Artless Tale ; Intended to Illustrate the Effects of Education. 2 vols., London, Ginger, 1804. [Stonehill.]

Complete Picture of Human Life ; or, Variety of food for the mind ; and including a collection of narrations, tales, stories, etc. With a frontispiece. Bolton. B. Jackson, 1787. [*Lancs.*]

Concealment. A Novel. 3 vols., London, John Warren, 1821. [B.M.]

Conduct. a Novel. 3 vols., London Printed at the Minerva Press, for A. K. Newman, 1814. [*Eng. Cat. :* Publisher's advert. : *Quarterly Review.*]

Confederates (The) : A Story. 3 vols., London, T. Hookham, 1823. [B.M.]

Confession of Count de Harcourt, containing His Amours, with several Ladies of Quality in the Courts of France, Italy, and England. With a frontispiece. 1743. [Holland.]

Confessions of a Beauty. From the French. 2 vols., London, Minerva Press, 1798. [New Ann. Reg. : Arthur Rogers.]

Confessions of a Coquet (The). A Novel. In a Series of Letters. London, W. Lane, 1785. [Arthur Rogers.]

Confessions of a Gamester (The). London, T. Hatchard, 1824. [B.M. : Elkin Mathews.]

Confessions of an Homœpathist. Dublin, Samuel B. Oldham ; London, Whittaker, 1846. [*Critic :* Publisher's advert.]

Conflict (The) ; or, the History of Miss Sophia Fanbrook. 3 vols., London, Francis Noble and John Noble, 1767. [B.M. : Pickering.]

Conirdan ; or the St. Kildians : a Moral Tale. By the Author of Hardenbrass and Haverill. London, Sherwood, 1817. [*Eng. Cat. : New Monthly Mag.*]

Conolly, Luke Aylmer. The Friar's Tale ; or, Memoirs of the Chevalier Orsino, with other Narratives. 2 vols., London, 1805. [*Bibliot. Brit. :* B.M. : Marks.]

Conquests of the Heart. 3 vols., 1785. [W. Brown.]

Conrad Blessington : A Tale. By a Lady. London, Longman, Rees, Orme, Brown, Green, & Longman, 1833. [B.M. : D. Webster.]

Conscience, Hendrik. The Lion of Flanders. 1838. [*Guide to Best Fiction.*]

—— Sketches from Flemish Life, in Three Tales : translated from the Flemish of Hendrik Conscience, With illustrations. London, Longman, Brown, Green and Longman, 1846. [Block : B.M. : *Critic.*]

Conscience, Hendrik. Tales of Flemish Life. London, Hamilton, 1840. [*Eng. Cat. : Guide to Best Fiction.*]
—— The Year of Miracles. 1837. [*Guide to Best Fiction.*]
Conscious Duplicity. A novel. 2 vols., London, William Lane, 1791. [Blakey.]
Consider Well What You Are About ; or, the History of Sarah and her Husband. By the author of " The Schoolfellows." London, 1837. [B.M. (5th edn.).]
Conspiracy (The). A Venetian Romance. 3 vols., London, Richard Bentley, 1834. [B.M.]
Constance ; a novel. The first literary attempt of a young lady. 4 vols., London, 1785. [B.M.]
Constance. A Tale Addressed to the Daughters of England. By the Author of Recantation. London, Rivington, 1848. [Ingpen.]
Constancy and Contrition. 3 vols., London, Richard Bentley, 1844. [B.M.]
Constancy ; A Moral Tale. London, John Hatchard, 1826. [B.M.]
Constant de Rebecque, Henri Benjamin. Adolphe : an Anecdote found among the papers of an unknown person. 3 vols., London, 1816. [*Bibliot. Brit. : Guide to Best Fiction : New Monthly Mag.*]
Constantia Beauchamp. 1777. [*Eng. Lit. in Germany.*]
Constantia, Or a True Picture of Human Life, in fifteen Evening Conversations. 2 vols., 1751. [W. Brown.]
Continuation of Vivian Grey (The). 3 vols., 1827. [*Blackwood's Edin. Mag.*]
Continuation of Yorick's Sentimental Journey. London, 1782. [Lowndes.]
Contrast, or The Opposite Consequences of good and evil Habits. The Bright Side of the Contrast exhibited in the Life of Sarah Meanwell. 1787. [*Eng. Lit. in Germany.*]
Contrast (The) ; or, the history of James and Thomas. A tale. Written for the use of Sunday Schools. Henley, [1800 ?] [B.M. (2nd edn.).]
Contrast (The) ; Or, Poverty and Riches. With two fragments. With woodcuts. Dundalk, Joseph Parkes, [1800 ?] [B.M.]
Contrast (The), or Scotland in 1745 and 1825. Wright, 1826. [*Edin. Mag. : Eng. Cat. : Quarterly Review.*]
Contrast (The), a tale, addressed to juvenile minds. Islington, 1829. [B.M.]
Convent (The), and Hester Marten. Aylesbury, 1848. [B.M.]
Convent of Grey Penitents, (The). 2 vols. [Cawthorn's Catalogue, 1810.]
Convent of St. Ursula ; (The). Or, Incidents of Otrago, An Italian Romance : With a frontispiece. London, 1809. [Murray Hill.]
Convent (The) : or, The History of Julia. 2 vols., London, T. Lowndes, 1767. [B.M. : W. T. Spencer.]

Convent Spectre, or, the Unfortunate Daughter. With Frontispiece. London, 1808. [Murray Hill.]
Conway, Derwent (*see* INGLIS, Henry David).
Cooke, James. **Jack Cade. An Historical** Romance. With illustrations. London, White, [*c.* 1840]. [Stonehill.]
Cooke, W. M. The Templar, a Novel, by the Author of " Hymenæus." London, Hugh Cunningham, 1845. [*Eng. Cat. :* Ingpen.]
Coombe, William (*see* COMBE).
Coombe Wood. 2 vols., 1783. [W. Brown.]
Cooper, Mrs. Moral Tales, consisting of : Osman, Almeria, Lucinda and Honoria, Gloriana, Alonzo, Belinda, Louisa and Harriet Serena, Benigna and Malevola, Pleasure and Virtue. London, Mawman, 1811. [G. Worthington.]
Cooper, Emily. Tales and Conversations. London, Fox, 1833. [B.M. : *Literary Gazette.*]
Cooper, James Ransom. Peter Bayssière, a Roman Catholic story. Translated [by James Ransom Cooper]. London, Simpkin, Marshall, 1835. [B.M.]
Cooper, Maria Susanna. Daughter or The History of Miss Emilia Royston and Miss Harriet Ayres. 1775. [*Eng. Lit. in Germany.*]
—— The Exemplary Mother ; or, Letters between Mrs. Villars and her Family. Published by a Lady, From the Originals in her Possession. 2 vols., London, 1769. [B.M. : *Eng. Lit. in Germany :* T. D. Webster.]
—— The History of Fanny Meadows. In a Series of Letters. By the Author of The Exemplary Mother. 2 vols., London, T. Becket, 1775. [Block : Fletcher.]
—— The Wife, or Caroline Herbert. By the late Author of " The Exemplary Mother." 2 vols., London, Becket and Porter, 1813. [Baker's Bookshop : Pickering.]
Cooper, Thomas. Captain Cobler ; or, the Lincolnshire Rebellion ; an historical romance of the reign of Henry VIII. London, 1850. [B.M.]
—— Wise Saws And Modern Instances. 2 vols., London, Jeremiah How, 1845. [B.M. : McLeish.]
Cope, H. Romances Of The Chivalric Ages. The Pilgrim Brothers. With plates. 2 vols., London, Edward Bull, 1833. [B.M.]
Cope, Richard. Robert Melville : Or Characters Contrasted. With a woodcut. Abergavenny, James Hiley Morgan, 1827. [B.M.]
Copson, H. J. The Gipsey's Warning ; or, Love and Ruin. An Entirely Original Romance of Real Life. With illustrations. London, Cousins, [*c.* 1830.]. [Stonehill.]

Coraly. A Novel. 3 vols., London, Longman, Hurst, Rees, Orme, and Brown, 1819.

Corbett, Miss M. The New Happy Week ; or, Holidays at Beechwood. Edinburgh, 1841. [B.M.]

Corbett, The Misses. The Busy-Bodies ; A Novel. By the Authors of " The Odd Volume." 3 vols., London, Longman, Rees, Orme, Brown, & Green ; and Adam Black, Edinburgh, 1827. [*Blackwood's Edin. Mag. :* B.M. : Publisher's advert.]

—— The Odd Volume. Edinburgh, Lizars, 1826. [B.M. : Ingpen : G. Worthington.]

—— The Odd Volume. Second Series. With 6 plates of music. London, Longman, Rees, Orme, Brown, & Green, 1827. [Clarke - Hall : Publisher's advert.]

—— Petticoat Tales. 2 vols., Edinburgh, W. and C. Tait, 1812. [B.M.]

—— The Sisters' Budget ; A Collection of Original Tales in Prose and Verse. By The Authors of " The Odd Volume,', &c. With contributions from Mrs. Hemans, Miss Mitford, Miss Jewsbury, Mrs. Hodson, Mrs. Kennedy, Mr. Macfarlane, Mr. Kennedy, Mr. H. G. Bell, Mr. Malcolm, Etc. 2 vols., London, Whittaker, Treacher, 1831. [B.M. : G. Worthington.]

—— Tales and Legends. By the Authors of " The Odd Volume," &c. 3 vols., Edinburgh, Cadell ; and Simpkin and Marshall, London, 1828. [B.M. : Elkin Mathews.]

Corner, Julia. The Baronet ; ou l'Amant malgré Lui. London, Smith and Elder, 1834. [*Eng. Cat. :* Arthur Rogers.]

—— Girls in Their Teens or Tales for Young Ladies. Containing, Always too Late and the Boarding School. London, Dean and Munday, [1830]. [Gumuchain.]

—— The Village School ; with the History, and what became of some of the scholars. London, [1848]. [B.M.]

Cornwallis, C. F., Pericles ; a tale of Athens in the eighty-third Olympiad. By the author of " A Brief Sketch of Greek Philosophy." 2 vols., London, Longman, Brown, Green & Longmans, 1846. [B.M. : *Eng. Cat. :* Publisher's advert.]

Corp, Harriet. An Antidote to the Miseries of Human Life, in the History of the Widow Placid and her daughter Rachel. London 1807. [B.M.]

—— Cœlebs Deceived. 2 vols., London, Baldwin, 1817. [*Eng. Cat. : Monthly Mag. : New Monthly Mag.*]

—— A Sequel to the Antidote to the Miseries of Human Life, containing a further account of Mrs. Placid and her daughter Rachel. By the Author of the " Antidote." London, Williams and

Smith, 1809. [B.M. : Leonard Hyman : Elkin Mathews.]

Corp, Harriet. Tales characteristic, descriptive, and allegorical. By the author of " An Antidote to the Miseries of Human Life," London, Baldwin, 1829. [B.M. : *Eng. Cat.*]

Corrected Temper (The) ; or, Bear and Forbear. London, 1849. [B.M.]

Correspondence of Two Lovers (The), Inhabitants of Lyons. Published from the French originals. 3 vols., London, T. Hookham ; and G. G. J. and J. Robinson, 1788. [Block.]

Corry, John. The Adventures of Felix and Rosarito ; Or, the Triumph of Love and Friendship. Containing An account of several interesting events During the late War, between France and Spain, in the Western Pyrenees. With an engraved frontispiece. London, Crosby ; T. Hurst ; Champante and Whitrow ; Wilmot and Hill, R. Ogle ; J. F. Hughes ; J. Stuart ; Didier ; and C. Chapple, [1782]. [*Bibliot. Brit. :* B.M. : *I. in F.*]

—— Edwy and Bertha ; Or, the Force of Connubial Love. With an engraved frontispiece. London, Crosby ; T. Hurst ; R. Dutton ; R. Ogle ; J. F. Hughes ; J. Stuart ; and C. Chapple, [1802]. [*Bibliot. Brit. :* B.M. : Stonehill.]

—— The Elopement, or, the Imprudent Connexion ; containing the adventures of Edmund and Letitia. London, [1810 ?]

—— The Mysterious Gentleman Farmer, or the Disguises of Love. 3 vols., 1808. [*Bibliot. Brit. :* Martin A. McGoff.]

—— Sebastian and Zeila, or, the Captive liberated by female generosity. London, [1805 ?] [B.M.]

—— The Suicide ; or, the progress of error. A moral tale. London, [1805 ?] [B.M.]

—— Tales for the Amusement of Young Persons. 1802. [*Bibliot. Brit.*]

Cospatrick of Raymondsholm. A Westland Tale. By the Author of Redmond the Rebel, or They met at Waterloo : St. Kathleen, &c. 2 vols., London, A. K. Newman, 1822. [B.M.]

Costello, Mrs. The Soldier's Orphan. A Tale. 3 vols., London, Longman, 1809. [Allibone : McLeish : G. Worthington.]

Costello, Louisa Stuart. Bearn and the Pyrenees : a legendary tour to the country of Henri IV. London, 1844. [B.M.]

—— Clara Fane ; Or, The Contrasts of a Life. 3 vols., London, Richard Bentley, 1848. [B.M. : Brough.]

—— Gabrielle ; Or, Pictures of a Reign. A Historical Novel. 3 vols., London, T. C. Newby ; and T. & W. Boone, 1843. [B.M.]

—— The Queen Mother, a Romance-

3 vols., London, Richard Bentley, 1842. [Allibone.]

Costello, Louisa Stuart. The Queen's Poisoner ; Or, France in the Sixteenth Century. A Romance. 3 vols., London, Richard Bentley, 1841. [B.M.]

Cottage Among the Mountains (The). A narrative of peculiarly interesting facts. By the author of " Conversations on Mind and Matter." [Thames Ditton], 1810. [B.M.]

Cottage Dialogues ; by the Author of " Michael Kemp." Cirencester, 1821. [B.M.]

Cottage Fire-side (The). Dublin, P. D. Hardy, [1815]. [Gumuchian.]

Cottage in Kent (The) ; or, The First of September. With a frontispiece [1810]. [Ingpen : Murray Hill.]

Cottage in the Wood (The) : A Swiss Tale Founded on Fact. London, L. B. Seeley, 1825. [B.M.]

Cottage on the Common (The), and the little Gleaners : by C. M. Author of " The Child and the Hermit." London, 1842. [B.M.]

Cottage Sketches, or active Retirement. 2 vols., 1812. [*New Monthly Mag.*]

Cottage Tales. By the Author of the Monitor, or, Sunday-School Remembrancer. Colchester, Swinburne, Walter, and Taylor, 1829. [B.M.]

Cottager's Assistant (The) ; or, The Wedding Present. By a Lady. London, 1834. [B.M.]

Cottager's Daughter (The) ; or, The Sorrows of Rosa. A Pathetic Tale. [1803]. [Ingpen.]

Cottager's Daughter (The). A tale of the nineteenth century. 2 vols., London, 1806. [B.M.]

Cottin, Sophie. Amelia Mansfield, a Novel. Translated from the French of Madame C * * * *. 4 vols., 1803. [B.M.]

—— Chevalier de Versenai, A Novel. 2 vols., London, Hughes, 1810. [*Monthly Mag.* : Stonehill.]

—— Clara ; a novel. 2 vols., London, 1808. [B.M.]

—— Elizabeth ; Or the Exiles of Siberia. A Tale founded upon Facts. From the French of Mad. Cottin. 1807. [Arthur Rogers.]

—— Malvina, By Madame C. * * * *, Authoress of Clare d'Albe, and Amelia Mansfield. Translated from the French, By Miss Gunning. 4 vols., London, Printed for T. Hurst ; C. Chapple ; and R. Dutton, by H. Reynell, 1804. [B.M.]

—— Matilda and Malek Adhel The Saracen ; a Crusade Romance. 4 vols., London, A K. Newman, 1816. [*Eng. Cat.* : Stephen Hunt.]

—— Theodore and Blanche, or the Victims of Love. A Novel. Translated from the French. 2 vols., London, Tipper, 1808. [*Bibliot. Brit.* : Stonehill.]

Cotton, Rev. S. G. The Three Whispers, And Other Tales. Dublin, Robertson, [c. 1850]. [*I. in F.*]

Counselling the Doubtful. London, [1849]. [B.M.]

Count de Rethel (The) : An Historical Novel. Taken from the French. 3 vols., London, Hookham, 1779. [Stonehill.]

Count de Santerre : A Romance. By a Lady. 2 vols., Bath, R. Cruttwell ; and C. Dilly, London, 1797. [Ingpen : *New Ann. Reg.*]

Count di Novini ; or, The Confederate Charthusians. A Neapolitan tale. 3 vols., London, G. G. & J. Robinson, 1799. [B.M.]

Count of Hoensdern (The), A German Tale. 3 vols., 1792. [*New Ann. Reg.*]

Count (The), Or Sublunary Life. By One in a high station. 3 vols., London, Thomas Cautley Newby, 1848. [B.M. : H. H. Langley.]

Count Roderic's Castle ; or, Gothic Times. A tale. 2 vols., London, W. Lane, 1794. [*Eng. Lit. in Germany : New Ann. Reg.* : Publisher's advert.]

Countess of Salisbury (The). To which is added, The Maid of Corinth. 3 vols., London, Richard Bentley, 1840. [B.M.]

Country and London (The). A tale for little boys and girls. By the author of " Aids to Development." London, Wertheim, 1849. [B.M. : *Eng. Cat.*]

Country Cousins (The) : or, a Journey to London. A Novel. 2 vols., London, Printed by W. Hoggard, for Francis Noble ; and John Noble, 1767. [Block : Fletcher.]

Country Curate (The), or Pastor's Fireside ; including the interesting history of Julia, of St. Cuthbert's Isle, and Louis de Montemar, a Spanish Nobleman. An affecting tale. London, [1820 ?] [B.M.]

Country Houses. 3 vols., London, Saunders and Otley, 1832. [B.M.]

Country ; or Old Michael and Young Maurice. [1844]. [B.M.]

Couper, Dr. Robert. The Tourifications of Malachi Meldrum, Esq., of Meldrum Hall. 2 vols., Aberdeen, 1803. [Dobell : Arthur Rogers.]

Course of a Revolution (The) ; or the Parthenopaean Republic—a historical tale of 1798. 3 vols., London, Saunders and Otley, 1849. [B.M. : *Eng. Cat.*]

Court Intrigue, or, the Victim of Constancy. An historical Romance. By the author of Mental Improvement [Sarah Green]. 2 vols., 1799. [*New Ann. Reg.* : Blakey.]

Court Intrigues. Or the Secret History Of Ardelisa, A Story founded on Facts, and illustrated with Anecdotes of Persons in real Life. London, E. Cabe, 1759. [B.M.]

Court Jester (The), or, Museum of Entertainment. London, [1790 ?] [B.M.]

Court of Holyrood. Fragments of an Old Story. Edinburgh, Macredie, Skelly, 1822. [Ingpen.]

Courtenay, Charles. Ereston, a Novel. 2 vols., 1809. [Allibone : *Bibliot. Brit.*]

Courtney, Mrs. Isabinda of Bellefield, A sentimental Novel. In a Series of Letters. 3 vols., 1796. [Allibone : *Bibliot. Brit.*]

Cousin Elizabeth. By the Author of "A Visit to the Seaside." London, J. Chapman, 1839. [B.M. : *Eng. Cat.*]

Cousin Gertrude. London, 1848. [B.M.]

Cousin Natalia's Tales. The Little Wooden Crucifix. The Goldsmith. The New Year's Wish. By the Translator of " Little Henry." With illustrations by Frances Corbaux. London, Cundall, 1841. [B.M. : *Eng. Cat.*]

Cousin Rachel's Visit. By a Lady. Wellington, Houlston, 1827. [B.M.]

Coventry, Francis. The History of Pompey the Little : Or, The Life and Adventures of a Lap-Dog. With a frontispiece. London, M. Cooper, 1751. [Block : B.M. : Ingpen.]

Cox, Mrs. Burton Wood. In a series of letters. By a Lady. 2 vols., Dublin, 1783. [B.M.]

Cox, George Valentine. Jeannette Isbelle : A Novel. 3 vols., London, John Richardson, 1837. [B.M. : James Glaisher.]

Coxe, Eliza A. Liberality and Prejudice. A Tale. 3 vols., London, B. and R. Crosby, 1813. [B.M. : Ingpen : *Quarterly Review.*]

Coxe, Frances Clare Adeline. The Camisard ; or, The Protestants of Languedoc. A Tale, 3 vols., London, George B. Whittaker, 1825. [B.M. : *Quarterly Review :* Stonehill.]

Coxe, Richard Charles. The Mercy at Marsden Rocks. A true tale. Newcastle, 1844. [B.M.]

Coxheath Camp : A Novel. In a Series of Letters. With a frontispiece and a chart. 2 vols., London, Fielding and Walker, 1779. [W. Brown : Pickering.]

Coyer, Abbé. Supplement to Lord Anson's Voyage round the World, containing a Discovery and Description of the Island of Frivola. By the Abbé Coyer. To which is prefixed an introf ductory Preface by the translator. London, 1752. [Allibone : *Bibliot-Brit.*]

Cozens, Charles. Adventures of a Guardsman. London, Richard Bentley, 1847. [Allibone : *Eng. Cat.*]

Crabb, Maria Joseph. Tales for Children in a Familiar Style. 1805. [*Camb. Hist. Eng. Lit.*]

Cradock, Lady Harriet. Anne Gray. A Novel. Edited by the Author of " Granby." [Thomas Henry Lister.] 3 vols., London, Saunders and Otley,

1834. [B.M. : Publisher's advert. : Arthur Rogers.]

Craik, Dinah Maria. Cola Monti ; Or the Story of a Genius. By the author of " How to win Love." With illustrations by Franklin. London, A Hall, [1849.] [B.M. : *Eng. Cat. :* Arthur Rogers.]

—— The Ogilvies ; a Novel. 3 vols., London, Chapman and Hall, 1849. [Allibone : B.M. : *Eng. Cat.*]

—— Olive, a Novel. By the Author of " The Ogilvies." 3 vols., London, Chapman and Hall, 1850. [Allibone : B.M. : *Eng. Cat.*]

—— Stella of the North, or the Foundling of the ship. A novel. By the author of Adelaide de Narbonne, &c. 4 vols., London, Lane and Newman, 1802. [Blakey.]

Craik, Helen. Henry of Northumberland ; or the Hermit's cell. A tale of the fifteenth century. 3 vols., [W. Lane, 1800]. [Blakey.]

—— Julia de Saint Pierre. A novel. 3 vols., London, William Lane, 1796. [*Minerva Press Catalogue :* Blakey] (*see* Adelaide de Narbonne).

Crandolph, A. J. The Mysterious Hand ; or, Subterranean Horrours ! A Romance. 3 vols., London, A. K. Newman, 1811. [*Bibliot. Brit. :* B.M. : Blakey.]

Craven, Elizabeth, (Margravine of Anspach). Modern Anecdotes of the Family of Kinkvervankotsdarsprakengotschderns. 1779. [*Bibliot. Brit. : Eng. Lit. in Germany.*]

—— The Soldier of Dierenstein : Or, Love and Mercy. An Austrian Story, By H. S. H. the M. of A. With a frontispiece. Newbury, Printed by T. Mayo, and published by J. White, London, 1802. [*Bibliot. Brit. :* B.M.]

Crawford, Mrs. A. The Lady of the Bedchamber. A Novel. 2 vols., London, T. C. Newby, 1850. [B.M. : *Eng. Cat. :* Wm. Smith.]

Crawfurd, Archibald. Tales of my Grandmother. 2 vols., Edinburgh, Archibald Constable ; and Hurst, Robinson, London, 1825. [B.M.]

Crayford : or, the Force of Influence. 2 vols., London, Newby, 1849. [B.M.]

Crazy Wright. And The Poor Stranger. (True Stories.) By the Author of Thomas Brown. With a woodcut. London, Houlston, N.D. No. 39 of Houlston's Series of Tracts. [Block.]

Crebillon, Claude Prosper Jolyot de. The Happy Orphans. An Authentic History of Persons in High Life, with a Variety of uncommon Events and surprizing Turns of Fortune. Translated and improved from the French Original. 2 vols., London, H. Woodgate and S. Brooks, 1759. [Ingpen.]

—— The Skimmer : or, The History of Tanzai and Neadarne. 2 vols., London, F. Galicke, 1742. [Pickering.]

Crebillon, Claude Prosper Jolyot de. The Sopha : A Moral Tale. Translated from the French Original of Monsieur Crebillon. 2 vols., London, T. Cooper, 1742. [Elkin Mathews : Murray Hill.]

Crespigny, Mrs. Champion de. The Pavilion. A Novel. 4 vols., London, Printed for William Lane at the Minerva Press, 1796. [Birrell & Garnett : B.M. : Stonehill.]

—— The Poor Soldier ; an American Tale, founded on a recent fact. Inscribed to Mrs. C. London, 1789. [*Bibliot. Brit.*]

Cripple (The). London, 1843. [B.M.]

Cripple of Rothenstein (The). Translated from the German. London, 1846. [B.M.]

Croffts, Mrs. Ankerwick Castle. A Novel. 4 vols., London, William Lane, 1800. [Allibone : *Bibliot Brit.*]

—— Salvador, or Baron de Montbelliard. 2 vols., London, Minerva Press, 1801. [Baker's Bookshop : Stonehill.]

Croft, Rev. Sir Herbert. Love and Madness. A Story too true : In a series of Letters between Parties whose Names would perhaps be mentioned, were they less known or less lamented. London, 1780. [B.M. : R. Hall.]

Croker, Miss M. S. The Question, Who is Anna ? A Tale. 3 vols., London, Printed for the Author, and published by J. Souter, 1818. [B.M. : *New Monthly Mag.*]

Croker, Thomas Crofton. The Adventures of Barney Mahoney. London, Fisher, Son, and Jackson, 1832. [*I. in F. :* Lib. of Congress : J. Preston.]

—— Daniel O'Rourke. 1828. [Allibone.]

—— Fairy Legends and Traditions of the South of Ireland. In 3 parts. London, John Murray, 1825–1828. [Allibone : B.M. : J. Preston.]

—— Legends of the Lakes ; Or, Sayings and Doings At Killarney. Collected chiefly from the Manuscripts of R. Adolphus Lynch, Esq. H. P. King's German Legion. With a map, illustrations by Daniel Maclise, and music. 2 vols., London, John Ebers, 1829. [B.M. : *I. in F. :* Sotheran.]

—— My Village, Versus " Our Village." By the Author of " Barney Mahoney." London, H. Fisher, R. Fisher, and P. Jackson, 1833. [B.M. : Lib. of Congress.]

Croly, Rev. George. Marston : Or the Soldier and Statesman. 3 vols., London, Henry Colburn, 1846. [B.M. : Martin A. McGoff : McLeish.]

—— Salathiel, A Story of The Past, The Present, and The Future. 3 vols., London, Henry Colburn, 1829. [Birrell & Garnett : Ingpen : Pickering.]

—— Tales of the Great St. Bernard. 3 vols., London, Henry Colburn, 1828. [Allibone : B.M. : Ingpen.]

Crompton, Susan F. Stories for Sunday Afternoons. London, J. Chapman, 1845. [Allibone : *Eng. Cat.*]

Cromwell in Ireland : A Historical Romance. 3 vols., London, Thomas Cautley Newby, 1847. [B.M. : *Critic.*]

Cronzbeck, Baron. Arminius ; or Germania Freed. Translated from the Third Edition of the German Original, Written by Baron Cronzeck. With an Historical and Critical Preface, by the celebrated Professor Gottsched, of Leipsic. 2 vols., London, Becker, 1764. [*Bibliot. Brit. :* Ingpen.]

Crookenden, Isaac. The Italian Banditti ; or, the Secretary History of Henry and Matilda. A Romance. With a frontispiece. London, 1809. [Murray Hill.]

—— Romantic Tales. The Revengeful Turk : or Mystic Cavern. The Distressed Nun : or Sufferings of Herfelia di Brindoli of Florence, and the vindictive Monk : or Fatal Ring. London, Fisher, 1802. [Stonehill.]

—— Spectre of the Turret ; or, Guolto Castle. A Romance. With a frontispiece. London, [1820]. [Maggs.]

Crosland, Mrs. Newton. Partners for Life, A Christmas Story, by Camilla Toulmin. With illustrations by Absolon. Orr, 1847. [B.M. : *Eng. Cat. :* Chas. Hutt.]

—— Toil and Trial. A Story of London Life. With a frontispiece by John Leech. London, A. Hall, 1849. [*Eng. Cat. :* Maggs.]

—— The Young Lord, and other tales. To which is added Victorine Durocher, by Mrs. Sherwood. London, Darton, 1849–1850. [B.M.]

Cross, R. The Adventures of John Le-Brun. Containing A Surprising Series of Entertaining Accidents in his own life. Also, Several Historical Accounts of the Private Memoirs of his Contemporaries. Being an Impartial History of his own Times. 2 vols., London, Hawkins, 1740. [Stonehill.]

Cross, W. The Disruption, a Scottish tale of recent times. Edinburgh, John Menzies, 1846. [B.M. : Publisher's advert.]

Crowe, Catherine. Adventures of Susan Hopley ; Or, Circumstantial Evidence. 3 vols., London, Saunders and Otley, 1841. [B.M. : *Guide to Best Fiction :* Lond. Lib.]

—— Light and Darkness ; or, Mysteries of Life. 3 vols., London, Henry Colburn, 1850. [B.M. : *Eng. Cat. :* McLeish.]

—— Men and Women Or Manorial Rights. By the Author of the " Adventures of Susan Hopley." 3 vols., London, Saunders and Otley, 1843. [B.M. : McLeish : *Tait's Edin. Mag.*]

—— The Night Side of Nature, or Ghosts and Ghost Seers. 2 vols.,

London, T. C. Newby, 1848. [Block : B.M. : *Guide to Best Fiction.*]

Crowe, Catherine. Pippie's Warning ; or, Mind your Temper. London, A. Hall, 1848. [B.M.]

—— The Story of Lilly Dawson. 3 vols., London, Henry Colburn, 1847. [B.M. : *Guide to Best Fiction.*]

Crowe, Eyre Evans. Tales. 3 vols., London, 1825. [Allibone.]

—— To-Day in Ireland. 3 vols., London, Charles Knight, 1825. [Block : B.M. : *I. in F.*]

—— Yesterday in Ireland. By the Author of " To-Day in Ireland." 3 vols., London, Henry Colburn, 1829. [B.M. : *I. in F.*]

Crowley, Thomas. Life and Adventures of M. de la Sarre ; containing a great many incidents presumed to be new, as not occurring in the common course of life. Rotterdam, 1751. [*Bibliot. Brit.*]

Crowquill, Alfred. Sketches of Pumps, Handled by Robert Cruikshank. With some temperate Spouting By Alfred Crowquill. With illustrations in Glyphography. London, D. Bogue, 1846. [B.M.]

Cruel Husband and Suffering Wife (The). Being a shocking account of the unheard of cruelties practised by one C——ss. a bricklayer's labourer. [London], [1800 ?]. [B.M.]

Cruel Husband (The) ; or, Devonshire Tragedy, wherein is related the account of Mr. J. Barton of Topsham, etc. Lodon, J. Pitts, [1810 ?]. [B.M.]

Crumpe, Miss. Geraldine of Desmond, or Ireland in the Reign of Elizabeth. An Historical Romance. 3 vols., London, Henry Colburn, 1829. [B.M. : *I. in F.*]

—— Isabel St. Albe : or Vice and Virtue. A Novel. 3 vols., Edinburgh, Archibald Constable ; and Hurst, Robinson, London ; and John Cumming, Dublin, 1823. [B.M. : Ingpen : *New Ann. Reg.*]

Crusade of Fidelis (The), a knight of the Order of the Cross ; being the history of his adventures, during his Pilgrimage to the Celestial City. Derby, H. Mozley, 1828. [B.M.]

Cullen, Margaret. Home. A Novel. 5 vols., London, J. Mawman, 1803. [Allibone : B.M. : Court Book Shop.]

—— Mornton. A Novel. 3 vols., London, Sherwood, 1814. [*Eng. Cat. : New Monthly Mag.*]

Cullen, Stephen. The Castle of Inchvally, a Tale. 3 vols., 1796. [Allibone : *New Ann. Reg.*]

—— The Haunted Priory ; Or, The Fortunes of the House of Rayo. A Romance. Dublin, W. Jones, 1794. [B.M. : *New Ann. Reg. :* Arthur Rogers.]

Cumberland, Richard. Arundel. By the Author of The Observer. 2 vols., London, 1789. [B.M. : W. Brown : McLeish.]

—— Henry, By the Author of Arundel. 4 vols., London, Charles Dilly, 1795. [B.M. : Parker & Son : Stonehill.]

—— John de Lancaster. A Novel. 3 vols., London, Lackington, Allen, 1809. [B.M. : Arthur Rogers : Stonehill.]

—— Original Tales. 2 vols., London, Miller and Pople, 1810. [Allibone : B.M. : H. B. Copinger.]

Cumming, Mrs. The Vicissitudes of Life ; or, the Balloon. A Canterbury Tale, for young persons. Canterbury, 1845. [B.M.]

Cunningham, Allan. Lord Roldan, A Romance. 3 vols., London, John Macrone, 1836. [Baker's Bookshop : B.M. : Stonehill.]

—— Paul Jones ; A Romance. 3 vols., Edinburgh, Oliver and Boyd ; Longman, Rees, Orme, Brown, & Green, 1826. [B.M. : Pickering : G. Worthington.]

—— Sir Michael Scott, A Romance. 3 vols., London, Henry Colburn, 1828. [B.M.]

—— Traditional Tales of the English and Scottish Peasantry. 2 vols., London, Taylor and Hessey, 1822. [B.M. : Dobell : Lib. of Congress.]

Cunningham, George Godfrey. Foreign Tales and Traditions Chiefly Selected From The Fugitive Literature of Germany. 2 vols., Glasgow, Blackie, Fullarton ; and A. Fullarton, Edinburgh, 1829. [B.M.]

Cunningham, John William. Sancho, or the Proverbialist. London, T. Cadell, 1816. [*New Monthly Mag. :* Stonehill.]

—— The Velvet Cushion. London, Cadell, 1814. [*Eng. Cat. :* Ingpen : *New Monthly Mag.*]

—— A World Without Souls. London, J. Hatchard, 1805. [A. Muirhead.]

Cupid and Hymen, or a Voyage to the Isles of Love and Matrimony, containing a most diverting Account of the Inhabitants of those two vast and populous Countries, their Laws, Customs, and Government, interspersed with many useful directions and cautions how to avoid the dangerous Precipices and Quicksands that these Islands abound with, and wherein so many thousands who have undertaken the Voyage, have miserably perished, Translated from the French original, to which is added The Batchelor's Estimate of the expenses attending a Married Life, The Married Man's Answer to it, and a vindication of the estimate, by John Single, of Gray's Inn, Esq. London, T. Cooper, 1742. [Pickering.]

Cure of the Gout, An Amusing Tale. With woodcuts. [1800]. [Combridges.]

Curious and Diverting History and Adventures of a Bedstead [The]. Containing many Singular and Interesting Amours, Tales and Narratives, particularly Lord K's Rapes and Seductions ; Peep into the Seraglio ; Intrigues of a Boarding School, London ; Licentiousness Displayed ; interspersed with others, forming one of the most moving histories, ever desplayed to the public, of Amours in High and Low Life. With 8 coloured plates. London, Smith [William Dugdale], [1840]. [*Cat. Lib. Prohib.*]

Curling, Captain Henry. John of England. An Historical Romance. 3 vols., London, Richard Bentley, 1846. [B.M. : Francis Edwards.]

—— Shakespere ; The Poet, the Lover, the Actor, the Man. A Romance. 3 vols., London, Richard Bentley, 1848. [B.M. : *Eng. Cat. :* Wm. Smith.]

—— The Soldier of Fortune. 3 vols., London, Richard Bentley, 1843. [B.M.]

Curran, H. G. Confessions of A Whitefoot. Edited by G. C. H. Esq. Barrister-at-Law. London, Richard Bentley, 1844. [B.M. : *I. in F.*]

Curse of Sentiment. 2 vols., 1787. [W. Brown.]

Curse of Ulrica (The) ; Or the White Cross Knights Or Riddarholmen. A Swedish Romance Of the Sixteenth Century. 3 vols., London, Black, Parry, 1815. [B.M. : *New Monthly Mag.*]

Curties, T. J. Horsley. Ancient Records ; Or, The Abbey of Saint Oswythe, A Romance. With a frontispiece. 4 vols., London, Minerva Press, 1801. [Stonehill.]

—— Ethelwina or The House of Fitz-Auburne. London, A. K. Newman, 1801. [*Eng. Cat. : Eng. Lit. in Germany.*]

—— The Monk of Udolpho.

—— St. Botolph's Priory ; or, the Sable Mask. An historic romance. 5 vols., London, 1806. [B.M.]

—— The Scottish Legend, or the Isle of Saint Clothair. A romance. 4 vols., London, William Lane, 1802. [B.M. : Blakey.]

—— The Watch Tower. 5 vols., London, A. K. Newman. [Publisher's advert, 1812.]

Cuthbertson, Catherine. Adelaide ; or, The Countercharm, A Novel. By the Author of Santo Sebastiano, &c. 5 vols., London, 1813. [Blackwell : *Quarterly Review :* Sexton.]

—— Ethelbert. By the Author of " Santo Sebastiano." 3 vols., 1830. [*New Monthly Mag.*]

—— Forest of Montalbano. A Novel. By the Author of Santo Sebastiano. 4 vols., London, G. Robinson, 1810. [B.M. : *Quarterly Review :* Stonehill.]

—— The Hut and the Castle ; A Romance. By the Author of " The Romance of the Pyrenees " ; " Santo Sebastiano ; or, The Young Protector," &c. 4 vols., London, Hurst, Robinson ; and Archibald Constable, Edinburgh, 1823. [B.M. : Fletcher : *New Monthly Mag.*]

Cuthbertson, Catherine. The Romance of the Pyrenees. 4 vols., London, G. and J. Robinson, 1803. [Baker's Bookshop : Pickering.]

—— Rosabella : Or, A Mother's Marriage. A Novel. By the Author of The Romance of the Pyrenees ; Santo Sebastiano, or, the Young Protector ; The Forest of Montalbano ; and Adelaide, or the Countercharm. 5 vols., London, Baldwin, Cradock, and Joy, 1817. [B.M. : Sexton : Stonehill.]

—— Santo Sebastiano ; Or, The Young Protector. A Novel. By the Author of " Adelaide." " The Romance of the Pyrenees," " The Forest of Montalbano," &c. &c. 5 vols., London, Printed at the Minerva Press, 1806. [Publisher's advert : T. D. Webster.]

—— Sir Ethelbert ; Or, The Dissolution of Monasteries. A Romance. By the Author of Santo Sebastiano ; The Romance of the Pyrenees, &c. &c. 3 vols., London, Longman, Rees, Orme, Brown, and Green, 1830. [B.M. ; *New Monthly Mag.*]

Cypriots (The), or a Miniature of Europe, in the Middle of the Fifteenth Century. By the Author of the Minstrel. 2 vols., 1795. [*New Ann. Reg.*]

Dacre, Charlotte. Confessions Of The Nun Of St. Omer. A Tale, By Rose Matilda. 3 vols., London, Printed by D. N. Shury ; for J. F. Hughes, 1805. [B.M.]

—— The Libertine.

—— [Edited by]. Recollections of a Chaperon ; edited by Lady Dacre. 3 vols., London, 1833. [McLeish : *Quarterly Review.*]

—— Zofloya ; or, The Moor : A Romance of the Fifteenth Century. 3 vols., London, 1806. [King.]

Dacresfield ; Or, Vicissitudes on Earth. A Novel. By Cordelia, Chief Lady at the Court of Queen Mab. 4 vols., London, Printed at the Minerva Press for A. K. Newman, 1820. [B.M. : Blakey.]

Daemon of Venice. By a Lady. Front. London, 1810. [Murray Hill.]

Dagley, Elizabeth Frances. The Birthday and Other Tales. With a frontispiece and an engraved title. London James Bulcock, 1828. [B.M.]

—— Fairy Favours, and Other Tales, By E. F. D. With a frontispiece and engraved title. London, William Cole 1825. [B.M.]

—— The Village Nightingale ; Or The Story of Esther Wallis. And Other

Tales. With a frontispiece and engraved title. London, N. Hailes, 1829. [B.M.]

Dagley, Elizabeth Frances. The Young Seer, Or Early Searches into Futurity. With an engraving by R. Baker after R. Dagley. London, Smith, Elder, 1834. [B.M.]

Dalberg, Baron de. Mehaled and Sedli ; Or, The History Of a Druse Family : With some account of the Druses, An Ancient People of Syria. 2 vols., London, Gale and Fenner, 1816. [Block : B.M. : *New Monthly Mag.*]

D'Alenson, Mons. The Bonze, or Chinese Anchorite. An Oriental Epic Novel. Translated from the Mandarine Language of Hoamchiram, a Tartarin Proselite. With a frontispiece and engraved titles. 2 vols., London, Dodsley, Becket and Hondt, E. Newbery, 1768. [T. D. Webster.]

Dalinda ; or, The Double Marriage. Being the Genuine History of a very Recent and Interesting Adventure. London, Corbett, 1749. [*Eng. Lit. in Germany :* Stonehill.]

Dallas, Robert Charles. Aubrey : A Novel. 4 vols., London, T. N. Longman and O. Rees, 1804. [Birrell and Garnett : Holland : Elkin Mathews.]

—— Felix Alvarez, or Manners in Spain Containing descriptive accounts of some of the Prominent Events of the Late Peninsular War ; and Authentic anecdotes illustrative of the Spanish Character ; interspersed with Poetry, original and from the Spanish. 3 vols., London, Baldwin, 1818. [Baker's Bookshop : *Eng. Cat. : New Monthly Mag.*]

—— The Knights : tales illustrative of the marvellous. 3 vols., London, 1808. [B.M.]

—— The Morlands. Tales illustrative of the Simple and Surprising. 4 vols., London, Longman, 1805. [B.M. : Ingpen.]

—— Percival, or Nature Vindicated. A Novel. 4 vols., London, Printed by A. Strahan for T. N. Longman and O. Rees, 1801. [Birrell and Garnett : Ingpen : Pickering.]

—— Sir Francis Darrell ; Or The Vortex : A Novel. 4 vols., London, Longman, Hurst, Rees, Orme, and Brown, 1820. [B.M. : Ingpen : McLeish.]

Dalton, James. Chartley The Fatalist. 3 vols., London, Edward Bull, 1831. [B.M. : *New Monthly Mag.*]

—— The Gentleman in Black. With illustrations by George Cruikshank, engraved by J. Thompson and C. Landells. London, William Kidd, 1831. [McLeish : Pickering : T. Thorp.]

—— The Invisible Gentleman, By the Author of " Chartley the Fatalist," " The Robber," &c. &c. 3 vols.,

London, Edward Bull, 1833. [B.M. : McLeish : Elkin Mathews.]

Dalton, James. The Old Maiden,s Talisman And Other Strange Tales. By the Author of " Chartley " ; " The Invisible Gentleman " ; and " The Gentleman in Black." 3 vols., London, Bull and Churton, 1834. [B.M. : Elkin Mathews.]

—— The Robber. By the Author of Chartley, the Fatalist. 3 vols., London, Edward Bull, 1832. [B.M. : *Metropolitan Mag.*]

Dalton, Maria Regina, [see ROCHE, Regina Maria].

Dame Partlet's Farm ; containing an account of the Great Riches she obtained by Industry, the good life she led, and alas, Good Reader ; her Sudden Death. To which is added A Hymn written by Dame Partlet just before her death and an Epitaph for her Tomb-Stone. With woodcuts. London, J. Harris, 1806. [Maggs.]

Dame Truelove's Tales, Now First Published. Useful Lessons for Little Misses and Masters. With a frontispiece and 21 plates. London, J. Harris, 1817. [P. M. Barnard : Arthur Rogers.]

Damer, Hon. Anne Seymour. Belmour : A Novel. 3 vols., London, J. Johnson, 1801. [Dobell : Pickering.]

Dandin, ——. The Dasa Kumára Charita, or Adventures of ten Princes. A series of tales. Edited by H. H. Wilson. 1846. [B.M.]

Danebury ; or the power of friendship. A tale ; with two odes. By a young lady. London, [1780 ?]. [B.M.]

Danger of the Passions, Or Syrian and Egyptian Anecdotes. 2 vols., 1770. [W. Brown.]

Dangerous Errors : A Tale. London, Lupton Relfe, 1822. [B.M. : *European Mag.*]

Dangerous Secrets. A Novel. 2 vols., London, Printed at the Minerva Press for A. K. Newman, 1815. [Baker's Bookshop : B.M. : Publisher's advert.]

Dangers of Dutchland (The) : A Tale for Youth, Descriptive of that Interesting Country. With plates. London, Edward Lacey, N.D., [Dobell.]

Dangers of Infidelity. 1812. [*New Monthly Mag.*]

Daniel, George. The Adventures of Dick Distich. Written after the manner of Fielding, Smollett, and Cervantes. 3 vols., London, 1812. [B.M. : *New Monthly Mag. :* Sotheby's.]

—— Merrie England in the olden time. With illustrations by John Leech and George Cruikshank. 2 vols., London, Richard Bentley, 1842. [*Eng. Cat. :* Lib. of Congress : Sotheran.]

Daniel, Robert Mackenzie. The Cardinal's Daughter. A Novel. 3 vols., London, Thomas Cautley Newby, 1847. [B.M.]

Daniel, Robert Mackenzie. The Grave Digger : A Novel. By the Author of "The Scottish Heiress." 3 vols., London, T. C. Newby, 1844. [B.M. : *Tait's Edin. Mag.*]

—— The Poor Cousin : A Novel. Edited by the author of "The Scottish Heiress ; " "The Young Widow ; " "The Young Baronet ; " etc. 3 vols., London, T. C. Newby, 1846. [B.M.]

—— The Scottish Heiress, A Novel. 3 vols., London, T. C. Newby ; and T. and W. Boone, 1843. [B.M.]

—— The Young Baronet. A Novel. By the Author of "The Scottish Heiress," "The Young Widow," &c., &c., &c. 3 vols., London, T. C. Newby, 1846. [B.M.]

—— The Young Widow. A Novel in Three Volumes. By the Author of the "Scottish Heiress," &c., &c., 3 vols., London, T. C. Newby. 1844. [B.M.]

Daniel, Mrs. Robert Mackenzie. Georgina Hammond, a novel. 3 vols., London, T. C. Newby, 1849. [B.M. (2nd edn.)]

—— Jeremiah Parkes ; A Novel. 3 vols., London, Thomas Cautley Newby, 1847. [B.M. : *Critic.*]

—— My Sister Minnie. A Novel. 3 vols., London, Thomas Cautley Newby, 1848. [B.M.]

—— Our Guardian. A Novel. 3 vols., London, T. C. Newby, 1849. [B.M.]

D'Arblay, Madame. Camilla : Or, A Picture of Youth. By the Author of Evelina and Cecilia. 5 vols., London, T. Payne, and T. Cadell, Jun., and W. Davies, 1796. [B.M. : Huntington : Stonehill.]

—— Cecilia, or Memoirs of an Heiress. By the Author of Evelina. 5 vols., London, T. Payne and T. Cadell, 1782. [Block : B.M. : Huntington.]

—— Evelina, Or, A Young Lady's Entrance into the World. In a Series of Letters. 3 vols., London, T. Lowndes, 1778. [Huntington : W. T. Spencer.]

—— The Wanderer ; Or, Female Difficulties. By the Author of Evelina ; Cecilia ; and Camilla. 5 vols., London, Longman, Hurst, Rees, Orme, and Brown, 1814. [B.M. : Huntington : Arthur Rogers.]

D'Arcy, Azilé. Prejudice ; or Physiognomy. A Novel. 3 vols., London, Printed at the Minerva Press, for A. K. Newman, 1817. [*Bibliot Brit. :* B.M. : *Monthly Mag.*]

D'Argens, J. B. de Boyer, Marquis. Memoirs of the Count du Beauval, including Some Curious Particulars relating to the Dukes of Wharton and Ormond, during their Exiles. Translated by Samuel Derrick. London, Cooper, 1754. [Stonehill.]

Darley, George. The Labours of Idleness ; Or Seven Nights' Entertainments. By Guy Penseval. London, John Taylor, 1826. [B.M. : Ingpen : Arthur Rogers.]

D'Arlincourt, Charles Victor Prevot, Vicomte. Charles the Bold ; or, the Recluse of the Wild Mountain, a Tale of the Fifteenth Century. With a folding frontispiece. London, William Cole, [182–]. [R. S. Frampton.]

—— The Recluse ; A Translation of "Le Solitaire." 2 vols., London, Henry Colburn, 1821. [B.M.]

—— The Renegade. Translated from the French. London, Minerva Press, 1803. [Stonehill.]

Darling, Peter Middleton. The Romance of the Highlands. 2 vols., Edinburgh, Ramsay, 1810. [Allibone : *Monthly Mag. :* Pickering.]

D'Arnaud, François Marie de Baculard. Fanny : or, the Happy Repentance. From the French. Dublin, 1777. [B.M.]

—— The History of Count Gleichen. Translated from the French of Arnaud. London, 1786. [B.M.]

—— The History of Sidney and Volsan. Translated from the French. Dublin, 1772. [B.M.]

—— Lorimon ; Or, Man in Every Stage of Life, A Novel, Translated from the French. 2 vols., London, Minerva Press, 1803. [Stonehill.]

—— The Tears of Sensibility. Translated from the French. By J. Murdock. 2 vols., 1773. [*Bibliot. Brit.*]

—— Warbeck ; a Pathetic Tale. [Translated by Sophia Lee]. 2 vols., London, W. Lane, 1786. [B.M. : E. M. Lawson : Arthur Rogers.]

D'Aubigne, Frances. The Express. A Novel. 3 vols., London, Minerva Press for A. K. Newman, 1819. [B.M.]

Daughter (The). 2 vols., London, 1810. [B.M.]

Daughter-in-Law (The), her Father, and Family. 2 vols., London, Printed at the Minerva Press, for A. K. Newman, 1813. [*New Monthly Mag. :* Publisher's advert.]

D'Aulnois, Marie-Catherine le Jumel de Berneville, Comtesse. The Earl of Douglas, an English Story. From the French of the Countess D'Anois. By the Translator of Dorval ; Observations on the Greeks ; Christina, Queen of Sweden, &c. &c. 3 vols., Lynn, Printed by W. Whittingham, 1774. [*Bibliot. Brit. :* Maggs.]

—— Fortunio. With illustrations. Edinburgh, Blackwood, 1847. [B.M. : *Eng. Cat.*]

—— History of Hypolitus, Earl of Douglas. London, 1741. [Lib of Congress.]

—— The History of the Tales of the Fairies. Newly translated from the French containing I. The tale of Graciosa and Prince Percinet II. The Blue-Bird and Florina, III. Prince Avenant. IV. The King of the Peacocks. V. Prince

Nonpareil VI. The Orange Tree. London, 1749. [B.M.]

D'Aulnois, Marie-Catherine le Jumel de Berneville, Comtesse. Queen Mab : Containing a Select Collection of only the Best, most Instructive and Entertaining Tales of the Fairies : viz., 1, Graciosa and Percinet. 2, The Fair One with the Golden Locks. 3, The Blue Bird. 4, The Invisible Prince. 5, The Princess Verenata. 6, The Princess Rosetta. 7, The Golden Bough. 8, The Orange-Tree and the Bee. 9, The Little Good Mouse. Written by the Countess D'Aulnoi. To which is added, A Fairy Tale in the ancient English Style, by Dr. Parnell : and Queen Mab's Song. With a frontispiece and woodcuts. London, J. Dodsley, 1770. [Ingpen : Pickering.]

—— Temple of the Fairies. Translated from the French of Various Authors. With a frontispiece and illustrations. 2. vols., London, Vernor and Hood, 1804. [Ingpen.]

Daunt, William J. O'Neill. The Gentleman in Debt. Cameron and Ferguson, 1848. [*I. in F.*]

—— Hugh Talbot : A Tale Of the Irish Confiscations Of the Seventeenth Century. Dublin, James Duffy, 1846. [B.M. : *I. in F.*]

Davenant, Or The Escape : An historical tale. London, Whittaker, Treacher, and Arnot, 1833. [B.M.]

Davenels (The) ; or, A Campaign of Fashion in Dublin. 2 vols., London, Henry Colburn, 1829. [*I. in F.*]

Davenport, Selina. An Angel's Form and a Devil's Heart. A Novel. 4 vols., London, Printed at the Minerva Press for A. K. Newman, 1818. [B.M.]

—— Donald Monteith, The Handsomest Man of the Age. A Novel. 5 vols., London, Printed at the Minerva Press for A. K. Newman, 1815. [B.M. : *New Monthly Mag.* : Stonehill.]

—— The Hypocrite ; Or, The Modern Janus. A Novel. 5 vols., London, Printed at the Minerva Press, for A. K. Newman, 1814. [B.M. : *Quarterly Review :* Stonehill.]

—— Italian Vengeance and English Forbearance. A Romance. 3 vols., London, A. K. Newman, 1828. [B.M.]

—— Leap Year ; Or Woman's Privilege. A Novel. 5 vols., London, Printed at the Minerva Press, for A. K. Newman, 1817. [B.M.]

—— The Original Of the Miniature. A Novel. 4 vols., London, Printed at the Minerva Press, for A. K. Newman, 1816. [B.M. : *New Monthly Mag.*]

—— Personation. A Novel. 3 vols., London, A. K. Newman, 1834. [B.M.]

—— Preference. A Novel. 2 vols., London, A. K. Newman, 1824. [B.M.]

—— The Queen's Page. A Romance. 3 vols., London, A. K. Newman, 1831. [B.M.]

Davenport, Selina. The Sons of the Viscount and the Daughters of the Earl, A Novel. Depicting recent Scenes in Fashionable Lift. By a Lady. 4 vols., London, Henry Colburn, 1813 [B.M. : Ingpen : Publisher's advert.]

—— The Unchanged. A Novel. 3 vols., London, A. K. Newman, 1832. [B.M.]

Davies, Edward. Elisa Powell ; or, Trials of Sensibility, a Series of Original Letters collected by a Welsh Curate. 2 vols., 1795. [J. G. Commin.]

Davis, Sir John Francis. Chinese Novels, translated from the Originals : to which are added, Proverbs and Moral Maxims, collected from their classical books. The whole prefaced by observations on the language and literature of China. By John Francis Davis. London, John Murray, 1822. [B.M. : Ingpen : McLeish.]

—— San-Yu-Low : or the three dedicated rooms. A tale, translated from the Chinese by J. F. Davis. Canton, P. P. Thomas, 1815. [B.M.]

Davys, Mary. The Accomplished Rake ; or, the Modern Fine Gentleman ; being the genuine memoirs of a person of distinction. London, 1756. [B.M.]

—— The Reform'd Coquet, or, Memoirs of Amoranda, A Novel. 1752. [Blackwell.]

Dawe, Ann. The Younger Sister. 2 vols., London, 1770. [B.M. : *Eng. Lit. in Germany.*]

Day, Isaac. Scenes for the Young, or Pleasing Tales. 1807. [*Camb. Hist. Eng. Lit.*]

Day, Thomas. The Children's Miscellany : in which is included the History of Little Jack. With a frontispiece. London, John Stockdale, 1788. [B.M.]

—— The History of Sandford and Merton, A Work Intended for the use of Children. With 2 illustrations. 3 vols., London, John Stockdale, 1783–1789. [Block : B.M. : Gumuchian.]

Day of Rest (The). With a woodcut. London, Houlston, N.D. No. 88 of Houlston's Series of Tracts. [Block.]

Days of Chivalry (The). A romance. 2 vols., [William Lane], 1797. [*New Monthly Mag.*]

Days of Queen Mary (The) ; or a Tale of the Fifteenth Century. London, Longman, 1823. [*Eng. Cat. : Quarterly Review.*]

Deacon, William Frederick. The Exile of Erin ; Or, The Sorrows Of a Bashful Irishman. 2 vols., London, Whittaker, 1835. [B.M. : *I. in F.*]

—— The Inn-Keeper's Album. London, Thomas M'Lean, 1823. [Kyrle Fletcher.]

—— November Nights ; Or Tales For Winter evenings. By The Author of "Warreniana." London, Thomas

Maclean, 1826. B.M. : *Quarterly Review.*]

Dead Man's Hollow ; or, the Bridal of Bodesden. A Romance. London, 1847. [B.M.]

Deale, —. Craven Derby ; Or, The Lordship by Tenure, Includes The Ladye of the Rose : An Historical Legend, Relating to the Great Founder of the Noble House of Darbye. By the Author of " Crockford's ; Or, Life in the West." 2 vols., London, Merric Smith, 1832–3. [B.M. : Wm. Smith.]

—— Life in the West ; or, The Curtain Drawn. A Novel. Dedicated, by Permission, to the Right Hon. Robert Peel, M.P. Containing Sketches, Scenes, Conversations, and Anecdotes of the Last Importance to Families, and Men of Rank, Fashion, and Fortune. Founded on Facts. By a Flat Enlightened. 2 vols., London, C. Chapple, 1828. [In 1828 was issued : " Crockford's Or Life in the West," which is the same work but published by Saunders and Otley.] [B.M. : Court Bk. Shop. : Marks.]

Death and Burial of Cock Robin (The). To which is added Pizarro and Alonzo ; or, industry better than gold. York, [1825 ?]. [B.M.]

Death-Bed Repentance. By a Clergyman. With a woodcut. London, Houlston, N.D. No. 75 of Houlston's Series of Tracts. [Block.]

Death's a Friend. A novel. By the author of the Bastard. 2 vols., London, 1788. [B.M.]

De Avellaneda (*see* FERNANDEZ DE AVELLANEDA).

De Balzac, Honoré (*see* BALZAC).

Debauchee Rewarded (The) ; or a warning to young men, being a true account how Captain John Dringle in courtship with Miss Jane Monrow attempted to ravish her. Stokesley, [1800 ?]. [B.M.]

De Beaulieu (*see* MALLÈS DE BEAULIEU).

De Beaumont, Elie. The History of the Marquis de Roselle. In a Series of Letters. Translated from the French. 2 vols., London, T. Becket, and P. A. De Hondt, 1765. [B.M. : Lib. of Congress : McLeish.]

—— The History of a Young Lady of Distinction. In a Series of Letters. 2 vols., London, F. Noble, 1754. [B.M. : Stonehill : Tregaskis.]

—— The New Clarissa. 2 vols., 1768. [*Bibliot. Brit. : Progress of Romance.*]

—— Novels for Grown Gentlemen and Ladies. [*Progress of Romance.*]

De Beaumont, Jeanne Marie Le Prince (*see* BEAUMONT).

De Beauvoir ; or, Second Love. 3 vols., London, Longman, Rees, Orme, Brown, and Green, 1828. [B.M.]

De Bernard (*see* BERNARD).

Deceitfulness of Pleaseure (The) ; or some account of my Lady Blithe. London,[1797 ?]. Cheap Repository. [B.M.]

Deception ; and Frederick, the faithful friend. London, 1848. [B.M.]

Decided Preference. A Tale, Founded upon facts. By an old Spinster. 2 vols., London, Simpkin, Marshall, 1842. [B.M.]

De Clifford ; or, Passion more Powerful than Reason. A Novel. 4 vols., London, Printed at the Minerva Press for A. K. Newman, 1820. [B.M.]

De Dalberg (*see* DALBERG).

De Fauqeus (*see* FAUQUES).

De Florian (*see* FLORIAN).

De Fontanieu, Gaspar Moise. Friend of Virtue. A Novel. From the French. By the Translater of the Effects of the Passions. 3 vols., London, Vernor, 1789. [Ingpen.]

De Genlis. Comtesse. Adelaide and Theodore, Or, Letters on Education. Translated from the French. 3 vols., London, Bathurst, 1783. [B.M. : Arthur Rogers : Stonehill.]

—— The Age of Chivalry ; or, Friendship of other Times : a moral and historical tale, abridged and selected from the Knights of the Swan, by Madame Genlis, by C. Butler. London, 1799. [*Bibliot. Brit. : B.M. : New Ann. Reg.*]

—— Alphonsine ; or, Maternal Affection. A novel. 4 vols., London, J. F Hughes, 1807. [B.M. (2nd edn.)]

—— Alphonso ; or, the Natural Son. 3 vols., London, 1809. [B.M. : *Monthly Mag.*]

—— Belisarius ; An Historical Romance. Translated from the French of Madame de Genlis. 2 vols., London, H. Colburn, 1808. [B.M. : Dobell.]

—— The Castle of Kolmeras. To which is added Ida Molten. London, 1804. [B.M.]

—— The Duchess de la Valliere. An Historical romance. Translated from the French. 2 vols., London, 1804. [Baker's Bookshop.]

—— The Duchess De la Vallière, And Madame De Maintenon. Romances. 2 vols., London, Henry Colburn, 1837. [Block : B.M. : *Eng. Cat.*]

—— The Duke of Lauzun. An Historical Romance. Interspersed with Numerous Anecdotes of the Court of Louis XIV., and forming a Companion to the Duchess de la Valliere. London, Henry Colburn, 1808. [Ingpen.]

—— The Impertinent Wife. London, A. K. Newman. [Publisher's advert., 1812.]

—— Jane of France. An Historical Novel. Translated from the French. 2 vols., London, Henry Colburn, 1816. [B.M. : *Eng. Cat. :* Holland.]

—— The Knights of the Swan ; or, the Court of Charlemagne : a historical and moral tale to serve as a continuation to the Tales of the Castle : and of which all the incidents that bear analogy to the French Revolution are taken from history. Translated from the French of Madame de Genlis by the Rev. Mr. Beresford. 3 vols., London, 1796. [Bailey Bros. : B.M. : *New Ann. Reg.*]

De Genlis, Comtesse. Lessons of a Governess to her Pupils. Translated from the French. 3 vols., London, 1792 [B.M.]

—— Madame de Maintenon. Translated from the French of Madame de Genlis. 2 vols., London, 1806. [Lib. of Congress : McLeish : Arthur Rogers.]

—— The New Aera ; Or, Adventures of Julien Delmour : Related by Himself. 4 vols., London, Henry Colburn, 1819. [Backus : B.M.]

—— Petrarch and Laura. London, Phillips, 1820. [Stonehill.]

—— Placide, A Spanish Tale. Translated from Les Battuecas of Madame de Genlis. By Alexander Jamieson. 2 vols., London, W. Simpkin and R. Marshall, 1817. [B.M. : *New Monthly Mag. : Quarterly Review.*]

—— Rash Vows, or, The Effects of Enthusiasm. A Novel. Translated from the French of Madame de Genlis. 3 vols., London, T. N. Longman and O. Rees, 1799. [B.M. : Pickering : Arthur Rogers.]

—— The Rival Mothers, Or Calumny. Translated from the French Of Madame de Genlis. 4 vols., London, Printed by A. Strahan for T. N. Longman and O. Rees, 1800. [B.M. : G. Sexton.]

—— Sainclair, or the Victim of the Arts and Sciences. Translated from the French. London, Dulau, 1808. [B.M. : *Eng. Cat.*]

—— The Siege of Rochelle ; Or, The Christian Heroine. Translated by R. C. Dallas. 3 vols., London, B. Dulau, 1808. [B.M. : Ingpen : Martin A. McGoff.]

—— Tales of the Castle : Or, Stories of Instruction and Delight. Being Les Veillées du Chateau, Translated into English By Thomas Holcroft. 5 vols., London, G. Robinson, 1785. [Birrell and Garnett : Block : Marks.]

—— The Young Exiles ; or, Correspondence of some Juvenile Emigrants : a work intended for the entertainment and instruction of Youth. From the French of Madame de Genlis. 3 vols., London, 1799. [B.M. : McLeish.]

— Zuma, Or the Tree of Health. To which are added Fair Pauline, Zeneida, the Reeds of the Tiber, etc. London, 1818. [Backus : B.M. : *New Monthly Mag.*]

De Gomez, Madeleine Angelique. Select Novels, Translated from the French. 1745. [Bailey Bros.]

De Goudar (*see* GOUDER).

De Guizot (*see* GUIZOT).

De Haviland (*see* HAVILAND).

De Herbster (*see* (HERBSTER).

De Jouy (*see* JOUY).

De Kock, Charles Paul. The Barber of Paris ; Or, Moral Retribution. 3 vols., London, Whittaker, 1839. [B.M. : Bumpus : Ingpen.]

—— The Modern Cymon, From the " Jean " of C. Paul de Kock. 2 vols., London, E. Marston, 1833. [B.M.]

—— Sister Anne : a Novel, Translated from the French by George W. M. Reynolds. London, 1840. [B.M. : Marks.]

De Lacy ; or Passion's Slave. A Novel. By the Author of Modes of Life, or Town and Country. 3 vols., London, A. K. Newman, 1828. [B.M.]

Delafaye (*see* LAFAYE-BRÉHIER).

De La Mark and Constantia ; or, Ancient Heroism. A Gothick Tale. With a frontispiece. London, Tegg, 1803. [Stonehill.]

De Lantier (*see* LANTIER).

De La Pasture, Count. Real Pearls In A False Setting. 3 vols., London, Saunders and Otley, 1839. [B.M.]

De La Roche, C. F. T. Amilec, Or the Seeds Of Mankind. Translated from the French, MDCCLIII. London, W. Needham, 1753. [B.M.]

De Laroche-Guilhem, Mlle. The History of Female Favourites. Of Mary De Padilla, under Peter the Cruel, King of Castile ; Livia, under the Emperor Augustus ; Julia Farnesa, under Pope Alexander the Sixth ; Agnes Soreau, under Charles VII. King of France ; and Nantilda, under Dagobert, King of France. London, Parker, 1772. [Ingpen.]

De La Solle, Henri François. Memoirs Of a Man of Pleasure, Or the Adventures of Versorand. [Translated by Sir John Hill.] 2 vols., London, T. Osborne, 1751. [B.M.]

Delaval. A novel. With a frontispiece. 2 vols., London, Printed at the Minerva Press, for William Lane, 1802. [Blakey.]

De Lavergne (*see* LAVAISSIÈRE DE LAVERGNE).

De La Villette, —. The Triumph of Truth. Translated from the French by R. Roberts. With a vignette title. 2 vols., 1775. [Dobell : Henry Start.]

Delepierre, Octave. Old Flanders ; Or, Popular Traditions and Legends of Belgium. 2 vols., London, T. C. Newby, 1845. [B.M.]

Delicate Embarrassment (The). 2 vols., London, Robinson and Roberts. [Publisher's advert., 1769.]

Delicate Objection (The), or Sentimental Scruple. 2 vols., London, W. Lane, 1775. (E. M. Lawson.]

De Lisle, Emma. Alinda, or the Child of Mystery. By the Author of " Ora and Juliet," etc. 1812. [B.M.]

De Lisle, Emma. Eva of Cambria ; or, The Fugitive Daughter. By Emma de Lisle. 3 vols., London, Printed at the Minerva Press, for A. K. Newman, 1810. [Publisher's advert. : Blakey (who says that this is not by De Lisle.)]

—— Fitz-Edward ; or, The Cambrians. A Novel. Interspersed with Pieces of Poetry. 3 vols., London, Printed at the Minerva Press, for A. K. Newman, 1811. [Elkin Mathews : Publisher's advert.]

—— Ora and Juliet ; or, Influence of First Principles. A Novel. By the author of Eva of Cambria, &c. 4 vols., London, Printed at the Minerva Press, for A. K. Newman, 1811. [Blakey : *Quarterly Review :* Stonehill.]

—— A Soldier's Offspring ; or, The Sisters. A tale. 2 vols., London, Minerva Press, 1810. [*Eng. Cat.* : Blakey.]

Dellingborough Castle ; or, The Mysterious Recluse. 2 vols., London, Lane, Newman. [Publisher's advert. ; Blakey.]

De Lobeira (*see* LOBEIRA).

De Lourdoueix, M. Charenton ; Or, The Follies of the Age : A Philosophical Romance. Translated from the French. With engravings by J. Shury. London, Baldwin, Cradock and Joy, 1818. [Block : B.M. : Arthur Rogers.]

De Luce (*see* LUCE).

Delusion. A Novel. 2 vols., London, Law and Whittaker, 1818. [B.M. : *New Monthly Mag.*)

De Mailles (*see* MAILLES).

De Maistre, J. G. Frederick Latimer : Or, The History Of a Young Man of Fashion. 3 vols., London, Printed by Luke Hansard, for T. Cadell, Jun. and W. Davies, 1799. [Baker's Bookshop : B.M. : Arthur Rogers.]

—— Count Xavier. A Journey round my Chamber. Translated from the French. By Mrs. John Outhwaite. London, 1818. [B.M.]

—— Journey round my Room. And, A Nocturnal Expedition round my Room. [London], Thomas, [1846]. [*Eng. Cat.* : Lib. of Congress.]

—— The Leper Of the City Of Aoste. A Narrative. Translated from the French, By Helen Maria Williams. London, George Cowie, 1817. [Allibone : Birrell and Garnett : B.M.]

De Marivaux, Pierre Carlet de Chamblain. The Life and Adventures of Indiana, The Virtuous Orphan. With copper-plates. London, C. Whitfield, 1746. [Arthur Rogers.]

—— Marianne. 1742. [*Progress of Romance.*]

—— Memoirs of the Countess de Bressol. By the Author of " The Virtuous Orphan." Translated by Joseph Collyer. 2 vols., London, 1743. [J. C. Hardy.]

De Marivaux, Pierre Carlet de Chamblain. Pharsamond ; Or, The New Knight-Errant. In which is introduced the Story of the Fair Anchoret. With that of Tarmiana and her unfortunate Daughter. Written originally in French, by M. de Marivaux. Translated by Mr. [J.] Lockman. 2 vols., London, C. Davis, 1750. [*Guide to Best Fiction* : John Orr : Pickering.]

—— The Virtuous Orphan ; or, The Life of Marianne, Countess of ——. 1784. [*Guide to Best Fiction.*]

De Merle (*see* MERLE).

Demetrius, a Russian Romance. 2 vols., London, Longman Hurst Rees Orme and Brown, 1813. [Block.]

Democrat (The), A Tale ; And The Hugonot, A Tale. 3 vols., London, Edward Bull ; and Hatchard, 1832. [B.M. : G. Worthington.]

De Montfort : Or, The Old English Nobleman. 3 vols., London, Richard Bentley, 1842. [B.M.]

De Montolieu (*see* MONTOLIEU).

De Moraes (*see* MORAES).

De Mouhy, Charles de Fieux, Chevalier. The Busy Body, or Successful Spy : being the entertaining history of Monsieur Bigand, a man infinitely inquisitive and entertaining. 2 vols., London, F. Cogan, 1742. [B.M. : McLeish : Dobell.]

—— Female Banishment ; Or, the Woman Hater. Originally wrote by the Chevalier de Mouhy, Author of the Fortunate Country Maid. 2 vols., [London, T. Lownds, 1759. [B.M. : Ingpen : Pickering.]

—— The Fortunate Country Maid. Being the Entertaining Memoirs of the Present Celebrated Marchioness of L.V. who from a Cottage, through a great Variety of Diverting Adventures, became a Lady of the First Quality in the Court of France, by her steady Adherence to the Principles of Virtue and Honour. Wherein are display'd The Various and Vile Artifices employ'd by Men of Intrigue, for seducing of Young Women ; with suitable Reflections. From the French of the Chevalier de Mouhy. 2 vols., London, F. Needham, 1740. [Dobell : Pickering.]

—— The Fortunate Orphan ; or, Memoirs of the Countess of Marlou, who, thro' a long Series of Uncommon Incidents and Adventures, was at length providentially conducted to the Honourable Condition she was entitled to by her most mysterious Birth.. Penn'd by Herself ; and Revis'd by the Chevalier de Mouhy. London, Needham, 1745. [B.M. : Stonehill.]

—— The Virtuous Villager, Or The Virgin's Victory. [*Progress of Romance.*]

Denniston, James. Legends of Galloway ; Being A Series of Traditions, Illustrative of its Ancient History.

Customs, Manners, and Superstitions. Edinburgh, Archibald Constable ; and Hurst, Robinson, London, 1825. [B.M. : Lib. of Congress.]

Denouement (The) ; or, History of Lady Louisa Wingrove. By a Lady. London, Robinson, 1784. [Stonehill.]

Dent, John. Force of Love. A Novel. 2 vols., 1786. [Allibone.]

Denton Hall ; or, The Rough Diamond. 3 vols., London, Boone, 1850. [B.M. : *Eng. Cat.*]

De Palmzeaux (*see* PALMZEAUX).

Dependence. By the Author of Little Sophy, and Recollections of a Beloved Sister. Derby, Henry Mozley, 1830. [B.M.]

De Quincey, Thomas. Klosterheim : Or, The Masque. By the English Opium-Eater. Edinburgh, William Blackwood ; and T. Cadell, London, 1832. [Block : B.M. : Ingpen.]

—— Walladmor : " Freely Translated into German from the English of Sir Walter Scott," [By Wilhelm Haering] and now Freely Translated from the German into English. 2 vols., London, Taylor and Hessey, 1825. [B.M. : Ingpen : Maggs.]

D'Erbine ; or, The Cynic. 3 vols., London, W. Simpkin and R. Marshall, 1829. [B.M.]

De Renneville, Madame. Charles and Eugenia. From the French of Madame de Renneville, By M.G. With a frontispiece. London, J. Souter, 1826. [B.M. : *Quarterly Review.*]

—— Miss Lovely de Macclesfield. The Domino Noir. Paris, 1811. [*Cat. Lib. Prohib.*]

Derenzy, Margaret Graves. The Old Irish Knight : A Milesian Tale of The Fifth Century. By the Author of " A Whisper to a Newly-Married Pair," " Parnassian Geography," &c. London, Poole and Edwards, 1828. [Block : B.M. : *I. in F.*]

Derenzy, S. S. Marian de Brittoon, or the Rector's orphan grand daughter. A novel.. 3 vols., London, 1822. [B.M.]

Derrick, Samuel. A Voyage to the Moon, with some Account of the Solar World : a Comical Romance, done from the French, by Samuel Derrick. Dublin, 1754. [Marks.]

De Segrais, M. Zayde, a Spanish History, written originally in French by M. de Segrais, revised, corrected by Mrs. Griffith. With a frontispiece. London, W. Lane, 1780. [Baker's Bookshop : Blakey.]

De Souza - Botelho, Adelaide Marie Emilie. Helen de Tournon : A Novel. Translated from the French. 2 vols., Longman, Hurst, Rees, Orme, and Brown, 1821. [B.M. : Pickering : Stonehill.]

Despaurrins, M. Neville Family, Founded on Facts. 3 vols., London, 1815. [*New Monthly Mag.*]

De Stael-Holstein, Madame A. L. G. Necker. Corinna, or Italy. 3 vols., London, Tipper, 1807. [Baker's Bookshop : B.M. : Lowndes.]

—— Corinna, or Italy. Translated by D. Lawler. 5 vols., London, Tipper, 1807. [B.M. : Stonehill.]

—— Corinne ; Or, Italy. Translated by Isabel Hill ; with metrical versions of the odes by L. E. Landon ; and a memoir of the authoress. 2 vols., London, R. Bentley, 1833. [B.M. : Lib. of Congress.]

—— Delphine. Translated from the French. 6 vols., London, J. Mawman, 1803. [B.M. : Court Bk. Shop : Pickering.]

—— (?), The Libertine Husband, a Novel, Translated from the French of Madame De Stael-Holstein. 2 vols., London, 1810. [Blackwell : B.M. : H. M. Fletcher.]

—— Zulma, and other Tales : to which is prefixed an Essay on Fictions. Translated from the French. 2 vols., London, Henry Colburn, 1813. [B.M. : *Eng., Cat. : Quarterly Review.*]

Destiny : Or, Family Occurrences : An Interesting Narrative. 2 vols., London William Burton, [c. 1800]. [B.M.]

Desultory Sketches And Tales Of Barbados. London, Henry Washbourne ; Fraser, Edinburgh ; Machen, Dublin ; and Smith, Glasgow, 1840. [B.M.]

De Vere, Marquis. The Life and Adventures of the Prince of Salerno : Containing an Account of his Adventures at Venice and in Hungary ; his Captivity at Venice, and Amour with an Ottoman Princess, together with his return to Italy ; with many entertaining descriptions of the Laws, Customs, and Manners of several Countries through which he travelled. London, J. Roson, 1770. [Dobell : Ingpen.]

De Vergy (*see* TREYSSAC DE VERGY).

De Vigny, Alfred Victor, Comte (*see* VIGNY, Alfred Victor, Comte de,).

Devil and Tom Walker (The) ; or, The Black Woodsman. A Legend of America. With a folding plate.. London, Duncombe, [c. 1800]. [Stonehill.]

Devil upon Crutches in England (The) ; Or, Night Scenes in London. A Satirical Work By a Gentleman of Oxford. London, Philip Hodges, etc. 1756. [W. Brown : Arthur Rogers : Murray Hill.]

De Voltaire (*see* VOLTAIRE).

Devonshire, Georgiana Cavendish, Duchess of. Emma ; or the Unfortunate Attachment. By the Author of The Sylph. 3 vols., London, Hookham, 1773. [B.M. : Stonehill.]

—— The Sylph. A Novel. 2 Vols.,

Lor don, T. Lowndes, 1779. [*Eng. Lit.* *in Germany :* Huth : Ingpen.]

De Wailly (*see* WAILLY).

Dialogue (A), between John Smith and Thomas Brown, Two Fellow-Apprentices, with a Particular Character of each. With a vignette title. London, Augustus Applegarth and Edward Cooper, N.D. [Court Bookshop.]

Dialogue of Courtship between Jockey and Maggy (A). In 5 parts. [Newcastle], 1775. [B.M.]

Dialogues between a Woman and a Virgin. London, R. Borewell, 1786. [*Cat. Lib. Prohib.*]

Dialogues of a Christian and a Jewess. London, R. Borewell, 1786. [*Cat. Lib. Prohib.*]

Dialogues of a Married Lady and Maid. London, R. Borewell, 1786. [*Cat. Lib. Prohib.*]

Dialogues of a Quaker and his Maid (The). London, R. Borewell, 1786. [*Cat. Lib. Prohib.*]

Diamonds and Toads ; Or the Mother And her two Daughters. With wood-cuts. Birmingham. T. Bloome ; and A. Carvalho, [1840 ?]. [B.M.]

Diary of a Little Dog (The). Supposed to be Written by Herself. London, Harvey and Darton, 1837. [B.M. : Gumuchian.]

Diary of a Nun. 2 vols., London, Henry Colburn, 1840. [B.M.]

Dibdin, Charles. Hannah Hewit ; or The Female Crusoe. 3 vols., London, C. Dibdin, [1792]. [B.M. : Murray Hill.]

—— The Younger Brother : A Novel, written by Mr. Dibden. 3 vols., London, For the Author, [1793]. [B.M. : *New Ann. Reg. :* Pickering.]

Dibdin, Robert William. The Village Rectory ; or Truth in fiction. London, Nisbet, 1846. [B.M. : *Eng. Cat.*]

Dibdin, Thomas Frognall. Cranmer, By A Member Of The Roxburghe Club, 3 vols., London, Henry Colburn, 1839. [B.M.]

—— The Belle Marianne ; a tale of truth and woe. London, 1824. [B.M. : Rev. W. Scott : *D.N.B.*]

Dick, The Day Scholar, a tale for little boys. By the author of " Mamma's Pictures," etc. Brentford, 1822. [B.M.]

Dick Field. London, 1843. [B.M.]

Dickens, Charles. The Battle of Life. A Love Story. With illustrations by Daniel Maclise, Clarkson Stanfield, Leech & Doyle. London, Bradbury and Evans, 1846. [Block : Maggs : W. T. Spencer.]

—— The Chimes : A Goblin Story of Some Bells that rang an Old Year out And a New Year in. With illustrations by Daniel Maclise, Doyle, Leech and Clarkson Stanfield. London, Chapman & Hall, 1845. [Block : B.M. : W.T. Spencer.]

Dickens, Charles. A Christmas Carol. In Prose. Being A Ghost Story of Christmas. With 4 illustrations by John Leech. &ondon, Chapman & Hall, 1843. [Block : B.M. : W. T. Spencer.]

—— The Cricket on the Hearth. A Fairy Tale of Home. With illustrations by Daniel Maclise, Clarkson Stanfield, John Leech, Doyle & Landseer. London, Printed and published for the Author by Bradbury & Evans, 1846. [Block : B.M. : W. T. Spencer.]

—— Dealings with the Firm of Dombey and Son, Wholesale, Retail and for Exportation. With 40 etchings by Hablot K. Browne. London, Bradbury and Evans, 1848. [Block : B.M. : W. T. Spencer.]

—— The Haunted Man, and the Ghost's Bargain. A Fancy for Christmas-Time, With illustrations by Clarkson Stanfield, John Tenniel, John Leech & Frank Stone. London, Bradbury & Evans, 1848. [Block : B.M. : W. T. Spencer.]

—— The Life and Adventures of Martin Chuzzlewit—his Relations, Friends, and Enemies. Comprising all his wills and his ways : with an Historical Record of what he did and what he didn't ; showing, moreover, who inherited the family plate, who came in for the silver spoons, and who for the wooden ladles : the whole forming a complete Key to the House of Chuzzlewit. Edited by Boz. With 40 illustrations by Phiz [H. K. Browne]. London, Chapman & Hall, 1844. [Block : B.M. : King.]

—— The Life and Adventures of Nicholas Nickleby. With 39 illustrations by Phiz [Hablot K. Browne], and a portrait after Daniel Maclise. London, Chapman & Hall, 1839. [Block : B.M. : W. T. Spencer.]

—— Master Humphrey's Clock. With illustrations by George Cattermole, Hablot [K.] Browne and Daniel Maclise. 3 vols., London, Chapman & Hall, 1840–1841. [Containing the first issue of " Barnaby Rudge " and " The Old Curiosity Shop,"] [Block : B.M. : W. T. Spencer.]

—— Oliver Twist ; or, the Parish Boy's Progress. By " Boz." With illustrations by George Cruikshank. 3 vols., London, Richard Bentley, 1838. [Block : King : W. T. Spencer.]

—— The Personal History of David Copperfield, the Younger, of Blunderstone Rookery. (Which he never meant to be published on any account.) With 40 etchings by Phiz [Hablot K. Browne]. London, Bradbury & Evans, 1850. [Block : B.M. : Maggs.]

—— The Pic Nic Papers. By Various Hands. Edited by Charles Dickens. With illustrations by George Cruikshank, Phiz [Hablot K. Browne], etc. 3 vols., London, Henry Colburn, 1841. [Block : B.M. : Maggs.]

Dickens, Charles. The Posthumous Papers of the Pickwick Club. With illustrations by R. Seymour, Phiz [Hablot K. Browne], and R. W. Buss. London, Chapman & Hall, 1837. [Block : B.M. : W. T. Spencer.]

—— Sketches by Boz, illustrative of everyday life and everyday people. With plates by George Cruikshank. 2 vols., London, Chapman and Hall, 1836. [Block : B.M. : W. T. Spencer.]

Did You Ever See Such Damned Stuff? Or so much the better, A Story without Head or Tail, Wit or Humour. A Parody of those French anti-clerical, semi-erotic, fairy tales, so much in vogue during the last century. London, C. G. Seyffort, 1760. [*Cat. Lib. Prohib.*]

Diderot, Denis. Les Bijoux Indiscrets, Or the Indiscreet Toys. Translated from the Congese Tongue. Printed at Mononmatapa. With illustrations. 2 vols., Tobago, Reprinted for Pierre Ragout, 1749. [Baker's Bookshop : W. Brown : Stonehill.]

—— James the Fatalist and His Master. From the French of Diderot. 3 vols., London, Robinson, 1797. [Baker's Bookshop : *New Ann. Reg.*]

—— The Natural Son. A Novel. Translated from the French of M. Diderot. 2 vols., London, T. N. Longman, 1799. [*New Ann. Reg. :* Stonehill.]

—— The Nun. Translated from the French. 2 vols., London, G. G. and J. Robinson, 1797. [B.M. : Arthur Rogers : Stonehill.]

Dignan, J. The Slave Captain ; A Legend of Liverpool. With plates. London, T. C. Newby, 1847. [Baker's Bookshop : B.M. : Salkeld.]

Dillon, Henry Augustus Dillon-Lee, Viscount. The Life and Opinions of Sir Richard Maltravers, an English Gentleman of the Seventeenth Century. 2 vols., London, Whittaker, 1822. [Stonehill.]

—— Rosaline de Vere. 2 vols., London, Treuttel and Würtz, Treuttel, Jun. and Richter, 1824. [B.M. : Clarke-Hall : G. Worthington.]

Dillon, Sir John Talbot. Alphonso and Eleonora ; or, the Triumphs of Valour and Virtue, etc. 2 vols., London, 1800. [B.M.]

Dinsdale, Joshua. Parmenides, Prince of Macedonia ; or, Fidelity Crowned. An Heroic Novel. Translated from the French. London, Wren, 1752. [W. Brown : Ingpen.]

Disasters of a Frolicsome Pig. London, 1849. [B.M.]

Discovery of the Island Frivola (A) ; or, The Frivolous Island. Translated from the French, now privately handed about at Paris, and said to be agreeable to the English Manuscripts concerning that Island, and its Inhabitants. Wrote

by order of A-l A-n. London, Payne, 1750. [Stonehill.]

Disinterested Love, or, The History of Sir Charles Royston, and Emily Lesley : In a Series of Letters. 2 vols., London, 1776. [*Eng. Lit. in Germany.*]

Disinterested Love ; or, the Modern Robin Grey, in a Series of Letters founded on Facts, By a Widow Lady. 2 vols., London, 1788. [Blackwell : B.M. : T. D. Webster.]

Disinterested Nabob (The), A Novel, interspersed with Genuine Descriptions of India, its Manners and Customs. 3 vols., London, 1787. [McLeish : Storey.]

Disobedience. A Novel. By the Author of Plain Sense. 4 vols., London, Printed for William Lane at the Minerva Press, 1797. [Backus : Arthur Rogers : Stonehill.]

Disraeli, Isaac. Flim-Flams ! or the life and errors of my uncle and the amours of my aunt with illustrations and obscurities, by Messrs. Tag, Rag and Bobtail. 3 vols., London, John Murray, 1805. [B.M.]

—— Lovers. 1799. [*Eng. Lit in Germany.*]

—— Loves of Mejnoun and Leila. 1797. [*Eng. Lit. in Germany.*]

—— Romances. London, Cadell and Davies, 1799. [Block : Ingpen : Pickering.]

—— Vaurien : Or, Sketches of the Times : Exhibiting Views of the Philosophies, Religions, Politics, Literature, And Manners of the Age. 2 vols., London. T. Cadell, junior and W. Davies ; and J. Murray and S. Highley, 1797. [B.M.]

Distinction : A Tale. By the Author of The Baroness. 2 vols., London, Seeley, Burnside ; and Seeley, 1845. [B.M.]

Distressed Lady (The), Or the Yorkshire Beauty made Happy. To which is added, Ovid's Art of Beauty. With a portrait. [1780]. [James Miles.]

Distressed Lady's Garland (The) ; or, a trial of true love. Worcester, [1785 ?]. [B.M.]

Distressed Lovers (The) ; or, the History of Edward and Eliza. 2 vols., London, Robinson and Roberts, 1767. [*Univ. Mag.*]

Distressed Orphan (The) ; or, Love in a Mad House. Interspersed with a great many Entertaining Letters. Written by herself. London, [1770 ?]. [B.M.]

Distressed Virtue or History of Miss Harriet Nelson. 1781. [*Eng. Lit. in Germany.*]

Diurnal Events ; Or The Antipodes to Romance. A Novel. By the Author of the Sailor and Soldier Boy. 4 vols., London, Printed at the Minerva Press, for A. K. Newman, 1816. [B.M. : *New Monthly Mag. :* Stonehill.]

Dix, John. Jack Ariel ; Or, Life on board an Indiaman. By the Author of the " Post Captain," " Travels in America," and a " Life of Chatterton." 3 vols., London, T. C. Newby, 1847. [B.M. : Maggs.]

Dodd, Dr. William (?). The Sisters ; Or, the History of Lucy and Caroline Sanson, Entrusted to a false friend. 2 vols., London, 1754. [B.M. : *Eng. Lit. in Germany* : Arthur Rogers.]

Dog of Knowledge (The) or Memoirs of Bob the Spotted Terrier Supposed to be written by Himself. By the Author of Dick, the little Poney. With a frontispiece. London, J. Harris, 1801. [*Guardian of Education* : Gumuchian.]

Dogherty, Mrs. Castle of Walforth and Monteagle. 4 vols., 1812. [Allibone.]
—— Ronaldsha. 3 vols., 1808. [Allibone.]

Doherty, Hugh. The Discovery : or The Mysterious Separation of Hugh Doherty, Esq., and Ann His Wife. By H.D., Esq. London, 1807. [Ingpen.]

Dolby, Thomas. Florestan : Or, The New Lord of the Manor. A Tale of Humanity. Comprising The History of a Rural Revolution From Vice and Misery to Virtue and Happiness. Dedicated to the Landed Proprietors of the United Kingdom. With a frontispiece and woodcut title. London, Joseph Rickerby. 1839. [B.M. : Ingpen.]

Dom Chavis (*see* CHAVIS).

Domestic Anecdotes With Moral Reflections. London, Francis Westley, 1825. [B.M. : *Edin. Mag.*]

Domestic Contrasts, or the different fortunes of Nancy and Lucy. In 3 parts. London, [1797 ?]. Cheap Repository. [B.M.]

Domestic Misery, Or the Victim of Seduction, A Pathetic Tale ; Addressed to the Unprincipled Libertine. London, Tegg and Castleman ; T. Hurst ; T. Brown, Edinburgh ; and B. Dugdale, Dublin, [1803]. [B.M. : Stonehill.]

Domestic Scenes. A Novel. By Lady Humdrum, Author of more Works than bear her name. 3 vols., London, Longman, Hurst, Rees, Orme, and Brown, 1820. [B.M. : Pickering : Publisher's advert.]

Domestic Scenes, or the Adventures of a Doll. Burnham, 1817. [B.M.]

Domestic Scenes ; a tale for the times. London, 1848. [B.M.]

Dominique the Resolute ; or, The Devil and the Deserter. With a frontispiece. London, Duncombe, [c. 1800]. [Stonehill.]

Domville, Sir W. The Three Sisters. A story translated [by Sir W. Domville] from the German. London, Privately Printed, 1842. [B.M.]

Donalda, or the Witches of Glensheill. 2 vols., London, A. K. Newman. [Publisher's advert., 1812.]

Donaldson, William. The Life and Adventures of Sir Bartholomew Sapskull, Baronet, by Somebody. With a frontispiece. 2 vols., 1768. [Arthur Rogers.]

Don't Stake a Pound to Raise a Crown. With a woodcut. London, Houlston, N.D. No. 78 of Houlston's Series of Tracts. [Block.]

Dorat, C. J. Fatal Effects of Inconstancy ; Or, Letters of the Marchioness de Syrcè, The Count de Mirbelle and Others. From the French. With a frontispiece. 2 vols., London, 1774. [Lib. of Congress : Arthur Rogers.]

Doris, Charles. A History of the Amours of Napoleon Bonaparte. Written by himself. 1816. [B.M.]

Dorothea ; or, A Ray of the New Light. 3 vols., London, Robinson, 1801. [Stonehill.]

D'Orville, Constant. Pauline ; or, The victim of the heart. From the French of d'Orville. 2 vols., [London, W. Lane, 1794]. [Blakey.]

Double Disappointment ; Or, The History of Charles Marlow. In a Series of Letters. 2 vols., London, 1774. [Ingpen.]

Double Marriage (The). 3 vols., 1792. [*New. Ann. Reg.*]

Double Surprise (The) ; A Novel, in a Series of Letters. 2 vols., London, 1783. [R. Hall.]

Double Trial (The) ; Or the Consequences of an Irish Clearing : A Tale of the present Day. 3 vols., London, Smith, Elder, 1832. B.M. : [Wm. Smith.]

Douglas, Christiana Jane. Anne Dysart : a tale of every-day life. 3 vols., London, Henry Colburn, 1850. [B.M. : *Eng. Cat.*]

Douglas, Francis. Rural Love, a tale. In the Scottish Dialect. To which is added a glossary. Aberdeen, 1759. [B.M.]

Douglas, J. Travelling Anecdotes through Various Parts of Europe. Volume I [all published]. With 6 plates. Rochester, 1782. [Blackwell.]

Douglas, Robert. Adventures of A Medical Student. With A Memoir of the Life of the Author. 3 vols., London, Henry Colburn, 1848. [B.M. : Elkin Mathews.]

Douglas and MacDonald ; or Industry better than Genius. By an authoress who has written several popular pieces. London, [1832 ?]. [B.M.]

Douglas, a narrative. By the Widow of a Clergyman. London, Nottingham, 1850. [B.M.]

Downes, Joseph. The Mountain Decameron. 3 vols., London, Richard Bentley, 1836. [B.M. : *Quarterly Review.*]

Dramatic Tales. The Zingaro Girl. A tale of Poland. With a frontispiece. London, Duncombe, N.D. [A. Filcek.]

Draper, Bourne Hall. Edwin ; or, The Motherless Boy. Interspersed with Pieces of Original Poetry. With steel engravings. London, Harvey and Darton, 1827. [B.M.]

—— Stories from Scripture on an Improved Plan. Old Testament. With illustrations. London, John Harris, [1830]. [Arthur Rogers.]

Draper, Sarah. Memoirs of the Princess of Zell, consort to King George the First. 2 vols., London, Minerva Press, 1796. [Stonehill : McLeish.]

Dreadful Fire (A) ; with Some account of those who escaped and those who perished. With a woodcut. London, The Religious Tract Society, N.D. No. 1593. [Block.]

Dream of Alcibiades (The). Translated from the Greek. London, H. Kent, 1749. [B.M.]

Dream of Fate (The), or Sarah the Jewess. A tale founded on the drama. By C. Z[arach]. Barnett. London, J. Duncombe, [1840 ?]. [B.M.]

Dream of Life (The). A Romance. With illustrations. London, Lloyd, [c.1840]. [Stonehill.]

Drop in the Ocean (A). By Agnes and Bessy. London, Joseph Masters, [1848]. [B.M.]

Druidess (The) : a tale of the fourth century. Translated from the German. London, Sharpe, [1846]. [B.M. : Critic.]

Drummond, Harriet. Lucy Seymour ; or, It is more blessed to give than to receive. Edinburgh, Hamilton, 1847. [B.M. : Eng. Cat. : Arthur Rogers.]

—— The Wilmot Family : or "They that deal truly are his delight." Edinburgh, Hamilton, 1848. [B.M. : Eng. Cat.]

Drury, Anna Harriet. Friends and Fortune, a moral tale. London, Parker, 1849. [B.M. : Eng. Cat.]

Du Bois, Dorothea. Theodora, a novel. 2 vols., London, 1770. [B.M.]

Du Bois, Edward. The Fairy of Misfortune ; or, the Loves of Octar and Zulima. An Eastern Tale. Translated from the French by the Author of A Piece of Family Biography. London, 1799. [B.M. : New Ann. Reg.]

—— Old Nick : A Satirical Story. By the Author of " A Piece of Family Biography," etc. 3 vols., London, Murray and Highley, 1801. [B.M. : Ingpen : McLeish.]

—— A Piece of Family Biography, Dedicated to George Colman. 3 vols., 1799. [Blackwell : New Ann. Reg.]

—— St. Godwin : A tale of the sixteenth, seventeenth, and eighteenth centuries. By Count Reginald De St. Leon. London, Wright, 1800. [B.M. : Arthur Rogers : Stonehill.]

Dubois, Henri L. Adolphe and Selanie ; or, the Power of Attachment. A moral tale. Edinburgh, 1824. [B.M.]

—— The History of a French Dagger ; an Anecdote of the Revolution. From the French. 2 vols., London, 1828. [B.M.]

Dubois-Fontanelle, J.G. Shipwreck and Adventures of Monsieur Pierre Viaud. Translated from the French, By Mrs. Griffith. London, 1771. [Lib. of Congress.]

Du Bosc, Jacques. The Accomplish'd Woman, Translated by a Gentleman of Cambridge. 2 vols., London, 1753. [B.M.]

Duchess of York (The). An English Story. 2 vols., London, William Lane, 1791. [Stonehill.]

Duclos, —. The Pleasures of Retirement, Preferable to the Joys of Dissipation ; Exemplified in the Life and Adventures of the Count de B——. Written by Himself. In Letters to a Friend. London, Wilkie, 1774. [Ingpen.]

Dudevant, A. L. A. D. Andrè. By George Sand. Translated by E. A. Ashurst. Edited by M. M. Hays. London, 1847. [Lib. of Congress.]

—— Consuello. 2 vols., London, Simms and McIntyre, 1847. [B.M. : Critic : Guide to Best Fiction.]

—— The Enchanted Lake : a tale. Translated by F. G. Shaw. London, 1850. [B.M.]

—— Indiana. 1850. [Guide to Best Fiction.]

—— Jacques. Translated by Anna Blackwell. London, 1847. [B.M. : Guide to Best Fiction.]

—— Journeyman Joiner ; or, The Companion of the Tour of France. H.G. Collins, 1847. [Eng. Cat. : Guide to Best Fiction : Lib. of Congress.]

—— The Last Aldini. 1847. [Guide to Best Fiction.]

—— Little Fadette ; a domestic story. With an analytical review of the life and writings of the author, by J. Mazzini. London, 1850. [B.M. : Guide to Best Fiction.]

—— The Master Mosaic Workers. 1847. [Guide to Best Fiction.]

—— Mauprat. By George Sand. Translated by Matilda M. Hays. 2 vols., London, Churton, 1847. [Critic : Guide to Best Fiction : Lib. of Congress.]

—— The Miller of Angibault. 1847. [Guide to Best Fiction]

—— The Mosaic Workers, a tale ; to which is added, The Orco ; a tradition. Translated from the French of George Sand by E.A.A. London, Clarke, 1844. [B.M. : Critic.]

—— The Sin of M. Antoine. With 11 engravings. London, E. Appleyard, 1848. [Publisher's advert.]

Dudevant, A. L. A. D. Spiridion. Translated from the French. London, Fox, 1842. [B.M. : Chave.]

—— The Uscoque ; a Venetian story. Translated by J. Bauer. London, G. Slater, [1850]. [B.M.]

Dudley, F. Amoroso. A Novel Founded on Fact. 2 vols., 1810. [Allibone : Blackwell.]

Dudley, John. Metamorphosis of Sona ; A Hindoo Tale : with a glossary. London, 1810. [B.M.]

Dudley Cranbourne : or a Woman's History. 3 vols., London, Richard Bentley, 1849. [B.M. : *Eng. Cat.*]

Duff, W. The History of Rhedi, the Hermit of Mount Ararat. An oriental tale. London, 1773. [B.M.]

D'Uffreux, M. The Siege of Aubigny, An Historical Tale [Translated by Thomas Manti]. N.D. [Blackwell.]

Dufour, Camilla. Aurora, or The Mysterious Beauty. Altered from the French. 2 vols., London, Crosby, 1803. [Ingpen.]

Dumas, Alexandre. The Chateau d'If : a Romance. Translated by E. Hardy. Simms and McIntyre, 1846. [W. T. Spencer.]

—— The Count of Monte Christo. With 20 illustration by M. Valentin. 2 vols., London, Chapman & Hall, 1846. [B.M. : King : Lib. of Congress.]

—— Francis the First : or, the Sculptor's Apprentice and the Provost's Daughter. 2 vols., London, [1849]. [B.M.]

—— George ; or, the Planter of the Isle of France. Translated from the French by G. J. Knox. 1846. [B.M.]

—— The Honey-Stew of the Countess Bertha. Translated from the French of Alexander Dumas, By Mrs. Cooke Taylor. With an engraved title and 5 plates. London, Jeremiah How, 1846. [Block : B.M. : Sotheran.]

—— Margaret of Navarre : or, the Massacre of St. Bartholomew's Eve. With a frontispiece. London, [1845]. [B.M.]

—— Marie Antoinette ; or, the Chevalier of the Red House, a tale of the French Revolution. London, [1846]. [B.M.]

—— Memoirs of a Physician. London, T. Hodgson, 1846. [B.M. : *Eng. Cat.*]

—— Pascal Bruno. A Sicilian Story. Edited by Theodore Hook. London, Henry Colburn, 1837. [B.M. : Publisher's advert.]

—— Pauline : a tale of Normandy. Translated from the French. [London], [1844]. [B.M.]

—— The Planter of the Isle of France. [Translated by J. Spring.] London, [1847]. [B.M.]

—— The Prisoner of If : or the Revenge of Monte Christo. London, [1846]. [B.M.]

Dumas, Alexandre. The Regent's Daughter : an Historical Romance. London, T. Hodgson, [1850]. [W. T. Spencer.]

—— The Three Musketeers ; or, the Feats and Fortunes of a Gascon Adventurer. By Alexander Dumas. Translated from the French, By William Barrow. London, Bruce and Wyld, 1846. [Block : B.M.]

—— Twenty Years After ; or the Further Feats and Fortunes of a Gascon Adventurer : being a Sequel to " The Three Musketeers," translated from the French by William Barrow. 2 vols., 1846. [Marks.]

Dumas, J. L. A. Gumal and Lina ; or, the African Children. An instructive and entertaining history, designed chiefly for the use of young people. Translated from the French by S. B. Moens. 2 vols., London, Duncan, 1817. [B.M.]

Dumenil, François Guillaume Ducray. The Blind Beggar ; or The Fountain of St. Catherine. A Novel. 4 vols., London, Printed by the Minerva Press for A. K. Newman, 1817. [B.M. Blakey]

—— Julien ; or, My Father's House. Translated from the French of Ducray Dumenil, by Mrs. Meeke. 4 vols., London, Minerva Press, 1807. [Blakey]

—— The Little Chimer ; a Tale, altered from the French of Ducry Dumenil. 4 vols., 1810. [*Quarterly Review.*]

—— The Novice of St. Ursula. By the Author of " A Tale of Mystery, " " Jeannette, " &c. 4 vols., London 1810. [*Monthly Mag. : Quarterly Review :* T. D. Webster.]

—— A Tale of Mystery, or Celina. A novel. Altered from the French of Ducray-Dumenil, by Mrs. Meeke. London, Printed at the Minerva Press for Lane and Newman, 1803. [Blakey]

—— Victor ; Or, the Child of the Forest. From the French of M. Ducray-Dumenil 4 vols., London, Minerva Press, 1802. [Stonehill ; Blakey.]

Duncan, Rev. Henry. The Cottage Fireside ; Or, The Parish Schoolmaster : A Moral Tale, Intended chiefly to convey, in an alluring form, An important practical lesson To Parents In the education of their children, And to young persons, In the duty of obedience, and the happiness of Good conduct. Edinburgh, Oliphant, Waugh, & Innes, 1816. [B.M.]

—— William Douglas ; or, The Scottish Exiles. A Historical Novel. 3 vols., Edinburgh, Oliver and Boyd ; and Longman, Rees, Orme, Brown, and Green, 1826. [B.M. : *Quarterly Review :* T. Thorp.]

—— The Young South Country Weaver ; or, A Journey to Glasgow : A Tale for the Radicals, And Maitland Smith, the

Murderer, A True Narrative. Edinburgh, Waugh and Innes, 1821. [B.M.]

Duncan, John (?). The Gambler's Wife ; or Murder Will Out. By the Author of " The Ordeal by Touch " " The Iron Mask," " The Assassins of the Cavern," &c. With woodcuts. London, Edward Lloyd [c. 1835]. [B. Ono : Stonehill.]
—— The Ordeal by Touch ; a Romance. London [1847] [B.M.].

Duncombe, Mrs. John. The Village Gentleman and the Attorney-at-Law. 2 vols., London, Published by Subscription, 1808. [Allibone : Baker's Bookshop : Arthur Rogers.]

Dunethvin ; Or, The Visit to Paris. A Novel. By a Lady Some time resident in France. 4 vols., London, Printed at the Minerva Press for A. K. Newman, 1818. [B.M. : *New Monthly Mag.*]

Dunleith Abbey ; Or, Malevolence Defeated : In which is displayed The Retribute Power of Providence Over those who injure The Innocent. With an engraving and a woodcut. London, John Arliss, N.D. [Court Bk. Shop.]

Dunlop, Donald M. Stanton. A tale. 2 vols., London [Bath], Longman, 1848. [B.M. : *Eng. Cat.*]

Dunn, Lady. The Benevolent Recluse. 2 vols., 1810. [*Monthly Mag.*]

Dunne, F. W. The Pirate of Bofine. An Historical Romance. 3 vols., London, A. K. Newman, 1832. [B.M.] : *I. in F.*]

Dunsany, : an Irish Story. 2 vols., London, Sherwood, 1818. [*Eng. Cat. : I. in F. : New Monthly Mag.*]

Duodecimo, Or The Scribbler's Progress, An Autobiography, written by an Insignificant Little Volume and published by itself. London, T. C. Newby, 1859. [B.M. : Ingpen.]

Du Plessis, L. F. A. Du Plessis's Memoirs ; Or, Variety of Adventures. With a description of some strolling players, amongst whom the Memorialist travell'd awhile, before his last departure from England. 2 vols., Dublin, 1757. [B.M. : Arthur Rogers.]
—— Richelieu ; or, the Broken Heart ; an historical tale. [Attributed to Catherine Grace Frances Gore.] London, Sams, 1826. [B.M. : *Eng. Cat. : Quarterly Review.*]

Duras, Claire L. R. Bonne, Duchesse de, —Edward. Translated from the French of the Author of Ourika. London, Longman, Rees, Orme, Brown, and Green, 1826. [B.M. : *Quarterly Review.*]
—— Ourika. London, Longman, Hurst, Rees, Orme, Brown, & Green. 1824. [B.M.]

Duros, Edward. Derwentwater, a Tale of 1715. 2 vols., London, William Kidd, 1830. [*Eng. Cat.: New Monthly Mag.: G. Worthington.*]

Duros, Edward. Otterbourne ; A Story of the English Marshes. By the Author of " Derwentwater." 3 vols., London, Richard Bentley, 1832. [B.M.]

Dyer, Robert. The Story of a Wanderer ; Founded upon his Recollections of Incidents in Russian and Cossack Scenes. London, Charles Knight, 1826. [B.M. : *New Monthly Mag.*]

Dyson, Mary Ann. Ivo and Verena, or the Snowdrop. London, Mozley, 1846. [*Eng. Cat. :* T. Thorp.]
—— Little Alice and her Sister. With a woodcut border to each page. London, James Burns, 1843. [B.M.]

Each Sex in Their Humour ; or, the Histories of the Families of Brightley, Finch, Fortescue, Shelburne, and Stevens, written by a Lady of Quality during her Travels abroad. 2 vols., London, For the Editor, 1764. [Lowe : Norman.]

Eagles, John. The Journal of Llewellin Penrose, a seaman. 4 vols., London, John Murray, 1815. [B.M. : Ingpen : Publisher's advert.]

Eardley Hall, A Tale by Ellen T——, Authoress of " Rose Sommerville," " Ravensdale," etc. etc. etc. With woodcuts. London, E. Lloyd, [1849 ?] [B. Ono.]

Earle, William, Jr. Welsh Legends : A Collection of Popular Oral Tales. With a frontispiece. London, Printed by J. D. Dewick for J. Badcock, 1802. [Backus : B.M. : Court Bk. Shop.]
—— The Welshmen, A Romance. 4 vols., London, 1901. [Allibone : B.M.]

Early Feuds ; Or Fortune's Frolics. A Novel. By the Author of Geraldwood, But which ? Villeroy, Sigismar, &c, [Henry Whitefield] 3 vols., London, Printed at the Minerva Press, for A. K. Newman, 1816. [B.M. : *New Monthly Mag.*]

Early Love, a tale. Edinburgh, 1814. [B.M.]

East, Timothy. The Modern Martyr. 2 vols., London, Frederick Westley and A. H. Davis ; John Boyd, Edinburgh ; R. Wrightson, Birmingham ; and G. Tyrrell, Dublin, 1829. [B.M.]

East India Sketch-Book. By a Lady. Second Series. 2 vols., London, Richard Bentley, 1833. [B.M.]

Easter Gift (The), Or The Way to be Very Good. A book very much wanted to be read by Parents as well as Children. With woodcuts. London, T. Carnan, 1781. [Arthur Rogers.]

Eastern Romance. Select Tales from the Arabian and other sources. London, Burns, [1843]. [B.M. : *Eng. Cat.*]

Eastern Tales, or Moral Allegories ; illustrative of the Manners and Customs of Oriental Nations : and designed for the instruction and amusement of youth. London, Chapple, 1811. [Ingpen : McLeish.]

Eastlake, Lady (*see* RIGBY, Elizabeth).

Easy Stories, for the Amusement and Information of Children of Four and Five Years old. With an engraving. London, N. Hailes, 1831. [B.M. : Gumuchian.]

Easy Tales for Little Children. London, 1849. [B.M.]

Eaton, Charlotte Anne. At Home and Abroad ; Or, Memoirs of Emily de Cardonnell. By the author of " Rome in the Nineteenth Century." " Continental Adventures." etc. A Novel. 3 vols., London, John Murray, 1831. [Baker's Bookshop : B.M. : Stonehill.]

—— Continental Adventures. A Novel. 3 vols., London, Hurst, Robinson, 1826. [B.M. : Ingpen : McLeish.]

—— Vittoria Colonna ; A Tale of Rome, In the Nineteenth Century. 3 vols., Edinburgh, William Blackwood ; and T. Cadell, London, 1827. [B.M. : Publisher's advert. : G. Worthington.]

Eaton, William Champion. The Heiress, a tale, Reading. 1846. [B.M.]

Eccentric Traveller (The). With 44 woodcuts. 4 vols., London, Longman, Rees, Orme, Brown, and Green, 1826. [B.M. : Ingpen : Arthur Rogers.]

Eda Morton and Her Cousins ; or School Room Days. London, T. Harrison, 1848. [B.M. : *Eng. Cat.*]

Edelfrida. A Novel. 4 vols., London, Hookham, 1792. [B.M. : Ingpen.]

Edgeworth, Mrs. Adelaide ; Or, The Chateau de St. Pierre. A Tale of the Sixteenth Century. 4 vols., London, Hughes, 1806. [B.M. : Ingpen.]

—— The Ballad Singer ; Or, Memoirs of the Bristol Family. A Novel. 4 vols., London, A. K. Newman, 1814. [B.M. : Cleverdon : *Eng. Cat.*]

—— The Wife, or a Model for Women. 3 vols., London, Printed at the Minerva Press, for A. K. Newman, 1810. [*Monthly Mag. :* Publisher's advert.]

Edgeworth, Maria. The Absentee. 1801. [*Guide to Best Fiction.*]

—— Belinda. 3 vols., London, J. Johnson, 1801. [Ingpen : McLeish : T. Thorp.]

—— Castle Rackrent, an Hibernian Tale. Taken from Facts, and from the Manners of the Irish Squires, before the Year 1782. [London], Printed for J. Johnson, by J. Crowder, 1800. [Birrell & Garnett : B.M. : Sotheran.]

—— Continuation of Early Lessons. [Volume I containing " Frank," and the beginning of " Rosamund " ; Volume II., containing the conclusion of " Rosamund," and " Harry and Lucy."] 2 vols., London, J. Johnson, 1814. [Elkin Mathews : Sotheran.]

—— Frank, being the sixth part of Early Lessons. By the Author of The Parent's Assistant. 6 vols., London, J. Johnson, 1801. [*Eng. Lit. in Germany :* Gumuchian.]

Edgeworth, Maria. Frank. Part I. [II., III., IV.], being the Seventh [8th., 9th., 10th] Part of Early Lessons. By the Author of " The Parent's Assistant." 4 vols., London, J. Johnson, 1801. [Elkin Mathews.]

—— Frank : a sequel to Frank, in Early Lessons. 3 vols., London, Printed for R. Hunter ; and Baldwin, Cradock & Joy, 1822. [Elkin Mathews : *Eng. Cat. :* T. Thorp.]

—— Garry Owen ; Or, The Snow-Woman And Poor Bob, The Chimney-Sweeper. With 4 woodcuts. London, John Murray, 1832. [B.M. : Gumuchian : Arthur Rogers.]

—— Harrington, a Tale ; And Ormond, a Tale. 3 vols., London, R. Hunter ; and Baldwin, Cradock & Joy, 1817. [B.M. : Ingpen : McLeish.]

—— Harry and Lucy concluded. Being the Last Part of " Early Lessons." 4 vols., London, R. Hunter ; and Baldwin, Cradock & Joy, 1825. [Ingram : Arthur Rogers : T. D. Webster.]

—— Helen, A Tale. 3 vols., London, Richard Bentley, 1834. [Block : B.M. Arthur Rogers.]

—— Leonora. 2 vols., London, J. Johnson, 1806. [B.M. : Ingpen : Arthur Rogers.]

—— The Little Dog Trusty, The Orange Miss and The Cherry Orchard. Being the Tenth Part of Early Lessons. 1801 [Arthur Rogers.]

—— The Modern Griselda. A Tale. London, J. Johnson, 1805. [T. D. Webster.]

—— Moral Tales for Young People. 3 vols., London, J. Johnson, 1801. [Francis Edwards : Ingram : Arthur Rogers.]

—— Orlandino. [Edinburgh.] 1848. [Block : Sotheran.]

—— The Parent's Assistant, or Stories for Children. 6 vols., London, J. Johnson, 1796. [B.M. (2nd edn.) : *Guide to Best Fiction.*]

—— Patronage. 4 vols., London, J. Johnson, 1814. [Ingpen : Marks : W. T. Spencer.]

—— Popular Tales. 3 vols., London, Printed for J. Johnson, by C. Mercier, 1804. [Clarke-Hall.]

—— Rosamond. A Sequel to Early Lessons. 2 vols., London, R. Hunter ; and Baldwin, Cradock & Joy, 1821. [Ingpen : Arthur Rogers : T. Thorp.]

—— Tales of Fashionable Life. 9 vols., London, J. Johnson, 1809-1812. [B.M. : Ingpen : W. T. Spencer.]

Edgeworth, Theodore. The Shipwreck ; or, Memoirs of an Irish Officer and his Family. 3 vols., London, Tregg, 1811. [*I in F.*]

Edinburgh : A Satirical Novel. By the Author of London ; or, a Month at Stevens's. 3 vols., London, Sherwood, Neely, and Jones, 1820. [Pickering : Arthur Rogers : D. Webster.]

Edith Leslie, A Novel. 3 vols., London, T. C. Newby, 1844. [B.M.]

Edith's Lesson, or the Old Fisherman. A tale. London, 1849. [B.M.]

Edmeston, James. Anston Park, a tale. London, Holdsworth, 1821. [B.M. : *Eng. Cat.*]

Edmond of Lateragh : a Novel founded on facts. 2 vols., Dublin, 1806. [*I. in F.*]

Edmonds, Mrs. Flora Mortimer : or, Six Months in the Country. London, 1850. [B.M.]

Edmund of the Forest. An historical novel. By the author of Cicely, or The rose of Raby, [Agnes Musgrave]. London, William Lane. 4 vols., 1797. [*New Ann. Reg.* Blakey.]

Edmund O'Hara, an Irish Tale. By the author of " Elmer Castle." Dublin, Curry, 1828. [B.M. : *I in F.*]

Edmund ; or, The child of the castle. A novel. 2 vols., [W. Lane, 1790.] [Blakey.]

Edridge, Rebecca. The Highest Castle and the Lowest Cave ; or, Events of the Days which are Gone. 3 vols., London, George B. Whittaker, 1825. [B.M. : *Edin. Mag.* : Ingpen.]

—— The Scrinium. 2 vols., London, G. and W. B. Whittaker, 1822. [B.M. : McLeish : Stonehill.]

Edward and George ; or, lessons from real life. London, 1818. [B.M.]

Edward and Harriet, or the Happy Recovery ; a sentimental novel. By a Lady. 2 vols., London, 1788. [B.M.]

Edward and Julia ; Or, Visits to the Village. With woodcuts. London, A. K. Newman, [1820 ?] [B.M.]

Edward and Laura, being a new Translation from the French, of the continuation of Rousseau's account of the Adventures of Lord B——. 2 vols., 1809. [*Monthly Mag.*]

Edward and Sophia, a Novel, by a Lady. 2 vols., 1787. [P. C. Cuttelle.]

Edward Beaumont : or, the Efficacy of Prayer. A narrative founded on facts. By a Lady. Dublin, 1844. [B.M.]

Edward de Courcy, An ancient fragment. 2 vols., London, W. Lane, 1794. [*New Ann. Reg.*: Publisher's advert.: Blakey.]

Edward Neville ; or, The Memoirs of an Orphan. 4 vols. London, Longman, Hurst, Rees, Orme, and Brown, 1823. [B.M. : Publisher's advert. : *Quarterly Review.*]

Edward, a Novel. 2 vols., London, 1774. [B.M. : *Eng. Lit. in Germany.*]

Edward, or the Pursuit of Happiness. London, Printed for T. Cadell and W. Davies, by J. M'Creery, 1820. [B.M.]

Edward, or Sorrows from Separation, An Interesting Narration Founded on Facts. 1791. [*Eng. Lit. in Germany.*]

Edward Orland ; or, Truth and Untruth. London, 1847. [B.M.]

Edward Wortley and the Exile of Scotland. 4 vols., London, Whiteley, 1819. [*Eng. Cat. : New Monthly Mag.*]

Edwin and Anna. 1785. [*Eng. Lit. in Germany.*]

Edwin ; or, The Heir of Aella. An Historical Romance. With a frontispiece. 3 vols., London, Minerva Press, 1803. [Stonehill, T. D. Webster.]

Edwin or, The Wandering Fugitive. An History founded on Facts. [1805.] [Ingpen.]

Edwy ; Son of Ethelred the Second : an Historic Tale. By a Lady. Addressed (by permission) to the Right Honourable the Countess of Westmorland. 2 vols., Dublin, Printed for the Authoress by John Rice, 1791. [G. Worthington.]

Effects of Groundless Hatred (The), Exemplified in The History of M. de Precelles. Founded on Facts. With woodcuts. London, James Wallis, [1840 ?] [B.M.]

Effects of Tyranny (The), or the History of Hamet, Prince of Persia. By Lawrence Lovesense. [London], R. Bassam, [1800 ?] [B.M.]

Effingham Hazard, the Adventurer. London, 1839. [B.M.]

Egan, Pierce. Finish to the Adventures of Tom, Jerry and Logic in their pursuits through Life in and out of London. With plates by Robert Cruikshank. London, G. Virtue, 1830. [T. Thorp.]

—— Life in London ; or, the Day and Night Scenes of Jerry Hawthorn, Esquire, and his friend Corinthian Tom, accompanied by Bob Logic, the Oxonian, in their Rambles and Sprees through the Metropolis. With 36 plates by George and I. R. Cruikshank and 3 folding sheets of music. London, Sherwood, Neely, & Jones, 1821. [Block : B.M. : Maggs.]

—— The Life of an Actor. With a frontispiece and 26 plates by T. Lane, & woodcuts. London, Arnold, 1825. [B.M. : Maggs : Marks.]

—— Real Life in London ; Or, the [(Volume II.) Further] Rambles and Adventures of Bob Tallyho, Esq. And his cousin, The Hon. Tom Dashall, [(Volume II.) &c.] Through the Metropolis ; Exhibiting a Living Picture of Fashionable Characters, Manners, and Amusements In High and Low Life. By An Amateur. With plates by Alken, Dighton, Brooke, Rowlandson, Heath, &c. 2 vols., London, Jones, 1821-1822. [Block : B.M. : Marks.]

Egan, Pierce, the Younger. Adam Bell. Clym O' The Cleugh. With a frontispiece. F. Hextall 1841. [Salkeld.]

—— Fair Rosamund. An Historical Romance. With woodcuts. London. Barth, 1844. [H. W. Fennell : Stonehill.]

Egan, Pierce, the Younger. Paul Jones. London, F. Hextall 1842. [B.M.]

—— The Pilgrims of the Thames, In Search of the National ! With illustrations by Pierce Egan, The Younger. London, Tegg, 1839. [Stonehill.]

—— Quintin Matsys, the Blacksmith of Antwerp. With an engraved frontispiece and woodcuts. London, Johnson, [1839]. [B.M. : *Eng. Cat. :* R. S. Frampton.]

—— Robin Hood and Little John ; Or, The Merry Men of Sherwood Forest. With illustrations by the Author. London, Foster and Hextall, 1839. [Dobell.]

—— The Thirteenth ; or, The Fatal Number. With illustrations. London, A. Vickers, 1849. [B.M. : Stonehill.]

—— Wat Tyler, or the Rebellion of 1831. With illustrations. London, Hextall, 1841. [B.M. : H. W. Fennell.]

Egbert, or, the Monk of Penmon. A Romance. By the author of two popular novels. 2 vols., London, 1810. [B.M.]

Eglantine, or the Flower that never fades ; an allegorical tale, altered from the French by the Author of A Narrative of three years residence in Italy. Dublin, 1828. [B.M.]

Eight Historical Tales, curious and instructive. London, 1801. [B.M.]

Elder, Abraham. Tales and Legends of the Isle of Wight : with the Adventures of the Author in Search of Them. London, Simpkin, Marshall, 1839. [B.M. : *Eng. Cat.*]

Elder Brother (The). [B.M.]

Elements of Tuition (The). And modes of Punishment ; in letters from Mdle. Dubouleau, a celebrated Parisian Tutoress, addressed to Miss Smart-Bum, Governess of a Young Ladies Academy at ——. Also Secrets of Mock Tutors who have taken a delight in administering Birch Discipline to their Female Pupils. With 8 coloured plates. [London, George Cannon], 1794 [1830] [*Cat. Lib. Prohib.*]

Elfrida ; Or, Paternal Ambition. A Novel. By a Lady. 3 vols., London, J. Johnson, 1786. [Block : P. L. Carver : *Eng. Lit. in Germany.*]

Eliezer ; or, the faithful servant. London, 1837. [B.M.]

Eliza Cleland, a novel. 3 vols., London, W. Lane, 1788. [Blakey]

Eliza Grimwood. A Legend of the Waterloo Road. London, Cousins, [c. 1840] [Stonehill.]

Eliza, or the pious Village Girl. London, 1823. [B.M.]

Elizabeth de Mowbray ; Or The Heir of Douglas. A Romance of the Thirteenth Century. 4 vols., London, Printed at the Minerva Press, for A. K. Newman, 1816. [B.M. Blakey.]

Elizabeth Percy, A Novel, Founded on Facts. Written by a Lady. 2 vols., London, Hamilton, 1792. [*New Ann. Reg. :* Stonehill.]

Ellen Harding, or the Tell-Tale. London, 1849. [B.M.]

——, or The Naughty Girl Reclaimed. With cut-out illustrations. 1811. [*Camb. Hist. Eng. Lit.*]

—— **Rushford.** A novel. 2 vols., London, William Lane 1794. [B.M. : Publisher's advert.]

—— **Walsingham ;** Or, Growth in Grace. By the author of " Nature and Grace exemplified," &c. &c. London, Houlston, 1836. [B.M.]

Ellen's Dream. With a vignette. London, James Burns, [1849]. [B.M.]

Ellerman, Charles F. The Amnesty ; Or, The Duke of Alba In Flanders. An Historical Novel Of the Sixteenth Century. 2 vols., London, Longman, Brown, Green, & Longmans, 1843. [B.M.]

Ellesmere, Francis, Earl of. The Mill : A Moravian Tale. Founded on Fact. With 7 illustrations. London, W. Nicol, 1829. [Pickering.]

Ellesmere Family (The) : A Tale of Unfashionable Life. By the Author of The West Indian. With a frontispiece. Wellington, Salop : F. Houlston, 1829. [B.M.]

Ellia, Felix. Norman Banditti ; or, the Fortress of Coustance, A Tale. 2 vols., London, [W. Lane.] 1798. [*New Ann. Reg.* Blakey.]

Elliott, Miss. History of the Hon. Mrs. Rosemont and Sir Henry Cardigan, In a Series of Letters. 1781. [*Eng. Lit. in Germany.*]

—— The Masqued Weddings, A Novel, in a Series of Letters. 2 vols., London, T. Hookham, 1781 [Pickering.]

—— The Portrait, a novel. 2 vols., London, 1783. [B.M.]

Elliott, Mary. The Adventures of Thomas Two-Shoes. Being a Sequel to that of " The Modern Goody Two-Shoes." With a folding frontispiece and 2 other plates. London, W. Darton, Jun., 1818. [Gumuchian.]

—— Confidential Memoirs ; Or, Adventures Of A Parrot, a Greyhound, a Cat, And a Monkey. With a frontispiece. London, William Darton, 1821. [B.M.]

—— The Contrast ; or, how to be happy. London, [1830 ?] [B.M.]

—— The Cousins ; or, quality before quantity. Conceit not merit. London. [1840]. [B.M.]

—— Grateful Tributes ; or, Recollections of Infancy. By M. Belson, Author of " Industry and Idleness," " Innocent Poetry," " Baby's Holiday," " Precept and Example," " The Mice and their Pic Nic," etc. With illustrations. London, W. Darton, Jun., 1813. [Mollie Green.]

Elliott, Mary. Idle Ann, or the Dunce Reclaimed. London, [1824 ?] [Algar : *Camb. Hist. Eng. Lit.*]

—— Industry and Idleness : a pleasing and instructive tale. London, Wm. Darton, Jun., 1811. [Algar : *Camb. Hist. Eng. Lit.*]

—— Little Lessons for little Folks : containing 1. The little Sweepers ; 2. The Mistake ; 3. The Widow and her only Son ; 4. Ask, and Learn ; 5. Village Annals ; or, Truth and Falsehood. London, 1818. [B.M.]

—— The Modern Goody Two Shoes. With 2 plates. London, W. Darton, 1819. [Algar : *Camb. Hist. Eng. Lit.* : J. G. Commin.]

—— The Orphan Boy or A Journey to Bath. Founded on Fact. With a frontispiece. London, W. Darton, 1812. [Dobell.]

—— Peggy and her Mammy. With a folding frontispiece and 2 plates. London, William Darton, 1819. [Gumuchian.]

—— The Ramble or More Paths than one. With a frontispiece and 2 plates. London, William Darton, [c. 1820]. [Gumuchian.]

—— Tales for Boys. London, Darton, 1839. [Allibone : *Camb. Hist. Eng. Lit : Eng. Cat.*]

—— Tales for Girls. With plates. London, Darton, [1845]. [*Camb. Hist. Eng. Lit.* : Clarke-Hall : *Eng. Cat.*]

—— Tales of Truth for Young People. London, Wm. Darton, [1836 ?] [B.M. : *Camb. Hist. Eng. Lit.* : *Eng. Cat.*]

—— The Truant Reclaimed. [London], W. Darton, [1824 ?]. [Algar : B.M.]

—— Truth our Best Friend. London, W. Darton, [1825]. [Algar : *Camb. Hist. Eng. Lit.*]

—— The Two Edwards ; or pride and prejudice unmasked. London, W. Darton, 1823. [Algar : B.M.]

—— William's Secret. With a folding frontispiece and 2 plates. London, William Darton, 1819. [Gumuchian.]

Ellis, Sarah Stickney. Family Secrets : Or, Hints to Those Who Would Make a Home Happy. With plates by Corbould. 3 vols., London, Fisher, 1841. [B.M. : Stephen Hunt.]

—— Fireside Tales for the Young. 4 vols., London, P. Young, 1842. [*Eng. Cat.* : Lib. of Congress.]

—— Home, Or The Iron Rule. A Domestic Story. 3 vols., London, Saunders and Otley, 1836. [B.M. : Lib. of Congress : Publisher's advert.]

—— Look to the End ; Or, The Bennets Abroad. 2 vols., London, Fisher, 1845. [B.M. : Lib. of Congress.]

—— Pictures of Private Life. With an engraving. London, Smith, Elder, 1833. [B.M.]

Ellis, Sarah Stickney. Pictures Of Private Life. Second Series. With an engraving. London, Smith, Elder, 1834. [B.M.]

—— Pictures Of Private Life. Third Series. With an engraving. London, Smith, Elder, 1837. [B.M.]

—— Pique. A Novel. 3 vols., London, Smith, Elder, 1850. [B.M. : Carver & Staniforth.]

—— Social Distinction ; Or, Hearts and Homes. 3 vols., London, Tallis, [1848-1849]. [B.M. : *Eng. Cat.* : Lib. of Congress.]

—— Temper and Temperament ; or, Varieties of Character. By the Author of " The Women of England." With plates. 2 vols., London, Fisher, [1846]. [B.M. : *Critic* : Lib. of Congress.]

Ellmer Castle. Dublin, Curry, 1827. [*I. in F.*]

Elmina, a Tale. With woodcuts. London, Harris, 1815. [F. Harvey.]

Elnathan; or, The Ages of Man. An Historical Romance. By a philosopher. 3 vols., London, A. K. Newman, 1811. [*Eng. Cat.* : *Quarterly Review* : Blakey]

Eloisa de Clairville. An historical novel, written during the reign of Philip Augustus, King of France. 2 vols., [W. Lane, 1770]. [Blakey.]

Eloise de Montblanc. A Novel. 4 vols. [London], William Lane]. 1796. [*New Ann, Reg.* : Blakey : T. D. Webster.]

Elson, Jane. Romance of the Castle. 2 vols., With a frontispiece. London, W. Lane, 1800. [Allibone : Blakey.]

—— The Village Romance. A Novel 2 vols., 1802. [Allibone.]

Elton, or the Heroine of Sorrow. A novel. London, 1812. [B.M.]

Elvina, A Novel. 2 vols., London, William Lane at the Minerva Press, 1792. [*New Ann Reg.* : Stonehill : Blakey].

Embarrassed Lovers, (The) ; or, The history of Henry Carey, Esq., and the Hon. Miss Cecilia Neville. In a series of letters. 2 vols., London, W. Lane, 1775. [Blakey].

Emigrant Orphans (The), and The convert of the select class. London, 1849. [B.M.]

Emigrants (The), a Gallic Tale. 2 vols., 1794. [*New Ann Reg.*]

Emilia and Alphonsus, a Novel, translated from the French. 2 vols., 1799. [*New Ann Reg.*]

Emily, a Novel. 3 vols., London, William Lane, 1792. [T. Thorp.]

Emily Grey, London, [1847]. [B.M.]

Emily or The History of a Natural Daughter. 1756. [*Eng. Lit. in Germany.*]

Emily : Or Traits of Principle. A Tale. By a Lady. London, Otridge and Rackham. 1824. [Elkin Mathews.]

Emily Percy ; or, The Heiress of Sackville. A Romance. By Ellen T——, Authoress of " Rose Sommerville,"

"Love and Honour," etc. With wood-cuts. London, E. Lloyd, [c. 1845]. [B. Ono : Stonehill.]

Emily, A tale for young persons. London, J. Harris, 1825. [B.M.]

Emily Trevor : or, the Vale of Elwy. By a Lady. London, Simpkin, 1850. [B.M.]

Emma and the little Silk-makers. A story. London, 1833. [B.M.]

Emma Dorvill. By a Lady. London, 1789. [B.M.]

Emma, Or the Child of Sorrow. 2 vols., Dublin, 1776. [Dobell : *Eng. Lit. in Germany*.]

Empronia. A tale to the heart. In a Series of th letters. 3 vols., [W. Lane, 1790]. [Blakey.]

Enchanted Mirror (The), a Moorish romance. Salisbury, J. Easton, 1799. [B.M.]

Enchantress (The) ; or, Where Shall I Find Her ? A Tale. By the author of Melbourne, Deloraine, Reginald, &c. [Mrs. Martin] London, Minerva Press, 1801. [B.M. : Stonehill : Blakey].

Engagement (The) : A Novel. 3 vols., London, Henry Colburn, 1841. [Black-well : [B.M.]

Engel, J. J. Lorenz Stark, A Character-istic Picture of A German Family. Translated from the German, By J. Gans. 2 vols., London, Treuttel and Würtz, Treuttel, Jun. and Richter, 1826. [B.M.]

Engel, M. E. Essays and Tales. From the German by Thomas Horne. 1808. [B.M.]

English, Clara. The Children in the Wood ; an instructive tale. London, Darton and Harvey, 1801. [B.M.]

English, Harriet. Conversations and Amusing Tales. Offered to the Publick for the Youth of Great Britain. With a frontispiece by Bartolozzi after Hamilton, and 12 vignettes. London, Printed for the Author by Charles Clarke, 1799. [B.M. : Gumuchian : Arthur Rogers.]

English, John. The Grey Friar, and the Black Spirit of the Wye. A Romance. 2 vols., London, Minerva Press, 1810. [Allibone : Blakey].

English Brothers, or Anecdotes of the Howard Family. 4 vols., [Cawthorn's Catalogue, 1810].

English Hermit (The), or, the Adventures of Philip Quarll. With woodcuts and a map by Bewick. York, Wilson and Spence, 1802. [John Pearson.]

English in India (The). And Other Sketches. By a Traveller. 2 vols., Lon-don, Longman, Rees, Orme, Brown, Green, and Longman, 1835. [B.M.: T. D. Webster.]

English Life ; Or, Manners at Home. In Four Pictures. 2 vols., London, G. Wightman. [*Eng. Cat.*]

English Night's Entertainments (The). First series contain a Day in Stowe Gardens. London, J. Gifford, 1826. [B.M. : Ingpen.]

English Nights Entertainments. The Misfortunes of Love, or the adventures, of Henry and Julia. To which is added the pathetic history of Leonora. London, 1800. [B.M.]

English Princess (The), or The Dutchess Queen. [T. D. Webster.]

Englishman in Paris (The) ; A Satirical Novel. With sketches of the Most Remarkable Characters that have recently visited that Celebrated Capital. 3 vols., London, Sherwood, Neely and Jones, 1819. [Ingpen : Pickering.]

Englishman's Fortnight in Paris (The) ; Or, The Art of Ruining Himself There in a Few Days. Translated from the French. London, Durham, 1777. [Ingpen.]

Ennersley, W. E. Edward's Cross ; Or, the Wife and the Friend. An Old English Tale. London, Dean and Munday, [1810]. [R. S. Frampton : Ingpen.]

Ennis, Alicia Margaret. The Contested Election ; Or A Courtier's Promises. 3 vols., London, Printed at the Minerva Press for A. K. Newman, 1820. [B.M. : *New Monthly Mag.* : Blakey.]

Entanglement (The) ; or, the History of Miss Eleonora Frampton, and Miss Anastasia Shaftoe. 2 vols., London, Noble, 1767. [*Univ. Mag.*]

Entertainer (The) ; containing great variety of instructive entertainment, for persons of every age, rank, or degree. Collected by Charles Tell-truth. 2 vols., London, 1766. [B.M.]

Entertaining and Instructive Tales. In two parts. Aberdeen, 1813. [B.M.]

Entertaining History of Little Goody Goose-cap (The), containing a variety of amusing and instructive adventures. With 2 plates. London, John Harris ; and Baldwin & Cradock, 1828. [J. D. Miller.]

Entertaining History of Old Robin Gray (The) : An Ancient Scotch Tale. London, Clements, 1789. [Stonehill.]

Entertaining History of Palidor and Fidele : written for the amusement and instruction of youth. London, [1786 ?] [B.M.)

Entertaining Juggler (The), or an ad-mirable teller. Translated from the Dutch, 1817. Madras. 1818. [B.M.]

Entertaining Novelist (The). [*Progress of Romance.*]

Entertaining Story-Teller (The). Fal-kirk, 1801. [B.M.]

Enthusiasm not Religion : a tale. By the late M.A.C. London, 1848. [B.M.]

Entire New Collection of Romances and Novels (An), Never Before Published. With plates. 1780. [Stonehill.]

Eötvös, Baron. The Village Notary; A romance of Hungarian life. Translated from the Hungarian of Baron Eötvös by Otto Wenckstern. With introductory remarks by Francis Pulszky. 3 vols., 1850. [Allibone : B.M.]

Erratics : By a Sailor. Containing Rambles in Norfolk, and Elsewhere. 3 vols., London, Oglivy, 1800. [Ingpen.]

Errors and their Consequences ; Or, Memoirs Of an English Family. 2 vols., London, Longman, Hurst, Rees, Orme, and Brown, 1819. [B.M.]

Errors of Sensibility (The). A novel. 3 vols., London Printed at the Minerva Press, for William Lane, 1793. [Blakey.]

Errym, Malcolm J., (*see* RYMER, James Malcolm).

Erskine, Esme Steuart. Alcon Malanzore, a Moorish tale. Brussels, 1815. [B.M.]

Erskine, Thos., Baron Erskine. Armata. A Fragment. Lond. John Murray, 1817. [F. S. Read : B.M.]

Escapes, Wanderings, and Preservation of a Hare (The). Related by Herself. With 3 engravings. London, J. and C. Evans, [1820].

Espinel, Vincente. The History of the Life of the Squire Marcos de Obregon. Translated into English from the Madrid edition of 1618, By Algernon Langton. 2 vols., London, 1816. [B.M. : *Guide to Best Fiction :* Lib. of Congress.]

Essay of Three Tales, translated from the German language. Ghent, 1820. [B.M.]

Essays and Tales. By a Popular Author. London, 1833. [B.M.]

Essington, R. W. The Island on the Mere ; a Cheshire Tale. By the Author of " The Legacy of an Etonian." Cambridge, 1847. [B.M.]

Esther ; or, The Two Mothers. From the French. With a vignette. London, James Burns, [1849]. [B.M.]

Ethelinda ; or, The Fair Maid of the Inn. An Interesting Tale. [1804]. [Ingpen.]

Étienne de Jouy (*see* JOUY).

Eugenia and Adelaide, A Novel. 2 vols., London, C. Dilly, 1791. [B.M.]

Eustace Fitz-Richard. A Tale of the Barons' Wars. By the Author of The Bandit-Chief, or Lords of Urvino. 4 vols., London, A. K. Newman, 1826. [B.M. : *New Monthly Mag. : Quarterly Review.*]

Euston, a novel. 2 vols. [Cawthorn's Catalogue, 1810].

Eustathius. Ismene and Ismenias, a novel. [Translated from the French by L. H. Le Moine]. London, 1788. [B.M.]

Eva ; or the Bridal Spectre. A Tale. London, 1830. [B.M.]

Evans, James Harington. The Old Man and His Grand-Daughter, at E——. London, Printed for the Author by E. Justins, 1817. [B.M.]

Evans, Robert. The Dream ; or, Noble Cambrians. 2 vols. [W. Lane, 1801]. [Blakey.]

Evans, Rev. Robert Wilson. The Rectory of Valehead. London, Smith, Elder, 1831. [B.M. (2nd edn.)]

Eve of San Marco (The). A Romance. 3 vols., 1812. [*Quarterly Review.*]

Eve of San Pietro (The). A Tale. 3 vols., London, T. Cadell and W. Davies, 1804. [B.M. : Birrell & Garnett.]

Evelyn Howard. Or Mistaken Policy. A Domestic Tale. 2 vols., London, Saunders and Otley, 1842. [B.M.]

Evening Amusement ; or, little stories for good children. London, 1827. [B.M.]

Evening Amusements for the Ladies ; or, original anecdotes, intended to promote a love of virtue in young minds. A series of letters. Dublin, 1789. [B.M.]

Evening Brush (The), or Laughable Jester for 1808, containing Entertaining Anecdotes, Humourous Stories, Whimsical Sayings, Irish Bulls, Tricks in Legerdemain, and Natural Magic. Curious Epigrams, Riddles, and Conundrums ; to which is annexed, The New Country Dances, together with a Variety of Toasts and Sentiments. With a frontispiece. London, J. Lee, [1808]. [Pickering.]

Evening Recreations ; or, a Collection of Original Stories, written by a Lady, for the Amusement of her Young Friends. [*Guardian of Education.*]

Evening Walk (The) ; a sentimental Tale. By a Youth of seventeen. London, 1795. [B.M. : *New Ann. Reg.*]

Evenings with the Old Story-Tellers. Select Tales from the Gesta Romanorum. London, Burns, 1845. [*Critic.*]

Everest, Mrs. Narratives of a Parent ; or, birth-day tales. London, 1845. [B.M.]

Eversfield Abbey : a novel. By the Authoress of the Aunt and the Niece. 3 vols., London, 1806. [B.M.]

Every Day Occurrences. 2 vols., London, Charles Knight, 1825. [B.M.]

Evil Eye (The), A Legend of Greece. With a folding frontispiece. London, Duncombe, [c. 1800]. [Stonehill.]

Example ; or, Family Scenes. London, 1832. [B.M.]

Example (The) ; or, The History of Lucy Cleveland, By a Young Lady. 2 vols., London, Fielding and Walker, 1778. [*Eng. Lit. in Germany : Westminster Mag.*]

Excursion of Osman (The), the son of Abdallah, Lord of the Vallies ; a political romance : including some anecdotes relative to a great northern family. With a frontispiece. Liverpool, T. Schofield, 1792. [B.M. : *Lancs. : New Ann. Reg.*]

Exile (The) : Or, Matilda of the Castle, And Rousina of the Alps ; An Historical Memoir. London, William Sams, 1820. [B.M.]

Expedition of Little Pickle (The), or, the Pretty Plotter. London, 1792. [B.M. : T. D. Webster.]

Explanation (The) : or, Agreeable Surprise. By a young lady. 2 vols., London, 1773. [B.M.]

Exquisite (The) : A Collection of Tales, Histories, and Essays. Funny, Fanciful, and Facetious. Interspersed with Anecdotes, Original and Select. Amorous Adventures. Piquant Jests, and Spicy Sayings. With illustrations. 3 vols., London, H. Smith [William Dugdale], [1842–1844]. [*Cat. Lib. Prohib.*]

Eyton, Elizabeth. The Fault was All His Own. A Novel, in a Series of Letters. By a Lady. 2 vols., London, G. Riley, 1771. [Allibone.]

Fables and Tales for the Ladies. To which are added miscellanies by another hand. London, 1750. [B.M.]

Fables Calculated for the Amusement and Instruction of Youth ; originally dedicated to a young Prince. Taken from the French. Taunton, 1789. [B.M.]

Fagg, Michael. The Life and Adventures of a Limb of the Law. Interspersed with Anecdotes of his Contemporaries, Members of the Legal Profession. London, Hancock, 1836. [G. Worthington.]

Fair Adulteress (The). A Novel. A Story Founded on Real Facts, and intended to encourage Virtue, by exposing Vice in its proper Colours : Being the Genuine History of the late Amours of two Persons of the First Rank. London, Printed for the Author, 1744. [B.M.]

Fair Adultress (The) : Or, The Treacherous Brother. Being the Secret Memoirs of a Certain Noble Family in the Island of Cyprus. Translated from the Greek. 1743. [T. D. Webster.]

Fair Cambrians (The). A novel. 3 vols. [W. Lane, 1790]. [Blakey.]

Fair Hibernian (The). 2 vols., London, 1789. [W. Brown.]

Fair Impostor (The), A novel. Written in a Series of Letters. 3 vols., London, T. Hookham, and J. Carpenter, 1792. [B.M. : Fletcher : Stonehill.]

Fair Wanderer (The) : or, the adventures of Ethelinda, Niece to the late Cardinal B——. London, F. Stamper & E. Downham, 1751. [B.M.]

Fairbank, William. The surprising life and adventures of M. Knowles. Nowcastle, [1805 ?]. [B.M.]

Fairy Birds from Fancy Islet, or the Children in the Forest : a new tale without an end. By the Author of " The Gipsies." London, 1846. [B.M.]

Fairy Ring (The) ; or, Emmeline. A moral tale. By a lady. [W. Lane, 1783]. [Blakey.]

Fairy Stories. Containing, I. The Blue Beard and Florina. III [*sic*]. The King of the Peacocks, and Rosetta. Whereunto is added, An excellent New Song, entitled, The Fairies Dance. With woodcuts. London, Printed and Sold in Aldermary Church Yard, [1750 ?] [B.M.]

Fairy Tales, for Youth ; By Catherine Calico. With engravings by H. Adlard. London, John Souter, 1826. [B.M.]

Fairy Tales Selected from the Best Authors. 2 vols., [London, William Lane, 1788]. [Blakey.]

Fairy Tales Translated from the German. Printed and Published for the Benefit of Manchester Athenaeum Bazaar. Salford, 1843. [B.M. : Arthur Rogers.]

Faithless Sea Captain (The) ; or, The Betray'd Virgin's Garland. With a woodcut. Manchester, G. Swindells, [c. 1794]. [*Lancs.*]

False Appearances ; or, Memoirs of Henry Auberville. Interspersed with Legendary Romances. Dublin, Porter, 1803. [Stonehill.]

False Gratitude or The History of Miss Rosemont, By a Lady. 1771. [*Eng. Lit. in Germany.*]

Familiar Tales for Young Children. By M. A. W. London, John Harris ; and W. Curtis, Plymouth, [1823]. [Arthur Rogers.]

Families of Owen and De Montfort (The). A Tale of Ancient Days. 3 vols., London, Printed at the Minerva Press for A. K. Newman, 1819. [B.M.]

Family of St. Richard, The Saxon (The). London, Toovey, 1844. [*Tait's Edin. Mag.*]

Family Picture Gallery ; Or Every-Day Scenes. Depicted By Many Close Observers, and by them Selected. 4 vols., London, John Booth, 1824. [B.M.]

Family Secrets : or a Page from Life's Volume. A Romance. London, 1846. [B.M.]

Family Sketches ; or, The history of Henry Dinmore. 2 vols. [W. Lane, 1789]. [Blakey.]

Famous Adventures of Captain John Avery of Plymouth, a Notorious Pirate. Falkirk, 1809. [B.M.]

Famous History of the Seven Wise Masters of Rome (The) ; Containing, Many Excellent and Delightful Examples, With Their Explanations ; and Modern Significations ; which (by way of Allusion) may be termed, An Historical Comparison of sacred and civil Transactions ; the better to make an impression on the Minds of Men. With woodcuts. London, Printed and

Sold in Aldermary Church Yard, [1750 ?]. [B.M.]

Famous History of the Seven Wise Mistresses of Rome (The) ; Wherein The Treachery of Evil Ministers is discovered, Innocency cleared, and the Wisdom of the Seven Wise Mistresses displayed. With woodcuts. London, Printed and Sold in Aldermary Church Yard, [1750 ?]. [B.M.]

Famous History of the Unfortunate Lovers Hero and Leander (The) ; Who Ended their Lives in the Sea for each other. With woodcuts. London, Printed and Sold in Aldermary Church Yard, [1750 ?]. [B.M.]

Fancy Fair (The). To which is added Star-Light. Or a Scene at Tweedale. London, J. Hatchard, 1833. [B.M.]

Fanny : the Amours of a West Country Young Lady, 1755. 2 vols.

Fanny and her Mother ; a story for children. London, 1831. [B.M.]

Fanny : a novel ; in a series of letters. Written by a Lady. 3 vols., London, 1785. [B.M.]

Fanny ; Or The Deserted Daughter. A Novel. Being the first literary attempt of A Young Lady. 2 vols., 1789. [W. Brown.]

Fantastical Excursion into the Planets (A). London, 1839. [B.M.]

Farmers (The) ; Or, Tales for the Times, Addressed to the Yeomanry of England. By The Author. London, C. and J. Rivington, 1823. [B.M.]

Farmer's Son of Kent (The). A tale. 2 vols., London, 1769. [B.M.]

Farrer, Henrietta Louisa. The Arrival at a new Home. By the author of " Tales of Kirkbeck." London, 1850. [B.M.]

—— Aunt Atta, a tale. 1850. [B.M.]

—— Baby's Baptism. London, 1848. [B.M.]

—— Carry and Milly. London, 1848. [B.M.]

—— Charles's Sum. London, W. J. Cleaver, 1849. [B.M.]

—— Harriet and Mary Bond. London, W. J. Cleaver, 1849. [B.M.]

—— The Little Traveller. London, W. J. Cleaver, 1849. [B.M.]

Farrow, Witham. The Bravo's Son ; or the Chief of St. Maldo, a romance. Interspersed with poetry. 2 vols., London, 1809. [B.M. : *Monthly Mag.*]

Fashionable Infidelity, Or Triumph of Patience. 3 vols., London, T. Hookham, 1789. [B.M.]

Fashionable Swindler (The) ; or, villainy displayed ; being the genuine history of G. R——. London, [1810]. [B.M.]

Fatal Effects of Deception. 3 vols., 1773. [W. Brown.]

Fatal Effects (The) ; or, Letters of the Marchioness de Syrce, the Count de Mirbelle, and others. Translated from the French. 2 vols., London, Wilkie, 1774. [Stonehill.]

Fatal Friendship. A novel. By a Lady. 2 vols., London, 1770. [B.M.]

Fatal Indifference (The) ; or the interesting history of Mrs. Matilda Markham. To which is added the history of Celestia, translated from the French. London, [1800 ?]. [B.M.]

Fatal Love ; or Letters from a Village. London, 1812. [*Quarterly Review.*]

Fatal Marriage (The) : a novel. 2 vols., London, 1785. [B.M.]

Fatal Obedience ; or the History of Mr. Freeland. 2 vols., London, [1780 ?] [B.M. : *Eng. Lit. in Germany.*]

Fatal Step (The) : or the history of Mrs. Brudenel. A novel. With a frontispiece. 2 vols., London, J. Almon, 1771. [B.M. : Dobell : Arthur Rogers.]

Fatality. 3 vols., 1796. [*New Ann. Reg.*]

Fate of Beauty (The) ; being the history of Anna Brown of Prescot. Manchester, A Swindells, [c. 1796–1799]. [*Lancs.*]

Fate of Graysdale (The). A Legend. 2 vols., London, John Duncan, 1829. [B.M.]

Father and Son (The) ; or Claremont. A desultory tale. [By Miss Taylor]. 3 vols., London, Minerva Press, 1806. [B.M. : Blakey.]

Father and Son (The), A Tale, By A Friend to Youth. London, Philanthropic Society, 1824. [B.M.]

Father Innocent, Abbot of the Capuchins ; Or, The Crimes of the Cloisters. London, Tegg and Castleman, [1803]. [B.M.]

Father John ; Or, Cromwell in Ireland. By S. E. A. Author of " Richard of York," " The Luddite's Sister," Etc. etc. London, Whittaker ; Curry, Dublin ; H. Perris, Liverpool, 1842. [B.M. : *I. in F.*]

Father Oswald, a genuine Catholic story. London, Dolman, 1842. [B.M. : *Eng. Cat.*]

Fatherless Fanny ; or, Adventures of the Countess of Werdensdorff. A Real and most Extraordinary Narrative. Written by Herself. With a frontispiece. London, Harrild, [c. 1810]. [Stonehill.]

Faulconstein Forest. A Romantic Tale. London, T. Hookham, Junior, and E. T. Hookham, 1810. [B.M. : *Monthly Mag.* : Arthur Rogers.]

Fauques, M. A. de. Oriental Anecdotes ; Or, The History of Haroun Al-Rachid. 2 vols., London, 1764. [Lib. of Congress.]

—— The Vizirs : Or, The Labyrinth. An Oriental Tale. With vignette titles. 3 vols., London, G. Riley, 1774. [Allibone : B.M.]

Faux Pas (The), or Fatal attachment. A novel. By C.L. 2 vols., London, Printed for the author, at the Minerva Press, by William Lane, 1800. [Blakey.]

Favourites, Beauties, and Amours, of Henry of Windsor. 3 vols., London, Sherwood, 1817. [*Eng. Cat.: New Monthly Mag.: Quarterly Review.*]

Favourites of Felicity. 3 vols., 1785. [W. Brown.]

Fearon, Henry. Old Dame Walder, a tale of Sussex life. London, 1847. [B.M.]

Feelings of the Heart ; Or the History of a Country Girl. Written by Herself and Addressed to a Lady of Quality. 2 vols., London, F. and J. Noble, 1772. [Ingpen.]

Fell, Mrs. The Peasant ; or, Female philosopher. 2 vols. [W. Lane, 1792]. *Minerva Press Catalogue :* Blakey.]

Female Adventurers (The). 1765. [*Eng. Lit. in Germany.*]

Female American (The) ; or, The Adventures of Unea Eliza Winkfield. Compiled by Herself. 2 vols., London, Printed for Francis Noble, and John Noble, 1768. [J. C. Hardy].

Female Constancy, Or the History of Miss Arabella Waldegrave. 2 vols., 1769. [W. Brown : *Eng. Lit. in Germany.*]

Female Foundling (The) ; Or, Virtue, Truth, and Spirit, Opposing every Difficulty. Shewing The Happy Success of Constant Love, In the true and entertaining Life of Mademoiselle D[orme]r. London, T. Walker, 1751. [Blackwell : B.M. : Pickering.]

Female Freemasons (The). 3 vols., London, Edward Bull, 1840. [B.M.]

Female Friendship, or, the Innocent Sufferer. A moral novel. 2 vols., London, 1770. [B.M.]

Female Intrepidity, or the Heroic Matron. A Tale. With a frontispiece and vignette by Thomas Rowlandson. London, Tegg, [c. 1800]. [Stonehill.]

Female Pilgrim (The), or Deserted Wife. By the author of " The Midnight Horrors." — " Spectre Mother." &c. With a frontispiece. London, Dean and Munday, N.D. [Court Bk. Shop.]

Female Politician (The) : or the Statesman unmask'd. A novel. By the author of The Prude. London, J. Wilford, 1773. [B.M.]

Female Sensibility ; or, The History of Emma Pomfret. A novel. Founded on facts. [W. Lane, 1783]. [Blakey.]

Female Soldiers ; Or, the Surprising Life and Adventures of Hannah Snell. With woodcuts. London, R. Walker, 1750. [B.M. : W. Brown.]

Female Werter (The). 2 vols., 1792. [*New Ann. Reg.*]

Fénélon, François de Salignac de la Mothe. The Adventures of Telemachus, Son of Ulysses, from the French of Messire François Salignac de la Mothe Fenelon, Archbishop of Cambray. A New Translation by Francis Fitzgerald. With a vignette and 24 engravings by M. Corbould. London, C. Taylor, 1792. [Marks : Pickering : Arthur Rogers.]

Fénélon, François de Salignac de la Mothe. The Adventures of Telemachus, the Son of Ulysses. In XXIV Books. To which is added, The Adventures of Aristonous. Done into English by Mr. Littlebury and Mr. Boyer. With a portrait, a map and 24 plates. 2 vols., London, Brotherton, Innys, Meadows, 1740. [Maggs.]

—— The adventures of Telemachus, the Son of Ulysses, translated from the French of Salignac de la Mothe-Fenelon, Archbiship of Cambray, by the late John Hawkesworth. Corrected and Revised by G. Gregory, with a Life of the Author, and a Complete Index, Historical and Geographical. With 12 engravings by Thomas Stothard. 2 vols., London, C. and G. Kearsley, 1795. [McLeish : Maggs : Marks.]

—— The Adventures of Telemachus, The Son of Ulysses. Translated from the French of Fenelon, Archbishop of Cambray [by John Hawkesworth]. With vignettes by Grignion & S. Wale. London, Printed for the Author by W. and W. Strahan, 1768. [James Miles : Parker & Son : Arthur Rogers.]

—— The Adventures of Telemachus. The Son of Ulysses. Translated from the French of Messire Francois Salignac de la Mothe-Fenelon, Archbishop of Cambray by Tobias Smollett. 2 vols., London, S. Crowder, 1776. [Ingpen : McLeish.]

Fenn, Eleanor Lady. Fables in Monosyllables. [*Camb. Hist. Eng. Lit.*]

—— The Fairy Spectator ; or, the invisible monitor. By Mrs. Teachwell and her family. London, 1789. [B.M. : *Camb. Hist. Eng. Lit.*]

—— The Juvenile Tatler. By a Society of young ladies under the tuition of Mrs. Teachwell. London, 1789. [B.M. : *Camb. Hist. Eng. Lit.*]

—— Little Tales for the Nursury. By Solomon Lovechild. London, Dean, [1848]. [B.M. : *Eng. Cat.*]

—— Mrs. Lovechild's Golden Present. London, John Newbery. [*Camb. Hist. Eng. Lit.*]

—— Sketches of Little Boys and Girls. By Solomon Lovechild. With a frontispiece and other illustrations. London, Dean, [1840]. [B.M. : Arthur Rogers.]

Fenton, Richard. Memoirs of an Old Wig. With a vignette title. London, Longman, 1815. [B.M. : Ingpen : Marks.]

Fenwick, Mrs. E. Infantine Stories. 1810. [*Camb. Hist. Eng. Lit.*]

—— The Life of Carlo. [*Camb. Hist. Eng. Lit.*]

—— Mary and her Cat. [*Camb. Hist. Eng. Lit.*]

Fenwick, Mrs. E. Secresy; or, The ruin on the rock. By a woman. London, Printed for the author, [1795]. [Blakey: Allibone.]

Ferdinand Franck ; an Autobiographical Sketch of the youthful days of a Musical Student. London, Ackermann. 1826. [*Eng. Cat. : New Monthly Mag.*]

Fergusson, Adam. The History of the Proceedings in the Case of Margaret, Commonly called Peg, only lawful Sister to John Bull, Esquire. London, W. Owen, 1761. [Ingpen: Arthur Rogers.]

Fernandez de Avellaneda,—. A Continuation of the History and Adventures of the Renowned Don Quixote De la Mancha. Translated from the Spanish of De Avellaneda into English by W. A. Yardley. London, Harrison, 1784. [B.M. : Ingpen.]

Ferrier, Susan Edmondstone. Destiny ; Or, The Chief's Daughter. By the Author of " Marriage." and " The Inheritance." 3 vols., Edinburgh ; Robert Cadell ; and Whittaker, London, 1831. [B.M. : Arthur Rogers : Stonehill.]

—— The Inheritance. By the Author of Marriage. 3 vols., Edinburgh, William Blackwood : & T. Cadell, London, 1824. [B.M. : McLeish : Arthur Rogers.]

—— Marriage ; A Novel. 3 vols., Edinburgh, William Blackwood ; and John Murray, London, 1818. [Block : B.M. : Ingpen.]

Festival of the Passions (The). Or Voluptuous Miscellany. By an Amateur. With engravings. Constantinople, Abdal Mustapha [London, George Cannon], [1828]. [*Cat. Lib. Prohib.*]

Festival of St. Jago. By the Author of the Private History of the Court of England [Sarah Green]. 2 vols., London, Printed at the Minerva Press, for A. K. Newman, 1810. [Publisher's advert : Blakey.]

Feuds of Luna and Perollo ; or, the Fortunes of the House of Pandolfina. An Historic Tale of the Sixteenth Century. 4 vols., London, A.K. Newman, 1821. [B.M. : Holland.]

Feval, Paul Henri-Corentin. The Loves of Paris. A Romance. Translated from the French by J. W. Ross. With illustrations. London, Vickers, 1846. [B.M. : Stonehill.]

Fiddle-Faddle's Sentimental Tour, in search of the amusing, picturesque, and agreeable. London, 1845. [B.M.]

Fidelia ; or the prevalence of fashion. London. 1821. [B.M.]

Fielding, Henry. Amelia. 4 vols., London, A. Millar, 1752. [King : Marks : Arthur Rogers.]

—— An Apology for the Life of Mrs. Shamela Andrews by Conny Keyber, London, A Lodd, 1741. [Hodgson.]

Fielding, Henry. The History Of the Adventures Of Joseph Andrews, And of his Friend Mr. Abraham Adams. Written in Imitation of The Manner of Cervantes, Author of Don Quixote. 2 vols., London, A. Millar, 1742. [B.M. : Francis Edwards : Maggs.]

—— (?) The History of Sir Harry Herald and Sir Edward Haunch. 3 vols., London, F. Noble and J. Noble, 1755. [Wm. Cross : *Eng. Lit. in Germany :* Pickering.]

—— The History of Tom Jones, A Founding. 6 vols., London, A. Millar, 1749. [King : Maggs : Quaritch.]

—— Miscellanies. 3 vols., London, Printed for the Author, 1743. [Contains first appearance of " The Life of Mr. Jonathan Wild the Great."] [Francis Edwards : McLeish : Maggs.]

Fielding, James Holroyd. Beauchamp ; Or, The Wheel of Fortune. A Novel. 4 vols., London, Printed at the Minerva Press, for A. K. Newman, 1817. [B.M. : *Monthly Mag. : New Monthly Mag.*]

Fielding, Sarah. The Adventures of David Simple : Containing an Account of his Travels through the Cities of London and Westminster, in Search of a Real Friend. By a Lady. 2 vols., London, Andrew Millar, 1744. [B.M. : Ingpen : Arthur Rogers.]

—— The Adventures of David Simple, Volume the Last, in which the History is Concluded. London , 1753. [Blackwell.]

—— Familiar Letters between the Principal Characters in David Simple and some others ; To which is added A Vision. By the Author of David Simple. 2 vols., London, Printed for the Author, 1747. [B.M. : Ingpen : G. H. Last.]

—— The Governess, or the Little Female Academy. By the author of David Simple. London, 1749. [Allibone : B.M. : *Eng. Lit. in Germany.*]

—— The History of Betty Barnes. 2 vols., London, D. Wilson and T. Durham, 1753. [B.M. : Elkin Mathews : Pickering.]

—— The History of The Countess of Delwyn. By the Author of David Simple. 2 vols., London, Andrew Millar, 1759. [Blackwell : B.M. : Arthur Rogers.]

—— The History of Ophelia. Published by the Author of David Simple. 2 vols., London, R. Baldwin, 1760. [*Eng. Lit. in Germany :* Pickering.]

—— The Lives of Cleopatra and Octavia. By the Author of " David Simple." London, Printed for the Author, 1757. [Ingpen : Pickering : Arthur Rogers.]

Fielding, Sarah, and **Collier,** Jane. The Cry : a new dramatic fable. 3 vols., London, R. and J. Dodsley, 1754. [B.M. : Ingpen : Arthur Rogers.]

Fiend of Normandy ; or, the Repentant Criminal. A romance of ancient times. London, 1821. [B.M.]

Fiévée, J. Suzette's Dowry ; or the History of Madame de Senneterre. Related by herself. Translated from the French. London, 1799. [B.M.]

—— Suzette's Marriage Portion. A Novel. Translated from the French Dublin, Ruth Pasley, 1802. [Ingpen.]

Fillan, A. D. Stories, traditionary and romantic, of the two Rebellions in Scotland in 1715 and 1745. London 1849. [B.M.]

Finch, Cathrine I. Noureddin, Or The Talisman of Futurity. An Eastern Tale. London, Smith, Elder, 1836. [B.M.]

Finch, Emily. The Last Days of Mary Stuart. 3 vols., London, T. & W. Boone, 1841. [B.M.]

Finesse. 2 vols., London, Richard Bentley, 1835. [B.M.]

Finger-Post (The). With a wood-cut. London, Houlston, N.D. No. 82 of Houston's Series of Tracts. [Block].

Finglass, Esther. The Recluse ; Or, History of Lady Gertrude Lesly. 2 vols., London, 1790. [Allibone.]

Fiorentino, G. The Novel from which the Play of the Merchant of Venice is taken ; from the Italian. 1755. [Allibone.]

Fire (The) : or never despair. With 3 plates. London, J. Harris, 1808. [Dobell.]

Fireside Companion (The) ; a literary, biographical and anecdotal book for all seasons ; being a series of tales, sketches, poems. London, [1850]. [B.M.]

Fire-Side Scenes. By the author of the Bachelor and Married Man. &c. &c. &c. 3 vols., London, Longman, Hurst, Rees, Orme, Brown, and Green, 1825. [B.M. : Ingpen : Publisher's advert.]

Fireside Stories ; or, Recollections of my Schoolfellows. By the author of " The Picture-Gallery." London, 1825. [B.M.]

First Collection of Pathetic, Sentimental and Moral Narratives (The) ; selected from the best authors. With engravings. London, 1807. [B.M.]

First Love ; or, The History of Lady Frances Sullivan. A Novel. 3 vols., London, Printed at the Minerva Press for William Lane, 1801. [A Margery : Blakey.]

First Voyage of Rodolph the Voyager (The), by G. D. L. [The second voyage. Edited by W. Sewell]. 2 vols., London, 1844. [B.M.]

Fish and the Ring (The) ; or the Fortunate Farmer's Daughter. Manchester, A. Swindells, [c. 1796-1799]. [*Lancs.*]

Fisher, Miss. Family Failings : a Novel. 3 vols., London, 1849. [B.M.]

Fisher, Joshua Bridges. The Hermitage. A Novel. 2 vols., Printed for the Author, 1796. [Stonehill.)

Fisher, Joshua Bridges. Pathetic Tales, Poems, etc. With a frontispiece. Printed for the Author, 1808. [Pickering.]

Fisher, Admiral William. The Petrel : a tale of the Sea. By a Naval Officer. 3 vols., London, Henry Colburn, 1850. [Allibone : B.M. : *Eng. Cat.*]

Fisherman (The) ; an Interesting Tale, for Young People. Bath, Steart ; Champonte, London. [*Guardian of Education.*]

Fisherman's Children (The), and Edith's English Home. By the author of " Hours of Childhood." London, Plymouth, 1848. [B.M.]

Fisherman's Daughter (The), a narrative from real life. Bungay, Brightly and Childs, 1816. [B.M.]

Fisherman's Hut (The), and other tales, for children. London, 1829. [B.M.]

Fisherman's Hut ; or, Alzendorf. A novel. 3 vols., London, Printed at the Minerva Press, for Lane, Newman, and Co. 1805. [Blakey.]

Fishermen (The) ; a tale for young persons. By the author of : " A Cup of Sweets." London 1815. [B.M.]

Fison, M. Giuseppe, the Italian boy ; by the author of " The German Shoemaker." London, 1846. [B.M.]

Fitzallen, Amelia. The Devoted One ; An Historical Novel. With an engraved title and plates. London, Printed by W. Hill, & published by John Saunders, 1835. [B.M.]

Fitzatherley, Mrs. Our Town ; Or, Rough Sketches Of Character, Manners, &c. By Peregrine Reedpen. 2 vols., London, Richard Bentley, 1834. [B.M. : Ingpen : Elkin Mathews.]

Fitz-George, George. Montauban and The Monk Hilario. A Legend of the Thirteenth Century. 3 vols., London, A. K. Newman, 1828. [B.M.]

Fitz-John, Matilda. Joan ! ! ! A Novel 4 vols., London, Hookham and Carpenter, 1796. [B.M. : *New Ann. Reg.* : Arthur Rogers.]

Flamank, James. The Curate of Steinhollt. A Tale of Iceland. 2 vols., London, Longman, 1837. [B.M. : Ingpen.]

Flammenberg, Lawrence. The Necromancer : Or the Tale of the Black Forest : founded on facts : Translated from the German of Lawrence Flammenberg, By Peter Teuthold. 2 vols., London, William Lane, 1794 [Pickering : Stonehill : Blakey.]

Fleet, Charles. Tales and Sketches for fireside reading. London 1849. [B.M.]

Fleming, Francis. The Life and Extraordinary Adventures, The Perils and Critical Escapes, of Timothy Ginnadrake, That Child of chequer'd Fortune. With 2 portraits. 3 vols., Bath, R. Cruttwell, [1771]. [Pickering : Sotheby's.]

Fletcher, Grenville. The Parricide's Grave.

Fletcher, Grenville Rhodomaldi, or the Castle of Roveggiano.
— Rosalviva, Or The Demon Dwarf. A Romance. 3 vols., London, Matthew Iley, 1824. [B.M. : Stonehill.]

Fletcher, Miss S. Gabrielle & Augustina ; Or, Virtue its own Reward. A Moral Tale For Young People. Translated from the French By Miss S. Fletcher. Coventry, N. Merridew ; and Longman, Hurst, Rees, and Orme, 1811. [B.M.]

Fletcher, Rev. W. The Deaf and Dumb Boy, a Tale ; with some account of the mode of educating the Deaf and Dumb. With a frontispiece and woodcuts. London, John W. Parker, 1837. [Block.]

Flights of Inflatus ; or the sallies, and adventures of a wild-goose philosopher. By the Author of the Trifler. 2 vols., London, 1791. [B.M.]

Flinders, Anne. Felix de Lisle. An Autobiography. London, Seeley, 1840. [Baker's Bookshop : *Eng. Cat.*]

Flohr, Apolline. The German Christmas Eve ; or, Deutscher Damen Weih-nachts-Körbchen. A picture of home life in Germany : comprising personal recollections, tales and sketches ; with directions for working beautiful and original patterns for knitting. Edited by A. Montgomery. London, [1847]. [B.M.]

Floods (The), a tale addressed to children and youth. London, 1834. [B.M.]

Flora and Her Children : or, the Holiday of the Flowers. London, [1850]. [B.M.]

Flora, The Beauty of the Scottish Border ; Being the Life of the Countess of Linford ; wherein are displayed the most exalted heroical, and interesting trials of female virtue, love, and constancy. Edited by her niece, the Hon. Lady Julia Drummond. With engravings. London, Virtue, 1830. [Internatl. Bk. Shop : Stonehill.]

Florentine Tales, with modern illustrations. London, 1847. [B.M.]

Florian, Jean Pierre Clavis de,—Claudine, or the Savoyarde. 1813. [B.M.]
— Eleazer and Naphtali, a Hebrew tale. With an introductory preface, illustrative of the ancient and present state of the Hebrews. Translated from the French of M. Florian, by J. Jones. London, 1816. [B.M.]
— Eleazer and Naphtaly, An Hebrew Tale, Translated from the French, By H. H. Young. London, Joseph John Leathwick, 1827. [B.M.]
— Estelle, by M. de Florian, with an Essay upon Pastoral, translated from the French by Mrs. Susanna Cummyng. 2 vols., London, Lee and Hurst, 1798. [B.M. : *New Ann Reg.. :* Stonehill.]
— Estelle, a Pastoral Romance. By M. De Florian, member of the French Academy. Translated by Mr.   [S.]

Maxey. With 7 plates by J. Mitan. London, T. Boosey, 1803. [Baker's Bookshop : Lib. of Congress : Pickering.]

Florian, Jean Pierre Clavis de. Galatea : a pastoral romance, imitiated from Cervantes. Translated by an officer. Dublin, 1791. [B.M.]
— Gonzalva of Cordova Or Grenada reconquered, now first translated from the French. 3 vols., 1793. [W. Brown : Martin A. McGoff : *New Ann Reg.*]
— The History of Numa Pompilius, Second King of Rome. Translated from the French of de Florian by Miss Elizabeth Morgan. 3 vols., London, T. Cadell, 1787. [Backus : B.M.]
— National Romances : From the French of Florian. Translated by Charlotte Herdman. London, Geo. Cowie, 1823. [Ewen-Munden.]
— New Tales, from the French of Florian. 1792. [*New Ann Reg.*]
— Stella, a pastoral romance. Translated from the French. By Miss E. Morgan. 2 vols., London, 1791. [B.M.]
— William Tell, or The Patriot of Switzerland. Freely translated from the French. With plates. London, J. Harris, 1823. [Arthur Rogers.]
— William Tell ; Or, Swisserland Delivered. A posthumous work of the Chevalier de Florian. Translated from the French. By William B. Hewetson. London, 1809. [Lib. of Congress : *Monthly Mag.*]
— Works of Chevalier de Florian ; containing Galatea, A Pastoral Romance, and other Characteristic Romances. Translated from the last Paris Edition by Mr. Robinson. To which is prefixed an Essay on Pastoral Romance by the Translator. 2 vols., 1786. [Arthur Rogers.]

Flower, William Balmbro'. Classical Tales and Legends. London, 1847. [Allibone : B.M.]
— Little Willie, the lame boy. A tale founded on fact. London, 1848. [B.M.]
— Rose Eglington, the stolen child. London, 1848. [B.M.]
— Tales of Faith and Providence. London, 1849. [Allibone : B.M.]
— Try again : or a day's misfortunes. London, 1848. [B.M.]

Flower Basket (The). A fairy tale. London, 1816. [B.M. : *New Monthly Mag.*]

Flying Dutchman (The) ; or, The Demon Ship. With woodcuts. London, Foster and Hextall, [c. 1835]. [Stonehill.]

Follies of St. James' Street (The). 2 vols., London, William Lane, 1789. [Pickering : Sotheran.]

Folly of Finery (The) ; or the history of Mary Lawson. London, Religious Tract Society, [1830 ?]. [B.M.]

Fontaine (*see* LA FONTAINE).

Fontanieu, Gaspar Moise de, (*see* DE FONTANIEU].

Fools' Pence (The). With a woodcut. London, The Religious Tract Society, N.D. [Block.]

Forbes, Duncan. The Adventures of Hatim Táï, a Romance. Translated from the Persian. By Duncan Forbes. London, 1830. [B.M.: *Quarterly Review*.]

Force of Example (The): Or, The History of Henry and Caroline ; written for the instruction and amusement of young persons. With a frontispiece by Scott after Kirk. London, E. Newbery, 1797. [B.M.: Gumuchian: Maggs.]

Force of Nature (The) ; or, the History of Charles, Lord Sommers. By the Editor of the Wanderer. 2 vols., London, Noble, 1767. [*Univ. Mag.*]

Ford Family in Ireland (The). A Novel. 3 vols., London, T. C. Newby, 1845. [B.M.: *I. in F.*]

Foreign Exclusives in London. 3 vols., London, Henry Colburn, 1830. [*New Monthly Mag.*]

Forman : a Tale. 3 vols., London, 1819. [*European Mag.* : T. D. Webster.]

Forrester. 3 vols., London, Whittaker, Treacher, 1830. [B.M.: *New Monthly Mag.*]

Forrester, Charles Robert. Castle Baynard ; Or, The Days of John. By Hal Willis, Student at Law. London, G. and W. B. Whittaker, 1824. [Allibone : B.M. : R. S. Frampton.]

—— Phantasmagoria of Fun : Edited and illustrated by Alfred Crowquill. 2 vols., London, Richard Bentley, 1843. [Birrell & Garnett : B.M. : G. H. Last.]

—— Sir Roland. A Romance of the Twelfth Century. By Hall Willis, Student at Law, Author of " Castle Baynard." 4 vols., London, A. K. Newman, 1827. [B.M.: Publisher's advert.]

Forresti ; or, The Italian Cousins. A Romance. By the Author of Valombrosa. 3 vols., London, Lane and Newman. 1806. [Publisher's advert : Blakey ; T. D. Webster.]

Forsaken (The). A Tale. 2 vols., London. Whittaker, 1836. [B.M. ; T. D. Webster]

Forster, A. V. Fatel Ambition. A Romance. 1811. [Allibone]

Forster, Rev. Edward. The Arabian Nights, Translated by The Reverend Edward Forster. With engravings after Robert Smirke. 5 vols., London, Printed for William Miller, by W. Bulmer, 1802. [B.M.]

Fortescue ; or, The Soldier's Reward : A Characteristic Novel. 2 vols., London, W. Lane, 1789 [Blakey.]

Fortnight's Ramble Through London (A). Being a Narrative of the Adventures of a Farmer's Son. 1795. [*Eng. Lit. in Germany*.]

Fortnum, Mrs. (*see* KING, Sophia).

Fortunate Employ ; Or, The Five Acres Ploughed. A Tale of Real Life. With a frontispiece. London, J. Hatchard, 1827. [B.M.]

Fortunate Man (The) ; Or, Poverty and Riches. To which is added, The History of the Peevish Child. With 15 woodcuts. London, T. Hughes, [1820 ?]. [B.M.]

Fortunate Transport (The) ; or, the Secret History of the Life and Adventures of Polly Haycock, alias Mrs. B——, the Lady of the Gold Watch. By a Creole. In 2 parts. London, [1750 ?]. [B.M.]

Fortune's Frolic : or the wonderful and comical marriage of the Young Edinburgh Lassie of 18, who went to the Harvest, being out of place, to an auld farmer of 70. [Edinburgh ?]. [1800 ?]. [B.M.]

Fortunes of Nigel (The), Lord Glenvarloch ; and Margaret Ramsay. An interesting narrative [founded on Sir Walter Scott's novel " The Fortunes of Nigel "]. London, [1825]. [B.M.]

Fortune of Roger de Flor : Or, The Almugavars. 3 vols., London, Richard Bentley, 1845. [B.M. : McLeish.]

Fortune-Teller (The). 2 vols., London, J. Bew, 1774. [W. Brown: T. Thorp.]

Foscari. A Venetian Tale, founded on Facts. London, Minerva Press, 179?. [Stonehill.]

Foscarini or The Patrician of Venice. 2 vols., London, Rowland Hunter, 1829. [B.M.]

Foster, Mrs. E. M. Concealment, or The Cascade of Llanfwarryhn. A tale. By the author of Miriam, Judith, Fedaretta, &c. London, Printed at the Minerva Press, for William Lane, 1801. [Blakey : *Minerva Press Catalogue*.]

—— The Duke of Clarence. An historical novel. By E. M. F. 4 vols., London, William Lane, 1795. [Blakey : *Minerva Press Catalogue* : T. D. Webster.]

—— Emily of Lucerne. By the author of The Duke of Clarence. 2 vols., [W. Lane, 1800]. [Blakey : *Minerva Press Catalogue.*]

—— Judith. A novel. By the author of Rebecca, Miriam Fitzmorris, &c. 2 vols., London, Printed at the Minerva Press, for William Lane, 1800. [*Minerva Press Catalogue* : Blakey.]

—— Rebecca. A novel. 2 vols., London, William Lane, 1799. [Blakey : *Minerva Press Catalogue.*]

Foundling (The), Or The History of Lucius Stanhope. With a frontispiece and 7 woodcuts. London, E. Newbery, 1787. [Gumuchian.]

Fouqué, Baroness. Tales by the Baroness Fouqué. London, Burns, 1845. [*Critic.*]

Fouque, Frederich Heinrich Karl, Baron de la Motte. The Magic Ring ; A Romance. From the German of Frederick, Baron de la Motte Fouqué. 3 vols., Edinburgh, Oliver and Boyd ; and Geo. B. Whittaker, 1825. [B.M. : *Critic :* G. Worthington.]

—— Ministrel-Love ; from the German of the Author of Undine. By George Soane, A.B. 2 vols., London, W. Simpkin, 1821. [Pickering.]

—— Minstrel-Love : A Romance From the German of Fouqué. A New Translation. With 9 illustrations. London, J. Burns, 1845. [B.M. : *Critic* : Lib. of Congress.]

—— The Outcasts. A Romance. Translated from the German By George Soane. 2 vols., London, G. and W. B. Whittaker, 1824. [Allibone : B.M.]

—— Romantic Fiction : select tales from the German of De la Motte Fouqué and others. London, Burns, [1843 ?]. [B.M. : *Eng. Cat.*]

—— Sintram and his Companions. A Northern Tale. From the German of the Baron de la Motte Fouqué. A New Translation. London, James Burns, 1841. [Block.]

—— Sintram and his Companions : A Romance. From the German of Frederic Baron de la Motte Fouqué [By Julius C. Hare]. London, C. and J. Ollier, 1820. [B.M. ; *Camb. Hist. Eng. Lit. :* Pickering.]

—— Sir Elidoc : an old Breton Legend : from the German. London, Mozley, 1849. [B.M. : *Eng. Cat.*]

—— Thiodolf, the Icelander. From the German. London, Burns, 1845, [B.M. : Lib. of Congress.]

—— Undine ; or, the Spirit of the Waters. A Miniature Romance. Translated from the German of Baron De La Motte Fouque, By the Rev. Thomas Tracy. London, J. Cunningham, 1840. [Block.]

—— Undine. A Romance. Translated from the German. By George Soane. London, W. Simpkin and R. Marshall, 1818. [B.M. : Robinson : Stonehill.]

—— Violina : a Miniature Romance. Translated from the German. London, Clarke, 1845. [Elkin Mathews.]

—— Wild Love and Other Tales, from the German, London, Burns, [1844]. [B.M. : Lib. of Congress.]

Four Interesting Tales. A Singular Adventure. The Robber. The Red Nose. The Newfoundland Dog. Glasgow, Printed for the booksellers, [1850 ?]. [B.M.]

Four Seasons (The). To which is added The Snow. With 14 woodcuts. London, Whitrow, [1820 ?]. [B.M.]

Fox, J. Santa-Maria ; or, the Mysterious Pregnancy. A romance. 3 vols., London, 1797. [B.M. : *New Ann. Reg.*]

Fox, J. Tancred. A Tale of Ancient Times. 2 vols., London, [W. Lane] 1791. [Allibone : Blakey.]

Fragment (A). [London ?, 1800 ?]. [B.M.]

Framery, Nicholas Étienne. Memoirs of the Marquis de St. Forlaix, Translated from the French, by Mrs. Brooke. 4 vols., 1770. [*Bibliot. Brit. :* Wm. Smith.]

—— Constance de Lindensdorf ; or, The Force of Bigotry. A tale. 4 vols. With a frontispiece. London, Lane, Newman, 1807. [Blakey.]

—— The Nun of Miserecordia ; or, The Eve of All Saints. A Romance. 4 vols., London, Minerva Press, for Lane, Newman, and Co., 1807. [Blakey]

Frances, Sophia. Vivonio ; or, The Hour of Retribution. A Romance. By a young lady. London, Minerva Press, 1806. [Publisher's advert, ; Blakey.]

Frances ; Or, The Two Mothers. A Tale. By M. S. 3 vols., London, Printed at the Minerva Press for A. K. Newman, 1819. [Block : B.M. : Internatl. Bk. Shop.]

Francis Lever, The Young Mechanic ; Being Incidents and Lectures Explanatory of The First Principles of Mechanics With some account of The Most Celebrated Engines, Ancient and Modern. With illustrations. London, John Harris, 1835. [Block : Gumuchian.]

Francis, the Philanthropist : An Unfashionable Tale. 3 vols., London, William Lane. 1786. [Stonehill : Blakey]

Frank and George. [London, 1820 ?]. [B.M.]

Frank Orby. A Novel. By One of the Eleven. 3 vols., London, Longman, 1833. [B.M. : Stonehill.]

Franklin, Thomas. Truth and Falshood : a tale. 1755. [B.M.]

Franklin, William. Loves of Camarúpa and Cámalatà, an ancient Indian tale, elucidating the customs of the orientals translated from the Persian [version by Na'ámat Allah?] by William Franklin. London, 1793. [B.M. : *Eng. Lit. in Germany :* Lowndes.]

Frankly, Mr. The History of Frugal, the Wild Bee. With a frontispiece and a woodcut vignette. London, [1816]. [Dobell : Gumuchian.]

Frascati's ; or Scenes in Paris. 3 vols., London, H. Colburn and R. Bentley. 1830, [T. D. Webster ; B.M. ; Publisher's advert.]

Fraser, James Baillie. Allee Neemroo, The Buchtiaree Adventurer. A Tale of Louristan. 3 vols., London, Richard Bentley, 1842. [B.M. : Glen.]

—— The Dark Falcon. A Tale of the Attruck. 4 vols., London, Richard Bentley, 1844. [B.M. : *Critic :* Holland.]

—— The Highland Smugglers. By the Author of "Adventures of a Kuzzilbash," "Persian Adventurer," &c. 3

vols., London, Henry Colburn and Richard Bentley, 1832. [B.M. : Pickering : Arthur Rogers.]

Fraser, James Baillie. The Khan's Tale. London, 1833. [Allibone : B.M.]

—— The Kuzzilbash. A Tale of Khorasan. 3 vols., London, Henry Colburn, 1828. [*Blackwood's Mag.* : B.M. : Lib. of Congress.]

—— Narrative of the Residence of the Persian Princes in London in 1835 and 1836, with an Account of their Journey from Persia and subsequent Adventures.. 2 vols., London, Richard Bentley, 1838. [G. Worthington.]

—— The Persian Adventurer : Being The Sequel of " The Kuzzilbash." 3 vols., London, Henry Colburn and Richard Bentley, 1830. [B.M. : Hodgson : Publisher's advert.]

—— Tales of the Caravanserai. 1833. [B.M. : Arthur Rogers.]

Freaks of Fortune (The ; or, Memoirs of Captain Conyers. A novel. London, 1740. [B.M.]

Frederic and Caroline, or the Fitzmorris Family. A novel. By the author of Rebecca, Judith, Miriam. [Mrs. E. M. Foster.] 2 vols., London, William Lane, 1800. [B.M. : Blakey.]

Frederica, or the Memoirs of a Young Lady, a novel, by a lady, dedicated to H.R.H. The Duchess of York. 3 vols., London, J. Ridgway, 1792. [T. Thorp.]

Frederica Risberg, a German Story. 2 vols., London. William Lane, 1793. [Blakey.]

Frederick. 1773. [*Eng. Lit. in Germany.*]

Frederick ; Or, Incidents Illustrative of the Beauties and Graces of Vital Piety, in The Domestic Circle. By the Author of " Eliza ; or, Traits of Character in Humble Life." With a frontispiece. London, Francis Westley, [1823]. [B.M.]

Frederick St. Clair ; or, the Infidel Reclaimed. London, Thomas Ward, 1837. [Publisher's advert.]

Frederick Wilding ; Or, The Ways of the World : A Novel. 3 vols., London, Baldwin and Cradock, 1832. [B.M.]

Free Grace displayed in the conversion of two unhappy prostitutes. London, 1798. [B.M.]

Freebooter's Bride (The) ; or, the Black Pirate of the Mediterranean : Including The Mystery of the Morescoes. A Romance Interspersed with Historical Allusions to the Reign of Charles V. 5 vols., London, A. K. Newman, 1829. [B.M.]

Freeman, Harriot Augusta. Astraea's Return ; or the Halcyon Days of France in the year 2440 : a Dream. Translated from the French by H. A. Freeman. London, 1797. [B.M.]

French, James. Clongibbon ; or, The White Knight of the Forest. Dublin, Duffy, 1845. [*I. in F.*]

French Protestant (The) ; a tale. By the author of the " Italian Convert." London, 1822. [B.M.]

Frere, Benjamin. The Adventures of a Dramatist On a Journey To the London Managers. 2 vols., London, Lackington, Allen, 1813. [B.M. ; F. Harvey : *New Monthly Mag.*]

—— The Modern Hero in the kingdom of Cathai. Translated from the French. Hereford, 1791. [B.M.]

—— Rank and Fashion ! Or, the Mazes of Life ; a novel. 3 vols., London, 1821. [B.M.]

Friendly Champions (The), or St. Louden Castle : an interesting tale, in which is pourtrayed the enterprising adventures of Earls' Rowallo and St. Clair against the Saracens in the Holy Land by an Etonian. With a frontispiece. London, J. Bailey, N.D. [Dobell.]

Friends and Lovers. 3 vols., 1812. [*Quarterly Review.*]

Friends (The), or The History of Billy Freeman and Tommy Truelove, proper to be imitated by all those who desire to be Good and Great. With a frontispiece and woodcuts. London, John Marshall, [c. 1800]. [Dobell.]

Friends (The) ; Or, Original Letters of a Person Deceased Now First Published from Manuscripts in his correspondant's Hands. 2 vols., London, Bell, 1773. [Baker's Bookshop : Ingpen : Stonehill.]

Friends (The) ; or, the triumph of innocence over false charges. A tale. London, 1822. [B.M.]

Friends (The) ; A True Tale of Woe and Joy : From the East. With an engraved frontispiece. London, George Wightman, 1830. [B.M.]

Friendship in a Nunnery ; or, The American Fugitive. 2 vols., London, Bew, 1778. [*Westminster Mag.*]

From Oxford to Rome : And How it Fared with some who lately Made the Journey. By a Companion Traveller. With a frontispiece. London, Longman, Brown, Green, & Longmans, 1847. [Block (3rd edn.).]

Frost, Thomas. The Black Mask ; or, The Mysterious Robber. With woodcuts. London, G. Purkess, [1850]. [B. Ono.]

—— Paul the Poacher. With woodcuts. London, G. Purkess, [1850]. [H. W. Fennell : B. Ono.]

Froude, James Anthony. Shadows of the Clouds. By Z. London, T. Harrison, 1847. [B.M. : *Eng. Cat.*]

Fruit Shop (The). A Tale. 2 vols., London, C. Moran, 1765. [Ashbee Collection.]

Fruitless Repentance (The) ; or, the History of Miss Kitty Le Fever. 2 vols., London, 1769. [B.M. ; *Eng. Lit. in Germany.*]

Fruits of Instruction (The) ; being an

account of the good conduct and happy death of Mary (W——), Elizabeth (B——), and Lydia (E——), three girls educated in a Sunday School in Kent. By the author of "Christian Records," &c. London, Ogle & Duncan, 1820. [B.M.]

Fry, Caroline. The Listener. 2 vols., London, James Nisbet, 1830. [B.M.]

—— Peggy Lum or A Hint to the Purchaser of Smuggled Goods. A Tale. With a plate. London, Baker and Fletcher, 1825. [Gumuchian.]

Fugitive of Folly (The) ; Intended as a Representative Sketch Of the Progress of Error, From Youth to Manhood : In a Miniature of Modern Manners, With Hints for the Regulation of the Police, &c. &c. By Thos. Thoughtless, Junior, Esquire. London, Printed for Charles Adams, 1793. [B.M. : Ingpen.]

Fuller, Anne. Alan Fitz-Osborne, An Historical Tale. 2 vols., Dublin, P. Byrne, 1786. [McLeish (1st Dublin edn.) : Pickering (1st Dublin edn.).]

—— The Convent : Or, the History of Sophia Nelson. By a young Lady. 2 vols., London, T. Wilkins, [1786]. [B.M. : *Eng. Lit. in Germany.*]

—— The Son of Ethelwolf : An Historical Tale. 2 vols., London, G. G. J. and J. Robinson, 1789. [Ingpen : Stonehill : Lyle H. Wright.]

Fullerton, Lady Georgiana. Ellen Middleton. A Tale. 3 vols., London, Edward Moxon, 1844. [B.M. : McLeish : Arthur Rogers.]

—— Grantley Manor. A Tale. 3 vols., London, Edward Moxon, 1847. [Block : B.M. : Brough.]

Fullom, Stephen Watson. The King and the Countess. A Romance. 3 vols., London, Henry Colburn, 1849. [B.M.]

Fun for the Parlour, or, All Merry Above Stairs, consisting of a great and pleasing Variety of Comic Lectures, delivered on Various Occasions, by Right Heads, Wrong Heads, Feather Heads, Heavy Heads, Wooden Heads, Brazen Heads, and by some Heads that are of no use to their Owners, many of which were never printed before ; exhibiting a droll Medley of Pleasing Tales, Entertaining Stories, Diverting Jests, Comical Bulls, Queer Puns, Quaint Sayings, Keen Waggeries, Brilliant Bon Mots, Smart Repartees, Merry Adventures, Droll Narrations, Wonderful Frolicks, Humourous Riddles, Puzzling Conundrums, Funny Rebusses, Whimsical Epigrams, Witticisms, and Strokes of Humour ; Entertaining to read, pleasing to hear, powerful in raising the Spirits, chearing the Heart, and brightening the Countenance, and are calculated to render Conversation agreeable, and to pass long Evenings with Wit and Merriment ; to which are added, Puzzles for the Wits, with their Solutions

which makes ye all as Wise as the Author. With a frontispiece. London, S. Bladon, 1771. [Pickering.]

Fun upon Fun : or the comical merry tricks of Leper the Taylor. In 2 parts. Glasgow, 1786. [B.M.]

Funeral of the Dairyman's Daughter (The) ; being the fifth part of her history. With a woodcut. London, J. Evans, N.D. [Block.]

Furbo, Francisco. Andrew of Padua, the Improvisatore : a tale from the Italian. And the Vindictive Father, from the Spanish of Leandra of Valladerras. London, 1820. [B.M.]

Furguss, Miss. The Thoughtless Ward, By a Lady. 1777. [*Eng. Lit. in Germany.*]

Gabrielle de Vergy, an historic tale. By the author of Anthony Leger, Esq. 2 vols., London, 1790. [B.M.]

Gainsayer Silenced (The) : Or, the Victory of Truth Delineated in the History of Henry Adam Of Longvale. A Narrative founded on fact. By the Author of Robin Rutherford. With a frontispiece. James Robertson ; M. Ogle, and Chalmers & Collins, Glasgow ; Baldwin, Cradock & Joy, John Hatchard, F. Westley, Simpkin & Marshall, William Booth, and Basil Stewart, London ; James Finlay, Newcastle ; and William Curry, Jun. Dublin, 1825, [B.M.]

Galland, Antoine. Arabian Nights Entertainments : consisting of One Thousand and One Stories, told by the Sultaness of the Indies to divert the Sultan from the Execution of a Bloody Vow he had made to marry a lady every Day, and have her cut off next Morning, to avenge himself for the Disloyalty of his first Sultaness. Translated into French from the Arabian MSS. by M. Galland, of the Royal Academy ; and now done into English from the last Paris Edition. 6 vols., London. 1763, [Maggs.]

—— The Arabian Nights' Entertainments : Or, The Thousand and One Nights. Accurately describing the Manners, Customs, Laws, and Religion Of The Eastern Nations. Translated from the French of M. Galland, By G. S. Beaumont. With engravings. 4 vols., London, Printed for Mathews and Leigh, by J. Moyes, 1811. [B.M. : Mudie's.]

Galt, John. The Annals of the Parish ; or, The Chronicle of Dalmailing ; During the Ministry of the Rev. Micah Balwhidder. Written by himself. Arranged and edited by the Author of "The Ayrshire Legatees." Edinburgh, William Blackwood. 1821. [B.M. : Ingpen : Arthur Rogers.]

—— The Ayrshire Legatees ; or, The Pringle Family. By the Author of "Annals of the Parish," &c. Edinburgh,

William Blackwood ; and T. Cadell, London, 1821. [B.M. : Ingpen : Arthur Rogers.]

Galt, John. Bogle Corbet ; Or, The Emigrants. 3 vols., London, Henry Colburn and Richard Bentley, [1831]. [B.M. : Ingpen : Arthur Rogers.]

—— The Earthquake ; A Tale. By the Author of " The Ayrshire Legatees." 3 vols., Edinburgh, William Blackwood ; and T. Cadell and W. Davies, London, 1820. [B.M. : Arthur Rogers.]

—— Eben Erskine ; Or, The Traveller. 3 vols., London, Richard Bentley, 1833. [B.M. : Francis Edwards : *New Monthly Mag.*]

—— The Entail : or The Lairds of Guppy. By the Author of Annals of the Parish, Sir Andrew Wylie, &c. 3 vols., Edinburgh, Wm. Blackwood ; and T. Cadell, London, 1823. [B.M. : Ingpen : Arthur Rogers.]

—— The Gathering of the West : (Originally published in Blackwood's Edinburgh Magazine). By the Author of The Ayrshire Legatees, The Entail, Annals of the Parish, etc. Edinburgh, William Blackwood ; and T. Cadell, London, 1823. [B.M.]

—— The Last of the Lairds : Or, The Life and Opinions Of Malachi Mailings, Esq., Of Auldbiggings. By the Author of Annals of the Parish, The Entail, Etc. Edinburgh, William Blackwood ; and T. Cadell, London, 1826. [Block : B.M.: Stonehill.]

—— Lawrie Todd ; Or, The Settlers in the Woods. 3 vols., London, Henry Colburn and Richard Bentley, 1830. [B.M. : Ingpen : McLeish.]

—— The Majolo : a Tale. 2 vols., London, Henry Colburn, 1816. [B.M. : *Eng. Cat. : New Monthly Mag.*]

—— The Member : An Autobiography. By the Author of " The Ayrshire Legatees," etc. etc. London, James Fraser, 1832. [B.M. : Ingpen : Arthur Rogers.]

—— The Omen. Edinburgh, William Blackwood ; and T. Cadell, London, 1825. [B.M.]

—— The Ouranoulogos ; or, the celestial volume. Illustrated by John Martin. London, 1833. [B.M.]

—— The Provost. By the Author of Annals of the Parish. Edinburgh, William Blackwood ; and T. Cadell, London, 1822. [B.M. : Ingpen : Arthur Rogers.]

—— The Radical : An Autobiography. By the Author of " The Member," " The Ayrshire Legatees." etc. etc. London, James Fraser, 1832. [B.M. Ingpen.]

—— Ringhan Gilhaize ; or The Covenanters. By the Author of " Annals of the Parish," " Sir Andrew Wylie," " The Entail." &c. 3 vols., Edinburgh, Oliver and Boyd, 1823. [B.M. : Ingpen : Arthur Rogers.]

Galt, John. Rothelan ; A Romance of the English Histories. By the Author of Annals of the Parish, Ringan Gilhaize, The Spaewife, &c. 3 vols., Edinburgh, Oliver and Boyd ; and Geo. B. Whittaker, London, 1824. [B.M. : Ingpen : McLeish.]

—— Sir Andrew Wylie, of that Ilk. By the Author of " Annals of the Parish," &c. 3 vols., Edinburgh, William Blackwood ; and T. Cadell, London, 1822. [Block : B.M. : Arthur Rogers.]

—— Southennan. 3 vols., London, Henry Colburn & Richard Bentley, 1830. [B.M. : Francis Edwards : Ingpen.]

—— The Spaewife ; A Tale of the Scottish Chronicles. By the Author of " Annals of the Parish," " Ringhan Gilhaize," &c. 3 vols., Edinburgh, Oliver & Boyd ; and G. & W. B. Whittaker, London, 1823. [B.M. : Ingpen : Pickering.]

—— Stanley Buxton ; Or, The Schoolfellows. By The Author of " Annals of the Parish." " Lawrie Todd." &c. &c. 3 vols., London, Henry Colburn and Richard Bentley, 1832. [Block : B.M.]

—— The Steam-boat. By the Author of Annals of the Parish ; Ayrshire Legatess ; Sir Andrew Wylie ; and the Provost. Edinburgh, Wm. Blackwood ; and T. Cadell, London, 1822. [B.M. : Ingpen : Arthur Rogers.]

—— The Stolen Child. A Tale of the Town. London, Smith, Elder, 1833. [B.M. : Ingpen : Arthur Rogers.]

—— Stories of the Study. 3 vols., London, Cochrane and M'Crone, 1833. [B.M. : McLeish.]

Gamble, John. Charlton, Or, Scenes in The North of Ireland ; A Tale. 3 vols., London, Baldwin, Cradock, and Joy. 1823. [B.M. : *I. in F.*]

—— Howard. 2 vols., London, Baldwin, Cradock, and Joy. 1815. [B.M. : Dobell: *I. in F.*]

—— Northern Irish Tales ; founded on Facts. 2 vols., London, Longman, Hurst, Rees, Orme, and Brown, 1818. [B.M. : *I. in F.* : Publisher's advert.]

—— Sarsfield, or Wanderings of Youth, an Irish Tale. 3 vols., London, 1814. [B.M. : *I. in F.* : *Quarterly Review.*]

Gambler's Dream (The). 3 vols., London, Edward Bull, 1837. [B.M.]

Gamester (The). With a woodcut. London, J. Marshall ; and R. White, [1796]. Cheap Repository. [B.M. : Court Bk. Shop.]

Gamester (The), a true story ; on which the tragedy of that name now acting at the Theatre Royal in Drury Lane is founded. Translated from the Italian. London, 1753. [B.M.]

Gardener, H. Poplar Grove ; a Romance. 3 vols., 1822. [*European Mag.*]

Gardiner, William. The Child of Providence ; Or, Montague In Search of Independence. With a frontispiece. Derby, Thomas Richardson ; Simpkin and Marshall, London, 1833. [B.M.]

—— Edward Westley ; or, Good Education, and the Consequences of not being taught a Trade. 1823. [*Quarterly Review.*]

—— The Fortnight's Visit ; containing original, moral, and interesting Tales. 1822. [*Quarterly Review.*]

—— The Magic Spell ; containing the history of Prince Lucillo and Princess Rayonette. London, 1819. [B.M.]

—— Original Tales of my Landlord's School. Collected from the writings of the Brachmins and translated from the Shanscrit. London, 1819. [B.M.]

—— The Shepherd Boy of Snowdon Hill ; containing the Adventures of David Jones, in various parts of Asia. With a frontispiece. London, T. Tegg, 1825. [Gumuchian.]

—— Story of Pigou, a Malay Boy. With a frontispiece by George Cruikshank. 1822. [W. T. Spencer.]

Gartshore, Mrs. Murray. Cleveland, a tale of the Catholic Church. London, Richard Bentley, 1847. [B.M. : *Eng. Cat.*]

Gascoigne, Mrs. M. A. Evelyn Harcourt ; a Novel. By the Author of " Temptation ; or, a Wife's Perils," " The School for Wives," &c. 3 vols., London, Henry Colburn, 1847. [*Critic :* Publisher's advert.]

—— The School for Wives. By the Authoress of " Temptation ; or, A Wife's Perils." 3 vols., London, Henry Colburn, 1841. [B.M. : Ingpen.]

—— Temptation ; Or, A Wife's Perils. 3 vols., London, Henry Colburn, 1839. [B.M. : Ingpen.]

Gaskell, Elizabeth Cleghorn. Libbie Marsh's Three Eras : A Lancashire Tale. London, Hamilton Adams, [1850]. [Sadleir.]

—— Lizzie Leigh : A Domestic Tale from " Household Words." By Charles Dickens [*sic*]. New York, Dewitt and Davenport, 1850. [Sadleir.]

—— Mary Barton : A Tale of Manchester Life. 2 vols., London, Chapman and Hall, 1848, [B.M. : Ingpen : Sadleir.]

—— The Moorland Cottage. By the Author of Mary Barton. With illustrations by Birket Foster. London, Chapman and Hall, 1850. [Ingpen : Arthur Rogers : Sadleir.]

—— The Sexton's Hero and Christmas Storms and Sunshine. Contributed by the Authoress of Mary Barton. For the benefiit of the Macclesfield Public Baths and Washhouses. Manchester, Johnson, Rawson, 1850. [Sadleir.]

Gaspey, George. Glory : A Tale of Morals drawn from History. With illus-

trations by John Absolon. London, William S. Orr, 1844. [B.M.]

Gaspey, Thomas. Calthorpe, Or Fallen Fortunes : A Novel. By the Author of " The Mystery ; or, Forty Years Ago." 3 vols., London, Longman, Hurst, Rees, Orme, and Brown, 1821. [Backus : B.M. : Publisher's Advert.]

—— History of George Godfrey. Written by Himself. 3 vols., London, Henry Colburn, 1828. [Baker's Bookshop : B.M. : Publisher's advert.)

—— The Lollards : A Tale, Founded on the Persecutions which marked the Early Part of the Fifteenth Century. By the Author of The Mystery, or Forty Years Ago ; and of Calthorpe, or Fallen Fortunes. 3 vols., London, Longman, Hurst, Rees, Orme, and Brown, 1822. [B.M. : Ingpen : *Quarterly Review.*]

—— " Many-Coloured Life : " Or, Tales of Woe and Touches of Mirth. By the Author of " The Lollards." " George Godfrey," &c. &c. London, Cunningham and Mortimer, 1842. [B.M. : Publisher's advert.]

—— The Mystery ; Or, Forty Years Ago. A Novel. 3 vols., London, Longman, Hurst, Rees, Orme and Brown, 1820. [B.M. : Ingpen : *New Monthly Mag.*]

—— Other Times ; Or, The Monks of Leadenhall. By the Author of The Lollards;—The Mystery ; Calthorpe, or Fallen Fortunes ; &c. &c. 3 vols., London, Longman, Hurst, Rees, Orme & Brown, 1823. [B.M. : Pickering : Publisher's advert.]

—— The Self-Condemned. A Romance. By the Author of " The Lollards,"— " Calthorpe," &c. &c. 3 vols., London, Richard Bentley, 1836. [B.M.]

—— The Witch-Finder ; Or, The Wisdom of Our Ancestors. A Romance. By the Author of " The Lollards," " Other Times," " Calthorpe," &c. 3 vols., London, Longman, Hurst, Rees, Orme, Brown, & Green, 1824. [B.M. : Ingpen : Arthur Rogers.]

Gatari, Geleazzo. The Fortunes of Francesco Novello Da Carrara Lord of Padua, An Historical Tale of the Fourteenth Century, From The Chronicles of Gataro, With Notes. By David Syme. Edinburgh, Constable ; and Hurst, Chance, London 1830. [B.M.]

Gathered Rose (The). London, 1845. [B.M.]

Geisweiler, Maria. Angelion, or the Wizard of Elis. From the German. 3 vols., London, A. K. Newman, 1816. [*Eng. Cat. : New Monthly Mag.*]

Gellert, Christian Fürchtegott. The Life of the Countess of G. . . . By Gellert, translated from the German, by a Lady. 2 vols., London, B. Law, [1747]. [Pickering.]

—— The Life of the Swedish Countess de G * * * Translated from the German by the Rev. Mr. N * * * * * . London, 1776. [B.M.]

General Entertainer (The), Three Hundred Tales and Fables, in which are contained the Lives and Intrigues of Great Personages. 2 vols., London, H. Slater, 1747. [Lowndes.]

General Lover, Or, Small Talker, A Series of Letters from a Lady in the West of England to Lady Anne D—— Abroad. Dublin, J. William, 1769. [Ingpen.]

Generosity, a novel. 3 vols., London, William Lane, 1792 : [Blakey.]

Generosity of an Arabian Prince. Singular Interposition of Providence. With woodcuts. London, James Wallis, [1840 ?]. [B.M.]

Generous Attachment (The). A Novel in a Series of Letters. 4 vols., London, Bew, 1787. [W. Brown : Stonehill.]

Generous Briton (The) ; or, The Authentic Memoirs of William Goldsmith, Esq. 2 vols., Dublin, Exshaw, 1766. [Ingpen (1st Dublin edn.)]

General Guardian (The) ; or, the History of Horatio Saville, Esq. ; and Miss Louisa C- - - -. 2 vols., London, Vernor and Chater, 1767. [Fletcher : *Univ. Mag.*]

General Man (The). An Eastern tale. Alnwick, [1830 ?]. [B.M.]

Genlis, Comtesse de (*see* DE GENLIS).

Gentle Moralist (The), or, a Smile for Prudence, and a Frown for Folly. With 3 plates. London, J. Harris, 1808. [Dobell.]

Gentleman Jack ; Or, Life on the Road. London, E. Lloyd, 1840. [H. W. Fennell.]

Genuine Copies of all the Love Letters and cards which passed between an illustrious personage and a noble lady, during the course of a late amour. Published by a proctor of Doctors Commons. London, T. Brown, [1780]. [Tregaskis.]

Genuine Memoirs of Miss Faulkner (The) ; otherwise Mrs. D ***1** n, or Countess of H*****x in expectancy. Containing the Amours and Intrigues of Several Persons of High Distinction, and remarkable Characters : with some curious Political Anecdotes, never before published. London, 1770. [McLeish.]

Genuine Memoirs of Miss Harriet Melvin and Miss Leonora Stanway. In a Series of Letters. By a Young Lady of Glocester. London, J. Fuller, 1772. [G. Worthington.]

George and Eliza, or a Journal of the Heart. 1810. [*Monthly Mag.*]

Georgiana and her Father ; or, Conversations on natural phenomena. London, Seeley, 1832. [B.M. : *Eng. Cat.*]

Georgie and Lizzie. By Cousin Kate. Edinburgh, Hamilton, 1849. [B.M.]

Geraldina, A Novel, Founded on a Recent Event. 2 vols., London, Robinson, 1798. [*New Ann. Reg.* : Stonehill.]

Geraldwood, a novel. By the author of Villeroy and Sigismar. 4 vols., London, 1801. [Baker's Bookshop : B.M.]

Gérard, L'Abbè Louis Philippe. The Count de Valmont ; or, The Errors of Reason. Translated from the French. 3 vols., London, Hatchard, 1805. [Stonehill.]

Gerrans, B. Tales of a Parrot ; done into English from a Persian manuscript, intitled Tooti Namêh. By a teacher of the Persic, Arabic, Hebrew, Syriac, Chaldaic, Greek, Latin, Italian, French and English languages. London, Printed for the translator at the Minerva Press, 1792. [Blakey.]

Gertrude : Agnes and Melite, and Amelia Douglas : tales by the author of " A Cup of Sweets." London, 1804. [B.M.]

Gertrude ; A Tale of The Sixteenth Century. 2 vols., London, Henry Colburn and Richard Bentley, 1830. [B.M.]

Getty, Edmund. The Last King of Ulster. 3 vols., London, James Madden, 1841. [B.M. : *I. in F.*]

Ghost of Harcourt (The). A romance. To which is added The Fair Maid of Portugal. London, Lane Newman and Co., 1803. [Blakey.]

Ghost of the Rock (The). A Romantic Story. To which is added The Fortunate Robbery. With a frontispiece. London, Roe, [1804]. [Ingpen.]

Ghost Stories. Collected with a Particular View to Counteract the Vulgar Belief in Ghosts and Apparitions, and to promote a rational estimate of the nature of phenomena commonly considered as Supernatural. With 6 plates by Thomas Rowlandson. London, R. Ackermann, 1823. [Francis Edwards : Ingpen : Arthur Rogers.]

Gibbons, Lee (*see* BENNETT, William).

Gibbes, Phoebe. The Life and Adventures of Mr. Francis Clive. 2 vols., Dublin, 1764. [B.M.]

Giberne, Charles. The Haunted Tower ; or, the adventures of Sir Egbert de Rothsay. London, R. Hunter, 1822. [B.M.]

Gibson, A. The Life of a Recluse. 2 vols., London, A. K. Newman, 1817. [B.M.]

Gibson, William.—Elidure and Ella ; A Cambrian Tale. London, 1805. [Allibone.]

Gifford, Arthur. The Omen, or Memoirs of Sir Henry Melville and Miss Julia Eastbrook. A Novel. 2 vols., London, Lowndes, 1785. [W. Brown : Stonehill.]

Gillies, Robert Pierce. The Confessions Of Sir Henry Longueville. A Novel. 2 vols., Edinburgh, Printed by James Ballantyne, for Longman, Hurst, Rees, Orme, and Brown, 1814. [B.M. : *New Monthly Mag.* : *Quarterly Review.*]

Gillies, Robert Pierce. German Stories : Selected from the Works of Hoffmann, De La Motte Fouquè, Pichler, Kruse, and Others. 3 vols., Edinburgh, William Blackwood ; and T. Cadell, London, 1826. [B.M. ; Dobell : Pickering.]

—— Palmario ; Or, The Merchant of Genoa. By the Author of " Tales of an Arctic Voyager," &c. &c. 3 vols., London, T. & W. Boone, 1839. [B.M.]

—— Ranulph de Rohais. A Romance Of the Twelfth Century. By the Author of " Tales of a Voyager to the Arctic Ocean." 3 vols., London, William Kidd, 1830. [B.M. : *New Monthly Mag.*]

—— Tales of a Voyager to the Arctic Ocean. 3 vols., London, Henry Colburn, 1826. [*Blackwood's Edin. Mag.* : B.M.]

—— Tales of a Voyager to the Arctic Ocean. Second Series. 3 vols., London, Henry Colburn, 1829. [B.M.]

——Thurlston Tales. By the Author of " Tales of a Voyager to the Arctic Ocean." 3 vols., London, John Macrone, 1835. [B.M.]

Gilliland, Thomas. The Trap : a moral, philosophical, and satirical work. 2 vols., London, 1808. [B.M.]

Gilmour ; Or, The Last Lockinge. 3 vols., London, Geo. B. Whittaker, 1824. [B.M.]

Gipsey Bride (The) ; Or, The Miser's Daughter." By the Author of " Jane Shore." With 6 plates. London, W. Bennett, 1841. [B.M. : Ingpen.]

Gipsies (The). London, Hatchard, 1842. [B.M.]

Giraldi, Giovanni Battista. The Story of the Moor of Venice. Translated from the Italian, with two essays on Shakspeare, and preliminary observations. By W. Parr. London, 1795. [B.M.]

Girard,—, The Genii : or, the Wonderful Adventures of Abou-Mirza. Imitated from the Arabian by Girard, and translated from the French of this author by C. Herdman, London, 1828. [B.M.]

Girl and her Basket of Eggs. With 8 woodcuts. London, Houlston, [c. 1820]. [Gumuchian.]

Glanville Family (The). By A Lady of Rank. 3 vols., London, Henry Colburn, 1838. [B.M. : Court Bookshop.]

Glascock, Captain William Nugent. Land Sharks And Sea Gulls. With 6 plates by George Cruikshank. 3 vols., London, Richard Bentley, 1838. [B.M. : Marks : Pickering.]

—— Naval Sketch-Book ; or, the Service Afloat and Ashore ; with characteristic reminiscences, fragments, and opinions on professional, colonial, and political subjects. Interspersed with copious notes. By an officer of rank. 2 vols., For the Author, 1826. [B.M. : G. Worthington.]

—— Naval Sketch-Book : Or, the Service Afloat and Ashore ; With Characteristic Reminiscences, Fragments, and Opinions. By the Author of the " Tales of a Tar." Second Series. 2 vols., London, Whittaker, 1834. [B.M.]

Glascock, Captain William Nugent, Sailors and Saints ; or, Matrimonial Manoeuvres. By the Authors of The " Naval Sketch Book." 3 vols., London, Henry Colburn, 1829. [B.M. : Maggs : Arthur Rogers.]

—— Tales of a Tar, With Characteristic Anecdotes. By One of the authors of " The Naval Sketch Book." London, Henry Colburn and Richard Bentley, 1830. [B.M. : Ingpen : Publisher's advert.]

Glasse, Francis. Memoirs of Andrew Winpenny, Count De Deux Sois, comprising numerous adventures in different countries, and exposing the craft and roguery practised in Life, By the Author of " Ned Clinton," etc. London, W. Strange, 1838. [Dobell.]

—— Ned Clinton ; Or, The Commissary : Comprising Adventures, and Events during the Peninsular War : With Curious and original Anecdotes of Military, and other Remarkable Characters. 3 vols., London, William Marsh, 1825. [B.M. : Marks.]

Glasse, George Henry. Louisa : A Narrative of Facts, supposed to throw Light on the Mysterious History of the Lady of the Hay-Stack. London, Rivington, 1801. [Ingpen.]

Gleig, George Robert. Allan Breck. By the Author of " The Subaltern," " Country Curate," &c. 3 vols., London, Richard Bentley, 1834. [B.M. : Ingpen : Arthur Rogers.]

—— Chelsea Hospital, And its Traditions. By the Author of " The Country Curate," " The Subaltern," " The Chronicles of Waltham," &c. 3 vols., London, Richard Bentley, 1838. [B.M. : Ingpen : James Miles.]

—— The Chelsea Pensioners. By the Author of " The Subaltern." 3 vols., London, Henry Colburn, 1829. [B.M. : McLeish : Arthur Rogers.]

—— The Chronicles of Waltham. By The Author of " The Subaltern," " The Country Curate." &c. 3 vols., London, Richard Bentley, 1835. [B.M. : Francis Edwards : Ingpen.]

—— The Country Curate. By the Author of " The Subaltern," and " The Chelsea Pensioners." 2 vols., London, Henry Colburn and Richard Bentley, 1830. [B.M. : Francis Edwards : Pickering.]

—— The Hussar. By the Author of " The Subaltern." 2 vols., London, Henry Colburn, 1837. [B.M. : Pickering : Publisher's advert.]

—— The Light Dragoon. By the author of " The Subaltern." 2 vols., London, Henry Colburn, 1844. [B.M. : *Eng. Cat.* : McLeish.]

Gleig, George Robert. The Subaltern. Edinburgh, William Blackwood, 1825. [M. Buxton Forman : J. Richardson : W. T. Spencer.]

—— The Veterans of Chelsea Hospital. By the Author of " The Subaltern," " Traditions of Chelsea College," " Country Curate," etc., 3 vols., London, Richard Bentley, 1842. [B.M. : Marks.]

Glencore Tower ; or, The Feuds of Scotland, 2 vols., London, Lane, Newman & Co. 1806. [Publisher's advert : Blakey.]

Glenfell, or Macdonalds and Campbells. An Edinburgh Tale of the Nineteenth Century. London, Sir Richard Phillip, 1820. [J. C. Hardy.]

Glenmore Abbey, by the Author of Ariel. 3 vols., London, A. K. Newman. [Publisher's advert, 1812.]

Glenullyn : Or, The Son of the Attainted. 3 vols., London, Edward Bull, 1841. [B.M.]

Gnorowski, S. B. Stanislaus of Cracow. An Historical Tale. London, Saunders and Otley, 1840. [B.M.]

Goadby, Robert. An Apology for the Life of Bampfylde Moore Carew. The whole taken from his own mouth. London, R. Goadby, [1749]. [B.M.]

Goals and Guerdons : Or, The chronicles of a life. By a very old lady.2 vols., London, Charles Ollier, 1848. [B.M.]

Godfrey de Hastings, a Romance. 3 vols., London, William Lane, 1798. [*New. Ann. Reg. :* Blakey.]

Godmother's Tales (The), by the author of Short Stories, Summer Rambles, Cup of Sweets, With a frontispiece. London, J. Harris, 1808. [B.M. : Dobell : Pickering.]

Godwin, C. Reine Canziani : A Tale of Modern Greece. 2 vols., London, Hurst, Robinson ; and A. Constable, Edinburgh, 1825. [B.M. : P. C. Cuttelle.]

Godwin, Catherine Grace. Alicia Grey : or, To Be Useful is to be Happy. London, Parker, 1837. [B.M. : *Eng. Cat.*]

—— Basil Harlow ; or, Prodigality is not Generosity. London, Parker, 1836. [B.M. : *Eng. Cat.*]

—— Cousin Kate ; Or, The Punishment of Pride : A Tale. With woodcuts. London, John W. Parker, 1836. [B.M.]

—— Josephine ; or, Early Trials. London, Parker, 1837. [B.M. : *Eng. Cat.*]

—— Louisa Seymour ; or Hasty Impressions. London, Parker, 1837. [B.M. : *Eng. Cat.*]

—— Scheming ; a tale. London, 1838. [B.M.]

Godwin, Edward. Christian Tales. Exon [Exeter], 1746. [B.M.]

Godwin, George. Facts and Fancies : A Collection of Tales and Sketches. London, Nickisson, 1844. [Allibone : B.M. : H. and J. Davey.]

Godwin, Mary Wollstonecraft. Mary, a Fiction. London, J. Johnson, 1788. [B.M. : King : Arthur Rogers.]

—— Original Stories, From Real Life ; With Conversations, Calculated to Regulate the Affections, And Form the Mind to Truth and Goodness. London, J. Johnson, 1788. [B.M. : Ingpen : Maggs.]

Godwin, William. Cloudesley : A Tale. By The Author of " Caleb Williams." 3 vols., London, Henry Colburn & Richard Bentley, 1830. [B.M. : Ingpen : Publisher's advert.]

—— Deloraine. 3 vols., London, Richard Bentley, 1833. [Birrell and Garnett : B.M. : Ingpen.]

—— Fables Ancient and Modern. Adapted for the Use of Children from Three to Eight Years of Age. By Edward Baldwin, Esq. With 36 copper plates. 2 vols., London, Thomas Hodgkins, 1805. [Court Bk. Shop : Elkin Mathews.]

—— Fleetwood, or, the New Man of Feeling. 3 vols., London, Richard Phillips, 1805. [B.M. : Kyrle Fletcher : Ingpen.]

—— Italian Letters : Or, The History of the Count de St. Julian. 2 vols., London, G. Robinson, 1784. [Algar : F. K. Brown's *Godwin :* W. Brown.]

—— Mandeville, A Tale of the Seventeenth Century In England. 3 vols., Edinburgh, Archibald Constable ; and Longman, Hurst, Rees, Orme & Brown, London, 1817. [B.M. : Ingpen : Arthur Rogers.]

—— St. Leon : A Tale of the Sixteenth Century. 4 vols., London, G. G. & J. Robinson, 1799. [Block : B.M. : Ingpen.]

—— Things As They Are ; or, the Adventures of Caleb Williams. 3 vols., London, B. Crosby, 1794. [Ingpen : King : Arthur Rogers.]

Godwin, William, Jun. Transfusion : By The Late William Godwin, Jun. With a memoir of his life and writings, By his father. 3 vols., London, John Macrone, 1835. [B.M. : G. Worthington.]

Goethe, Johann Wolfgang. Faust : a dramatic poem, by Goethe. Translated into English prose, with remarks on former translations, and notes. By the translator of Savigny's Of the Vocation of our Age for Legislation and Jurisprudence [A. Hayward]. London, 1833. [Wm. Heinemann.]

—— Faustus : a Dramatic Mystery ; The Bride of Corinth ; The First Walpurgis Night. Translated from the German of Goethe, and illustrated with notes, by John Anster. London, Longman, 1835. [B.M. : Wm. Heinemann.]

—— Goethe's Novel. Translated from

the German. London E. Moxon, 1837. [B.M.: Elkin Mathews.]

Goethe, Johann Wolfgang. Heliodora, or the Grecian Minstrel. Translated [by W. A. Lindau] from the German of Baron Goethe. London, Dutton, 1804. [Oswald's *Bibliog. of Goethe.*]

—— The Sorrows of Werter ; A German Story, founded on Fact. 2 vols., London, J. Dodsley, 1779. [Ingpen : Arthur Rogers.]

—— The Sorrows of Werter. Translated By F. Gotzberg. London, 1802. [B.M.]

—— The Sorrows of Werter. Translated by Dr. Pratt. With engraved title. [1813 ?] [B.M. (2nd edn.)]

—— The Sorrows of Werter. Translated from the French edition of M. Aubry, [or rather of Count F. W. K. Schmettau ?] by J. Gifford. 2 vols., London, 1789. [B.M.]

—— The Sorrows of Werter ; Translated from the German of Goethe by W. Render. London, 1801. [Lib. of Congress.]

—— Wilhelm Meister's Apprenticeship. A Novel. From the German of Goethe, [Translated by Thomas Carlyle.] 3 vols. Edinburgh, Oliver and Boyd; and G. & W. B. Whittaker, London, 1824. [Block : B.M. : Arthur Rogers.]

—— Wilhelm Meister's Apprenticeship. A novel from the German of Goethe. Translated by R. Dillon Boylan. London, Bohn, 1846. [B.M.]

Going Too Far : A Tale For All Ages. 2 vols., London, Baldwin, Cradock and Joy, 1825. [B.M.]

Golden Legends. Containing " The Bracelet,"—" The Locket," And " The Signet Ring." 3 vols., London, Saunders and Otley, 1833. [B.M.]

Golden Marriage (The) : A Romance of Deep Interest. With illustrations. London, E. Lloyd, [c. 1835]. [Stonehill.]

Goldsmid, Isabel. Shadows and Sunshine. A tale. By the author of " Viola." London, Longman, 1850. [B.M. : *Eng. Cat.*]

—— 'Tis an Old Tale, and Often Told. London, Published for the Author, by Robert Jennings, 1839. [B.M.]

Goldsmith, Mary. Casualties. A Novel. 2 vols., London, T. Hughes, 1804. [B.M. : Ingpen.]

Goldsmith, Oliver. The Citizen of the World ; or Letters from a Chinese Philosopher Residing in London to his Friends in the East. 2 vols., London, Printed for the author, 1762. [B.M. : Marks : Quaritch.]

—— The Memoirs of a Protestant, condemned to the Galleys of France, for his Religion. Written by Himself. Comprehending an Account of the various Distresses he suffered in Slavery ; and his Constancy in supporting almost every Cruelty that bigotted Zeal could inflict or Human Nature sustain ; also a Description of the Galleys, and the Service in which they are employed. The whole interspersed with Anecdotes relative to the General History of the Times, for a Period of Thirteen Years ; during which the Author continued in Slavery, 'till he was at last set free, at the Intercession of the Court of Great Britain. Translated from the original, just published at the Hague. By James Willington, 2 vols., London, R. Griffiths, and E. Dilly, 1758. [Block : B.M. : Iolo Williams.]

Goldsmith, Oliver. The Mystery Revealed ; Containing a Series of Transaction and Authentic Testimonials, Respecting the supposed Cock-Lane Ghost : Which have hitherto been concealed from the Public. London, W. Bristow ; and C. Ethrington, York, 1742 [for 1762]. [Iolo Williams.]

—— The Vicar of Wakefield : A Tale. Supposed to be written by Himself. 2 vols., Salisbury, Printed by B. Collins for F. Newbury, 1766. [B.M. : Maggs : Quaritch.]

Goldsmith's Widow (The) ; and other tales. London, [1847]. [B.M.]

Golland, Mrs. (*see* HAYNES, Miss C. D.).

Gomersall, Mrs. A. The Citizen, A Novel. 2 vols., London, Scatcherd & Whitaker, 1790. [B.M.]

—— The Disappointed Heir. 2 vols., London, 1796. [Allibone : *New Ann. Reg.*]

—— Eleanora, A Novel. 2 vols., London, 1789. [Allibone.]

Gomez, Madeleine Angelique de, (*see* DE GOMEZ].

Gomez and Eleonora, translated from a Spanish Manuscript. 2 vols., 1798. [*New Ann. Reg.*]

Gooch, Elizabeth Sarah Villa-Real,— The Contrast. A Novel. 2 vols., 1794. [*New Ann. Reg.* : T. D. Webster.]

—— Fancied Events : or, the Sorrows of Ellen. A Novel. 2 vols., London, George Cawthorn, 1799. [Court Bk. Shop.]

—— Sherwood Forest, or Northern Adventures. A Novel. 3 vols., 1804. [R. W. Burl.]

—— Truth and Fiction. 4 vols., London, 1801. [Baker's Bookshop.]

—— The Wanderings of the Imagination. 2 vols., London, 1796. [B.M. : *New Ann. Reg.*]

Good Effects of Sincere and Constant Prayer (The), exemplified in the history of the Dobson family. London, Rivington, 1803. [*Guardian of Education.*]

Good Farmer (The) : Or The Entertaining History Of Thomas Wiseman ; who procured Riches and a Good Name, by the Paths of Virtue and Industry. With woodcuts. Banbury, J. G. Rusher, [1810]. [King.]

Good Father (The), And Prudent Son. To which is added, The Mother, A Poem. With 15 woodcuts. London, Whitrow, [1820?]. [B.M.]

Good Humour ; or My Uncle, The General. By a Third Cousin. 2 vols., London, T. Egerton, 1820. [B.M. : *Eng. Cat.* : T. Thorp.]

Good Mother's Legacy (The). With a woodcut. London, Howard & Evans ; J. Hatchard ; Hazard & Binns, Bath, [1795]. Cheap Repository. [Block : B.M. : Court Bk. Shop.]

Good News in Bad Times ; Or Piety and Patriotism the best Source of Consolation in Seasons of Public Distress. With a woodcut. A Single folio leaf. York, Carrall, [18- -]. [B.M.]

Good Shepherd and his little lambs (The). A Story for little Children, by an Uncle. London, J. H. Jackson, 1848. [B.M.]

Goodall, William. The Adventure of Captain Greenland : Written in imitation of all those wise, learned, witty and humorous authors, who either already have, or hereafter may write in the same stile and manner. 4 vols., London, R. Baldwin, 1752. [Bailey Bros. : Tregaskis.]

Goodricke, Henry. Lindor and Adelaide, A Moral Tale. In which are exhibited the effects of the late French Revolution on the Peasantry of France. By the Author of " Observations on Doctor Price's Revolution Sermon." London, 1791. [T. D. Webster.]

Gordon, Mrs. The Fortunes Of The Falconars. 3 vols., London, Saunders and Otley, 1844. [B.M. : Arthur Rogers.]

—— Kingsconnell, a tale. 3 vols., London, T. C. Newby, 1850. [B.M. : McLeish : Arthur Rogers.]

Gordon, Alexander. Macgrigor and Clarendon, or The Recluse Lovers. A Novel. Aberdeen, Chalmers, 1821. [Ingpen.]

Gordon, Percival. Giovanni Sbogarro, a Venetian Tale, taken from the French, by Percival Gordon. 2 vols., London, Baldwin, 1820. [*New Monthly Mag.*]

Gore, Catherine Grace Frances, Agathonia. A Romance. London, Edward Moxon, 1844. [Birrell and Garnett : B.M. : G. Worthington.]

—— The Ambassador's Wife. 3 vols., London, Richard Bentley, 1842. [B.M.]

—— The Banker's Wife ; Or, Court and City. A Novel. 3 vols., London, Henry Colburn, 1843. [B.M.]

—— The Birthright, And other Tales. 3 vols., London, Henry Colburn, 1844. [B.M.]

—— The Cabinet Minister. By the Authoress of " Mothers and Daughters," " Mrs. Armytage," " The Heir of Selwood," &c. 3 vols., London, Richard Bentley, 1839. [B.M. : James Glashier : McLeish.]

Gore, Catherine Grace Frances. Castles in the Air. A Novel. 3 vols., London, Richard Bentley, 1847. [B.M. : *Critic*]

—— Cecil, Or, The Adventures of a Coxcomb. A Novel. 3 vols., London, Richard Bentley, 1841. [B.M. : Francis Edwards : *Guide to Best Fiction.*]

—— Cecil, a Peer, A Sequel to Cecil, or the Adventures of a Coxcomb. By the same author. 3 vols., London, T. and W. Boone, 1841. [Birrell and Garnett : B.M. : Francis Edwards.]

—— Courtier of the Days of Charles the Second, And other Tales. 3 vols., London, Henry Colburn, 1839. [Allibone : *Eng. Cat.*]

—— The Débutante ; Or, The London Season. 3 vols., London, Richard Bentley, 1846. [B.M. : *Critic.*]

—— The Diamond and the Pearl, a Novel. 3 vols., London, Henry Colburn, 1848. [B.M. : *Eng. Cat.*]

—— The Diary Of A Désennuyée. 2 vols., London, Henry Colburn, 1836. [B.M. : Ingpen : Lib. of Congress.]

—— The Dowager ; Or The New School for Scandal. 3 vols., London, Richard Bentley, 1840. [B.M. : James Glaisher.]

—— The Fair of May Fair. 3 vols., London, Henry Colburn and Richard Bentley, 1832. [B.M. : Ingpen.]

—— Fascination, And Other Tales. Edited by Mrs. Gore. 3 vols., London, Henry Colburn, 1842. [B.M.]

—— Greville : Or, A Season in Paris. 3 vols., London, Henry Colburn, 1841. [B.M. : E. Hector.]

—— The Hamiltons Or The New Aera. By the Author of " Mothers and Daughters." 3 vols., London, Saunders and Otley, 1834. [Baker's Bookshop : B.M.]

—— The Heir of Selwood : Or, Three Epochs of a Life. By the Authoress of " Mothers and Daughters," " Mrs. Armytage." and " Stokeshill Place." 3 vols., London, Henry Colburn, 1838. [B.M. : Elkin Mathews.]

—— Hungarian Tales. By the Author of " The Lettre de Cachet." 3 vols., London, Saunders & Otley, 1829. [B.M. : Clarke-Hall : Ingpen.]

—— The Inundation ; or Pardon and Peace. With plates by George Cruikshank. London, Willoughby, [1843]. [Block : *Eng. Cat.*]

—— The Lettre de Cachet ; A Tale. The Reign of Terror ; A Tale. London, J. Andrews, 1827. [B.M.]

—— The Man of Fortune, And Other Tales. 3 vols., London, Henry Colburn, [1842. [B.M.]

—— Manners of the Day, Or, Women as they are. 3 vols., London, 1841. [Allibone.]

—— Mary Raymond, And Other Tales. By The Authoress of " Mothers and Daughters," &c. &c. 3 vols., London, Henry Colburn, 1838. [B.M.]

Gore, Catherine Grace Frances. Memoirs of a Peeress ; Or The Days of Fox. Edited by Lady Charlotte Bury. 3 vols., London, Henry Colburn, 1837. [Block : B.M. : G. Worthington.]

—— Men of Capital. 3 vols., London, Henry Colburn, 1846, [B.M.]

—— Modern Chivalry, Or a New Orlando Furioso. With illustrations by George Cruikshank. 2 vols., London, Mortimer, 1843. [B.M. : Chas. Hutt.]

—— Modern French Life. Edited by Mrs. Gore. 3 vols., London, Richard Bentley, 1842. [B.M.]

—— The Money-Lender. 3 vols., London, Henry Colburn, 1843. [B.M.]

—— Mothers and Daughters ; A Tale of the Year 1830. 3 vols., London, Henry Colburn and Richard Bentley, 1831. [B.M. : G. Worthington.]

—— Mrs. Armytage ; Or, Female Domination. By the Authoress of " Mothers and Daughters." 3 vols., London, Henry Colburn, 1836. [B.M. : C. Howes.]

—— New Year's Day, a Winter's tale. With plates by George Cruikshank. London, Fisher, [1846]. [Block (2nd edn.) : B.M. (2nd edn.)].

—— The Opera : A Novel. By the Author of " Mothers and Daughters." 3 vols., London, Henry Colburn and Richard Bentley, 1832. [B.M.]

—— Peers and Parvenus. A Novel. 3 vols., London, Henry Colburn, 1846. [B.M. : E. Hector : Ingpen.]

—— Pin Money ; A Novel. By the authoress of " The Manners of the Day." 3 vols., London, Henry Colburn and Richard Bentley, 1831. [B.M.]

—— Polish Tales. By the Authoress of " Hungarian Tales." 3 vols., London, Saunders and Otley, 1833. [B.M.]

—— The Popular Member, The Wheel of Fortune, Etc., 3 vols., London, Richard Bentley, 1844. [B.M.]

—— Preferment : Or, My Uncle the Earl. 3 vols., London, Henry Colburn, 1840. [Baker's Bookshop : B.M. : McLeish.]

—— Romances of Real Life. By the Author of " Hungarian Tales." 3 vols., London, Henry Colburn, 1829. [B.M. : Wm. Brown.]

—— Self. By the Author of " Cecil." 3 vols., London, Henry Colburn, 1845. [Baker's Bookshop : B.M. ; Publisher's advert.]

—— The Sketch Book of Fashion. By the Author of " Mothers and Daughters." 3 vols., London, Richard Bentley, 1833. [B.M.]

—— Sketches Of English character. 2 vols., London, Richard Bentley, 1846. [B.M.]

—— The Snow-Storm, A Christmas Story. With plates by George Cruikshank. London, Fisher [1845]. [Block : B.M. : W. T. Spencer.]

Gore, Catherine Grace Frances. Stokeshill Place ; Or The Man of Business. By the Authoress of " Mrs, Armytage," " Mothers and Daughters," etc., 3 vols., London, Henry Colburn, 1837. [B.M. : H. H. Langley : Publisher's advert.]

—— The Story Of a Royal Favourite. 3 vols., London, Henry Colburn, 1845. [B.M. : Clarke-Hall : Publisher's advert.]

—— Temptation And Atonement, And other tales. 3 vols., London, Henry Colburn, 1847. [B.M.]

—— Theresa Marchmont ; Or, The Maid of Honour. A Tale. London, J. Andrews, 1824. [B.M. : Arthur Rogers.]

—— The Tuileries. A Tale. By the Author of " Hungarian Tales." "Romances of Real Life," &c. &c. 3 vols., London, Henry Colburn and Richard Bentley, 1831. [B.M. : Ingpen : Pickering.]

—— The Woman of the World. A Novel. By The Authoress of the Diary of a Désennuyée. 3 vols., London, Henry Colburn, 1838. [Baker's Bookshop : B.M.]

—— Women As They Are ; Or, The Manners of the Day. 3 vols., London, Henry Colburn and Richard Bentley, 1830. [B.M. (2nd edn.)]

Gore, Mary. Raymond and Other Tales. 3 vols., London, 1838. [Arthur Rogers.]

Gorey Cup of Condor's Well (The) : a tale of mystery : by an old seaman. London, 1842. [B.M.]

Gorgy, Jean Claude. Blansay. A tale of incidents in life. From the French. By the author of *Victorina, Louis and Nina*, &c. 2 vols. [W. Lane, 1790: Blakey: T. D. Webster.]

—— Lidora ; An Ancient Chronicle. From the French. 2 vols., London, Printed at the Minerva Press, 1791. [Ingpen.]

—— Louis and Nina ; or, An excursion to Yverdun. 2 vols. [W. Lane, 1789.] [Blakey.]

—— St. Alma. A novel. Translated from the French of J. C. Gorgy, by Mrs. Helme. 2 vols. [Blakey.]

—— Sentimental Tablets of the Good Pamphile, written in the months of August, September, October and November, 1795, by M. Gorgy. Translated from the French by P. S. Dupuy [and Charles Lamb] of the East-India House. With a frontispiece and a page of music. London, Printed at the Philanthropic Reform, 1795. [B.M. : King.]

—— Victorina. An interesting and incidental tale. By the Author of *Blansay, Louis and Nina*, &c. Translated from the French. 2 vols., [W. Lane, 1790.] [Blakey.]

Gospel Stories. [*Literary Annalist.*]

Goss, Prothesia S. The Piedmontese Envoy ; or, the men, manners, and religion of the Commonwealth. A tale. London, [1844 ?]. [B.M.]

Gotha, or, Memoirs of the Wurzburg Family. Founded on Facts. 2 vols., London, 1811. [Baker's Bookshop : T. D. Webster.]

Gothic Legends, A Tale of Mystery. With woodcut on title. London, A Seale, 1802. [Dobell.]

Gothic Story of De Courville Castle (The) ; or the Illegitimate Son. London, [1825 ?] [B.M.]

Goudar, Ange de. Chinese Spy. 1764. [*Eng. Lit. in Germany*.]

Goulbourne, E. Frederick de Montford. By the Author of Pursuits of Fashion. 3 vols., London, Ebers, 1811. [Baker's Bookshop : *Eng. Cat. :* Stonehill.]

Governess (The), or Courtland Abbey. 1797. [*New Ann Reg.*]

Governess (The) ; or, Evening Amusements at a boarding school. London, Vernor and Hood, 1800. [B.M.: *Guardian of Education*.]

Grace Dermott ; or, Help for the afflicted. London, Religious Tract Society, 1849. [B.M.]

Grafigny, Madame F. d'I. de H. The Letters of a Peruvian Princess. Also, as a sequel, The Letters of Aza, by Ignatius Hungari de la Marche-Courmont. To which are prefixed, A Life of Madame De Grafigny, and a short Biographical Notice of Marche-Courmont. Translated from the French by William Mudford. With a frontispiece. London. Sherwood, Neely and Jones, 1809. [Ingpen.]

—— Letters written by a Peruvian Princess. Translated from the French. London, 1748. [B.M.]

Graglia, G. A. The Castle of Eridan ; Or, The entertaining and surprising History Of the Valiant Don Alveres, And the beautiful Eugenia, Duchess of Savoy. London, Hurst, Baldwin, 1800. [B.M. : G. Worthington.]

Graham, E. S. Voyage to Locuta. By Lemuel Gulliver, Jun. London, J. Hatchard, 1818. [Gumuchian : *New Monthly Mag.*]

Graham, Malcolm. Florence Graham ; or, The Pirate's Daughter. By the author of " The Life of Nelson." With illustrations. London, E. Lloyd, 1847. [B.M. : Stonehill.]

—— The Robber Chief ; Or, the Foundling of the Forest. A Romance. By the Author of " The Black Pirate, or the Phantom Ship," " Florence Graham, or the Pirate's Daughter ; " " The Life of Nelson," &c. &c. &c. With plates. London, William Emans, 1840. [H.W. Fennell : B. Ono.]

Graham, Mrs. [*see* BARRY, Mrs.].

Grand Le. Tales of the Twelfth and Thirteenth Centuries. 2 vols., 1786. [W. Brown.]

Grand Assizes (The) ; Or General Gaol Delivery. With a woodcut. London, J.

Marshall, [1796]. Cheap Repository. Sunday Reading. [B.M.]

Grandpapa's Drawer Opened. With a frontispiece. London, Houlston, 1833. [Court Bk. Shop (2nd edn.)]

Grant, Anne. Letters From The Mountains ; Being the real Correspondence of a lady Between the years 1773 and 1803. 3 vols., London, Longman, Hurst, Rees, & Orme ; J. Hatchard, Mrs. Cook, 1806. [King.]

Grant, James. Adventures Of An Aide-de-camp : Or, A Campaign in Calabria. 3 vols., London, Smith, Elder, 1848. [B.M. : Lib. of Congress.]

—— Joseph Jenkins ; Or, Leaves from the Life of a Literary Man. By the Author of " Random Recollections," " The Great Metropolis," &c. &c. 3 vols., London, Saunders and Otley, 1843. [B.M. : G. Worthington.]

—— The Romance of War : Or, The Highlanders In France and Belgium. A Sequel to The Highlanders in Spain. London, Henry Colburn, 1846-1847. [B.M. : Fletcher.]

—— The Romance of War : Or, The Highlanders in Spain. 4 vols., London, Henry Colburn, 1846–1847. [B.M. : Mudie's : T. Thorp.]

—— The Scottish Cavalier. An historical romance. 3 vols., London, Henry Colburn, 1850. [B.M.]

—— Sketches in London. With 24 plates by " Phiz " and others. London, Thomas Tegg, 1838. [B.M. : T. Thorp.]

—— Travels in Town. By the Author of " Random Recollections of the Lords and Commons." " The Great Metropolis," etc. etc. 2 vols., London, Saunders and Otley, 1839. [G. Worthington.]

—— Walter Fentor or the Scottish Cavalier. 3 vols., 1850. [Noel Broadbent.]

Grant, James Gregor. Rufus Or The Red King. A Romance. 3 vols., London, Saunders and Otley, 1838. [B.M.]

Grant, John O'Brien. The Husband-Hunter ; Or, " Das Schiksal." By Denis Ignatius Moriarty, Esq. Author of " The Wife-Hunter." 3 vols., London, Richard Bentley, 1839. [B.M. : James Glaisher.]

—— Innisfoyle Abbey. A Tale of Modern Times. By Denis Ignatius Moriarty, Esq. Author of the " Wife Hunter," The " Husband Hunter," &c. 3 vols., London, C. Dolman, 1840. [B.M.]

—— The Wife Hunter, And Flora Douglas : Tales by The Moriarty Family. Edited by Denis Ignatius Moriarty, Esq. 3 vols., London, Richard Bentley, 1838. [B.M.]

Grant, Joseph. Tales of the Glens ; With Ballads and Songs. To which is Prefixed, A Memoir of the Author, By Robert Nicoll. Edinburgh, Fraser ; and Henry Washbourne, 1836. [B.M.]

Grant, Mrs. M. A. Tales, founded on Facts. London, Boosey, 1820. [*Eng. Cat: New Monthly Mag.*]

Gratitude, or, the Juvenile Writers. With 2 plates. London, J. Harris, 1808. [Dobell.]

Grattan, Thomas Colley. Agnes de Mansfeldt. A Historical Tale. 3 vols., London, Saunders and Otley, 1836. [B.M.]

—— The Heiress of Bruges ; A Tale Of the Year Sixteen Hundred. 4 vols., London, Henry Colburn and Richard Bentley, 1830. [Block : McLeish.]

—— High-Ways and By-Ways ; Or Tales of the Roadside, Picked up in the French Provinces. By A Walking Gentleman. London, G. and W. B. Whittaker, 1823. [B.M. : *Quarterly Review.*]

—— High-Ways and By-Ways ; Or, Tales of the Roadside, Picked up in the French Provinces. By A Walking Gentleman. Second Series. 3 vols., London, Henry Colburn, 1825. [B.M. : Dobell : G. Worthington.]

—— High-Ways and By-Ways ; Or, Tales of the Roadside, Picked up in the French Provinces. By A Walking Gentleman. Third Series. 3 vols., London, Henry Colburn, 1827. [*Blackwoods' Edin. Mag.* : B.M. : Dobell.]

—— Jacqueline of Holland. A Historical Tale. 3 vols., London, Henry Colburn and Richard Bentley, 1831. [Baker's Bookshop : B. M. : McLeish.]

—— Legends Of the Rhine And of The Low Countries. By The Author of " Highways and By-Ways ", etc. 3 vols., London, Henry Colburn and Richard Bentley, 1832. [B.M. : T. Thorp : T. D. Webster.]

—— The Master Passion ; and Other Tales & Sketches. With a portrait. 3 vols., London, Henry Colburn, 1845. [Allibone : *Critic :* Publisher's advert.]

—— Tales. 1832. [*Literary Gazette.*]

—— Traits of Travel ; Or, Tales of Men and Cities. By the Author of " High-ways and By-ways." 3 vols., London, Henry Colburn, 1829. [B.M. : Ingpen.]

Graves, Richard. Columella ; Or, The Distressed Anchoret. A Colloquial Tale. By the Editor of the Spiritual Quixote. With a frontispiece. 2 vols., London, J. Dodsley, 1779. [B.M. : Holland : Ingpen.]

—— Plexippus. 2 vols., 1790. [Sotheby's.]

—— The Spiritual Quixote, or The Summer's Ramble of Mr. Geoffrey Wildgoose. A Comic Romance. With vignette titles. 3 vols., London, J. Dodsley, 1773. [B.M. : Dobell : Arthur Rogers.]

—— The Triflers, by an Adept in the Art of Trifling, to which is added The Rout, also The Farmer's Son. With a frontispiece. Printed for the Author's Executrix, 1805. [Kyrle Fletcher.]

Graves, Richard, the Younger. Eugenius ; Or, Anecdotes of the Golden Vale. An Embellished Narrative of Real Facts. With frontispieces. 2 vols., London, J. Dodsley, 1785. [B.M. : Ingpen : Arthur Rogers.]

Great Bear's Story (The). The Vizier and the Woodman. London, Wright, 1841. [B.M. (2nd edn.)]

Great Wheel (The) ; or, the Fair Field of Fortune. A dream. By the author of " The Village Bride." London, 1830. [B.M.]

Green, George Smith. The Life of Mr. J. Van, being a series of many extraordinary events and surprizing vicissitudes. 2 vols., London, [1750 ?] [B.M.]

Green, Sarah. Carthusian Friar.

Green, Sarah (?). Charles Henly ; or, The fugitive restored, 2 vols., [W. Lane 1790.] [*Minerva Press Catalogue :* Blakey.]

—— The Fugitive, Or Family Incidents. By the Author of Private History of the Court of England, Romance Readers and Romance Writers, &c. &c. 3 vols., London, Black, Parry, 1814. [B.M. : *European Mag. : New Monthly Mag.*]

—— Good Men of Modern Date. 3 vols., 1812. [*Quarterly Review.*]

—— Gretna Green Marriages ; Or, The Nieces. A Novel, 3 vols., London, A. K. Newman, 1823. [B.M.]

—— Mental Improvement for a young lady, on her entrance into the world ; addressed to a favourite niece. London, William Lane, 1793. [B.M. : Blakey.]

—— Parents and Wives ; Or, Inconsistency and Mistakes. A Novel. 3 vols., London, A. K. Newman, 1825. [B.M. : *Edin. Mag.*]

—— The Reformist ! ! ! A Serio-Comic-Political Novel. 2 vols., London, Minerva Press, 1810. [B.M. : Stonehill.]

—— Romance Readers and Romance Writers : a satirical novel. 3 vols., London, T. and E. T. Hookham, 1810. [B.M. : *Monthly Mag.*]

—— The Royal Exile, or Victims of Human Passions. 4 vols., 1810. [*New Monthly Mag. : Quarterly Review.*]

—— Scotch Novel Reading ; or, Modern Quackery. A Novel *Really* Founded on Facts. By A Cockney. 3 vols., London, A. K. Newman, 1824. [B.M.]

—— Who is the Bridegroom ? Or Nuptial Discoveries. A Novel. 3 vols., London, A. K. Newman, 1822. [B.M. : *New Monthly Mag. : Quarterly Review.*]

Green, William Child. Abbot of Montserrat ; Or, The Pool of Blood. A Romance. 2 vols., London, A. K. Newman, 1826. [B.M. : *New Monthly Mag. : Quarterly Review.*]

Green, William Child. The Algerines ; Or, The Twins of Naples. 3 vols., London, A. K. Newman, 1832. [B.M. : *Metropolitan Mag.*]

—— Alibeg the Tempter. A Tale Wild and Wonderful. 4 vols., London, A. K. Newman, 1831. [B.M.]

—— The Woodland Family, or The Sons of Error and Daughters of Simplicity. With an engraved title-page and plates. London, Joseph Emans, 1824. [Pickering.]

Green Bushes (The), or a Hundred Years Ago. 1847. [Noel Broadbent.]

Green's First Tales for Little Children. With plates. London, Darton and Clark, [1844 ?]. [Block.]

Gregory, Sir William. Paddiana, Or Scraps and sketches of Irish Life, present and past, By the Author of " A Hot Water Cure." With a frontispiece. 2 vols., London, Richard Bentley, 1847. [B.M. : Clarke-Hall : *I. in F.*]

Gresley, Sir Roger. Sir Philip Gasteneys : A Minor. London, Henry Colburn, 1829. [B.M. : Ingpen : G. Worthington.]

Gresley, Rev. William. Bernard Leslie, or a tale of the last ten years. London, Masters, 1842. [B.M.]

—— Coniston Hall ; or, the Jacobites : an Historical Tale. With woodcuts. London, Burns, 1846. [*Critic :* T. D. Webster.]

—— The Siege of Lichfield : a tale, illustrative of the Great Rebellion. With illustrations. London, Masters, 1840. [B.M. : Dobell.]

Grey, Catherine Maria. Alice Seymour. A Tale. London, J. Hatchard, 1831. [B.M.]

—— Aline. An old friend's story. By the Author of " The Gambler's Wife," " Daughters," " Sybil Lennard," &c. &c. &c. 3 vols., London, T. C. Newby, 1848. [B.M.]

—— The Belle of the Family ; Or, The Jointure. A Novel. By the Author of " The Young Prima Donna," " The Little Wife," &c. &c. 3 vols., London, T. C. Newby, 1843. [B.M. : *Tait's Edin. Mag.*]

—— The Bosom Friend. A Novel. By the Author of " The Gambler's Wife," " The Young Prima Donna," &c. &c. &c. 3 vols., London, T. C. Newby, 1845. [B.M.]

—— Daughters. A Novel. By the Author of " The Gambler's Wife," " Sybil Lennard," &c. 3 vols., London, Thomas Cautley Newby, 1847. [B.M. : H. B. Copinger : McLeish.]

—— The Duke. A Novel. 3 vols., London, Richard Bentley, 1839. [B.M. : McLeish.]

—— Hyacinthe ; or, The Contrast. By the Authoress of " Alice Seymour." 3 vols., London, James Cochrane, 1835. [Pickering.]

Grey, Catherine Maria. The Little Wife ; And the Baronet's Daughters. 3 vols., London, Saunders and Otley, 1841. [B.M.]

—— An Old Country House. A Novel. By the author of " The Gambler's Wife," etc. 3 vols., London, T. C. Newby, 1850. [B.M. : H. B. Copinger.]

—— The Old Dower House, A Tale of Bygone Days. By the Author of " The Young Prima Donna," " The Belle of the Family," &c. &c. &c., 3 vols., London, T. C. Newby, 1844. [B.M. : *Tait's Edin. Mag.*]

—— The Rectory Guest. A novel. By the author of " The Gambler's Wife." 3 vols., London, T. C. Newby, 1849. [B.M. : *Eng. Cat.*]

—— Sybil Lennard. A Novel. By the Author of " The Young Prima Donna," " The Gambler's Wife," etc. 3 vols., London, Thomas Cautley Newby, 1846. [*Critic.*]

—— The Young Prima Donna : A Romance of the Opera. 3 vols., London, Richard Bentley, 1840. [B.M.]

Grey, Elizabeth Caroline. Vileroy, or the Horrors of Zindorf Castle. With woodcuts, London, E. Lloyd, [1844.] [B.M. : B. Ono : M. Summers.]

Grey, Hon. Mrs. De Lisle ; or, The Distrustful Man. 3 vols., London, Edward Bull, 1828. [The second edition was entitled " De Lisle ; or the Sensitive Man."] [B.M. : Ingpen.]

—— The Trials of Life. By the Author of " De Lisle." 3 vols., London, Edward Bull, 1829. [B.M. : Pickering : T. Thorp.]

—— The Way of the World. By the Author of " De Lisle," and " The Trials of Life." 3 vols., London, Edward Bull, 1831. [B.M. : Clarke-Hall : McLeish.]

Grierson, Miss. Lily Douglas, a simple story. Leith, 1821. [B.M. (2nd edn.)]

—— Pierre and his Family ; or, a Story of the Waldenses. By the author of " Lily Douglas." Edinburgh, Hamilton, 1823. [B.M.]

—— The Visit, or mamma and the children. By the Author of " Lily Douglas," etc. Edinburgh, 1824. [B.M.]

Griffin, Elizabeth. The Friends. Or, The Contrast Between Virtue and Vice. A Tale Designed for the Improvement of Youth. With a frontispiece by G. Murray after Thurston and woodcuts. Oxford and London, Crosby and Letterman, 1798. [Gumuchian.]

Griffin, Gerald [Edit. by]. The Christian Physiologist. Tales illustrative of the five senses : their mechanism, uses and government. Edited by the author of the Collegians, etc. London, 1830. [B.M. : *I. in F.*]

Griffin, Gerald. The Collegians. 3 vols., London, Saunders & Otley, 1829. [B.M. : Ingpen : Pickering.]

—— The Duke of Monmouth. By the

Author of " The Munster Festivals," &c.
3 vols., London, Richard Bentley, 1836.
[B.M.]

Griffin, Gerald. Holland Tide : or
Munster Popular Tales. London, W.
Simpkin and R. Marshall, 1827.
[Publisher's advert ; T. D. Webster.]

—— The Invasion. By the Author of
"The Collegians," &c. 4 vols., London,
Saunders and Otley, 1832. [B.M. :
Guide to Best Fiction : Elkin Mathews.]

—— The Rivals. Tracy's Ambition. By
the Author of " The Collegians." 3
vols., London, Saunders and Otley, 1829.
[*New Monthly Mag. :* G. Worthington.]

—— Tales of the Munster Festivals
Containing, Card Drawing ; The Half
Sir ; and Suil Dhuv, the Coiner. By the
Author of " Holland-Tide, or Irish
Popular Tales." 3 vols., London,
Saunders and Otley, 1827. [B.M. :
Pickering : T. D. Webster.]

—— Tales of my Neighbourhood. By
the Author of " The Collegians." 3 vols.,
London, Saunders and Otley, 1835.
[B.M. : *I. in F.*]

—— Talis Qualis, Or, Tales of the Jury
Room. 3 vols., London, Maxwell, 1842.
[B.M. : Elkin Mathews : G. Worthington.]

Griffin, James. The Freebooter of the
Alps. A Romance. 2 vols., London, A.
K. Newman, 1821. [B.M.]

Griffith, Elizabeth. The History of
Lady Barton, A Novel in Letters. 3
vols., London, T. Davies and T. Cadell,
1771. [B.M. : Maggs : Arthur Rogers.]

—— The Princess of Cleves, An Historical Novel, Revised and Corrected by
Mrs. Griffith. London, William Lane,
1780. [Ingpen : Blakey.]

—— The Story of Lady Juliana Harley.
A novel. In letters. 2 vols., London,
T. Cadell, 1776. [Maggs.]

Griffith, Elizabeth and Richard. The
Delicate Distress. A Novel. In Letters,
by Frances, and The Gordian Knot, or
Dignus Vindice Nodus. A Novel. In
Letters, by Henry, 4 vols., London,
1769. [T. D. Webster.]

—— A Series of Genuine Letters between Henry and Frances. 4 vols.,
London. 1757. [B.M.]

—— Two Novels in Letters, By the
Author of Henry and Frances. 4 vols.,
1769. [Blackwell : T. D. Webster.]

Griffith, Richard. Something New. 2
vols., London, 1772. [Ingpen :
Sotheby's]

—— The Triumvirate : Or The Authentic Memoirs of A[ndrew], B[eville] and
C[arewe], 2 vols., London, W. Johnston,
1764. [Block : Ingpen : Arthur Rogers.]

Griffith, Sophia. She would be A
Heroine. 3 vols., London, Baldwin,
Cradock, & Joy ; and Doig & Stirling,
Edinburgh, 1816. [B.M. : *New Monthly
Mag. :* Wm. Smith.]

Griffiths, Griffiths Ap. The Sons of St.
David. A Cambro-British historical
Tale, Of the Fourteenth Century. With
explanatory Notes and References. 3
vols., London, Printed at the Minerva
Press for A. K. Newman, 1816. [B.M. :
New Monthly Mag.]

Grimm, Jakob Ludwig Karl and Wilhelm. German Popular Stories, Translated from the Kinder und Hans Mär-
chen [by Edgar Taylor]. Collected by
M. M. Grimm. From Oral Tradition.
With 22 etchings by George Cruikshank. 2 vols., London, [Vol I] C.
Baldwyn, 1823. [Vol II] James Robins,
1826. [Block : Gumuchian : Maggs.]

Grimstone, Mary Leman. The Beauty
of the British Alps ; or, Love at First
Sight. With illustrations. Plymouth,
Bennett, 1825. [Stonehill.]

—— Character ; Or, Jew and Gentile :
A Tale. 2 vols., London, Charles Fox,
1833. [B.M.]

—— Cleone, A Tale of Married Life.
2 vols., London, Effingham Wilson,
1834. [B.M. : Elkin Mathews.]

—— Louisa Egerton ; or, Castle Herbert. A Tale from Real Life. With
illustrations. London, Virtue, 1830.
[B.M. : Stonehill.]

—— Quintus Servinton. A tale, founded
upon incidents of real occurrence. 3
vols., Hobart Town, 1830. [B.M.]

—— Woman's Love. A Novel. 3 vols.,
London, Saunders and Otley, 1832.
[B.M.]

Grosse, Marquis von. The Dagger.
Translated from the German of Grosse.
London, 1795. [Baker's Bookshop.]

—— The Genius, or the Mysterious
Adventures of Don Carlos de Grandez,
by the Marquis Von Grosse, translated
from the German by Joseph Trapp.
2 vols., 1797. [*New Ann. Reg.*]

—— Horrid Mysteries. A Story. From
the German of the Marquis of Grosse,
By P. Will. 2 vols., London, William
Lane, 1796. [*Holden's Reprints : New
Ann. Reg. :* Blakey.]

Grossett, Emilia. The Monastery of St.
Mary ; or the White Maid of Avenal :
a Scottish Tale. With a frontispiece.
London, J. Bailey, [c. 1820]. [Marks.]

Grossett, Emilia. The Spirit of the
Grotto ; or, The Castle of St. George.
A Romance. With a frontispiece. Lon-
don, Mason, [c. 1800]. [Stonehill.]

Grossi, Tommaso. Marco Visconti : a
Novel. Translated from the Italian by
A. D. [Alice Frances Dugdale.] London,
Charing Cross Publishing Co., N.D.
[G. Worthington.]

—— Marco Visconti : A Romance Of
the Fourteenth Century. From the
Italian of Tommaso Grossi by Miss
Caroline Ward. 2 vols., London, Smith,
Elder, 1836. [B.M. : Ingpen.]

Guards (The). A Novel. 3 vols., London, T. Clerc Smith, 1827. [B.M. : Ingpen : Tregaskis.]

Guellette, Thomas Simon. Chinese Tales; Or The Marvellous Adventures Of the Fum-Hoam. Translated from the French of Thomas Simon Gueulette. Oriental Tales. Translated from the French of The Comte de Caylus. London, Walker and Edwards, 1817. [Court Bk. Shop : *Monthly Mag.*]

—— Tartarian Tales ; Or A Thousand and One Quarters of Hours. Written in French by the celebrated Mr. Guellettee, Author of the Chinese, Mogul, and other Tales. The Whole now for the first Time translated into English, By Thomas Flloyd. With a frontispiece. London, J. and R. Tonson, 1759. [Birrell and Garnet : Grafton : Ingpen.]

Guénard, Madame. The Three Monks ! ! ! From the French. 2 vols., London, [1803.] [B.M.]

Guest, Lady Charlotte. Mabinogion, from the Llyfr Coch o Hergest and other Ancient Welsh MSS., With an English Translation and Notes. By Lady Charlotte Guest. With facsimiles. 3 vols., 1828-1845. [James Miles.]

Guichard, Eleonore. The Bracelet : or, the Fortunate Discovery, Being the history of Miss Polly * * * * *. Translated with some alterations from a French work, entitled, " Mèmoires de Cècile." 2 vols., London, [1759]. [B.M.]

Guilty Tongue (The). By the author of " The Last Day of the Week." London, Seeley, 1827. [B.M. : *Eng. Cat.*]

Guion, Miss. The Life, and Singular Memoirs, of Matilda, Countess de Lausanne ; or, The Unfortunate Victim of Paternal Ambition : A Gothic Story. To which is added the Castle of Formosa ; or the Treacherous Moor ; and The Rivals, or Love and Superstition, a Terrific Tale Founded on Fact. With a frontispiece. London, Fisher, 1802. [Stonehill.]

Guizot, Élizabeth Charlotte Pauline de. Madame de Guizot's Tales for Youth. Translated from the French. London, Hamilton, Adams, 1838. [B.M.]

—— The Young Student ; or, Ralph and Victor. From the French, by S. Jackson, London, Bogue, 1844. [B.M.]

Gulliver's Last Voyage, describing Bally-mugland, or the floating island. London, William Cole. 1825. [*Edin. Mag.* : Norman.]

Gulzara, Princess of Persia ; Or, The Virgin Queen. Collected from the original Persian. London, John Souter, 1816. [B.M. : Ingpen : Pickering.]

Gunnersbury, Amelia. Memoirs of a Demi-rep of Fashion ; or the Private History of Miss Amelia Gunnersbury, containing curious Anecdotes of Persons of the First Rank, which illustrate

many celebrated and eminent characters. With a frontispiece. 2 vols., Dublin, 1776. [B.M. : Pickering.]

Gunning, Elizabeth. Dangers through Life, Or, The Victim of Seduction. 3 vols., London, Printed at the Minerva Press, for A. K. Newman, 1812. [Blackwell : Publisher's advert.]

—— The Exile of Erin, a novel. 3 vols., 1808. [B.M.]

—— The Farmer's Boy ; A Novel. With a Portrait. 4 vols., London, Printed by J. Cundee for B. Crosby ; T. Hurst and M. Jones, 1802. [Birrell & Garnett : Francis Edwards : Fletcher.]

—— Lord Fitzhenry. A Novel. 3 vols., 1794. [*New Ann. Reg.*]

—— The Orphans of Snowdon. 3 vols., 1797. [*New Ann. Reg.*]

—— The Packet, A Novel. 4 vols., 1794. [Blackwell : B.M. : McLeish.]

Gunning, Susannah. Anecdotes of the Delborough Family. A Novel. 5 vols., London, Printed at the Minerva Press for William Lane, 1792. [*Eng. Lit. in Germany* : Ingpen : McLeish.]

—— Barford Abbey, A Novel : In a Series of Letters. 2 vols., London, T. Cadell and J. Payne, 1768. [B.M. : Pickering : Arthur Rogers.]

—— The Count de Poland. 4 vols., Published for the Author, 1780. [*Eng. Lit. in Germany* : T. D. Webster.]

—— Delves. 2 vols., 1796. [*New Ann. Reg.*]

—— Family Pictures, A Novel, Containing curious and interesting Memoirs of several Persons of Fashion in W—re, By a Lady. 2 vols., Dublin, 1764. [Blackwell.]

—— The Foresters. A Novel Adapted from the French. By Miss Gunning. 4 vols., London, Sampson Low, 1796. [B.M. : *New Ann. Reg.* : Arthur Rogers.]

—— The Gipsey Countess : A Novel. 4 vols., 1799. [*New Ann. Reg.*]

—— Love at First Sight. A Novel. From the French. With alterations and additions. 5 vols., London, H. Lowndes, 1797. [B.M. : *New Ann. Reg.*]

—— Memoirs of Madame Barneveldt, from the French, by Miss Gunning. 2 vols., 1795. [*New Ann. Reg.*]

—— Memoirs of Mary. A Novel. 5 vols., London, J. Bell, 1793. [B.M. : Ingpen : *New Ann. Reg.*]

Gustavus : Or, The Macaw ; A Story to teach Children the Value of Things, Translated from the German. With a frontispiece. London, Darton, Harvey and Darton, 1814. [B.M. : Sotheran.]

Gutherie, William. The Friends. A Sentimental History ; describing Love as a Virtue, As well as a Passion. 2 vols., London, T. Waller, 1754. [B.M. : Maggs : Stonehill.]

Guthrie, William. The Mother, or The Happy Distress. A Novel. By the Author of the Friends. 2 vols., London, Printed for the Author by J. Wilkie, 1759. [Baker's Bookshop.]

Guttierez, Valentin Llanos. Don Esteban ; Or, Memoirs of a Spaniard. Written by Himself. 3 vols., London, Henry Colburn, 1825. [B.M. : Pickering : Publisher's advert.]

—— Memoirs of Don Juan van Halen ; comprising the Narrative of his Imprisonment in the Dungeons of the Inquisition at Madrid, and of his Escape, his Journey to Russia, his Campaign with the Army of the Caucasus. 2 vols., 1830. [A. V. Turner.]

—— Sandoval ; Or, The Freemason. A Spanish Tale. By The Author of " Don Esteban." 3 vols., London, Henry Colburn, 1826. [B.M. : Publisher's advert : *Quarterly Review*.]

Guy, Henry. Angelina ; or, Mystic Captives. With a Frontispiece. London, 1808. [Murray Hill.]

Gwynn, Albinia. History of the Honourable Edward Mortimer, By a Lady. 2 vols., London, C. Dilly, 1785. [Stonehill : T. Thorp.]

—— The Rencontre, Or, Transition of a Moment. A Novel. In a Series of Letters. By a Lady. [London, W. Lane, 1784.] [Huth : Blakey.]

Haas, James D. Anthony Traugott, the Potter Musician. An instructive tale. From the German. By James D. Haas. 1849. [B.M.]

Hack, Maria. English Stories, Illustrating Some of the most interesting Events And Characters Between the Accession of Alfred And The Death of John. With frontispiece. 2 vols., London, Darton, Harvey, and Darton, 1820. [Block : B.M. : Sanders.]

—— English Stories. Second Series ; including the period between the Accession of Henry the Third, and the Death of Henry the Sixth. London, Harvey and Darton, 1820. [B.M. : *Camb. Hist. Eng. Lit.* : Ernest Cooper.]

—— English Stories. Third Series, Illustrating the Progress of the Reformation under the Tudor Princes. With a frontispiece. London, Harvey and Darton, 1825. [B.M. : Ingpen.]

—— Grecian Stories ; taken from the Works of Eminent Historians : with explanatory conversations. London, 1819. [B.M. : *Camb. Hist. Lit.*]

—— Harry Beaufoy ; Or, the Pupil of nature. With a frontispiece by H. Melville after E. B. Hack. London, Harvey and Darton, 1821. [B.M. : Gumuchian : Sotheran.]

—— Winter Evenings ; or, tales of travellers. 4 vols., London, Harvey, 1818. [B.M.]

Hack, Maria. (?) The Winter-Scene ; to amuse and instruct the rising generation. By M. H. London, 1818. [B.M.]

Hackney-Coachman (The). [1796.] Cheap Repository. [B.M.]

Hadassah, or the adopted Child. By the author of " Jessie Barton." London, [1847]. [B.M.]

Hadleigh Grove, or The History of Sir Charles Dawers and the fair Jessica. A Novel. 2 vols., 1773. [*Eng. Lit. in Germany*.]

Hadley, George. Argal ; Or the Silver Devil, Being The Adventures of An Evil Spirit, Comprising a series of interesting Anecdotes in public and private Life, with which the Demon became acquainted in various Parts of the World, during his Confinement in the Metalline Substance to which he was condemned. Related by himself. 2 vols., [Volume I] London, T. Vernon ; and Rawson, Hull [1793]. [Volume II] London, Vernor and Hood ; and Rawson, Hull. [1793]. [B.M. : *New Ann. Reg.*]

Hahn-Hahn, Ida, Countess. The Countess Faustina. By Ida, Countess Hahn-Hahn. Translated from the German by H.N.S. London, Ollivier, 1844. [B.M. : *Critic* : McLeish.]

—— Sigismund Forster ; a Tale. London, Hayward and Adam, 1846. [Publisher's advert.]

—— Ulrich ; a Tale. 2 vols., London, Hayward and Adam, 1846. [Publisher's advert.]

Hainsforth, J.H. A Legend of the Tower of London. With a Frontispiece and woodcuts. London, Lloyd, [1840]. [Hollings.]

Hakewill, James. Coelebs. A Novel. 1812. [Allibone.]

Hales, J. M. H. The Astrologer ; or the Eve of San Sebastian : A Romance. 3 vols., London, 1820. [*New Monthly Mag.*]

—— De Willenberg ; Or, The Talisman. A Tale of Mystery. 4 vols., London, A. K. Newman, 1821. [B.M.]

Hall, Anna Maria. The Buccaneer ; A Tale. 3 vols., London, Richard Bentley, 1832. [B.M. : Guntrip & Richardson : Ingpen.]

—— The Forlorn Hope. A Story of Old Chelsea. By Mrs. S. C. Hall. With woodcuts. [On cover :] Printed and Sold in Aid of the Fund for Building the Hospital for Consumption and Diseases of the Chest in Old Brompton, [1845]. [Block.]

—— The Juvenile Budget ; or, Stories for Little Readers. With illustrations by H. K. Browne. London Chapman and Hall, 1837. [*Publisher's advert.* : Sexton.]

—— Lights and Shadows Of Irish Life. By Mrs. S. C. Hall. 3 vols., London, Henry Colburn, 1838. [B.M. : Lib. of Congress : McLeish.]

Hall, Anna Maria. Little Chatterbox : A Tale. By Mrs. S. C. Hall. With illustrations by John Absolon. London, Wm. S. Orr, 1844. [B.M.]

—— Marian ; Or, A Young Maid's Fortunes. By Mrs. S. C. Hall. 3 vols., London, Henry Colburn, 1840. [Block : B.M. : T. Thorp.]

—— Midsummer Eve : A Fairy Tale of Love. With woodcuts after Maclise, Landseer, etc., London, 1848. [B.M. : Parker & Son : Sotheran.]

—— Number One : A Tale. By Mrs. S. C. Hall. With illustrations by John Absolon. London, Wm. S. Orr, 1844. [B.M.]

—— Obstinacy. A Tale. With a frontispiece. London, Longman, Rees, Orme, Brown, & Green, 1826. [B.M. : Publisher's advert. : *Quarterly Review.*]

—— The Outlaw. By the Author of " The Buccaneer," &c. 3 vols., London, Richard Bentley, 1835. [B.M.]

—— Sketches of Irish Character. 2 vols., London, 1829. [Allibone : B.M.]

—— Sketches of Irish Character : Series Second. London, Westley and Davis, 1831. [Allibone : B.M. : *Guide to Best Fiction.*]

—— Stories of the Irish Peasantry. 1840. [*I. in F.*]

Hall, Anna Maria. The Swan's Egg. Edinburgh, 1850. [B.M.]

—— Tales of Woman's Trials. By Mrs. S. C. Hall. London, Houlston, 1835. [B.M. : Lib. of Congress.]

—— Uncle Horace, A Novel, By the Author of " Sketches of Irish Character," " The Buccaneer," &c. &c. 3 vols., London, Henry Colburn, 1837. [B.M. : Brough : Publisher's advert.]

—— The Whiteboy ; A Story of Ireland in 1822. 2 vols., London, Chapman and Hall, 1845. [B.M. : *Guide to Best Fiction :* Publisher's advert.]

Hall, Anna Maria, and **Foster,** Mrs. Jonathan. Stories and Studies from the Chronicles and History of England. 2 vols., London, Darton, 1847. [B.M. : *Eng. Cat.*]

Hall, Captain Basil. Patchwork. 3 vols., London, Edward Moxon, 1841. [B.M. : Francis Edwards : Foyle.]

Hall, Clara. The Shepherd Brothers, an Interesting Historical Tale. With plates. London, Edward Lacey, N.D. [Block.]

—— The Sisters. A Pleasing Domestic Story founded on fact and other tales. With a frontispiece by Fenner after D. Lynch, 3 plates and 5 woodcuts. London, Edward Lacey, [1830]. [Gumuchian.]

Hall, Henry Haverard. The Benevolent Eccentric ; Or, Conscript of Switzerland, A Tale. Founded on Facts. With the Pleasures of the Soul, A Poem. With a frontispiece. London, Printed and Published, for the Author, [1815]. [B.M.]

Hall, Mrs. S. C. (*see* HALL, Anna Maria).

Hall, Thomas. " Effects " and Adventures of Raby Rattler, Gent. With plates by Samuel P. Fletcher. 1845. [B.M. : H. M. Fletcher : Marks.]

—— The Lord of the Manor ; or, Lights and Shades of Country Life. 2 vols., London, Shoberl, 1849. [B.M.]

—— Roland Bradshaw, His Struggles and Adventures on the Way to Fame, (dedicated to the Youth of England) By the Author of " Raby Rattler." With 28 Plates by S. P. Fletcher. London, Sherwood, Gilbert and Piper, 1848. [B.M. : T. D. Webster.]

Hall, W. Female Confessions, or Scenes in Life. 2 vols., [Cawthorn's Catalogue, 1810.]

Hall and the Manor House (The). A novel. 3 vols., London, T. C. Newby, 1849. [B.M. : *Eng. Cat.*]

Haller, Albrecht von. Usong. An Eastern Narrative. Written in German by Baron Haller. 2 vols., London, Printed for the Translator, by F. Newbury and J. Walter, 1772. [B.M. : Tregaskis : T. D. Webster.]

Halloran, Lieut. L. Boutcher. Rescued Fragments of Cabin Memorandums. Plymouth, W. Curtis, 1826 [B.M.]

Hamel, The Obeah Man. 2 vols., London, Hunt and Clarke, 1827. [B.M. : Ingpen : Publisher's advert.]

Hamerton, Mrs. Mrs. Leslie and Her Grandchildren : A Tale. London, Charles Tilt, 1827. [B.M.]

Hamilton, Alexander. The Doomed. 3 vols., London, Smith, Elder, 1832. [B.M.]

—— Edith of Glammis. By Cuthbert Clutterbuck, Of Kennaquhair, F.S.A., &c. &c. 3 vols., London, Smith, Elder, 1836. [B.M.]

Hamilton, Ann. Adventures of a Seven-Shilling Piece. 2 vols., London, 1811. [B.M. : Chas. Hutt : *I. in F.*]

—— The Irishwoman in London. A Modern Novel. 3 vols., London, Hughes, 1810. [B.M. : *I. in F.*]

—— The Maiden Wife ; or, the Heiress of De Courcy. 4 vols., London, 1812. [*New Monthly Mag.*]

—— A Winter at St. James's, or Modern Manners : a Novel. 4 vols., 1811. [Marks.]

Hamilton, Count Anthony. History of May Flower. A Circassian tale. Salisbury, 1796. [B.M. : (2nd edn.)]

—— Select Tales of Count Hamilton, Author of the Life and Manners of the Count de Grammont, Translated from the French. 2 vols., London, J. Burd, 1760. [Baker's Bookshop : B.M. : Dobell.]

Hamilton, C. G. Amy Harrington ; or a Sister's love. By C. G. H. [London], Nisbet, 1848. [B.M.]

Hamilton, C. G. Constance Lyndsay; or the Progress of Error. By C. G. H. Edinburgh, Hamilton, 1849. [B.M.]

—— The Curate of Linwood: or the real strength of the Christian Ministry; by C. G. H. London, Hamilton, 1845. [B.M.]

—— Margaret Waldegrave; or, the power of truth. Edinburgh, Hamilton, 1846. [B.M.]

—— Norman Leslie; a tale of Scottish History in the sixteenth century. By C. G. H. London, Nisbet, 1850. [B.M.]

Hamilton, Elizabeth. The Cottagers of Glenburnie; A Tale for the Farmer's Ingle-Nook. Edinburgh, Printed by James Ballantyne; for Manners and S. Cheyne, 1808. [Pickering: T. D. Webster.]

—— Memoirs of Modern Philosophers. 3 vols., Bath, R. Cruttwell, 1800. [Ingpen: Stonehill: T. Thorp.]

—— Translation of the Letters of a Hindoo Rajah. Written previous to, and during the Period of his Residence in England, to which is prefixed a Preliminary Dissertation on the History, Religion and Manners of the Hindoos. 2 vols., London, G. G. and J. Robinson, 1796. [Ingpen: *New Ann. Reg.*]

Hamilton, Emma. The Betrothed Cousins. A Tale. London, Printed for the Author, 1810. [B.M.]

—— " I can't afford it " and other Tales. 2 vols., London, 1813. [B.M.]

Hamilton, James. The Happy Home. By the author of " Life in earnest." London, 1848. [B.M.]

Hamilton, Terrick. Antar. A Bedoueen Romance. Translated from the Arabic. By Terrick Hamilton. 4 vols., London, John Murray, 1819-1820. [Ingpen: McLeish: Pickering.]

Hamilton, Captain Thomas. The Youth and Manhood Of Cyril Thornton. 3 vols., Edinburgh, William Blackwood; and T. Cadell, London, 1827. [B.M.: McLeish: Tregaskis.]

Hamlain, Or The Hermit of the Beach. A Moral Reverie calculated for the instruction and amusement of youth. London, Newbery, 1799. [Arthur Rogers.]

Hammer, Joseph Von. New Arabian Nights' Entertainments, Selected from the Original Oriental MS. By Jos. Von Hammer: and now first translated into English By The Rev. George Lamb. 3 vols., London, Henry Colburn, 1826. [B.M.: Marks: Arthur Rogers.]

Hampstead Murder (The) ; or, The Prediction. With woodcuts. London, Lloyd, 1845. [Stonehill.]

Hampton Court ; Or, The Prophecy Fulfilled. 3 vols., London, Richard Bentley, 1844. [B.M.: *Critic.*]

Hannay, David. Ned Allen; or the Past Age. 2 vols., London, Longman, 1849. [B.M.: *Eng. Cat.*]

Hannay, James. A Claret Cup: For Naval Messes, and the Public Generally. Further reminiscences and sketches of Percival Plug, R.N. London, J. & D. A. Darling, 1848. [B.M.: Publisher's advert.]

—— Hearts are Trumps. An Amphibious Story. London, 1849. [B.M.]

—— King Dobbs, Sketches in Ultra-Marine. With illustrations. London, J. & D. A. Darling, 1849. [B.M.: Publisher's advert.]

—— Singleton Fontenoy, R.N. 3 vols., London, Henry Colburn, 1850. [B.M.]

Hans the Miser, a tale of Central Germany To which is added Perrin and Lucette. The Curious Girl reformed. Divine Providence. The Farm and the Presbytery. Derby, 1846. [B.M.]

Hansard, M. A. E. The Friends; Or The Influence of Religion, A Tale For Young persons entering into life. London, Hatchard, 1834. [B.M.]

Hanway, Mary Ann. Andrew Stuart, or The northern wanderer. A novel, 4 vols., London, William Lane, 1800. [Blakey.]

—— Christabelle, The Maid of Rouen. A Novel Founded on Facts. 4 vols., London, Longman, Hurst, Rees, Orme, and Brown, 1814. [B.M.: *European Mag.*]

—— Ellinor, or the World as it is. A Novel. 4 vols., W. Lane, 1798. [*New Ann. Reg.*: Blakey.]

—— Falconbridge Abbey. A Devonshire Story. 5 vols., London, Minerva Press, 1809. [B.M.: Blakey.]

Happiness and Misery : being the history of a few days in the lives of two cottagers. 1836. [B.M. (new edn).]

——; a Tale for the Grave and the Gay. 2 vols., London, Francis Westley, 1821. [Baker's Bookshop: B.M.: Pickering.]

Happy Bride (The), or, the virtuous country maid rewarded, etc. London, [1825 ?]. [B.M.]

Happy Change (The). With a woodcut. London, The Religious Tract Society, N.D. No. 1607. [Block.]

Happy Cottagers (The), or, the Breakfast, Dinner and Supper. To which is added, The Shepherd's Boy, reading to the poor Widow. With 9 woodcuts. Manchester. A. Swindells, [c. 1796-1799]. [*Lancs.*]

Happy Discovery, or, The History of Miss Emilia Creswell. 2 vols., London, J. Wilkie, 1769. [Ingpen.]

Happy Family (The), or, Memoirs of Mr. and Mrs. Norton, intended to shew the delightful effects of filial obedience. London, [1786]. [B.M.: Arthur Rogers.]

Happy Restorations. Three narratives; entitled, The Great Preparation, The Young Footman, The Second Hand Dress. London, [1849]. [B.M.]

Happy Sequel (The), Or The History of Isabella Mordaunt. A Tale for Young People. With a frontispiece. London, J. Harris, 1814. [Gumuchian : Arthur Rogers.]

Happy Spinster (The) of Lancashire, Or the True Story Of Poor Blind Ellen : With an Account of the strange old Woman who lived with her, whom she maintained for Two Guineas a Year, allowed by the Parish. With a woodcut. Nottingham, Sutton, [1810 ?]. [B.M. : Court Bk. Shop.]

Happy Waterman (The). With a frontispiece. London, J. Marshall. [1800 ?]. Cheap Repository, [Block : B.M.]

Harden Hall ; Or, The Three Proposals : A Novel. Edited by the Hon. F—— B——. 3 vols., London, Smith, Edler, 1847. [B.M. : T. D. Webster.]

Hardenbrass and Haver III ; Or, The Secret of the Castle, A Novel. Containing A Madman and no madman—Who Walks—Deeds of Darkness. &c. Remarkable characters, incidents, adventures, &c. &c. Instructive and entertaining. 4 vols., London, Sherwood, Neely, 1817. [Backus : B.M. : *New Monthly Mag.*]

Harding, Anne Raikes. Correction. A Novel. 3 vols., London, Longman, Hurst, Rees, Orme, and Brown, 1818. [B.M. : *New Monthly Mag.*]

—— Decision. A Tale. By The Author of Correction. &c. 3 vols., London, Longman, Hurst, Rees, Orme, and Brown, 1819. [B.M. : Pickering : Publisher's advert.]

—— Dissipation. A Tale of Simple Life. By the Author of "Realities," "Correction," &c. 4 vols., London, A. K. Newman, 1827. [B.M. : Publisher's advert.]

—— Experience. A Tale for all Ages. By the Author of Corrections, Realities, Dissipation &c. 4 vols., London, A. K. Newman, 1828. [B.M. : *Quarterly Review.*]

—— Realities, *Not* a Novel. A Tale from Real Life. By the Author of Correction, Decision, Refugees, &c. 4 vols., London, A. K. Newman, 1825. [B.M. : *Edin. Mag.* : Pickering.]

—— The Refugees, An Irish Tale. By The Author of Correction, Decision, &c. &c. 3 vols., London, Longman, Hurst, Rees, Orme, & Brown, 1822. [B.M. : *I. in F.* : T. Thorp.]

Hardwicke, Countess of. The Court of Oberon, or, Temple of the Fairies : A Collection of Tales Of Past Times. Originally Related by Mother Goose, Mother Bunch, and Others, Adapted to the Language and Manners of the present period. London, J. Harris, 1823. [Block.]

Hardy, Miss. Owen Glendower. An Historical Romance. 2 vols., London, 1849. [Allibone.]

Hardy, Elizabeth. Michael Cassidy ; or, the Cottage Gardener. A tale for small beginners. London, Thames Ditton, 1845.

Hardy, Philip Dixon. Legends, Tales, and Stories of Ireland. With engravings. Dublin, John Cumming, 1837. [B.M. : *I. in F.*]

Hare (The) ; or, Hunting incompatible with Humanity. Written as a Stimulus to Youth towards a proper Treatment of Animals. London, Vernor and Hood, 1799. [*Guardian of Education.*]

Häring, Georg Wilhelm Heinrich. The Burgomaster of Berlin. By Willibald Alexis. 1843. [*Guide to Best Fiction.*]

Harkin, Hugh. The Quarterclift : or, the Adventures of Hudy McGuiggen. With illustrations. Belfast [1841]. [*I. in F.*]

Harkness, Hugh. Love, War, and adventure. Tales. 3 vols., London, E. Churton, 1846. [B.M. : Publisher's advert.]

Harley, Mrs. The Castle of Mowbray, an English Romance. By the Author of *St. Bernard's Priory.* London, 1788. [B.M. : *Eng. Lit. in Germany.*]

—— The Countess of Hennebon. An historical novel. By the author of *The Priory of St. Bernard,* 3 vols., [W. Lane, 1789.] [Blakcy.]

—— Saint Bernard's Priory. An old English tale ; being the first literary production of a young lady. London, for the authoress, 1786. [B.M. : *Eng. Lit. in Germany* : Blakey.]

Harley, Edward. The Veteran ; Or, Matrimonial Felicities. 3 vols., London, Longman, Hurst, Rees, Orme, and Brown, 1819. [B.M. : *European Mag.* : Publisher's advert.]

Harley Beckford. 3 vols., London, Baily, 1849. [B.M.]

Harold the Exile. 3 vols., London, * * * * * * *, 1819. [B.M. : T. D. Webster.]

Harpe, M. de la. Memoirs of Prince Menzikoff, favourite of Peter the Great. [Probably translated by Matthew Iley.] London, Matthew Iley, 1819. [Elkin Mathews.]

Harriet and Her Cousin ; or, prejudice overcome. Edinburgh, 1823. [B.M. (2nd edn.).]

Harriett, Or the Innocent Adultress. 2 vols., London, 1771. [Cat. Lib. Prohib.]

Harris, Alexander. The Emigrant Family : or, the Story of an Australian Settler. By the Author of " Settlers and Convicts." 3 vols., London, Smith, Elder, 1849. [B.M. : Elkin Mathews.]

Harris, Catherine. Edwardina, a Novel. Dedicated to Mrs. Souter Johnson. London, Printed for the Author at the Minerva Press, 1800. [G. Worthington : Blakey.]

Harrison, W. H. Christmas Tales, Historical and Domestic. With engravings. London, A. K. Newman, [1838 ?]. [Court Bk. Shop.]
—— Tales Of A Physician. London, Robert Jennings, 1829. [B.M.]
—— Tales Of A Physician. Second Series. London, Jennings and Chaplin, 1831. [B.M.]
—— Waldemar, a tale of the Thirty Years' War. 1833. [B.M. : Arthur Rogers.]

Harry and Archie : or first and last Communion. In 2 parts. London, Masters, [1848]. [B.M.]

Harry and William Or The Two Cousins. A Tale. With 4 engravings. London, Harvey and Darton, 1821. [Gumuchian.]

Hartlebourn Castle. 2 vols., 1793. [*New Ann. Reg.*]

Hartley, Mary Ann. Claudine Mignot ; Surnamed La L'Hauda, or, the Praised one. Dedicated, by Permission, To Lady Campbell. 3 vols., London, T. C. Newby, 1844. [B.M. : *Tait's Edin. Mag.*]
—— Indian Life : A Tale of the Carnatic. 3 vols., London, Saunders and Otley, 1840. [B.M.]

Hartley House. Calcutta : a Novel of the days of Warren Hastings. 1789. [*Guide to Best Fiction.*]

Hartstonge, Mathew Weld. The Eve of All-Hallows ; or, Adelaide of Tyrconnell ; A Romance. 3 vols., London, G. B. Whittaker, 1825. [*I. in F.* : H. H. Ward.]

Harvest Home. With cuts. London, Lloyd. [c. 1840] [Hollings.]

Harvey, Jane. The Ambassador's Secretary. A Tale. 4 vols., London, A. K. Newman, 1828. [B.M.]
—— Auberry Stanhope ; or, Memoirs of an author, 3 vols., London, Printed at the Minerva Press, for A. K. Newman, 1813. [Publisher's advert : Blakey.]
—— Brougham Castle. A Novel. 2 vols., London, Printed at the Minerva Press for A. K. Newman, 1816. [B.M. : *New Monthly Mag.*]
—— The Castle of Tynemouth. A tale. 2 vols., Newcastle-upon-Tyne, 1830. [B.M. (2nd edn.).]
—— Ceraline. 4 vols., London, 1821. [B.M.]
—— Ethelia, a novel. 3 vols., London, Printed at the Minerva Press, 1810. [*Monthly Mag.* : Publisher's advert.]
—— Minerva Castle. A tale. 3 vols., [Minerva Press, 1802]. [Blakey.]
—— Mountalyth, A Tale. 3 vols., London, Baldwin, Cradock and Joy, 1823. [B.M.]
—— Records Of a Noble Family. 4 vols., London, Sold by Longman, Hurst, Rees, Orme and Brown ; and Printed and sold by H. Mozley, Gainsborough,

September, 1814. [B.M. : *European Mag. : Quarterly Review.*]

Harvey, Jane. Singularity. A Novel. 3 vols., London, A. K. Newman, 1822. [B.M. : Stonehill.]
—— Warkfield Castle. A tale. 3 vols., [Minerva Press, 1802.] [Blakey.]

Hasworth, H. H. The Lady of the Cave ; or, Mysteries of the fourteenth century. An historical romance. 3 vols., London, Minerva Press, 1802. [Allibone : Blakey.]

Hatchway, Lieut. The Greenwich Pensioners. 3 vols., London, Henry Colburn, 1838. [B.M. : McLeish : Arthur Rogers.]

Hatfield, Miss. She Lives in Hopes ; Or, Caroline. A Narration founded upon facts. (By Permission) Dedicated to Her Royal Highness The Princess of Orange and Nassau. 2 vols., London, Published for the Authoress, 1801. [B.M.]

Hatred, or the Vindictive Father, A Tale of Sorrow. 3 vols., London, Minerva Press, 1802. [Blackwell.]

Hatton, Ann. Cambrian Pictures ; Or, Every One Has Errors. By Ann of Swansea. 3 vols., London, Printed at the Minerva Press, for A. K. Newman, [1810.] [B.M. (Date erased) : Publisher's advert : Blakey.]
—— Cesario Rosalba ; Or, The Oath of Vengeance. A Romance. By Ann of Swansea. 5 vols., London, Printed at the Minerva Press for A. K. Newman, 1819. [B.M. : *Quarterly Review* : Blakey.]
—— Chronicles Of an Illustrious House ; Or the Peer, the Lawyer, and the Hunchback. A Novel. Embellished with Characters and Anecdotes of well-known persons. By Ann of Swansea, Author of Cambrian Pictures, Sicilian Mysteries, Conviction, Secret Avengers, &c. &c. 5 vols., London, Printed at the Minerva Press for A. K. Newman, 1816. [B.M. : *New Monthly Mag.*]
—— Conviction ; Or, She is Innocent ! A Novel. By Ann of Swansea, Author of Cambrian Pictures, Sicilian Mysteries, &c. &c. 5 vols., London, Printed at the Minerva Press for A. K. Newman, 1814. [B.M. : Publisher's advert. : *Quarterly Review.*]
—— Deeds of the Olden Time. A Romance. 5 vols., London, A. K. Newman, 1826. [B.M.]
—— Gerald Fitzgerald ; An Irish Tale. By Ann of Swansea. 5 vols., London, A. K. Newman, 1831. [B.M. : *I. in F.*]
—— Gonzalo de Baldivia ; Or, A Widow's Vow. A Romantic Legend. Inscribed, By Permission, to William Wilberforce, Esq. By the Author of Cambrian Pictures, Sicilian Mysteries, Conviction, Secret Avengers, Chronicles of an Illustrious House, &c. &c. 4 vols., London, Printed at the Minerva Press, for A. K. Newman, 1817. [B.M.]

Hatton, Ann. Guilty or not Guilty ; Or, A Lesson for Husbands. A Tale. 5 vols., London, A. K. Newman, 1822. [B.M.]
—— Lovers and Friends ; Or, Modern Attachments. A Novel. By Anne of Swansea. 5 vols., London, Printed at the Minerva Press for A. K. Newman, 1821. [Block : B.M.]
—— Secret Avengers ; Or, The Rock of Glotzden. A Romance. By Anne of Swansea. 4 vols., London, Printed at the Minerva Press for A. K. Newman, 1815. [B.M. : *European Mag.* : Publisher's advert.]
—— Secrets in every Mansion ; Or The Surgeon's Memorandum-Book. A Scottish Record. By Anne of Swansea. 5 vols., London, Printed at the Minerva Press for A. K. Newman, 1818. B.M. : [*New Monthly Mag.* : Blakey.]
—— Sicilian Mysteries, or, the Fortress Del Vechii, a Romance, by Ann of Swansea. 5 vols., London, Printed at the Minerva Press, for A. K. Newman, 1812. [B.M. : Publisher's advert. : *Quarterly Review.*]
—— Uncle Peregrine's Heiress. A Novel. By Ann of Swansea. 5 vols., London, A. K. Newman, 1828. [B.M.]
—— Woman's A Riddle. A Romantic Tale. By Ann of Swansea. 4 vols., London, A. K. Newman, 1824. [B.M.]
Hauff, Wilhelm. The Banished : a Swabian Historical Tale. Edited by James Morier. 3 vols., London, Henry Colburn, 1839. [Block : B.M. : Francis Edwards.]
—— The Christmas Roses, and other tales, chiefly translated from the German. London, Addey, 1845. [B.M.]
—— Lichtenstein, or the Swabian League. An Historical Romance. Translated from the German. By F. Woodley and W. Lauder, London, 1846. [Baker's Bookshop.]
Haughty Duchess (The), or Death and the Lady. To which is added, The Miller taken in, and A furnished table. Glasgow, [1815]. [B.M.]
Haunted Fire of Uller (The), an Iernian Legend. By J. L. O. S. Dublin, [1810 ?]. [B.M.]
Haunted Tower (The), or the Wonderful Events that occurred in the Life of Angela Modeni, an Orphan brought up by the Marchioness Di Montmorenci ; with an Interesting Account of - - - her Capture by a Troop of Banditti ; the Rivalry of the Captain and Lieutenant ; the Horrid Deeds afterwards perpetrated. With a frontispiece. London, William Cole, [c. 1825]. [Marks.]
Haunted Woman (The) ; or, Passion and Perseverance. A Tale of Startling Interest. With woodcuts. London, Lea, N.D. [Stonehill.]
Haviland, Mrs. M. de. Sentiment Not Principle : Or, An Old Man's Legacy.

2 vols., London, Whittaker, 1835. [B.M.]
Haweis, Thomas. Siberian Anecdotes, A Novel. Containing Real Histories and Living Characters, 3 vols., London, Lowndes, 1783. [B.M. : F. Dahl : Stonehill.]
Hawes, Barbara. Tales of the North American Indians and adventures of the early Settlers in America. London, Jarrold, 1844. [Allibone : B.M.]
Hawke, Cassandra, Lady. Julia de Gramont. By The Right Honorable Lady H****. 2 vols., London, Printed by T. Bensley, for B. White, 1788. [B.M. : Stonehill : Lyle H. Wright.]
Hawker, Admiral Edward. Arthur Montague, or An Olny Son at Sea. By A Flag Officer. 3 vols., London, Saunders and Otley, 1850. [B.M. : *Eng. Cat.* : Maggs.]
Hawkesworth, John. Almoran and Hamet. An Oriental Tale. 2 vols., London, Printed by C. Say. For H. Payne & W. Cropley, 1761. [Birrell & Garnett : B. M. : Court Bk. Shop.]
Hawkins, Laetitia Matilda. Annaline ; Or Motive-Hunting. 3 vols., London, James Carpenter, 1824. [B.M.]
—— The Countess and Gertrude ; Or, Modes of Discipline. 4 vols., London, F. C. and J. Rivington, 1811. [B.M. : Ingpen : McLeish.]
—— Heraline ; Or, Opposite Proceedings. 4 vols., London, F. C. and J. Rivington ; and T. Hookham, 1821. [B.M. : Pickering : T. D. Webster.]
—— Rosanna ; Or, a Father's Labour Lost. 3 vols., London, Rivington, 1814. [B.M. : Ingpen : McLeish.]
Hawkwood, A Romance of Italy. 3 vols., London, Saunders and Otley, 1840. [B.M.]
Haworth, Euphrasia Fanny. The Pine Tree Dell, and Other Tales. 2 vols., London, J. Andrews, 1827. [B.M.]
Hayley, William. Douglas D'Arcy ; Some passages in The Life of an Adventurer. London, F. J. Mason, 1834. [B.M. : G. Worthington.]
—— The Young Widow ; Or The History of Cornelia Sedley, In a Series of Letters. 4 vols., London, G. G. J. and J. Robinson, 1789. [W. Brown : Pickering : T. D. Webster.]
Haynes, Miss C. D. Augustus & Adelina ; Or, The Monk of St. Bernardine. A Romance. 4 vols., London, Printed at the Minerva Press for A. K. Newman, 1819. [B.M. : T. D. Webster.]
—— Eleanor ; Or, The Spectre of St. Michael's. A Romantic Tale. 5 vols., London, Printed at the Minerva Press for A. K. Newman, 1821. [B.M.]
—— The Foundling of Devonshire ; Or, "Who is She ? " A Novel. 5 vols., London, Printed at the Minerva Press for A. K. Newman, 1818. [B.M. : *Monthly Mag.*]

Haynes, Miss C. D. The Maid of Padua ; Or, Past Times. A Venetian Tale. By Mrs. Golland. 4 vols., London, A. K. Newman, 1835. [B.M.]

—— The Ruins of Ruthvale Abbey. A Novel. By Mrs. Golland, (Late Miss Haynes). 4 vols., London, A. K. Newman, 1827. [*Blackwood's Edin. Mag.* : B.M. : Publisher's advert.]

—— The Witch of Aysgarth. By Mrs. Golland. 3 vols., London, A. K. Newman, 1841. [B.M.]

Haynes, D. F. Pierre and Adeline, or, The Romance of the Castle. 2 vols., London, 1814. [Allibone : *Quarterly Review.*]

Hays, Mary. Family Annals, or the Sisters. London, 1817. [*New Monthly Mag.*]

—— Memoirs of Emma Courtney. 2 vols., London, 1796. [B.M. : *New Ann. Reg.*]

—— The Victim of Prejudice. 2 vols., London, Johnson, 1799. [*New Ann. Reg.* : Stonehill.]

Hays, Matilda M. Helen Stanley, A Tale. London, E. Churton, 1846. [B.M. : *Critic* : Publisher's advert.]

Haywood, Eliza. L'Entretien de Beaux Esprits. Being the sequel to La Belle Assemblée. [Translated by Eliza Haywood.] 2 vols., London, 1834. [B.M.]

—— The Fortunate Foundlings : Being the Genuine History of Colonel M[anne]rs, and his Sister Madam du P——y, the Issue of the Hon. Ch[arl]es M[anne]rs, Son of the late Duke of R[ut]l[an]d. London, 1744. [Francis Edwards.]

—— The History of Jemmy and Jenny Jessamy. By the Author of The History of Betsy Thoughtless. 3 vols., London, T. Gardner, 1753. [Block : B.M. : Arthur Rogers.]

—— The History of Miss Betsy Thoughtless. 4 vols., London, T. Gardner, 1751. [*Guide to Best Fiction* : Parker & Son : Sotheby's.]

—— The Husband. In answer to the Wife. London, T. Gardner, 1756. [B.M. : Murray Hill.]

—— The Invisible Spy. By Exploralibus. 4 vols., London, T. Gardner, 1755. [B.M. : W. Brown : Arthur Rogers.]

—— Life's Progress through the Passions ; Or, The Adventures of Natura. By the Author of The Fortunate Foundling, London, T. Gardner, 1748. [Ingpen : T. D. Webster.]

—— Modern Characters, Illustrated by Histories in Real Life, and Address'd to the Polite World. 2 vols., London, T. Gardner, 1753. [Dobell : Pickering.]

—— The Unfortunate Princess, Or the Ambitious Statesman, Containing the Life and Surprising Adventures of the Princess of Ijaves. With a frontispiece. London, 1741. [Bailey Bros. : B.M.]

Haywood, Eliza. The Virtuous Villager, or the Virgin's Victory ; being memoirs of a very great lady at the Court of France, written by herself. Translated from the original [or rather written] by the author of La Belle Assemblée, 2 vols., London, 1742. [B.M.]

—— The Wife. By Mira, one of the authors of the "Female Spectator." London, T. Gardner, 1756. [B.M. : Tregaskis.]

Hazel, Harry. The Corsair. The Foundling of the Sea. A Romance. With woodcuts. London, Lloyd, 1847. [Stonehill.]

Hazlitt, William. Liber Amoris. Or, The New Pygmalion. With a Vignette Title. London, Printed for John Hunt by C. H. Reynell, 1823. [Block : B.M. : Tregaskis.]

He Is Found At Last : or, Memoirs of the Beverley Family. 2 vols., London, F. & J. Noble, 1775. [B.M.]

Head, Miss. Rybrent de Cruce. 3 vols., London, Henry Colburn, 1829. [B.M. : Pickering.]

Healey, Miss. Henry Sinclair, or the Ghosts of Haverford Hall. With a vignette and a frontispiece. London, Dean & Munday, N.D. [Court Bk. Shop.]

Hearts of Steel. By the author of " Wilderhess." 3 vols., London, Wightman, 1825. [*Edin. Mag.* : *Eng. Cat.*]

Hebrew Tales, Selected and Translated from Ancient Hebrew Works. 1826. [*Quarterly Review.*]

Hebrew Talisman (The). London, [1840 ?]. [B.M.]

Hedge, Mary Ann. The Flatterer, or, False Friendship. A tale. London, Baldwin, Cradock and Joy, 1822. [B.M.]

—— Life ; or, Fashion and Feeling. A Novel. 3 vols., London, A. K. Newman, 1822. [B.M.]

—— Man ; or, Anecdotes National and Individual : an historic mélange for the amusement of youth. London, A. K. Newman, 1822. [B.M. : *Quarterly Review.*]

—— Radama ; or, The Enlightened African. 1824. [*Camb. Hist. Eng. Lit.*]

—— The Retreat ; Or, Sketches from Nature. A Descriptive Tale. By the Author of Affection's Gift, Treasures of Thought. Letters on History, &c. 2 vols., London, Baldwin, Cradock, and Joy ; and Swinborne and Walter, Colchester, 1820. [B.M. : *New Monthly Mag.*]

—— Samboe ; or the African Boy, by the author of " Twilight Hours improved." London, Harvey, 1823. [B.M. : *Eng. Cat.*]

Heerfort and Clara. 3 vols., 1789. [W. Brown.]

Hefford, John. Crestyphon, a Theban tale : and the Vandal Robbery, a Carthaginian tale. London, 1820. [B.M.]

Heighway, Osborn T. W. Frederic and Louisa, a novel, by the author of Adeline. 4 vols., London, William Lane, Minerva Press. 1792. [*New Ann. Reg.* : T. Thorp : Blakey.]

Heir of Montague (The). A novel. 3 vols., London, Minerva Press 1797-1798. [Baker's Bookshop : B.M. : Blakey.]

Heiress and Her Suitors (The). London, Saunders and Otley, 1838. [B.M.]

Heiress of the Castle of Morlina (The) ; or, the Domains of Isabella di Rotaldi Restored : and the Usurper Secluded. To which is added The Story of Shabraco and Sabrina ; or the Mystery Developed. With a frontispiece. London, Fisher, 1802. [Stonehill.]

Heiress (The). A Tale, Founded on Facts. By E. H. London, James Burns, 1839. [B.M.]

Helen Halsey. A Tale of the Borders. A Romance of Deep Interest. With woodcuts. London, Lloyd, [1847]. [B.M. : Stonehill.]

Helen Porter : or, A Wife's Tragedy and A Sister's Trials. A Romance. By the Author of " The Hangman's Daughter." With woodcuts. London, E. Lloyd, [c. 1840]. [Stonehill.]

Helen Sinclair, a Novel, by a Lady. 2 vols., 1799. [*New Ann. Reg.*]

Helena, A Novel. By a Lady of Distinction. London, W. Richardson, 1788. [B.M. : *Eng. Lit. in Germany.*]

Heliodorus. The Adventures of Theagenes and Chariclea. A Romance. Translated from the Greek of Heliodorus. 2 vols., London, Stafford, 1789. [McLeish : Stonehill.]

Helme, Elizabeth. Albert ; or, the Wilds of Strathnavern. 4 vols., 1799. [New Ann. Reg. : T. D. Webster.]

—— Attic Fragments. By the Author of the " Modern Times." London, Knight, 1825. [*Edin. Mag.* : *Eng. Cat.* : *Quarterly Review.*]

—— Clara and Emmeline ; Or, the Maternal Benediction. A Novel. By the Author of Louisa ; or, the Cottage on the Moor. 2 vols., London, G. Kearsley, 1788. [B.M.]

—— Duncan and Peggy : A Scottish Tale. 2 vols., London, J. Bell, 1794. [Hodgson : Pickering.]

—— The Farmer of Inglewood Forest ; or, An Affecting Portrait of Virtue and Vice. With a frontispiece. 4 vols., London, William Lane at the Minerva Press, 1796. [*New Ann. Reg.* : Publisher's advert. : Stonehill.]

Helme, Elizabeth. Instructive Rambles In London, and The Adjacent Villages. Designed to amuse the mind, and improve the understanding of youth. With a frontispiece. London, T. N. Longman, and O. Rees ; and E. Newbery, 1800. [Baker's Bookshop : Block.]

Helme, Elizabeth. James Manners, Little John, and their Dog bluff. London, 1799. [B.M.]

—— Louisa. Or, the Cottage on the Moor. 2 vols., London, G. Kearsley, 1787. [B.M. : *Eng. Lit. in Germany.*]

—— Modern Times ; Or The Age we live in. A Posthumous Novel. 3 vols., Brentford, 1814. [B.M. : *European Mag.* : *New Monthly Mag.*]

—— The Pilgrim of the Cross ; or, the Chronicles of Christabelle de Mowbray. An ancient legend. 4 vols., Brentford, P. Norbury, 1805. [B.M.]

—— St. Clair of the Isles ; Or, The Outlaws of Barra. A Scottish Tradition. 4 vols., London, Longman, 1803. [Baker's Bookshop : *Eng. Lit. in Germany* : Ingpen.]

—— St. Margaret's Cave : or, The Nun's Story. An ancient legend. 4 vols., London, 1801. [B.M. : *Eng. Lit. in Germany.*]

Helme, William. Henry Stukeley, or the Effects of Dissipation. 3 vols., 1794. [*New Ann. Reg.*]

Helvetius, Claude Adrien, (Attributed to) The Child of Nature, improved by Chance. A Philosophical Novel. 2 vols., London, 1774. [Blackwell : B.M. : *Eng. Lit. in Germany.*]

Hemet, John. Contradictions ; or, Who could have thought it ? A Novel, from the French, by John Hemet. 2 vols., London, 1799. [B.M. : *New Ann. Reg.*]

Hemphill, Barbara. Freida the Jongleur. 3 vols., London, 1857. [B.M.]

—— Lionel Deerhurst ; Or, Fashionable Life Under the Regency. Edited by the Countess of Blessington. 3 vols., London, Richard Bentley, 1846. [B.M.]

Hendriks, Rose Ellen. Alice Lemington. 3 vols., 1847. [James Glaisher.]

—— The Astrologer's Daughter. An Historical Novel. 3 vols., London, T. C. Newby, 1845. [B.M.]

—— Charlotte Corday ; An Historical Tale. London, R. Groombridge, 1846. [B.M.]

—— Ella, the Ballet Girl ; a tale. London, 1831. [B.M.]

—— The Idler Reformed. A Tale. 3 vols., London, R. Groombridge, 1846. [B.M.]

—— Jenny Lind. A Tale. 2 vols., London, E. Churton, 1848. [B.M.]

Hendriks, Rose Ellen. Political Fame. London, 1847. [B.M.]

—— The Young Authoress. 3 vols., London, John and Daniel Darling, 1847. [B.M.]

Hennebon, Or The Countess of Montfort ; And Bertha of Burgundy. 3 vols., London, Richard Bentley, 1835. [B.M.]

Henningsen, Charles Frederick. Sixty Years Hence. A Novel. By the Author of " The White Slave," " Revelations of Russia," " Eastern Europe and the

Emperor Nicholas." 3 vols., London, Thomas Cautley Newby, 1847. [McLeish.]

Henningsen, Charles Frederick. The White Slave ; Or, The Russian Peasant Girl. By the Author of " Revelations of Russia." 3 vols., London, Henry Colburn, 1845. [B.M. : T. Thorp : G. Worthington.]

Henrietta and Her Cousins. By S. F. R. London, 1822. [B.M.]

Henrietta of Gerstenfeld, A German Story. 2 vols., London, William Lane, 1787-1788. [H. M. Fletcher. : Blakey.]

Henry, John. The Foundling of Cordova, A Moorish Tale. 3 vols., London, Thomas Hurst ; Amyot, Paris, 1842. [B.M.]

Henry and Edward : or, familiar conversations on the elements of science. By the author of " The Decoy." 2 vols., London, 1828. [B.M.]

Henry and Isabella ; Or, The Reverses of Fortune, A Novel. 2 vols., London, Crosby, 1811. [Stonehill.]

Henry and James ; Or, A Rational Education Preferable to Riches. True Elevation of Mind Displayed In Condescension and Humanity. With woodcuts. London, James Wallis, [1840 ?]. [B.M.]

Henry De Beauvais. A Novel. 2 vols., [W. Lane, 1798]. [Blakey.]

Henry Domville ; Or, A Younger Son. By Himself. 2 vols., London, Chapman and Hall, 1847. [B.M. : James Glaisher.]

Henry Fitzosmond. A Moral Tale. London, James Asperne, 1818. [Ingpen.]

Henry Fitzroy, The Young Midshipman. 1823. [Holland.]

Henry Freemantle. 2 vols., [Cawthorn's Catalogue, 1810.]

Henry Somerville ; a Tale by the Author of Hallerbourn Castle. 2 vols., London, 1797. [B.M. : *New Ann. Reg.*]

Henry, a Tale. 2 vols., 1793. [*New Ann. Reg.*]

Henry Willoughby. 2 vols., 1798. [*New Ann. Reg.*]

Herbert, Caroline. Human Life, With Variations ; Or The Chapter of Accidents. London, Longman, Hurst, Rees, Orme, and Brown ; and Lake, Uxbridge, 1817. [Baker's Bookshop : B.M.]

Herbert, William. Ella Rosenberg. A Romance. 2 vols., London, Hughes, 1808. [B.M. : Stonehill.]

Herbert, William. The Spanish Outlaw. A tale. 4 vols., London, 1807. [B.M.]

Herbert. Hon. William. Hedin, or the Spectre of the Tomb, a tale. London, 1820. [*Monthly Mag.*]

Herbster, Madame de. The Cavern ; or, The Two Sisters. An Interesting Tale. From the French of Madame de Herbster. By E. A. Smythe. With a frontispiece. London, Whittingham and Arliss, 1816. [Block.]

Herbster, Madame de. The Cavern ; or, The Two Sisters, A Translation of the French Tale of Le Souterrain, ou les deux Soeurs, 1811. [*Quarterly Review.*]

—— The Cavern of Roseville, or, the Two Sisters. A Tale. Translated from the French of Madame Herbster, by Alexander Jamieson. London, Whittaker, 1817. [B.M. : *Eng. Cat. : Quarterly Review.*]

Heriot, John. The Half-Pay Officer ; Or, Memoirs of Charles Chanceley. A Novel. 3 vols., London, 1788. [Allibone : Arthur Rogers.]

—— The Sorrows Of the Heart. A Novel. 2 vols., London, J. Murray, 1787. [Allibone : B.M. : Francis Edwards.]

Hermit (The), and the wandering Infants. With woodcuts. Dundalk, J. Parks, [1800 ?]. [B.M.]

Hermit of the Grove (The) ; or, the Fatal Effects of Gaming. A Tale, Alas ! Too True. With a frontispiece. London, Printed by T. Maiden, For Ann Lemoine, And J. Roe, [1804]. [Block : Ingpen.]

Hermit of Mount Dragon (The), A Sardinian Narrative, and The Sufferings of Zimeo. With a frontispiece. [c. 1800.] [Arthur Rogers.]

Hermit of the Rock (The ; or, The History of the Marchioness de Lausanne, and the Comte de Luzy. Translated from a French Manuscript. 3 vols., London, F. Noble, 1779. [*Eng. Lit. in Germany :* Holland : Pickering.]

Hermitage (The) ; a British Story. York, 1772. [B.M.]

Hero (The), or the Adventures of a Night : a romance. 2 vols., London, Allman, 1817. [*Eng. Cat. : Monthly Mag.*]

Heroic Life and Exploits of Siegfried the Dragon Slayer (The). An old German story. With 8 plates by William Kaulbach. London, Joseph Cundall ; and David Bogue, 1848. [Block : B.M.]

Heroic Virtue : or, the Noble Sufferers. Exemplified in the Illustrious Lives, of several Noblemen and Ladies, viz. Don Lopez and Tereza. By the Author of****. London, 1749. [B.M.]

Heroick Princes (The) ; or, the Conscious Lovers. With 8 copper plates. London, M. Cooper, 1755. [J. C. Hardy.]

Heron, Mrs. Conversation ; Or, Shades of Difference. A Novel. 3 vols., London, A. K. Newman, 1821. [B.M.]

Heron, M. The Conflict ; a Sentimental Tale. 2 vols., London, 1793. [Allibone : *New Ann. Reg.*]

Hervey, Elizabeth. Amabel : Or Memoirs of a Woman of Fashion. 4 vols., London, Henry Colburn, 1813. [B.M. : Ingpen : Stonehill.]

—— Melissa and Marcia ; or the Sisters : a Novel. 2 vols., London, Wm Lane, 1788. [B.M. : Huth : T. D. Webster.]

Hervey, Elizabeth. The Mourtray Family. A Novel. 4 vols., London, R. Faulder, 1800. [Huth : Ingpen : W. T. Spencer.]

Heseltine, William. The Last of the Plantagenets : An Historical Romance, Illustrating Some of the Public Events, and Domestic And Ecclesiastical Manners, Of the Fifteenth and Sixteenth Centuries. London, Smith, Elder, 1829, [B.M. : H. B. Copinger : Marks.]

Hesitation ; Or, To Marry, or, Not to Marry ? 3 vols., London, Printed by Strahan and Spottiswoode, for Longman, Hurst, Rees, Orme, and Brown, 1819. [B.M. : *European Mag. :* Publisher's advert.]

Heun, Carl Gottlieb Samuel. Liesli, a Swiss tale Translated from the German by J. D. Haas. London, G. B. Whittaker, 1826. [B.M. : *New Monthly Mag.*]

Hewlett, Esther. Eliza Harding ; a Tale, founded on Facts. London, Holdsworth, 1821. [*Investigator*.]

—— The Little Cowslip-Gatherers or What a penny will do. With 3 plates. London, William Darton, [1820]. [Gumuchian.]

—— The Old Man's Head : or, Youthful Recollections. With copper-plates. London, [1825 ?]. [B.M.]

—— The Poplar Grove. or, Little Harry and his Uncle Benjamin : a Tale for Youth. London, 1841. [B.M.]

Hewlett, Joseph Thomas. College Life ; Or, the Proctor's Note-Book. 3 vols., London, Henry Colburn, 1843. [B.M. : *Quarterly Review*.]

—— Dunster Castle, An Historical Romance of the Great Rebellion. 3 vols., London, Henry Colburn, 1846. [B.M.]

—— Great Tom Of Oxford. By the Author of " Peter Priggins," &c. 3 vols., London Henry Colburn, 1846. [B.M. : W. T. Spencer : Stonehill.]

—— The Parish Clerk. By the Author of " Peter Priggins." Edited by Theodore Edward Hook. 3 vols., London, Henry Colburn, 1841. [B.M. : Elkin Mathews.]

—— Parsons and Widows. By the Author of " Peter Priggins," " The Parish Clerk," &c. 3 vols., London, Henry Colburn, 1844. [B.M. : *Critic*.]

—— Peter Priggins, The College Scout. Edited by Theodore Hook. With illustrations by Phiz [Hablot K. Browne]. 3 vols., London, Henry Colburn, 1841, [B.M. : W. T. Spencer : A. V. Turner.]

Hey, Richard. Edington : A Novel. 2 vols., London, 1796. [Allibone : Ingpen : *New Ann. Reg.*]

Hide and Seek ; or, The Old Woman's Story. 3 vols., London, Lane, Newman and Co. [Publisher's advert : Blakey.]

Hifford, John. Theban and Carthaginian Tales. London, Iley, 1820. [*Eng. Cat. : New Monthly Mag.*]

Higginson, Lieut. Francis. The Smugglers, a Chronicle of the Coast Guard. Vol. I [no more published]. London, 1843. [B.M.]

Higginson, Francis, S. Manderville, Or, The Hibernian Chiliarch : A Tale. 2 vols., London, Thomas Dolby, 1825. [B.M. : Ingpen.]

High Life, A Novel. 3 vols., London, Saunders and Otley, 1827. [B.M. : Trehaskis : *Univ. Mag.*]

Highland Cottage, A Pleasing Tale of Youth. To which is added, Benevolence, a Fragment. With woodcuts. [1810]. [Ellis.]

Highland Inn (The). With woodcut titles. 2 vols., London, Henry Colburn, 1839. [B.M. : G. Worthington.]

Highlander (The) ; Or, A Tale of my Landlady. By E. H. H. 2 vols., London, Printed at the Minerva Press for A. K. Newman, 1819. [B.M. : *Quarterly Review*.]

Hilaria. The Festive Bawd. London, John Martin, 1798. [*Cat. Lib. Prohib.*]

Hildebrand : Or, The Days of Queen Elizabeth. An Historical Romance. By the Author of " The King's Son." 3 vols., London, John Mortimer, 1844. [B.M.]

Hilditch, Ann. Mount Pelham. A novel. By the author of Rosa de Montmorien. 2 vols., [W. Lane, 1789]. [Blakey.]

—— Rosa de Montmorien. A Novel. 2 vols., London, William Lane, 1787. [Allibone : B.M. : Stonehill.]

Hill, George Delgarno. Scenes of 1792 ; or a Tale of Revolution. London, Rivington, 1848. [Baker's Bookshop : B.M.]

Hill, Isabel. Brother Tragedians. A Novel. 3 vols., London, Saunders and Otley, 1834. [B.M. : Publisher's advert.]

Hill, " Sir " John. The Adventures Of Mr. George Edwards, A Creole. London, T. Osborne, 1751. [B.M. : Francis Edwards : Pickering.]

—— The Conduct of Married Life. Laid down in a Series of Letters, written by the Honourable Juliana-Susannah Seymour, to a Young Lady, her Relation, lately Married. London, Baldwin, 1753. [*Eng. Lit. in Germany :* Stonehill : T. D. Webster.]

—— The History Of a Woman of Quality : Or, The Adventures Of Lady Frail. By an Impartial Hand. London, M. Cooper, and G. Woodfall, 1751. [B.M. : Pickering.]

—— Letters from the Inspector to a Lady with Genuine Answers. Both printed verbatim from the originals. 1752. [B.M. : Arthur Rogers.]

Hill, Mary. Anselmo, or the Day of Trial, a Romance. 4 vols., London, Printed at the Minerva Press, for A. K. Newman, 1813. [*Eng. Cat. :* Publisher's advert. : Blakey.]

Hill, Mary. The Forest of Comalva, a novel, containing sketches of Portugal, Spain, and part of France. 3 vols., London, 1809. [B.M.]

Hillary, Joseph. The Parish Priest in Ireland. Cork, Mathews, [1814]. [*I. in F.*]

Hillyard, William. Catalina ; or, The Spaniard's Revenge. With woodcuts. London, Dicks, 1847. [Publisher's advert.]

Historical Tales of the Southern Counties. 2 vols., London, Saunders and Otley, 1838. [B.M. : Foyle.]

Histories of the Good-Natured Boy, and the Ill-Natured Boy (The). With woodcuts. Wellington, Salop, F. Houlston, N.D. [B.M. (4th edn.),]

Histories of some of the Penitents in the Magdalen-House (The), as supposed to be related by Themselves. 2 vols., London, 1760.

History and Adventures of Ben the Soldier (The). London, [1800 ?]. [B.M.]

History and Adventures of Don Alfonso Blas de Lirias (The), Son of Gil Blas of Santillane. Translated from the Spanish Original. London, C. Ward and R. Chandler, 1741. [B.M. : Ingpen.]

History and Adventures of Frank Hammond (The). London, R. Griffiths, 1755. [H. B. Wheatley (2nd edn.).]

History and Character of Grace Snodgrass (The). Glasgow, Chalmers & Collins, 1821. [B.M. (2nd edn.).]

History and Comical Adventures of Harlequin (The), and his pleasing companion Columbine. With woodcuts. [London], [c. 1790]. [B.M.]

History and Comical Transactions of Lothian Tom (The). Edinburgh, [1785 ?]. [B.M.]

History of Abou Casem (The), and His Two Remarkable Slippers. To which is added, the History of the Master Cat or Puss in Boots. With 6 woodcuts. Chelmsford, I. Marsden, [1815]. [Gumuchian.]

History of Alfred and Thomas (The) ; To which is added, The Blacksmith. With 14 woodcuts. London, T. Hughes, [1820 ?]. [B.M.]

History of All Real and Threatened Invasions (The). Windsor, 1794.

History of Amanda. 1758. [*Eng. Lit. in Germany.*]

History of Amelia Harcourt and Lousa Darlington. 1777. [*Eng. Lit. in Germany.*]

History of Amintor and Teresa (The). London, W. Owen, 1769. [B.M. : W. Brown.]

History of Ann and Her leven Sisters (The) ; Displaying the Various Adventures They encountered in their Travels, &c. &c. &c. With a frontispiece. London, T. Hughes, 1815. [B.M.]

History of Automathes, who was left 19 Years on a desolate Island. 1745. [W. Brown.]

History of a Banbury Cake (The) ; An entertaining Book For Children. With woodcuts. Banbury, J. G. Rusher, [1835 ?]. [B.M.]

History of Barbarossa and Pollyana. 1756. [W. Brown.]

History of Barnaby Boulton (The). By the Author of " Thomas Brown," &c. &c. With a woodcut. London, Houlston, N.D. No. 80 of Houlston's Series of Tracts. [Block.]

History of the Basket Maker (The), Or Vanity Reproved, and Industry Rewarded. A Peruvian Tale. With 17 woodcuts. Chelmsford, I. Marsden, [1815]. [Gumuchian.]

History of Benjamin St. Martin (The), a Fortunate Foundling. Interspersed with Curious Anecdotes and Narratives of the Love-Affairs of some Persons in High Life. 2 vols., London, J. Coote, 1759. [Pickering.]

History of Betsy Green (The), a Sunday Scholar. London, Religious Tract Society, [1830 ?] [B.M.]

History of the Blind Beggar of Bethnal Green (The) ; Shewing His Bireh [sic] and Parentage ; His going to the Wars, losing his Sight, and turning Beggar at Bethnal Green. Of his getting Riches and the Education of his Daughter ; who is courted by a young Knight. Of the Beggur's [sic] dropping Gold with the Knight's Uncle, Of the Knight's Marriage with the Beggar's Daughter ; and the Discovery of his famous Pedigree. With woodcuts. London, Printed and Sold in Aldermary Church Yard, [1750 ?]. [B.M.]

History of Buckhaven. With a woodcut on the title-page. Edinburgh, [1812].

History of Captain and Miss Rivers (The). 3 vols., London, T. Hookham, 1787. [Pickering.]

History of the Celebrated Nanny Goose (The). From the Original Ms. Wirksworth, James Whitaker, 1840. [Arthur Rogers.]

History of Charles Falkland, Esq., and Miss Louisa Saville. A Novel. In a series of letters. 2 vols., [London], 1787. [B.M.]

History of Charles Jones (The), The Footman. Written by Himself. With a woodcut. London, J. Marshall, and R. White, [1796]. [B.M. : Court Bk. Shop.]

History of Charles Mandeville (The), a Sequel to Lady Julia, by Mrs. Brooke. 2 vols., London, W. Lane, 1790. [*Bibliot. Brit.* : Borrow Head Bookshop : T. D. Webster.]

History of Charles Munson ; or, the Truant Reclaimed. (Frederic and Matilda). With engravings. Dundalk, J. Park, [1800 ?]. [B.M.]

History of Charlotte Summers (The), the Fortunate Parish Girl, 2 vols., London, Printed for the Author, [1740]. [Block : B.M. : Dobell.]

History of the Children in the Wood (The) ; Or Murder Revenged. With woodcuts. London, Printed and Sold in Aldermary Church Yard, [1750 ?]. [B.M.]

History of Cleanthes and Celemene Written by a person well acquainted with all the principal characters from their original. 2 vols., London, 1757. [B.M.]

History of Clorana (The), the Beautiful Arcadian ; or, Virtue Triumphant. London, Printed in the Year 1737. [Stonehill.]

History of Count Bertram (The), an Italian Nobelman, whose ambition roused the jealousy of a rival courtier, who caused him to be banished from his native country, and deprived of his estate, etc., London, [1816 ?]. [B.M.]

History of the Curate of Craman, By an Unbeneficed Clergyman. 1777. [*Eng. Lit. in Germany.*]

History of the Davenport Family (The). In which is displayed A Striking Contrast between Haughty Indolence and Healthful Activity, In the Characters of the Young Davenports, and their Cousins Sophia and Amelia Easy. Interspersed with Moral Reflections. By H. S. Vol. I. With engravings. London, E. Newbery, [1800 ?]. [B.M. : Court Bk. Shop.]

History of Diligent Dick (The) ; or, Truth will out, though it be hid in a well. London, [1797 ?]. Cheap Repository. [B.M.]

History of Dr. John Faustus (The). Shewing How he Sold himself to the Devil to have Power to do what he pleased for twenty-four Years. Also, Strange Things done by Him and his Servant Mephistopholes. With an Account how the Devil came for him, and tore him to Pieces. With woodcuts. London, Printed and Sold in Aldermary Church Yard, [1750 ?]. [B.M.]

History of Eliza (The). Written by a Friend. 2 vols., London, J. Dodsley. 1767. [B.M. : Pickering.]

History of Eliza Musgrove. 2 vols., London, 1769. [T. D. Webster.]

History of Eliza Warwick (The). 2 vols., London, Bew, 1778. [*Eng. Lit. in Germany* : Arthur Roger : Stonehill.]

History of Ellen (The). London [1830 ?]. [B.M.]

History of Emma (The), or the Victim of Depravity ; wherein is exemplified In the Sufferings of this interesting Female, the Miserable effects of deviating from the Paths of Virtue. With the Life of Kitty Clark, who, from a Mistaken notion of Revenge, left her Uncle's House, and entered into a Licentious Course of gay Living with a Noble Lord : After whose Death she underwent a variety of Scenes ; and Died an object of the utmost misery. With a frontispiece. London, Dean and Munday, N.D. [Court Bk. Shop.]

History of the Emperor Manalay (The), and his virtuous wife. A story taken from ancient history. Newcastle, [1795.] [B.M.]

History of Euphemia's Little Scholars, Mary and Frances, founded upon fact. London, 1822. [B.M.]

History of the Family at Smiledale (The), presented to all little Boys and Girls. With a frontispiece and 12 woodcuts by Bewick. London, E. Newbery. [1790].

History of Fanny Mason. London, C. and J. Rivington, 1823. [B.M.]

History of Fanny Mills (The) ; or no one too young to do good. London, [1797 ?] [B.M.]

History of Fanny Seymour (The). London, William Bathoe, 1753. [B.M. : Pickering.]

History of Filchum Cantum (The); or, a merry and diverting dialogue between Apollo, a Senator, Foolish Harry, Silly Billy. By J. G. Gent., a Moral Philosopher, London, 1749. [B.M.]

History of Fortunatus. Containing Various surprising Adventures. Among which he acquired a Purse, that could not to be emptied. And a Hat that carried him wherever he wished to be. With woodcuts. London, Printed and Sold in Aldermary Church Yard, [1750 ?]. [B.M.]

History of the Fortune-Teller in the Old Bailey (The), Exhibiting the Intrigues and Characters of Several Personages of the First Rank, and some Droll and Familiar Scenes, drawn from Real Life. 1764. [Marks.]

History of Four Kings (The), Their Queens and Daughters. Kings of Canterbury, Colchester, Cornwall and Cumberland. Being the Merry Tales of Tom Hodge And his School-Fellows. With woodcuts. London, Printed and Sold in Aldermary Church Yard, [1750 ?]. [B.M.]

History of the Frolicksome Courtier (The), And the Jovial Tinker. With woodcuts. [London], Printed and Sold in Aldermary Church Yard, [1750 ?]. [B.M.]

History of George Desmond ; founded on facts which occurred in the East Indies. Wellington, 1821. [B.M.]

History of George Mason (The). London, 1844. [B.M.)

History of Georgina Neville (The) : or, the Disinterested Orphan. A novel, being the first literary attempt of a young lady. London, 1791. [B.M.]

History of Hector, Prince of Troy (The) ; Or, the Three Destructions of Troy. The First and Second Time by Hercules, and the Third Time by the Greeks. Together with The noble Actions of Hector, Achilles, the Amazon Queen, and divers other Princes. With woodcuts. London, Printed and Sold in Aldermary Church Yard, [1750 ?]. [B.M.]

History of Honest Roger (The) ; founded on fact. By a Clergyman. London, Religious Tract Society, [1830 ?]. [B.M.]

History of Honoria (The), being the Adventures of a Young Lady. Interspersed with the Histories of Emilia, Julia and others. By a Young Gentleman. London, 1754. [McLeish.]

History of the Human Heart (The). Or, the Adventures Of a Young Gentleman. London, J. Freeman, 1749. [*Rochester Reprints.*]

History of Idle Jack Brown (The). Containing the Merry Story of the Mountebank, with some Account of the Bay Mare Smiler, Being the Third Part of the Two Shoemakers. With a woodcut. London, J. Marshall ; With R. White, [1796]. Cheap Repository. [B.M. : Court Bk. Shop.]

History of Israel Jobson (The), the Wandering Jew, translated from the original Chinese [or rather, written] by M. W. London, J. Nicholson, 1757. [B.M.]

History of Jack and the Giants (The). In 2 Parts. With woodcuts. London, Printed and Sold in Aldermary Church Yard, [1750 ?]. [B.M.]

History of Jack of Newbery (The), Called The Clothier Of England. With wood-cuts. London, Printed and Sold in Aldermary Church Yard, [1750 ?]. [B.M.]

History of Jack Sheppard (The) : his wonderful exploits and excapes. A romance founded on facts. Illustrated from drawings after J. Sketch. London, 1839. [B.M.]

History of Jane Price and Sarah Lightfoot. London, C. & J. Rivington, 1825. [B.M.]

History of Jane Shore, Mistress to Edward IV. Shewing How she came to be Concubine to the King. With a frontispiece. London, 1809. [J. Richardson.]

History of John Steady and Edward Careless. Otley, [1815 ?]. [B.M.]

History of John Wise (The), a poor boy. London, Religious Tract Society, [1830 ?]. [B.M.]

History of Johnny Armstrong (The), Of Westmoreland. With woodcuts. London, Printed and Sold in Aldermary Church Yard, [1750 ?]. [B.M.]

History of Joshua Trueman Esq. (The), And Miss Peggy Williams. 2 vols., London, 1754. [B.M. : *Eng. Lit. in Germany.*]

History of Judith Potts (The). By the Author of "A Week at Christmas." With a frontispiece. Wellington, Houlston, 1829. [B.M.]

History of Julius Fitz-John (The). 3 vols., London, Sherwood, 1818. [*Eng. Cat. : New Monthly Mag.*]

History of the King and the Cobler. 2 parts. London, [1780 ?]. [B.M.]

History of La Rivere (The). Translated from the French. London, 1766. [B.M.]

History of Lady Bettesworth and Captain Hastings. In a series of letters. 2 vols., London, 1780. [B.M. : T. D. Webster.]

History of Lady Emma Melcombe. 3 vols., 1787. [W. Brown.]

History of Lady Louisa Stroud (The), and the Honourable Miss Caroline Stretton. 2 vols., London, 1764. [B.M.]

History of Lady Lucy Fenton. 1768. [*Eng. Lit. in Germany.*]

History of Lawrence Lazy (The). Containing His Birth and Slothful Breeding ; how he served the Shoemaker, his Wife, the Squire's Cook, and the Farmer ; which by the Laws of Lubberland, was accounted High Treason. His Arraignment and Trial ; and happy Deliverance from the many Treasons laid to his Charge. With woodcuts. London, Printed and Sold in Aldermary Church Yard, [1750 ?]. [B.M.]

History of the Life and Adventures of Mr. Anderson (The). Containing His Strange Varieties of Fortune In Europe and America. Compiled from his own Papers. London, W. Owen, 1754. [B.M. : Murray Hill.]

History of the Life and Death of that most Noble Knight Sir Bevis, of Southampton (The). Containing, His Acts of Chivalry in various Battles, and in slaying Giants, Monsters, Wild Beasts, &c. With woodcuts. London, Printed and Sold in Aldermary Church Yard, [1750 ?]. [B.M.]

History of the Life and Glorious Actions of the Mighty Hercules, of Greece (The). Containing, His encountering and overcoming, Serpents, Lions, Monsters, Giants, Tyrants, and powerful Armies. — His taking Cities, Towns, Kings, and Kingdoms ; together with the unfortunate Manner of his Death. With woodcuts. London, Printed and Sold in Aldermary Church Yard, [1750 ?]. [B.M.]

History of Little Ann. With a Fragment. With woodcuts. Dundalk, J. Parks, [1800 ?]. [B.M.]

History of Little King Skilful (The). York, Wilson. [*Guardian of Education.*]

History of Lord Aimworth (The), **and The Honourable Charles Hartford, Esq.** In a Series of Letters. A Novel.

By the author of Dorinda Catesby and Ermina, or the Fair Recluse. 3 vols., 1773. [Blackwell : McLeish : Sotheby's.]

History of Lord Ashborn and the Honourable Miss Howe, or The reclaimed libertine, By the Author of Frederick, the fortunate beggar. 1773. [*Eng. Lit. in Germany.*]

History of Lord Belford (The), and Miss Sophia Woodley, in a Series of Letters. 3 vols., London, Francis Noble, 1784. [B.M.]

History of Lord Clayton and Miss Meredith (The). 2 vols., London, Robinson and Roberts, 1769. [J. C. Hardy.]

History of Lord Stanton, By a Gentleman of the Middle Temple, author of the Trial. 1774. [*Eng. Lit. in Germany.*]

History of Lucy Wellers (The). Written by a Lady. 2 vols., London, 1753. [B.M. : *Eng. Lit. in Germany.*]

History of Major Bromley and Miss Clifford (The). 2 vols., London, 1767. [B.M.]

History of Margaret, Sister to John Bull. 1761. [W. Brown.]

History of Martin and James (The) ; or, the Reward of Industry. Designed for the Improvement of Children. With woodcuts. London, Harvey and Darton, 1833. [Block.]

History of Mary, the Maid of the Inn : A Melancholy and Affecting Narrative : detailing her Unfortunate Attachment, her Singular Courage, . . . discovers her Lover to be both a Robber and a Murderer : with an Account of his Trial and Execution; the Forlorn Wanderings of the Unfortunate Mary, who became a wretched Maniac, . . . from the Celebrated Poem by Robert Southey, which is here added. With a frontispiece. Derby, Thomas Richardson, [c. 1830.] [Marks.]

History of Mary Prince (The), To which is added the Narrative of Asa-Asa, a captured African. 1831. [B.M.]

History of Mary Wood (The), The House-Maid ; Or, The Danger of False Excuses. With a woodcut. London, Howard & Evans ; J. Hatchard ; Hazard & Binns, Bath, [1796 ?]. Cheap Repository. [Court Bk. Shop.]

History of Master Jackey and Miss Harriot (The). Glasgow, Lumsden. [*Guardian of Education.*]

History of the Matrimonial Adventures of a Banker's Clerk, with the Pretended Lady Ann Frances Caroline Boothby, otherwise Sister to the Duke of Beaufort. One series of Letters addressed to Mr. George N— at Newcastle-upon-Tyne, London, G. Henderson, 1762. [W. Brown : Ingpen.]

History of Michael Kemp (The), the happy Farmer's Lad. In 2 parts. Bath, 1819. [B.M.]

History of the Miss Baltimores (The) ; In a Series of Letters. 2 vols., 1783. [Blackwell.]

History of Miss Dorinda Catsby and Miss Emilia Faulkner. 2 vols., London, 1772. [B.M.]

History of Miss Emilia Beville. 2 vols., London, Printed by W. Hoggard for Francis Noble and John Noble, 1768. [Block : *Eng. Lit. in Germany.*]

History of Miss Harriot Fitzroy (The), and Miss Emilia Spencer. By the Author of Lucenda Courtney. 2 vols., London, W. Hoggard for Francis Noble and John Noble, 1767. [*Eng. Lit. in Germany :* Pickering.]

History of Miss Harriott Fairfax (The). Written by a Lady. London, T. Sabine, [1780 ?]. [B.M.]

History of Miss Indiana Danby (The). By a Lady. 2 vols., London, J. Dodsley, 1765. [B.M. : *Eng. Lit. in Germany.*]

History of Miss Katty N ‑ ‑ ‑ ‑ (The), written by herself. London, F. Noble, [1757]. [B.M.]

History of Miss Lucinda Courtney, in a Series of Letters by Herself to her friend Miss Constantia Bellmour. 1764. [*Eng. Lit. in Germany.*]

History of Miss Maria Barlowe (The). a series of letters. 2 vols., London, Fielding & Walker, 1777. [B.M.]

History of Miss Pamela Howard (The) ; By the Author of Indiana Danby. 2 vols., London, T. Lowndes, 1773. [B.M.: Arthur Rogers.]

History of Miss Pittborough (The). In a series of letters. By a Lady. 2 vols., London, 1767. [B.M.]

History of Miss Sommerville, Written by a lady. 1769. [*Eng. Lit. in Germany.*]

History of Montellion, the Most Valiant and Renowned Knight of the Oracle (The). Son to Perocles, the valiant Knight of Assyria, and the fair Constantia ; the Daughter of the Emperor of Persia. Containing Many strange and wonderful Adventures of his Parents, relating to their Love-Exploits. With woodcuts. London, Printed and Sold in Aldermary Church Yard, [1750?]. [B.M.]

History of Mother Bunch of the West (The) : Containing Many Rarities out of her Golden Closet of Curiosities. Part the Second. With woodcuts. London, Printed and Sold in Aldermary Church Yard, [1750 ?]. [B.M.]

History of Mother Shipton (The). With woodcuts. London, Printed and Sold in Aldermary Church Yard, [1750 ?]. [B.M.]

History of Mr. Bragwell (The) ; or the Two Wealthy Farmers. Part III. With a woodcut. London, J. Marshall, and R. White, [1796]. Cheap Repository. [B.M. : Court Bk. Shop.]

History of Mr. Stanley and Miss Temple, A Rural Novel. 1773. [*Eng. Lit. in Germany.*]

History of Netterville (The). A Chance Pedestrian. 2 vols., London, J. Cundee, 1802. [Fletcher.]

History of Nicolas Pedrosa (The), and his escape from the Inquisition in Madrid. A tale. Glasgow, J. & M. Robertson, 1802. [B.M.]

History of the Noble Marquis of Salus and Patient Grissel (The). With woodcuts. London, Printed and Sold in Aldermary Church Yard, [1750 ?]. [B.M.]

History of Old Hardy (The), the Soldier. London, Religious Tract Society, [1830. [B.M.]

History of an old Lady and her Family (The). London, M. Cooper, 1754. [Block.]

History of a Pin (The), as related by itself. Interspersed with a Variety of Anecdotes ; Pointing out to the Youth of both Sexes, the Superiority of a generous Mind, over one that is narrow and uncultivated. By the Author of The Brothers, A Tale for Children, &c. London, E. Newbery, 1798. [B.M. : Court Bk. Shop.]

History of Polly Willis, an Orphan. 1755. [*Eng. Lit. in Germany.*]

History of Primrose Prettyface (The), who was raised from being the Daughter of a Poor Cottager to Great Riches. With 2 plates. London, 1830. [Francis Edwards.]

History of Prince Fatal (The), and Prince Fortunatus. [1825 ?]. [B.M.]

History of Reynard the Fox (The). With woodcuts. London, Printed and Sold in Aldermary Church Yard, [1750 ?]. [B.M.]

History of Reynard the Fox (The), Bruin the Bear, &c. London, G. Smith, 1756. [B.M. : Ingpen.]

History of Robin Hood (The) ; and of all the Notable Exploits performed by him and his merry men. With 9 woodcuts. Manchester, A. Swindells, [c. 1796-1799]. [*Lancs.*]

History of Rory O'More, A tale of the Irish Rebellion. Also, the History of the Fish and the Ring : or, the Fortunate Farmer's Daughter. Newcastle [1838 ?]. [B.M.]

History of a Savage Girl (The), Caught Wild in the Woods of Champagne. Newly Translated from the French of Madam H - - - t London, R. Davidson, [c. 1750]. [Ingpen : Stonehill.]

History of Sawney Beane and his family, robbers and murderers, etc. Birmingham, [1810 ?]. [B.M.]

History of a School Boy (The), &c. London, Crosby, N.D. [*Guardian of Education.*]

History of the Sieges of Aquileia and Berwick (The). Being the Story on which the new Tragedy of Aquileia is founded. With some Remarks on that Play. London, 1760. [McLeish.]

History of Sir Charles Beaufort (The). Containing the Genuine and Interesting Memoirs of a Family of Distinction in the South of England. Displaying the Miseries that may arise from acting contrary to that peculiar Character which Nature has given to both the Sexes. 2 vols., London, T. Lownds, 1766. [Pickering.]

History of Sir Charles Dormer and Miss Harriet Villers (The) ; in which are exemplified, from a late Catastrophe in real Life, the Contrast of Virtue and Vice, and the dangerous and fatal Consequences arising from Confidents and Intermeddlers in Family Affairs. By a Lady. 2 vols., London, J. Roson, 1770. [Publisher's advert.]

History of Sir Geoffry Restless. 2 vols. [By Henry Man.] 1791. [W. Brown.]

History of Sir Henry Clarendon. 2 vols., London, 1785. [B.M. : W. Brown.]

History of Sir Roger and his Son Joe (The). 2 vols., London, J. Scott, 1750. [Pickering.]

History of the Sleeping Beauty in the Wood. An oriental [*sic*] tale. [London], J. Pitts, [1810 ?]. [B.M.]

History of Sophia Shakespear (The). London, W. Reeve ; H. Slater, 1753. [J. C. Hardy.]

History of Sophron and Tigranes. With woodcuts. 1809. [Salkeld.]

History of a Tame Robin (The), Supposed to be written by Himself. With a frontispiece. London, Darton Harvey and Darton, 1817. [Kennard : Mayhew : Arthur Rogers.]

History of that Celebrated Lady Ally Croaker (The). [London], [1780 ?]. [B.M.]

History of Thomas Martin or " A Little that the Righteous Man Hath, is Better than great riches of the Ungodly." London, C. & J. Rivington, 1823. [B.M.]

History of Tom Jones the Foundling, In His Married State (The). London, Robinson, 1750. [Chas. Hutt : Stonehill.]

History of Tom Long the Carrier (The). With woodcuts. London, Printed and Sold in Aldermary Church Yard [1750 ?]. [B.M.]

History of Tom White (The), The Postillion. With a woodcut. London, Howard and Evans ; J. Hatchard; Hazard and Binns, Bath, N.D. Cheap Repository. [Court Bk. Shop.]

History of Tommy Playlove (The), and Jacky Lovebook, wherein is shewn the Superiority of Virtue over Vice, however Dignified by Birth or Fortune. With 13 woodcuts. Glasgow, J. Lumsden, 1819. [Pickering.]

History of Tommy Titmouse (The). With woodcuts. London, J. Harris, 1809. [B.M.]

History of Two Modern Adventurers (The). 2 vols., London, 1757. [B.M.]

History of Two Orphans. London, W. Owen, 1756. [Publisher's Announcement at end of Life and Memoirs of Mr. Ephraim Tristram Bates, 1756.]

History of the Two Wealthy Farmers (The) ; Or, a New Dialogue, between Mr. Bragwell and Mr. Worthy. Part IV. With a woodcut. London, J. Marshall ; and R. White, [1796]. Cheap Repository. Sunday Reading. [B.M. : Court Bk. Shop.]

History of Valentine and Orson (The). Reader ; you'll find this little Book contains Enough to answer thy Expence and Pains ; And if with Caution you will read it thro', 'Twill both Instruct thee and Delight thee too. With woodcuts. London, Printed and Sold in Aldermary Church Yard, [1750 ?]. [B.M.].

History of the White Cat (The), A Fairy Tale. With woodcuts. Birmingham, T. Bloomer ; and A. Carvalho, London, [1840 ?]. [B.M.]

History of Whittington (The), Who was afterwards Lord Mayor of London, and his Cat. To which is added, The Father's Secret, a Tale. Gateshead, J. Marshall, N.D. [Block.]

History of Wilhelmina Susannah Dormer, containing a wonderful series of events. London, [1750 ?]. [B.M.]

History of Will. Brown (The), The Poacher, And his Daughter Betsey. With Some Account of Squire Field's Family. With a woodcut. London, The Religious Tract Society, [1830 ?]. [B.M. : Court Bk. Shop.]

History of Will Ramble (The), a Libertine. 2 vols., London, 1755. [Thorpe.]

History of Young Edwin (The) and his Sister Jessy, &c. written for the purpose of making every little Girl and Boy good and happy. London, E. Newbery, 1797. [Publisher's advert.]

Hita, G. P. de. Civil Wars of Granada. Translated by T. Rodd. London, 1803. [Lib. of Congress.]

Hitchener, William Henry. St. Leonard's Forest, Or the Child of Chance. A Novel. 2 vols., London, Chapple, 1813. [Stonehill.]

—— The Towers of Ravenswold, or Days of Ironside. 2 vols., London, 1814. [*New Monthly Mag. : Quarterly Review.*]

Hitchon, Miss A. L. M. A parental present of pretty stories : or evening amusement for good children. London, Fisher, 1837. [B.M.]

Hoare, George Richard. The Young Traveller ; a Tale. 1812. [Allibone.]

Hockley, William Browne. The Memoirs of a Brahmin ; Or, The Fatal Jewels, By the Author of " Pandurang Hari," " The Zenana," " Vizier's Son," &c. &c. &c. 3 vols., London, T. C. Newby ; and T. & W. Boone, 1843. [B.M.]

—— Pandurang Hari, Or Memoirs of a Hindoo. 3 vols., London, Geo. B. Whittaker, 1826. [B.M. : *Edin. Mag. : Guide to Best Fiction.*]

—— The Vizier's Son Or the Adventures of a Mogul. By the author of Pandurang Hari, Or Memoirs of a Hindoo, The Zenana, &c. 3 vols., London, Saunders and Otley, 1831. [B.M.]

—— The Zenana ; Or A Nuwab's Leisure Hours ; By the Author of " Pandurang Hari ; or Memoirs of a Hindoo." 3 vols., London, Saunders and Otley, 1827. [*Blackwood's Edin. Mag. : B.M. : McLeish.*]

Hodson, Margaret. First Impressions ; or, The portrait. A novel. By Mrs. Holford. 4 vols., [W. Lane, 1800.] [Blakey.]

—— Italian Stories. Translated by Miss Holford, Author of Wallace. London, J. Andrews, 1823. [B.M. : Pickering : *Quarterly Review.*]

—— Warbeck of Wolfstein. 3 vols., London, Rodwell and Martin, 1820. [B.M. : Ingpen : Pickering.]

Hofer, the Tyrolese. By the Author of " Claudine," " Always Happy." With 12 plates. London, Harris, 1824. [B.M. : Gumuchian.]

Hoffman, Ernst Theodor Amadeus. The Devil's Elixir. From the German of E. T. A. Hoffmann. 2 vols., Edinburgh, William Blackwood ; and T. Cadell, London, 1824. [B.M. : G. Worthington.]

Hoffmann, Heinrich. The English Struwelpeter, or pretty stories and funny pictures for little children. After the German of H. H. Leipzig, [1848]. [B.M. (4th edn.).]

Hofland, Barbara. Adelaide ; Or, the Intrepid Daughter : a tale, including anecdotes of Henry the Great and the Massacre of St. Bartholomew. By the author of " Theodore." London, J. Harris, 1823. [B.M.]

—— The Affectionate Brothers. A tale. With a frontispiece and an engraved title. London, A. K. Newman, 1816. [Blakey.]

—— Beatrice, A Tale Founded on Facts. 3 vols., London, Longman, Rees, Orme, Brown, and Green, 1829. [B.M. : McLeish.]

—— The Captives in India, A Tale ; And A Widow and a Will. 3 vols., London, Richard Bentley, 1834. [B.M.]

—— Czarina ; An Historical Romance of the Court of Russia. 3 vols., London,

Henry Colburn, 1842. [B.M. : G. Worthington.]

Hofland, Barbara. Daniel Dennison, And the Cumberland Statesman. 3 vols., London, Richard Bentley, 1846. [B.M.]

—— The Daughter of a Genius ; A Tale for Youth. London, Harris, 1823. [B.M. : Cleverdon : *Eng. Cat.*]

—— The Decision. A Novel By the Author of Caroline Ormsby. 3 vols., London, Longman, 1811. [Allibone : C. Howes : *Quarterly Review.*]

—— Elizabeth and her three beggar boys. London, A. K. Newman, [1830 ?]. [B.M. : Arthur Rogers.]

—— Ellen, the Teacher. [Allibone.]

—— Emily's Reward ; or, the holiday trip to Paris. London, 1844. [B.M.]

—— Energy, A Tale. With an engraved title and a frontispiece. London, A. K. Newman, 1838. [B.M. : Brough.]

—— Farewell Tales. London, A. Hall, 1840. [B.M.]

—— A Father as he should be. A Novel. 4 vols., London, Printed at the Minerva Press, for A. K. Newman, 1815. [B.M. : *European Mag. :* Publisher's advert.]

—— Fortitude. A Tale. With a frontispiece and engraved title. London, A. K. Newman, 1835. [B.M.]

—— Godmother's Tales. With an engraved title and a frontispiece. London, A. K. Newman, 1842. [Arthur Rogers.]

—— The Good Grandmother And her Offspring ; A Tale. London, R. Hunter, 1817. [Birrell & Garnett : B.M. : Arthur Rogers.]

—— The History of a Clergyman's Widow and her Young Family. By the Author of An Officer's Widow and her Young Family. With a frontispiece. London, Printed at the Minerva Press for A. K. Newman, 1812. [B.M. : *Camb. Hist. Eng. Lit. : Quarterly Review.*]

—— The History of an Officer's Widow and her young family. London, 1809. [B.M.]

—— Humility. A Tale. London, A.K. Newman, 1837. [B.M.]

—— Integrity. A Tale. With a frontispiece. London, Longman, Hurst, Rees, Orme & Brown, 1823. [B.M. : *New Monthly Mag. :* Publisher's advert.]

—— Katherine. A Tale. 4 vols., London, A. K. Newman, 1828. [B.M.]

—— The King's Son : A Romance of English History. Edited by Mrs. Hofland. 3 vols., London, Henry Colburn, 1843. [B.M.]

—— The Maid of Moscow, Or Iwanowna. 2 vols., 1816. [Blackwell.]

—— Matilda ; Or, The Barbadoes Girl. A Tale for young People. By the Author of the Clergyman's Widow and Family, Merchant's Widow and Family, Affectionate Brothers, Panorama of Europe, The Sisters, &c. With a frontispiece. London, Printed at the Minerva Press, for A. K. Newman, 1816. [B.M.]

Hofland, Barbara. The Merchant's Widow and her Family. By the author of The Officer's Widow and Her Family ; Clergyman's Widow and Family ; Daughter-in-law, &c. With a frontispiece. London, Printed at the Minerva Press, for A. K. Newman, 1814. [Stonehill : Blakey.]

—— Moderation. A Tale. With a frontispiece. London, Longman, Hurst, Rees, Orme, Brown, and Green, 1825. [B.M. : Guntrip & Richardson : Publisher's advert.]

—— Patience and Perseverance ; Or, the Modern Griselda. A Domestic Tale. By the Author of " Says She to Her Neighbour, What ? " &c. 4 vols., London, Printed at the Minerva Press for A. K. Newman, 1813. [B.M. : Ingpen : Marks.]

—— Reflection. A Tale. With a frontispiece. London, Longman, Rees, Orme, Brown & Green, 1826. [B.M. : Gumuchian : Maggs.]

—— Rich Boys and Poor Boys. With a frontispiece and an engraved title. [1836]. [Arthur Rogers.]

—— Says she to her Neighbour, What ? By an Old-fashioned Englishman. 4 vols., London, Printed at the Minerva Press, for A. K. Newman, 1812. [Allibone : B.M. : Publisher's advert.]

—— Self-Denial. With a frontispiece. London, Longman, Rees, Orme, Brown, & Green, 1827. [B.M. : Maggs : Publisher's advert.]

—— The Sisters. A Domestic Tale. London, Printed at the Minerva Press, for A. K. Newman, 1814. [Ingpen : Publisher's advert : Blakey.]

—— The Son of a Genius : A Tale, for the Use of Youth. With a frontispiece. London, John Harris, 1817. [Sotheran.]

—— The Stolen Boy, An Indian Tale. With a Frontispiece. London, A. K. Newman. [1830 ?]. [B.M.]

—— Tales Of The Manor. 4 vols., London, Longman, Hurst, Rees, Orme, and Brown, 1822. [B.M. : Maggs.]

—— Tales Of The Priory. 4 vols., London, Longman, Hurst, Rees, Orme, and Brown, 1820. [B.M. : Maggs : *Quarterly Review.*]

—— Theodore, or the Crusaders. A Tale for Youth. With 12 plates. London, [1815]. [Arthur Rogers.]

—— The Unloved One ; A Domestic Story. 3 vols., London, Henry Colburn, 1844. [B.M.]

—— The Visit to London ; or, Emily and her Friends. 4 vols., London, Printed at the Minerva Press, for A. K. Newman, 1814. [Publisher's advert. : *Quarterly Review :* Blakey.]

Hofland, Barbara. William and his Uncle Ben. 1826. [*Camb. Hist. Eng. Lit.*]

—— York House, Or, Conversations in a Ladies' School : Founded on Fact. By Domina. London, J. Dennett for Williams 1813. [Birrell & Garnett.]

—— The Young Cadet or Henry Delamire's Voyage to India. London, John Harris, 1821. [Arthur Rogers.]

—— The Young Crusoe ; or, The Shipwrecked Boy. A Tale. London, Newman, [c. 1820]. [Stonehill.]

—— The Young Pilgrim, or Alfred Campbell's Return to the East. With a frontispiece. London, Harris, 1826. [B.M. : *Eng. Cat. : Quarterly Review.*]

Hogg, James. Altrive Tales : collected among the peasantry of Scotland, and from foreign adventurers. By the Ettrick Shepherd. With illustrations by George Cruikshank. Vol I [No more published]. London, J. Cochrane, 1832. [Allibone : B.M. : G. Worthington.]

—— The Brownie of Bodsbeck ; And Other Tales. 2 vols., Edinburgh, William Blackwood ; and John Murray, London, 1818. [Block : B.M. : Stonehill.]

—— Dramatic Tales ; By the Author of "The Poetic Mirror." 2 vols., Edinburgh, Ballantyne, 1817. [B.M. : Elkin Mathews.]

—— The Private Memoirs and Confessions of a Justified Sinner : Written by Himself : With a detail of curious traditionary facts, And other evidence, by the Editor. With a facsimile. London, Longman, Hurst, Rees, Orme, Brown, & Green, 1824. [Block : B.M. : Arthur Rogers.]

—— The Shepherd's Calendar. 2 vols., Edinburgh, William Blackwood ; and T. Cadell, London, 1829. [Block : B.M. : Pickering.]

—— Tales Of the Wars of Montrose. 3 vols., London, James Cochrane, 1835. [B.M. : McLeish.]

—— The Three Perils of Man ; or War, Women, and Witchcraft. A Border Romance. 3 vols., London, Longman, Hurst, Rees, Orme, & Brown. 1822. [B.M. : Ingpen : Arthur Rogers.]

—— The Three Perils of Woman ; Or, Love, Leasing, and Jealousy. A Series of Domestic Scottish Tales. 3 vols., London, Longman, Hurst, Rees, Orme, Brown, and Green, 1823. [B.M. : *New Monthly Mag. :* Sotheby's.]

—— Winter Evening Tales, Collected among The Cottagers in the South of Scotland. 2 vols., Edinburgh, Oliver and Boyd ; and G. and W. B. Whittaker, 1820. [B.M. : Ingpen : Arthur Rogers.]

Hogg, Thomas Jefferson. Memoirs of Prince Alexy Haimatoff. Translated from The Original Latin Manuscripts. Under the Immediate Inspection of The Prince, by John Brown, Esq.

London, T. Hookham, Jun. and E. T. Hookham, 1813. [*Ashley Lib. :* B.M. : Publisher's advert.]

Hogg, Thomas Jefferson. Two Hundred and Nine Days ; or The Journal of a Traveller on the Continent. 2 vols., London, Hunt, 1827. [B.M. : *Eng. Cat. :* Ingpen.]

Holberg, Ludwig, Baron. A Journey to the World Under-Ground, being the Subterraneous Travels of Nicholas Klimius. Translated from the Original. London, T. Astley : and B. Collins, Salisbury, 1742. [B.M. : Arthur Rogers : Victorius.]

Holbrook, Ann Catherine. Constantine Castriot ; an historical tale ; taken from authentic documents of the memorable siege of Malta, in the year 1565. Rugeley, 1829. [B.M.]

—— Realities and Reflections. A series of original tales, founded on facts. Thame, [1834]. [B.M. (4th edn.).]

—— Tales, serious and instructive with moral reflections. Uttoxeter, 1821. [B.M.]

Holcraft, Richard. Tales from the German. London, Longman, Rees, Orme, Brown, & Green ; Oliver & Boyd, Edinburgh ; and Robertson & Atkinson, Glasgow, 1826. [B.M. : Arthur Rogers.]

Holcroft, Fanny. Fortitude and Frailty ; A Novel. Inscribed to the Revered Memory of her Lamented Father. 4 vols., London, Printed by W. Clowes, for W. Simpkin and R. Marshall, 1817. [B.M. : *Quarterly Review :* Arthur Rogers.]

—— The Wife and the Lover. 3 vols., London, Henry Colburn, 1813. [Allibone : Publisher's advert. : *Quarterly Review.*]

Holcroft, Thomas. The Adventures of Hugh Trevor. 6 vols., London, Shepperson & Reynolds, 1794-97. [Birrell & Garnett : B.M. : Arthur Rogers.]

—— Alwyn : Or the Gentleman Comedian. 2 vols., London, Fielding and Walker, 1780. [B.M. : Ingpen.]

—— An Amorous Tale of the Chaste Loves of Peter the Long, And of His Most Honoured Dame Blanche Bazu, His Feal Friend Blaise Bazu, And the History of the Lovers' Well. Imitated from the Original French by Thomas Holcroft. London, G. G. J. and J. Robinson, 1786. [Birrell & Garnett.]

—— Anna St. Ives : A Novel. 7 vols., London, Shepperson and Reynolds, 1792. [B.M. : *Guide to Best Fiction :* Murray Hill.]

—— The Family Picture ; or domestic dialogues on amiable subjects ; illustrated by histories. 2 vols., London, 1783. [B.M.]

—— Memoirs of Bryan Perdue : a Novel. 3 vols., London, Longman, Hurst, 1805. [B.M. : Arthur Rogers : Stonehill.]

111

Holder, Rev. Mr. The Secluded Man ; or, The history of Mr. Oliver. 2 vols., London, 1798. [Blakey.]

Holdsworth, Arthur Howe. Gomerock Castle ; or, the Grave of the Unknown. London, 1844. [B.M.]

Holford, Mrs. M. Calaf. A Persian Tale. 2 vols., London, Minerva Press, 1798. [*New Ann. Reg.* : Stonehill.]

Holford, Margaret. [*See* HODSON, Margaret.)

Holiday Present, containing Anecdotes of Mr. and Mrs. Jennet and their little Family. With woodcuts. York, 1797. [J. G. Commin.]

Holiday Visit (The), and other tales ; being sketches of childhood, designed for juvenile readers. London, Harvey, 1826. [B.M.]

Holidays at Brighton ; or, seaside amusements. London, 1834. [B.M.]

Holland, John. The Old Arm-Chair ; or, Recollections of a Bachelor. A Tale. By Sexagenarius. With a frontispiece. London, Henry Fisher, 1824. [B.M. : Elkin Mathews : Norman.]

Hollings, Captain W. The Bytal Pucheesee : Translated into English. By Captain W. Hollings. Calcutta, W. Ridsdale, 1848. [B.M.]

Holloway, William. The Baron of Lauderbrooke. A tale. London, A. Lemoine, 1800. [B.M.]

—— Dovedell Hall ; Or, The Fortunate Exiles, Weymouth, Love, 1792.

Holmes, Elizabeth. Scenes in our Parish By a " Country Parson's " Daughter. Bristol, J. Chilcott, 1830. [B.M.]

—— Scenes in our Parish. By a " Country Parson's " Daughter. Second Series. London, J. Hatchard, 1832. [B.M.]

Holmes, W. H. M. Oakleigh ; Or the Minor of Great Expectations. With illustrations by T. Onwhyn. 3 vols., London, T. C. Newby, 1843. [B.M. : G. Worthington.]

Holstein, Anthony Frederick. The Assassin of St. Glenroy : or, the Axis of Life. A novel. 4 vols., London, A. K. Newman. 1810. [B.M. : Monthly Mag. : Blakey.]

—— Bouverie, or the Pupil of the World. 5 vols., London, Printed at the Minerva Press, for A. K. Newman, 1812. [*Eng. Cat.* : Publisher's advert. : *Quarterly Review.*]

—— The Discontented Man ; Or Love and Reason. A Novel. 3 vols., Printed at the Minerva Press for A. K. Newman, 1815. [B.M. : Publisher's advert : Blakey.]

—— The Inhabitants of the Earth ; or, The Follies of Women. A Novel. 3 vols., London, A. K. Newman, 1811. [B.M. : *Quarterly Review.*]

—— L'Intriguante, or the Woman of the World. 4 vols., London, Printed at the Minerva Press, for A. K. Newman, 1814. [Publisher's advert.]

Holstein, Anthony Frederick. Isadora of Milan. 5 vols., London, Printed at the Minerva Press, for A. K. Newman, 1812. [Publisher's advert.]

—— Lady Durnevor ; or, My Father's Wife. 3 vols., London, Printed at the Minerva Press, for A. K. Newman, 1813. [Publisher's advert : Blakey.]

—— Love, Mystery, and Misery ! A Novel. 2 vols., London, Printed by the Minerva Press, for A. K. Newman, 1810. [B.M. : *Monthly Mag.* : Publisher's advert.]

—— The Miseries of an Heiress. 4 vols., Printed at the Minerva Press, for A. K. Newman, 1810. [Publisher's advert. : *Quarterly Review.*]

—— The Modern Kate ; or, A Husband Perplexed. 2 vols., London, Printed at the Minerva Press, for A. K. Newman, 1811. [Publisher's advert. : *Quarterly Review.* : Blakey.]

—— Sir Owen Glendowr, and other tales. 3 vols., London, Lane, Newman, 1808. [Publisher's advert : Blakey.]

—— The Scotchwoman. 3 vols., London, Printed at the Minerva Press, by A. K. Newman, 1814. [*New Monthly Mag.* : Publisher's advert : Blakey.]

Holstein, Esther. Ernestina ; A Novel. 2 vols., 1801. [Allibone.]

Home for the Holidays. London, J. Chidley, 1835. [B.M. (2nd edn.)]

Home Happiness ; or, Three Weeks in Snow. With a frontispiece. London, Hatchard, 1838. [Block.]

Home Mission (The) : an Irish Story ; founded on fact. Dublin, Robertson, 1840. [B.M. : *I. in F.*]

Homely, Martha. Maids as they are not and Wives they Are. 4 vols., London, J. D. Dewick, 1803. [Fletcher.]

Honest London Spy (The) : exhibiting the base and subtle intrigues of the Town, in a number of essays, serious and comical. By Peeping Tim. To which is added, The Obliging Husband and Imperious Wife, in a number of pleasant dialogues. Galway, [1779]. [B.M.]

Honesty, the Best Policy, being the history of a Ferryman. London, Religious Tract Society, [1830 ?]. [B.M.]

Honor Delafont ; or, the Mother's Prayer. By the Author of " Sunsetting." London, 1849. [B.M.]

Honour and Shame. A Novel. 3 vols., London, Richard Bentley, 1845. [B.M.]

Hood, Thomas. National Tales. With Lithographs by T. Dighton. 2 vols., London, William H. Ainsworth, 1827. [Birrell & Garnett : B.M. : Arthur Rogers.]

—— Tylney Hall. 3 vols., London, A. H. Baily. 1834. [Birrell & Garnett : B.M. : James Glaisher.]

Hood, Thomas. Up the Rhine. With woodcuts. London, A. H. Baily. 1840. [Block.]

Hook, James. Pen Owen. 3 vols., Edinburgh, William Blackwood; and T. Cadell, London, 1822. [B.M.: John Orr: Arthur Rogers.]

—— Percy Mallory. By the Author of Pen Owen. 3 vols., Edinburgh, William Blackwood; and T. Cadell, London, 1824. [B.M.: Ingpen: Pickering.]

Hook, Sarah Ann. Secret Machinations; a Novel. 4 vols., London, 1804. [Allibone.]

—— The Widowed Bride, or, Celina. a Novel. 3 vols., 1802. [Allibone.]

Hook, Theodore Edward. Births, Deaths, and Marriages. By the Author of "Sayings & Doings;" "Maxwell;" "John Brag;" &c. 3 vols., London, Richard Bentley, 1839. [B.M.]

—— Fathers and Sons: A Novel. With a portait. 3 vols., London, Henry Colburn, 1842. [B.M.: G. Worthington.]

—— Gilbert Gurney. By the Author of "Sayings and Doing," "Love and Pride," etc. 3 vols., London, Whittaker, 1836. [B.M.: Ingpen: J. Preston.]

—— Gurney Married: A Sequel to Gilbert Gurney. By the Author of "Sayings and Doings." 3 vols., London, Henry Colburn, 1838. [B.M.: Clarke-Hall: Ingpen.]

—— Jack Brag. By the Author of "Sayings and Doings," "Maxwell," &c. 3 vols., London, Richard Bentley, 1837. [B.M.: Pickering: J. Preston.]

—— Love and Pride. By the Author of "Sayings and Doings," etc. 3 vols., London, Whittaker, 1833. [Birrell & Garnet: B.M.: W. Brown.]

—— The Man of Sorrow. 3 vols., London, 1809. [Allibone.]

—— Maxwell. By the Author of "Sayings and Doings." 3 vols., London, Henry Colburn & Richard Bentley, 1830. [Birrell & Garnet: B.M.: Publisher's advert.]

—— The Parson's Daughter. By the Author of "Sayings and Doings." &c. 3 vols., London, Richard Bentley, 1833. [B.M.: W. Brown: Ingpen.]

—— Peregrine Brunce; Or, Settled at last. A Novel. 3 vols., London, Richard Bentley, 1842. [B.M.]

—— Precepts and Practice. With a portrait. 3 vols., London, Henry Colburn, 1840. [B.M.: Guntrip & Richardson: Ingpen.]

—— Sayings and Doings. A Series Of Sketches from Life. 3 vols., London, Henry Colburn, 1824. [B.M.: Foyle: Lib. of Congress.]

—— Sayings and Doings, Or Sketches from Life. Second Series. 3 vols., London, Henry Colburn, 1825. [B.M.: Ingpen: Elkin Mathews.]

—— Sayings and Doings; Or Sketches from Life Third Series. 3 vols.,

London, Henry Colburn, 1828. [B.M.: Clarke-Hall: Ingpen.]

Hook, Theodore Edward. Tentamen; or, an Essay towards the History of Whittington and his Cat, by Dr. Vicesimus Blenkinsop. With a vignette portrait. 1820. [Allibone: Dobell.]

Hookham, ——. The Modern Husband; A Novel. 2 vols., 1769. [Allibone.]

Hoole, Innes. Hearts *versus* Heads; Or, Diamond Cut Diamond. A Novel. 3 vols., London, A. K. Newman, 1823. [B.M.: Stonehill.]

—— Scenes at Brighton; Or, "How Much?" A Satirical Novel. 3 vols., London, A. K. Newman, 1821. [B.M.: Ingpen: Marks.]

—— Society and Solitude. A Novel. 3 vols., London, A. K. Newman, 1821. [B.M.]

Hooton, Charles. Adventures of Bilberry Thurland. With etchings by A. Hervieu. 3 vols., London, Richard Bentley, 1836. [B.M.: Ingpen: W. T. Spencer.]

—— Colin Clink. With illustrations by John Leech. 3 vols., London, Richard Bentley, 1841. [B.M.: James Glaisher.]

—— Launcelot Wedge. A novel. 3 vols., London, T. C. Newby, 1849. [B.M.]

—— Woodhouselee; Or, The Astrologer. 3 vols., London, Parry, 1848. [B.M.]

Hope, Thomas. Anastasius: Or, Memoirs of a Greek; Written at the Close of The Eighteenth Century. 3 vols., London, John Murray, 1819. [B.M.: Cleverdon: Arthur Rogers.]

Horne, M. J. [*See* ADVENTURES OF NAUFRAGUS.]

Horne, Richard Hengist. The Good-Natured Bear. A story for children of all ages. London, Joseph Cundall, 1846. [B.M.]

Horrible Revenge (The), or, the Assassin of the Solitary Castle. With illustrations. London, J. Fairburn, [1830?] [B.M.]

Horrors of Oakendale Abbey. By the Author of Elizabeth. [Mrs. Carver.] London, Minerva Press, 1797. [Stonehill: *Minerva Press Catalogue.*]

Hort, Lieut.-Col. J. J. The Days when we had Tails on us. With 12 illustrations. London, J. & D. A. Darling, 1848. [Publisher's advert.]

—— The Horse Guards. By the Two Mounted Sentries. With 12 illustrations. London, J. & D. A. Darling, 1848. [Publisher's advert.]

—— The Man who eloped with his own Wife. London, J. D. Darling, 1850. [B.M.: Lib. of Congress.]

—— Penelope Wedgebone: The Supposed Heiress. With 8 plates by Alfred Ashley. London, J. & D. A. Darling. 1850. [Block: B.M.: T. D. Webster.]

113

Hort, Lieut.-Col. J. J. The Secretary. A Novel. 3 vols., London, J. & D. A. Darling, 1850. [B.M.]

—— The White Charger, that cost me £200 ; lost me £70,000 ; drove me from Society ; eventually deprived me of my friends ; and finally compelled me to quit the Service. By the Author of " The Horse Guards," " The Days when we had Tails on us," &c. With 2 illustrations by Alfred Ashley. London, J. & D. A. Darling, 1850. [B.M. : Publisher's advert.]

Horwood, Caroline. The Castle of Vivaldi; Or, The Mysterious Injunction. A novel. 4 vols., London, Minerva Press, 1810. [Ingpen : *Monthly Mag. :* Blakey.]

—— Drawing-Room Tales, historical and traditional. London, [1820 ?]. [B.M.]

—— Original Moral Tales for Children. [Allibone.]

—— St. Otsburg ; or, the Carmelite Monk : A Romance. 4 vols., 1811. [*Quarterly Review.*]

Houghton, Mary. The Border Chieftains ; Or, Love and Chivalry, A Novel. 3 vols., London, Printed at the Minerva Press, for A. K. Newman, 1813. [Publisher's advert. : *Quarterly Review* : Stonehill.]

—— The Mysteries of the Forest. 3 vols., London, A. K. Newman, 1810. [*Eng. Cat. : Monthly Mag. : Quarterly Review.*]

House of Lancaster (The) ; Or, The Story of Ap Thomas. An Historical Novel. 2 vols., London, J. F. Hughes, 1810. [Blackwell : B.M. : Murray Hill.]

House of Marley. A Novel. 2 vols., London, William Lane, 1797. [Blakey.]

House That Jack Built (The). A diverting story for children of all ages. [London], Aldermary Church-York, [1770 ?]. [B.M.]

Howard, Miss. Married Life ; or, Faults on all sides. 5 vols., London, Minerva Press, 1811. [Blakey.]

Howard, Anne. Mary Spencer ; a tale for the times. London, 1844. [B.M.]

—— Ridley Seldom, or, The way to keep Lent. A Tale for the times. London, 1845. [B.M.]

Howard. Lieut. the Hon. Edward Granville George. Jack Ashore. By the Author of " Rattlin the Reefer," " Outward Bound," &c. &c. 3 vols., London, Henry Colburn, 1840. [B.M. : *Guide to Best Fiction :* Sadleir.]

—— The Old Commodore. By the Author of " Rattlin the Reefer," &c. 3 vols., London, Richard Bentley, 1837. [B.M. : Sadleir : T. Thorp.]

—— Outward Bound ; Or The Merchant's Adventures. By The author of " Rattlin, the Reefer," " The Old Commodore," &c. 3 vols., London, Henry Colburn, 1838. [B.M. : Sadleir : T. Thorp.]

Howard, Lieut. the Hon. Edward Granville George. Rattlin, The Reefer. Edited by the author of " Peter Simple." With etchings by A. Hervieu. 3 vols., London, Richard Bentley. 1836. [B.M. : Henry : Sadleir.]

—— Sir Henry Morgan The Buccaneer. By The author of " Rattlin the Reefer," " Outward Bound," " Jack Ashore," &c. With a portrait. 3 vols., London, Henry Colburn, 1842. [B.M. : Sadleir.]

Howard, Lady Harriet. The Birthday : a tale for the Young. By the Author of " Gideon," etc. London, 1844. [B.M.]

Howard, Mary Matilda. Brampton Rectory, or, the Lesson of Life. London, Parker, 1849. [B.M.]

—— Compton Merivale. Another leaf from the lesson of life. By the Author of Brampton Rectory ; or, the Lesson of Life. London, Parker, 1850. [Baker's Bookshop : B.M. : G. Worthington.]

Howard Castle ; Or A Romance From the Mountains. By a North Briton. 5 vols., London, Printed at the Minerva Press, for A. K. Newman, 1817. [B.M. : *Monthly Mag. : New Monthly Mag.*]

Howell, Mrs. Anzoletta Zadoski. A Novel. 2 vols., London, Lane, Minerva Press, 1796. [A. Filcek : Ingpen : Stonehill.]

—— Georgina, a Novel. With a frontispiece. 2 vols., London, William Lane, 1796. [Allibone : *New Ann. Reg. :* Pickering.]

—— Rosenberg. A legendary tale. By a lady. 2 vols., London, W. Lane, 1789. [Ingpen : *Minerva Press Catalogue :* Blakey.]

—— The Spoiled Child ; a Novel. 2 vols., London, Minerva Press, 1797. [Allibone : *New Ann. Reg. :* Stonehill.]

Howison, John. Tales of the Colonies. 2 vols., London, Henry Colburn and Richard Bentley, 1830. [B.M. : Francis Edwards : Publisher's advert.]

Howitt, Mary. Alice Franklin. A tale. Another part of " Sowing and Reaping." London, 1843. [B.M.]

—— The Childhood of Mary Leeson. [London, 1848]. [B.M.]

—— The Children's Year. With 4 illustrations by John Absolon, from original designs by Anna Mary Howitt. London, Longman, Brown, Green, and Longmans, 1847. [Block.]

—— The Citizen of Prague. Translated by Mary Howitt. 3 vols., London, Henry Colburn, 1846. [*Critic.*]

—— Hope on, Hope ever ! a tale. London, 1840. [B.M.]

—— Little Coin, Much Care ; or How poor men live. A tale. London, [1842]. [B.M.]

—— Love and Money. An every day tale. London, [1843]. [B.M.]

—— My Uncle the Clockmaker. A tale. Illus. London, William Tegg. [1844]. [B.M. : Block.]

114

Howitt, Mary. No Sense Like Common Sense ; or, Some passages in the Life of Charles Middleton, Esq. With a frontispiece and an engraved title. London, Thomas Tegg, 1843. [B.M.: Gumuchian.]
—— The Seven Temptations. London, Richard Bentley, 1834. [B.M. : *Eng. Cat.*]
—— Sowing and Reaping : or, What will come of it ? London, 1841. [B.M. (2nd edn.).]
—— Strive and thrive. A tale. London, 1840. [B.M.]
—— Tales in Prose. With plates. London, William Darton, [1836]. [Colbeck.]
—— The two Apprentices. A tale for youth. London, 1844. [B.M.]
—— Which is the Wiser ; or people abroad. A tale for youth. London, 1842. [B.M.]
—— Wood Leighton ; Or, A Year in the Country. 3 vols., London, Richard Bentley, 1836. [Backus : Block : B.M.]
—— Work and Wages ; or, Life in Service. London, 1842. [B.M.]
Howitt, William. The Hall and the Hamlet ; or scenes and characters of country life. 2 vols., London, Henry Colburn, 1848. [B.M. : Publisher's advert. : G. Worthington.]
—— The Life and Adventures of Jack of the Mill, Commonly called " Lord Othmill " ; created, for his Eminent Services, Baron Waldeck and Knight of Kilcottie. A Fireside Story. With 40 woodcuts by G. F. Sargent. 2 vols., London, Longman, Brown, Green, and Longmans, 1844. [B.M. : Pickering : Publisher's advert.]
—— Pantika : Or, Traditions Of the Most Ancient Times. 2 vols., London, Whittaker, 1835. [B.M. : Pickering.]
Hubback, Mrs. J. The Younger Sister : a novel. 3 vols., London, T. C. Newby, 1850. [Allibone.]
Hubbub (The) ; or, the history of Farmer Russel, the hard-hearted overseer. London, J. Marshall, [1797 ?]. Cheap Repository. [B.M.]
Huber, V. A. Francis and Josepha, A Tale By William Fardley. From the German of Huber. 1808. [B.M.]
—— Stories of Spanish Life. From the German of Huber. Edited by Lieut.-Col. Craufurd. 2 vols., London, Henry Colburn, 1837. [B.M. : Lib. of Congress.]
Hudson, Mrs. Almack's. A Novel. 3 vols., London, Saunders & Otley, 1826. [B.M. : Court Bk. Shop : John Smith.]
Hughes, Anne. Caroline ; or, The Diversities of Fortune : A Novel. 3 vols., 1787. [*Eng. Lit. in Germany* : Blakey.]
—— Henry and Isabella ; or, A Traite through Life. By the Author of " Caroline, or The Diversities of Fortune." 4 vols., London, William Lane, 1788. [B.M. : *Eng. Lit. in Germany* : Stonehill.]

Hughes, Anne. Jemima. A novel. By the author of Zoriada, or Village annals, &c. With a frontispiece. London, William Lane, 1795. [Blakey : Ingpen : Stonehill.]
Hughes, Mary. The Alchemist. By the Author of " Ornaments Discovered ; " " The Metamorphoses, Or Effects of Education ; " " Aunt Mary's Tales for her Nephews and Nieces," &c. With frontispiece. London, Printed for William Darton, Jun. By R. and A. Taylor, 1813. [B.M.]
—— Aunt Mary's Tales, for the Entertaiment and Improvement of Little Girls. With a frontispiece. London, Darton, Harvey and Darton, 1817. [Arthur Rogers.]
—— The Metamorphoses ; Or, the Effects of Education, a Tale. By the Author of Aunt Mary's Tales. With a frontispiece. London, William Darton, Jun. 1818. [B.M. : Gumuchian.]
—— The Ornaments Discovered : a Story in two parts. By the Author of Aunt Mary's Tales. London, Darton, 1815. [*Eng. Cat. : New Monthly Mag.*]
—— The Orphan Girl ; a moral tale. London, W. Darton, 1819. [B.M. : *Camb. Hist. Eng. Lit.* : Arthur Rogers.]
—— Pleasing and instructive Stories for young children. With 6 plates. London, [1830 ?]. [B.M.]
—— The Rebellious School-Girl ; a tale. London, 1821. [B.M.]
—— Something new from Aunt Mary. (The Little Adventurer. Founded on fact.) London, W. Darton, 1820. [B.M.]
Hughes, Robert. Coberley Hall. A Gloucestershire Tale of the Fourteenth Century. With a frontispiece. Cheltenham, Griffith, 1824. [Stonehill.]
Hughes, William. The Three Students Of Gray's Inn. A Novel. 3 vols., London, T. C. Newby, 1846. [B.M. : McLeish.]
Hugill, Mrs. Isidora of Gallicia. 2 vols., 1797. [*Eng. Lit. in Germany : New Ann. Reg.*]
Hugo, Victor. Hans of Iceland. With illustrations by George Cruikshank. London, J. Robins, 1825. [Block : B.M. : Arthur Rogers.]
—— The Last Day of a Condemned, From the French of Victor Hugo. With Observations on Capital Punishment, by Sir P. Hesketh Fleetwood. London, Smith, Elder, 1840. [B.M. : Arthur Rogers : Victorius.]
—— The Noble Rival ; Or, The Prince of Congo. With illustrations. London, George Peirce, [1845]. [B.M. : Court Bk. Shop.]
—— Notre-Dame ; A Tale of the " Ancien Régime ; " From the French of M. Victor Hugo ; With a Prefatory Notice, Literary and Political Of his Romances. By the Translator of Thierry's " History of the Conquest of

England by the Normans," And of Wilson's Edition of "Lafayette, Louis-Philippe, and The Revolution of 1830." [William Hazlitt.] With a portrait. 3 vols., London, Effingham Wilson, 1833. [B.M.]

Hugo, Victor. The Slave King, from the Bug-Jargal of Victor Hugo. 1833. [B.M.: Arthur Rogers.]

Huish, Robert. Edwin and Henry ; Or, the Week's Holiday. With woodcuts by Branston after Brook. D. Mackay, [1810].

—— Fatherless Rosa ; Or, The Dangers of The Female Life. 1834. [Ingpen.]

—— Fitzallan By a Blue. With engraved titles and plates. 2 vols., London, Thomas Kelly, 1832. [B.M.]

—— The Nun of Gnadenzell. A Romance. With woodcuts. London, Edward Lloyd, 1846. [B.M.: B. Ono.]

—— Our Grandpapa's chest : being a companion to our Grandmamma's clock : containing a series of tales. London, Allman, [1850]. [B.M.]

—— The Progress of Crime ; or, Authentic Memoirs of Marie Manning. With woodcuts. London, 1849. [B.M.: Holland : Stonehill.]

Hull, Thomas. Genuine Letters from a Gentleman to a Young Lady his Pupil. Calculated to form the Taste, Regulate the Judgment, and improve the Morals. Now first revised and published by T. Hull. 2 vols., London, Bell, 1772. [B.M.: Stonehill.]

—— The History of Sir William Harrington. Written some years since, and revised and corrected by the late Mr. Richardson. 4 vols., London, Bell, 1771. [Stonehill.]

Human Frailties. A Novel interspersed with poetry. By the author of "The Observant Pedestrian." London, 1803. [B.M.]

Human Heart (The). London, Taylor and Hessey, 1824. [B.M.]

Human Nature : a Novel. 1815. [*New Monthly Mag.*]

Human Vicissitudes, or Travels into unexplored Regions. 2 vols., 1798. [*New Ann. Reg.*]

Hume, Grace Stuart. Alice, or Infidelity ; The Trifler ; and My Aunt Anne. Three Tales. 5 vols., London, A. K. Newman, 1823. [B.M.: *New Monthly Mag.*]

Humorous Adventures of Jump Jim Crow. Glasgow, [1840 ?]. [B.M.]

Humourist, (The): A Collection of Entertaining Tales, Anecdotes, Repartees, Witty Sayings, Epigrams, Bon Mots, Jeu d'Esprits, &c. Carefully selected. With 40 plates by George Cruikshank. 4 vols., London, James Robins, 1819-1820. [Block : Sawyer.]

Hundred Years Hence ; or The Memoirs of Charles, Lord Moresby, Written by Himself. London, Longman, Rees, Orme, Brown, & Green, 1828. [B.M.]

Hunt, James Henry Leigh. Sir Ralph Esher, or Adventures of A Gentleman of the Court of Charles II. 3 vols., London, Henry Colburn and Richard Bentley, 1832. [Dr. A. Mitchell describes an earlier issue: "Sir Ralph Esher ; or, Memoirs of the Court of Charles II. 3 vols., 1830."]. [B.M.: Ingpen : Publisher's advert.]

Hunt, Robert. Panthea, the Spirit of Nature. London, H. Bohn, 1849. [B.M.: Lib. of Congress.]

Hunt, Thornton. The Foster-Brother : A Tale of The War of Chiozza. Edited by Leigh Hunt. 3 vols., London, T. C. Newby, [1845]. [King.]

Hunter, Maria. Ella, or He's always in the Way. 2 vols., London, W. Lane, 1798. [*New Ann. Reg.* : Blakey.]

—— Fitzroy; Or, The Impulse of the Moment. A Novel. 2 vols., London, William Lane, 1792. [Baker's Bookshop : Arthur Rogers : Blakey.]

—— Lady McLairn, the Victim of Villainy. 4 vols., London, 1806. [Baker's Bookshop.]

Hunter, Rachel. Family Annals ; or, worldly wisdom. A novel. 5 vols., London, 1808. [B.M. (2nd edn.).]

—— The History of the Grubthorpe Family, or the Old Batchelor and his Sister Penelope. 3 vols., Norwich, W. Robberds, 1802. [P. C. Cuttelle : Francis Edwards.]

—— Letitia ; or, the Castle without a Spectre. 4 vols., London, 1801. [B.M.]

—— Letters from Mrs. Palmerstone to her Daughter, inculcating morality by entertaining narratives. 3 vols., London, 1803. [B.M.]

—— The Schoolmistress ; a moral tale for young ladies. 2 vols., London, Printed at the Minerva Press, for A. K. Newman, 1811. [B.M.: Publisher's advert.]

—— The Unexpected Legacy. 2 vols., London, A. K. Newman. [Publisher's advert, 1812.]

Huntington, Jedediah Vincent. Lady Alice ; or, the New Una. A Novel. 3 vols., London, 1849. [McLeish.]

Huntley, Sir Henry Veel. Peregrine Scramble ; or Thirty Years Adventures of a Blue Jacket. 2 vols., London, Richard Bentley, 1849. [B.M.]

Hurlstone, Isaac. The Fatal Interview ; Or the Danger of Unbridled Passion. A Controversy, designed to improve and Strengthen the mind in virtue and piety. London, Simpkin, Marshall 1835. [B.M.]

Hurry, Mrs. Moral Tales for Young People. 1807. [*Camb. Hist. Eng. Lit.*]

Hurry, Mrs. Ives. Rational Amusement for leisure hours ; consisting of interesting tales for the mental improvement of Youth. With a frontispiece and 13 woodcuts. London, J. Harris, 1804. [B.M.]

Hurry, Mrs. Ives. Tales Of Instruction And Amusement, Written for the use Of Young Persons. With frontispieces. 2 vols., London, E. Newbery, 1795. [B.M. : Victorius.]

Hurstone, H. P. Dorinda Grafton. A domestic tale. 3 vols., London, 1808. [B.M.]

Hurstone, J. P. An Autumn in Cheltenham ; or, Mysteries in High Life. A fashionable novel. 3 vols., London, 1808. [B.M.]

Husband and Wife (The) ; or, The Matrimonial Martyr. By Mrs. Bridget Bluemantle. 3 vols., Minerva Press, 1807. [Blakey.]

Husband Forced to be Jealous (The) : or, the Good Fortune of those Women that have Jealous Husbands. Being the Secret History of several Noble Persons ; a very Entertaining History, and founded on Real Facts, and not the Result of an inventive Fancy, as many Books are. Translated from the French. London, John Lever, 1765. [Block (2nd edn.).]

Husband Hunters ! ! ! A Novel. By the Author of Montreithe, or The Peer of Scotland. [Amelia Beauclerc.] 4 vols., London, Printed at the Minerva Press, for A. K. Newman, 1816. [B.M. : *New Monthly Mag.* : Blakey.]

Husband Hunting : or, the Mother and Daughters. A tale. 3 vols., London, G. B. Whittaker, 1825. [B.M. : *Edin. Mag.*]

Husband's Resentment (The); Or, the History of Lady Manchester. A Novel. 2 vols., London, T. Lowndes, 1776. [B.M. : Tregaskis.]

Hutchinson, Miss A. A. Exhibitions of the Heart ; a Novel. Dedicated (by Permission) to the Queen. 4 vols., London, Printed for the Author, 1799. [B.M. : Elkin Mathews.]

—— Friends Unmasked ; or Scenes in Real Life. A novel founded on facts. 3 vols., London, Longman, 1812. [B.M. : *New Monthly Mag.*]

Hutchinson, P. O. Chronicles of Gretna Green. 2 vols., London, Richard Bentley, 1844. [Bailey Bros. ; B.M. : *Eng. Cat.*]

Hutton, Catharine. Miser Married. A Novel. 3 vols., London, Longman. Rees, Orme & Brown, 1813. [J. C. Hardy : Murray Hill.]

—— Oakwood Hall, A Novel ; Including a Description of The Lakes Of Cumberland and Westmoreland, And A part of South Wales. 3 vols., London, Printed by Strahan and Spottiswoode, for Longman, Hurst, Rees, Orme, and Brown, 1819. [B.M. : Publisher's advert.]

—— The Welsh Mountaineer : A Novel. 3 vols., London, Longman, Hurst, Rees, Orme, and Brown, 1817. [B.M. : *Literary Panorama : New Monthly Mag.*]

Hutton, George. Amantes ; a Novel. London, 1794. [Allibone.]

Hutton, R. N. Jealousy, a novel. By the Author of " Five Years in the East." 3 vols., London, T. C. Newby, 1849. [B.M. : Foyle.]

Hyde Nugent. A Tale of Fashionable Life. 3 vols., London, Henry Colburn, 1827. [B.M. : Elkin Mathews.]

Hyppolitus ; or, the Wild Boy. A novel. Translated from the French. 4 vols., London, Lane, Newman, and Co. 1805. [B.M.]

I Can Do Without It. With a woodcut. London, Houlston, N.D. No. 46 of Houlston's Series of Tracts. [Block.]

I Heard It Said So. By the Author of " Thomas Brown," &c &c. With a woodcut. London, Houlston, N.D. No. 49 of Houlston's Series of Tracts. [Block.]

Iberian Tales and Novels. As they were publickly rehearsed for the entertainment of the Spanish Nobility : by that celebrated Lady Donna Isabella. Containing many surprizing amours. London, 1745. [B.M.]

Ida of Austria ; or, the Knights of the Holy Cross. A Romance. 3 vols., 1811. [*Quarterly Review.*]

Idalia. A novel. Founded on facts. 2 vols., London, Minerva Press, 1800. [Baker's Bookshop.]

Idiot Heiress (The). A Novel. 2 vols., London, Minerva Press, 1805. [Stonehill.]

Idolatry of the Heart (The). A Tale by Eliza. With a frontispiece. Derby, [1830]. [Gilbert Jamieson.]

Iliff, Mrs. The Prior Claim. 2 vols., London, Printed at the Minerva Press, by A. K. Newman, 1813. [Publisher's advert.]

Iliff, Edward Henry. Angelo ; a Novel. 2 vols., London, 1796. [Allibone : *New Ann. Reg.*]

I'll Consider of It. A Tale. In which " Think I to myself " is partially considered. 3 vols., London, 1812. [B.M. : *Quarterly Review.*]

Ill Effects of A Rash Vow (The) ; a novel, in a series of letters. 2 vols., London, William Lane, 1789. [Blakey.]

Illusions of Sentiment, A Descriptive and Historic Novel. London, Axtell, 1788. [Stonehill.]

I'm Afloat, I'm Afloat : or, Roderick the Rover. A Romance. With woodcuts. London, E. Lloyd, [1848]. [B.M. : B. Ono.]

Imaginary Adultress (The). 2 vols., London, Printed by E. Thomas for Corri, 1808. [B.M.]

Immelina, Countess de Mansfield. A German tale. 3 vols., [W. Lane.], 1799. [*New Ann. Reg.*]

117

Imogen. A pastoral romance. From the ancient British. 2 vols., [W. Lane, 1784]. [Blakey.]

Impartial History of the Life, Amours, Travels and Transactions of Mr. John Barker, Lord Mayor of London. 1741. [*Cat. Lib. Prohib.*]

Impetuous Lover (The), or the Guiltless Parricide. By A. G. Esquire. 2 vols., London, 1757. [B.M.]

Important Trifles. Chiefly designed for the entertainment and instruction of youth, 3 vols., London, R. Snagg, 1793. [B.M.]

Improving Tales. Containing The Storm ; Beauty and Deformity ; the Midshipman and Athlone Castle. London, Newman, 1825. [B.M.]

In School and Out of School or the History of William and John. An interesting Tale. By One who knows Both. With a frontispiece and 2 plates by S. Bellin after R. Seymour. London, Dean and Munday, 1827. [Arthur Rogers.]

In What Manner Little Henry came to the Knowledge of God. A story for children, from the German. London, 1827. [B.M.]

Inatulla. Bahar-Danush ; or, Garden of Knowledge. An Oriental Romance. Translated from the Persic of Einaiut Oolah by Jonathan Scott. 3 vols., Shrewsbury, J. and W. Eddowes, 1799. [Baker's Bookshop : B.M. : Maggs.]

—— Tales (the Baar Danesh) translated from the Persian of Inatulla of Delhi [by Alexander Dow]. 2 vols., London, 1768. [Allibone : B.M. : *Progress of Romance.*]

Inchbald, Elizabeth. Nature and Art. 2 vols., London, 1796. [*Guide to Best Fiction :* Parker & Son : Arthur Rogers.]

—— A Simple Story. 4 vols., London, G. G. J. and J. Robinson, 1791. [B.M. : Ingpen : Pickering.]

Incognita (The) ; or, Emily Villars. A novel. In a series of letters. 2 vols., [W. Lane, 1783.] [Blakey.]

Incredulous Boy (The) ; Or, The Story Of George Berry. And Stratagem of a Scotch Pedlar. With woodcuts. London, James Wallis, [1840 ?]. [B.M.]

Indian Adventurer (The) ; or History of Mr. Vanneck, a novel, founded on facts. London, W. Lane, 1780, [Blakey.]

Indian Juggler ; or, The True History of Old Shusco. With a woodcut. London, William Jones, N.D. [Block.]

Indiscreet Marriage, Or Henry and Sophia Somerville. 3 vols., 1779. [W. Brown.]

Industry : A Tale of Real Life, consisting of a Series of Interesting Occurrences, illustrative of Felicity accruing from a Steady Perseverance in Diligence and Economy. London, H. R. Thomas, 1825. [Elkin Mathews.]

Infant Stories : intended to convince little girls that to be good is to be happy. In words not exceeding two Syllables. With illustrations. London, Harvey and Darton, 1825. [Block : B.M.]

Infantile Tales, With a Continuation of the History of the Little Curricle of Yellow Pasteboard. With woodcuts. London, J. Harris, 1803. [Dobell.]

Influence and Example ; Or, The Recluse. A Tale. By the Author of " Dangerous Errors." London, Lupton Relff, 1823. [B.M. : Ingpen : *Quarterly Review.*]

Ingemann, Bernhard Severin. Waldemar Surnamed Seir, or the Victorious. Translated from The Danish of B. S. Ingemann By a Lady [Jane Frances Chapman]. 3 vols., London, Saunders and Otley, 1841. [B.M.]

Inglis, Henry David. The New Gil Blas ; Or, Pedro of Penaflor. 3 vols., London, Longman, Rees, Orme, Brown, Green, & Longman, 1832. [B.M. : Francis Edwards : Ingpen.]

—— Scenes from the Life Of Edward Lascelles, Gent. With illustrations by George Cruikshank. 2 vols., Dublin, William Curry, Jun., Simpkin, Marshall, London ; Fraser, Edinburgh, 1837. [B.M.]

—— Solitary Walks through Many Lands. 2 vols., London, Hurst, 1828. [*Eng. Cat. : Quarterly Review.*]

—— Tales of Ardennes. By Derwent Conway. London, G. B. Whittaker, 1825. [B.M.]

Inhuman Stepmother (The) ; or, the History of Miss Harriot Montague. Founded on Facts. 2 vols., London, J. Roson, 1770. [Publisher's advert.]

Injured Innocence : Or the Rape of Sarah Woodcock. A Tale Founded on Facts. Compiled partly from the Trial of Lord Baltimore, partly from papers found after his decease, and arranged without the ommital of any of the facts, given in evidence by Sarah Woodcock, at the Trial. By S—— J—— Esq. of Magdelene College, Oxford. Author of " The Lustful Turk," " The Inutility of Virtue," " Seducing Cardinal," " Scenes in the Seraglio," " Seduction of Sontag," " Domestic Discipline, or every one to his own Taste." With 8 lithographs. New York, Printed for the Booksellers [London, William Dugdale, 1840]. [*Cat. Lib. Prohib.*]

Inklings of Adventure. 3 vols., 1836. [Clarke-Hall : T. Thorp.]

Innocence Betrayed ; or the perjured lover. Being a true account of Miss Sarah Moreton. York, J. Kendrew, [1820 ?]. [B.M.]

Inquisition (The). 2 vols., 1797. [*New Ann. Reg.*]

Insinuating Bawd (The), and the repenting harlot. To which is added The six nights rambles, etc. [London], 1758. [B.M.]

118

Integrity, or the Artist Stanton and his daughters. By S. S. J. London, Palmer, 1849. [B.M.]

Integrity, or the History of Sophia Francourt, from the French. 2 vols., London, W. Beilby, 1790. [T. Thorp.]

Interesting Adventures of a Little White Mouse (The). With woodcuts. Birmingham, T. Bloomer ; and A. Carvalho, London, [1840 ?). [B.M.]

Interesting Story of Edwin and Julia (The) ; being a rational enquiry into the nature of things. In a series of letters. By a Doctor of Physic, M.A. London, [1788]. [B.M.]

Interesting Tales, Consisting of Isidore, Arthur, The Clear-sighted Blind Man, Robert and the Hogshead. Translated from the French by a Lady. London, Vernor and Hood, 1805. [Ingpen : T. D. Webster.]

Interesting Tales, Selected and Translated from the German. Containing : The Biography of a Spaniel, The Mask, The Florist, The Robber, The April Fool, The Idiot. London, Printed for W. Lane, by the Minerva Press, 1797. [Baker's Bookshop : Ingpen : *Minerva Press Catalogue.*]

Intrigue a la Mode, Or the Covent Garden Atlantis, containing the Adventures of the most celebrated ladies of the neighbourhood. London, 1761. [*Cat. Lib. Prohib.*]

Intriguing Beauty, and the Beauty without Intrigue. 3 vols., London, T. & J. Allman, 1819. [B.M.]

Inutility of Virtue (The). Translated from the French by Dr. —— of Magdalen College, Oxford. With 8 plates. London, Madam Le Duck [J. B. Brookes], 1830. [*Cat. Lib. Prohib.*]

Invasion (The), Or What Might have Been. A Novel. 2 vols., London, Symonds, 1798. [B.M. : *New Ann. Reg. :* Stonehill.]

Invisible Man (The) ; Or Duncam Castle. A novel from the French. 2 vols., London, Printed at the Minerva Press for William Lane, 1800. [Stonehill : Blakey.]

Involuntary Inconstant, Or the History of Miss Frankfort. 2 vols., 1772. [W. Brown.]

Iphigenia, a novel. 3 vols., London, William Lane, 1791. [Baker's Bookshop : Blakey.]

Ireland, Samuel William Henry. The Abbess. A Romance. 4 vols., 1799. [*Gentleman's Mag. : New Ann. Reg.*]

—— The Woman of Feeling. 4 vols., London, 1804. [B.M.]

Irish Coquette (The), A Novel. With a frontispiece. 3 vols., London, Saunders and Otley, 1844. [B.M. : *I. in F.*]

Irish Girl (The) : A Religious Tale. By the author of Coelebs Married. With an illustration. London, Walker, 1814. [B.M. : *I. in F.*]

Irish Guardian (The) : A Pathetic Story ; By a Lady. 2 vols., Dublin, 1776. [*I. in F.*]

Irish Pearl (The) ; a Tale of the Time of Queen Anne. Dublin, Oldham, 1850. [B.M. : *I. in F.*]

Irish Peasant (The) ; Or the History of Peter Lacy, And his wife Susan. With a woodcut. London, Printed by Augustus Applegarth, for the Religious Tract Society, [c. 1823]. [Block.]

Irish Priest (The) ; or, What for Ireland ? London, Longman, Brown, Green, &c., 1847. [B.M. : *I. in F.*]

Irish Schoolboy (The). [London], Religious Tract Society, [1830 ?]. [B.M.]

Irish Widow (The). Founded on facts. Dublin, 1828. [B.M.]

Irishman at Home (The) : characteristic sketches of the Irish Peasantry. With 5 woodcuts by George Measom. Dublin, McGlashan & Orr, 1849. [B.M. : *I. in F.*]

Irishman (The) ; or, The Favourite of Fortune : a satirical novel, founded upon facts. 2 vols., London, 1772. [B.M. : *I. in F.*]

Irishmen (The) ; a Military-Political Novel ; by A Native Officer. 2 vols., London, Newman, 1810. [B.M. : *I. in F.*]

Iron Shroud (The) ; Or, Italian Revenge. With a woodcut vignette. Glasgow, Printed for the Booksellers, [1840 ?] [B.M.]

Isaacs, Mrs. Earl Osric ; or the Legend of Rosamund, a Romance. 4 vols., London, Chapple, 1820. [*Eng. Cat. : Monthly Mag.*]

—— Ella St. Lawrence ; Or, the Village of Selwood And its Inhabitants : A Novel. 4 vols., London, C. Chapple, 1809. [B.M. : *Monthly Mag.*]

—— Glenmore Abbey ; or, The Lady of the Rock. A Novel. By the author of Ariel. London, Minerva Press, 1805.

—— Tales of To-day. 3 vols., London, C. Chapple, 1816. [B.M. : *New Monthly Mag.*]

—— The Wandering of Fancy ; consisting of miscellaneous pieces in prose and verse. London, 1812. [*Quarterly Review.*]

Isabel de Barsas ; A Tradition of the Twelfth Century. 3 vols., London, Baldwin, Cradock, and Joy, 1823. [B.M. : *New Monthly Mag.*]

Isabel, or, Influence. London, 1850. [B.M.]

Isabella. A Novel. By the Author of "Rhoda," &c. 3 vols., London, Henry Colburn, 1823. [B.M. : Ingpen : Arthur Rogers.]

Isabella: Or, The Rewards of Good-Nature. A Sentimental Novel Intended Chiefly to Convey United Amusement and Instruction to the Fair Sex. By the Author of the Benevolent Man and the History of Lady Anne Neville. 2 vols., London, Bell, 1776. [Arthur Rogers.]

Isdell, Sarah. The Irish Recluse. 3 vols., 1809. [*Monthly Mag.*]

Isn't It Odd? By Marmaduke Merrywhistle. 3 vols., London, G. & W. B. Whittaker, 1822. [B.M. : James Glaisher : Ingpen.]

It Was Me, A Tale, by Me, one who cares for Nothing or Nobody. 2 vols., London, Printed at the Minerva Press, by A. K. Newman, 1813. [Blackwell : Publisher's advert : Stonehill.]

Italian Convert (The), A Narrative, Founded on Fact. With a frontispiece. London, Printed for Francis Westley by J. Haddon, 1821. [B.M.]

Italian Marauders (The). A Romance By Anna Matilda. 4 vols., 1809. [*Monthly Mag.*]

Itanoka. 2 Parts. Frontispiece. London, 1810. [Murray Hill.]

Ivy Castle. 2 vols., 1794. [*New Ann. Reg.*]

Jack and Gill, and old Dame Gill. [London], [1810 ?]. [B.M.]

Jack Tench ; or, the Midshipman turned Idler. By Blowhard. With vignette title and 17 plates and cuts by Perch. London, W. Brittain. 1841 [1842]. [B.M. : Marks : Hollings.]

Jackson, James. The Chivalry of Scotland, In the Days of King Robert Bruce, Including The Royal Hunt of Roslin, In which the life of Sir William St. Clair was staked by Bruce, against the Foest and Estate of Pentland, near Edinburgh ; A Tale of Roslin Castle. With a frontispiece. Edinburgh, Bell and Bradfute, 1848. [Block.]

Jacobs, Friedrich C. W. Allwin and Theodore. For The Perusal of Children. Translated from the German. Hamburg, F. Perthes, 1804. [B.M.]

James, George Payne Rainsford. Adra, or the Peruvians ; the Ruined City. London, 1829. [B.M.]

—— Agincourt. A Romance. 3 vols., London, Richard Bentley, 1844. [Block : B.M. : Clarke-Hall.]

—— The Ancient Régime : A Tale. 3 vols., London, Longman, Brown, Green, & Longmans, 1841. [B.M. : E. Hector : McLeish.]

—— Arabella Stuart. A Romance From English History. 3 vols., London, Richard Bentley, 1844. [B.M. : Lib. of Congress : McLeish.]

—— Arrah Neil ; Or, Times of Old. 3 vols., London, Smith, Elder, 1845. [Block : B.M. : Lib. of Congress.]

—— Attila. A Romance. By the Author of " The Gipsy," " Mary of Burgundy," " One in a Thousand," &c. &c. 3 vols., London, Longman, Rees, Orme, Brown, Green, & Longman, 1845. [B.M. : Lib. of Congress : McLeish.]

James, George Payne Rainsford. Beauchamp : Or, The Error. 3 vols., London, Smith, Elder, 1848. [Block : B.M. : Lib. of Congress.]

—— A Book of the Passions. With 16 steel engravings. London, Longman, Orme, 1839. [B.M. : Kyrle Fletcher : Sotheran.]

—— The Castle of Ehrenstein : Its Lords Spiritual and Temporal ; Its Inhabitants, Earthly and Unearthly. 3 vols., London, Smith, Elder, 1847. [Block : B.M. : Ingpen.]

—— Charles Tyrrell ; Or, The Bitter Blood. With a portrait. 3 vols., London, Richard Bentley, 1839. [B.M. : James Glaisher : Lib. of Congress.]

—— The Commissioner ; Or, De Lunatico Inquirendo. With 28 steel plates by Phiz [Hablot K. Browne]. Dublin, William Curry, Jun., 1843. [Birrell & Garnett : B.M. : Lib. of Congress.]

—— The Convict. A Tale. 3 vols., London, Smith, Elder, 1847. [B.M. : Ingpen : McLeish.]

—— Corse de Leon ; Or, The Brigand. A Romance. Dedicated by Permission to His Majesty the King of the Belgians. 3 vols., London, Longman, Orme, Brown, Green, & Longmans, 1841. [B.M. : Foyle : Ingpen.]

—— Dark Scenes of History. 3 vols., London, T. C. Newby, 1849. [Allibone : B.M. : Lib. of Congress.]

—— Darnley ; Or, the Field of the Cloth of Gold. By the author of " Richelieu," &c. 3 vols., London, Henry Colburn and Richard Bentley, 1830. [B.M. : Ingpen ; McLeish.]

—— Delaware ; Or, The Ruined Family. A Tale. 3 vols., Edinburgh, Robert Cadell ; and Whittaker, London, 1833. [B.M.]

—— De L'Orme. By the Author of " Richelieu," and " Darnley." 3 vols., London, Henry Colburn and Richard Bentley, 1830. [Allibone : Block : B.M.]

—— The Desultory Man By the Author of " Richelieu." " The Gipsy," &c. 3 vols., London, Saunders and Otley, 1836. [Block : B.M. : Lib. of Congress.]

—— Eva St. Clair ; And Other Collected Tales. 2 vols., London, Longman, Brown, Green, & Longmans, 1843. [Allibone : B.M.]

—— The False Heir. 3 vols., London, Richard Bentley, 1843. [B.M. : Lib. of Congress : Maggs.]

—— The Fight of the Fiddlers : A Serio-Comic Verity. With illustrations by H. K. Browne. London, David Bogue, 1849. [B.M. : Ingpen : Pickering.]

—— Forest Days. A Romance of Old Times. 3 vols., London, Saunders and Otley, 1843. [B.M. : Lib. of Congress : McLeish.]

James, George Payne Rainsford. The Forgery, Or, Best Intentions. 3 vols, London, T. C. Newby, 1849. B.M. : Ingpen : Lib. of Congress.]

—— Gaston de Foix. A Romance Of the Sixteenth Century. 3 vols., London, John Mortimer, 1844. [B.M.]

—— The Gentleman Of The Old School. A Tale. 3 vols., London, Longman, Orme, Brown, Green & Longmans, 1839. [B.M. : Lib. of Congress : Maggs.]

—— The Gipsy ; A Tale. By the Author of " Richelieu," " Mary of Burgundy," &c. &c. 3 vols., London, Longman, Rees, Orme, Brown, Green & Longman, 1835. [B.M. : Ingpen : Lib. of Congress.]

—— Gowrie : Or, The King's Plot. With a frontispiece. London, 1848. Allibone : Lib. of Congress : T. Thorp.]

—— Heidelberg. A Romance. 3 vols., London, Smith, Elder, 1846. [B.M. : Lib. of Congress : W. T. Spencer.]

—— Henry Masterton ; Or the Adventures of a Young Cavalier. By the Author of " Richelieu," " Darnley," &c. 3 vols., London, Henry Colburn and Richard Bentley, 1832. [B.M. : Lib. of Congress : McLeish.]

—— Henry of Guise : Or, The States of Blois. 3 vols., London, Longman, Orme, Brown, Green, & Longmans. 1839. [B.M. : Lib. of Congress : Wm. Smith.]

—— The Huguenot : A Tale Of The French Protestants. By the Author of " The Gipsy," " The Robber," &c. &c. 3 vols., London, Longman, 1839. [B.M. : Ingpen : Lib. of Congress.]

—— The Jacquerie ; Or, The Lady and the Page. An Historical Romance. 3 vols., London, Longman, Brown, Green, & Longmans, 1841. [Block : B.M. : Lib. of Congress.]

—— John Jones's Tales for little John Jones's (taken from the History of England). 2 vols., London, 1849. [Allibone : B.M.]

—— The King's Highway : A Novel. 3 vols., London, Longman, Orme, Brown, Green & Longmans, 1840. [Allibone : B.M. : Chas. Hutt.]

—— The Last of the Fairies. With illustrations by Henry Vizetelly after John Gilbert. London, Willoughby, [1847], [Block : B.M. : Lib. of Congress.]

—— The Life and Adventures of John Marston Hall. By the author of " Darnley," " Richelieu," " Henry Masterton," " Mary of Burgundy," &c. 3 vols., London, Longman, Rees, Orme, Brown, Green, & Longman, 1834. [B.M. : Lib. of Congress : Magg.]

—— The Man at Arms : Or, Henri de Cerons. A Romance. London, Richard Bentley, 1840. [B.M. : McLeish : Arthur Rogers.]

—— Margaret Graham : A Tale, Founded on Facts. 2 vols., London,

Parry, 1848. [Block : B.M. : Lib. of Congress.)

James, George Payne Rainsford. Mary of Burgundy ; Or, The Revolt of Ghent, by the author of " Darnley," " Richelieu," " Henry Masterton," &c. 3 vols., London, Longman, Rees, Orme, Brown, Green, & Longman, 1833. [B.M. : Brough : Arthur Rogers.]

—— Morley Ernstein, Or The Tenants of the Heart. 3 vols., London, Saunders and Otley, 1842. [B.M. : McLeish : Arthur Rogers.]

—— My Aunt Pontypool. 3 vols., London, Saunders and Otley, 1835. [Allibone : B.M. : Arthur Rogers.]

—— The Old Oak Chest : A Tale of Domestic Life. 3 vols., London, T. C. Newby, 1850. [Allibone : B.M. : Lib. of Congress.]

—— One in a Thousand ; Or, The Days of Henry Quatre. By the author of " The Gipsy," " Mary of Burgundy," &c. &c. 3 vols., London, Longman, Rees, Orme, Brown, Green, and Longman, 1835. [Birrell & Garnett : Block : B.M.]

—— Philip Augustus ; Or, The Brothers in Arms. By the Author of " Darnley." " De L'Orme," &c. 3 vols., London, Henry Colburn and Richard Bentley, 1831. [B.M. : Lib. of Congress : McLeish.]

—— Richelieu, A Tale of France. 3 vols., London, Henry Colburn, 1829. [Halkett & Laing give the sub-title as *A Tale of the Court of France*.] [B.M. : McLeish : W. T. Spencer.]

—— The Robber : A Tale. By the Author of " Richelieu," " The Gipsy," " Attila," &c. 3 vols., London, Longman, Orme, Brown, Green, & Longmans, 1838. [B.M. : Lib. of Congress : Sanders.]

—— Rose D'Albret ; Or Troublous Times. A Romance. 3 vols., London, Richard Bentley, 1844. [Block : B.M. : Lib. of Congress.]

—— Russell : A Tale Of The Reign of Charles II. 3 vols., London, Smith, Elder, 1847. [Allibone : B.M. : Lib. of Congress.]

—— Sir Theodore Broughton ; Or, Laurel Water. 3 vols., London, Smith, Elder, 1848. [B.M. : Lib. of Congress : Arthur Rogers.]

—— The Smuggler. A Tale. 3 vols., London, Smith, Elder, 1845. [B.M. : Ingpen : Arthur Rogers.]

—— The Step-Mother, or Evil Doings. Printed for Private Circulation, 1845. [Arthur Rogers.]

—— The String of Pearls. By The Author of " Darnley," &c. 2 vols., London, Richard Bentley, 1832. [B.M. : McLeish : Elkin Mathews.]

—— A Whim, and its Consequences. 3 vols., London, Smith, Elder, 1847. [McLeish : Elkin Mathews : G. Worthington.]

James, George Payne Rainsford. The Woodman ; a romance of the times of Richard III. 3 vols., London, T. C. Newby, 1849. [T. Thorp.]

James, J. A. The Pastor's Daughter. With introduction by the author of " The Anxious Inquirer." London, [1844]. [B.M.]

James, J. H. The Banks of the Wye : or Two Summers at Clifton. By the Author of A Winter in Bath. 4 vols., London, F. Crosby, [c. 1810]. [Ingpen.]

—— Corinna of England, and a Heroine in the Shade. A modern romance, by the author of " The Winter in Bath," etc. 2 vols., London, B. Crosby, 1809. [B.M.]

—— The Splendour of Adversity : a domestic story. By the author of " Black Rock House," " Winter in Bath," " Corinna of England," " The Dead Letter Office." 3 vols., London, 1814. [B.M. : *New Monthly Mag.*]

—— A Winter in Bath. By the Author of two popular novels. 4 vols., London, F. Crosby, [1807]. [Ingpen.]

James, J. W. The Wolf of the Black Forest ; or, the Mysterious Murder. London, [1850]. [B.M.]

James, Thomas Andrew. Count Cagliostro : Or, The Charlatan. A Tale of The Reign of Louis XVI. 3 vols., London, Edward Bull, 1838. [B.M.]

James Dowell ; or, a sequel to " The Poor Man and the Pauper." London, 1842. [B.M.]

James Forbes ; A Tale, Founded on Facts. London, J. Hatchard, 1824. [B.M.]

James Hatfield And the Beauty of Buttermere : A Story of Modern Times. With illustrations by Robert Cruikshank. 3 vols., London, Henry Colburn, 1841. [B.M.]

James Jarvis. Part I [and Part II]. With a woodcut. London, Houlston, N.D. No. 65 of Houlston's Series of Tracts. [Block.]

Jameson, —. A Trip to London ; Or, the Humours of a Berwick Smack. Interspersed with Topographical Notices. Edinburgh, Underwood, 1815. [B.M. : *Eng. Cat. :* Stonehill.]

Jameson, Anna Brownell. Ashford Rectory, or the Spoiled Child Reformed, with a short introduction to the Science of Architecture and Heraldry. With a frontispiece. London, Whittaker, 1820. [*Eng. Cat. :* T. Thorp.]

—— The House of Ravenspur. A Romance. By Mrs. Jamieson. 4 vols., London, G. and W. B. Whittaker, 1822. [B.M. : Ingpen : Pickering.]

—— Visits and Sketches at Home and Abroad, with Tales and Miscellanies now first collected, and a new edition of the " Diary of an Ennuyée." 4 vols., London, Saunders & Otley, 1834. [Elkin Mathews.]

Jamieson, J. Congal and Fenella ; a Tale, Founded on Macbeth. London, 1791. [Allibone : B.M.]

Jane Hudson, the American girl ; or Exert Yourself. London, 1848. [B.M.]

Janet and Harry. A tale founded on fact. London, 1827. [B.M.]

Janson, C. Edward Fitz-York. 4 vols., [Cawthorn's Catalogue, 1810.]

Jaquelina of Hainault, an Historical Novel, by the Author of the Duke of Clarence. 3 vols., 1798. [*New Ann. Reg.*]

Jaqueline of Olzeburg, or Final Retributions. A Romance. London, Chappelle, 1800. [G. Worthington.]

Jauffret, L. F. The Little Hermitage. A Tale ; Illustrative of the Arts of Civilized Life. With 2 engravings. London, Richard Phillips, 1805. [Gumuchian : Sotheran.]

—— The Travels of Rolando ; containing, In a supposed Tour Round the World, Authentic Descriptions of the Geography, Natural History, Manners, and Antiquities Of Various Countries. Translated from the French of L. F. Jauffret. 4 vols., London, Richard Phillips, 1804. [B.M.]

Jealousy ; or, The Dreadful Mistake. By a clergyman's daughter. 2 vols., [W. Lane, 1801]. [Blakey.]

Jeannette and Jeannot ; or, The Conscript's Vow. A Romance. With woodcuts. London, E. Lloyd, [c. 1840]. [B. Ono : Stonehill.]

Jeary, Eliza. Marina and Amelia ; Or, The History Of Two Female Friends. Presented as A Token of Regard To The Juvenile World. London, Printed for the Author, by W. Justins, 1808. [B.M.]

Jem Gudgeon, Or Radical Conduct. By A Reformer. Being a continuation of " Will Waver, or Radical Principles." Oxford, Printed by W. Baxter, for J. Parker ; and F. C. and J. Rivington, 1821. [B.M.]

Jenkin, Henrietta Camilla. Lost and Won ; Or, The Love Test. By the Author of " The Maid's Husband." 3 vols., London, Henry Colburn, 1846. [B.M.]

—— The Maid's Husband. 3 vols., 1844. [James Glaisher.]

—— The Smiths. A Novel. By the Author of " The Maid's Husband," " Wedlock ; or, Yesterday and to-day." 3 vols., London, T. C. Newby, 1843. [B.M.]

—— Wedlock ; Or, Yesterday and To-day. By the author of " The Maid's Husband." 3 vols., London, Richard Bentley, 1841. [B.M.]

Jenkins, Mrs. Cardinal De Retz : A Literary Curiosity. 2 vols., 1844. [James Glaisher.]

Jenner, Rev. Charles. Letters from Altamont in the Capital, to his Friends in the Country. London, 1767. [B.M. : Dobell : *Eng. Lit. in Germany.*]

—— Letters from Lothario to Penelope. To which is added Lucinda, a Dramatic Entertainment of Three Acts. 2 vols., London, Becket and De Hondt, 1769. [Stonehill.]

—— Louisa: a Tale. To which is added an Elegy to the memory of Lord Lyttelton. London, 1774. [B.M.]

—— The Placid Man : Or, Memoirs of Sir Charles Beville. 2 vols., London, J. Wilkie, 1770. [B.M. : Ingpen : Maggs.]

Jenner, Mrs. J. Melmoth House : A Novel. 3 vols., London, Printed for the Author, 1866. [B.M. : *New Monthly Mag.*]

Jennet Gill and other tales. London, [1850 ?]. [B.M.]

Jennings, Hargrave. The Ship of Glass ; Or, The Mysterious Island. A Romance. 3 vols., London, Thomas Cautley Newby, 1846. [B.M.]

Jephson, Robert. The Confessions of Jean Baptiste Couteau, citizen of France, written by himself : and translated from the original French [actually written] by R. Jephson. 2 vols., London, 1794. [B.M.]

Jephthah : or, The Maid of Gilead. Edinburgh, 1840. [B.M.]

Jerningham, Edward. The Nunnery, Or The History of Miss Sophia Howard. 2 vols., 1767. [Dobell : *Eng. Lit. in Germany.*]

Jerrold, W. Blanchard. The Disgrace to the Family. A Story of Social Distinctions. With 12 plates by Phiz [Hablot K. Brown]. 1848. [Danielson.]

Jerrold, William Douglas. The Chronicles of Clovernook ; With some account of The Hermit of Bellyfulle. With a frontispiece. London, Punch Office, 1846. [Block : B.M. : *Critic.*]

—— A Man Made of Money. With 12 plates by John Leech. London, Punch Office, 1849. [Allibone : B.M. : Arthur Rogers.]

—— Men of Character. With illustrations by W. M. Thackeray. 3 vols., London, Henry Colburn, 1838. [B.M. : Arthur Rogers.]

—— Punch's Letters to his Son. Corrected and Edited, from the MSS. in the Alsatian Library, by Douglas Jerrold. With 24 illustrations by Douglas Jerrold. London, Wm. S. Orr, 1843. [Elkin Mathews.]

—— The Story of a Feather. With a frontispiece by John Leech. London, Punch Office, 1844. [Baker's Bookshop : Elkin Mathews : Pickering.]

Jesse, Edward. Scenes and Tales of Country Life, with Recollections of Natural History. With woodcuts. London, 1844. [Dobell : Sotheran.]

Jessie Barton : or "Not at Home." London, Religious Tract Society, [1845 ?]. [B.M.]

Jessy ; or, the Bridal Day. A novel. Written by a Lady. 2 vols., London, 1771. [B.M.]

Jessy ; Or, The Rose of Donald's Cottage. A Tale. By the Author of the Bravo of Bohemia, &c. 4 vols., London, Printed at the Minerva Press for A. K. Newman, 1818. [B.M. : *New Monthly Mag.*]

Jesuitism and Methodism. A Novel. 2 vols., London, Printed for the Author, and Published by Saunders and Otley, 1829. [B.M.]

Jew and the Foundling (The). A Romance. With illustrations. London, Lloyd, 1847. [Stonehill.]

Jewels (The) ; or Michael Ashdell's Trial. A Narrative founded on facts. London, 1842. [B.M.]

Jewry, Laura. The Forest and the Fortress : a Romance of the Nineteenth Century. 3 vols., 1850. [Allibone.]

—— Kirkholme Priory ; Or, Modern Heroism. A Tale. By the Author of "The Ransom." 3 vols., London, Richard Bentley, 1847. [B.M.]

—— The Ransom. A Tale of the Thirteenth Century : Founded on a Family Tradition. 3 vols., London, T. C. Newby, 1846. [Allibone : B.M. : *Critic.*]

Jewsbury, Geraldine Endsor. The Half-Sisters. 2 vols., 1854. [Allibone.]

—— Zoe. The History of two Lives. 3 vols., London, Chapman & Hall, 1845. [B.M. : McLeish : Publisher's advert.]

Jewsbury, Maria Jane. Phantasmagoria ; Or Sketches of Life and Literature. 2 vols., London, Hurst, Robinson, 1825. [*Edin. Mag. :* Elkin Mathews : Mudie's.]

—— The Three Histories. The History of an Enthusiast. The History of a Nonchalant, The History of a Realist. London, Westley, 1830. [Stonehill.]

Jireh : A Scene in the Pastoral Life Of the Author. London, Thomas Ward, 1836. [B.M.]

Joanna, Or The Female Slave. A West Indian Tale. Founded on Stedman's Narrative of an Expedition against the revolted Negroes of Surinam. London, Lupton Relfe, 1824. [B.M.]

Joe Oxford, Or The Runaway. 3 vols., 1830. [Backus.]

John and Henry ; or the Disobedient Child. By M. C. A sincere Friend of youth. With woodcuts. London, Harvey and Darton, 1842. [Block.]

John Bull and his Wonderful Lamp : A New Reading of an Old Tale, By Homunculus. With 6 plates by the Author. London, John Petheram, 1849. [Dobell.]

Johns, John. Good out of Evil : a tale of a cellar. London, Christian Tract Society, 1838. [B.M.]

Johns, Richard. Legend and Romance, African and European. 3 vols., London, Richard Bentley, 1839. [B.M.]
—— The Schoolfellows, Or, A By-way to fame. 3 vols., London, Richard Bentley, 1841. [B.M.]
Johnson, Anna Maria. Calista. 2 vols., London, W. Lane [1789]. [Publisher's advert, 1790: Blakey.]
—— Monmouth: A Tale, Founded on Historic Facts. Inscribed to His Grace the Duke of Buccleugh. 3 vols., London, W. Lane, 1790. [Blackwell: Pickering.]
—— The Platonic Guardian; or, The history of an orphan. By a lady. 3 vols. [W. Lane, 1787]. [Minerva Press Catalogue: Blakey.]
Johnson, Arthur. Dinan. A Romance. London, G. and W. B. Whittaker, 1821. [Baker's Bookshop: B.M.: Pickering.]
Johnson, Mrs. D. The Brothers in High Life; Or, The North of Ireland, A Novel. 3 vols., London, Kearsley, 1813. [Allibone: Blackwell: Stonehill.]
Johnson, Samuel. The Prince of Abissinia. A Tale. [Rasselas.] 2 vols., London, R. and J. Dodsley, 1759. [B.M.: King: McLeish.]
Johnson, Theophilus. Phantoms; or, The adventures of a gold headed cane. Containing a general descriptive and picturesque view of human life. 2 vols., London, William Lane, 1783. [Blakey.]
Johnson, Wilhelmina. The Ranger of the Tomb; or, Gipsy's Prophecy. A Romance. With woodcuts. London, E. Lloyd, 1847. [B.M.: B. Ono.]
Johnston, Miss. Ellen. A Tale of Ireland. London, Painter, 1843. [B.M.: *I. in F.*]
Johnston, Mary. Domestic Tales; Containing The Merchant's Wife And Her Sister. London, G. and W. B. Whittaker, 1822. [B.M.]
—— The Lairds of Glenfern. Or, Highlanders of the Nineteenth Century. A Tale. 2 vols., London, Printed at the Minerva Press, for A. K. Newman, 1816. [B.M.: *New Monthly Mag.*]
Johnstone, Charles. The Adventures Of Anthony Varnish; Or, A Peep at the Manners of Society. By an Adept. 3 vols., London, William Lane, 1786. [B.M.: *Eng. Lit. in Germany;* T. D. Webster.]
—— Chrysal; Or, The Adventures of a Guinea. Wherein are exhibited Views of several striking Scenes, with curious and interesting Anecdotes of the most Noted Persons in every Rank of Life, whose Hands it passed through in America, England, Holland, Germany, and Portugal. By an Adept. 4 vols., London, T. Beckett, 1760-1765. [Dobell: Maggs: Pickering.]
—— The History of Arsaces, Prince of Betlis. By the Editor of Chrysal. 2 vols., London, T. Becket, 1774. [B.M.: Mollie Green: Ingpen.]
—— The History Of John Juniper, Esq.

Alias Juniper Jack. Containing The birth, parentage, and education, Life, adventures, and character Of That most wonderful and surprizing Gentleman. By the editor of The Adventures of a Guinea. 3 vols., London, R. Baldwin, 1781. [B.M.: Ingpen: King.]
Johnstone, Charles. The Pilgrim, or, A Picture of Life; in a Series of Letters, written mostly from London By a Chinese Philosopher, to his Friend at Quang-Tong. By the Editor of Chrysal. 2 vols., London, T. Cadell, [1775]. [B.M.: *Eng. Lit. in Germany*: McLeish.]
—— The Reverie: Or A Flight to the Paradise of Fools. Published by the Editor of The Adventures of a Guinea. 2 vols., London, T. Becket and P. A. de Hondt, 1763. [An unauthorised edition (*see* B.M.) was issued at Dublin by Dillon Chamberlaine in 1762.] [B.M.: Arthur Rogers: Stonehill.]
Johnstone, Mrs. Christian Isobel. Clan-Albin: A National Tale. 4 vols., Edinburgh, John Moir for Macredy, Skelly & Muckersy, 1815. [The imprint on the B.M. copy is " London, Printed for Longman, Hurst, Rees, Orme & Brown, London; Macredie, Skelly, and Muckersy, Edinburgh; and John Cumming, Dublin, 1815."] [Allibone: *Literary Gazette*; T. D. Webster.]
—— Diversions of Hollycot, or the Mother's Art of thinking. By the author of Clan-Albin. Edinburgh, 1828. [B.M.]
—— [Edited by]. The Edinburgh Tales. Conducted by Mrs. Johnstone. 3 vols., Edinburgh, William Tait; Chapman and Hall, London; John Cumming, Dublin, 1845-1846. [B.M.: Elkin Mathews: Mrs. Villiers.]
—— Elizabeth de Bruce. By the Author of Clan-Albin. 3 vols., Edinburgh, William Blackwood: and T. Cadell, London, 1827. [B.M.: Clarke-Hall: Holland.]
——Nights Of the Round Table: Or, Stories of Aunt Jane and her friends. By the Author of " The Diversions of Hollycot," " Clan-Albin," " Elizabeth de Bruce," &c. &c. First Series. Edinburgh, Printed by John Johnstone, For Oliver and Boyd, and Simpkin and Marshall, 1832. [B.M.]
—— Nights of the Round Table: Or, Stories of Aunt Jane and her friends. By the Author of "The Diversions of Hollycot," " Clan-Albin," " Elizabeth de Bruce," &c. &c. Second Series. Edinburgh, Printed by John Johnstone, for Oliver and Boyd; and Simpkin and Marshall, 1832. [B.M.]
Jolly, James. The Young Enthusiast In Humble Life. A Simple Story. With a Biographical Introduction. London, James Fraser, 1833. [B.M.]
Jolly Sailor's Jester (The), or BritishTars' Companion, containing a numerous Selection of Nautical Tales, Frolicsome

Jokes, Smart Repartees, Witty Quibbles, Queer Puns, Irish Bulls, Strange Oddities, Humorous Adventures; together with all the best Things ever said by Ben Block, and his Merry Shipmates, the whole calculated to give an additional Amusement to the Leisure Hour, when the Circling Grog warms each generous Tar to drink to Wives and Sweethearts. With a frontispiece. London, T. Sabine, [1788]. [Pickering.]

Jones, Miss. The False Step. And The Sisters. 3 vols., London, Edward Bull, 1832. [B.M.: Elkin Mathews.]

Jones, E. H. St. Pierre. Rockaven: A Tale of the Thirteenth Century. With plates. 3 vols., London, Printed at The Caxton Press, by H. Fisher, 1827. [*Blackwood's Edin. Mag.*: B.M.: Ingpen.]

Jones, Ernest Charles. The Wood-Spirit. A Novel. 2 vols., London, T. & W. Boone, 1841. [B.M.]

Jones, Evan. Bards, or Towers of Morven, 1809. [Cawthorn's Catalogue.]

Jones, George, The Expatriated: a tale of modern Poland. By Leigh Cliffe. London, 1836. [B.M.]

—— Margaret Coryton. By Leigh Cliffe. 3 vols., London, R. & S. A. Bielefeld; and Galignani, Paris, 1829. [B.M.]

—— Supreme Bon Ton: and Bon Ton by Profession. A Novel. By the Author of " Parga," etc. 3 vols. London, J. C. Spence, 1820. [B.M.]

—— Temptation. A Novel. By Leigh Cliffe. Author of " The Knights of Ritzberg,"—"Parga," " Supreme Bon Ton," &c. 3 vols., London, J. C. Spence, 1823. [B.M.: *New Monthly Mag.*]

Jones, Harriet. Belmont Lodge. A Novel. 2 vols., London, Printed for the Author at the Minerva Press, 1799. [Ingpen.]

—— The Family of Santraile; or The Heir of Mentault: a Romance. 4 vols., 1908 [Allibone.] (Cawthorn's Catalogue gives this as *Emily of Santraile*)

Jones, James Athearn. Haverhill; Or, Memoirs Of an Officer in the Army of Wolfe. 3 vols., London, T. & W. Boone, 1831. [B.M.]

—— Tales of an Indian Camp. 3 vols., London, Henry Colburn and Richard Bentley, 1829. [B.M.]

Jones, John. Hawthorn Cottage; or, the Two Cupids: A Tale. 2 vols., London, James Asperne, 1815. [Allibone: B.M.]

Jones, Rev. Joseph. Osborne, Or The Country Gentleman. A Tale for the Times. Oxford, D. A. Talboys; Hatchard, London, 1833. [B.M.]

Jones, Louisa. Rosina; or, The Village Maid. With a frontispiece. London, J. S. Pratt, 1843. [Block.]

Jones, Stephen [?]. The Life and Adventures of a Fly. Supposed to have been written by himself. With woodcuts by Bewick. London, E. Newbery, [1800 ?]. [B.M.]

Joseph, E. L. Warner Arundell. The Adventures of a Creole. 3 vols., London, Saunders and Otley, 1838. [B.M.]

Journal of a Governess (The). By E. W. With a frontispiece. Brighton, 1823. [Arthur Rogers.]

Journal of Penrose (The), a seaman. 4 vols., London, 1815. [*New Monthly Mag.*]

Journey to London (The), Or the History of the Selby Family. 2 vols., 1744. [*Eng. Lit. in Germany*: T. Thorp.]

Journey to the Moon (A). And Interesting Conversations with the Inhabitants, respecting the Condition of Man. By the Author of " Worlds Displayed." With a woodcut. London, J. Evans, N.D. [Block.]

Jouy, Victor Joseph Étienne de. The Hermit in Italy, Or Observations of the Manners and Customs of Italy; being a continuation of the Sketches of French Manners. 3 vols., London, Geo. B. Whittaker, 1825. [B.M.: T. Thorp.]

Jouy, Victor Joseph Étienne de, and **Jay,** Antoine. The Hermit in Prison; Translated from the French of E. Jouy, and A. Jay. 2 vols., London, G. and W. B. Whittaker, 1823. [B.M.: Ingpen: McLeish.]

Judith; or, the Prophetess of Bethulia. A romance from the Apocrypha. London, Hatchard, 1849. [B.M.]

Julia, The Curate's Daughter, Her Journey to London, N.D. [Salkeld.]

Julia Fitz-Clarence. 3 vols. [Cawthorne's Catalogue, 1810]

Julia of Ardenfield. A Novel. 2 vols., London, 1816. [*New Monthly Mag.*: T. D. Webster.]

Julia Ormond; or, the New Settlement. By the authoress of " The Two Schools." London, 1850. [B.M.]

Julia St. Pierre. A Tale of the French Revolution. With woodcuts. London, E. Lloyd, [1848]. [B.M.: B. Ono: Stonehill.]

Julian of Osnaberg; or, The Siberian Exile. Edinburgh, 1820. [F. Dahl.]

Juliana. A novel, by the Author of " Francis, the Philanthropist." 3 vols., London, William Lane, 1786. [B.M.: Blakey.]

Juliana Ormeston, the fraternal Victim. 4 vols., 1792. [*New Ann. Reg.*]

Juliet; or, The cottager. In a series of letters. By a lady. 2 vols. [W. Lane, 1789]. [Blakey.]

Julius; or, the Deaf and Dumb Orphan. A Tale, founded on the popular Play of Deaf and Dumb. London, Newbery, 1801. [*Guardian of Education.*]

Justina; Or, Religion Pure and Undefiled. A Moral Tale. 2 vols., London, A. K. Newman, 1823. [B.M.]

Juvenile Adventures of David Ranger, Esq. (The). from an Original Manuscript found in the Collections of a late noble Lord. 2 vols., London, P. Stevens, 1757. [Allibone: Myers: Stonehill.]

Juvenile Adventures of Miss Kitty F . . . . r (The), 2 vols., London, Stephen Smith, 1759. [*Cat. Lib. Prohib.*]

Juvenile Amulet (The); A Pledge of Affection. With plates. [Printed on different coloured papers.] London, Edward Lacey, [1840 ?]. [B.M.]

Juvenile Christmas Tales. With woodcuts by Bewick. 1811. [Howard Samuel.]

Juvenile Emigrants, a novel. 2 vols. London, Symonds, 1799.

Juvenile Fabulist (The). A Collection of Familiar Fables, Adapted to the Capacities of Children. With woodcuts. London, Dean and Munday, [1820 ?]. [B.M.]

Juvenile Library. With 16 woodcuts. London, Whitrow, [1820]. [Tregaskis.]

Juvenile Memoirs, being Original Tales of a Moral Tendency for Young Ladies and Gentlemen. With plates. 1823. [Adrian Hammond.]

Juvenile Olio. (The); or Mental Medley; consisting of original essays, moral and literary tales, fables, reflections, written by a Father, chiefly for the use of his children. London, 1796. [B.M.]

Juvenile Sketch Book (The); or, pictures of youth. Tales. London, H. R. Thomas, 1825. [B.M.]

Juvenile Stories and Dialogues; composed chiefly in words of two syllables, for the use of Schools. London, Vernor and Hood, 1801. [*Guardian of Education.*]

Juvenile Tales. Comprising: Mary and her Cat, etc. London, Darton and Clark, [1830]. [B.M.]

Kalee-Krishnan Behadur (*See* BEHADUR).

Kanor, A Tale, Translated from the Savage. London, R. Griffiths, 1750. [Blackwell: B.M.]

Kanousky, Or The Young Indian. With a frontispiece. London, Simpkin and Marshall; Darton and Harvey; J. Eedes; J. W. Burnham, Wycombe; and Bradford, Thame, 1828. [B.M.]

Karamzin, Nikolai Mikhailovich. Russian Tales By Karamsin. Translated by J. B. Elrington. London, 1803. [B.M.: *Guide to Best Fiction.*]

—— Tales from the Russian of N. Karamsin. [Translated by A. A. Feldborg.] London, 1804. [B.M.: *Guide to Best Fiction.*]

Kavanagh, Julia. Madeleine: A tale of Auvergne, Founded on fact. London, Richard Bentley, 1848. [Allibone: B.M.: *Guide to Best Fiction.*]

—— Nathalie; a tale. 3 vols., London Henry Colburn, 1850. [B.M.: *Guide to Best Fiction.*]

—— The Three Paths. A Story for Youth. London, Chapman and Hall, 1848. [Allibone: B.M.]

Kaye, Sir John William. Doveton; Or, The Man of Many Impulses. By the Author of " Jerningham." 3 vols., London, Smith, Elder, 1837. [B.M.]

—— Jerningham; Or, The Inconsistent Man. 3 vols., London, Smith, Elder, 1836. [B.M.]

—— Peregrine Pultuney; Or, Life in India. 3 vols., London, John Mortimer, 1844. [B.M.]

Keate, George. Sketches from Nature; Taken and Coloured in a Journey to Margate. Published from the Original Designs. 2 vols., London, J. Dodsley, 1779. [B.M.: Arthur Rogers: G. Worthington.]

Keelivine, Christopher. Tales and Sketches of the West of Scotland. Edinburgh, Oliver and Boyd, 1824. [G. Worthington.]

Keene, Rev. H. G. Persian Fables, for Young and Old. With 18 engravings. London, John W. Parker, 1820. [Publisher's advert.]

Keightley, Thomas. Tales and Popular Fictions: Their Resemblance and Transmission from Country to Country. With plates by W. H. Brooke engraved on wood by G. Baxter. London, Whittaker, 1834. [G. Worthington.]

Keir, Mrs. James. Interesting Memoirs. By a Lady. In 2 volumes. London, A. Strahan, and T. Cadell, 1786. [Court Book Shop. 3rd edn.]

—— The History of Miss Greville. By the Author of Interesting Memoirs. 3 vols., London, Printed and Sold for the Author, at Carruther's and T. Cadell, 1787. [B.M.: Martin A. McGoff: Arthur Rogers.]

Kellet, Alexander [*See* MENTAL NOVELIST].

Kelly, Mrs. The Fatalists; Or, Records of 1814 and 1815. A Novel. 5 vols., London, A. K. Newman, 1821. [B.M.: Dobell.]

—— The Matron of Erin: A National Tale. 3 vols., London, Simpkin and Marshall; and Richard Coyne, Dublin, 1816. [B.M.: *New Monthly Mag.*: D. Webster.]

Kelly, Dennis Burrowes. The Manor of Glenmore: Or, The Irish Peasant. By A Member of the Irish Bar. 3 vols., London, Edward Bull, 1839. [B.M.: *I. in F.*]

Kelly, Frances. Domestic Comforts. A tale, founded on facts, for the use of young people. With a frontispiece. London, Minerva Press, 1808. [B.M.]

Kelly, Hugh. Memoirs of a Magdalen: or, The History of Louisa Mildmay. Now first published from a Series of Original Letters. 2 vols., Dublin, P. Wilson, J. Exshaw, J. Murphy, H. Saunders, W. Sleater, J. Potts, D. Chamberlain, J. Hoey, jun., J. Williams, & T. Ryder, 1767. [B.M.: W. T. Spencer.]

Kelly, Isabella. The Abbey of St. Asaph. A novel. By the author of Madeline, or The castle of Montgomery. With a frontispiece. 3 vols. [W. Lane, 1795.] [Blakey.]

—— The Baron's Daughter: a Gothic romance. 4 vols., London, 1802. [B.M.]

—— Eva. A novel. Dedicated by permission to Her Royal Highness the Duchess of Gloucester. 3 vols. London, Printed at the Minerva Press, for William Lane, 1799. [Blakey.]

—— Jane de Dunstanville; or, Characters as they are. 4 vols., 1813. [*Quarterly Review*.]

—— Jocelina, or the Rewards of Benevolence. 2 vols., London, 1797. [*Eng. Lit. in Germany*: Huth: New Ann. Reg.]

—— Madeline; or, The Castle of Montgomery, a novel. London, William Lane, 1794. [*New Ann. Reg.*: Blakey.]

—— A Modern Incident in Domestic Life. 2 vols., Brentford, P. Norbury, 1803. [B.M.]

—— The Ruins of Avondale Priory. A novel. 3 vols., London, William Lane, 1796. [B.M.: *New Ann. Reg.* Blakey.]

——Ruthinglenne, or The critical moment. A novel. Dedicated by permission, to Lady Dalling. 3 vols. London, Printed at the Minerva-Press, for William Lane, 1801. [Blakey.]

—— The Secret. A Novel. 4 vols., Brentford, P. Norbury, 1805. [B.M.]

Kelly, R. N. De Renzey.

—— Frederick Dornton; Or, The Brothers. A Novel. 4 vols., London, A. K. Newman, 1822. [Baker's Bookshop: Blackwell: B.M.]

Kelty, Mary Ann. The Favourite of Nature. A Tale. 3 vols., London, G. & W. B. Whittaker, 1821. [B.M.: Ingpen: Marks.]

—— Mamma and Mary, discoursing Upon Good and Evil. In Six Dialogues. With woodcuts. London, Harvey and Darton, N.D. [Block, 2nd edn.]

—— Osmond, A Tale. By the Author of " The Favourite of Nature." 3 vols., London, G. and W. B. Whittaker, 1822. [B.M.: Francis Edwards: *Quarterly Review*.]

—— The Story of Isabel; By the Author of " The Favourite of Nature," &c. &c. &c. 3 vols., London, Longman, Rees, Orme, Brown, & Green, 1826. [B.M.: Publisher's advert.: *Quarterly Review*.]

—— Trials; A Tale. By the Author of " The Favourite of Nature," &c. &c. 3 vols., London, G. and W. B. Whittaker, 1824. [B.M.: Glen: Marks.]

Kemp, Mrs. Rachel Cohen, the Usurer's daughter. Bath, Binns, [1850]. [B.M.: *Eng. Cat.*]

Kendall, A. Derwent Priory; or Memoirs of an Orphan, in a Series of Letters. 2 vols., 1798. [*Eng. Lit. in Germany*: New Ann. Reg.]

Kendall, A. The School for Parents: by the Author of Derwent Priory. To which is prefixed, Pity recommended to Youth, a tale. London, [1810 ?]. [B.M.]

Kendall, Edward Augustus. Burford Cottage And its Robin-Red-Breast. By The Author of Keeper's Travels. London, Thomas Tegg; Tegg, Wise, and Tegg, Dublin; Griffin, Glasgow; and J. and S. A. Tegg; Sydney, 1835. [B.M.: Ingpen.]

—— The Canary Bird. A Moral Fiction. Interspersed with Poetry. By the Author of The Sparrows, Keeper's Travels, The Crested Wren, etc. With a frontispiece. London, Printed for E. Newbery, by J. Cundel, 1799. [Mollie Green: Gumuchian.]

—— The English Boy At The Cape: An Anglo-African Story. By the Author of Keeper's Travels. With frontispieces. 3 vols., London, Whittaker, 1835. [B.M.: Arthur Rogers.]

—— Keeper's Travels in Search of his Master. With a frontispiece. London, E. Newbery, 1798. [B.M.: Dobell: Arthur Rogers.]

—— The Stories of Senex; Or Little histories of Little People. London, E. Newbery, 1800. [B.M.: Arthur Rogers.]

—— The Swallow: A Fiction. Interspersed with Poetry. With a frontispiece. London, Printed for E. Newbery, By T. Baylis, 1800. [B.M.: Court Bookshop: Arthur Rogers.]

Kendrick, Tertius T. C. The Travellers. A Tale, Illustrative of the Manners, Customs, and Superstitions Of Modern Greece. 3 vols., London, C. S. Arnold, 1825. [B.M.: *Edin. Mag.*]

Kenley, Marianne. The Cottage of the Appenines, or the Castle of Novina. A romance. 4 vols., Belfast, 1806. [B.M.]

Kennedy, Mrs. De Clifford; Or, Passion more Powerful than Reason. A Novel. 4 vols., London, 1820. [*New Monthly Mag.*: Parker & Son.]

Kennedy, Grace. Anna Ross, A Story for Children. By the Author of " The Decision," etc. With 6 etchings. Edinburgh, William Oliphant, 1824.

—— Dunallan; Or, Know What you Judge; A Story. By the Author of " Decision," &c. &c. 3 vols., Edinburgh, W. Oliphant, 1825. [B.M.: Ingpen: McLeish.]

—— Father Clement. A Roman Catholic story. By the author of "The Decision," etc. Edinburgh. 1823. [B.M.]

—— Jerry Allan, the Lame Girl. 1822. [Allibone.]

—— Philip Colville: or A Covenanter's Story. Unfinished. By the Author of " The Decision," " Father Clement," &c. &c. Edinburgh, W. Oliphant, 1825. [*Edin. Mag.*: Elkin Mathews.]

—— Willoughby; Or Reformation. The Influence of Religious Principles. By the Author of " The Decision," " Caroline Ormsby," " Village Counsel," &c. &c. 2 vols., London, C. and J. Rivington, 1823. [B.M.]

Kennedy, Mrs. Quintin. The Voice of Conscience: A Narrative founded on fact. London, Fisher, [1840]. [B.M.]

Kennedy, William. An Only Son; A Narrative By The Author of "My Early Days." London, Frederick Westley and A. H. Davis, 1831. [B.M.]

Kent, Anne. Evelyn Stuart; Or, Right *versus* Might. By Adrian. 3 vols., London, Richard Bentley, 1846. [B.M.]

Kentish, Mrs. The Gipsy Daughter; or, the Noble Orphan. London, Davis, 1839. [B.M.]

—— How to be happy: or, The Cottage of Content; the Cottage on fire; and the Water-cress Boy. With engravings. London, [1840 ?]. [B.M.]

—— Maid of the Village. London, Virtue, 1836. [W. T. Spencer.]

Kept Mistress (The). London, J. Morgan, 1761. [B.M.: W. Brown: Pickering.]

Kerr, Ann. Adeline St. Julian; Or, The Midnight Hour. A Novel. 2 vols., London, 1799. [*New Ann. Reg.*]

—— Edric the Forester; Or, the Mysteries of the Haunted Chamber. An historical romance. London, Clements, Romancist and Novelists' Library, 1841. [B.M.: Arthur Rogers.]

—— The Heiress di Montalde; or, the Castle of Bezanto: a novel. 2 vols., London, 1799. [B.M.]

Kett, Rev. Henry. Emily, A Moral Tale. Including Letters From A Father to his daughter, Upon the Most Important Subjects. 2 vols., London, Rivingtons, Payne, Lunn, Egerton; and Hatchard, 1809. [Pickering: *Quarterly Review*.]

Key to Drama (A); or Memoirs, Intrigues, and Atchievements, of Personages, who have been chosen by the most celebrated Poets, as the fittest Characters for Theatrical Representations. Vol. 1. [All published.] Containing the Life, Character and secret history of Macbeth. By A Gentleman. London, J. Browne, 1768. [J. C. Hardy.]

Kiddershaw, J. Swedish Mysteries; or, The Hero of the Mines of Dalecarlia. A Tale. Translated from a Swedish Manuscript by Johanson Kiddershaw. 3 vols., London, Printed for William Lane at the Minerva Press, 1801. [F. Dahl: Blakey.]

Kidgell, Rev. John. The Card. With a frontispiece and another plate. 2 vols., London, Printed for the Maker and sold by J. Newbery, 1755. [B.M.: Ingpen: Stonehill.]

—— Fables Originales. Original Fables. With engravings. 2 vols., London, 1763. [B.M.]

—— Original Fables. (*See* " Fables Originales " by this author.)

Kilner, Dorothy. Adventures of a Hackney Coach (The). 2 vols., London, 1781. [W. Brown.]

Kilner, Dorothy. The Adventures of a Pincushion. Designed chiefly for the Use of Young Ladies. With woodcuts. London, John Marshall, [1780]. [B.M.]

—— Anecdotes Of a Boarding-School; Or, an Antidote to the Vices Of those Useful Seminaries. By M. P. 2 vols., London, John Marshall, [1800 ?]. [B.M.]

—— Edward the Orphan. A tale founded on facts. With illustrations. London, [1824 ?]. [Baker's Bookshop: B.M.]

—— Jemina Placid; or, the advantage of good-nature, exemplified in a variety of familiar incidents. London. J. Marshall, [1800 ?]. [B.M. (3rd edn.)]

—— The Life and Perambulation of a Mouse, by M. P. With a frontispiece and woodcuts. London, John Marshall, [1803]. [B.M.: Arthur Rogers.]

—— Memoirs of a Peg-Top. By the Author of Adventures of a Pincushion. With a frontispiece & 27 woodcuts. London, John Marshall. N.D. [Court Book Shop.]

—— The Rational Brutes Or Talking Animals. By M. Pelham. With a frontispiece. London, J. Harris. 1803. [Gumuchian.]

—— The Review Or Three Day's Pleasure. A Story written in the last century. By M. P. With 2 plates. London, John Marshall, 1820. [Gumuchian.]

—— The Rotchfords; Or, The Friendly Counsellor: Designed for the Instruction and Amusement of the Youth of Both Sexes, by M. P. [Mary Pelham.] 2 vols., London, John Marshall, [1790]. [B.M.: Arthur Rogers: Baker's Bookshop.]

Kilverstone Castle, or the Heir restored. A Gothic Story. London, [1799]. [B.M. (mutilated).]

Kimball, Richard B. Saint Leger; or, the Threads of Life. London, 1850. [B.M.]

Kimber, Edward. The Life and Adventures of Joe Thompson. Written by himself. With a portrait. 2 vols., London, Hinton & Frederick, 1750. [B.M.: Ingpen: Arthur Rogers.]

—— Maria: The Genuine Memoirs of an Admired Lady of Rank and Fortune. 1764. [*Eng. Lit. in Germany*: Ingpen.]

King, Frances Elizabeth. The Rector's Memorandum Book, Being The Memoirs Of A Family in the North. London, Printed for the Editor, [1819.] [B.M.]

King, Harriot Rebecca. Nuneham Park; Or the Summer Holidays. A Sequel to Oakdale Cottage; Or the Christmas Holidays. London, John Souter, 1831. [B.M.]

—— Oakdale Cottage; or, The Christmas Holidays. An Original Tale, Dedicated to the Young Ladies of her own establishment. London, J. Souter, 1829. [B.M.]

King, Richard John. Anschar. A Story of the North. London, Parker, 1850. [B.M.]

King, Sophia. The Adventures of Victor Allen. 2 vols., London, 1805. [Allibone: B.M.]

—— Cordelia, or, a Romance of real Life. 2 vols., London, Minerva Press, 1799. [Fletcher: Blakey.]

—— The Fatal Secret, Or, Unknown Warrior, A Romance of the Twelfth Century, with Legendary Poems. London, Printed for the Author, by J. G. Barnard, 1801. [B.M.]

—— Waldorf; or, the Dangers of Philosophy. A philosophical tale. 2 vols., London, 1798. [B.M.: *New Ann. Reg.*]

King Can Do No Wrong (The). London, 1832. [B.M.]

King Henry IV., being a specimen of Shakspeare's Plays, furnished in imitation of the Waverley Novels, &c. 2 vols., London, 1826. [*New Monthly Mag.*]

King Henry the Fourth. 2 vols., [1782]. [Allibone.]

King's Daughter (The); London, 1849. [B.M.]

Kingsley, Charles. Alton Locke, Tailor and Poet: An Autobiography. 2 vols., London, Chapman and Hall, 1850. [*Eng. Cat.*: Kyrle Fletcher: T. Thorp.]

Kingston, William Henry Giles. The Albatross, Or, Voices from the Ocean. A Tale of the Sea. 3 vols., London, H. Hurst, 1849. [Bailey Bros.: B.M.]

—— The Circassian Chief. A Romance of Russia. 3 vols., London, Richard Bentley, 1843. [B.M.: Arthur Rogers: G. Worthington.]

—— The Prime Minister. An Historical Romance. 3 vols., London, Richard Bentley, 1845. [B.M.]

Kinsman of Mahomet, Or Memoirs of a French Slave at Constantinople. 2 vols., 1774. [W. Brown.]

Kirkby, John. The Capacity and Extent of the Human Understanding; Exemplified in the Extraordinary Case of Automathes: A Young Nobleman; who was Accidentally left in his Infancy, upon a desolate Island, and continued Nineteen Years in that solitary State, separate from all Human Society. A Narrative abounding with many surprizing Occurrences, both Useful and Entertaining to the Reader. London, R. Manby and Cox, 1745. [B.M.: Arthur Rogers: Stonehill.]

Kirwan, A. V. The Widow of Calcutta; and other Sketches. By a Traveller. 2 vols., 1841. [James Glaisher.]

Kitty's Attalantis. London, J. Harrison, [1766]. [Ashbee Collection.]

Kletke, Hermann. The Savoyard Boy And his Sister: Adapted from the German of H. Kletke. By James D. Haas. With illustrations by John Absolon. London, Wm. S. Orr, 1844. [B.M.]

Kniegge, Baron (*see* KUIEGGE).

Knight, Ellis Cornelia. Dinarbas; A Tale: Being a Continuation of Rasselas, Prince of Abissinia. London, C. Dilly, 1790. [B.M.: Ingpen: Stonehill.]

—— Marcus Flaminius; or, a view of the military, political and social life of the Romans, in a series of letters from a patrician in the year 762 from the foundation of Rome to 769. 2 vols., London, 1792. [B.M.]

—— Sir Guy de Lusignan. A Tale of Italy. 2 vols., London, Saunders and Otley, 1833. [B.M.; McLeish: Storey.]

Knight, H. Gally. Phrosyne, a Grecian tale; Alashtar, an Arabian tale. London, 1817. [*New Monthly Mag.*]

Knight of the Glen (The). An Irish romance. By the author of the Castles of Wolfnorth and Monteagle. 2 vols., London, 1815. [B.M.: *New Monthly Mag.*]

Knight of Newbrough (The); or, the Abbot of Byland: a tale of the Fauconberg's. London, 1847. [B.M.]

Knights (The), or Sketches of the Heroic Age. 1797. [*New Ann. Reg.*]

Knorring (*see* VON KNORRING).

Knowles, James Sheridan. Fortescue. A Novel. London, Privately printed, 1846. [B.M.]

—— George Lovell, A Novel. 3 vols., London, Edward Moxon, 1847. [B.M.: Lib. of Congress: Sotheran.]

—— The Magdalen, and Other Tales. London, J. Moxon, 1832. [Baker's Bookshop: *Literary Gazette.*]

Knox, Captain Charles H. Hardness, Or The Uncle. 3 vols., London, Saunders and Otley, 1841. [B.M.]

—— Harry Mowbray. With woodcuts. London, 1843. [B.M.: R. Hall: T. D. Webster.]

—— Softness. A Novel By The Author of " Hardness." 3 vols., London, Saunders and Otley, 1841. [B.M.]

—— Traditions of Western Germany. The Black Forest, the Neckar, the Odenwald, The Taunus, the Rhine, and the Moselle. 3 vols., London, Saunders and Otley, 1841. [B.M.]

Knox, Rev. James Spencer. Pastoral Annals. London, Seeley, 1840. [*I. in F.*]

Kock, Charles Paul de (*see* DE KOCK).

Koromantyn Slaves (The); Or, West-Indian Sketches. By the Author of "The Solace of an Invalid," &c. &c. &c. London, J. Hatchard, 1823. [B.M.]

Kosewitz, W. F. Von. Eccentric Tales, from the German of W. F. Von Kosewitz. With plates by George Cruikshank after sketches by Alfred Crowquill. London, J. Robins, 1827. [B.M.: F. Harvey: Pickering.]

Kotzebue, Augustus von. The Constant Lover or William and Jeanette: A Tale. From the German of A. von Kotzebue. To which is prefixed An Account of the Literary Life of the Author. 2 vols., London, J. Bell, 1799. [B.M.: *New Ann. Reg.*: Stonehill.]

Kotzebue, Augustus von. The Guardian Angel: a story for youth, from the German of Kotzebue. Translated by Annabella Plumptre. London, Vernor and Hood, 1802. [Allibone: Dobell: *Guardian of Education*.]
—— The History of my Father, or how it happened that I was born, a Romance, translated from the German of Kotzebue. 1799. [*New Ann. Reg.*]
—— Ildegerte, Queen of Norway. From the German of Augustus von Kotzebue, author of The Stranger. By Benjamin Thompson, Jun. translator of The Stranger, as performed at the Theatre Royal, Drury Lane. London, William Lane, 1798. [Blakey.]
—— Novelettes. 3 vols., London, Phillips, 1807. [Ingpen.]
Kramer, Prof. [C. B. E. Naubert]. Herman of Unna: A Series of Adventures of the Fifteenth Century, in which the Proceedings of the Secret Tribunal under the Emperors Wenceslaus and Sigismond, are Delineated. Written in German. 3 vols., London, G. G. and J. Robinson, 1794. [Blackwell: Ingpen: Marks.]
—— Walter de Monbary, Grand Master of the Knights and Templars. An Historical Romance. From the German of Professor Kramer. 4 vols., London, Printed at the Minerva Press for Lane and Newman, 1803. [Pickering: Blakey: Bernard Whyte.]
Krasinski, Count Henryk. Mary Barton: An Historical Tale. 3 vols., 1846. [James Glaisher.]
—— The Poles In The Seventeenth Century. An Historical Novel. With a Sketch of the Polish Cossacks. 3 vols., London, T. C. Newby. 1843. [Baker's Bookshop: B.M.: Arthur Rogers.]
Kuiegge, Baron Adolf Franz Friedrich Ludwig von. The German Gil Blas; or The Adventures of Peter Claus. Translated from the German of Baron Kniegge [*sic*]. 3 vols., London, 1793. [B.M.: *New Ann. Reg.*]

La Coquetterie; Or, Sketches of Society in France and Belgium. 3 vols., London, T. & W. Boone, 1832. [B.M.: E. M. Lawson: G. Worthington.]
La Soubrette; Or, the Adventures and Recollections Of Theresa Dornay. A Narrative founded on facts. 3 vols., London, Madden and Malcolm, 1845. [B.M.]
La Souriciere. The Mouse-Trap. A Facetious and Sentimental Excursion Through part of Austrian Flanders and France. Being a Divertisement for both sexes. By Timothy Touchit. 2 vols., London, J. Parsons, 1794. [Ashbee Collection.]

Lachlan, Elizabeth. Leonora; Or, The Presentation at Court. Being The First of a Series of Narratives Called Young Ladies' Tales. By the Author of " Private Education;" " The Poor Girl's Help;" " Early Education;" " The Youth's French Guide;" etc. etc. 2 vols., London, Longman, Rees, Orme, Brown, and Green, 1829. [B.M.]
Laclos, P. A. F. Choderlos de. Dangerous Connections: Or, Letters Collected in a Society by M. C * * * * De L * * * * and Published for the Instruction of Other Societies. 4 vols., London, 1784. [Lib. of Congress: *New Monthly Mag.*: Arthur Rogers.]
Ladies Miscellany (The): being a Collection of Novels, calculated to promote a Noble and Generous Love in both Sexes. With a frontispiece. 2 vols. London, M. Cooper and W. Brown, [c. 1760]. [J. C. Hardy.]
Lady Godiva (The); or, Peeping Tom of Coventry. A Romance. With woodcuts. London, E. Lloyd, [1849]. [B. Ono.]
Lady Hamilton; or, Nelson's Legacy. A Romance of Real Life. With woodcuts. London, E. Lloyd, [1849]. [B.M.: B. Ono.]
Lady Jane Grey: an Historical Tale. 2 vols., London, Printed for William Lane, at the Minerva, 1791. [Block].
Lady Jane's Pocket. A Novel. By the Author of Silvanella, or the Gipsey. 4 vols., London, Printed at the Minerva Press for A. K. Newman, 1815. [B.M.: Publisher's advert.]
Lady of Martendyke (The). A historical tale of the Fifteenth Century. By a Lady. 4 vols., London, 1813. [Baker's Bookshop.]
Lady's Drawing Room (The). Being a Faithfull Picture of the Great World, in which the various Humours of both Sexes are Display'd. Drawn from the Life, and Interspersed with Entertaining and Affecting Novels. London, M. Cooper, 1744. [B.M.: Ingpen: T. Thorp.]
Lady's Revenge (The). A Tale founded on Facts; [to which is added: Anecdote of a Brazilian Slave; also Extraordinary Instance of Rigid Justice in a Magistrate]. With a frontispiece. London, S. Carvalho, [1817]. [Marks.]
Lady's Tale (The); Or, The History of Drusilla Northington. 2 vols., London, Noble, 1786. [B.M.: Stonehill.]
Laech, Rev. F. The Noble Exile. A Tale founded on Fact. London, N.D. [Block.]
Lafaye-Bréhier, Julie de. Family Suppers; Or, Evening Tales for Young People; In which instruction is blended with Amusement. Translated by Lady Mary H * * * * * * from the French of Madame Delafaye. With 16 woodcuts. 2 vols., London, J. Souter, 1818. [B.M.]
—— Fortune's Reverses; or, the young Bernese; a tale for youth, translated

130

from the French of Mdme. J. de la Faye. By E. Bowles, 2 vols., Swaffham, 1830. [B.M.]

Lafontaine, August Heinrich Julius. Age and Youth; or, The Families of Abendstedt. A novel. From the German of Lafontaine. 4 vols., London, Printed at the Minerva Press, for A. K. Newman, 1813. [B.M.: Publisher's advert.: Blakey.]

—— Baron de Fleming. or, The Rage of Nobility. 3 vols. [Minerva Press, 1804]. [Blakey.]

—— Baron de Fleming, the Son; or The Rage of Systems. A novel. From the German of Augustus La Fontaine. London, Printed at the Minerva-Press, for Lane, Newman, and Co., 1804 [Blakey.]

—— Clara Duplessis, and Clairant: The History of a Family of French Emigrants. Translated from the German. 3 vols., London, Longman, 1797. [Ingpen: *New Ann. Reg.*]

—— Dolgorucki and Menzikof. A Russian tale. From the German of Augustus La Fontaine. 2 vols., London, Lane, Newman, and Co., 1805. [B.M.: Blakey.]

—— Edward and Annette. A moral tale from the German of A. Lafontaine. London, 1807. [B.M.]

—— The Family of Halden; A Novel. Translated from the German. 4 vols., London, Bell, 1799. [B.M.: Stonehill.: T. D. Webster.]

—— Family Quarrels. A Novel. 3 vols., London, J. Dean, 1811. [B.M.: *Quarterly Review*.]

—— Henrietta Bellmann; or, the new family picture; a novel, 2 vols., London, 1804. [B.M.: T. D. Webster.]

—— Hermann and Emilia. 4 vols., London, Minerva Press, 1805. [Publisher's advert: Blakey.]

—— Lobenstein Village. A novel. Translated by Mrs. Meeke, from the French of Augustus La Fontaine. With a frontispiece. 4 vols., London, Minerva Press, 1804. [Blakey; T. D. Webster.]

—— Love and Gratitude; or, Traits of the Human Heart. Six novels, translated from A. La Fontaine. Prepared for the press by Mrs. Parsons. 3 vols., Brentford, 1804. [B.M.]

—— The Man of Nature, or Nature and Love from the German of Miltenberg, by W. Wennington, with Notes illustrative and comparative, by the Translator. London, 1799. [B.M.: *Gentleman's Mag.: New Ann. Reg.*]

—— Odd Enough, to be sure! or, Emilius in the world. A novel. From the German. [Translated by John Hemet.] 2 vols., London, Lane & Newman, 1802. [B.M.]

—— The Rake and the Misanthrope. A Novel. From the German [by Mary Charlton]. 2 vols., London, Minerva Press, 1804. [Stonehill: Blakey.]

Lafontaine, August Heinrich Julius. Raphael; or Peaceful Life. Translated from the German by Mrs. Green. 2 vols., London, J. Taylor, 1812. [B.M.: *New Monthly Mag.*]

—— The Reprobate. A novel. Translated by the author of " The Wife and the Mistress " [Mary Charlton], &c. 2 vols., London, Lane and Newman, 1802. [B.M.: Blakey.]

—— Rodolphus of Werdenberg. Translated from the German of La Fontane [*sic*]. 2 vols., London, 1805. [B.M.]

—— Romulus. A Tale of Ancient Times. Translated from the German of Augustus Lafontaine by the Rev. P. Will. 2 vols., London, Phillips, [1799]. [Ingpen.]

—— Saint Julien. From the German. With additional notes, historical and explanatory. 2 vols., London, William Lane, 1799. [B.M.: Blakey.]

—— Saint Julien; or Memoirs of a Father, Translated from the German of Augustus la Fontaine. London, J. Bell, 1798. [B.M.]

—— The Village Pastor and his Children. A novel. From the German of Augustus La Fontaine. 4 vols. [Minerva Press, 1803]. [Blakey.]

Lairds of Fife (The). 3 vols., Edinburgh, Constable; and Hurst, Chance, London, 1828. [B.M.: Elkin Mathews: *Quarterly Review*.]

Lajetchnikoff, —. The Heretic. Translated from the Russian of Lajetchnikoff by Thomas B. Shaw. 3 vols., Edinburgh, William Blackwood, 1844. [Ingpen: Arthur Rogers.]

Lake, Eliza. The Wheel of Fortune. 3 vols., London, J. F. Hughes. [Publisher's advert., 1806.]

Lakeby, Edward. The Earldom Restored, An Event in High Life. 2 vols., London, Smith, Elder; Edinburgh: John Hamilton; Glasgow: John Smith; Aberdeen: A. Brown, and L. Smith; Dundee: Frederick Shaw, 1837. [B.M.]

Lakshmana Mudaliyár. The Tootinameh; or Tales of a Parrot: in the Persian Language; with an English Translation. Calcutta, A. Upjohn, 1792. [Henry Young.]

La Martelière, Jean Henri Ferdinand. The Three Gil Blas, or Follies of Youth. A novel. From the French of La Martelière. 4 vols., London, Minerva Press, 1804. [B.M.: Stonehill: Blakey.]

Lamartine de Prat, Marie Louis Alphonse de. Genevieve, or, the History of a Servant-Girl: translated from the French of M. de Lamartine by Andrew R. Scoble. London, Bohn, 1850. [Allibone: B. M.]

—— Gethsemane, or the Death of Julia; translated from the French. By I. H. Urquhart. London, A. H. Baily, 1838. [B.M.]

Lamartine de Prat, Marie Louis Alphonse de. Jocelyn. An Episode. Translated from the French, by Mme. F. H. Jobert. Paris, 1837. [B.M.]

—— Jocelyn. An episode. Journal found in the house of a village curate. Translated by R. Anstruther. London, 1844. [B.M.]

Lamb, Lady Caroline. Ada Reis. A Tale. 3 vols., London, John Murray, 1823. [Birrell & Garnett: B.M.: Lib. of Congress.]

—— Glenarvon. 3 vols., London, Henry Colburn, 1816. [B.M.: Ingpen: Bernard Whyte.]

—— Graham Hamilton. 2 vols., London, Henry Colburn, 1822. [Birrell & Garnett: B.M.; King.]

Lamb, Charles. The Adventures of Ulysses. With a frontispiece and engraved title. London, Baldwin, 1808. [*Eng. Cat.*: Maggs.]

—— (attributed to). Felissa or the Life and Opinions of a Kitten of Sentiment. With 12 plates. London, J. Harris, 1811. [Block: Gumuchian: Arthur Rogers.]

—— King Lear. With 3 copper-plates. London, Printed for the Proprietors of The Juvenile Library, 1808. [*Ashley Lib.*]

—— Othello. With 3 plates. No publisher's name or place of publication. [1807]. [*Ashley Lib.*]

—— Rome and Juliet. With 3 plates. No publisher's name or place of publication. [1807 ?]. [*Ashley Lib.*]

—— A Tale of Rosamund Gray and Old Blind Margaret. London, Lee and Hurst, 1798. [B.M.: *Eng. Lit. in Germany*: *New Ann. Reg.*]

—— Timon of Athens. With 3 Copper Plates. London, Printed for Thomas Hodgkins, by Richard Taylor, 1807. [*Ashley Lib.*]

Lamb, Charles and Mary. Mrs. Leicester's School; Or The History of Several Young Ladies, Related by Themselves. London, M. J. Godwin, 1809. [B.M.: Gumuchian: Ingram.]

—— Tales from Shakespear. Designed For the Use of Young Persons. With 20 plates engraved by William Blake after drawings by William Mulready. 2 vols., London, Thomas Hodgkins, 1807. [*Ashley Lib.*: Gumuchian: Ingram.]

Lamb, Mary. The Merchant of Venice. With 3 copper-plates. London, Printed for the Proprietors of The Juvenile Library, 1808. [*Ashley Lib.*]

—— The Midsummer Night's Dream. With 3 copper-plates. London, M. J. Godwin, 1811. [*Ashley Lib.*]

—— The Winter's Tale. With 3 copper-plates. London, M. J. Godwin, 1809. [*Ashley Lib.*]

Lambe, George. The Mysteries of Ferney Castle; a Romance. 4 vols., 1809. [*Monthly Mag.*]

Lambert, Hon. Camden Elizabeth. The Bar-Sinister, Or Memoirs of an Illegitimate. Founded on Facts. 2 vols., London, Smith, Elder, 1836. [B.M.: Elkin Mathews.]

—— Ella; Or The Emperor's Son. 3 vols., London, Henry Colburn, 1838. [B.M.]

Lamont, Martha Macdonald. The Fortunes of Woman: Memoirs, edited by Miss Lamont. 3 vols., London, Henry Colburn, 1849. [B.M.]

—— The Gladiator, a tale of the Roman Empire. London, Longman, 1840. [B.M.]

Lamp of the Sanctuary (The). A Catholic story. London, T. Richardson, [1850 ?]. [B.M.]

Lancashire Collier Girl (The). A True Story. With a woodcut. London, J. Marshall, [1798 ?]. Cheap Repository. [Block: B.M.]

Lancaster, Agnes. The Abbess of Valtiera; Or The Sorrows of a Falsehood. A Romance. 4 vols., London, Printed at the Minerva Press, for A. K. Newman, 1816. [B.M.: *New Monthly Mag.*: Blakey.]

Landon, Letitia Elizabeth. Duty and Inclination: A Novel, 3 vols., London, Henry Colburn, 1838. [B.M.]

—— Ethel Churchill: Or, The Two Brides. By the Author of " The Improvisatrice," " Francesca Carrara," " Traits and Trials of Early Life," etc. etc. 3 vols., London, Henry Colburn, 1837. [B.M.: *Guide to Best Fiction*: Publisher's advert.]

—— Francesca Carrara. By The Author of Romance and Reality, The Venetian Bracelet, &c. &c. 3 vols., London, Richard Bentley, 1834. [Allibone: B.M.: G. Worthington.]

—— Lady Anne Granard; Or, Keeping up appearances. By L. E. L. (The late Mrs. Maclean). With a portrait. 3 vols., London, Henry Colburn, 1842. [B.M.]

—— Romance And Reality. By L. E. L. Author of " The Improvisatrice," " The Venetian Bracelet," &c. &c. &c. 3 vols., London, Henry Colburn and Richard Bentley, 1831. [Allibone: B.M.: Lib. of Congress.]

—— Traits and trials Of Early life. By L. E. L. London, Henry Colburn, 1836. [B.M.: Lib. of Congress.]

Landor, Edward Wilson. Lofoden: Or, The Exiles of Norway. 2 vols., London, Smith, Elder, 1849. [B.M.: *Eng. Cat.*: Lib. of Congress.]

Landor, Robert Eyres. The Fawn of Sertorius. 2 vols., London, Longman, Brown, Green, & Longmans, 1846. [B.M.: Elkin Mathews: Publisher's advert.]

—— The Fountain of Arethusa. 2 vols., London, Longman, Brown, Green, & Longmans, 1848. [Baker's Bookshop: B.M.: Lib. of Congress.]

Landor, Walter Savage. Pericles and Aspasia. 2 vols., London, Saunders and Otley, 1836. [B.M.: *Guide to Best Fiction.*]

Lane, Amelia. The Fortress, An Historical Tale Of The Fifteenth Century, From Records of the Channel Islands. With lithographs. 3 vols., London, Edward Bull, 1840. [B.M.]

Lane, Edward. The Fugitives; or, A Trip to Canada. An interesting Tale, Chiefly Founded on Facts; Interspersed with Observations on the Manners, Customs, &c. of the Colonists and Indians. London, Effingham Wilson, 1830. [B.M.]

Lane, Edward William. The Thousand and One Nights, Commonly called, in England, The Arabian Nights' Entertainments. A New Translation from the Arabic, with copious notes. By Edward William Lane. With woodcuts after William Harvey. 3 vols., London, Charles Knight, 1839-1840-1841. [B.M.: Maggs: Parker & Son.]

Lane's Annual Novelist. A collection of moral tales, histories, and adventures, selected from the magazines, and other periodical publications for the year. With a vignette. 2 vols. [W. Lane, 1786]. [Blakey.]

Langhorne, John. The Effusions of Friendship and Fancy. In several letters to and from select Friends. London, T. Becket and P. A. De Hondt, 1763. [Baker's Bookshop.]

—— Frederic and Pharamond; or, the Consolations of Human Life. London, T. Becket and P. A. de Hondt, 1769. [B.M.: Ingpen: Elkin Mathews.]

—— The Letters that passed between Theodosius and Constantia; After she had taken the Veil. Now first published from the original Manuscript. London, T. Becket and P. A. De Hondt, 1763. [Baker's Bookshop: Ingpen: Elkin Mathews.]

—— Solyman and Almena. London, H. Payne and W. Cropley, 1762. [McLeish: Pickering: Lyle H. Wright.]

Lansdell, Sarah. Manfredi, Baron St. Osmund. An old English Romance. 2 vols., London, William Lane, 1796. [*New Ann. Reg.*: Blakey.]

—— The Tower; or the Romance of Ruthyne. By the Authoress of " Manfredi." 3 vols., 1789. [*New Ann. Reg.*: D. Webster.]

Lansdowne, Baron. Alexis; Or, The Young Adventurer. A Novel. London, T. Cooper, 1746. [B.M.: Stonehill: Webster.]

Lantier, Étienne François de. Adolphe and Blanche; Or, Travellers in Switzerland. Translated from the French. 4 vols., London, Printed by M. Allen, for John Badcock, 1803-4. [B.M.: Court Bk. Shop.]

La Pie Voleuse (*see* PIE VOLEUSE).

Lara, Catherine. Durval and Adelaide. 1796. [*New Ann. Reg.*]

—— Lewis de Boncoeur. 2 vols., 1796. [*New Ann. Reg.*]

Laroche, Marie Sophie von. The History of Lady Sophia Sternheim, attempted from the German of Mr. Wieland [or rather of Laroche, published by Wieland; translated by J. Collyer]. London 1776. [*Bibliot. Brit.* : B.M.: *Guide to Best Fiction.*]

Laroche-Guilhem (*see* DE LAROCHE-GUILHEM).

Lascivious Hypocrite (The). Or the Triumph of Vice. Translated from the French work " Le Tartuffe Libertine." London, 1783. [*Cat. Lib. Prohib.*]

Last Man (The), or Omegarus and Syderia, a romance in futurity. 2 vols., London, 1806. [B.M.]

Last of the O'Mahonys (The), And other Historical Tales Of The English Settlers In Munster. 3 vols., London, Richard Bentley, 1843. [B.M.: *I. in F.*]

Lathom, Francis. Astonishment! ! ! A romance of a century ago. 2 vols., London, Longman, 1802. [B.M.: Stonehill.]

—— The Castle of Ollada. A romance. 2 vols. [W. Lane, 1795]. [Blakey: Publisher's advert.]

—— Fashionable Mysteries; or, the Rival Duchesses, And other Tales. 3 vols., London, A. K. Newman, 1829. [B.M.]

—— The Fatal Vow; Or, St. Michael's Monastery, A Romance. 2 vols., London, Crosbie, 1807. [B.M.: Stonehill.]

—— Human Beings, a Novel. 3 vols., London, 1807. [B.M.]

—— The Impenetrable Secret, Find it out! A novel. 2 vols. With a frontispiece. London, Printed at the Minerva Press, for Lane, Newman, and Co., 1805. [Blakey.]

—— Italian Mysteries; Or, More Secrets than One. A Romance. 3 vols., London, Printed at the Minerva Press for A. K. Newman, 1820. [B.M.: *New Monthly Mag.*]

—— Live and Learn; Or, The First John Brown, His Friends, Enemies, and Acquaintance, In Town and Country. A Novel. 4 vols., London, A. K. Newman, 1823. [B.M.: *New Monthly Mag.*]

—— London; or, Truth Without Treason. A Novel. 4 vols., London, Minerva Press, 1809. [Stonehill.]

—— Men and Manners, a novel. 4 vols., London, 1799. [Baker's Bookshop: *New Ann. Reg.*: Murray Hill.]

—— The Midnight Bell, A German Story, Founded on Incidents in Real Life. 3 vols., 1798. [*Eng. Lit. in Germany*: Holden's Reprints: *New Ann. Reg.*]

—— The Mysterious Freebooter; or, The Days of Queen Bess. A Romance. 4 vols., London, Minerva Press, 1806. [E. M. Lawson: Publisher's advert.: Stonehill.]

Lathom, Francis. Mystic Events; Or, The Vision of the Tapestry. A Romantic Legend Of the Days of Anne Boleyn. 4 vols., London, A. K. Newman, 1830. [B.M.]
—— The One-Pound Note, And other Tales. 2 vols., London, Printed at the Minerva Press for A. K. Newman, 1820. [B.M.]
—— The Polish Bandit; Or, Who is my Bride? And Other Tales. 3 vols., London, A. K. Newman, 1824. [B.M.: A. Filcek.]
—— Puzzled and Pleased; Or, The Two Old Soldiers: And other Tales. 3 vols., London, A. K. Newman, 1822. [B.M.: Stonehill.]
—— The Romance of the Hebrides; or, wonders never cease! 3 vols., London, A. K. Newman, 1809. [B.M.: Blakey.]
—— The Unknown; or, The Northern Gallery. A Romance. 3 vols., London, Printed at the Minerva Press, for Lane, Newman, & Co., 1808. [Blakey.]
—— Very Strange, But Very True! or, The History of an Old Man's Young Wife. A Novel. 4 vols., London, Newman, 1821. [Stonehill.]
—— Young John Bull; or, Born Abroad and Bred at Home. A Novel. 3 vols., London, A. K. Newman, 1828. [B.M.]
Lathy, Thomas Pike. The Invisible Enemy; or, The Mines of Wielitska. A Polish legendary romance. 4 vols., London, Lane, Newman, 1806. [B.M.]
—— The Paraclete. A Novel. With a frontispiece. 5 vols., London, Printed at the Minerva Press; for Lane, Newman, 1805. [B.M.: Blakey.]
—— Usurpation; or The inflexible uncle. A novel. 3 vols., London, Lane, Newman 1805. [Publisher's advert.: Blakey.]
Lauder, Sir Thomas Dick. Highland Rambles, and Long Legends to Shorten the Way. 2 vols., Edinburgh, 1837. [Allibone: B.M.: *Camb. Hist. Eng. Lit.*]
—— Legendary Tales of the Highlands. A Sequel to Highland Rambles. With 6 plates by Hablot K. Browne. 3 vols., London, Henry Colburn, 1841. [Anderson Galleries: B.M.: Pickering.]
—— Lochandhu, A Tale of the Eighteenth Century. With vignette titles. 3 vols., Edinburgh, Archibald Constable; and Hurst, Robinson, London. 1825. [Blackwell: B.M.: Pickering.]
—— The Wolfe of Badenoch: An Historical Romance of the Fourteenth Century, by the Author of Lochandhu. 3 vols., Edinburgh, Cadell; and Simpkin and Marshall, London, 1827. [Block: Maggs: Publisher's advert.]
Laugh and be Fat, or Food for all Parties: The Spangled Lora, Country 'Squires, Jolly Sailor, Hearty Farmer, Merry Soldier, John the Footman, and Dolly the Dairy Maid, a general collection of the Best Jests, calculated to Banish Sorrow, Relieve Care, and make the Heart Merry, the whole containing all the wit of the present times, and suited to all Capacities that are disposed for Mirth and Good-Humour. With a frontispiece. London, W. Lane, [1790]. [Pickering: Robson.]
Laugh and be Fat: or, The Merry Jester: containing a choice collection of Tales, Repartees, etc., etc. Manchester, J. Imeson, 1784. [*Lancs.*]
Laughable Adventures of Charles and Lisette (The); or, the Beards. To which is added, the Strolling Student. London, 1796. [B.M.]
Laura, or original letters. A sequel to the Eloisa of J. J. Rousseau. From the French. 2 vols., London, W. Lane, 1790. [Blakey: Murray Hill.]
Laura and Augustus. An Authentic Story. In a Series of Letters by a Young Lady. 3 vols., London, Cass, 1784. [Ingpen: Arthur Rogers: Stonehill.]
Laura Blundell and Her Father. A novel. 3 vols., London, Printed at the Minerva Press, for A. K. Newman, 1812. [Internat. Bk. Shop: Publisher's Advert.: *Quarterly Review.*]
Laura Valcheret. A Tale for Adolescence, by the author of Observations on Works of Fiction. London, Henry Colburn, 1814. [Publisher's advert.]
Laura Valmont. A Novel Written by a Lady. London, Charles Dilly, 1791. [B.M.: W. Brown.]
Laurence, Miss H. London In The Olden Time; Or, Tales Intended to illustrate the Manners and Superstitions of its Inhabitants, From the twelfth to the sixteenth century. Longman, Hurst, Rees, Orme, Brown, and Green, 1825. [B.M.: *Edin. Mag.*]
—— London in the Olden Time; or, Tales Intended to illustrate the Manners and Superstitions of its Inhabitants from the twelfth to the sixteenth century. Second Series. London, Longman, Rees, Orme, Brown, & Green, 1827. [B.M.]
Laurence, Sarah. Stories selected from the History of Greece. London, Published for the Author, 1820. [Sotheran.]
Laurentia. A novel. 2 vols., London, 1790. [B.M.]
Lavaissière de Lavergne, Alexandre Marie Anne de. The Fair Circassian; or, The Gulf of Smyrna. From the French of A. de Lavergne. London, [1849 ?]. [B.M.]
Lavallée, Joseph. Letters of a Mameluke, or a moral and critical picture of the manners of Paris. With notes by the Translator. From the French. 2 vols., London, 1804. [B.M.]
Lavergne (*see* LAVAISSIÈRE DE LAVERGNE).
Lavinia Fitz-Aubyn, With other Tales; Sketched from Life. 4 vols., London, P. Martin; and J. Rees, Bristol, 1816. [B.M.]

Lawler, Dennis. The Soldier's Cottage; A Tale. London, Printed for the Editor, By E. Thomas, 1808. [B.M.]
—— Vicissitudes in Early Life; or the history of Frank Neville, a serio-comic, sentimental and satirical tale; interspersed with comic sketches, Anecdotes of Living Characters and Original Poetry. London, C. Chapple. [1807]. [B.M.: Norman.]

Lawrence, Herbert. The Contemplative Man, or the History of Christopher Crab, Esq.; of North Wales. 2 vols., London, J. Whiston, 1771. [Blackwell: W. Fletcher.]
—— The Life and Adventures of Common Sense; An Historical Allegory. 2 vols., [London], Montagu Lawrence, 1769. [B.M.: W. Brown: Maggs.]

Lawrence, James Henry. The Empire of the Nairs, Or the Rights of Women. An Utopian Romance. 4 vols., London, T. Hookham, 1811. [B.M.: Dobell: *Quarterly Review.*]

Layton, Mrs. Frederick. Hulme Abbey. A Novel. 3 vols., London, Fearman, 1820. [*Eng. Cat.*: Arthur Rogers: T. Thorp.]

Leadbetter, Mary. Cottage Dialogues among the Irish Peasantry. With notes and a preface by Maria Edgeworth. London, J. Johnson, 1811. [B.M.: *I. in F.*]
—— Cottage Dialogues among the Irish Peasantry. Second Series. London, J. Johnson, 1813. [*I. in F.*]
—— and **Shakleton,** Elizabeth. Tales for Cottages, accommodated to the present Condition of the Irish Peasantry. Dublin, 1814. [B.M.: *New Monthly Mag.*]

Learning at a Loss, Or, The Amours of Mr. Pendant and Miss Hartley, A Novel. 2 vols., London, Printed for the Author, 1778. [Stonehill.]

Lebrun, Pigault. The Barons of Felsheim. A romance. From the French of Pigault Lebrun, author of My Uncle Thomas, Monsieur Botte, &c. London, Lane, Newman, and Co., 1804. [Blakey.]
—— Brick Bolding; or What is Life? An English, French, and Italian Romance. From the French. 2 vols. [Minerva Press, 1804]. [Blakey.]
—— The First Night of my Wedding. From the French of Pigault Lebrun. 2 vols. [Minerva Press, 1804]. [Blakey.]
—— The History of a Dog. Written And published By a Gentleman of his acquaintance. Translated from the French of Pigault Lebrun, Author of The Barons of Felshaim, Monsieur Botte, My Uncle Thomas, &c. &c. London, Printed at the Minerva Press for Lane, Newman, 1804. [Court Bk. Shop.]
—— Monsieur Botte, a Romance. 3 vols., London, Minerva Press, 1803. [Stonehill.]

Lebrun, Pigault. My Uncle Thomas. From the French of Pigault Lebrun. 4 vols. [W. Lane]. 1801 [Blakey.]
—— Papa Brick; Or, What is Death. An English, French and Italian Romance, being the suite of Brick Bolding. From the French of Pigault Lebrun. London, The Minerva Press, 1804. [Arthur Rogers.]
—— The Polanders, The Lying Family, and the Life of My Uncle, with His Portfolio. Translated from the French of Pigault Lebrun. 2 vols., London, Printed at the Minerva Press, for Lane, Newman, 1805. [B.M.: A. Filcek: Ingpen.]
—— The Shrovetide Child; or the Son of a Monk. A novel translated from the French. 2 vols., London, 1797. [B.M.: *New. Ann. Reg.*]

Leckie, Mrs. Stories for the Young. Edinburgh, 1841. [B.M.]
—— The Village School. A Story for Girls. Edinburgh, 1837. [B.M.]

Lee, Hannah, F. The Log-Cabin; or, The World Before you. By the Author of "Three Experiments of Living." London, J. Chapman, 1844. [B.M.: Lib. of Congress.]

Lee, Harriet. Canterbury Tales for the Year 1797. 5 vols., London, G. G. and J. Robinson, 1797-9. [Second volume by Sophia Lee.] [Baker's Bookshop: Block: B.M.]
—— The Errors of Innocence; a Novel. 5 vols., 1786. [Allibone: *Eng. Lit. in Germany.*]
—— Kruitzner: or, the German's tale. London, John Murray, 1822. [*Quarterly Review* (New edn.).]

Lee, Margaret. Clara Lennox; Or, The Distressed Widow. A Novel. Founded on Facts. Interspersed with an Historical Description of The Isle of Man. 2 vols., London, Printed for the Authoress, by J. Adlard, 1797. [Allibone: B.M.: *New Ann. Reg.*]

Lee, Nelson. The Life of a Fairy. Illustrated by Alfred Crowquill. [London], John & A. Darling, [1850]. [Adrian Hammond: Publisher's advert.]

Lee, Sophia. The Life of a Lover. In a Series of Letters. 6 vols., London, G. and J. Robinson, 1804. [B.M.: Pickering: Arthur Rogers.]
—— Ormond; or the Debauchee; comprehending Sketches of real Characters, and illustrative of the Manners and Customs of Fashionable Life, at the Close of the year 1809. 3 vols., 1810. [*Quarterly Review.*]
—— The Recess; or, a Tale of other Times. By the Author of the Chapter of Accidents. 3 vols., London, T. Cadell, 1785. [B.M.: McLeish: Arthur Rogers.]
—— (*see* also LEE, Harriet, Canterbury Tales for the Year 1797.)

Lefanu, Alicia. Don Juan de Las Sierras, Or, El Empecinado. A Romance. 3 vols., London, A. K. Newman, 1823. [B.M.: *New Monthly Mag.*]

—— Helen Monteagle. 3 vols., London, Sherwood, 1818. [Allibone: Ingpen: *New Monthly Mag.*]

—— Henry the Fourth of France. A Romance. 4 vols., London, A. K. Newman, 1826. [B.M.: Stonehill.]

—— The India Voyage; a Novel. 2 vols. [Allibone.]

—— Leolin Abbey. A Novel. 3 vols., London, Printed by Strahan and Spottiswoode for Longman, Hurst, Rees, Orme, & Brown, 1819. [B.M.: Publisher's advert.]

—— Strathallan. 4 vols., London, Sherwood, Neely and Jones, 1816. [B.M.: Ingpen: McLeish.]

—— Tales of a Tourist. Containing The Outlaw, and Fashionable Connexions. 4 vols., London, A. K. Newman, 1823. [B.M.: *European Mag.*]

Lefanu, Joseph Sheridan. The Cock and Anchor, Being A Chronicle of old Dublin City. 3 vols., Dublin, William Curry, Jun.; Longman, Brown, Green and Longmans, London; Fraser, Edinburgh, 1845. [B.M.]

—— The Fortunes of Colonel Torlogh O'Brien: A Tale of the Wars of King James. With plates by Hablot K. Browne. Dublin, James McGlashan, 1847. [B.M.: Colbeck: Arthur Rogers.]

Legacy (The), a Novel. With a frontispiece [By Mrs. Carver]. 2 vols., London, William Lane, 1799. [*New Ann. Reg.*]

Legend of Cloth Fair (A): And other tales. With illustrations by Phiz [Hablot K. Browne]. London, J. W. Southgate, 1840. [B.M.]

Legends and Traditionary Stories. London, Burns, [1843]. [B.M.: *Eng. Cat.*]

Legends of Terror! And Tales of the Wonderful and Wild. Original and Select. With woodcuts. London, Printed by T. Richardson [for] Sherwood, Gilbert, and Piper, 1826. [Block.]

Legouvé, J. M. E. B. The Maniac, a tale; or a view of Bethlem Hospital: and the Merits of Women, a poem from the French by Amelia Bristow. London, 1810. [B.M.]

Le Grand, Monsieur. Tales of the Minstrels. Translated from the French. With a frontispiece. London, Egerton, [c. 1775]. [Stonehill.]

Leicester, Caroline. Fanny and her mamma, containing a series of interesting and useful conversations on various subjects. Dublin, 1848. [B.M.]

Leicester, Peter. Ada Greville; or, Woman's Constancy. 3 vols., London, Churton, 1850. [B.M.]

—— Arthur of Britanny, An Historical Tale. By The Author of " The Templars." 3 vols., London, Whittaker, Treacher, 1831. [B.M.]

Leicester, Peter. Bosworth Field; Or, The Fate of a Plantagenet. An Historical Tale. By the Author of "Arthur of Britany," &c. 3 vols., London, J. Cochrane, 1835. [B.M.]

—— The Templars. An Historical Novel. 3 vols., London, Whittaker, Treacher, 1830. [B.M.: *New Monthly Mag.*]

Leigh, Sir Samuel Egerton. Munster Abbey, A Romance: interspersed with reflections on Virtue and Morality. 3 vols., Edinburgh, 1797. [B.M.: *New Ann. Reg.*: T. D. Webster.]

Leigh, W. H. The Emigrant: a tale of Australia. London, Simmons, 1847. [B.M.]

Leinstein, Madame. The Fatal Scarf; Or, A Sister's Vengeance. A Legend of Cuth-Ionor. With a frontispiece. London, Dean and Munday, [1825 ?]. [B.M.: Ingpen.]

Leland, Rev. Thomas. Longsword, Earl of Salisbury. An Historical Romance. With frontispieces by Grignon. 2 vols., London, W. Johnston, 1762. [B.M.: Ingpen: Arthur Rogers.]

Le Maire, Henri. The French Gil Blas, or adventures of H. Lanson. Translated from the third edition in French [of Le Maire]. 4 vols., London, 1793. [B.M.: *New Ann. Reg.*]

Lemira of Lorraine. A Romance. 3 vols., London, G. and W. B. Whittaker, 1822. [Blackwell: B.M.: Stonehill.]

Lemon, Mark. The Enchanted Doll: A Fairy Tale for Little People. With a frontispiece, title and illustrations by Richard Doyle. London, Bradbury and Evans, 1849. [B.M.: Gumuchian: Arthur Rogers.]

Lennep (*see* VAN LENNEP).

Lennox, Charles. The Duchess de la Vallière; a Historical Novel, from the French. 2 vols., London, 1814. [Allibone.]

Lennox, Charlotte. Euphemia. 4 vols., London, T. Cadell, and J. Evans, 1790. [Allibone: B.M.: W. Brown.]

—— The Female Quixote; Or the Adventures Of Arabella. 2 vols., London, A. Millar, 1752. [B.M.: Ingpen: Maggs.]

—— Henrietta. By the Author of " The Female Quixote." 2 vols., London, A. Millar, 1758. [B.M.: Maggs: Arthur Rogers.]

—— Hermione, or the Orphan Sisters. A Novel. 4 vols., London, Minerva Press, 1791. [Stonehill.]

—— The History of Sir George Warrington, or The Political Quixote. By the Author of the Female Quixote. 3 vols., London, 1797. [*New Ann. Reg.*: Arthur Rogers: Sotheby's.]

—— The Life of Harriot Stuart. Written by herself. 2 vols., London, J. Payne and J. Bouquet, 1751. [B.M.: Pickering: Tregaskis.]

—— Memoirs for the History of Madame de Maintenon and of the Last Age.

Translated from the French By the Author of the Female Quixote. 5 vols., London, A. Millar and J. Nourse, 1757. [Pickering.]

Lennox, Charlotte. The Memoirs of the Countess of Berci. Taken from the French. By the author of the Female Quixote. 2 vols., London, A. Millar, 1756. [B.M.]

—— Sophia. 2 vols., London, James Fletcher, 1762. [B.M.: Arthur Rogers: Stonehill.]

Lennox, Lord William Pitt. Compton Audley; Or, Hands not Hearts. 3 vols., London, Richard Bentley, 1841. [Baker's Bookshop: B.M.: Ingpen.]

—— The Tuft-Hunter. 3 vols., London, Henry Colburn, 1843. [B.M.]

Lennox Family (The); or, What do you think of the World? 3 vols., 1812. [*New Monthly Mag.*: *Quarterly Review.*]

Le Noir, Elizabeth Anne. Clara de Montfier; a moral tale. With original poems. 3 vols., Reading, Printed for the author, 1808. [Title of second edition reads "The Maid of La Vendée."] [B.M.: *Monthly Mag.*]

—— Village Anecdotes; or, The Journal of a Year, From Sophia to Edward. With Original Poems. 3 vols., London, 1804. [B.M.: *Camb. Hist. Eng. Lit.*]

—— Village Annals, a Scene in Domestic Life. 2 vols., 1803. [*Camb. Hist. Eng. Lit.*]

Leon, Elizabeth. The Mysterious Voice; with other tales and allegories. London, Painter, 1849. [B.M.]

Leonora: Or, Characters Drawn from Real Life. Containing A Great Variety of Incidents, Interspers'd with Reflections moral and entertaining. 2 vols., London, Thomas Davies, 1745. [B.M.]

Lermos and Rosa; or, The Fortunate Gipsey: An Interesting Adventure, which really Happened in Spain, about forty years ago. With a frontispiece. London, Tegg, 1805. [Stonehill.]

Leroy, Christopher Edward. Outalissi; A Tale of Dutch Guiana. London, J. Hatchard, 1826. [*Blackwood's Edin. Mag.*: B.M.: *Literary Gazette.*]

Lerr, Anne. Mysterious Count, a Novel. 1803. [Allibone.]

Les Jumelles; or, the Twins. [By Symonds.] London, J. Barfield, 1828. [B.M.: Block.]

Le Sage, Alan René. The adventures of Gil Blas of Santillane. A New Translation by the Author of Roderick Random [Tobias Smollett]. With plates. 4 vols., London, J. Osborne, 1750. [Parker & Son: Pickering: Arthur Rogers.]

—— The Adventures of Gil Blas of Santillane. A New Translation, by Percival Proctor. With engravings. 2 vols., London, Printed for the Translator, 1774. [B.M.: Mudie's.]

—— The Adventures of Gil Blas of Santillane. Translated by B. Heath

Malkin. With illustrations by Robert Smirke. 4 vols., London, Longman, 1809. [B.M.: G. H. Last: Parker & Son.]

Le Sage, Alan René. The Adventures of Gil Blas of Santillana, newly Translated from the French by Martin Smart. With copperplate engravings. 4 vols., London, R. Phillips, 1807. [B.M.: Marks: A. V. Turner.]

—— Adventures of Gil Blas of Santillane. With a Biographical Notice of the Author, by Jules Janin. Translated by Joseph Thomas. With illustrations by Tony Johannot. London, 1841. [Lib. of Congress.]

—— The Adventures of Robert Chevalier, called de Beauchêne, Captain of a Privateer in New-France. 2 vols., London, 1745. [B.M.]

—— Asmodeus; Or, The Devil on Two Sticks, With a Biographical Notice of the Author, by Jules Janin; Translated by Joseph Thomas. With illustrations by Tony Johannot. London, J. Thomas, 1841. [B.M.: Dobell: Marks.]

—— The Bachelor of Salamanca. From the French, by James Townsend. 2 vols. London, 1822. [Allibone: Lib. of Congress.]

—— The Bachelor of Salamanca; or, Memoirs of Don Cherubin de la Ronda. In three parts. Translated by Mr. Lockman. 2 vols., London, A. Bettesworth, 1737-1739. [B.M.]

—— The Devil upon Crutches, from the Diable Boiteux. A new translation, to which are now first added Asmodeus's Crutches. A critical letter upon the work, and dialogues between Two Chimneys of Madrid. With plates. 2 vols., London, J. Osborn, 1750. [Tregaskis.]

—— The History of Vanillo Gonzales, Surnamed the Merry Bachelor, Translated from the French of Le Sage. 2 vols., 1797. [*New Ann. Reg.*]

—— Le Diable Boiteux: or, the Devil upon Two Sticks. Translated from the last Paris edition, very much enlarg'd. 2 vols., London, 1741. [B.M.: McLeish.]

—— Spanish Tales; Translated From Le Sage And Selected from other Authors: Wherein are contained A Description of Madrid, Grenada, Saragoza, Seville, Milan, Parma, Palermo, &c. &c. By Mrs. Frederick Layton. 3 vols., London, Hatchard; Barrett, Bath; and Dighton, Cambridge, 1816. [B.M.: Stonewall Jackson: Marks.]

Leslie, Mrs. Fireside Stories; plain tales of Aunt Deborah and her friends. By the author of A Plain Story, &c. 3 vols. [London, Minerva Press, 1806: Blakey.]

—— A Plain Story. 4 vols., London, Printed at the Minerva-Press, for William Lane, 1801. [Blakey: *Minerva Press Catalogue*].

Leslie, James. The Cotter's Tale-Book for the Winter Evenings. Aberdeen, 1839. [B.M.]

—— Willie and Meggie's Marriage, with a hundred cuts of homespun yarn therewith interwoven. Aberdeen, 1837. [B.M. (2nd edn.).]

Lesson for Lovers, Or History of Col. Melville and Lady Charlotte Richley. 2 vols., 1783. [W. Brown.]

Lester, Elizabeth B. The Quakers. A Tale. London, Baldwin, 1817. [B.M.: Ingpen: T. D. Webster.]

Le Suire, Robert Martin. The French Adventurer; Or, Memoirs Of Gregoire Merveil, Marquis d'Erbeuil. Translated From the French of M. Le Suire. 3 vols., London, Printed for John Bew, 1791. [B.M.]

Letitia and Laura: a moral tale. By a Mother. London, W. Darton, 1824. [B.M.]

Letters Between Clara and Antonia, in which are interspersed the interesting memoirs of Lord Des Lunettes, a character in real life. 2 vols., London, J. Bew, 1780. [B.M.: Publisher's advert.]

Letters Between Emilia and Harriet. London, 1762. [B.M.]

Letters Between an English Lady And Her Friend at Paris. In which are contained The Memoirs Of Mrs. Williams. By a Lady. 2 vols., London, T. Becket, and P. A. De Hondt, 1770. [B.M.: *Eng. Lit. in Germany*: Stonehill.]

Letters Between Master Tommy and Miss Nancy Goodwill, containing the history of their Holiday Amusements. With woodcuts. London, 1770. [B.M.]

Letters from Cockney Lands. 1826. [*Quarterly Review.*]

Letters from Elizabeth Williams to Anne Mowbray; Or, Justice to Ourselves and others, The consequence of True Piety. Wellington, Houlston, 1829. [B.M.]

Letters from Henrietta to Morvina. Interspersed with anecdotes, historical and amusing, of the different courts and countries through which she passed. Founded on Facts. 2 vols., London, Bew, 1777. [B.M.: *Westminster Mag.*]

Letters from Sophia to Mira: Containing the Adventures of a Lady; In which The several Situations, most common in Female Life, are naturally described. London, R. and J. Dodsley, 1763. [B.M.: T. D. Webster.]

Letters of Charlotte (The), during her connexion with Werter. 2 vols., London, 1786. [Ingpen.]

Letters of Miss Riversdale. A novel. 3 vols., London, J. Johnson, 1803. [B.M.: Arthur Rogers.]

Letters of Ortis to Lorenzo, translated from the Originals, published at Milan. London, Henry Colburn, 1814. [*Eng. Cat.: New Monthly Mag.*]

Letters to Little Henry, from his Aunt. London, 1841. [B.M.]

Letters to my Sisters Or Octavia Arden. London, James Nisbet, 1826. [B.M.]

Letters Written from Lausanne, Translated from the French. 2 vols., 1799. [*New Ann. Reg.*]

Lever, Charles James. Arthur O'Leary: His Wanderings and Ponderings In Many Lands. Edited by His friend, Harry Lorrequer. With a portrait and 9 plates by George Cruikshank. 3 vols., London, Henry Colburn, 1844. [B.M.: King: Maggs.]

—— Charles O'Malley, the Irish Dragoon. Edited by Harry Lorrequer. With a frontispiece, vignettes and 20 plates by Phiz [Hablot K. Browne]. 2 vols., Dublin, William Curry, Jun., 1841. [B.M.: Ingpen: Lib. of Congress.]

—— Confessions of Con Cregan: The Irish Gil Blas. With illustrations by Phiz [Hablot K. Browne]. 2 vols., Orr, [1850]. [B.M.: Noel Broadbent: Maggs.]

—— The Confessions of Harry Lorrequer, Late Captain in the —th Regiment of Foot. With a frontispiece, a vignette, and 20 plates by Phiz [Hablot K. Browne]. Dublin, William Curry, 1839. [Block: B.M.: Lib. of Congress.]

—— Diary and Notes Of Horace Templeton, Esq. Late Secretary of Legation at ——. 2 vols., London, Chapman and Hall, 1848. [B.M.: Noel Broadbent: Lib. of Congress.]

—— Jack Hinton, the Guardsman. With a portrait, plates and woodcuts by Phiz [Hablot K. Browne]. Dublin, William Curry, Jun.; William S. Orr, London; Fraser, Edinburgh, 1843. [The above is the first part of " Our Mess."] [Block: Lib. of Congress: Maggs.]

—— The Knight of Gwynne: A Tale of The Time of the Union. With 40 plates by " Phiz " [Hablot K. Browne]. London, Chapman and Hall, 1847. [Block: B.M.: Lib. of Congress.]

—— The O'Donoghue; A Tale of Ireland Fifty Years Ago. With plates by Hablot K. Browne. Dublin, William Curry, Jun.; William S. Orr, London; Fraser, Edinburgh, 1845. [Block: B.M.: Lib. of Congress.]

—— Roland Cashel. With illustrations by Phiz [Hablot K. Browne]. London, Chapman and Hall, [1850]. B.M.: Kyrle Fletcher: Maggs.]

—— St. Patrick's Eve; Or, Three Eras in the Life of an Irish Peasant. With illustrations by Phiz [Hablot K. Browne]. London, Chapman & Hall, 1845. [Block: B.M.: Lib. of Congress.]

—— Tales of the Trains: being some Chapters of Railroad Romance, By Tilbury Tramp, Queen's Messenger. With illustrations by " Phiz" [Hablot K. Browne]. W. S. Orr, 1845. [Noel Broadbent: Francis Edwards: Maggs.]

Lever, Charles James. Tom Burke of "Ours." With illustrations by Phiz [Hablot K. Browne]. 2 vols., Dublin, 1844 [The above is the second part of "Our Mess."] [B.M.: Lib. of Congress: McLeish.]

Leverland, Gervase C. The Virtuous Wife: a Sentimental Tale. By G. C. L. With a portrait. Sudbury, Privately printed, 1812. [B.M.: Marks: T. Thorp.]

Levey, —. Bob Norberry; or, Sketches from the Note Book of an Irish Reporter; edited by Captain Prout. With 18 illustrations by Henry Macmanus and others. Dublin, James Duffy, 1844. [B.M.: *I. in F.:* Marks.]

Levinge, Sir Richard George Augustus. Cromwell Doolan; or, life in the army. By the Author of "Echoes from the Backwoods?" 2 vols., London, 1849. [B.M.]

Levis, Duke de. The Carbonaro. A Piedmontese Tale. 2 vols., London, Henry Colburn, 1829. [B.M.: Arthur Rogers.]

Lewes, George Henry. Ranthorpe; or, a Poet's First Struggles. London, Chapman and Hall, 1847. [B.M.: E. Hector: Ingpen.]

—— Rose, Blanche, And Violet. 3 vols., London, Smith, Elder, 1848. [B.M.: Holland: Chas. Hutt.]

Lewis, I. Terrific Tales. London, 1804. [Lib. of Congress.]

Lewis, L. Lord Walford; a Novel. 2 vols., London, 1789. [Allibone.]

Lewis, Miss M. G. Ambition. 3 vols., London, T. Cadell; and W. Blackwood, Edinburgh, 1825. [B.M.: *Edin. Mag.*]

—— The Jewish Maiden. A Novel. By the Author of "Ambition, &c." 4 vols., London, A. K. Newman, 1830. [B.M.: *New Monthly Mag.*]

Lewis, Matthew Gregory. Ambrosio, or The Monk, a Romance. 3 vols., London, [1795]. [John Pearson.]

—— The Castle of Lindenberg, or the History of Raymond and Agnes; with the Story of the Bleeding Nun. With 2 plates. London, S. Fisher. 1798. [P. C. Cuttelle.]

—— Feudal Tyrants; or, The Counts of Carlsheim and Sargans. A Romance. Taken from the German. 4 vols., London, J. F. Hughes, 1806. [B.M.: Bumpus Exhibition: Elkin Mathews.]

—— Koenigsmark the Robber; or, the Terror of Bohemia: in which is included, the Affecting History of Rosenberg and Adelaide, and their Orphan Daughter. London, Dean and Munday, [c. 1815 ?]. [B.M.: Stonehill.]

—— The Monk. (*See* Ambrosio.)

—— Romantic Tales. 4 vols., London, Printed by D. N. Shury, for Longman, Hurst, Rees, and Orme, 1808. [Birrell & Garnett: B.M.: Stonehill.]

Lewis, Robert. Adventures of a Rake. 1759. [Allibone.]

Lewis Tyrrell; or, the Depraved Count: including The pathetic Adventures and tragical end of Ella Clifford and Oscar Henry Hampden; the Victims of Treachery. An English Tale of the Fourteenth Century. With a frontispiece. London, Dean & Munday, [1825 ?]. [B.M.: Court Bk. Shop.]

Liardet, Frederick. Tales, by a Barrister. 3 vols., London, Chapman and Hall, 1844. [B.M.: McLeish: Stonehill.]

Liberal American (The). A novel, in a series of letters, by a lady. 2 vols., London, William Lane, 1785. [Blakey.]

Libertine Husband Reclaimed and Virtuous Love Rewarded. 1775. [*Eng. Lit. in Germany.*]

Libertines (The). A Novel. 2 vols., Cambridge, Robinson, 1798. [B.M.: *Eng. Lit. in Germany:* Ingpen.]

Library of Fiction (The), Or Family Story-Teller; Consisting of Original Tales, Essays, and Sketches of Character. With plates. 2 vols., London, Chapman and Hall, 1836-7. [Block: King: Arthur Rogers.]

Library of French Romance. In 2 parts [all published]. London, [1847]. [B.M.]

Life, Adventures and Amours of Sir R[ichard] P[errot] who so recently had the honour to present the F[lintshire] Address at the English Court. London, J. Brough, 1770. [B.M.: Ingpen.]

Life, Adventures, Intrigues and Amours of the Celebrated Jemmy Twitcher (The). Exhibiting many striking proofs to what Baseness the Human Heart is capable of descending. The whole faithfully compiled from Authentic Materials. London, Jonathan Brough, [1770]. [B.M.: *Cat. Lib. Prohib.*]

Life and Adventures of Anthony Leger, Esq. (The), or The Man of Shifts. 3 vols., London, T. Wilkins, 1789. [*Eng. Lit. in Germany:* T. Thorp.]

Life and Adventures of a Cat (The). London, Willoughby Mynors, 1760. [Ingpen: Maggs.]

Life and Adventures of the Celebrated Dr. Faustus (The); relating his First Introduction to Lucifer, and Connection with Infernal Spirits; his Method of Raising the Devil and his Final Dismissal to the Tremendous Abyss of Hell. London, [1825]. [Maggs.]

Life and Adventures of John Nicol (The). London, Cadell, 1822. [*Eng. Cat.: European Mag.*.]

Life and Adventures of Lady Anne, The Little Pedlar (The). By the Author of the "Blue Silk Workbag," "Harcourt Family," &c. With a frontispiece. London, J. Souter, 1823. [B.M.]

Life and Adventures of Mathew Bishop of Deddington in Oxfordshire. Written by himself. London, 1744. [B.M.]

Life and Adventures of Mr. Pig and Miss Crane. [1835 ?]. [B.M.]

Life and Adventures of Paul Plaintive (The), compiled from original Documents. 2 vols., 1811. [*Quarterly Review.*]

Life and Adventures of Sir Bartholomew Sapskull (The). By Somebody. 2 vols., London, 1768. [B.M.]

Life and Adventures of Toby, the Sapient Pig; with his opinions on men and manners. Written by himself, etc. London, [1805]. [B.M.]

Life and Astonishing Adventures of John Daniel, A Smith at Royston. 1770. [W. Brown.]

Life and Confessions of Humphrey Humbug (The). With a brief account of his family, from 1 Anno Mundi to 1835 Anno Christi, related by himself. London, 1835. [B.M.: Arthur Rogers.]

Life and Death of Fair Rosamond. London, [1750 ?]. [B.M.]

Life and Death of a Monkey; Or, The Village of Alton. A Tale. 2 vols., London, Edmund Lloyd, 1820. [B.M. (2nd edn.).]

Life and Death of a Monkey (The); a tale for young persons. London, 1814. [*New Monthly Mag.*]

Life and Death of St. George (The), The Noble Champion of England. With woodcuts. London, Printed and Sold in Aldermary Church Yard, [1750 ?]. [B.M.]

Life and Extraordinary Adventures of Lucy Amelia Gordon, (The), who was well known, some years since, as the Handsome Servant Maid of Grosvenor Square. A true narrative, written by herself. J. Ker. [N.D.] [Block.]

Life and Heroic Actions of Balbe Berton (The), Chevalier de Grillon, Surnamed the Brave. Translated from the French by a Lady, and revised by Mr. [Samuel] Richardson, Author of Clarissa, etc. 2 vols., London, Woodgate, [1760 ?] [B.M.: Ingpen.]

Life and Memoirs of Mr. Ephraim Bates (The), commonly called Corporal Bates, a broken-hearted Soldier. London, W. Owen, 1756. [B.M.]

Life and Opinions of Miss Sukey Shandy (The), of Bow Street, Gentlewoman. In a series of letters to her dear brother, Tristram Shandy, Gent. London, R. Stevens, 1760. [Tregaskis.]

Life and Real Adventures of Hamilton Murray (The), written by himself. 3 vols., London, 1759. [B.M.]

Life and Surprising Adventures of Blue-Eyed Patty (The). Wolverhampton, [1810 ?]. [B.M.]

Life and Surprising Adventures of Jack Shepperd (The). London. G. Purkess, 1849. [H. W. Fennell.]

Life and Surprizing Adventures of Crusoe Richard Davis (The). 2 vols., London, F. Noble; and J. Noble, N.D. [Dr. Hubert Norman.]

Life and Surprizing Adventures of Don Antonio De Trezzanio, who was Self-Educated, and lived Forty-five Years in an uninhabited Island in the East Indies. Written by Salandio the Hermit, who found him there, and afterwards brought him to Goa. Translated from the Portuguese. With plates. London, H. Serjeant, 1766. [Pickering].

Life and Surprizing Adventures of F. Reveep (The). Translated into English by Mr. Transmarine. [1770 ?]. [B.M.]

Life and Times of Dick Whittington (The). An Historical Romance. With 22 plates. London, Hugh Cunningham, 1841. [H. W. Fennell.]

Life as it is; or, A Peep into Fashionable Parties. A novel. 3 vols. Minerva Press, 1807. [Blakey.]

Life Boat (The); or, The Stranded Ships on the Bar of Memel. Being An Authentic and Interesting Account of the remarkable Deliverance of Three Ships' Companies by the Crew of the Robert and Margaret. With a woodcut. London, Augustus Applegarth and Edward Cowper, N.D. [Block.]

Life for Life; or, "the Law written in the heart." A brief tale for 1850. London, Ollivier, [1850]. [B.M.]

Life in the Irish Militia; or, Tales of the Barrack Room. London, Ridgway, 1847. [*I. in F.*]

Life of Alexander Alexander (The). 2 vols., 1830. [*New Monthly Mag.*]

Life of a Fox (The), Written by himself. With illustrations by Thomas Smith. 1843. [Blackwell.]

Life of a Midshipman (The), A Tale Founded on Facts: And intended to correct An Injudicious Predilection in Boys for The Life of a Sailor. With a frontispiece by F. Howard. London, Henry Colburn and Richard Bentley, 1829. [B.M.: R. Walter Gibson: H. Gray.]

Life of Miss Louisa Selby (The). [*Cat. Lib. Prohib.*]

Life of Mrs. Gooch (The), Written by Herself, Dedicated to the Public. 3 vols., London, Printed for the Authoress. 1792. [Holland.]

Life of Patty Saunders. Written by Herself. London. W. Owen, 1752. [Elkin Mathews.]

Life of Rolla (The). A Peruvian Tale: including a description of the Temple of the Sun, to which are added Six Peruvian Fables. With a frontispiece. London, Newbery, 1800. [Arthur Rogers.]

Life: A Romance. By * * *. 3 vols., London, T. C. Newby, 1844. [B.M.]

Life, smooth and rough as it runs. London, 1815. [B.M.]

Life, Travels and Adventures of Christopher Wagstaff, Grandfather to Tristram Shandy, interspersed with a suitable variety of matter. 2 vols., 1762. [Allibone: Chas. Hutt.]

Life-Lore: Lessons from the childhood of Nolan Fairfield. London, Longman, Brown, Green and Longmans, 1847. [B.M.: *Critic.*]

Life's Lessons; A Tale. By the author of " Tales that might be true." London, Charles Tilt, 1839. [B.M.]

Life's Stepping Stones; or the History of Fanny Grey. In 2 parts. London, 1850. [B.M.]

Lillian Arundel, a Story for Children. London, 1843. [B.M.]

Lilliputian Story Teller (The). 1785. [*Camb. Hist. Eng. Lit.*]

Limbourg, Jean Philippe de. New Amusements of the German Spa. Written in French in the Year 1763. Decorated with Views of Spa and its Environs. To which are Added Novels, containing certain Histories, Anecdotes and Adventures. With 6 folding plates. 2 vols., London, L. Davis, 1764. [B.M.: Dobell: D. Webster.]

Lindamara, or an Old Maid in search of a Husband. 3 vols., 1810. [B.M.]

Lindridge, James. The Life and Adventures of Jack Rann; alias sixteen-string Jack, the highwayman, With illustrations. London, Purkess, [1845 ?]. [B.M.]

—— Tales of Shipwrecks and Adventures at Sea with celebrated voyages, amusing tales and anecdotes. Edited by James Lindridge. With illustrations. London, W. M. Clark, 1846. [B.M.]

Linley, William. The Adventures Of Ralph Reybridge: Containing Sketches Of Modern Characters, Manners, And Education. 4 vols., London, Richard Phillips, 1809. [B.M.: G. Sexton.]

—— Forbidden Apartments. A tale. 2 vols. London, Printed at the Minerva Press, for William Lane, 1800. [Blakey.]

Linton, Eliza Lynn. Amymone. A Romance Of the days of Pericles. By the Author of " Azeth the Egyptian." 3 vols., London, Richard Bentley, 1848. [B.M.]

—— Azeth, the Egyptian. A Novel. 3 vols., London, Thomas Cautley Newby, 1847. [B.M.]

Linton, Henry P. The Curate of Elmdale: a tale of the Irish Tithe Agitation, during the years 1830 to 1836. London, Seeley, 1848. [B.M.: *Eng. Cat.*]

Linwood, Mary. Leicestershire Tales. 4 vols., Printed for the Author, 1808. [Backus: Blackwell: B.M.]

Lionel; Or, The Last of the Pevenseys. A Novel. 3 vols., London, Longman, Hurst, Rees, Orme, & Brown, 1818. [B.M.: *New Monthly Mag.*]

Lisle (*see* DE LISLE).

Lister, Charles. The College Chums. A Novel. 2 vols., London, T. C. Newby, 1845. [B.M.: *Critic.*]

Lister, Maria Theresa. Dacre: A Novel. Edited by The Countess of Morley.

3 vols., London, Longman, Rees, Orme, Brown, Green and Longman, 1834. [B.M.: Francis Edwards: A. Margery.]

Lister, Thomas Henry. Arlington, A Novel. By the Author of " Granby." 3 vols., London, Henry Colburn and Richard Bentley, 1832. [B.M.: W. Brown: *Quarterly Review.*]

—— Granby. A Novel. 3 vols., London, Henry Colburn, 1826. [Birrell & Garnett: Block: B.M.]

—— Herbert Lacy. By the Author of Granby. 3 vols., London, Henry Colburn, 1828. [B.M.: Kyrle Fletcher: Ingpen.]

Literary Amusements; Or, Evening Entertainer. By a Female Hand. Containing, The History of Mr. Allen. The Life of an Authoress. The Enchanted Rose. History of Nourzhatel. Fatal Curiosity. The Fox-hunters. Effects of Seduction. Letter on Suicide. On the Studies of Women. William and Phebe. Thoughts on Friendship. On Rural Simplicity. 2 vols., Dublin, Printed by T. Henshall, for S. Price, W. & H. Whitestone, T. Walker, J. Beatty, E. Cross and R. Burton, 1782. [B.M.]

Literary Box (The), containing the Contributions of the Evelyn Family, consisting of instructing and amusing Tales, in prose and verse, suited to all ages. By the Author of " The Welcome Visitor." With 12 engravings. London, John Harris, 1824. [Gumuchian.]

Little Adam The Gardener. With a vignette. London, James Burns, [1849]. [B.M.]

Little Annie and her Sisters, By E. W. H. With a frontispiece. London, J. Masters. 1839. [B.M.]

Little Arthur. [London]. Religious Tract Society, [1830 ?]. [B.M.]

Little Basket-Maker (The), and other tales. (Translated from the German). With 4 illustrations. London, Joseph Cundall, 1848. [B.M.]

Little Basket-Makers. London, Religious Tract Society, [1830 ?]. [B.M.]

Little Budget for Little Girls (The). By Old Humphrey. With woodcuts. London, The Religious Tract Society, N.D. [Court Book Shop.]

Little Charles the Gardener. With a woodcut. London, Houlston, N.D. No. 68 of Houlston's Series of Tracts. [Block.]

Little Curricle of Yellow Pasteboard (The), With a Variety of Infantile Tales. With woodcuts. London, J. Harris, 1803. [Dobell.]

Little Deserter (The), or Holiday Sports An amusing Tale Dedicated to all good boys. Altered from the French. With 15 engravings. Edinburgh, Oliver & Boyd, [1810 ?]. [Arthur Rogers.]

Little Dog Dash. A tale. Wellington, 1828. [B.M.]

Little Dove (The); a story for children. Translated from the German. London, 1828. [B.M.]

Little Errand Girl (The), showing the benefits of affliction. London, Religious Tract Society, [1830 ?]. [B.M.]

Little Forget-Me-Not (The). London 1841. [B.M.]

Little Frank and Other Tales. London, 1838. [B.M.]

Little Girl and Her Bible (The). [London,] Religious Tract Society, [1830 ?]. [B.M.]

Little Grey Mouse (The); Or, The History of Rosabelle and Paridel. With woodcuts. Wellington, N.D. [Ingpen.]

Little Italians (The), Or, The lost children of Mont St. Bernard. With a vignette and a frontispiece. London, James Burns, [1849]. [B.M.]

Little Juba; or, the Adventures and Vicissitudes of a Lap Dog. With a frontispiece. London, Printed for J. Harris, by J. Swan, 1802. [Mollie Green: *Guardian of Education*.]

Little Martin or the Redbreast. From the German. With a vignette. London, James Burns, [1849]. [B.M.]

Little Mary. With woodcuts. London, Religious Tract Society, [1830]. [B.M.]

Little Mary; a tale for children. Illustrative of some Scripture truths. London, Simpkin, 1845. [B.M.: *Eng. Cat.*]

Little Maurice and his Uncle. London, 1840. [B.M.]

Little Moralists (The); Or, The History Of Amintor and Florella, The pretty little Shepherd and Shepherdess Of the Vale of Evesham. With woodcuts. London, E. Newbery, 1792. [F. Hollings.]

Little Mountaineers of Auvergne (The); Or, The Adventures Of James and Georgette. Altered from the French, and Adapted to the Perusal of Youth. With a frontispiece. London, R. & L. Peacock, 1801. [Block: B.M.: Arthur Rogers.]

Little Peace-Maker (The). London, Religious Tract Society, [1830 ?]. [B.M.]

Little Prisoner (The); or Passion and Patience: and, Amendment; or Charles Grant and his Sister. By the authors of Hugh Latimer, Little Quaker. London, Dean & Munday, 1828. [B.M.]

Little Prisoner; or, a Visit to the Island of Malta. Founded on Fact. With a frontispiece. London, Harvey and Darton, [1822]. [Mollie Green.]

Little Robinson (The), and Other Tales. Edinburgh, William and Robert Chambers. 1848. [Block.]

Little Savoyard (The). London, 1849. [B.M.]

Little Selina. London, Tyler & Reed, [1840 ?]. [B.M.]

Little Stories for Little Children. [Translated from the German by W. B. F.]. London, 1848. [B.M.]

Little Stories of One and Two Syllables for Little Children. London, 1849. [B.M.]

Little Susan and Her Lamb. London, The Religious Tract Society, [1830 ?]. [B.M.]

Little Wanderers (The); or, the surprising history of two pretty orphans. London, 1806. [B.M.]

Little Warbler of the Cottage (The) and her dog Constant. With 6 engravings. London, J. Harris, 1816. [Gumuchian.]

Littlejohn, P. The Cypher; or, The world as it goes. A novel. 3 vols. [W. Lane, 1791]. [Blakey.]

—— Henry. A novel. By the author of The cypher; or, The world as it goes. 2 vols. [W. Lane, 1793]. [Blakey.]

—— The Mistake: or Something Beyond a Joke. 3 vols., London, J. Bonsor, 1800. [Allibone: Fletcher.]

Littleton, C. M. The Enchanted Ring Front. London, 1810. [Murray Hill.]

Living Waters by the Pilgrim's Path. A tale for the young. [By] J. G. F. London, [1850 ?]. [B.M.]

Llewellin, Mrs. Read, and Give it a Name. A Novel. 4 vols., London, Printed at the Minerva Press, for A. K. Newman, 1813. [Publisher's advert.: *Quarterly Review*: Blakey.]

Llewelyn's Heir; Or, North Wales: Its Manners, customs and Superstitions During the last century. Illustrated by A Story Founded on Fact. 3 vols., London, Smith, Elder, 1846. [B.M.: Kyrle Fletcher.]

Lloyd, Charles, Junior. Edmund Oliver. By Charles Lloyd. 2 vols., Bristol: Printed by Bulgin and Rosser, For Joseph Cottle, 1798. [*Ashley Lib.*: B.M.: *Eng. Lit. in Germany*.]

—— Isabel: A Tale: By Charles Lloyd. 2 vols., London, Longman, Hurst, Rees & Orme; and Sherwood, Neeley and Jones, Ulverstone, 1810. [*Ashley Lib.*]

Lloyd, Sarah Maria. The Folly & Mischief of Prejudice & Obstinacy; Illustrated in the History of Tommy Sole And his Great-Grandmother. A tale founded on facts. With a woodcut. London, Houlston, N.D. No. 29 of Houlston's Series of Tracts. [Block.]

Lobeira, Vasco de. Amadis of Gaul [From the Spanish Version of Garciordonez de Montalvo, By Robert Southey]. 4 vols., London, Printed by N. Biggs for T. N. Longman and O. Rees, 1803. [Baker's Bookshop: B.M.]

Locke, J. de Clinton. The Swiss Family Robinson. Second Series. Being The Continuation of the Work Already Published under that Title. Translated from the French, By J. de Clinton Locke. 2 vols., London, Sampson Low, 1849. [B.M.: Bernard Whyte.]

Lockhart, John Gibson. The History Of Matthew Wald. Edinburgh, William

Blackwood; and T. Cadell, London, 1824. [B.M.: Ingpen: A. Margery.]

Lockhart, John Gibson. Reginald Dalton. By the Author of Valerius, and Adam Blair. 3 vols., Edinburgh, William Blackwood; and T. Cadell, London, 1823. [Birrell & Garnett: Block: B.M.]

—— Some Passages in The life of Mr. Adam Blair Minister of the Gospel At Cross-Meikle. Edinburgh, William Blackwood; and T. Cadell, London, 1822. [B.M.]

—— Valerius; A Roman Story. 3 vols., Edinburgh, William Blackwood; and T. Cadell, London, 1821. [Birrell & Garnett: B.M.: Arthur Rogers.]

Loftus, George, (?). Milford House; or, folly as it flies. By a late officer of the Third Guards. 3 vols., London, W. Lindsell, 1814. [B.M.: *New Monthly Mag.: Quarterly Review.*]

Logan, Eliza. Restalrig; or, The Forfeiture. By the Author of St. Johnstoun, or John Earl of Gowrie. 2 vols., Edinburgh, Machlachlan & Stewart; and Simpkin & Marshall, 1829. [B.M.]

—— St. Johnstoun; Or, John, Earl of Gowrie. 3 vols., Edinburgh, Machlachlan and Stewart, 1823. [B.M.: Ingpen: McLeish.]

Logan. A Family Story. 4 vols., London, A. K. Newman, 1823. [*Eng. Cat.: New Monthly Mag.*]

Lohmann, Emilie Friederike Sophie. Self-Devotion: or, the Prussians at Hochkirch. A free translation from the German. Lichfield, 1849. [B.M.]

Lomas, J. R. W. De La Macy, A Tale of Real Life. 2 vols., London, Effingham Wilson, 1834. [B.M.: Elkin Mathews.]

London Courtship: or a New Road to Matrimony. Consisting of original letters which passed between a celebrated Young Lady of the City of London and several of her suitors. London, [1759 ?]. [B.M.]

London Jingles and Country Tales for Young People. Bunbury, J. G. Rusher, [1840 ?]. [B.M.]

London; or a Month at Stevens's. By a Late Resident. A Satirical Novel. 3 vols., London, Sherwood, 1819. [B.M.: Ingpen: T. Thorp.]

Loney,—. Sebastian and Isabel; or, The Invisible Sword. [T. D. Webster.]

Long, Lady Catharine. Sir Roland Ashton. A Tale of the Times. 2 vols., London, James Nisbet. 1844. [Allibone: B.M.]

Long, Edward. The Anti-Gallican; Or, The History and Adventures of Harry Cobham, Esquire. Inscribed to Louis XVth; by the Author. With a frontispiece. London, T. Lownds, 1757. [B.M.: W. Brown: A. Rogers.]

Long Engagements. A Tale of the Affghan Rebellion. London, Chapman and Hall, 1846. [*Critic*: Publisher's advert.]

Long Lost Found (The). Parts 1-3 [all published]. With illustrations by H. K. Browne. 1847. [B.M.]

Long Pack (The). A Northumbrian Tale, an hundred years old. With a woodcut. Barnard Castle, J. Atkinson, N.D. [Block.]

Longest Day (The); or, The Village Festival. By Simon Twig. London, [1839]. [B.M.]

Longueville, Peter. The Hermit; or, The adventures of Philip Quarll. London, William Lane, 1786. [Blakey.]

Longus. Daphnis and Chloe, A Pastoral Novel. Now first selectly translated into English from the original Greek of Longus [by Rev. C. P. Le Grice]. Penzance, Printed for the Author by T. Vigurs, 1803. [Birrell & Garnett: B.M.]

—— Lives, Amours, and surprising Adventures of Daphnis and Chloe. With woodcuts. 1746. [W. Brown.]

Lord of Hardivyle, (The), an Historical Legend of the Fourteenth Century, London, W. Trepass, 1800. [J. C. Hardy.]

Lossius, C. F. Cumal and Lina, Or The African Children. An Instructive and Entertaining History for the use of Young People Translated from the French by S. B. Moens. With Plates. 2 vols., 1817. [Backus: B.M.: Arthur Rogers.]

Lost Manuscripts of a Blue Jacket (The). Newcastle, F. Crewe, 1850. [B.M.]

Loudon, Agnes. Tales for Young People by Agnes Loudon. Edited by Mrs. Loudon. With illustrations from designs by Gilbert. Engraved by Folkard. London, Kerby, 1846. [B.M.]

—— Tales of School Life. With illustrations by John Absolon. London, Grant, 1850. [B.M.]

Loudon, Jane C. The Mummy, A Tale of the Twenty-Second Century. 3 vols., London, Henry Colburn, 1827. [B.M.: Arthur Rogers: Victorius.]

—— Prose and Verse. Birmingham, Wrighton, 1824. [Stonehill.]

——Stories of A Bride; By the Author of The Mummy. 3 vols., London, Henry Colburn and Richard Bentley, 1829. [B.M.]

Loudon, Margracia. Dilemmas of Pride. By the Author of First Love. 3 vols., London, Bull & Churton, 1833. [B.M.: Elkin Mathews.]

Loudon, Margracia. First Love. A Novel. 3 vols., London, Saunders and Otley, 1830. [B.M.: *New Monthly Mag.*: T. D. Webster.]

—— Fortune-Hunting: A Novel. By The Author of " First Love." 3 vols., London, Henry Colburn & Richard Bentley, 1832. [B.M.: Elkin Mathews.]

—— Maternal Love: a novel. 3 vols.,

London, T. C. Newby, 1849. [Allibone: B.M.: *Eng. Cat.*]

Louis and Nina, Or An Excursion to Yverdun. 2 vols., 1789. [Martin A. McGoff.]

Louisa Forrester; or Characters drawn from Real Life. 3 vols., London, W. Lane, 1789. [B.M.: Maggs: Stonehill.]

Louisa Matthews. 3 vols., 1793. [W. Brown: *New Ann. Reg.*]

Louisa, or the Reward of an Affectionate Daughter. A novel, 2 vols., London, 1790. [B.M.: T. D. Webster.]

Louisa; Or, Virtue in Distress. Being the History of a natural Daughter of Lady * * * *. London, A. and C. Corbett, 1760. [B.M.: Huth.]

Louisa; or, the virtuous villager, a Roman Catholic tale, translated from the French, for the use of the Catholic schools. Dublin, 1832. [B.M.]

Louisa Wharton. A story, founded on facts: written by herself, in a series of letters to a friend. London, [1780?]. [B.M.]

Lourdoueix (*see* DE LOURDOUEIX).

Louvet de Couvray, Jean Baptiste. Emily de Varmont; or, a Divorce dictated by Necessity. To which are added, The Amours of Father Sévin. From the French of Louvet de Couvray. 3 vols., London, 1798. [B.M.]
—— Life and Adventures of the Chevalier de Faublas. 4 vols., London, 1793. [Lib. of Congress.]

Love and Avarice, or the Fatal Effects of preferring Wealth to Beauty, by a Lady of Shropshire. London, 1748. [Myers.]

Love and Crime; or the Mystery of the Convent. London, [1845]. [B.M.]

Love and Friendship: or, The Fair Fugitive. Exemplified in the Histories of two Families of Distinction, in the West of England; and intispers'd with a Variety of Characters, and several pleasing and interesting Incidents. Dublin, 1757. [D. Webster.]

Love & Horror; an Imitation of the Present, & a model for all future romances. By Ircastrensis. London, 1815. [*New Monthly Mag.*]

Love at First Sight; or, the History of Miss Caroline Stanhope. 3 vols., London, 1773. [B.M.]

Love at First Sight: or, the history of Miss Lydia Harmwood. London, 1821. [B.M.]

Love in a Barn, or the Country courtship. In 3 parts. [Newcastle]. [1780?]. [B.M.]

Love in High Life, or the Amours of a Court. London, [1760?]. [B.M.]

Love in a Tub; or the wine-merchant taken in. To which are added, Charlie and his Lalland bride, The Scottish brose. Toasts and Sentiments. Glasgow, [1820?]. [B.M.]

Love Lost: a Tale. London, 1826. [*New Monthly Mag.*].

Love of Evelina for Lord Armond: and the adventures of a young lady, who was confined in the hollow of an oak tree. Falkirk, 1821. [B.M.]

Love Story (A). By a Bushman. 2 vols., London, Cunningham and Mortimer, 1842. [Publisher's advert.]

Lovel Castle; or the Rightful Heir Restored. A Gothic tale. With a frontispiece. London, [1825?]. [B.M.: Dobell.]

Lovell, George William. The Trustee. By the Author of The Tragedy of " The Provost of Bruges," &c. 3 vols., London, Henry Colburn, 1841. [B.M.]

Lover, Samuel. Handy Andy: A Tale of Irish Life. With illustrations by the author. London, Frederick Lover and Richard Groombridge, 1842. [B.M.: Ingpen: King.]
—— Legends and Stories of Ireland. With etchings by the Author. Dublin, W. F. Wakeman, 1831. [Colbeck: Marks: Sotheby's.]
—— Legends and Stories of Ireland. Second series. With illustrations by W. Harvey and by the Author. London, Baldwin and Cradock, 1834. [*Eng. Cat.*: G. Worthington.]
—— [Edited by], Popular Tales and Legends of the Irish Peasantry. With illustrations by Samuel Lover. Dublin, William Frederick Wakeman, 1834. [Block: B.M.: *I. in F.*]
—— Rory O'More: A National Romance. With 15 illustrations by the author. 3 vols., London, Richard Bentley, 1837. [B.M.: *Guide to Best Fiction*: T. Thorp.]
—— Treasure Trove; the First of a Series of Accounts of Irish Heirs; a Romantic Tale of the last Century. With 26 etchings by the Author. London, Frederick Lover, 1844. [B.M.: Danielson: Sotheran.]

Lovers' Labours. [Cawthorn's Catalogue, 1810].

Lover's Quarrel (The). Being the pleasant history of Fair Rosamond whose love was obtained by Tommy Potts. [1775?]. [B.M.]

Loves of Mirtil, Son of Adonis. With plates. 1770. [W. Brown.]

Loves of the Saints (The); or, the diverting history of Sandy and Bobby, etc. 1825. [B.M.]

Love's Perils, or Theodore and Amyntor, a Romantic Love Tale, on which is founded the Grand Melo Drame performed at the Surrey Theatre. With a plate. London, Kemmish, and Stevens, [1820]. [Pickering.]

Love's Pilgrimage. A Story Founded on Facts. Compiled from the Journal of a Deceased Friend. 3 vols., London, T. N. Longman, 1796. [B.M.: *New Ann. Reg.*: Stonehill.]

Lovett, John. The Citizen of the World. London, 1793. [B.M.]

Lowndes, Hannah Maria. The Child of Mystery; Or, The Cottager's Daughter.

A Tale of Fashionable Life. With engravings. London, William Evans, 1837. [B.M.: Ingpen: McLeish.]

Lowndes, Hannah Maria. The Curate's Daughters, or the Twin Roses of Arundale. A Domestic Story. With plates. London, W. Emans, [c. 1835]. [Ingpen.]

—— Emily Moreland, or Maid of the Valley. With illustrations. London, George Virtue, 1829. [Marks: W. T. Spencer.]

—— The Forged Note, Or Julian and Marianne. With plates. 1824. [Guntrip.]

—— The Gamblers; or the Treacherous Friend: a moral tale. By the author of several popular works. London, 1824. [B.M.]

—— The Gipsey Chief; or, The Haunted Oak. A Tale of Other Days. With illustrations. London, Virtue, [1840]. [B.M.: Stonehill.]

—— The Gipsey Girl, or the Heir of Hazel Dell, a romantic tale. With plates. London, J. & F. Tallis, 1836. [B.M.: Rawlinson: Stonehill.]

—— The Gipsy Mother; or the miseries of enforced marriages. By the Authoress of Emily Moreland. With illustrations. London, [1835 ?]. [B.M.: G. Sexton.]

—— Gretna Green, or The Elopement of Miss D—— with a Gallant Son of Mars. With illustrations. London, John Tallis, 1821. [Blackwell: Murray Hill.]

—— The Love Token; or the Mistress and her Guardian. A domestic story. London, Virtue, [1844 ?]. [B.M.]

—— The Outlaw's Bride. A Romantic Tale. With illustrations. London, Virtue, 1838. [Ingpen: Stonehill.]

—— The Pride of the Village; Or, The Farmer's Daughters. A Domestic Story. With a frontispiece by George Cruikshank. London, Virtue, [1830]. [Dobell: Ingpen: Marks.]

—— Rosaline Woodbridge. 3 vols., London, Matthew Iley, 1827. [An edition with plates, and the sub-title: *or The Midnight Visit. A Romantic Tale*, was published the same year by Virtue in one volume.] [B.M.: Ingpen: Stonehill.]

—— The Scottish Chieftains; or, The Perils of Love and War. With illustrations. London, George Virtue, 1831. [Baker's Bookshop: Block: Marks.]

—— The Strangers of the Glen; or the Travellers Benighted. With plates. [c. 1830]. [Blackwell.]

—— Trials of Love; or Woman's Reward. A Romance of Real Life. With plates. London, Printed for the Proprietors, by McGowan, 1849. [Block.]

—— Village Scandal; or, the Gossip's Tale, A Picture of Real Life. With illustrations. London, William Emans, 1835. [B.M.: Court Bk. Shop: Stonehill.]

—— The Wedding Ring: Or, Married and Single; A Domestic Tale. By Hannah Maria Jones. 4 vols., London, George Virtue, 1824. [R. Stotesbury.]

Lowther, G. Gerald; A Tale of Conscience. 2 vols., London, John W. Parker, 1840. [B.M.]

Lubin and Rosetta; Or, Love and Innocence: A Pastoral Tale. With an engraving. London, Dean and Munday, 1811. [Court Bk. Shop.]

Lucas, Charles. The Abissinian Reformer; or, the Bible and the Sabre. A novel. 3 vols., London, 1808. [B.M.: Arthur Rogers.]

—— Gwelygordd; Or, The Child of Sin. A Tale of Welsh Origin. By the Author of The Infernal Quixote, Abyssinian Reformer, Castle of St. Donats, &c. &c. 3 vols., London, Printed at the Minerva Press for A. K. Newman, 1820. [B.M.: *New Monthly Mag.*]

—— The Infernal Quixote. A Tale of the Day. With a frontispiece. 4 vols., London, William Lane, 1801. [B.M.: Pickering.]

Lucas, Mrs. Martin. Treachery. 3 vols., London, T. C. Newby, 1848. [B.M.]

Lucas, William. The Duellists, Or Men of Honour. A Story calculated to shew the Folly, Extravagance and Sin of Duelling. With a frontispiece. London, Albion Press, 1805. [Arthur Rogers.]

Luce, Joan de. Curiosity. A Novel. 3 vols., London, A. K. Newman, 1822. [B.M.]

Lucelle; or, The Young Indian. A Romance. With woodcuts. London, E. Lloyd, [1847]. [B.M.: B. Ono.]

Lucinda Hartley or Adventures of an Orphan, Containing the Humorous History of Mr. Goodwin. 1790. [*Eng. Lit. in Germany.*]

Lucinda, or The Angry Father, a Domestic Tale. With a plate. London, Kemmish, and Stevens. [c. 1820]. [Pickering.]

Lucky and Unlucky (The). With a woodcut. London, The Religious Tract Society, N.D. No. 1609. [Block.]

Lucretia or Virtue the Best Dowry. 1790. [*Eng. Lit. in Germany.*]

Lucy Ashbourne; or, Solitude Sweetened; exhibiting the influence of true religion in rendering life happy. A tale founded on fact. London, 1833. [B.M.]

Lucy Morley: or, a Child's passage from death unto life: by a Sunday School teacher. London, 1840. [B.M.]

Lucy Neal: or Negro life, love, mirth and character. London, 1847. [B.M.]

Lucy; or, " I will not be naughty again, Papa." [London], [Religious Tract Society], [1830 ?]. [B.M.]

Lucy Unwin; Or, Prejudice Reproved: And other tales. With an engraving. London, Darton and Harvey, 1836. [B.M.]

Lucy's Pilgrimage; Or the Branch of Roses. With a vignette. London, James Burns, [1849]. [B.M.]

Luke Somerton; or, The English Renegade. A Romance. By the Author of

"Treachery," "Temptation," "Poverty," Etc. With woodcuts. London, Edward Lloyd, 1845. [B.M.: B. Ono.]

Lumley House. A novel. The first attempt of a young lady. 3 vols. [W. Lane, 1787]. [Blakey.]

Lundie, Mrs. J. C. The Children of the Manse. By . . . London, 1850. [B.M.]

Lusignan, or the Abbaye of La Trappe. A novel. 4 vols., London, Minerva Press, 1801. [Stonehill: Blakey.]

Lustful Turk (The). Part the First. A History Founded on Facts. Containing an Interesting Narrative of the cruel fate of two young English ladies, named Silvia Carey, and Emily Barlow. Fully explaining how Emily Barlow, and her servant, Eliza Gibbs, on their passage to India, were taken prisoners by an Algerian Pirate, and made a present of to the Dey of Algiers; who on the very night of their arrival debauched Emily. —Containing also every possible particular of the Artful Plans laid by the Dey, to get possession of the person of Silvia Carey—how he effected his purpose—with the particulars of her becoming a victim to his libidinous desires. Which recital is also interspersed with the Histories of several other ladies confined in the Dey's Harem. One of which gives an account of the horrid practices then carrying on in several French and Italian convents by a Society of Monks, established in Algiers, under pretence of redeeming Christian slaves; but who, in reality, carried on an infamous traffic in young girls. Also an account of the sufferings of Eliza Gibbs from the flogging propensities of the Bey of Tunis. With many other curious circumstances, until the reduction of Algiers by Lord Exmouth; by which means these particulars became known.—The whole compiled from the Original Letters, by permission of one of the sufferers. By an Arcadian A8. To be had of all the principal Booksellers in town and country. 1828. [*Cat. Lib. Prohib.*]

Lymbunner, A. L. The Fall of the Nan Soung. A Tale of the Mogul Conquest of China. 3 vols., London, Saunders and Otley, 1846. [B.M.: *Critic.*]

Lynch, Theodora Elizabeth. The Cotton-Tree; or, Emily, the little West Indian. A tale. London, Theobald, 1847. [B.M.]

—— The Family Sepulchre: a tale of Jamaica. London, A. Hall, [1848]. [B.M.]

—— Maude Effingham. A tale of Jamaica. London, A. Hall, 1849. [B.M.]

Lyndon, Charlotte. The Steadfast ones; or, Safe at last. Brighton, Hamilton, 1849. [B.M.: *Eng. Cat.*]

—— The Voice of Ida; a tale. London, Hamilton, 1848. [B.M.: *Eng. Cat.*]

Lynn, Eliza, (*see* LINTON, Eliza Lynn).

Lynn Haverhill; Or The Life of a Soldier. 3 vols., 1838. [James Glaisher.]

Lyttleton, George Lord. The Court Secret: a Melancholy Truth. Now first translated from the Original Arabic. By an Adept in the Oriental Tongues. London, T. Cooper, 1741. [Birrell & Garnett: Holland.]

Lyttleton, M. La Belle Sauvage: or, A Progress through the Beau-Monde. A Novel. 2 vols., London, Printed at the Minerva Press for Lane and Newman, 1803. [B.M.: Ingpen: Blakey].

—— Fiesco, Count of Lavagne. A novel. 4 vols., [Minerva Press, 1805]. [Blakey.]

—— Follies of Fashion: a dramatic novel. London, 1801. [B.M.]

—— The German Sorceress. 3 vols. [Minerva Press, 1803]. [Blakey.]

—— Isabel; or, The orphan of Valdarno. By a student of Trinity College. [Minerva Press, 1802.]

—— The Lottery of Life; or, the Romance of a Summer. 3 vols., London, Printed at the Minerva Press, 1802. [Baker's Bookshop.]

—— Peregrine, or the Fool of Fortune. A Novel. By the author of The Follies of Fashion, Lottery of Life, La Belle Sauvage, &c. 3 vols., London, Printed at the Minerva Press, 1803. [Baker's Bookshop: B.M.: Blakey.]

Lytton, Edward Bulwer, Lord. Alice Or The Mysteries. A Sequel to " Ernest Maltravers." By the Author of " Pelham," " Rienzi," " The Student," &c. &c. 3 vols., London, Saunders and Otley, 1838. [Birrell & Garnett: B.M.: Ingpen.]

—— The Caxtons; A Family Picture. 3 vols., Edinburgh, William Blackwood, 1849. [Block: Ingpen: McLeish.]

—— Devereux. A Tale. By The Author of " Pelham." 3 vols., London, Henry Colburn, 1829. [B.M.: Ingpen: Arthur Rogers.]

—— The Disowned. By the Author of " Pelham." 4 vols., London, Henry Colburn, 1829. [Ingpen: Pickering: Arthur Rogers.]

—— Ernest Maltravers By the Author of " Pelham," "Eugene Aram," " Rienzi," &c. &c. 3 vols., London, Saunders and Otley, 1837. [B.M.: Elkin Mathews: Poynder, Hunt.]

—— Eugene Aram. A Tale. By the Author of " Pelham," " Devereux," &c. 3 vols., London, Henry Colburn & Richard Bentley, 1832. [B.M.: Ingpen: Arthur Rogers.]

—— Falkland. London, Henry Colburn, 1827. [B.M.: Ingpen: *Literary Gazette.*]

—— Godolphin. A Novel. 3 vols., London, Richard Bentley, 1833. [B.M.: *New Monthly Mag.*: Pickering.]

—— Harold, The Last of the Saxon Kings; By the Author of " Rienzi;" " The Last of the Barons;" Etc. etc.

etc. 3 vols., London, Richard Bentley, 1848. [B.M.: Ingpen: Arthur Rogers.]

Lytton, Edward Bulwer, Lord. The Last Days Of Pompeii. By the Author of "Pelham," "Eugene Aram," "England, and the English." &c. &c. 3 vols., London, Richard Bentley, 1834. [Block: B.M.: Arthur Rogers.]

—— The Last of the Barons. By The Author of "Rienzi." 3 vols., London, Saunders and Otley, 1843. [Block: B.M.: King.]

—— Leila; or The Siege of Granada: and Calderon the Courtier. By the Author of "Eugene Aram." With engravings. London, 1838. [Arthur Rogers.]

—— Lucretia, Or The Children of Night. By the Author of "Rienzi," Etc. etc. 3 vols., London, Saunders & Otley, 1846. [Elkin Mathews.]

—— Night and Morning. By the Author of "Rienzi," "Eugene Aram," &c. &c. 3 vols., London, Saunders and Otley, 1841. [Baker's Bookshop; B.M.: McLeish.]

—— Paul Clifford. By the Author of "Pelham," "Devereux," &c. 3 vols., London, Henry Colburn and Richard Bentley, 1830. [B.M.: McLeish: Maggs.]

—— Pelham; or the Adventures of a Gentleman. 3 vols., London, Henry Colburn, 1828. [Block: B.M.: Arthur Rogers.]

—— The Pilgrims of the Rhine. By the Author of "Pelham," "Eugene Aram," &c. With plates. London, Saunders and Otley, 1834. [Block: Arthur Rogers: A. V. Turner.]

—— Rienzi The Last of the Tribunes. By the Author of "Eugene Aram," "Last Days of Pompeii," &c. &c. 3 vols., London, Saunders and Otley, 1835. [B.M.: Ingpen: Publisher's advert.]

—— The Student. A Series of Papers, By the Author of "Eugene Aram," "England and the English," &c. &c. 2 vols., London, Saunders and Otley, 1835. [Block: Ingpen: Pickering.]

—— Zanoni. By The Author of "Night and Morning," "Rienzi," etc. 3 vols., London, Saunders & Otley, 1842. [B.M.: Maggs: Publisher's advert.]

Lytton, Rosina Lady. Bianca Capello. An Historical Romance. By Lady Lytton Bulwer. 3 vols., London, Edward Bull, 1843. [B.M.: Lib. of Congress: Elkin Mathews.]

—— The Budget Of The Bubble Family. By Lady Lytton Bulwer. With frontispieces. 3 vols., London, Edward Bull, 1840. [B.M.: Francis Edwards: Lib. of Congress.]

—— Cheveley; Or, The Man of Honour. 3 vols., London, Edward Bull, 1839. [Lib. of Congress.]

—— Memoirs of a Muscovite. Edited by Lady Bulwer Lytton. 3 vols., London,

T. C. Newby, 1844. [B.M.: Elkin Mathews.]

Lytton, Rosina Lady. The Peer's Daughters. A Novel. 3 vols., London, T. C. Newby, 1849. [Lib. of Congress: Elkin Mathews.]

—— The Prince-Duke And The Page, A Historical Novel. Edited by Lady Lytton Bulwer. 3 vols., London, T. and W. Boone, 1841. [B.M.: Ingpen.]

M.D.'s Daughter (The), A Novel Of the Nineteenth Century. 3 vols., London, T. & W. Boone, 1842. [B.M.]

Mabel Carrington: a novel. By the Author of "The Blacksmith's Daughter," 3 vols., London, [1849]. [B.M.]

Maberly, Hon. Catherine Charlotte. Emily: Or, The Countess of Rosendale. A Novel. With a frontispiece. 3 vols., London, Henry Colburn, 1840. [B.M.: Ingpen: Lib. of Congress.]

—— Fashion And its Votaries. 3 vols., London, Saunders and Otley. 1848. [B.M.: Lib. of Congress.]

—— Leontine; Or, The Court of Louis the Fifteenth. 3 vols., London, Henry Colburn, 1846. [B.M.: Critic.]

—— The Love-Match. A Novel. By the Author of "Emily." 3 vols., London, Henry Colburn, 1841. [B.M.: Lib. of Congress: McLeish.]

—— Melanthe. Or, The Days of the Medici. A Tale of the Fifteenth Century. 3 vols., London, John Mitchell, 1843. [B.M.: Holland: Lib. of Congress.]

Macauley, Elizabeth Wright. Tales of the Drama. Founded on the Tragedies of Shakespeare, Massinger, Shirley, and on the Comedies of Steele, Farquhar, Cumberland. Chiswick, Sherwood, 1822. [B.M.: Kyrle Fletcher: Lib. of Congress.]

Macausland, Miss. Adelaide's Gift: or, New Year's Day. Edinburgh, 1848. [B.M.]

MacCarthy, Daniel. The Free Lance: a Historical Romance. 3 vols., London, Richard Bentley, 1844. [B.M.: Critic.]

—— The Siege of Florence: An Historical Romance. 3 vols., London, Henry Colburn, 1840. [B.M.: Ingpen.]

MacChronicle, Ronald. Burton. A Novel. 3 vols., London, A. K. Newman, 1825. [B.M.]

—— Legends of Scotland. First Series. Containing Fair Helen of Kirkonnel, and Roslin Castle. 3 vols., London, A. K. Newman, 1822. [B.M.]

—— Legends of Scotland. Second Series. Containing Daft Marget. 3 vols., London, A. K. Newman, 1823. [B.M.: Quarterly Review.]

—— Legends of Scotland. Third Series. Containing Edward Falconer. 3 vols., London, A. K. Newman, 1828. [B.M.]

MacCombie, Thomas. Arabin; or, the Adventures of a Colonist in New South

Wales. With an essay on the Aborigines of Australia. London, Simmonds, 1845. [Allibone: B.M.: *Eng. Cat.*]

M'Cormick, Captain Thomas. The Rambler of Fortune; Or Sketches Of The early part Of a Military Life. London, Printed for the Author by P. Boyle, 1803. [B.M.]

MacCrindell, Rachel. The Convent; a Narrative founded on Fact. London, Aylott, 1848. [B.M.]
—— The English Governess. A tale of real life. London, Aylott, 1844. [Baker's Bookshop: B.M.: *Eng. Cat.*]
—— The School-Girl in France; a Narrative. London, Seeley, 1840. [Allibone: B.M.: *Eng. Cat.*]

McDermot, Martin. The Mystery Developed. A Novel. 3 vols., London, A. K. Newman, 1825. [B.M.]

Macdonald, Andrew. Laura; A Novel. By the Author of the Independent. 2 vols., London, C. Elliot & T. Kay; and Charles Elliot, Edinburgh, [1790]. [B.M.: Myers.]

Macdonald, Diana Louisa. Villa Verocchio: or the Youth of Leonardo da Vinci. A tale. London, Longman, 1850. [B.M.]

MacDonald; or, the Great Mistake. A story of real life. London, [1849]. [B.M.]

Macdonnell, Eneas. The Hermit Of Glenconella; A Tale. London, G. Cowie, 1820. [B.M.: *I. in F.*: *New Monthly Mag.*]

Macdonough, Captain Felix. The Hermit Abroad. By the Author of the Hermit in London, and The Hermit in the Country. 4 vols., London, Henry Colburn, 1823. [B.M.: Ingpen: Publisher's advert.]
—— The Hermit in the Country; Or, Sketches of English Manners. 4 vols., London, Henry Colburn, 1820-22. [B.M.: McLeish: Arthur Rogers.]
—— The Hermit in Edinburgh; Or, Sketches of Manners and Real Characters and Scenes in the Drama of Life. 3 vols., London, Sherwood, Jones, 1824. [Baker's Bookshop: B.M.: Bernard Whyte.]
—— The Hermit in London; or, Sketches of English Manners. 5 vols., London, Henry Colburn, 1819-1820. [B.M.: Ingpen: *Quarterly Review*.]
—— The Heroine of The Peninsula; Or, Clara Matilda of Seville. By the Author of the " Hermit in London," and other popular works. 2 vols., London, Sherwood, Gilbert and Piper; C. Chapple; A. K. Newman, 1826. [B.M.: *Quarterly Review*.]
—— The Highlanders: A Tale. By the Author of The Hermit in London, Hermit Abroad, &c. 3 vols., London, Henry Colburn, 1824. [B.M.: Kyrle Fletcher.]
—— The Wandering Hermit, by the author of the Hermit in London. Paris, 1823. [B.M.]

Macfarlane, Charles. The Armenians. A Tale of Constantinople. 3 vols., London, Saunders and Otley, 1830. [B.M.: *New Monthly Mag.*]
—— The Camp of Refuge. 2 vols., London, Charles Knight, 1844. [B.M. *Critic.*]
—— The Dutch in the Medway. By the author of " The Camp of Refuge." London, 1845. [B.M.]
—— A Legend of Reading Abbey, By the author of " The Camp of Refuge." London, Charles Knight, 1845. [B.M.]
—— The Romance of History. Italy. 3 vols., London, Edward Bull, 1832. [B.M.: *Metropolitan Mag.*]

M'Gauran, —. Walter Clayton: A Tale of the Gordon Riots. 3 vols., London, T. C. Newby, 1844. [B.M.]
—— The Will; Or, The Half-Brothers. A Romance. 3 vols., London, Richard Bentley, 1846. [B.M.]

M'Gennis, Alicia. Strathbogie; Or The Recluse of Glenmorris. A Romance. 5 vols., London, Printed at the Minerva Press, for A. K. Newman, 1817. [B.M.: *New Monthly Mag.*: Blakey.]

MacGowan, John. Infernal Conference; Or, Dialogues of Devils, By the Listener. 2 vols., London, G. Keith, 1772. [Mudie's.]

MacKay, Charles. Longbeard, Lord of London: A Romance. 3 vols., London, Edward Bull, 1841. [B.M.]

MacKay, Margaret. The Family at Heatherdale: or, the influence of Christian principles. Edinburgh, Hamilton, 1837. [B.M.: *Eng. Cat.*]

Mackenzie, Anna Maria. Dusseldorf, or, the Fratricide. A Romance. With a frontispiece. 3 vols., London, William Lane, 1798. [*New Ann. Reg.*: Blakey.]
—— The Gamesters: A Novel. By the authoress of Burton-Wood and Joseph. 3 vols., London, R. Baldwin, 1786. [B.M.: *Eng. Lit. in Germany.*]
—— The Irish Guardian, Or, Errors of Eccentricity. London, Longman, Hurst, 1809. [B.M.: Ingpen.]
—— Martin and Mansfeldt, or the Romance of Franconia. 3 vols., London, Minerva Press, 1802. [B.M.]
—— Mysteries Elucidated, A novel. By the author of Danish massacre, Monmouth, &c. With a frontispiece. 3 vols., London, William Lane, 1795. [Blakey.]
—— Slavery, or, The Times. By the Author of Monmouth, The Danish Massacre, &c. 2 vols., London, 1792. [*New Ann. Reg.*: T. D. Webster.]

Mackenzie, Colin. The Young Muscovite; Or, The Poles in Russia. Edited by Captain Frederic Chamier, R.N. 3 vols., London, Cochrane and M'Crone, 1834. [B.M.]

Mackenzie, Henry. Julia de Roubigné. A Tale. In a Series of Letters. Published

148

By the Author of The Man of Feeling and The Man of the World. 2 vols., London, W. Strahan and T. Cadell; and W. Creech, Edinburgh, 1777. [Birrell & Garnett: B.M.: Ingpen.]

Mackenzie, Henry. The Man of Feeling. London, T. Cadell, 1771. [B.M.: W. T. Spencer: Stonehill.]

—— The Man of Honour, And The Reclaimed. 2 vols., London, Richard Bentley, 1834. [B.M.]

—— The Man Of the World. In Two Parts. 2 vols., London, W. Strahan; and T. Cadell, 1773. [B.M.: Dobell: Pickering.]

—— Story of La Roche. 1779. [*Eng. Lit. in Germany*.]

Mackenzie, Mary Jane. Geraldine; Or, Modes of Faith and Practice. A Tale. By a Lady. 3 vols., London, T. Cadell and W. Davies; and W. Blackwood, Edinburgh, 1820. [B.M.: *Monthly Mag*.: Stonehill.]

—— Private Life; or, Varieties of Character and Opinion. By the Author of " Geraldine ", &c. &c. 2 vols., London, T. Cadell; and W. Blackwood, Edinburgh, 1829. [Block: B.M.: Guntrip & Richardson.]

Mackenzie, Mrs. Almeria D'Aveiro. 3 vols., London, A. K. Newman. [Publisher's advert. 1812.]

Mackenzie, R. Shelton. Mornings at Matlock, a Collection of Stories. 3 vols., London, Colburn, 1850. [Allibone: B.M.: *Eng. Cat*.]

—— Titian. A Romance of Venice. 3 vols., London, Richard Bentley, 1843. [B.M.: Kyrle Fletcher: T. D. Webster.]

—— The Travellers or Morning at Matlock. 3 vols., London, 1850. [Baker's Bookshop.]

Mackintosh, Margaret. The Cottager's Daughter; a tale founded on facts, betwixt 1685 and 1688. To which are added miscellaneous pieces . . . songs. Edinburgh, 1836. [B.M.]

Maclellan, Frances. Evenings Abroad. By the Author of " Sketches of Corfu." With a frontispiece. London, Smith, Elder, 1836. [B.M.]

M'Leod, D. B. Lily M'Nab; Or The Heiress of Dunelf. A Tale of modern times. London, Simpkin, Marshall; D. Marples, Liverpool, 1845. [B.M.]

MacLeod, Miss E. H. Belmont's Daughter. A Fashionable Novel. 4 vols., London, A. K. Newman, 1830. [B.M.]

—— Geraldine Murray. A Tale of Fashionable Life. By E. H. P. Late Miss M'Leod. 4 vols., London, A. K. Newman, 1826. [B.M.: McLeish: Publisher's advert.]

—— Principle! A Fashionable Tale. 4 vols., London, A. K. Newman, 1824. [B.M.]

—— Tales of Ton; The First Series; Containing Fashionable Characters. A Novel. 4 vols., London, A. K. Newman, 1821. [B.M.]

MacLeod, Miss E. H. Tales of Ton; The Second Series. 4 vols., London, A. K. Newman, 1821. [B.M.]

—— Tales of Ton. Third Series. 4 vols., London, A. K. Newman, 1822. [B.M.]

M'Millan, Mr. Julia; or, The Adventures of the Daughter of a Village Curate; Describing her Journey from Elmwood to London. To which is Added The Happy Couple; or, the Rector of South-Green. With a frontispiece. London, Hughes, 1800. [Stonehill.]

McMullan, Mary Ann. The Wanderings of a Goldfinch; or Characteristic Sketches in the Nineteenth Century. London, Longman, 1816. [Ingpen: *New Monthly Mag*.]

MacNally, Louisa. Eccentricity: A Novel. 3 vols., Dublin, Printed at the Hibernia Press Office, for J. Cumming, 1820. [B.M.: *New Monthly Mag*.: Stonehill.]

MacNeil; or the Scottish Orphans. A Story. Edinburgh, Hamilton, 1823. [B.M.: P. C. Cuttelle.]

MacNeil, Hector. The Scottish Adventurers, or, The Way to Rise: An Historical Tale. 2 vols., Edinburgh, William Blackwood, 1812. [Allibone: Pickering: *Quarterly Review*.]

MacNish, Robert. The Modern Pythagorean, a Series of Tales, Essays, and Sketches. With the Author's Life, by D. M. Moir. 2 vols., Edinburgh, 1838. [B.M.: Lib. of Congress.]

MacPherson, James. The Iliad of Homer, translated into English prose. 2 vols., 1773. [Allibone.]

M'Sparran, Archibald. The Legend of M'Donnell, and the Norman de Borgos. Belfast, 1829. [*I. in F*.]

McTaggart, Anne. Memoirs Of A Gentlewoman Of The Old School. By a Lady. 2 vols., London, Hurst, Chance, 1830. [B.M.: P. C. Cuttelle.]

Mad Pranks of Tom Tram (The), Son in Law to Mother Winter. Together with His Merry Jests, Odd Conceits, and pleasant Tales, very delightful to read. In 3 parts. With woodcuts. London, Printed and Sold in Aldermary Church Yard, [1750 ?]. [B.M.]

Madden, Richard Robert. The Mussulman. 3 vols., London, Henry Colburn and Richard Bentley, 1830. [B.M.: Ingpen: Publisher's advert.]

Madge Blarney the Gipsey Girl. London, John Marshall, [1797 ?]. Cheap Repository. [B.M.]

Madness the Rage: Or Memoirs of a Man without a Name. 2 vols., London, Sherwood, Neely and Jones, 1810. [Elkin Mathews: *Monthly Mag*.]

Magdalen (The), or, the Penitent of Godstow, an historical Novel. 3 vols., 1812. [*Quarterly Review*.]

Magi and the Star (The). London,

Simpkin, Marshall, 1845. [Block: B.M.: *Critic*.]

Magic and Mesmerism An Episode of The Eighteenth Century And Other Tales. 3 vols., London, Saunders and Otley, 1843. [B.M.]

Magician and Robbers (The); or, the Astrologer's Prediction. To which is added, The wonderful sagacity of a dog: an anecdote. Newcastle, [1805]. [B.M.]

Maginn, William. The Red Barn, A Tale, Founded on Fact. With plates. London, John Bennett, 1831. [Stonehill.]

—— The Suicide; a Tale founded on Facts. By the Author of the " Red Barn." No. 1 [all published]. London, [1825 ?]. [B.M.]

—— Tales of Military Life. By the Author of " The Military Sketch Book." 3 vols., London, Henry Colburn, 1829. [B.M.: Ingpen.]

—— Whitehall; or, The Days of George IV. London, William Marsh, [1827]. [B.M.: G. Worthington.]

—— and **Ollier,** Charles. John Manesty, The Liverpool Merchant. With illustrations by George Cruikshank. 2 vols., London, John Mortimer, 1844. [Allibone: Block: Arthur Rogers.]

Magnanimous Amazon (The); or, Adventures of Theresia, Baroness van Hoog. With Anecdotes of other Eccentric Persons. London, Vernor and Hood, 1796. [*New Ann. Reg.*: Stonehill.]

Mahmoud. 3 vols., London, E. Churton, 1835. [B.M.]

Mahony, Francis Sylvester. Facts and Fictions from Italy. By Don Jeremy Savonarola, Benedictine Monk. Addressed during the Last Two Winters to Charles Dickens, Esq.: being an Appendix to his " Pictures." London, R. Bentley, 1847. [B.M.: Marks.]

Maid of Kent (The). 3 vols., London, 1790. [B.M.]

—— **of the Mountain** (The); or, The Female Alcade. A Spanish Story. Also the Affecting History of Ines de Cordove; or, The Unfortunate Lovers. With a frontispiece. London, Ker, [*c.* 1810]. [Stonehill: Murray Hill.]

—— **of Quality** or The History of Lady Lucy Layton. 1770. [*Eng. Lit. in Germany.*]

Maiden Monarch (The); Or, Island Queen. 2 vols., London, R. Hastings, 1840. [B.M.: James Glaisher.]

Mailles, Jacques de. The Right Joyous and Pleasant History of the Feats, Gests and Prowesses of the Chevalier Bayard, The Good Knight without Fear and without Defeat. By the Loyal Servant. [Translated by Sara Coleridge]. 2 vols., London, John Murray, 1825. [B.M.: Ingpen.]

Mainwaring, Mrs. M. Moscow; Or, The Grandsire. An Historical Tale. 3 vols., London, A. K. Newman, 1822.

[B.M.: *European Mag.*: *New Monthly Mag.*]

Mainwaring, Mrs. M. The Suttee; or, The Hindoo Converts. By Mrs. General Mainwaring. 3 vols., London, A. K. Newman, 1830. [B.M.: *New Monthly Mag.*]

Maistre (*see* De Maistre).

Makanna; Or, the Land of the Savage. 3 vols., London, Simpkin and Marshall, 1834. [B.M.]

Malan, Rev. Caesar Henri Abraham. The Eldest Son. Translated from the French. London, J. Nisbet, 1826. [B.M.]

—— Good Boys: or, Examine Yourselves. (Translated from " Les braves et honnêtes Garçons de Genève.") London, Religious Tract Society, [1825 ?]. [B.M.]

—— The Image Boys, translated from the French. London, Religious Tract Society, [1830 ?]. [B.M.]

—— Missions at Home. A true narrative Translated from the French. London, James Nisbet, 1826. [B.M.]

—— The Mountain Peasants. Translated from the French. London, J. Nisbet. 1822. [B.M.]

——Narratives for the Young. In 8 parts. London, Religious Tract Society, [1826 ?]. [B.M.]

—— The Poor Watchmaker of Geneva. London, 1822. [B.M.]

—— Simon the Rebel. A true narrative. London, 1844. [B.M.]

—— Sketches for Youth. London, Seeley, 1845. [Allibone.]

—— The True Cross: a narrative. Translated from the French. London, J. Nisbet, 1834. [B.M.]

—— The Two Old Men of La Vosges. Translated from the French. London, 1822. [B.M.]

—— The Valaisane, or Women of the Valais. Translated from the second French edition. London, 1822. [B.M.]

—— The Village School. From "L'Ecole de Valdámont." London, Religious Tract Society, [1830 ?]. [B.M.]

Malcolm, John. Tales of Field and Flood; With Sketches of Life at Home. Edinburgh, Oliver and Boyd; and Simpkin and Marshall, 1829. [B.M.: G. Worthington.]

Malcolm Douglas: or, the Sybilline Prophecy: A romance. 3 vols., London, [1812]. [B.M.: *New Monthly Mag.*]

Malden, Miriam. Hope; Or, Judge without prejudice. A Novel, 4 vols., London, Printed at the Minerva Press, for A. K. Newman, 1813. [B.M.: Publisher's advert.: *Quarterly Review.*]

—— Jessico Mandeville; a Novel. 1804. [Allibone.]

Malet, Lady. Violet; Or, The Danseuse: A Portraiture Of Human Passions and Character. 2 vols., London, Henry Colburn, 1836. [B.M.: Ingpen: Publisher's advert.]

Mallès de Beaulieu, Madame. The

Young "Robinson", An Interesting Narrative of a French Cabin-Boy, who was ship-wrecked on an uninhabited Island. With a frontispiece and a vignette title. London, Holloway and Thomas, 1825. [B.M.]

Mamma and her Child. London, [1843]. [B.M.]

Mamma's Absence; or, "The Written Rules." London, Seeley, [1849]. [B.M.]

—— **Stories,** Read by herself to her Little Girl. With 7 plates. London, Darton, Harvey and Darton, 1812. [Sotheran.]

Mammon in London; Or, The Spy of the Day. 2 vols., London, W. Sams, 1823. [B.M.: Arthur Rogers.]

Man, Henry. Mr. Bentley, The Rural Philosopher: A Tale. 2 vols., London, W. Goldsmith, 1775. [B.M.: *Eng. Lit. in Germany*: Arthur Rogers.]

Man of Benevolence (The). London, the Author; 1789.

Man of Failing (The); a tale. 2 vols., London, William Lane, 1789. [Blakey.]

Man of Pleasure in Paris (The). Or an Account of the Pleasures of that Capital: In a series of Letters from Sir Charles P * * * * * to Lady Emily C * * * *. With 4 plates. Paris, [London, J. B. Brookes], 1808. [*Cat. Lib. Prohib.*]

Man of Sensibility (The); or the History of Edward and Matilda. 2 vols., London, Vernor, 1810. [B.M.: *Monthly Mag.*]

Manasseh, a tale of the Jews. London, Hatchard, 1842. [B.M.: *Eng. Cat.*]

Mancur, John Henry. Constance: or, the Star of the Ballet. An Interesting Narrative. With woodcuts. London, E. Lloyd. [1848]. [B.M.: B. Ono.]

—— Henri Quatre; Or, the Days of the League. 3 vols., London, Whittaker, 1834. [B.M.: *Eng. Cat.*: Wm. Smith.]

Mandeville; or, The Last Words of a Maniac; A Tale of the Seventeenth Century in England. Written by Himself. Volume 4 [a Continuation of William Godwin's *Mandeville*, but not by Godwin.] London, Wilson, 1818. [Ingpen: *New Monthly Mag.*]

Mandeville: or, The Lynmouth Visitors. By a Lady. Barnstaple, Brightwell, 1839. [B.M.]

Manfredi, or the Mysterious Hermit: an Interesting and Original Romance. With a vignette title and a frontispiece. London, G. Stevens, [*c.* 1810]. [Marks.]

Mangin, Edward. George The Third. A Novel. 3 vols., London, James Carpenter, 1807. [B.M.: Pickering.]

—— More Short Stories. London, 1830. [B.M.]

Manners, Captain. The Boon. 3 vols., 1810. [*Monthly Mag.*: *Quarterly Review.*]

Manners of the Day (The), a Novel. 3 vols., London, Henry Colburn, 1830. [*Eng. Cat.*: *New Monthly Mag.*]

Manning, Anne. The Maiden and Married Life of Mary Powell, afterwards Mistress Milton. London, 1850. [*Guide to Best Fiction*: Lib. of Congress.]

Manning, Anne. Stories from the History of Italy, from the invasion of Alaric to the present time. London, Baldwin, 1831. [B.M.]

—— Village Belles. A Novel. 3 vols., London, Baldwin and Cradock, 1833. [B.M.: H. H. Langley.]

Manœuvres of Don Pedro Antos (The), The Famous Swindler of Segovia, Consisting of Various Ludicrous Adventures. With a frontispiece. [1803]. [Ingpen.]

Man-o'-War's Man. By Bill Truck. 1843. [Arthur Rogers.]

Mansion-House (The): A novel. By a Young Gentleman. [James Norris Brewer] 2 vols., London, William Lane, 1796. [*New Ann. Reg.*: Blakey.]

Mant, Alicia Catherine. The Canary Bird. With a frontispiece. London, J. Harris, 1817. [B.M.: T. Thorp.]

—— Caroline Lismore, Or The Errors of Fashion. A Tale. With a frontispiece by Corbould. London, Law and Whittaker, 1815. [Ingpen: Marks: *New Monthly Mag.*]

—— The Cottage in the Chalk-Pit. London, Harvey and Darton, 1822. [Ingpen.]

—— Ellen: or, The Young Godmother. A Tale for Youth. By a Young Lady. Southampton. T. Skelton, 1812. [Baker's Bookshop: B.M.: Gumuchian.]

—— Margaret Melville And The Soldier's Daughter; Or, Juvenile Memoirs: Interspersed with Remarks on the Propriety of Encouraging British Manufactures. With a frontispiece. London, R. & R. Gilbert, 1818. [B.M.: Ingpen: *New Monthly Mag.*]

—— Montague Newburgh; Or, The Mother and Son. With a frontispiece. 2 vols., London, Law and Whittaker, 1817. [B.M.: Court Book Shop: Ingpen.]

—— Tales for Ellen. By the author of Ellen, the young godmother. London, 1825. [Allibone: B.M.: *Camb. Hist. Eng. Lit.*]

—— The Young Naturalist, A Tale. With a frontispiece. London, H. Holloway, 1824. [B.M. (2nd edn.).]

Manuscripts from the Diary of a Physician. With illustrations. 2 vols., London, E. Lloyd, 1844. [R. S. Frampton.]

Manzoni, Alessandro. The Betrothed Lovers: A Milanese Story of the Seventeenth Century. With The Column of Infamy. 3 vols., London, Longman, Brown, Green, and Longmans, 1845. [Block.]

—— The Betrothed Lovers; A Milanese Tale of the XVIIth Century. Translated from the Italian [by C. Swan]. 3 vols., Pisa, Capurro, 1828. [B.M.: Ingpen: *Quarterly Review.*]

—— I Promessi Sposi. The Betrothed; a new translation. Illus. 2 vols., London, J. Burns, 1844. [B.M.: *Critic*.: T. D. Webster.]

Maple Vale; or, the history of Miss Sidney. 3 vols., London, 1791. [B.M.]

Marcella: or, The Missionary Abroad and At Home. Containing Sketches and Incidents from Life. 2 vols., London, J. Hatchard, 1828. [B.M.: *Quarterly Review*.]

Marcet, Jane. Bertha's Visit to her Uncle in England. 3 vols., London, John Murray, 1830. [B.M.: Clarke-Hall.]

—— Mary's Grammar, interspersed with stories. London, Longman, 1835. [B.M.: *Eng. Cat*.]

—— The Seasons, Stories for very young Children. By the author of " Conversations on Chemistry." 4 vols., London, Longman, 1832. [B.M.: *Eng. Cat*.]

—— Stories for young children, by the author of " Conversations on Chemistry." London, 1831. [B.M.]

—— Willy's Grammar, interspersed with stories for the use of children. London, 1845. [B.M.]

—— Willy's Holidays; or, Conversations on different kinds of Governments, intended for Young Children. London, 1836. [B.M.: P. C. Cuttelle: Arthur Rogers.]

Marchant, M. A. Rudolph and Adelaide; or, The Fort of St. Fernandos. A Novel. 3 vols., London, Sherwood, 1811. [*Quarterly Review*: Stonehill.]

Margam Abbey, An Historical Romance of the Fourteenth Century. London, John Green, 1837. [B.M.: Kyrle Fletcher.]

Margaret at Home: by the author of " A Visit to Bury St. Edmunds." London, Grant, 1847. [B.M.]

Margaret of Navarre, Queen. Novels, Tales and Stories. Written originally in French by Margaret de Valois, Queen of Navar, and printed by order of the French King. Translated into English by several hands. (First part) [all published]. London, 1750. [B.M.]

Margaret Russell: an Autobiography.

Margaretta (Countess of Rainsford). A Sentimental Novel. 2 vols., London, Johnson and Payne, 1769. [*Eng. Lit. in Germany*: Huth.]

Maria Cecilia; Or, Life and Adventures of the Daughter of Achmet III, Emperor of the Turks. From the French. 2 vols., [London, W. Lane, 1788.]. [Blakey.]

Maria Harcourt. A Novel. Written in Daily Journals (never before attempted). By the Author of " Lord Winworth." " Phebe," etc. 2 vols., London, 1788. [B.M.]

Maria Menzikoff and Fedor Dolgoronki. A Russian Tale Founded on Fact in which is detailed Vicissitudes and strange events. With a frontispiece.

London, J. Bailey, [*c.* 1812]. [Arthur Rogers.]

Maria; Or, A Shandean Journey of a Young Lady, Through Flanders and France, during the Summer of 1822. By My Uncle Oddy. London, John Hatchard, 1823. [B.M.]

Maria; or, the Vicarage. A novel. 2 vols., London, 1796. [B.M.: *New Ann. Reg*.]

Mariamne; or, Irish anecdotes. A novel. by the author of Ashton Priory, Benedicta, Powis Castle, &c. &c. 2 vols. [W. Lane, 1793]. [Blakey.]

Marian. A Novel. 3 vols., 1812. [*New Monthly Mag*.: *Quarterly Review*.]

Maria's Reward; Or the Voice of the Dead. By the Author of Jane and her Teacher; George Wilson and his Friend; The Lady at the Farm-House, &c. With a frontispiece. London, James Nisbet, 1825. [B.M.]

Mariotti, L. The Black Gown Papers. 2 vols., London, J. Chapman, 1846. [*Eng. Cat*.: Foyle: T. D. Webster.]

Marishall, Jean. The History of Alicia Montague. By the Author of Clarinda Cathcart. 2 vols., London, 1767. [*Eng. Lit. in Germany*: D. Webster.]

—— The History of Miss Clarinda Cathcart, and Miss Fanny Renton. 2 vols., London, 1766 [B.M.: Murray Hill.]

Marivaux, Pierre Carlet de Chamblain de, (*see* DE MARIVAUX).

Mark, J. Endless Entertainment, or Comic, Terrific and Legendary Tales. With 18 woodcuts. London, G. Herbert, [1826]. [*Edin. Mag*.: Marks: *Quarterly Review*.]

Marley, Daniel, (?). The History of Mr. Charles Fitzgerald and Miss Sarah Stapleton. In Five Books. Dublin, James Hoey, 1770. [Pickering.]

Marly; Or a Planter's Life in Jamaica. Glasgow, Richard Griffin; and Hunt and Clarke, London, 1828. [B.M.]

Marmacopt, Albert. The Wharbroke Legend: A Tale of the Dead. 2 vols., London, Ogle, Duncan; and Ogle, Allardice, and Thomson, Edinburgh, 1820. [B.M.: Dobell: *New Monthly Mag*.]

Marmontel, Jean François. Belisarius. London, P. Vaillant, 1767. [Baker's Bookshop: B.M.]

—— Belisarius. A new translation. London, M. Cooper, 1768. [B.M.]

—— Belisarius. Translated by F. Ashmore. London, Harrison, 1789. [B.M.]

—— Belisarius. A new edition, London, Vernor & Hood, 1794. [B.M.]

—— Marmontel's Tales, Selected and abridged, for the Instruction and amusement of Youth, by Mrs. Pilkington. With woodcuts by Bewick. London, 1799. [B.M.: *Camb. Hist. Eng. Lit*.: *New Ann. Reg*.]

—— Moral Tales. [Translated by C. Dennis and R. Lloyd.] 2 vols., London,

T. Becket and P. A. De Hondt, 1764. [B.M.: G. Worthington.]

Marmontel, Jean François. Select Moral Tales. Translated from the French By a Lady [Miss R. Roberts]. Gloucester, 1763. [B.M.]

—— The Tales of an Evening; Followed by The Honest Breton. Translated from the French. 4 vols., London, J. Bew, 1792-1794. [B.M.: Stonehill.]

Marriage of St. Pierre (The); or Ingratitude, Adultery, and Murder, an interesting narrative found among the baggage of Capt. Dumain. With a frontispiece. London, Redriffe, [182–]. [R. S. Frampton.]

Marriage Present (A), Or Some Account of Sarah and William, In two Parts. Chelsea, N.D.

Marriott, E. F. Black-eyed Susan, or, The Sailor's Bride. A nautical romance. With woodcuts. London, Edward Lloyd, 1845. [B.M.: B. Ono.]

Marryat, Captain Frederick. The Children of the New Forest. 2 vols., London, H. Hurst, [1847]. [B.M.]

—— The Diary of a Blasé. By the author of Jacob Faithful, Peter Simple, etc. Philadelphia, E. L. Carey and A. Hart, 1836. [Sadleir.]

—— Jacob Faithful By the Author of "Peter Simple," "The King's Own," &c. 3 vols., London, Saunders & Otley, 1834. [B.M.: Ingpen: Arthur Rogers.]

—— Japhet, In Search of a Father. By the Author of "Peter Simple," "Jacob Faithful," &c. 3 vols., London, Saunders and Otley, 1836. [B.M.: Ingpen: T. Thorp.]

—— Joseph Rushbrook; Or, The Poacher. By the author of Peter Simple. 3 vols., London, Longman, Orme, Brown, Green, 1841. [Baker's Bookshop: B.M.: Ingpen.]

—— The King's Own. By the Author of "The Naval Officer." 3 vols., London, Henry Colburn and Richard Bentley, 1830. [B.M.: Guntrip & Richardson: Ingpen.]

—— The Little Savage [Edited by Frank S. Marryat]. With illustrations. 2 vols., London, H. Hurst, 1848-1849. [B.M.: Ingpen: Tregaskis.]

—— Masterman Ready; Or, The Wreck of the Pacific. Written for Young People. With illustrations. 3 vols., London, Longman, Orme, Brown, Green, & Longmans, 1841-1842. [Block: B.M.: Ingpen.]

—— The Mission, Or, Scenes in South Africa. Written for Young People. 2 vols., London, Longman, Brown, Green, & Longmans, 1845. [Block: B.M.: Ingpen.]

—— Mr. Midshipman Easy. By the Author of "Japhet, in Search of a Father," "Peter Simple," "Jacob Faithful," &c. 3 vols., London, Saunders

and Otley. 1836. [B.M.: Gumuchian: Ingpen.]

Marryat, Captain Frederick. Narrative of the Travels and Adventures of Monsieur Violet in California, Sonora, and Western Texas. 3 vols., London, Longman, Brown, Green & Longmans, 1843 [B.M.]

—— The Naval Officer; Or Scenes and Adventures in the Life of Frank Mildmay. 3 vols., London, Henry Colburn. 1829. [B.M.: Arthur Rogers.]

—— Newton Forster; Or, The Merchant Service. By the author of "The Kings Own." 3 vols., London, James Cochrane, 1832. [B.M.: Ingpen; Pickering.]

—— Olla Podrida. By The Author of "Peter Simple," &c. &c. 3 vols., London, Longman, Orme, Brown, Green and Longmans, 1840. [B.M.: Ingpen: A. V. Turner.]

—— The Pacha of Many Tales By the Author of "Peter Simple," "Jacob Faithful," &c. 3 vols., London, Saunders and Otley, 1835. [Block: B.M.: Ingpen.]

—— Percival Keene. 3 vols., London, Henry Colburn, 1842. [Block: B.M.: Ingpen.]

—— Peter Simple. By the author of "Newton Foster," "The King's Own," &c. 3 vols., London, Saunders and Otley, 1834. [B.M.: Kyrle Fletcher: King.]

—— The Phantom Ship. 3 vols., London, Henry Colburn. 1839. [B.M.: Ingpen.]

—— The Pirate, and the Three Cutters. With 20 illustrations by Clarkson Stanfield. London, Published for the Proprietor by Longman, Rees, Orme, Brown, Green and Longman, 1836. [B.M.: McLeish: Arthur Rogers.]

—— Poor Jack. With illustrations by Clarkson Stanfield. London, Longman, Orme, Brown, Green, and Longmans, 1840. [B.M.: Lib. of Congress: Arthur Rogers.]

—— The Privateer's-Man, One Hundred Years Ago. 2 vols., London, Longman, Brown, Green, and Longmans, 1846. [B.M.: Ingpen: Maggs.]

—— The Settlers in Canada. Written for Young People. With frontispieces. 2 vols., London, Longman, Orme, Brown, Green and Longmans, 1844. [Block: B.M.: Ingpen.]

—— Snarleyow, Or The Dog Fiend. By the author of "Peter Simple," "Frank Mildmay," &c. 3 vols., London, Henry Colburn, 1837. [B.M.: Ingpen: Arthur Rogers.]

—— Stories of the Sea. New York, Harper, 1836. [This is the American edition of *The Pirate and Three Cutters*. It also contains the first appearance in book form of Marryat's *Moonshine*, which was previously in *The Keepsake* Annual.] [Sadleir.]

—— Valerie, An Autobiography. 2 vols.,

London, Henry Colburn, 1849. [B.M.: Ingpen.]

Marsden, William. Memoirs of a Malayan Family. Written by Themselves and Translated from the Original by W. Marsden. 1830. [T. Thorp.]

Marsh, Anne. Adelaide Lindsay. A novel. Edited by the author of Emilia Wyndham, Two Old Men's Tales, etc. 3 vols., London, Henry Colburn, 1850. [B.M.: *Eng. Cat.*]

—— Angela. A Novel. By the Author of "Emilia Wyndham," "Two Old Men's Tales," &c. 3 vols., London, Henry Colburn, 1848. [Allibone: Block: B.M.]

—— Aubrey. By the Author of "Emilia Wyndham." London, 1841. [B.M.]

—— Bellah, a tale of La Vendee. From the French. Edited by the Author of "Two Old Men's Tales." 1847. [B.M.]

—— Emilia Wyndham. By the Author of "Two old men's tales," "Mount Sorel,' etc. 3 vols., London, Henry Colburn, 1846. [B.M.: McLeish: Elkin Mathews.]

—— Father Darcy. An Historical Romance. By the Author of "Mount Sorel," "Emilia Wyndham," &c. 2 vols., London, Chapman and Hall, 1846. [Allibone: B.M.: Publisher's advert.]

—— Lettice Arnold: A Tale. By the Author of "Emilia Wyndham," etc. London, Henry Colburn, 1850. [B.M.: *Eng. Cat.*]

—— Mordaunt Hall, or, A September Night. By the author of "Two Old Men's Tales." 3 vols., London, Henry Colburn, 1849. [B.M.: *Eng. Cat.*: G. H. Last.]

—— Mount Sorel; Or, The Heiress of the De Veres. By The Author of the "Two Old Men's Tales." 2 vols., London, Chapman and Hall, 1845. [Block: B.M.: Arthur Rogers.]

—— Norman's Bridge; Or, The modern Midas. By the Author of "Emilia Wyndham," "The two old men's tales," &c. 3 vols., London, Richard Bentley, 1847. [B.M.: *Critic*: *Eng. Cat.*]

—— Tales of the first French Revolution. Collected by the author of "Emilia Wyndham." London, T. Hodgson, 1849. [B.M.: *Eng. Cat.*]

—— Tales Of the Woods and Fields. A Second Series Of "The Two Old Men's Tales." 3 vols., London, Saunders & Otley, 1836. [B.M.: *Quarterly Review*: W. T. Spencer.]

—— The Triumphs of Time. By the Author of "Two Old Men's Tales." 3 vols., London, Richard Bentley, 1844. [Baker's Bookshop: B.M.: Holland.]

—— Two Old Men's Tales. The Deformed and The Admirals Daughter. 2 vols., London, Saunders and Otley, 1834. [Ingpen: *Quarterly Review*.]

—— The Wilmingtons. By the author of "Two Old Men's Tales." 3 vols., London, Henry Colburn, 1850. [B.M.: Wm. Brown : *Eng. Cat.*]

Marshall, Mrs. Henwick Tales. [*Camb. Hist. Eng. Lit.*]

Marshall, Edmund. Edmund and Eleonora: Or Memoirs of the Houses of Summerfield & Gretton. A Novel. 2 vols., London, Printed for John Stockdale, by W. Epps, Margate, 1797. [B.M.: *New Ann. Reg.*: Arthur Rogers.]

Marshall, Thomas Henry. The Irish Necromancer; Or, Deer Park. A Novel. 3 vols., London, A. K. Newman, 1821. [B.M.]

Marten, Ambrose. The Stanley Tales, Original & Select chiefly collected By the late Ambrose Marten, of Stanley Priory Teesdale. 4 vols., London, W. Morgan, [1826]. [Block: *Quarterly Review.*]

Marten, Thomas. The Marriage; a Novel. 2 vols., 1771. [Allibone].

Martin, Miss. St. Etienne: A Romance of the First Revolution. 3 vols., London, T. C. Newby, 1845. [B.M.: *Critic.*]

Martin, E. Friar Hidalgo; a Romance. 1807. [Allibone.]

Martin, H. Helen of Glenross, A Novel By the Author of Historic Tales. 4 vols., London, Robinson, 1802. [Stonehill.]

Martin, Mary Letitia. Julia Howard, a Romance. 3 vols., London, 1850. [B.M.]

Martin, Miss. The Changeling; a Novel, by the Author of "Canvassing." 3 vols., London, Saunders and Otley, 1848. [*Times Literary Supplement.*]

Martin, Mrs. Deloraine. A domestic tale. 2 vols., London, William Lane, 1798. [*Minerva Press Catalogue*: Blakey.]

—— Jeannette. A novel. By the author of Melbourne, Reginald, Deloraine, &c. 4 vols., London, Printed at the Minerva Press, for William Lane, 1800. [*Minerva Press Catalogue*: Blakey.]

Martin, S. A Sister's Stories. By the author of "Three Years' Residence in Italy." With illustrations. Kirkby Lonsdale, A. Foster, 1833. [B.M.]

Martineau, Harriet. The Billow and the Rock. A Tale. London, Charles Knight, 1846. [Block.]

—— Dawn Island. A Tale. Written for the National Anti-Corn Law Bazaar, May, 1845. With a frontispiece and an engraved title. Manchester, 1845. [Block: B.M.: Gilbert Jamieson.]

—— Deerbrook. A Novel. 3 vols., London, Edward Moxon, 1839. [Blackwell: B.M.: Ingpen.]

—— Feats on the Fiord. A Tale of Norway. London, Charles Knight, 1844. [Block.]

—— Five Years of Youth; Or, Sense and Sentiment. With plates. London, Harvey and Darton, 1831. [B.M.: Arthur Rogers: T. D. Webster.]

Martineau, Harriet. Forest and Game Law Tales. 3 vols., London, Edward Moxon, 1845-1846. [B.M.: *Critic:* T. D. Webster.]

—— The Hour and the Man. A Historical Romance. 3 vols., London, Edward Moxon, 1841. [B.M.: Lib. of Congress: McLeish.]

—— Illustrations of Political Economy. 9 vols., London, Charles Fox, 1832-1834. [Block: *Camb. Bib. of Eng. Lib.*]

—— Illustrations of Taxation. No. 1 [—V]. In 2 parts. London, 1834. [Allibone: B.M.]

—— Ireland, a Tale. London, Charles Fox, 1832. [*I. in F.*]

—— Mary Campbell; a Tale. 1837. [Allibone.]

—— The Playfellow: a series of tales. (The Settlers at Home. The Peasant and the Prince. Feats on the Fiord. The Crofton Boys.) In 4 parts. London, Charles Knight, 1841. [Baker's Bookshop: B.M.: *Camb. Hist. Eng. Lit.*]

—— Poor Laws and Paupers Illustrated. 1. The Parish, a tale. [2. The Hamlets, a tale. 3. The Town, a tale. 4. The Land's End, a tale.] In 4 parts. London, Charles Fox, 1833-1834. [Allibone: B.M.]

—— Traditions of Palestine. Edited by Harriet Martineau. London, Longman, Rees, Orme, Brown, and Green, 1830. [Baker's Bookshop: B.M.]

Marvellous Magazine and Compendium of Prodigies. Consisting of The Southern Tower, or Conjugal Sacrifice, and Retribution; The Veiled Picture, a Tale of Mystery; Domestic Misery; Highland Heroism; Albani; Father Innocent; Abbot of the Capuchins. With illustrations. London, T. Hurst, 1802. [Baker's Bookshop.]

Marvellous Pleasant Love-Story (A). 2 vols., London, Printed at the Minerva Press, for W. Lane, 1801. [B.M.: McLeish: Elkin Mathews.]

Mary and Fanny. A Narrative. By Juvenis. With a frontispiece. London, Printed at the Minerva Press, for A. K. Newman, 1816. [B.M.: *New Monthly Mag.*]

Mary Aston Or The events of a year. London, Saunders and Otley, 1845. [B.M.]

Mary Atkins; or, Nature and grace. London, 1842. [B.M.]

Mary Gray, the Sunday Scholar. London, Religious Tract Society, [1830 ?]. [B.M.]

Mary Harland; or the Journey to London, A tale of humble life. Edinburgh, 1828. [B.M.]

Mary Jones, Or The Soldier's Daughter. An Interesting Story. With a woodcut. London, Augustus Applegarth and Edward Cowper, N.D. [Block: Court Bk. Shop.]

Mary Parker; or, the Shoemaker's Wife.

By the authoress of "Tales for the Bush." Exeter, 1846. [B.M.]

Mary Phillips; or, good reasons to my village neighbours for receiving the Sacrament. London, 1822. [B.M.]

Mary Price; or, The Memoirs of a Servant-Maid. With illustrations. London, (*c.* 1840.) [Stonehill.]

Masaniello, The Fisherman King of Naples. With illustrations. London, G. Peirce, [1845]. [B.M.]

Maskell, M. W. Old Tapestry; A Tale of Real Life. 2 vols., Edinburgh, Printed by James Ballantyne for W. and C. Tait; and G. and W. B. Whittaker, 1819. [B.M.: Stonehill.]

Masquerades; or What you Will, By the Author of Eliza Warwick. 4 vols., London, J. Bew, 1780. [*Eng. Lit. in Germany.*]

Massie, W. Alice Paulet: A Sequel to Sydenham, Or, Memoirs of a Man of the World. By the Author of " Sydenham." 3 vols., London, Henry Colburn & Richard Bentley, 1831. [B.M.: James Glaisher: Publisher's advert.]

—— Fitzwiggins. A Novel. By the Author of " Sydenham," Etc. 3 vols., London, Richard Bentley, 1840. [B.M.: Glen: T. D. Webster.]

—— Lionel Wakefield. By the Author of " Sydenham." 3 vols., London, Richard Bentley, 1836. [B.M.]

—— Sydenham; Or, Memoirs of A Man of the World. 3 vols., London, Henry Colburn and Richard Bentley, 1830. [B.M.: Clarke-Hall: Lib. of Congress.]

Massouf; or, the Philosophy of the Day. An Eastern Tale. London, Minerva Press, 1802. [B.M.: Stonehill.]

Mathews, Mrs. The Phantom, Or Mysteries of the Castle. A Tale of Other Times. London, Baldwin, 1825. [Ingpen.]

Mathews, Mrs. C. Anecdotes of the Clairville Family; to which is added the History of Emily Wilmont. York, T. Wilson & R. Spence, 1802. [B.M.]

—— Griffith Abbey, or Memoirs of Eugenia. 2 vols., London, 1807. [B.M.]

—— Simple Facts; or, the History of an Orphan. 2 vols., London, 1793. [B.M.: *New Ann. Reg.*]

Matilda and Fanny, or, the Sisters of Rosedale; an interesting narrative. London, Dean & Munday, [1828]. [B.M.]

——; Or the Adventures of an Orphan, An Interesting Tale. With a frontispiece. London, Tegg and Castleman, [1803]. [B.M.]

Matilda: or, The efforts of virtue. A novel. in a series of letters, by a lady, 3 vols., London, William Lane, 1785. [Blakey.]

Matilda St. Aubin. A sketch. 2 vols. [W. Lane, 1793]. [Blakey.]

Matthew, Charlotte. Introspection; or, a peep at real characters. 4 vols., Bath, R. Cruttwell, 1801. [Baker's Bookshop: Maggs.]

Matthew, Richard. Courtly Annals; Or, Independence the True Nobility. A Novel. 4 vols., London, Printed at the Minerva Press for A. K. Newman, 1814. [Ingpen: Publisher's advert.: *Quarterly Review*.]

Matthews, Mrs. Perplexities, or the Fortunate Elopement. 3 vols., London, 1794. [Baker's Bookshop: *New Ann. Reg.*]

Maturin, Charles Robert. The Albigenses. A Romance. By the Author of "Bertram," A Tragedy: "Woman; or, Pour et Contre," &c. 4 vols., London, Hurst, Robinson; & A. Constable, Edinburgh, 1824. [B.M.: Arthur Rogers: Stonehill.]

—— Fatal Revenge; Or, The Family of Montorio. A Romance. By Dennis Jasper Murphy. 3 vols., London, Longman, Hurst, Rees, and Orme, 1807. [Birrell & Garnett: B.M.: Ingpen.]

—— Melmoth The Wanderer: A Tale. By the Author of "Bertram," &c. 4 vols., Edinburgh, Archibald Constable; and Hurst, Robinson, London, 1820. [Block: B.M.: Arthur Rogers.]

—— The Milesian Chief. A Romance. By the Author of Montorio and The Wild Irish Boy. 4 vols., London, Henry Colburn, 1812. [B.M.: *I. in F.*: *Quarterly Review*.]

—— The Wild Irish Boy. A Novel. By the Author of Montorio. 3 vols., London, Longman, 1808. [B.M.: *I. in F.*: Pickering.]

—— Women; Or, Pour et Contre. A Tale. By The Author of "Bertram," &c. 3 vols., Edinburgh, Printed by James Ballantyne for Archibald Constable; and Longman, Hurst, Rees, Orme, and Brown, 1818. [Birrell & Garnett: Block: B.M.]

Maturin, Edward. The Irish Chieftain; or, The Isles of Life and Death. Glasgow, Griffin, 1848. [*I. in F.*]

Maurice, John Frederick Denison. Eustace Conway: Or, The Brother and Sister. A Novel. 3 vols., London, Richard Bentley, 1834. [B.M.]

Maurice Powell: An Historical Welsh Tale of England's Troubles. 3 vols., London, Baldwin, Cradock, and Joy, 1821. [B.M.: Woore.]

Max Wentworth. 3 vols., London, Saunders and Otley, 1839. [B.M.: James Glaisher.]

Maxwell, Caroline. Alfred of Normandy: or, the Ruby Cross. An historical romance, 2 vols., London, Seale, 1808. [B.M.: Ingpen.]

—— The Earl of Desmond; or, O'Brien's Cottage. An Irish story. 3 vols., London, 1810. [B.M.]

—— Lionel; or, The Impenetrable Command. An historical romance. 2 vols., London, Lane, Newman, 1808. [Cawthorne's Catalogue: Blakey.]

Maxwell, William Hamilton. The Bivouac; or Stories of The Peninsular War. 3 vols., London, Richard Bentley, 1837. [B.M.]

Maxwell, William Hamilton. Captain O'Sullivan; Or, Adventures Civil, Military, and Matrimonial, Of a Gentleman on half pay. 3 vols., London, Henry Colburn, 1846. [B.M.]

—— The Dark Lady of Doona. By the author of "Stories of Waterloo." 1834. [B.M.: Arthur Rogers.]

—— The Fortunes of Hector O'Halloran and his Man Mark Antony O'Toole. With 27 etchings by Richard Doyle and John Leech. London, Richard Bentley, [1842-1843]. [B.M.: G. H. Last.]

—— My Life. By the author of "Stories of Waterloo," "Wild Sports of the West," &c. &c. &c. 3 vols., London, Richard Bentley, 1835. [B.M.]

—— O'Hara; Or, 1798. 2 vols., London, J. Andrews; and Miliken, Dublin, 1825. [B.M.: *Edin. Mag.*: *I in. F.*]

—— Stories of Waterloo; and other Tales. 3 vols., London, Henry Colburn and Richard Bentley, 1829. [B.M.: Guntrip: Stonehill.]

—— Wild Sports of the West, With Legendary Tales, and Local Sketches. By the Author of "Stories of Waterloo." With plates & woodcuts. 2 vols., London, Richard Bentley, 1832. [B.M.: Arthur Rogers.]

May Day; Or, Anecdotes of Miss Lydia Lively. Intended to Improve and Amuse the Rising Generation. London, John Marshall, 1787. [B.M.: Sotheran.]

Mayhew, Augustus Septimus and Henry. The Good Genius that turned Everything into Gold, or The Queen Bee and the Magic Dress, a Christmas Fairy Tale by the Brothers Mayhew. With 4 etchings and 4 glyphographs by George Cruikshank. London, D. Bogue, 1847. [B.M.: F. Hollings: Marks.]

—— The Greatest Plague of Life; or The Adventures of a Lady in search of a Good Servant. By One who has been "Almost Worried to Death." Edited by the Brothers Mayhew. With 12 etchings by George Cruikshank. London, David Bogue, [1847], [Blackwell: B.M.: F. Hollings.]

—— The Image of his Father; or, One Boy is more Trouble than a Dozen Girls: being a Tale of a Young Monkey. By the Brothers Mayhew. With illustrations by "Phiz" [Hablot K. Browne]. London, H. Bohn, 1848. [B.M.: *Eng. Cat.*]

—— The Magic of Kindness; Or the Wondrous Story of the Good Huan. By the Brothers Mayhew. With illustrations by George Cruikshank and Kenny Meadows. London, Darton, [1849]. [B.M.: *Eng. Cat.*: Chas. Hutt.]

Mazeppa; Or the Wild Horse of the Ukraine. A Romance. With illustrations. London, E. Lloyd, 1850. [B.M.: H. W. Fennell: Stonehill.]

Meany, Stephen Joseph. The Terry Alt: a Tale of 1831. 3 vols., 1841. [*I. in F.*]

Medley (The): consisting of tales, serious and humorous, in prose and verse, partly original. With 5 plates, London, 1806. [B.M.: T. D. Webster.]

Medwin, Thomas. Lady Singleton; Or, The World as it is. 3 vols., London, Cunningham & Mortimer, 1843. [B.M.]

Meeke, Mary. The Abbey of Clugny. A Novel. 3 vols., London, Printed at the Minerva Press, 1795. [*New Ann. Reg.*: Blakey.]

—— Amazement. A novel. 3 vols., London, Printed at the Minerva-Press, for Lane, Newman & Co. 1804. [Blakey.]

—— Anecdotes of the Altamout Family. A novel. By the author of The Sicilian, &c. London, Printed at the Minerva Press, for William Lane, 1800. [Blakey.]

—— Conscience. A Novel. 4 vols., London, Printed at the Minerva Press, for A. K. Newman, 1814. [B.M.: Publisher's advert.: *Quarterly Review.*]

—— Count St. Blancard, or, The prejudiced judge, a novel. By Mrs. Meek. With a frontispiece. 3 vols., London, William Lane, 1795. [*New Ann. Reg.*]

—— Ellesmere. A novel. 4 vols., London, W. Lane, 1799. [B.M.]

—— Harcourt. A novel. By the author of The Mysterious Wife, &c. 4 vols., London [W. Lane, 1799]. [Blakey: *New Ann. Reg.*]

—— Independence. A novel. By Gabrielli. 4 vols. [W. Lane, 1802]. [Blakey.]

—— Laughton Priory. By Gabrielli, Author of Mysterious Wife, Mysterious Husband, &c. 4 vols., London, A. K. Newman, 1809. [Blakey: Publisher's advert.]

—— Matrimony, the Height of Bliss, or the Extreme of Misery. A novel. 4 vols., London, Minerva Press, 1811. [*Quarterly Review*: Blakey.]

—— Midnight Weddings. A novel. 3 vols., London, W. Lane, 1802. [B.M.]

—— Mysterious Husband. A Novel. By Gabrielli, author of The Mysterious wife, &c. &c. 4 vols., London, Minerva Press, 1801. [Blackwell: Blakey.]

—— The Mysterious Wife. A novel. By Gabrielli. 4 vols., London, William Lane, 1797. [*New Ann. Reg.*: Blakey.]

—— The Nine Days' Wonder. 3 vols., London, Minerva Press, [1804]. [Publisher's advert: Blakey.]

—— The Old Wife and Young Husband. A novel. 3 vols., London, Printed at the Minerva Press, for Lane, Newman, and Co. 1804. [Blakey.]

—— Palmira and Ermance. A novel. By Mrs. Meeke. 3 vols. [W. Lane, 1797]. [Blakey.]

—— Something Odd! A Novel. 3 vols., London, Minerva Press, 1804. [Blackwell.]

—— The Spanish Campaign; Or, The Jew. A Novel. 3 vols., London, Printed at the Minerva Press for A. K. Newman, 1815. [B.M.: *European Mag.*: Publisher's advert.]

Meeke, Mary. Stratagems Defeated. A Novel. By Gabrielli, Author of Laughton Priory; Mysterious Wife, Mysterious Husband; Harcourt, &c. 4 vols., London, Printed at the Minerva Press, for A. K. Newman, 1811. [B.M.: Publisher's advert: Blakey.]

—— " There is a Secret, Find it out! " A Novel. 4 vols., London, Printed at the Minerva Press, for Lane, Newman, 1808. [B.M.]

—— The Veiled Protectress; Or, The Mysterious Mother. A Novel. 5 vols., London, Printed at the Minerva Press for A. K. Newman, 1819. [B.M.: *New Monthly Mag.*]

—— What Shall Be, Shall Be. A Novel. 4 vols., London, A. K. Newman, 1823. [B.M.: *New Monthly Mag.*: *Quarterly Review.*]

—— Which is the Man? A novel. With a frontispiece. 4 vols., London, W. Lane, Minerva Press, 1801. [B.M.: Parker: Stonehill.]

—— The Wonder of the Village. 3 vols., London, Lane, Newman, 1805. [Publisher's advert.: Blakey.]

Mcikle, James. Killinchy; or, The Days of Livingston. Belfast, McComb, 1839. [*I. in F.*]

Meinhold, Wilhelm. Mary Schweidler, the Amber Witch. The most Interesting Trial for Witchcraft ever known. Printed from an imperfect manuscript by her father Abraham Schweidler. Edited by W. Meinhold, Translated from the German by Lady Duff Gordon. London, John Murray, 1844. [B.M.: *Eng. Cat.*: Arthur Rogers.]

Melbourne. A Novel, by the Author of " Deloraine " [by Mrs. Martin], 3 vols., London, Minerva Press, 1798. [Baker's Bookshop: Stonehill: Blakey.]

Melcombe Lodge; Or, Traits of Family Pride! A Novel, By a Lady. 4 vols., Lynn, Printed by and for W. Whittingham, And published by Baldwin, Cradock, and Joy, London, 1819. [B.M.]

Melmoth, Courtney (*see* PRATT, Samuel Jackson).

Melville, Theodore. The Benevolent Monk; or, the Castle of Olalla. A romance. 3 vols., London, Crosby, 1807. [B.M.]

—— The Irish Chieftain and his Family. A Romance. 4 vols., London, Printed at the Minerva Press, for Lane, Newman, 1809. [B.M.: Ingpen: *I. in F.*]

Melwin Dale, A Novel, In a Series of Letters. By a Lady. 2 vols., London, William Lane, 1786. [Huth.]

Memis, Mrs. John Smythe. Precipitance: A Highland Tale. By a Lady. 2 vols., Edinburgh, Printed for the Author, 1823. [B.M.: Ingpen: *Quarterly Review.*]

Memoir of Jane Martin and her little brother. By a Lady. 1843. [B.M.]

Memoir of Maria * * *, a Converted Jewess. London, 1844. [B.M. (5th edn.).]

Memoirs and Adventures of a Flea; In Which are Interspersed Many Humorous Characters and Anecdotes. 2 vols., London, Axtell, 1785. [King: Stonehill.]

Memoirs and Opinions of Mr. Blenfield. By the author of *Tales of Sympathy* London, W. Lane, 1790. [Blakey.]

Memoirs of the Ancient House of Clarendon. A novel. 3 vols., London, William Lane, 1796. [*New Ann. Reg.*: Blakey.]

Memoirs of Antonina, Queen of Abo. Displaying her Private Intrigues, And Uncommon Passions. With Family Sketches And curious Anecdotes of Great Persons. Translated from the French. With a portrait. 2 vols. in 1. London, E. Bentley, 1791. [Ashbee Collection.]

Memoirs of a Babylonian Princess written by herself and translated into English. 2 vols., London, 1844. [B.M.]

Memoirs of a Baroness. 2 vols., 1792. [*New Ann. Reg.*]

Memoirs of the Bashaw Count Bonneval, From his Birth to his Death. With a frontispiece. London, Withers, 1750. [Ingpen.]

Memoirs of Captain Shelburne. Second Edition. To which is now added, Henry and Charlotte; or, The Fatal Shipwreck. A tale. Sommers Town, 1799. [B.M.]

Memoirs of Charley Crofts, containing numerous highly entertaining Anecdotes. Written by himself. Cork, 1829. [B.M.]

Memoirs of the Chevalier Pierpoint. 2 vols., London, R. and J. Dodsley, 1763. [Pickering: Stonehill.]

Memoirs of a Coquet; Or the History of Miss Harriot Airy. By the Author of Emily Willis; Or, the History of a Natural Daughter. London, Printed by W. Hoggard, for Francis Noble; and John Noble, 1765. [B.M.: Pickering.]

Memoirs of Davy Dreamy (The), Edited by Flit. 1839. [B.M.]

Memoirs of Dick, The Little Pony; intended for the Instruction and Amusement of Little Masters and Misses, supposed to be written by Himself. With woodcuts. London, N. Hailes, 1821. [Sotheran.]

Memoirs of Female Philosophers. By a Modern Philosopher of the Sex. 2 vols., London, 1808. [Blackwell: B.M.]

Memoirs of Fidelis and Harriot (The): wherein The Contrast between Virtue and Vice is fully exhibited from a real Fact. Transacted in the year 1720. Preserved in the original Manuscript of Mrs. Harvey. Dublin, 1753. [T. D. Webster.]

Memoirs of a French Lady of Pleasure (The). London, 1797. [*Cat. Lib. Prohib.*]

Memoirs of Harriot and Charlotte Meanwell, Who from a State of Affluence are reduced to the greatest Distress. Containing many Particulars in the Intercourse of their Lives, both entertaining and instructive to young Persons of either Sex. Written by Themselves. London, Printed for the Authors, 1757. [Pickering.]

Memoirs of John Bull (The). A Domestic Servant. London, 1797. [*Cat. Lib. Prohib.*]

Memoirs of Lady Harriot Butler: now first published from Authentic Papers, in the Lady's own hand-writing. 2 vols., London, 1741. [B.M.: McLeish.]

Memoirs of the Life and Adventures of Sobrina. 2 vols., London, 1755. [T. D. Webster.]

Memoirs of the Life and Gallant Exploits of the Old Highlander (The). London, 1791. [*Cat. Lib. Prohib.*]

Memoirs of the Life and Remarkable Exploits of Dennis Neale, alias John Clarke, otherwise called the Second Turpin, who was executed at Tyburn for Robbing on the Highway; a Full Account of his Extraordinary Adventures and most daring Robberies. London, T. Parker, and R. Griffiths, 1754. [Pickering.]

Memoirs of the Life, Sufferings, and Surprising Adventures of a Noble Foreigner at * * * * * * *. To which are added some instructive remarks on the vicissitudes of fortune. Written by himself. London, C. Corbett, 1752. [B.M.]

Memoirs of a London Doll, written by herself. Edited by Mrs. Fairstar. London, 1846. [B.M.]

Memoirs of the Love and State-Intrigues of the Court of H[anover] From the Marriage of the Princess of Z[elle] To the Tragical Death of Count K[onigsmarc]k. A Home-Truth, written originally in High German by the celebrated Countess of K—k, sister to that unfortunate nobleman. London, 1743. [Ingpen: Arthur Rogers.]

Memoirs of Lydia Tongue Pad, and Juliana Clack-it, etc. London, M. Thrush, [1750 ?]. [B.M.]

Memoirs of M. de Brinboc: Containing Some Views of English and Foreign Society. 3 vols., London, T. Cadell and W. Davies, 1805. [B.M.]

Memoirs of Maitre-Jacques, Of Savoy. 2 vols., Bath, Hazard, 1775. [*Eng. Lit. in Germany*: Stonehill.]

Memoirs of a Man of Fashion, Written by Himself. 3 vols., 1821. [G. H. Last.]

Memoirs of a Man of Honour. Translated from the French. 1747. [Arthur Rogers.]

Memoirs of the Manstein Family; pathetic, sentimental, humorous and satirical. 2 vols., London, Lowndes,

1783. [*Eng. Lit. in Germany*: R. Hall: Huth.]

Memoirs of Maria, A Persian Slave. 2 vols., 1790. [Crowe.]

Memoirs of the Marquis de Villebon, In a Series of Letters. A Novel founded on facts. 2 vols., Salisbury, 1796. [F. Hollings: *New Ann. Reg.*]

Memoirs of Miss Arabella Bolton (The). Containing a genuine account of the treatment she received from the Hon. Col. L——l, etc. 2 vols., London, 1770. [B.M.: W. Brown.]

Memoirs of Miss D'Arville, or the Italian Female Philosopher, in a Series of Adventures founded on fact. Translated from the Italian. With frontispieces. 2 vols. London, 1764. [Lowe].

Memoirs of the Montague Family. 3 vols., London, Lloyd, 1817. [*Eng. Cat.: Monthly Mag.*]

Memoirs of Myself. By Pill Garlick. London, John Miller; and N. Mahon, and M. Keen, Dublin, 1816. [B.M.: *New Monthly Mag.*: Pickering.]

Memoirs of the Nutrebian Court; With the history of the Princess de Barnaville, and the Count de L——; And many affairs relating to a certain Fine Gentleman. 2 vols., London, M. Laugham, 1747. [B.M.]

Memoirs of Oliver Cromwell and his Children. Supposed to be written by Himself. 3 vols., 1816. [Ingpen: *New Monthly Mag.*]

Memoirs of an Oxford Scholar, containing his amour with the beautiful Miss L——., of Essex, and interpsers'd with several entertaining incidents, Written by Himself. London, 1756. [B.M.: W. Brown: Dobell.]

Memoirs of a Printer's Devil; Interspersed with Pleasing Recollections, Local Descriptions, and Anecdotes. Gainsborough, Printed and sold by J. M. Mozley for the Author, 1793. [B.M.]

Memoirs of a Schoolmaster (The). Bath. 1790. [*Cat. Lib. Prohib.*]

Memoirs of a Scots Heiress Addressed to the Right Honourable Lady Constance ****** By the author of Constance, etc., 3 vols., London, T. Hookham, 1791. [B.M.: Elkin Mathews.]

Memoirs of Sir Charles Belville, or The Placid Man. 2 vols., 1773. [W. Brown.]

Memoirs of Sir Charles Goodville and His Family: in a series of letters to a friend. 2 vols., London, D. Browne; and Whiston and White, 1753. [Tregaskis: T. D. Webster.]

Memoirs of a Social Monster; Or, The History of Charles Price. London, Kearsley, 1786. [Ingpen.]

Memoirs of Thule, Or the Island of Love. 2 vols., 1744. [W. Brown.]

Memoirs of Two Beloved Pupils. London, Religious Tract Society, 1840. [B.M.]

Memoirs of Two Young Gentlemen. Exhibiting The most striking instances of the seduction and snares to which young people are liable, the horrors consequent upon vice and dissipation, the amazing efficacy of divine grace in conversion, the pleasures of a religious life, and the joy of dying in the Lord. Interspersed with Awful warnings to companions in iniquity, serious exhortations to improve the time of divine forbearance and benignity, and remarkable anecdotes of the glories of redeeming love and mercy in the salvation of some persons of the most abandoned characters. The whole Designed To humble and reclaim the sons of vice and profaneness, to animate devout aspirers to heaven, to repress self-righteousness, exalt the righteousness of God, and promote the sacred interests of religion and virtue. Edinburgh, J. Reid, 1768. [B.M.]

Memoirs of a Young Lady of Family. Being a succinct account of the capriciousness of fortune, and an accurate survey of the heart of that incomprehensible animal called Man. London, J. Scott, 1758. [B.M.]

Memoirs of a Young Lady of Quality (The). A Platonist. 3 vols., London, R. Baldwin, 1756. [B.M.: Dobell: Pickering.]

Memory. By the Author of " Margaret Whyte," " The Two Lambs," etc. etc. With a frontispiece. Wellington, Salop, 1824. [Gumuchian.]

Men and Women. A Novel. Dedicated to Sir James Mackintosh. By the author of " What You Please," "Tourville," etc. 3 vols., Bristol, J. Lansdown, 1805. [Baker's Bookshop: Pickering.]

Mental Novelist and Amusing Companion, a collection of histories, essays, & novels: containing Historical description of the Indians in North America. Curious odd thoughts. History of Milo, the bruiser. The man of spirit; or History of Alacer. Humourous & wonderful history of the Lancashire witches. History of the unfortunate man of honour. The final philosopher. Unheard-of sufferings of David Menzies, amongst the Cherokees, and his surprizing deliverance. The innocent suicide, a tale. Dialogue between Miss Prater and Lady Dunny, on ghosts. Series of dilemmas and difficulties of an officer of marines. With many other curious literary productions of Alexander Kellet, Esq., London, W. Lane. 1783. [W. Brown: Blakey.]

Mental Triumph. 3 vols., 1789. [W. Brown.]

Mental Wanderings: or Fragments, on Priestcraft and Superstition. A Tale of other Times. By Phileleuthenius. Liverpool, 1819. [B.M.]

Mercenary Marriage (The), or The History of Miss Shenstone. 1773. [*Eng. Lit. in Germany.*]

Mercier, Louis Sébastian. Memoirs of the Year Two Thousand Five Hundred. Translated from the French [by William Hooper]. 2 vols., London, Robinson, 1772. [B.M.: Ingpen: Stonehill.]

Merelina; Or, Such is Life: In a Series of Letters. By T. T. T. London, Longman; Chelmsford, H. Guy; Colchester, Knibb, Dennis; Maldon, Youngman, 1842. [B.M.: Publisher's advert.]

Merle, William Henry De. Bathurst; or, Church, State, and Country, as they were. A Novel. By the Author of " Melton de Mowbray," &c. 3 vols., London, T. C. Newby, 1850. [B.M.]

—— Glenlonely; Or the Demon Friend. 3 vols., London, Longman, Rees, Orme, Brown, Green, & Longman, 1837. [The B.M. and the Ingpen copies have only " Glenlonely " as the title.] [B.M.: Halkett & Laing: Ingpen.]

Merle, William Henry De. Melton de Mowbray: Or, The Banker's Son. A Novel. 3 vols., London, R. Bentley, 1838. [B.M.: McLeish.]

Merrivane, Mark. Life at Full Length; Or Men and things as they are, As they are not, And As they ought to be: Consisting of Comical Fictions, and facts undisguised. With frontispieces by T. Onwhyn. 3 vols., London, T. C. Newby, 1844. [B.M.: *Critic.*]

Merry Frolick; or the Comical Cheats of Swalpo, a Notorious Pick-Pocket. And the merry Pranks of Roger the Clown. With woodcuts. London, Printed and sold at the Printing-Office in Bow-Church-Yard, [1785]. [Maggs.]

Merry Medley (The); or, a Christmass-Box for gay gallants and good companions. Containing stories and jokes and jovial songs, set for the voice, violin, and modish Country Dances. Dedicated to the Lovers of Fun, by C. F. London, [1745 ?]. [B.M.]

Merry Tales (The), Or the Wise Men of Gotham. With woodcuts. London, Printed and Sold in Aldermary Church Yard, [1750 ?]. [B.M.]

Merrye Englaunde; or, The Goldene Daies of Goode Queene Besse. London, Charles Dolman, 1841. [Block.]

Meteyard, Eliza. The Doctor's Little Daughter. London, A. Hall, 1850. [Allibone: B.M.: *Eng. Cat.*]

—— Struggles for Fame. A Novel. 3 vols., London, T. C. Newby, 1845. [B.M.: *Critic.*]

Metropolis (The), A Novel, By the Author of Little Hydrogen, or The Devil on Two Sticks in London. 3 vols., 1819. [Blackwell.]

Michel, Nicholas. Henry of Monmouth: Or the Field of Agincourt. 3 vols., London, Saunders and Otley, 1841. [B.M.]

Michel, Nicholas. Trevor Hastings, Or the Battle of Tewkesbury. By the Author of " Henry of Monmouth." 3 vols., London, Saunders and Otley, 1842. [B.M.]

Middleton, Joseph. Marmaduke Lorrimer; a novel. 3 vols., London, 1850. [B.M.: McLeish.]

—— Stanhope. A Domestic Novel. London, Saunders and Otley, 1845. [B.M.]

Midnight Assassin (The); Or, Confession of the Monk Rinaldi; Containing a complete History of his Diabolical Machinations and unparalleled Ferocity. Together with A Circumstantial Account of that Scourge of Mankind The Inquisition; with the Manner of Bringing to trial those unfortunate beings who are at its disposal. With a frontispiece. London, Tegg, [1802]. [Ingpen.]

Midnight Groan (The); or, the Spectre of the Chapel: involving an exposure of the horrible secrets of the nocturnal assembly. A Gothic romance. With a frontispiece. London, 1808. [B.M.: Murray Hill.]

Midnight Horrors; or, the Bandit's Daughter. An Original Romance. With a frontispiece. London, Dean and Munday, [1810 ?]. [B.M.: Stonehill.]

Midnight Hour (The); or, Fatal Friendship. London, Lemoine and Roe, [*c.* 1804]. [Stonehill.]

Midnight Ramble (The): or, The Adventures of two Noble Females. London, B. Dickinson, 1754. [B.M.]

Midnight Rambler (The); or, New Nocturnal Spy, for the present Year. Containing a Complete Description of the Modern Transactions of London and Westminster from the hours of Nine in the Evening, till Six in the Morning. Exhibiting great Variety of Midnight Scenes and Adventures in Real Life, both Serious and Comic. With a frontispiece. London, Cooke, [*c.* 1790]. [Stonehill.]

Midnight, the Signal, In Sixteen Letters to a Lady of Quality. With vignette titles. 2 vols., London, Dodsley, 1779. [Bailey Bros.: *Eng. Lit. in Germany*: James Glaisher.]

Midsummer Holydays; or, a long Story; written for the Improvement and Entertainment of Young Folk. London, 1788. [B.M.]

Mildred Winnerley; or, The Curse of Beauty. By the Author of " Amy," " The Wife's Tragedy," &c. With woodcuts. London, E. Lloyd, [1849 ?]. [B. Ono.]

Miles, E. Violet Hill, or Memoirs of Cordelia, a fair foundling. London, 1791. [Baker's Bookshop.]

Miles, Henry Downes. Claude du Val, A Romance. With illustrations. London, T. White, 1840. [R. S. Frampton.]

—— Dick Turpin; the Highwayman. With woodcuts. London, [*c.* 1845.] [Stonehill.]

Milistina: or, The Double Interest. A Novel. Dedicated to the Marchioness Townshend. 2 vols., London, 1797. [T. D. Webster.]

Military Adventures of Johnny New-come, with an Account of his Campaigns on the Peninsula and in Pall Mall; with Sketches by Rowlandson; and Notes. By an Officer. With 15 plates by Thomas Rowlandson. London, 1815. [Maggs.]

Millener's Girl (The); or, The Interesting and Authentic Adventures of Fanny Bilson; a Country Clergyman's Daughter To which is added the True Story of Anna; the Orphan of Worcestershire. With a frontispiece. London, Hughes, 1802. [Arthur Rogers: Stonehill.]

Miller, F. B. Tales of Travel: Consisting of Narratives of Various journeys Through Some of the most interesting parts Of the World. With Plates. London, Harvey and Darton, 1833. [Block: B.M.]

Miller, Johann Martin. Siegwart: a monastic tale. Translated from the German. By L. M. Hawkins. 3 vols., London, 1806. [B.M.]

—— The Siegwart. Sigevart. A tale translated from the German. by H. L. 1799. [B.M.: *New Ann. Reg.*]

Miller, Lydia Falconer. Little Amy's Birthday, and other tales. A story-book for autumn. London, Routledge, 1846. [B.M.: *Eng. Cat.*]

—— The Little Foundling, and other tales. A Story Book for Summer. Written for young children. By Harriet Myrtle. With a frontispiece. London, Joseph Cundall, [1840].

—— The Man of Snow, and other tales. London, Routledge, 1848. [B.M.: *Eng. Cat.*]

—— A Story Book Of the Seasons: Spring. Written for young children. With illustrations by John Absolon. London, Joseph Cundall, 1845. [B.M.]

—— A Story Book Of the Seasons: Summer. Written for young children. With illustrations by J. Absolon. London, Joseph Cundall, 1846. [B.M.]

Miller, Thomas. A Day in the Woods; A Connected Series of Tales and Poems. London, Smith, Elder, 1836. [B.M.: Sotheran.]

—— Fair Rosamond; Or The Days of King Henry II. An Historical Romance. 3 vols., London, Henry Colburn, 1839. [B.M.: B. Halliday.]

—— Fortune and Fortitude; exemplified in the lives of Jack Hardy and Augustus Errantdale. London, Darton, 1848. [Allibone: B.M.]

—— Gideon Giles the Roper. With 36 illustrations by Edward Lambert. London, T. Miller, 1841. [B.M.: *Eng. Cat.*: T. Thorp.]

Miller, Thomas. Godfrey Malvern; or, the Life of an Author. With 27 plates by "Phiz" [H. K. Browne]. 2 vols., London, H. Bohn, 1842-1843. [B.M.: *Eng Cat.*: R. Hall.]

—— Lady Jane Grey; An Historical Romance. 3 vols., London, Henry Colburn, 1840. [Baker's Bookshop: B.M.]

—— Royston Gower; Or, The Days of King John. An Historical Romance. 3 vols., London, Henry Colburn, 1838. [B.M.: *Guide to Best Fiction.*]

Millikin, Anna. Plantagenet; a Tale of the Twelfth Century. 2 vols., London, 1802. [Allibone.]

—— The Rival Chiefs; or, The Battle of Mere. [Minerva Press, 1805]. [Blakey.]

Millingen, John Gideon. Adventures of An Irish Gentleman. 3 vols., London, Henry Colburn and Richard Bentley, 1830. [B.M.]

—— Jack Hornet; Or, The March of Intellect. By the Author of "The Adventures of an Irish Gentleman." 3 vols., London, Richard Bentley, 1845. [B.M.: *Critic.*]

—— Stories Of Torres Vedras. By the Author of "Adventures of an Irish Gentleman." 3 vols., London, Richard Bentley, 1839. [B.M.: T. D. Webster.]

Millman's Tales, Adapted for The Higher Classes of Youth. London, John Souter, 1831. [B.M.]

Mills, John. A Capful of Moonshine; or, 'Tis not all Gold that glitters. London, 1849. [B.M.]

—— D'Horsay: Or, The Follies of the Day. By a Man of Fashion. With a portrait, vignette on title-page & 10 plates by George Standfast. London, William Strange, 1844. [B.M.: Marks: Rosebery.]

—— The English Fireside: A Tale of the Past. 3 vols., London, Saunders and Otley, 1844. [B.M.: James Glaisher: E. M. Lawson.]

—— The Old English Gentleman, Or, The Fields and the Woods. 3 vols., London, Henry Colburn, 1841. [B.M.]

—— The Old Hall; Or, Our Hearth and Homestead. 3 vols., London, T. C. Newby, 1845. [B.M.: Elkin Mathews.]

—— The Stage Coach; Or, The Road of Life. With illustrations. 3 vols., London, Henry Colburn, 1843. [B.M.]

Milman, Edward Augustus. The Way-side Cross; or, the Raid of Gomez, a tale of the Carlist War. London, John Murray, 1847. [Allibone: B.M.]

Miltie, Baron Karl von. The Twelve Nights. London, Whittaker, Treacher, 1831. [B.M.: Ingpen.]

Milton, Henry. Lady Celia Farrencourt; a Novel. 3 vols., 1845. [Allibone.]

—— Rivalry. 3 vols., London, John Ollivier, 1840. [B.M.: James Glaisher.]

Minifies, Susannah and Margaret. The

Cottage; A Novel: In a Series of Letters. 3 vols., London, 1769. [T. D. Webster.]

Minifies, Susannah and Margaret. The Histories of Lady Frances S— and Lady Caroline S—. Written by the Miss Minifies. 4 vols., London, R. and J. Dodsley, 1763. [Block: B.M.: Huth.]

—— The Picture. A Novel. 3 vols., London, J. Johnson, 1766. [Pickering.]

Minor (The); Or, History of George O'Nial, Esq. 2 vols., Dublin, Watson, 1787. [Stonehill: T. D. Webster.]

Minstrel (The); Or, Anecdotes of Distinguished Personages in the Fifteenth Century. 3 vols., London, Hookham and Carpenter, 1793. [Blackwell: B.M.: Stonehill.]

Miranda; or, Three Steps, and which is the best. London, 1850. [B.M.]

Miriam. A novel. By the Author of Frederick & Caroline. Wm. Lane, 1800. [*Eng. Lit. in Germany*: Blakey.]

Miriam Coffin, Or The Whale-Fishermen: A Tale. 3 vols., London, Whittaker, 1834. [B.M.]

Miriam, a Jewish Tale. 1826. [*Quarterly Review*.]

Mirror of Seduction. 1810. [*Quarterly Review*.]

Miseries and Pleasures of Matrimony (The); Or, The First Husband and the Second. A Novel. 4 vols., London, Printed at the Minerva Press for A. K. Newman, 1815. [B.M.: *New Monthly Mag.*: Publisher's advert.]

Miseries of Poor Simple Innocent Silly Tam (The). [Edinburgh ?], [1810 ?]. [B.M.]

Miser's Secret; or, the Days of James the First. An historical romance. 3 vols., London, Saunders & Otley, 1850. [B.M.]

Misfortunes of Love (The). A novel. Translated from the French. 2 vols. [William Lane, 1785]. [Blakey.]

Miss Aylmer; Or, The Maid's Husband. 3 vols., London, Richard Bentley, 1840. [B.M.]

Miss C—y's Cabinet of Curiosities, or The Green Room broke open. By Tristram Shandy Gent. Utopia [London], 1765. [B.M.]

Missionary Stories. In 22 parts. London, 1842-1843. [B.M.]

Mistaken Evil (The), A True Story. London, J. Marshall, N.D. [J. D. Miller.]

Mister, Mary. The Adventures of a Doll. Compiled with the hope of affording amusement and instruction. With a frontispiece. London, Darton and Harvey, 1816. [Gumuchian.]

—— Mungo the Little Traveller. [*Camb. Hist. Eng. Lit.*]

—— Tales from the Mountains. By the author of Mungo, the Little Traveller.

London, 1814. [B.M. (2nd edn.).]

Mister Humfries' Clock. "Bos" maker. A miscellany of striking interest. With illustrations. London, 1840. [B.M.]

Mistletoe (The). A German tale of Christmas. By the author of "The Wedding Bells." London, Allman, 1847. [B.M.]

Mistress of Royalty (The); or the Loves of Florizel and Perdita. London, 1814. [*New Monthly Mag.*]

Mitchell, Agnes W. The Smuggler's Son; and other tales and sketches. In prose and verse. By A. W. M. 1842. [B.M.]

Mitchell, John. The Female Pilgrim; or, the Travels of Hephzibah. Under the Similitude of a Dream. In which is given An historical Account of the Pilgrim's Descent, and a Description of her native Country, with the State of the Inhabitants thereof; the Reason why, and Manner how, she left the Place of her Nativity, in Search of a better Country; the kind of Entertainment she met with on the Road; the Dangers she went through, with her safe Arrival at the Country she travelled in Search of. Interspersed with Variety of Reflections, Dialogues, Songs, &c. The Whole calculated equally for Instruction and Entertainment, and suited to all Capacities. With plates, London, J. Chalmers, 1793. [B.M.]

Mitchell, Nicholas. The Eventful Epoch; Or, the Fortunes of Archer Clive. 3 vols., London, Simpkin, Marshall, 1846. [B.M.: *Critic.*]

—— The Fatalist, Or the Fortunes of Godolphin. By An Essayist on the Passions. 3 vols., London, William Edwards, 1840. [B.M.]

—— The Traduced. An Historical Romance. 3 vols., London, T. and W. Boone, 1842. [B.M.]

Mitford, Mrs. The Cousins. London, Darton, [1849]. [B.M.]

—— Disobedient Joseph. London, [1849]. [B.M.]

—— Frank and his Christmas Gift; or, the true worth of a sovereign. London, [1849]. [B.M.]

—— The Overturned Chaise. London, [1849]. [B.M.]

Mitford, Mary Russell. Belford Regis; Or Sketches Of a Country Town. 3 vols., London, Richard Bentley, 1835. [B.M.: Ingpen: Arthur Rogers.]

—— Country Stories. London, Saunders and Otley, 1837. [B.M.: Cleverdon: Ingpen.]

—— Lights and Shadows Of American Life. Edited by Mary Russell Mitford. 3 vols., London, Henry Colburn and Richard Bentley, 1832. [B.M.: Lib. of Congress.]

—— Our Village: Sketches of Rural

Character & Scenery. London, G. & W. B. Whittaker, 1824. [B.M.: Arthur Rogers: Varda.]

Mitford, Mary Russell. Our Village: Sketches of Rural Character and Scenery. Second Series. London, Whittaker, 1826. [B.M.: Kyrle Fletcher: T. Thorp.]

—— Our Village: Sketches of Rural Character and Scenery. Third Series. London, Whittaker, 1828. [B.M.: Kyrle Fletcher: *Quarterly Review.*]

—— Our Village: Sketches of Rural Character and Scenery. Fourth Series. London, Whittaker, Treacher. 1830. [B.M.: Kyrle Fletcher: Arthur Rogers.]

—— Our Village: Sketches of Rural Character and Scenery. Fifth Series. London, Whittaker, 1832. [B.M.: Kyrle Fletcher: T. Thorp.]

—— Tales for Young People. With a frontispiece. 1840. [Wm. Smith.]

Mock-Monarchs (The); or, the Benefits of High Blood. 2 vols., London, [1754 ?]. [B.M.]

Modern Amours or A Secret History of Adventures of Some Persons of the First Rank, Faithfully Related from the Author's own Knowledge of each Transaction. With a Key Prefixed. 1733. [*Eng. Lit. in Germany.*]

Modern Antique (The); or, the Muse in the Costume of Queen Anne. 1813. [*Quarterly Review.*]

Modern Atalantis (The); or, the Devil in an Air-Balloon. Containing the characters and secret memoirs of the most conspicuous persons of high quality of both sexes in the island of Libertusia, etc. London, 1784. [B.M.: W. Brown.]

Modern Fine Gentleman (The). A novel. 2 vols., London, 1774. [B.M.]

Modern Lovers, or the Adventures of Cupid. 1756. [W. Brown.]

Modern Manners; Or, A Season at Harrogate. 2 vols., London, Longman, Hurst, Rees, Orme, & Brown, 1817. [B.M.: *Monthly Mag.*]

Modern Miniature (The), a novel. 2 vols., 1792. [*New Ann. Reg.*: T. Thorp.]

Modern Rake (The). Or the Life and Adventures of Sir Edward Walford Containing a Curious and Voluptuous History of his luscious intrigues, with numerous women of fashion, his laughable faux pas, feats of gallantry, debauchery, dissipation, and concubinism. His numerous rapes, seductions, and amatory scrapes. Memoirs of the Beautiful Courtezans, with whom he lived; with some Ticklish Songs, Anecdotes, Poetry, etc. With plates. London, J. Sudbury, 1824. [*Cat. Lib. Prohib.*]

Modern Times, or Anecdotes of the English Family. 3 vols. [Cawthorn's Catalogue, 1810].

Modes of Life; or, Town and Country. A Novel. 3 vols., London, A. K.

Newman, 1823. [B.M.: *New Monthly Mag.*]

Mogridge, George. Amos Armfield; Or, the Leather-covered Bible. London, The Religious Tract Society, [1845]. [B.M.]

—— Aunt Upton and her nephews and nieces. London, 1841. [B.M.]

—— The Encourager. With woodcuts. London, The Religious Tract Society, [1835 ?]. [B.M.: Court Bk. Shop.]

—— The Juvenile Culprits. By the author of "The Juvenile Moralists." Wellington, 1829. [B.M.]

—— The Juvenile Moralists. By the author of "The Juvenile Culprits." Wellington, 1829. [B.M.]

—— Mirth and Morality, A Collection of Original Tales, By Carlton Bruce. With 20 woodcuts by George Cruikshank. London, T. Tegg; R. Griffin, Glasgow; J. Cumming, and W. F. Wakeman, Dublin, 1834. [B.M.: Marks.]

—— Play Hours: or, the Happy Children. London, [1843 ?]. [B.M.]

Mohn, Lady Isabella. Geraldine Hamilton; Or, Self-Guidance. A Tale. 2 vols., London, Richard Bentley, 1832. [B.M.: *I. in F.*: Pickering.]

Moir, David Macbeth. The Life of Mansie Wauch, Tailor in Dalkeith. Written by Himself. Edinburgh, William Blackwood; & T. Cadell, London, 1828. [Block: B.M.: Arthur Rogers.]

Molesworth, John Edward Nassau. Overbury; or, some advantages of an established and endowed Church, and some evils of the "Voluntary System." A tale. London, 1834. [B.M.]

—— Tales from the scrap-book of a Country Clergyman. London, 1831. [B.M.]

Molesworth, Mary. Claude; or the Double Sacrifice. 2 vols., London, Henry Colburn, 1850. [Allibone: B.M.: *Eng. Cat.*]

—— A Stumble on the Threshold: a Story of the Day. London, Ollivier, 1848. [B.M.: *Eng. Cat.*]

Molly Gay; or, the aged Christian widow. By the author of "Charity in Religion." London, 1846. [B.M.]

Momus's Cabinet of Amusement, The New Encyclopaedia, or World of Wit, a Choice Selection of Bon Mots, Puns, Epigrams, and Humorous Tales in Prose and Verse; also Anecdotes of Eminent and Eccentric Persons, calculated to Enliven the Mind and Exhilarate the Spirits, in Difficult Times. With a frontispiece. London, [1800 ?]. [B.M.]

Monastic Ruins; or, The Invisible Monitor. A Romance. To which is added, The Brazier. A Tale. With a frontispiece. London, Printed by T. Maiden, For Ann Lemoine, And J. Roe, [1804 ?]. [Block.]

Monimia. A novel. 2 vols. [W. Lane, 1791]. [Blakey.]

Monitress (The); or, the œconomy of female life in a series of letters from Mary Dawes Blackett to her daughter. London, [1791]. [B.M.]

Monk and the Vine-Dresser (The): Or, the Emigrants of Bellesme. A Moral Tale. By a Lady. Edinburgh, Manners & Miller, A Constable and Brown & Crombie; and Constable, Hunter, Park and Hunter, London, 1809. [Sidgwick & Jackson.]

Monk of the Grotto (The); or, Eugenio & Virginia. A Tale. From the French [of Pigault Lebrun?]. 2 vols., London, Minerva Press, 1800. [Stonehill: Blakey.]

Monkey Man. A single folio sheet. [Edinburgh], [1830?]. [B.M.]

Monkland, Mrs. Life in India; or, The English at Calcutta. 3 vols., London, Henry Colburn, 1828. [B.M.]

—— The Nabob at Home; Or, The Return to England. By the Author of " Life in India." 3 vols., London, Henry Colburn, 1842. [B.M.]

—— The Nabob's Wife. By The Author of " Village Riminiscences " [*sic*]. 3 vols., London, Richard Bentley, 1837. [B.M.]

—— Village Reminiscences. By an old maid. 3 vols., London, Richard Bentley, 1834. [B.M.]

Monks and the Robbers (The); a tale of the Fifteenth Century. 2 vols., London, 1808. [B.M.: McLeish.]

Monk's Daughter; or, Hypocrisy punished. 3 vols., 1812. [*Quarterly Review.*]

Monks of St. Andrews (The); or, the Castle of Haldenstein. London, [1825]. [B.M.]

Monkton, Charles. Some Account of Myself. By Charles Earl of Erpingham. 4 vols., London, W. Simpkin & R. Marshall, 1817. [B.M.: *Monthly Mag.*: *New Monthly Mag.*]

Montagu, Frederic. Compensation; and by whom received. London, Finey, 1847. [B.M.: *Eng. Cat.*]

—— Mary Ashley the Factory Girl: or, Facts upon Factories. In 2 parts. London, 1839. [B.M.]

Montague, Edward. The Castle of Berry Pomeroy. A Novel. 2 vols., Lane, Newman, 1806. [Allibone: Blakey.]

—— The Daemon of Sicily; a Romance. 4 vols., 1807. [Allibone.]

—— The Legends of a Nunnery. A romance. 4 vols., London, 1807. [B.M.]

—— Modern Characters. A Novel. 3 vols., London, 1808. [B.M.: Ingpen.]

Montalba, Anthony R. Fairy Tales from All Nations. With illustrations by Richard Doyle. London, Chapman and Hall, 1849. [B.M.: Lowndes.]

Montalbion, Kate. Caledonia; or the Stranger in Scotland. 4 vols., 1810. [*Monthly Mag.*: *Quarterly Review.*]

—— The Spanish Lady, and the Norman Knight. A romance of the eleventh century. 2 vols., London, J. F. Hughes, 1810 [1816]. [B.M.: *Monthly Mag.*]

Montalde; or, the Honest Breton. An Interesting Tale. With a frontispiece. London, Printed for T. Maiden, For Ann Lemoine, And J. Roe, [1804?]. [Block.]

Montengon, Don Pedro. Eudoxia; Daughter of Belisarius. A Novel. Translated from the Spanish by Charles Hervey Smith. 2 vols., London, Stockdale, 1818. [Stonehill.]

Montesquieu, Charles Secondat, Baron de. Miscellaneous Pieces. London, 1759. [Contains " Eleven New Persian Letters," " The Temple of Gnidus," and " Lysimachus."] [Stonehill.]

—— The Temple of Gnidus, and Arsaces and Ismenia, Translated from the French of Charles de Secondat, Baron de Montesquieu. London, J. Wright, 1797. [B.M.: Pickering.]

Montford Castle or The Knight of the White Rose. 2 vols., 1795. [*Eng. Lit. in Germany*: *New Ann. Reg.*]

Montgomery, Mrs. A. Ashton Hall; a Novel. London, 1846. [Allibone.]

Montgomery, James. The Whisperer; or, Tales and Speculations, by Gabriel Silvertongue. London, J. Johnson, 1798. [Norman.]

Montgomery, M. M. Lights and Shadows of German Life. 2 vols., London, Edward Bull, 1833. [B.M.]

Montgomery; Or The West Indian Adventurer, a Novel, by A Gentleman Resident in the West Indies. 3 vols., Jamaica, Printed at the Office of the " Kingston Chronicle," 1812. [B.M.: King.]

Montolieu, Jeanne Isabelle Bottens, Baroness de. Caroline of Lichtfield; A Novel. Translated from the French [of Madame Montolieu]. By Thomas Holcroft. 3 vols., London, G. G. J. and J. Robinson, 1786. [W. Brown: Holland: Ingpen.]

—— Christina: or, Memoirs of a German Princess. By the Author of Caroline of Lichtfield. 2 vols., London, 1808. [B.M.]

—— Tales. 3 vols., 1805. [T. D. Webster.]

Montreithe; Or, The Peer of Scotland. A Novel. [Amelia Beauclerc]. 4 vols., London, Printed at the Minerva Press, for A. K. Newman, 1814. [B.M.: Publisher's advert.: Blakey.]

Montrose, or the Gothic Ruin, a Novel. 3 vols., 1799. [Mayhew: *New Ann. Reg.*]

Montville; Or, The Dark Heir of the Castle. A Novel. 3 vols., London, A. K. Newman, 1826. [B.M.: *Edin. Mag.*: *Quarterly Review.*]

Moodelliar, T. V. Pleasant Stories from Gladwin's Persian Moonshee, with a close translation and their Analysis on the Opposite Sides. Madras, 1832. [Dobell: Stonehill.]

Moodie, Mrs. Mark Hurdlestone. The Gold Worshipper. 2 vols., 1853. [Arthur Rogers.]

Moore, Clara. Burton, or the Bright Halfpenny. By the Author of " The Cottage on the Common." London, 1848. [B.M.: Alger.]

Moore, Edward. The Mysteries of Hungary. A Romantic History, Of the Fifteenth Century. 3 vols., London, Printed at the Minerva Press, for A. K. Newman, 1817. [B.M.: *New Monthly Mag.*]

—— Sir Ralph de Bigod, A Romance of the Nineteenth Century. 4 vols., Minerva Press, 1811. [*Quarterly Review.*]

—— The Story of Mr. and Mrs. Wilson. 1753. [*Eng. Lit. in Germany.*]

Moore, Frances, (?). All's right at last: or The History of Miss West. 2 vols., London, 1774. [B.M.]

—— The History of Charles Mandeville. A sequel to Lady Julia, by Mrs. Brooke. 2 vols., London, W. Lane, 1790. [Blakey: Borrow Head Bookshop: T. D. Webster.]

—— The History of Emily Montague. By the Author of Lady Julia Mandeville. 4 vols., London, J. Dodsley, 1769. [B.M.: Arthur Rogers: Stonehill.]

—— The History of Lady Julia Mandeville. By the Translator of Lady Catesby's Letters. 2 vols., London, R. and J. Dodsley, [1763]. [B.M.: *Eng. Lit. in Germany*: Martin A. McGoff.]

—— Manners: A Novel. 3 vols., London, Baldwin, Cradock, and Joy, 1817. [B.M.: Ingpen: Pickering.]

—— A Year and a Day. A Novel. By Madame Panache, Author of Manners, 2 vols., London, Baldwin, Cradock, and Joy, 1818. [B.M.: Ingpen: Marks.]

Moore, George. The Courtezan; An English Tale, an illustration of the Passion of Revenge. 1808. [Ingpen.]

—— Gransville Abbey: a Romance. 3 vols., London, 1801. [T. D. Webster.]

—— The Married Man; An English Tale: In which is attempted an illustration of The Passion of Jealousy, In Its effects on the human mind. [No Publisher, or place of publication, 1811]. [B.M.: Ingpen.]

—— Tales of the Passions. London, Printed at the Minerva Press, for A. K. Newman, 1814. [Publisher's advert.]

—— Theodosius de Zulvin, The Monk of Madrid, a Spanish Tale. 2 vols., 1802. [Sexton.]

Moore, Hannah W. Ellen Ramsay. 3 vols., London, Longman, Hurst, Rees, Orme, Brown, & Green, 1824. [B.M.: Publisher's advert.]

Moore, Dr. John. Edward. Various Views of Human Nature, taken from Life and Manners Chiefly in England. By the Author of Zeluco. 2 vols., London, A. Strahan and T. Cadell, 1796. [B.M.: Ingpen: Arthur Rogers.]

Moore, Dr. John. Mordaunt: Sketches of Life, Character, and Manners, In Various Countries; Including the Memoirs of A French Lady of Quality. 3 vols., London, 1800. [B.M.: Clarke-Hall: Francis Edwards.]

—— The Post Captain, or The Wooden Walls Well Manned, comprehending a View of Naval Society and Manners. With a vignette title. London, Tegg, 1806. [King: G. Worthington.]

—— Zeluco. Various Views of Human Nature, taken from Life and Manners, Foreign and Domestic. 2 vols., London, A. Strahan and T. Cadell, 1789. [B.M.: Ingpen: Marks.]

Moore, Marian. Ariana and Maud; a Novel. 3 vols., [Minerva Press]. 1803. [Allibone: Blakey.]

—— Lascelles. Interspersed with Characteristic Sketches from Nature. 3 vols., London, Minerva Press, 1802. [Blackwell: Blakey.]

Moore, Oliver. The Staff Officer; Or, The Soldier of Fortune. A Tale of Real Life. 3 vols., London, Cochrane and Pickersgill, 1831. [B.M.: Ingpen: Pickering.]

Moore, Mrs. Robert. Evelyn Mountjoy; Or, Views of Life. A Novel. 4 vols., London, Longman, Hurst, Rees, Orme, & Brown. 1819. [B.M.: Publisher's advert.: Quarterly Review.]

Moore, Sidney O. Annie Gray. London, 1850. [B.M.]

Moore, Thomas. Confessions of an Oxonian. By Thomas Little. With 36 plates by J. Findlay. 3 vols., London, J. J. Stockdale, 1826. [B.M.]

—— The Epicurean. A Tale. London, Longman, Rees, Orme, Brown, & Green, 1827. [B.M.: Galloway: Ingpen.]

—— Memoirs of Captain Rock, The Celebrated Irish Chieftain, with Some Account of his Ancestors. Written by Himself. London, Longman, 1824. [B.M.: Ingpen: Elkin Mathews.]

—— Travels of an Irish Gentleman in Search of a Religion. With Notes and Illustrations by the Editor of " Captain Rock's Memoirs." 2 vols., London, Longman, 1833. [B.M.: Elkin Mathews.]

Moore, Thomas George. The Bachelor: a novel. 3 vols., London, 1809. [Allibone: B.M.: T. D. Webster.]

Moraes, Francisco de. Palmerin of England. Corrected by Robert Southey from the Original Portuguese of Francisco de Moraes. 4 vols., London, Longman, 1807. [G. Worthington.]

Moral, Matthew, [Mary Pilkington]. The Novice; or, The Heir of Montgomery Castle. A Novel. 3 vols., London, Printed at the Minerva Press for A. K. Newman, 1814. [B.M.: Publisher's advert.: Blakey.]

Moral Amusement; Or, A Selection of Tales, Histories, And Interesting Anecdotes; Intended to Amuse and Instruct Young Minds. With a frontispiece. London, Vernor and Hood; and F. Newbery, 1799. [B.M.]

Moral Budget of my Uncle Newbury (The). By the Author of " Twelve Moral Maxims of my Uncle Newbury." With woodcuts. London, Houlston, 1830 [B.M.]

Moral Courage and Other Tales. With a frontispiece. Edinburgh, William and Robert Chambers, 1850. [Block.]

Moral Legacy (The); Or, Simple Narratives. London, William Miller, 1801. [*Eng. Lit. in Germany*: Ingpen.]

Moral Tales, By a Father. London, John Harris.

Moral Tales. Eugenio; Mr. V——; Beggar and his Dog. With a vignette. Poughnill, G. Nicholson, 1801. [Block.]

Mordaunt, Henry. Chronicles of the Ton. 3 vols., 1815. [Sotheby's.]

More, Hannah. Coelebs in Search of a Wife: Comprehending Observations on Domestic Habits and Manners, Religion and Morals. 2 vols., London, T. Cadell & W. Davies. 1808. [Ingpen: H. H. Langley: Lyle H. Wright.]

—— Dan and Jane; or, Faith and works. A Tale. London, 1796. Cheap Repository. [B.M.]

—— Hints Towards Forming the Character of a Young Princess. 2 vols., London, T. Cadell and W. Davies, 1805. [B.M.: Arthur Rogers: W. T. Spencer.]

—— The History of Hester Wilmot, etc. In 2 parts. London, [1800 ?]. Cheap Repository. [B.M.]

—— Jack Brown in Prison; Or, The Pitcher never goes so often to the Well but it is broke at last. Being the Fourth Part of the History of the Two Shoemakers. With woodcuts. London, J. Marshall; and R. White, [1796]. Cheap Repository. [B.M.: Court Book Shop.]

—— The Shepherd of Salisbury-Plain. Part I [& II]. With woodcuts. London, J. Marshall, [1820 ?]. Cheap Repository. [Block: B.M.]

—— The Two Shoemakers, Part VI. Dialogue the Second. On the Duty of carrying Religion into our Amusements. With a woodcut. London, Howard and Evans, [1796]. Cheap Repository. [B.M.]

More, Sarah. The Cheapside Apprentice; Or, the History of Mr. Francis H * * * *. Fully setting forth the Danger of Playing with Edge Tools. Shewing also, how a Gay Life may prove a short one; and that a merry Evening may produce a sorrowful Morning. With a woodcut. London, J. Marshall; and R. White. [1800 ?]. Cheap Repository. [B.M.: Court Bk. Shop: Tregaskis.]

More Minor Morals: or, an introduction to the Winter family: with Aunt Eleanor's stories interspersed. 1821. [B.M.]

More Short Stories in Words of Two Syllables. By the Author of " Short Stories in one Syllable," &c. With a frontispiece. London, J. Harris, 1808. [B.M.: Gumuchian.]

Moreland, Olivia. The Charms of Dandyism; Or Living in Style. By Olivia Moreland, Chief of the Female Dandies; and Edited by Captain Ashe. 3 vols., London, Printed at the Minerva Press for A. K. Newman, 1819. [B.M.: King: Maggs.]

Morell, Sir Charles, (*see* RIDLEY, James.)

Moreton; or, The Doomed House. A Romance. With illustrations. London, Lloyd, [*c.* 1847]. [B.M.: Stonehill.]

Morgan, Ann Jane. Amiable Willie; Or, " Are you Ready ?" By Ann Jane. With a woodcut. London, Benjamin L. Green, 1848. [B.M.]

—— Death-Bed Repentance; Or, The Disappointed Minister. By Anne Jane. With a woodcut. London, Benjamin L. Green, 1848. [B.M.]

—— Irish Dick. By Ann Jane. With a woodcut. London, Benjamin L. Green, 1848. [B.M.]

—— Old Betty And The Ragged Money. By Ann Jane. With a woodcut. London, Benjamin L. Green, 1848. [B.M.]

Morgan, J. M. The Revolt of the Bees. London, Longman, 1826. [*Blackwood's Mag.*: B.M.: *Eng. Cat.*]

Morgan, Sydney, Lady. Absenteeism. London, Henry Colburn, 1825. [B.M.: Ingpen.]

—— The Book of the Boudoir. 2 vols., London, Henry Colburn, 1829. [Kyrle Fletcher: McLeish.]

—— Dramatic Scenes from Real Life. 2 vols., London, Saunders and Otley, 1833. [B.M.: *I. in F.*: Pickering.]

—— Florence Macarthy: An Irish Tale. [Edited by Sir T. C. Morgan.] 4 vols., London, Henry Colburn, 1818. [B.M.: Ingpen: Arthur Rogers.]

—— The Missionary, An Indian Tale, By Miss Owenson. With a portrait. 3 vols., London, Stockdale, 1811. [Bailey Bros.: Stonehill: T. D. Webster.]

—— The Novice of Saint Dominick. By Miss Owenson, Author of St. Clair. 4 vols., London, Richard Phillips, 1806. [Ingpen: Pickering: Stonehill.]

—— The O'Briens and the O'Flahertys; A National Tale. 4 vols., London, Henry Colburn, 1827. [B.M.: Ingpen: Arthur Rogers.]

—— O'Donnel. A National Tale. 3 vols., London, Henry Colburn, 1814. [B.M.: Dobell: Ingpen.]

—— Patriotic Sketches of Ireland, Written in Connaught. 2 vols., London, Phillips, 1807. [B.M.: Ingpen: Arthur Rogers.]

—— The Princess; Or The Beguine. 3 vols., London, Richard Bentley, 1835. [B.M.: Ingpen: Lib. of Congress.]

Morgan, Sydney, Lady. St. Clair; Or, the Heiress of Desmond. By S[ydney] O[wenson]. London, E. Harding; S. Highley; and J. Archer, 1803. [B.M.: Pickering: Arthur Rogers.]

—— The Wild Irish Girl; A National Tale. By Miss Owenson. 3 vols., London, Richard Phillips, 1806. [*Guide to Best Fiction*: Ingpen: Pickering.]

—— Woman and her Master. 2 vols., London, Bryce, 1840. [B.M.: *Eng. Cat.*]

—— Woman; Or, Ida of Athens. By Miss Owenson. 4 vols., London, Longman, 1809. [B.M.: Ingpen: Pickering.]

—— & Sir Thomas Charles. The Book without a Name. With a portrait. 2 vols., London, Henry Colburn, 1841. [B.M.: H. B. Copinger: Kyrle Fletcher.]

Moriarty, Denis Ignatius (*see* GRANT, John O'Brien).

Moriarty, Henrietta Maria. Brighton in an Uproar: A Novel, founded on Facts. 2 vols., London, Henry Colburn, 1811. [*Eng. Cat.* : *Quarterly Review*.]

—— Crim. Con. A novel, founded on facts. 2 vols., London, 1818. [Allibone: B.M.]

Morier, James Justinian. Abel Allnutt. A Novel. By the Author of " Hajji Baba," " Zohrab the Hostage," " Ayesha," &c. 3 vols., London, Richard Bentley, 1837. [B.M.: Ingpen: Arthur Rogers.]

—— The Adventures of Hajji Baba, of Ispahan. 3 vols., London, John Murray, 1824. [B.M.: Maggs: Arthur Rogers.]

—— The Adventures of Hajji Baba, of Ispahan, in England. 2 vols., London, John Murray, 1828. [B.M.: King: Arthur Rogers.]

—— Ayesha. The Maid of Kars. By the Author of " Zohrab," " Hajji Baba," &c. 3 vols., London, Richard Bentley, 1834. [Block: B.M.: Arthur Rogers.]

—— Martin Toutround; A Frenchman in London in 1831. Translated from an unpublished French MS. London, Richard Bentley, 1849. [Allibone: B.M.: *Eng. Cat.*]

—— The Mirza. 3 vols., London, Richard Bentley, 1841. [B.M.: Kyrle Fletcher: T. Thorp.]

—— An Oriental Tale, By The Author of Hajji Baba. Printed for sale in aid of the funds of the Sussex County Hospital. With a frontispiece after the author's drawing. Brighton, W. Leppard, [1839]. [B.M.: Arthur Rogers: W. T. Spencer.]

—— Zohrab the Hostage. By the Author of " Hajji Baba." 3 vols., London, Richard Bentley, 1832. [Blackwell: B.M.: Arthur Rogers.]

Morley, G. T. Unnatural Uncle. 2 vols., London, 1805. [Allibone.]

Morley, Henry. The Dream of the Lilybell, tales and poems; with translations of the " Hymns to Night " from the German of Novalis and Jean Paul's

" Death of an Angel." London, Sherwood, 1845. [Allibone: B.M.: *Eng. Cat.*]

Morrington, Isabella. Cottage of Merlin Vale; a Novel. 1809. [Allibone.]

Morris, Peter. Peter's Letters to His Kinsfolk. With a portrait. 3 vols., Edinburgh, William Blackwood, 1819. [B.M.: Kyrle Fletcher: T. Thorp.]

Mortimer, Edward. Montoni, or the Confessions of the Monk of Saint Benedict. A romance. 4 vols., London, 1808. [B.M.]

Mortimer, Frances Clare Adeline (*see* COXE).

Mortimer Delmar; And Highfield Tower. Tales By the Author of " Conrad Blessington." 3 vols., London, Saunders and Otley, 1838. [B.M.]

Mortimers (The), or The Vale of Machynllaeth. 3 vols., London, R. P. Moore, 1828. [B.M.]

Morton, A. The Charmed Scarf. A Tale. London, Romancist and Novelists' Library, 1841. [B.M.: Ingpen.]

Moser, Joseph. The Hermit of Caucasus, An Oriental Romance. 2 vols., 1796. [Blackwell: *New Ann. Reg.*]

—— Moral Tales: consisting of the Reconciliation, Clementia and Malitia, Charles and Maria, the Best Heart in the World. London, 1797. [B.M.: *New Ann. Reg.*]

—— Tales and Romances, of Ancient and Modern Times. 5 vols., London, T. Hurst. 1800. [Baker's Bookshop: Pickering.]

—— Turkish Tales. 2 vols., London, William Lane, 1794. [*New Ann. Reg.*: Blakey.]

Moss, Misses C. and M. The Romance of Jewish History. 3 vols., London, Saunders and Otley, 1840. [B.M.: Kyrle Fletcher: Lib. of Congress.]

—— Tales Of Jewish History. 3 vols., London, Miller & Field, 1843. [B.M.]

Moss-Troopers. A Border Tale. By the Author of Bannockburn, &c. 3 vols., London, A. K. Newman, 1826. [Baker's Bookshop: B.M.: *Quarterly Review*.]

Mosse, Henrietta Rouviere. Arrivals from India; or Time's a great Master. A novel. 4 vols., London, Printed at the Minerva Press, for A. K. Newman, 1812. [*New Monthly Mag.*: Publisher's advert.: Blakey.]

—— The Blandfords; or, Fate and Fortune. A Novel. 4 vols., London, A. K. Newman, 1829. [B.M.]

—— A Bride and No Wife. A Novel. 4 vols., London, Printed at the Minerva Press for A. K. Newman, 1817. [B.M.: *New Monthly Mag.*]

—— Craigh-Melrose Priory; Or, Memoirs Of the Mount Linton Family. A Novel. By a Lady. 4 vols., London, C. Chapple, 1815. [B.M.: *New Monthly Mag.*]

—— A Father's Love And A Woman's Friendship; Or, The Widow and her Daughters. A Novel. 5 vols., London,

A. K. Newman, 1825. [B.M.: *Edin. Mag.*]

Mosse, Henrietta Rouviere. Gratitude; and Other Tales. 3 vols., London, A. K. Newman, 1826. [B.M.: *Edin. Mag.*]

—— A Peep at Our Ancestors. An historical romance. 4 vols., With a frontispiece. London, Lane, Newman, 1807. [B.M.: Blakey: Saintsbury's *Eng. Novel.*]

—— Woman's Wit & Man's Wisdom; Or, Intrigue. A Novel. 4 vols., London, A. K. Newman, 1827. [B.M.]

Most Delectable History of Reynard the Fox (The), And of his son Reynardine. A revised version of an old romance. From the edition of 1701, with an Introduction. 1844. [Ingpen.]

Mother Bunch's Closet Newly Broke Open. Containing, Rare Secrets of Art & Nature, Tried and Experienced By Learned Philosophers, and Recommended to all Ingenious Young Men and Maids. Teaching them, in a natural Way, how to get good Wives and Husbands. By our loving Friend Poor Tom, for the King, a Lover of Mirth, but a Hater of Treason. Part the First. With woodcuts. London, Printed and Sold in Aldermary Church Yard, [1750 ?]. [B.M.]

Mother Bunch's Fairy Tales. Published for the Amusement of all those Masters and Misses who by Duty to their Parents, and Obedience to their Superiors, Aim at Becoming Great Lords and Ladies. With plates. London, F. Newbery, 1773. [Arthur Rogers.]

Mother-in-Law; Or the Innocent Sufferer. Interspersed with the Uncommon and Entertaining Adventures of Mr. Hervey Faulconer. 2 vols., London, F. Noble, 1757. [Ingpen.]

Motherless Mary. A Tale shewing that goodness even in poverty is sure to meet its proper reward. With 6 engravings. London, J. Harris, 1818. [Court Bk. Shop.]

Mother's Gift (The); or, a Present for Little Children who are good. 1770. [*Camb. Hist. Eng. Lit.*]

Motley, James. Tales of the Cymry; with notes illustrative and explanatory. London, Longman, 1848. [B.M.]

Mouhy, Charles de Fieux, Chevalier de (*see* DE MOUHY).

Mouldy, Malachi. Stonehenge; Or, The Romans in Britain. A Romance of the Days of Nero. 3 vols., London, Richard Bentley, 1842. [B.M.: Ingpen.: T. D. Webster.]

Mountain Chief (The); or, The Descendant of William Tell. 4 vols., 1810. [*Quarterly Review.*]

Mountain Hermit (The); or, the History of Solitary Simon. Newcastle, [1810 ?]. [B.M.]

Mountford, William. Martyria: a Legend wherein are contained homilies, conversations and incidents of the reign of Edward the Sixth. London, J. Chapman, 1845. [B.M.: Lib. of Congress.]

Mountjoye, F. L. C. D'Aveyro; or, The Head in the Glass Cage. A Novel. Translated from the French by F. L. C. Montjoye. 4 vols., London, 1803. [T. D. Webster.]

—— Mount Pausillipo. 5 vols., 1803. [Allibone.]

Mouse-Trap (The). 2 vols., 1794. [*New Ann. Reg.*]

Mower, Arthur. The Welch Mountaineer. 2 vols., London, B. Crosby, 1811. [B.M.: *Quarterly Review*: Stonehill.]

—— The White Cottage. A Tale. Edinburgh, William Blackwood; and T. Cadell and W. Davies, London, 1817. [B.M.: *Quarterly Review*: Sexton.]

—— Zulneida: A Tale of Sicily. By the Author of The White Cottage. 3 vols., London, John Macrone, 1837. [B.M.]

Mozeen, Thomas. Young Scarron. Dublin, Sam Price and Richard Wilson, 1752. [B.M.: Ingpen: Tregaskis.]

Mozley, Harriet. The Fairy Bower, or, the History of a Month. A tale for young people. London, John & Charles Mozley, 1841. [B.M.: *Eng. Cat.*: John Orr.]

—— The Lost Brooch; Or, The History of Another Month. A Tale for Young People by the Author of " The Fairy Bower." 2 vols., London, James Burns, 1841. [Block: B.M.]

—— Louisa, or, The Bride. London, John and Charles Mozley, 1842. [B.M.]

Mr. St. George, a true story. By John Bull. London, Printed for Citizen Lee, [1795 ?]. [B.M.]

Mrs. Cleveland, and the St. Clairs, &c. 3 vols., London, Richard Bentley, 1836. [B.M.]

—— **Maberly;** Or, The World as it will be. 3 vols., London, John Macrone, 1836. [B.M.]

—— **Wilberforce** Or The Widow and her Orphans. A Tale. 2 vols., London, Saunders and Otley, 1838. [B.M.]

Much to Blame. A Tale By a Celebrated Author. 3 vols., London, John Templeman, 1824. [B.M.]

Mudford, William. Augustus and Mary; Or, The Maid of Buttermere. A Domestic Tale. With a frontispiece. London, Printed for M. Jones, by E. M'Millan, 1803. [Court Book Shop.]

—— The Five Nights of St. Albans. 3 vols., Edinburgh, William Blackwood; and T. Cadell, London, 1829. [B.M.: Elkin Mathews: Publisher's advert.]

—— Nubilia in Search of a Husband. [Cawthorn's Catalogue, 1810.]

—— The Premier. 3 vols., London, Henry Colburn and Richard Bentley, 1831. [B.M.: T. D. Webster.]

—— Stephen Dugard. A Novel. By the Author of " Five Knights of St. Albans," etc. 3 vols., London, Richard Bentley, 1840. [B.M.: Hodgson.]

Mudford, William. Tales and Trifles, from Blackwood's and other popular magazines. 2 vols., London, W. Tegg, 1849. [B.M.]

Mudie, Robert. Glenfergus. 3 vols., Edinburgh, Oliver and Boyd, 1820. [B.M.: *Monthly Mag.: Quarterly Review.*]

Mujnoon; Or The Distracted Lover. A Tale From the Persian, 1785.

Muller, Captain Richard. Memoirs Of the Right Honorable Lord Viscount Cherington, Containing A Genuine Description Of the Government, and Manners Of the Present Portuguese. 2 vols., London, J. Johnson, 1782. [B.M.]

Mullion, Mary. The Curate's Daughter, A Tale for Young Persons. London, G. & W. B. Whittaker, 1823. [B.M.]

Mulso, Thomas. Callistus; Or, The Man of Fashion; and Sophronius; or, the Country Gentleman. In three dialogues. Dublin, Exshaw, 1769. [Stonehill.]

Munchausen at Walcheren; or a continuation of the renowned Baron's surprising travels and exploits at Walcheren, the Dardanelles, Talavera, Cintra, and the particulars of a wonderful Turtle-Feast with Sir W. . . . C . . . . when preparing to attack Flushing. London, 1811. [B.M.]

Munro, Georgina C. Charles Harcourt; Or, The Adventures of a Legatee. 3 vols., London, Richard Bentley, 1843. [B.M.]

—— The Voyage of Life. A Tale Of the Land and the Ocean. 3 vols., London, Richard Bentley, 1844. [B.M.: McLeish.]

Murder in the Wood (The). London, [1797 ?]. Cheap Repository. [B.M.]

Murdered Bride (The), or the Victim of Treachery. With plates. London, William Emans, [1820]. [H. W. Fennell.]

Murdoch, John. Pictures of the Heart, sentimentally delineated in the danger of the passions, an allegorical tale: The Adventures of a Friend of Truth, an oriental history, in two parts. The Embarrassments of Love, a novel: and The Double Disguise, a drama in two acts. 2 vols., London, 1783. [B.M.]

Murphy, Arthur (?). Isabella: or, The Memoirs of a Coquette. Dublin, James Hoey, 1761. [*I. in F.*]

Murphy, Dennis Jasper (*see* (MATURIN, Charles Robert).

Murphy, Elizabeth H. F. The Levite; Or, Scenes two hundred years ago. 3 vols., London, John Ollivier, 1845. [B.M.: *Critic.*]

Murphy, James Cavanagh. The Arabs in Spain, an Historical Romance. 2 vols., London, Churton, 1840. [Allibone: *Eng. Cat.*]

Murray, Mrs. Henry Count of Kolinski. [Cawthorn's Catalogue, 1810.]

—— A Polish Tale. London, 1810. [Allibone.]

Murray, Hon. Charles Augustus. The Prairie-Bird. 3 vols., London, Richard Bentley, 1844. [B.M.: Clarke-Hall: Elkin Mathews.]

Murray, Hamilton. Mildred Vernon; A Tale of Parisian Life In the Last days of the Monarchy. 3 vols., London, Henry Colburn, 1848. [B.M.]

Murray, Hugh. Corasmin, or, the Minister; a romance. By the author of The Swiss Emigrants. 3 vols., London, Longman, Hurst, Rees, 1814. [Blackwell: B.M.: Pickering.]

—— The Swiss Emigrants; a Tale. London, Longman and Rees, 1804. [Allibone: B.M.: G. Worthington.]

Murray, John. The Travels of the Imagination: A True Journey from Newcastle to London in a Stage Coach, with Observations upon the Metropolis by J. M. London, E. and C. Dilly, 1773. [Ingpen.]

Murray, John Fisher. The Viceroy. 3 vols., London, John Murray, 1841. [B.M.]

Musaeus, Johann Karl August. The Diverting History of Number Nip, Lord of the Giant Mountains in Germany: with the pranks with which travellers are harassed who enter his territories. London, S. Fisher, 1804. [B.M.]

—— The Enchanted Knights; or, the Chronicle of the Three Sisters. (The Demon of the Ring.) Translated [by A. Sagorski] from the German of Musaeus. In 2 parts. London, H. Cunningham, 1845. [B.M.]

—— Physiognomical Travels, Preceded by a Physiognomical Journal. Translated from the German of J. C. A. Musaeus. By Anne Plumptre. To which is prefixed, A Short Sketch of the Life and Character of the Author, By his Pupil Kotzebue. 3 vols., London, T. N. Longman, 1800. [Pickering.]

—— Popular Tales Of The Germans. Translated from the German [of J. C. A. Musaeus by William Beckford]. 2 vols., London, J. Murray, 1791. [B.M.: Huntington: Maggs.]

Musgrave, Agnes. Cicely, or the Rose of Raby. An Historical Novel. 4 vols., London, William Lane, 1795. [*New Ann. Reg.*: Blakey.]

—— The Solemn Injunction. A novel. 4 vols., London, W. Lane, 1798. [B.M.]

Musnicki, L. N. H. The Camp of the Crusaders; an historical sketch: and other tales. London, [1848 ?]. [B.M.]

—— Roxolana, the Podolian; a tale of the sixteenth century. London, [1850 ?]. [B.M.]

Mutual Attachment; or, The memoirs of Victoria de Ponty. A novel. Translated from the French. [W. Lane, 1784]. [Blakey.]

Mutability of Human Life or Memoirs of Adelaide, Marchioness of Melville. 1777. [*Eng. Lit. in Germany.*]

My Bird and My Dog. A tale for youth. By the author of The Citizen's Daughter, Idiot Heiress, &c. With a frontispiece, London, Printed at the Minerva Press for A. K. Newman & Co. 1816. [Blakey.]

My Children's Diary, or The Moral of the Passing Hour. With a frontispiece and a vignette. London, Sampson, Low, 1825. [Ingpen.]

My Grandfather Gregory. With woodcuts. London, The Religious Tract Society; and J. Nisbet, [c. 1834]. [Block.]

My Grandfather's Farm; Or, Pictures of Rural Life. Edinburgh, Oliver and Boyd; and Geo. B. Whittaker, London, 1829. [B.M.: H. H. Langley: Stonehill.]

My Old Cousin; Or, A Peep into Cochin-China. A Novel. By the Author of Romantic Facts, or which is his Wife? Veronica, or The Mysterious Stranger, &c. 3 vols., London, Printed at the Minerva Press for A. K. Newman, 1819. [B.M.: *New Monthly Mag.*: Blakey.]

My Own Story: a Tale of Old Times. With an illustration by George Petrie. Dublin, Curry, 1829. [B.M.: *I. in F.*]

My Own Times. 2 vols., 1812. [*New Monthly Mag.*]

Myrtle, Harriet (*see* MILLER, Mrs. Lydia Falconer.)

Myrtle (The); or, The effects of love. A novel. In a series of letters. By a lady. 3 vols. [W. Lane, 1785]. [Blakey].

Mysteries of Oronzo; or, The Murderer's Doom. A Romance of the Thirteenth Century. With illustrations. London, Elliot, 1841. [Stonehill.]

Mysterious Dagger (The); or, the Avengers. [London, 1842 ?]. [B.M.]

Mysterious Father, Or Trials of the Heart. A Novel. Written by a Lady. 4 vols., London, Albion Press, 1805. [Ingpen.]

Mysterious Florentine (The), a Romance. 4 vols., 1809. [*Monthly Mag.*: Cawthorn's Catalogue.]

Mysterious Foundling (The); or, The Heir Restored. In which is Included, The Adventures of a Misanthrope. With a frontispiece. London, Langley, [c. 1810]. [Stonehill.]

Mysterious Man (The). A Novel. By the Author of Ben Bradshawe; the Man without a head. 3 vols., London, T. C. Newby, 1844. [B.M.: *Tait's Edin. Mag.*]

Mysterious Novice (The): or, Convent of the Grey Penitents: Including the Memoirs of Augustus and Wilhelmina. An Original Romance. With a frontispiece. London, Arliss, 1809. [Stonehill.]

Mysterious Omen (The); or, Awful Retribution. An Original Romance. Including the Crimes of Count Caraffa, the Murderer and the Adventures of his son Leonardi, the Banditti Captain. With a frontispiece. London, Harrild, 1812. [B.M.: Stonehill.]

Mysterious Penitent (The); The Norman Chateau. A Romance. Dublin, H. Colbert, 1801. [Pickering (1st Dublin edn.).]

Mysterious Pilgrim (The); or, Fatal Duplicity. An Italian Romance. To which is added, The Hibernian Mendicant. With a frontispiece. London, Langley and Belch, 1810. [Stonehill.]

Mysterious Sisters (The), a Spanish Romance. 2 vols., London, J. F. Hughes. [Publisher's advert, 1806.]

Mystery upon Mystery, a tale of earlier times. By the author of the Baron de Falkenheim. With a frontispiece. 4 vols., London, Minerva Press, 1808. [B.M.: Blakey.]

Mystic Castle (The); or, Orphan heir. A romance. By the author of The wanderer of the Alps. [By Mr. Singer]. 2 vols., London, William Lane, 1796. [Blakey.]

Mystic Tower (The); or, Villainy Punished. A Romance. With a frontispiece. London, Kaygill, [c. 1799]. [Stonehill.]

Mystic Cottager of Chamouny (The). A Novel. 2 vols., London, William Lane, 1794. [*New Ann. Reg.*: Blakey.]

Nabob (The). A novel. In a series of letters. By a lady. 2 vols., London, William Lane, 1785. [Blakey.]

Naish, W. (?). The Negro Slave. A tale addressed to the women of Great Britain. London, 1830. [B.M.]

Nannie and Jane; or, the World no Friend. London, 1823. [B.M.]

Napier, Mrs. C. Moral Stories for Children. London, Bowdery and Kerby, 1819.

Napier, Elizabeth. The Nursery Governess, by E. Napier, published after her death by her husband, Colonel C. J. Napier. London, 1834. [B.M.]

Nares, Edward. I Says, Says I; a Novel. By Thinks-I-To-Myself. 2 vols., London, J. Johnston, 1812. [B.M.: Ingpen: *Quarterly Review*.]

—— Think's-I-To-Myself. A Serio-Ludicro, Tragico-Comico, Tale, Written by Think's-I-To-Myself-Who? 2 vols., London, Sherwood, Jones, 1811. [B.M.: Arthur Rogers: Stonehill.]

Narrative (A), of the Extraordinary Adventures of four Russian Sailors. To which is added, A Droll Story of a Fisherman. Glasgow, J. & M. Robertson, 1801. [B.M.]

Narrative (A), of the Extraordinary Adventures of four Russian Sailors. To which is added the story of the King and Fairy Ring. Glasgow, [1815 ?]. [B.M.]

Narritive [*sic*] (A), of the extraordinary adventures of four Russian Sailors, who were cast away on the desert Island of East Spitzbergan, in Greenland. To which is added a description of the Island of Barbadoes. London, [1785 ?]. [B.M.]

Nathan, Eliza. Elvington.
—— Langreath, A Tale. 3 vols., London, G. and W. B. Whittaker, 1822. [Blackwell: B.M.]

Nathan, Isaac. The Southern Euphrosyne and Australian Miscellany, containing Oriental moral tales, original anecdote, and music. London, [1848 ?]. [B.M.]

National Feeling; or, The History of Fitzsimon: a Novel, with Historical and Political Remarks; by An Irishman. 2 vols., Dublin, 1821. [*I. in F.*]

Nature, A Novel. 1770. [W. Brown].

Navy at Home (The). 3 vols., London, 1831. [Maggs.]

Neale, Erskine. The Bishop's Daughter. By the Author of " The Life-Book of a Labourer." London, Routledge, 1842. [B.M.: *Eng. Cat.*]
—— The Blank Book of a Small Colleger. London, Thos. Boys, 1824. [B.M.: Kyrle Fletcher.]
—— Experiences Of a Gaol Chaplain; Comprising Recollections of Ministerial Intercourse With Criminals of various classes, With their Confessions. 3 vols., London, Richard Bentley, 1847. [B.M.]
—— Self-Sacrifice; or, the Chancellor's Chaplain. By the author of " The Bishop's Daughter," &c. &c. London, Bogue, 1844. [B.M.: *Tait's Edin. Mag.*]
—— Whychcotte of St. John's; Or, The Court, The Camp, the Quarter-Deck, And The Cloister. 2 vols., Londdon, Effingham Wilson, 1833. [B.M.: McLeish: Elkin Mathews.]

Neale, John Mason. Agnes de Tracy: a tale of the times of S. Thomas of Canterbury. Cambridge, Thomas Stevenson, 1843. [Block: B.M.: *Eng. Cat.*]
—— Ayton Priory; or, the Restored Monastery. Cambridge, Rivington, 1843. [B.M.: *Eng. Cat.*]
—— Deeds of Faith. Stories for children from Church history. London, Joseph Masters, 1850. [B.M.: *Eng. Cat.*]
—— Duchenier; or the Revolt of La Vendée. By the Author of " Stories of the Crusades." London, Joseph Masters, 1848. [B.M.: Block.]
—— Evenings at Sackville College: Legends for Children. London, Joseph Masters, N.D. [Block.]
—— Shepperton Manor: a tale of the times of Bishop Andrewes. London, Cleaver, 1845. [B.M.: *Eng. Cat.*]
—— Stories from Heathen Mythology and Greek History for the Use of Christian Children. London, Joseph Masters, 1847. [B.M.: Arthur Rogers.]
—— Stories of the Crusades. I. De Hellingley. II. The Crusade of S. Louis. London, Masters, 1846. [B.M.: *Eng. Cat.*.]
—— Victories of the Saints: stories for children from Church history. London, Cleaver, 1850. [B.M.: *Eng. Cat.*]

Neale, William Johnson. The Captain's Wife. By The Author of Cavendish, The Flying Dutchman, Naval Surgeon, Port Admiral, Etc. etc. etc. 3 vols., London, T. and W. Boone, 1842. [B.M.: T. Hutt: Maggs.]

Neale, William Johnson. Cavendish: Or, The Patrician at Sea. 3 vols., London, Henry Colburn and Richard Bentley, 1831. [B.M.: Maggs: Publisher's advert.]
—— The Flying Dutchman: A Legend of the High Seas. By the Author of "Cavendish," "Gentleman Jack," "Paul Periwinkle," &c. &c. 3 vols., London, Henry Colburn, 1839. [B.M.: T. Hutt.]
—— Gentleman Jack. A Naval Story. By The Author of " Cavendish," &c. &c. 3 vols., London, Henry Colburn, 1837. [B.M.: Maggs: Publisher's advert.]
—— Lawyers in Love. 3 vols., 1844. [Allibone.]
—— The Lost Ship; Or, The Atlantic Steamer. By the Author of " Cavendish," " The Flying Dutchman," &c. 3 vols., London, Henry Colburn, 1843. [B.M.: T. Hutt: Maggs.]
—— The Naval Surgeon. By the Author of " Cavendish," " The Flying Dutchman," " Paul Periwinkle," &c. &c. 3 vols., London, Henry Colburn, 1841. [B.M.: T. Hutt.]
—— Paul Periwinkle; or, the Pressgang. In Three Books. By the Author of " Cavendish," etc. With 40 etchings by Phiz [Hablot K. Browne]. London, Willoughby, [1841]. [Block: B.M.: Marks.]
—— The Port Admiral; A Tale of the War. By the Author of " Cavendish." 3 vols., London, Cochrane and M'Crone, 1833. [B.M.: T. Hutt: *Quarterly Review.*]
—— The Priors of Prague: By The Author of " Cavendish." 3 vols., London, John Macrone, 1836. [B.M.: Maggs: Stonehill.]
—— Will Watch. From the Autobiography of a British Officer. By The Author of Cavendish, Etc. etc. 3 vols., London, James Cochrane, 1834. [B.M.: T. Hutt: Maggs.]

Neapolitan (The), or the Test of Integrity, by Ellen of Exeter. [Anna Maria Mackenzie]. 3 vols., London, Minerva Press, 1796. [Blakey.]

Ned Delaney. Dublin, 1823. [B.M.]

Needham, Camilla. Ada A Tale. London, Saunders and Otley, 1838. [B.M.]
—— Village Annals: or, the Story of Hetty Jones. Part III. London, 1850. [B.M. (2nd edn.)]

Neele, Henry. The Romance of History. England, 3 vols., London, Edward Bull, 1828. [B.M.]

Neotetaeria; A Country Tale for London Readers; Contained in The first letter of Mr. Humphrey Blinkinsop, To his Nephew. With notes, illustrations, and a postscript. London, C. Chapple, 1812. [B.M. (2nd edn.)]

Neri, Mary Anne. The Hour of Trial: a tale. 3 vols., London, 1808. [Allibone: B.M.]

Net-Maker of Bagdad; or, The Fool and his Cousin. An Eastern Tale. With a frontispiece. London, Ann Lemoine and J. Roe, [1807]. [Ingpen.]

Network; or Thought in Idleness. London, Maunder, 1826. [B.M.: *Eng. Cat.*]

Never Wrong; or the Young Disputant, and " It was only in Fun." Tales for the Young. London, 1850. [B.M.]

New Atalantis (A). For the Year One thousand Seven hundred and Fifty-eight [1759 & 1760]. London, 1758-1760. [Stonehill.]

New British Universal Jester (The), or the Wit's Companion, containing all the Fun, Humour, and Wit which have lately flowed from the Universities, the Theatres, Country Wakes, Fairs, and all Places of Public Resort, in Town and Country, including all the Humorous Jests, Funny Jokes, Droll Adventures, Frolicksome Tales, Witty Quibbles, Merry Stories, Smart Repartees, Youthful Pranks, Irish Bulls, Wise Sayings, Facetious Puns, Clever Epigrams, Comical Epitaphs, Conundrums, Toasts, Sentiments, etc., etc., which will expel Care, drown Grief, banish the spleen, improve the Wit, Create Mirth, Entertain Company, and give the Reader a light Heart and Cheerful Countenance, the whole teaching the agreeable Art of Story-telling, and Furnishing Pieces of Wit for the Amusement and Improvement of both Sexes. With a frontispiece. Southwark, W. Kemmish, [1795]. [Pickering.]

New Care-Killer (The), Or, Exquisite Effusions of Wit and Humour, Whimsical Adventures; Laughable Tales; Curious Scenes; Droll Transactions; Extravagances in Love; and other Extraordinary Good Things. With 3 plates. Hughes, 1823. [W. T. Spencer.]

New Collection of Gothic Stories (A). Rodolpho; or, The Banditti of the Castle. The Story of Frederico; or, the Ruin of the House of Vilaineuf. Athelbert; or, The Phantom of the Castle. A Tale of Horror. The Mysterious Vision; or, Perfidy Punished; and Henry de Montmorency, A Terrific Story. With a frontispiece. London, Fisher, 1801. [Stonehill.]

New Description of Merryland (A), containing a Topographical, Geographical, and Natural History of that Country. Bath, W. Jones, 1741. [Pickering.]

New Entertaining Novelist (The). Being a selection of stories from the most approved modern authors. Glasgow, 1785. [B.M.]

New Gleaner (The); or, entertainment for the fireside: consisting of tales moral and humorous. Second Series. 2 vols., Salford, W. Cowdroy, Jun., 1809. [B.M.]

New Landlord's Tales; Or, Jedediah in the South. 2 vols., London, T. Hookham, 1825. [B.M.]

New Lodger (The). London, 1843. [B.M.]

New Modern Story Teller, or Universal Entertainer; Being a Collection of Merry, polite, grave, moral, entertaining and improving Tales, related with that Modesty so as not to offend the most delicate Ear, and at the same time calculated to inspire Mirth among all Degrees of People, of whatsoever Age, Sex, or Opinion. Each Story embellished with proper Mottos, suitable to the Subject, and moral Introductions to prepare and entertain the Minds of the Readers. Among which are The Lass's mistake in her lovers question. Justice save all. An old woman basted with butter. The merry revenge. The parson and his horned horse. An old woman the best physician. The arch methodist. The humour of the spur. The faithful dog. The positive cobler. The lucky disaster. Danger of being inquisitive. Infallible receipt to cure a drunkard. A new quirk for the lawyers. Bravery rewarded. The courageous highwayman. Double diligence, &c. &c. &c. With a frontispiece (repeated). 2 vols., London, For the Author, 1767. [B.M.: Ingpen: W. T. Spencer.]

New Monk (The), a romance. By R. S. Esq. London, William Lane, 1798. [Blakey.]

New Sylph (The), or, Guardian Angel. A Story. London, W. Lane, 1788. [Pickering.]

New Tom Thumb (The), with an account of his wonderful exploits as related by Margery Meanwell. With illustrations. London, J. Harris, 1814. [B.M.]

Newell, Richard H. Baldwin; Or, A Miser's Heir. A Serio-Comic Tale. By An Old Bachelor. 2 vols., London, Printed at the Minerva Press for A. K. Newman, 1820. [B.M.]

Newgate. A Romance. With woodcuts. London, E. Lloyd, [1847]. [B.M.: H. W. Fennell: B. Ono.]

Newman, Cardinal John Henry. Loss and Gain. London, James Burns, 1848. [Block: B.M.: *Guide to Best Fiction.*]

Newminster Abbey, or the Daughter of O'More. A novel, founded on facts and interspersed with original poetry. 2 vols., London, 1808. [B.M.: T. D. Webster.]

Newspaper Wedding (The): Or an advertisement for a husband. A Novel. Founded on incidents which arose in consequence of an advertisement that appeared in the Daily Advertiser of July 29, 1772. Including a number of letters on the subject of love and marriage. 2 vols., London, R. Snagg, 1774. [Tregaskis.]

Newton, Emma. The Modern Unbeliever. London, Simpkin, 1847. [*Critic.*]

Newton, J. H. Hofer, The Patriot of the Tyrol. An Historical Romance. By the author of " William Tell." With illustrations. London, Peirce, 1845. [B.M.: Stonehill.]

—— William Tell, The Hero of Switzerland. An Historical Romance. With illustrations. London, T. Paine, [c. 1850]. [B.M.: Stonehill.]

Newton, Rev. John. Cardiphonia; or, The Utterance of the Heart; in the Course of Real Correspondence. By the Author of " Omicron's Letters." 2 vols., London, Buckland, 1781. [B.M.: Stonehill.]

Nice Distinctions: A Tale. Dublin, Printed at the Hibernia Press for I. Cumming; and Longman, Hurst, Rees, Orme, & Brown, London, 1820. [B.M.: *I. in F.*]

Nicholai, Friedrich. The Life and Opinions of Sebaldus Nothanker. From the German of Freidrich Nicholai [by Thomas Dutton]. 3 vols., London, C. Lowndes, 1798. [*New Ann. Reg.: Pickering.*]

Nicholson, Mr. Catherine; or, The wood of Llewellyn. A descriptive tale. By the author of The Village of Martindale and Orlando and Seraphina. With a frontispiece. 2 vols. [W. Lane, 1788]. [*Minerva Press Catalogue:* Blakey.]

—— Orlando and Seraphina: a Turkish story. 2 vols., London, William Lane, 1787. [B.M.: Ingpen: *Minerva Press Catalogue*].

—— The Solitary Castle, a romance of the eighteenth century. By the author of *The Village of Martindale.* With a frontispiece. 2 vols., London, W. Lane, 1789. [B.M.: G. Worthington: Blakey.]

—— The Village of Martindale: A novel. 2 vols., London, W. Lane, 1787. [*Minerva Press Catalogue:* Blakey: W. Brown.]

Nicholson, Renton. Cockney Adventures and Tales of London Life. With 42 woodcuts. London, 1838. [B.M.: H. W. Fennell: W. T. Spencer.]

Nickleby Married. With 22 plates. London, John Williams, 1840. [Noel Broadbent.]

Nicloux, Maria Louisa. A Week's Amusement, Translated from the French of Maria Louisa Nicloux, by Adolphus William Barnes. London, C. Chapple, 1823. [B.M.]

Niebuhr, Barthold Georg. Stories from Greek History: in a series of tales related to his son, by B. G. Niebuhr. Translated from the German. London, D. Nutt, 1843. [B.M.]

Niemcewicz, Julius Ursinus. Levi and Sarah; Or The Jewish Lovers. A Polish Tale, By Julius Ursinus Niemcewicz. Translated from the German Edition, With A Preface and Notes, By the Editor. London, John Murray, 1830. [B.M.: *New Monthly Mag.:* T. D. Webster.]

Nieritz, Carl Gustav. The Foundling, or the School of Life. Edinburgh, 1850. [B.M.]

Night Adventurer (The); or, the Palaces and Dungeons of the Heart. A Romance. With woodcuts. London, Edward Lloyd, 1846. [B.M.: B. Ono.]

Night Hag (The); or, Saint Swithin's Chair: A Romance, on which is founded The Popular Drama Now performing with unbounded Applause At Astley's Amphitheatre. With a frontispiece. London, J. Bailey, N.D. [Court Book Shop.]

Night Watch (The); or, Tales of the Sea. 2 vols., London, Henry Colburn, 1828. [B.M.: Stonehill.]

Nina, an Icelandic Tale, for Young Persons. With a frontispiece. London, J. Harris, 1821. [Publisher's advert.]

Nixon, Captain. The Ramble of Philo, and his Man Sturdy. 2 vols., London, W. Lane, 1788. [B.M.: *Minerva Press Catalogue:* Blakey.]

No Enthusiasm; A tale Of the present times. 2 vols., London, Francis Westley, 1822. [B.M.: Storey.]

No Virtue Without Struggle: No Struggle without Reward. With a vignette. London, James Burns,]1849]. [B.M.]

Nobility Run Mad, or Raymond and His Three Wives. A Novel. By the author of the Sailor Boy and Soldier Boy. 4 vols., London, Minerva Press, 1802. [Stonehill: Blakey: B.M.]

Noble Cornutos (The). Being a series of tales for the amusement of the fashionable world. 2 vols., London, 1808.

Noble Enthusiast (The); a modern romance. 3 vols., London, William Lane, 1792. [Blakey.]

Noble Wanderers (The). A Novel. 2 vols., London, Minerva Press, 1802. [Stonehill.]

Nocturnal Revels, Or History of King's Place, and other Modern Nunneries. 2 vols., 1779. [W. Brown.]

Nominal Husband (The): or, Distress'd Innocence. A true secret history, taken from an Old Saxon Manuscript. London, 1750. [B.M.]

Nooth, Charlotte. Eglantine; Or, the Family of Fortescue. A Novel. 2 vols., London, A. J. Valpy, 1816. [B.M.: *New Monthly Mag.*]

Norah Dalrymple, a woman's story. 3 vols., London, T. C. Newby, 1850. [B.M.: *Eng. Cat.*]

Norah Toole, and other tales, illustrative of national and domestic manners. By a Lady. London, 1844. [B.M.]

Norgate, T. S. Essays, Tales and Poems. Norwich, 1795. [B.M.: Ingpen.]

Norman, Elizabeth. Child of Woe, 3 vols., 1789. [Allibone: W. Brown.]

Norman Abbey; A Tale of Sherwood

Forest. By a Lady. 3 vols., 1832. [James Glaisher: *Metropolitan Mag.*]

Normanby, Constantine Henry Phipps, Marquis of. The Contrast, By the Author of " Matilda," " Yes and No," &c. &c. 3 vols., London, Henry Colburn & Richard Bentley, 1832. [B.M.: Elkin Mathews: *Quarterly Review.*]

—— The English at Home. By the Author of " The English in Italy," &c. 3 vols., London, 1830. [*New Monthly Mag.*: T. D. Webster.]

—— The English in France. By the Author of " The English in Italy." 3 vols., London, Saunders and Otley, 1828. [B.M.: Pickering.]

—— The English in Italy: A Novel. 3 vols., London, Saunders & Otley, 1825. [B.M.: Ingpen: Pickering.]

—— Historiettes, or Tales of Continental Life. By the Author of " The English in Italy." 3 vols., London, Saunders and Otley, 1827. [*Blackwood's Edin. Mag.*: Block: Pickering.]

—— Matilda; A Tale of the Day. London, Henry Colburn, 1825. [B.M.: Ingpen: *Quarterly Review.*]

—— The Prophet of St. Paul's; a Novel. [Allibone.]

—— Yes and No: A Tale of the Day. By the Author of " Matilda." 2 vols., London, Henry Colburn, 1828. [B.M.: Ingpen: Arthur Rogers.]

Norrington, Or the Memoirs of a Peer. London, Hurst, Chance, 1830. [Baker's Bookshop: B.M.: Holland.]

Norris, Mrs. Euphronia, or the Captive. 3 vols., 1810. [*Monthly Mag.*]

—— Second Love; or, the Way to be Happy. A Novel. 2 vols., London, 1805. [T. D. Webster.]

North, William. Anti-Coningsby; Or, The new generation grown old. By an Embryo, M.P. 2 vols., London, T. C. Newby, 1844. [B.M.: Clarke-Hall.]

—— Anti-Punch; Or The Toy-Shop in Fleet-Street. A Romance of the Nineteenth Century. By the Author of " Anti-Coningsby "—" The Impostor, or Born without a Conscience "—"Zadora," &c. With woodcuts. London, E. Dipple, 1847. [B.M.]

—— The City of the Jugglers; Or, Free-Trade in Souls. A Romance of the " Golden " Age. With 4 plates by F. H. T. Bellew. London, H. J. Gibbs, 1850. [Block: B.M.: H. B. Copinger.]

—— The Imposter; Or, Born without a conscience. By the Author of " Anti-Coningsby." With illustrations. 3 vols., London, T. C. Newby, 1845. [B.M.: *Critic.*]

Northern Cottage (The); or the effect of Bible reading. By P.D.H. Dublin, Bentham and Hardy, 1827. [B.M.]

Northmore, Thomas. Memoirs of Planetes; Or, A Sketch of the Laws and Manners of Makar. By Phileleutherus Devoniensis. 1795. [Arthur Rogers.]

Norton, Hon. Caroline Elizabeth Sarah. The Wife And Woman's Reward. 3 vols., London, Saunders & Otley, 1835. [B.M.]

Norval and Julia, or, the Mysterious Rock. Where Julia's Mother was Immured for more than Ten Years by her Cruel Husband. A Scottish Tale. London, T. and R. Hughes, N.D. [Block.]

Noted History or Mother Grim [The], commonly called Goody Grim's witty tales. [Newcastle ?], [1780 ?]. [B.M.]

Notoriety; or, Fashionables Unveiled. 3 vols., 1812. [*Quarterly Review.*]

Nott, J. Sappho. After a Greek Romance. London, 1803. [Baker's Bookshop.]

Novello, Mary Sabilla. A Day In Stowe Gardens. London, J. & H. L. Hunt, 1825. [B.M.]

Nugent, George Grenville, Lord. Legends Of the Library at Lilies, By the Lord and Lady there. 2 vols., London, Longman, Rees, Orme, Brown, Green, and Longman, 1832. [B.M.: H. B. Copinger: Sotheran.]

Nun and Her Daughter (The); or, Memoirs of the Courville Family. A novel. [By Helen Craik]. 4 vols., London, Lane, Newman, and Co., 1805. [B.M.: Blakey: *Minerva Press Catalogue.*]

Nun of St. Agatha. An Historical Romance of the Sixteenth Century. 3 vols., London, A. K. Newman, 1830. [B.M.: *New Monthly Mag.*]

Nun [The]; or, the Adventures of the Marchioness of Beauville. London, J. Roson, 1771. [Court Bk. Shop.]

Nun (The); or, Memoirs of Angelique; an interesting tale. Also the Adventures of Henry de Montmorency; a tale. To which is added, the Surprising Life of Mrs. Dholson, London, Tegg & Castleman, [1803]. [B.M.]

Nuñes, Leonardo. Edward and Frances; an historical tale, illustrative of some remarkable events relative to English History, in the sixteenth century. Translated from the Spanish by J. Willasey. Lancaster, 1829. [B.M.]

Nunnery for Coquettes (The). London, T. Lowndes, 1771. [B.M.: Pickering.]

Nursery Tales; consisting of The Wasp in the Peach, Cleanliness is next to Godliness, The Tale-Bearer. London, [1840]. [B.M.]

Oakcliffe Hall; or, The Fatal Effects of Feudal Quarrels. A Tale of the Fifteenth Century. London, Cole, [*c.* 1820]. [Stonehill.]

Oakley, Peregrine. Aureus; Or, the Life and Opinions of a Sovereign. Written by Himself. London, George Wightman, 1824. [Block: B.M.: Ingpen.]

Observant Pedestrian (The), or a

Donkey Tour to Brighton. 3 vols., London, 1815. [*New Monthly Mag.*]

Observant; or, Traits of the heart, in a solitary tour from Caernarvon to London: by the author of *The Mystic Cottager*. 2 vols., London, William Lane, 1795. [Blakey.]

Oby Sedgwick, or Country Conversations. By Epsilon. 1812. [*New Monthly Mag.*]

Ocean Child (The). A Domestic Tale. By the Author of "Clarisse," "Temptation," "Paul the Reckless," &c. With woodcuts. London, E. Lloyd, [1846]. [B.M.: H. W. Fennell: B. Ono.]

O'Connor, E., (Attributed to). Almeria Belmore. 1789. [*Eng. Lit. in Germany.*]

Odd Moments; Or, Time Beguiled. With a frontispiece by S. Freeman after H. Corbould. London, Thomas Boys, 1825. [B.M.]

Oddest of all Oddities (The); being a choice collection of all the odd tales, verses, adventures, that have been spoken, sung, and recited by various Odd Fellows. Compiled by Oddicurio. London, 1820. [B.M.]

O'Donovan, John. The Banquet of Dun Na n-Gedh, and the Battle of Magh Rath. With a translation and notes by John O'Donovan. Dublin, Irish Archaeological Society, 1842. [B.M.: *I. in F.*]

Oehlenschläger, Adam Gottlob. Wayland Smith. With the amplified Legend by Oehlenschlager. 1847. [B.M.: *Guide to Best Fiction.*]

Officer's Daughter (The); or a Visit to Ireland in 1790. By the Daughter of a Captain in the Navy. 4 vols., 1810. [*Quarterly Review.*]

Officer's Daughters, or Emily and Kitty; in words of three syllables. London, Miller [*c.* 1820]. [Nat. Mag. Co.]

Offspring of Fancy. 2 vols., 1778. [W. Brown.]

O'Flanagan, Theophilus. Deirdri, or, The Lamentable Fate of the Sons of Usnach. Dublin, John Barlow, for the Gaelic Society of Dublin, 1808. [B.M.: *I. in F.*]

Ogle, Nathaniel. Mariamne: an historical novel of Palestine. 3 vols., London, G. B. Whittaker, 1825. [B.M.: McLeish.]

O'Halloran; or the Insurgent Chief. An Irish historical Novel of 1798. 1825. [*Edin. Mag.: Quarterly Review.*]

O'Keefe, Adelaide. Dudley. 3 vols., London, Printed by Strahan and Spottiswoode, for Longman, Hurst, Rees, Orme, and Brown, 1819. [Backus: B.M.: Publisher's advert.]

—— Llewellin, A Tale. 3 vols., London, C. Cawthorn, 1799. [B.M.: Stonehill.]

—— Patriarchal Times; Or, The Land of Canaan: A Figurate History. In Seven Books. Comprising Interesting Events, Incidents, and Characters, Founded on The Holy Scriptures. 2 vols., London, Gale and Curtis, 1811. [B.M.: Pickering.]

O'Keefe, Adelaide. Zenobia, Queen of Palmyra; A Narrative, Founded on History. By the Author of Patriarchal Times. 2 vols., London, for J. Debrett; and F. C. and J. Rivington, 1814. [Court Book Shop: Dobell: Ingpen.]

Old Castle (The); or, the Forty Knights and the Fair Penitent. A romance. London, [1810 ?]. [B.M.]

Old Daddy Gander's Fairy Tales. . . . The Bleeding Finger, etc. Front. Lond. 1804. [Murray Hill.]

Old Earl and His Young Wife (The), 3 vols., London, Richard Bentley, 1841. [B.M.]

Old Heads Upon Young Shoulders. [*Progress of Romance.*]

Old Oak Chest (The); or, a Book a great Treasure. By the author of " Charlie's Discoveries." London, Harvey, [1840 ?]. [B.M.]

Old Roger Bond. With woodcuts. London, Religious Tract Society, 1836. [B.M.]

Old Times and New; or, Sir Lionel and his Protégée. A Novel. 4 vols., London, Printed at the Minerva Press, for A. K. Newman, 1812. [*New Monthly Mag.*: Publisher's advert.: Blakey.]

Old Times Revived; a Romantic Story of the Ninth Age. By Eyestas. 4 vols., 1809. [*Monthly Mag.*]

Old Travelling Woman (The), Nanny Ford. London, 1843 [B.M.].

Old Wives' Tales. London, F. C. and J. Rivington, 1821. [B.M.]

Oliphant, Margaret. Merkland. By the Author of Margaret Maitland. 3 vols., London, Henry Colburn, 1850. [B.M.: *Eng. Cat.*]

—— Passages in the Life of Mrs. Margaret Maitland of Sunnyside. Written by herself. 3 vols., London, Henry Colburn, 1849. [B.M.: *Chambers' Cyclop. Eng. Lit.*: Holland.]

Olivia, or, the Orphan. A tale. By a Lady of Distinction. 2 vols., London, M. Iley, 1820. [B.M.]

Ollier, Charles. Altham and his Wife. A Domestic Tale. London, C. & J. Ollier, 1818. [B.M.: *New Monthly Mag.*]

—— Ferrers. A Romance of the Reign of George the Second. 3 vols., London, Richard Bentley, 1842. [B.M.]

—— Inesilla, Or, The Tempter, A Romance; With other Tales. London, E. Lloyd; and William Blackwood, Edinburgh, 1824. [B.M.]

O'Neill, Mrs. The Bondman. A Story of the Times of Wat Tyler. London, Smith Elder, 1833. [B.M.: *Eng. Cat.*: Arthur Rogers.]

Onesimus; Or, the Run-away servant converted. A True Story: Shewing What a wonderful Improvement in his Condition Onesimus experienced after he became a Christian. To which is added An affectionate Address to all those unhappy Persons, both Men and Women, who, like Onesimus, have left their Home and have got into any bad Way of living, and who have also a Mind to hear how they may get out. With a woodcut. London, J. Marshall, and R. White, [1796]. Cheap Repository. Sunday Reading. [B.M.: Court Bk. Shop.]

Only Child (The); or Portia Bellenden. A Tale. London, 1821. [T. D. Webster.]

Opie, Amelia. Adeline Mowbray, Or the Mother and Daughter: A Tale. 3 vols., London, Longman, Hurst, Rees, & Orme; and A Constable, Edinburgh, 1805. [Court Bk. Shop: Ingpen: McLeish.]

—— Dangers of Coquetry. A Novel. 2 vols., London, W. Lane, 1790. [Blakey.]

—— Detraction Displayed. London, Longman, Rees, Orme, Brown, and Green; and S. Wilkin, Norwich, 1828. [B.M.: Ingpen: Arthur Rogers.]

—— The Father and Daughter. A Tale in Prose, With an Epistle from the " Maid of Corinth to her Lover," and Other Poetical Pieces. London, Longman, Hurst, Rees, and Orme, 1801. [*Eng. Lit. in Germany*: Publisher's advert.]

—— Happy Faces; or, benevolence and selfishness, and The Revenge. London, S. O. Beeton, [1830 ?]. [B.M.]

—— Illustrations of Lying, in all its Branches. 2 vols., London, Longman, Hurst, Rees, Orme, Brown, & Green, 1825. [B.M.: Arthur Rogers: Stonehill.]

—— Madeline, A Tale. 2 vols., London, Longman, Hurst, Rees, Orme, & Brown, 1822. [Birrell & Garnett: B.M.: Arthur Rogers.]

—— New Tales. 4 vols., London, Longman, Hurst, Rees, Orme, and Brown, 1818. [Block: B.M.: Ingpen.]

—— Simple Tales. 4 vols., London, Longman, Hurst, Rees, Orme, and Brown, 1806. [Ingpen: Publisher's advert.: G. Worthington.]

—— Tales of the Heart. 4 vols., London, Longman, Hurst, Rees, Orme, and Brown, 1820. [Block: B.M.: Arthur Rogers.]

—— Tales of the Pemberton Family; for the use of children. With illustrations. London, 1825. [B.M.]

—— Tales of Real Life. 3 vols., London, Longman, Hurst, Rees, Orme, and Brown, 1813. [B.M.: *Eng. Cat.*: Arthur Rogers.]

—— Temper, Or Domestic Scenes. A Tale. 3 vols., London, Longman, Hurst, Rees, Orme, and Brown, 1812. [Allibone: B.M.: *Quarterly Review.*]

—— Valentine's Eve. 3 vols., London, Longman, Hurst, Rees, Orme, and

Brown, 1816. [B.M.: Pickering: *Quarterly Review.*]

Opie, Amelia. A Wife's Duty. A Tale. London, Grove, 1847. [Ingpen.]

Oppressed Captive; Being an historical novel, deduced from the distresses of real life, in an impartial and candid account of the unparallel'd sufferings of Caius Silius Nugenius, now under confinement in the Fleet Prison, at the suit of an implacable and relentless parent. 1757. [Dobell.]

Orange Girl of Venice (The). A Romance. With woodcuts. London, E. Lloyd, [*c.* 1847]. [B. Ono: Stonehill.]

Ordeal (The). A novel. 3 vols., London, Gale, Curtis & Fenner. 1813. [B.M.]

Order and Disorder. A Tale, Recommended to the Perusal of all Little Girls who wish to be Neat, Notable, and Industrious. With a frontispiece. 1825. [Arthur Rogers: Renier.]

Orderson, J. W. Creoleana; Or, Social and Domestic Scenes and Incidents in Barbados in Days of Yore. London, Saunders and Otley, 1842. [B.M.: *Eng. Cat.*: Lib. of Congress.]

Oriental Tales, Collected from an Arabian Manuscript in the Library of the King of France. With woodcuts. 2 vols., London, 1745. [Lowndes.]

Oriental Wanderings; Or, The Fortunes of Felix. A Romance. By T. E. 3 vols., London, A. K. Newman, 1824. [B.M.]

Original Anecdotes, Or the History of Haroun Alrachid. 2 vols., Dublin, 1764. [Dobell.]

Original Stories and Anecdotes, through which are conveyed a mother's observations to her children, &c. London, 1808. [B.M.]

Original Tales for Children. 2 vols., London, 1827. [B.M.]

Original Tales, Histories, Essays and Translations. By different hands. Edinburgh, 1785. [B.M.]

Original Tales; or, true stories for my little grandchildren. London, Ward, 1849. [B.M. (3rd edn.)]

Orlebar, Mrs. Cuthbert. Cinderella: a fairy tale. By the author of " Harry and Walter." 1848. [B.M.]

Ormsby, Anne. Memoirs of a family in Swisserland: founded on facts. 4 vols., London, 1802. [B.M.]

—— The Soldier's Family; or, Guardian Genii. A romance. 4 vols., London, B. Crosby, 1807. [Allibone: B.M.]

Orphan Heiress of Sir Gregory (The). An Historical Fragment of the last Century. London, Sampson, Low, 1799. [Fletcher: *New Ann. Reg.*]

Orphan of Bollenbach (The), or Polycarp the Adventurer. 1797. [*New Ann. Reg.*]

Orphan of Nepaul (The), A Tale of Hindustan. London, Saunders and Otley, 1840. [B.M.]

Orphan (The); or, the entertaining history

of little Goody Goosecap by Toby Teachem. London, John Marshall, [1786 ?]. [B.M.]

Orphan (The); a romance. By Mootoo. London, A. Hall, 1850. [B.M.]

Orphan Sisters (The): a tale founded on facts. By the author of Memoir of Mary Ann P——. London, 1822. [B.M.]

Orphan's Choice (The): a Tale. By E * * * * *. Author of "The Cousins." London, 1830. [B.M.]

Orphans of Llangloed (The). A modern tale. By the author of Lusignan. 3 vols., London, Printed at the Minerva Press, for Lane and Newman, 1802. [Blakey.]

Orrery, Roger Boyle, Earl of. Parthenissa, that most fam'd Romance, the Six Parts Compleat. London, 1776. [Blackwell.]

O'Ruarc: an Irish Tale. Dublin, Milliken, 1832. [*I. in F.*]

Osborne, Fanny. The Voice of Many Waters: a tale for young people. London, E. Wilson, 1848. [B.M.: *Eng. Cat.*]

O'Shaughnessy, P. The Miser's Fate. A Romance. With woodcuts. London, G. Purkess, [1848]. [B.M.: *B. Ono.*]

Osier Bed at Camberwell (The): A Tale of Mystery! Including The Trial, Confession, and Execution Of James Greenacre, For the Murder of Hannah Brown; And of Sarah Gale, Who was Convicted and Transported for Life as an Accessory. With illustrations. London, John Saunders, N.D. [Court Bk. Shop.]

Osmond, J. S. Gil Blas Corrected; divested of offensive passages. 4 vols., London, 1798. [Allibone.]

Osmyn the Unknown. With illustrations. London, E. Dipple, 1847. [Publisher's advert.]

Ospringe, Emily. Contemplation, Cowardice, & Vicissitude, Interesting Tales for the Amusement and Instruction of the Young. With illustrations. London, Edward Lacey, N.D. [Block.]

Oswald Castle, or Memoirs of Lady Sophia Woodville. By a Lady. Dublin, 1789. [Arthur Rogers.]

Oswick, The Bold Outlaw. A Tale of the eighth century. London, T. Hurst, 1802. [B.M.]

O'Tara, Mac Erin. Thomas Fitz-Gerald The Lord of Offaley. A Romance of the Sixteenth Century. Being the first of a projected series illustrative of The History of Ireland. 3 vols., London, A. K. Newman, 1825. [B.M.]

Ottawah, The Last Chief of the Red Indians of Newfoundland. London, E. Appleyard, 1848. [Publishers' advert.: Stonehill.]

Ottley, Thomas Henry. The English in India. By the Author of "Pandurang Hari," and "The Zenana." 3 vols., London, W. Simpkin and R. Marshall, 1828. [B.M.]

—— Rustum Khan: or Fourteen Nights'

Entertainment at the Shah Bhag, or Royal Gardens at Ahmedabad. 3 vols., London, Pubd. for the Author by W. Sams, 1831. [Elkin Mathews.]

Oulton, Walley C. The Wonderful Story Teller or New Pocket Library of Agreeable Entertainment. Consisting Entirely of a Great Variety of Valuable Articles Not included in the Wonderful Magazine: Containing A Miscellaneous Collection of Remarkable Stories, Surprising Narratives, Wonderful Occurences, Singular Events, Whimsical Tales, Striking Anecdotes, Odd Sayings, Supernatural Visions, Absurd Characters, Extraordinary Memoirs, &c. &c. &c. in the Wonderful Phenomena of Nature. Dedicated to the Numerous Purchasers of the Wonderful Magazine, and the Public at large. With a frontispiece. London, [*c.* 1800]. [T. D. Webster.]

Our Own Times. With a woodcut. London, Houlston, N.D. No. 30 of Houlston's Series of Tracts. [Block.]

Ouseley, Sir William. The Bakhtyar Nameh, or Story of Prince Bakhtyar and the Ten Viziers; a Series of Persian Tales. From a Manuscript in the Collection of Sir William Ouseley. London, 1801. [McLeish.]

Out of Town; Or, The Recess. Containing Passages of the Life and Adventures of Arthur Melmont. 3 vols., London, Edward Churton, 1835. [B.M.]

Outcast (The); a Story of the Modern Reformation. Dublin, Curry, 1831. [*I. in F.*]

Outline, Oliver. New Canterbury Tales; or the Glories of the Garrison. London, Henry Colburn, 1811. [B.M.: Publisher's advert.: *Quarterly Review.*]

Outlines of Truth. London, Hatchard, 1825. [*Edin. Mag.: Eng. Cat.*]

Outsiders of Society (The); Or, the Wild Beauties of London. London, 1843. [H. W. Fennell.]

Owenson, Sydney (*see* MORGAN, Sydney, Lady).

Oxenford, John, and **Feiling,** C. A. Tales from the German, comprising specimens from the most celebrated authors. Translated by J. Oxenford and C. A. Feiling. London, Chapman and Hall, 1844. [B.M.: *Eng. Cat.*: Lib. of Congress.]

Paalzow, Henriette von (*see* VON PAALZOW).

* * * * **Packet Broke-Open** (The); or, a letter from Miss Blandy in the shades below, to Captain Cranstoun in his exile above, etc. London, M. Cooper, 1752. [B.M.]

Paddy and Thomas: a conversation between two Irishmen, with an interesting account of what happened to Thomas. London, [1810 ?]. [B.M.]

Paget, Eliza. Ellen. London, 1838. [Allibone.]

Paget, Eliza. Self-Dependence. A Tale. With a frontispiece. London, Darton and Harvey, 1838. [B. M.: Ingpen.]
—— The Way of Peace. a tale. Derby, 1829. [B.M.]

Paget, Francis Edward. Caleb Kniverton, the Incendiary; a Tale. Oxford, 1833. [Allibone: B.M.]
—— The Hope of the Katzekopfs, a Fairy Tale by William Churne of Staffordshire. Rugeley, 1844. [Ian Colvin.]
—— Owlet of Owlestone Edge. 1837. [Allibone.]
—— The Pageant; or, Pleasure and its Price. A Tale of the upper Ranks of Society. London, 1843. [T. D. Webster.]
—— Tales of the Village. 3 vols., 1840-1841. [Allibone: B.M.]
—— Tales of the Village Children. 2 vols., 1843-1844. [Allibone: Ian Colvin.]
—— The Warden of Berkingholt; or, Rich and Poor. Oxford, Joseph Masters, 1843. [B.M.: *Eng. Cat.*]

Palace of Enchantment (The), or Entertaining and Instructive fairy tales: containing Fortunio Perfect love Princess Rosetta White Mouse Princess Vereneta, Florio and Florello Golden Bough Queen and country girl Wonderful wand King and fairy ring Princess Fair Star, and Prince Chery. With 3 illustrations, London, W. Lane, 1788. [Blakey.]

Palais Royal (The). An Historical Romance. By the Author of " Henri Quatre; or, the Days of the League." 3 vols., London, Henry Colburn, 1844. [B.M.]

Palmer, Alicia Tyndal. The Daughters Of Isenberg: A Bavarian Romance. 4 vols., London, Lackington, Allen, 1810. [B.M.: Ingpen: *Quarterly Review.*]
—— The Husband and the Lover; an Historical Moral Romance. 3 vols., 1809. [Allibone: *Monthly Mag.*]
—— The Sons of Altringham, a Novel. 3 vols., London, Lackington, Allen, 1811. [Allibone: B.M.: *Quarterly Review.*]

Palmer, Charlotte. Female Stability: Or, the History Of Miss Belville. In a Series of Letters. 5 vols., London, F. Newbery, 1780. [B.M.: *Eng. Lit. in Germany.*]

Palmer, John. The Haunted Cavern: A Caledonian Tale. London, B. Crosby, 1796. [B.M.: *Eng. Lit. in Germany*: Stonehill.]
—— Like Master Like Man. A Novel. By the Late John Palmer, of the Theatre Royal, in the Haymarket, son to the deceased and celebrated John Palmer, of the Theatre Royal, Drury Lane, and of the above-mention'd Theatre. With a Preface, by George Colman, The Younger. 2 vols., London, Printed for the relief of the Author's Widow, 1811. [Blackwell: B.M.: Ingpen.]

Palmer, John. The Mystery of the Black Tower, a romance. 2 vols., London, Printed for the author by William Lane, 1796. [*New Ann. Reg.:* Blakey.]
—— The Mystic Sepulchre, or such things have been. A Spanish romance. 2 vols., London, 1807. [B.M.]

Palmzeaux, Michael de. Misogug: Or, Women as they are, A Chaldean Tale. Translated from the French. 2 vols., London, C. Elliott, 1788. [B.M.: Arthur Rogers: G. Worthington.]

Paltock, Robert. The Life and Adventures of Peter Wilkins, a Cornish Man: Relating particularly, his Shipwreck near the South Pole; His wonderful Passage thro' a subterranneous Cavern into a kind of new World; his there meeting with a Gawry or flying Woman, whose Life he preserv'd, and afterwards married her; his extraordinary Conveyance to the Country of Glurns and Gawrys, or Men and Women that fly. Likewise a Description of this strange Country, with the Law, Customs, and Manners of its Inhabitants, and the Author's remarkable Transactions among them. Taken from his own Mouth, in his Passage to England from off Cape Horn in America, in the Ship Hector. With an Introduction, giving an Account, of the surprising Manner of his coming on board that Vessel, and his Death on his landing at Plymouth in the year 1739. By R. S., a Passenger in the Hector. With 6 plates. 2 vols., London, J. Robinson & R. Dodsley, 1751. [*Bookworm*: B.M.: Maggs.]
—— Memoirs of the Life of Parnese, a Spanish Lady of Vast Fortune Written by herself: shewing the irresistible Force of Education. With a true account of the hardships she suffered, in Man's apparel, for eight Years, in different Countries, in the Prosecution of a Virtuous Amour with Rockbartez; her Escape from Slavery with Sarpeta, her master's Daughter; their Flight into Persia; her accidental marriage there to Rockbartez; and Return. Interspersed with the Story of Beaumont and Sarpeta. Translated from the Spanish Manuscript, by R. P[altock]. London, W. Owen, 1751. [B.M.: Dobell: McLeish.]

Palzow (*see* VON PAALZOW).

Pamela in High Life, or Virtue Rewarded in a Series of Letters to Her Parents, wherein a Faithful Account is given of her actions from her Marriage to her Death. London, Mary Kingman, 1741. [Arthur Rogers.]

Parasite. Dublin, 1765. 2 vols. [Elkin Mathews.]

Pardoe, Julia S. H. The Confessions Of A Pretty Woman. 3 vols., London, Henry Colburn, 1846. [Block: B.M.: *Critic.*]
—— Flies in Amber. 3 vols., London,

Shoberl, 1850. [Allibone: B.M.: *Eng. Cat.*]

Pardoe, Julia S. H. The Hungarian Castle. 3 vols., London, T. & W. Boone, 1842. [B. M.: Lib. of Congress: Wm. Smith.]

—— Lord Morcar of Hereward. A Romance of the Times of William the Conqueror. 4 vols., London, A. K. Newman, 1829. [Blackwell: B.M.: Arthur Rogers.]

—— The Mardens And The Daventrys. Tales, By the author of " Traits and Traditions of Portugal," &c. 3 vols., London, Saunders and Otley, 1835. [B.M.: Publisher's advert.]

—— The Rival Beauties. A Novel. 3 vols., London, Richard Bentley, 1848. [B.M.: Lib. of Congress: T. D. Webster.]

—— The Romance of the Harem. 3 vols., London, Henry Colburn, 1839. [B.M.: Elkin Mathews.]

—— Speculation, A Novel By the Author of " Traits and Traditions of Portugal." 3 vols., London, Saunders and Otley, 1834. [B.M.]

—— Traits and Traditions of Portugal. Collected during a residence in that Country. 2 vols., London, Saunders and Otley, 1833. [B.M.]

Pardon, George Frederick. The Faces in the Fire; A Story for the Season. By Redgap. With a frontispiece and 2 plates by T. H. Nicholson. London, Willoughby, [1850]. [B.M.: Dobell: T. Thorp.]

Parental Duplicity, or the Power of Artifice, by P. S. M. 3 vols., 1797. [*New Ann. Reg.*]

Parental Stories; or, a father's present to his children. Edinburgh, [1835 ?]. [B.M.]

Paris, John Ayrton. Philosophy in Sport Made Science in Earnest; Being An attempt to illustrate the first principles of natural philosophy. By the aid of Popular Toys and Sports. With 21 woodcuts by George Cruikshank. 3 vols., London, Longman, Rees, Orme, Brown and Green, 1827. [Block: B.M.: Victorius.]

Paris Chit-Chat, Or a View of the Society, Manners, Customs, Literature and Amusements of the Parisians, being a translation of " Guillaume le Franc-Parleur " and a sequel to " The Paris Spectator." 3 vols., 1816. [Blackwell.]

Parish Clerk (The); a Tale. 1823. [*Quarterly Review.*]

Parish Election (The). With a woodcut. London, Houlston, N.D. No. 77 of Houlston's Series of Tracts. [Block.]

Parker, Mrs. Decision And Indecision; Or, The Two Cousins. By the wife of a Wesleyan Minister. With a frontispiece. London, J. Mason, 1833. [B.M.]

Parker, Emma. Elfrida, Heiress of Belgrove. A novel. London, 1811. [B.M.]

—— The Guerilla Chiefs. 2 vols., London, 1815. [*New Monthly Mag.*]

Parker, Emma. Self-Deception. In a Series of Letters. 2 vols., London, T. Egerton, 1816 [B.M.: Pickering.]

Parker, Frances S. The Guiding Star, and other Tales. London, Hurst, 1835. [B.M.: (2nd edn.): *Eng. Cat.*]

Parker, G. A View of Society and Manners in High and Low Life, being the Adventures in England, Ireland, Scotland, Wales, France, of Mr. Parker. Including a History of the Stage Itinerant. 2 vols., London, Printed for the Author, 1781. [Baker's Bookshop.]

Parker, Mary Elizabeth. Alfred, 3 vols., 1802. [Allibone.]

—— Orwell Manor. A novel. 3 vols., London, Printed for the Author at the Minerva Press, 1795. [Arthur Rogers: T. Thorp: Blakey.]

Parker, Thomas. La Bruja: The Witch, or a Picture of the Court of Rome found among the MSS. of a Respectable Theologian, A Great Friend of that Court. Translated from the Spanish by Markophrates. With a frontispiece and engraved title. London, Hatchard, 1840. [G. Worthington.]

Parnell, William. Julietta, Or The Triumph of Mental Acquirements over Personal Defects. London, J. Johnson, 1802. [Ingpen: Pickering: Norman.]

—— Maurice and Berghetta, Or The Priest of Rahery. A Tale. London, Rowland Hunter, 1819. [Allibone: Ingpen: Elkin Mathews.]

Parr, William. Harry and his Mother; A Monitory Tale, intended chiefly for youth. With illustrations. London, W. Darton, [1812.] [Gumuchian.]

Parrott, Marianne. The Pastor's Family; Or, The Sister Preceptress. By the Authoress of " The Son and the Ward." London, Harvey and Darton; and N. Hailes, 1831. [B.M.]

—— The Son and the Ward; or, Selfishness Corrected: A Tale for Youth. London, Longman, Rees, Orme, Brown, and Green, 1829. [B.M.]

Parry, Catherine. Eden Vale. A Novel. 2 vols., London, John Stockdale, 1784. [B.M.: W. Brown.]

Parsons, Eliza. Anecdotes of Two Well-Known Families. Written by a Descendant and Dedicated to the First Female Peer in England. Prepared for the Press by Mrs. Parsons. 3 vols., London, T. N. Longman, 1798. [Ingpen: *New Ann. Reg.*]

—— Castle of Wolfenbach; a German story. 2 vols. With a frontispiece. London, William Lane, 1793. [*Holden's Reprints*: Blakey.]

—— The Convict, or Navy Lieutenant. A novel. 4 vols., Brentford, P. Norbury, 1807. [B.M.]

—— Ellen and Julia. 2 vols. With a frontispiece. [W. Lane, 1793]. [Blakey.]

—— The Errors of Education. 3 vols., London, William Lane, 1791. [Blakey.]

Parsons, Eliza. The Girl of the Mountains. A novel. 4 vols., London, William Lane, 1797. [*New Ann. Reg.:* Blakey.]
—— The History of Miss Meredith, A Novel. 2 vols., London, Printed for the Author, 1790. [B.M.: H. B. Copinger.]
—— Lucy. A Novel. 3 vols., London, Minerva Press, 1794. [B.M.: *New Ann. Reg.:* Stonehill.]
—— Murray House. "A plain unvarnished tale." 3 vols., Brentford, 1804. [B.M.]
—— The Mysterious Visit, A Novel founded on facts. 4 vols., Brentford, Norbury, 1802. [Stonehill.]
—— The Mysterious Warning. A German Tale. With a frontispiece. 4 vols., London, William Lane, 1796. [B.M.: Ingpen: Blakey.]
—— An Old Friend with a New Face. 3 vols., 1797. [*New Ann. Reg.*]
—— The Valley of St. Gothard, a Novel. 3 vols., Brentford, Norbury, 1799. [*New Ann. Reg.:* Stonehill.]
—— The Voluntary Exile. 5 vols., London, William Lane, 1795. [B.M.: *New Ann. Reg.:* Pickering.]
—— Woman As She Should Be; or, Memoirs of Mrs. Menville. A Novel. 4 vols., London, Minerva Press, 1793. [Blackwell: *New Ann. Reg.:* Arthur Rogers.]
—— Women As They Are. A Novel. 4 vols., London, William Lane, 1796. [Pickering: Arthur Rogers: Stonehill.]
Parsons, Mrs. G. Thornberry Abbey, A Tale of the Established Church. London, Dolman, 1846. [B.M.: *Critic.*]
Parson's Wife (The). A novel. Written by a Lady. 2 vols., London, 1789. [B.M.]
Partings and Meetings: A Tale, Founded on Facts. London, J. B. Bell, 1830. [B.M.]
Passages from the Life of a Daughter at Home. 1845. [T. Thorp.]
Pastimes of a Convent (The); Or the Amorous Advantages of Father Andouillard, with a Dissertation on the Advantages of Flagellation, Preceded by Recollections of the Youth of Raymond de B. and of his amorous adventures. Brussels [London, James Ferguson and Louis Chappuis], 1798 [1830]. [*Cat. Lib. Prohib.*]
Pastor Chief (The); Or, The Escape of the Vaudois. A Tale of The Seventeenth Century. 3 vols., London, Cunningham & Mortimer, [1843]. [B.M.: Publisher's advert.]
Pasture, Count De la, (see DE LA PASTURE).
Pastorals in Prose. Or, moral tales, for the amusement of youth. London, [1790 ?]. [B.M.]
Paterson, Samuel. Another Traveller; Or, Cursory Remarks and Critical Observations made upon a Journey through part of the Netherlands in the latter end of the Year 1766. By Coriat

Junior. 3 vols., London, J. Johnson, 1767. [Ellis: Ingpen.]
Patmore, Peter George. Chatsworth, The Patrician. [Edited by Robert Plumer Ward.] London, Cochrane and M'Crone, [1830]. [B.M.: Ingpen.]
—— Mirror of the Months. London, G. B. Whittaker, 1826. [B.M.: Pickering.]
Patrick, Mrs. F. C. The Irish Heiress, a novel. 3 vols., London, William Lane, 1797. [Allibone: *New Ann. Reg.:* Blakey.]
—— The Jesuit. Or, The History of Antony Babington, Esq. An historical Novel. 3 vols., 1799. [Allibone: *Eng. Lit. in Germany: New Ann. Reg.*]
—— More Ghosts! By the wife of an officer, author of The Irish Heiress. 3 vols., London, William Lane, 1798. [Allibone: Blakey.]
Patterson, Paul. The Playfair Papers, Or Brother Jonathan, The Smartest Nation in all Creation. With engravings by Robert Cruikshank. 3 vols., London, Saunders and Otley, 1841. [B.M.]
Paturot, Jerome. The Vane of the Steeple. 2 vols., London, 1845. [*Critic.*].
Paul the Reckless; or, the Fugitive's Doom. London, 1846. [B.M.]
Paxton, Mrs. Life as it is. A Second Series of Original Tales. London, Darton, 1844. [Allibone: B.M.: *Eng. Cat.*]
—— The Veil Lifted; or, incidents of private life. A series of original tales. London, W. Brittain, 1843. [Allibone: B.M.]
—— The Young Physician, a Narrative. London, W. Brittain, 1846. [Allibone: *Eng. Cat.*]
Pazos, Dôna Francisca. Ofelia; Or The Child of Fate. 2 vols., London, Thomas Hurst, 1835. [B.M.]
Peaceful Villa (The), an Eventful Tale. 2 vols., 1793. [W. Brown: *New Ann. Reg.*]
Peacock, Lucy. The Adventures of the Six Princesses of Babylon, in their Travels to the Temple of Virtue; An Allegory. London, Printed for the Author by T. Bensley, 1785. [Block: B.M.: Arthur Rogers.]
—— Ambrose and Eleanor; Or, The Adventures of Two Children Deserted On an Uninhabited Island. Translated from the French. With Alterations, Adapting it to the Perusal of Youth, for whose Amusement and Instruction it is designed. By the Author of The Adventures of the Six Princesses of Babylon; Juvenile Magazine; Visit for a Week, &c. With a frontispiece. London, R. and L. Peacock, 1796. [B.M.]
—— Emily; or, the Test of Sincerity. London, 1816. [B.M.]
—— Friendly Labours, Or, Tales and Dramas For the Amusement and

Instruction of Youth. With frontispieces. 2 vols., Brentford, Printed by and for P. Norbury, 1815. [B.M.]

Peacock, Lucy. The Knight of the Rose. An allegorical narrative. By the author of the Six Princesses of Babylon. London, 1793. [B.M.]

—— The Little Emigrant. A Tale. By the author of the adventures of the Six Princesses of Babylon. With a frontispiece. London, 1799. [B.M.: J. Richardson.]

—— Patty Primrose Or The Parsonage House. By the Author of " A Visit for a Week," etc. With a frontispiece. London, Darton, Harvey and Darton, 1816. [Gumuchian.]

—— The Rambles of Fancy; Or, Moral and Interesting Tales. Containing, The Laplander, The Ambitious Mother, Letters from—Lindamira to Olivia, Miranda to Elvira, Felicia to Cecilia, The American Indian, The Fatal Resolution, The Creole. By the Author of the Adventures of the Six Princesses of Babylon. 2 vols., London, Printed by T. Bensley, for the Author, 1786. [B.M.]

—— The Visit for a Week; Or, Hints On the Improvement of Time. Containing Original Tales, Anecdotes from Natural and Moral History, &c. Designed for the Amusement of Youth. By the Author of the Six Princesses of Babylon, Juvenile Magazine, And Knight of the Rose. London, Printed for Hookham and Carpenter; and for the Author, 1794. [B.M.]

Peacock, Thomas Love. Crotchet Castle. By the Author of Headlong Hall. London, T. Hookham, 1831. [Block: B.M.: Arthur Rogers.]

—— Headlong Hall. London, T. Hookham, Jun., 1816. [Block: B.M.: Ingpen.]

—— Maid Marian, by the Author of Headlong Hall. London, T. Hookham; and Longman, Hurst, Rees, Orme, and Browne, 1822. [Block: B.M.: Ingpen.]

—— Melincourt. By the Author of Headlong Hall. 3 vols., London, T. Hookham, Jun.; and Baldwin, Cradock, & Joy, 1817. [Block: B.M.: Ingpen.]

—— The Misfortunes of Elphin. By the Author of Headlong Hall. London, Thomas Hookham, 1829. [Block: B.M.: Ingpen.]

—— Nightmare Abbey: By the Author of Headlong Hall. London, T. Hookham, Jun.; & Baldwin, Cradock, & Joy, 1818. [Block: B.M.: Arthur Rogers.]

Peake, Lieut. Charles. The Saucy Jack, & The Indiaman. By a Blue Jacket. 2 vols., London, R. Bentley, 1840. [B.M.]

Peake, Eliza. Honour! A Tale. London, Saunders and Otley, 1844. [Allibone: B.M.]

—— Jealousy And Revenge. Tales. With illustrations. 2 vols., London, Saunders and Otley, 1845. [Allibone: B.M.]

Peake, Richard Brinsley. Cartouche, The Celebrated French Robber. 3 vols., London, Hugh Cunningham, 1844. [Allibone: B.M.]

Peake, William. Court Intrigues. A Novel. 3 vols., London, T. C. Newby, 1845. [B.M.: *Critic.*]

Pearl Fisher of St. Domingo (The). A Tale of the Buccaniers. With illustrations. London, Peirce, [c. 1840]. [Stonehill.]

Pearl Necklace and the Scarlet Frock (The); with the Evening walk. Tales for children. By the authoress of " A Year's residence in the country." Norwich, 1831. [B.M.]

Pearson, S. The Medallion 3 vols., 1794. [*New Ann. Reg.*]

Peck, Frances. The Bard of the West, Commonly called Eman ac Knuck, or Ned of the Hills. An Irish Historical Romance, Founded on Facts of the Seventh Century. 3 vols., London, Baldwin, Cradock & Joy; and John Cumming, Dublin, 1818. [Backus: B.M.: *New Monthly Mag.*]

—— The Life and Acts of the Renowned and Chivalrous Edmund of Erin, commonly called Emun ac Knuck or Ned of the Hills, &c. 3 vols., 1818. [*I. in F.*]

—— The Maid of Avon. A novel, for the Haut Ton. By an Irishwoman. 3 vols., London, Minerva Press, 1807. [Blakey.]

—— Napoleon; or, The Mysteries of the Hundred Days, An Historical Novel. London, Simpkin and Marshall, 1826. [Ingpen: *New Monthly Mag.*: *Quarterly Review.*]

—— Vaga, or a View of Nature. 3 vols., London, Printed at the Minerva Press, for A. K. Newman, 1815. [Publisher's advert (2nd edn.).]

—— The Welch Peasant Boy. A Novel. By the author of The Maid of Avon. 3 vols., London, 1808. [B.M.: Blakey.]

—— Young Rosiniere, or Sketches of the World, a novel. 3 vols. [Cawthorn's Catalogue, 1810].

Pedantry, Superstition, & Temperance, Instructive and Entertaining Stories for Young People. With illustrations. London, Edward Lacey, N.D. [Block.]

Pedder, James. The Yellow Shoe-Strings; Or, The Good Effects of Obedience to Parents. With a frontispiece. London, William Darton, [1814]. [B.M.: Court Book Shop: Arthur Rogers.]

Pedlars. Dublin, 1826. [B.M.]

Peep at the Theatres. A satirical, critical, and moral Novel. 3 vols., 1812. [*Quarterly Review.*]

Peers, John Witherington. A Visit to the Rectory of Passy; With Sketches of Character and Scenery. London, J. Hatchard, 1826. [B.M.]

Peggy and Patty; Or, The Sisters of

Ashdale. 4 vols., London, Dodsley, 1783. [T. D. Webster.]

Penitent (The), A Domestic Story Of the Nineteenth Century. London, Saunders and Otley, 1839. [B.M.]

Penitent Father (The). 2 vols., 1793. [*New Ann. Reg..*]

Penn, James. The Farmer's Daughter of Essex. London, 1767. [B.M.]

—— The Surry Cottage. London, The Author, and Bladon, 1779. [B.M.]

Pennie, John Fitzgerald. Corfe Castle; Or Keneswitha. With an engraved title. London, Hurst, Robinson, 1824. [B.M.]

—— The Tale of a Modern Genius, or the Miseries of Parnasus. 3 vols., London, 1827. [E. M. Lawson.]

Pennington, Lady Sarah. Letters on Different Subjects, amongst which are interspers'd the Adventures of Alphonso, after the Destruction of Lisbon. 4 vols., London, To be had by the Subscribers, 1766. [Francis Edwards: Stonehill.]

Penrose, Elizabeth. Tales and Conversations; Or The New Children's Friend. By Mrs. Markham. 2 vols., 1832. [Butland.]

Penruddock, A Tale. By The Author of ' Waltzburg.' 3 vols., London, Whittaker, 1835. [B.M.]

Percival, Margaret. The Irish Dove; or, Faults on both Sides. A tale. By the author of " Rosa, the Work-Girl." Dublin, Robertson, 1849. [B.M.: *I. in F.*]

—— Rosa, the Work-Girl. A tale. By a Young Lady. Dublin, 1847. [B.M.]

Percival, Thomas. A Father's Instruction, Consisting of Moral Tales, Fables, and Reflections: designed to promote The Love of Virtue. 1776. [*Eng. Lit. in Germany.*]

Percy, Clara. The Changeling of Fortune. A Sketch from Real Life. With a frontispiece. London, William Cole, [1830 ?]. [B.M.: Arthur Rogers.]

Percy Stephen. Robind Hood and his Merry Foresters. London, 1841. [Allibone.]

Percy, Thomas, (Edited by). The Matrons. Six Short Histories. London, Dodsley, 1762. [Ingpen.]

Percy, or the Friends. 1797. [*New Ann. Reg.*]

Peregrine, Peter. Matilda Montfort. 4 vols., 1809. [*Monthly Mag.*]

Perfidy Detected! Or, The Children In the Wood Restored, By Honestas, the Hermit of the Forest. Who were supposed to have been either murdered or starved to death, by order of their inhuman Uncle, being The Continuation of the History of the Children in the Wood. With woodcuts. Banbury, J. G. Rusher, [1835 ?]. [B.M.]

Perjured Lover (The), or the History of Thomas Beaumont, an Oxford student, and Miss Lucia Bannister, etc. London, T. Sabine, [1790 ?]. [B.M.]

Perpetual Almanack: Or, Gentleman Soldier's Prayer-Book. Showing how a Soldier was taken before the Mayor of the City he was in, for using Cards in the Church during divine Service; being a Droll, Merry, and Humourous Account of an Odd Affair that happened to a Private Soldier, in the 60th Regiment of foot. [A Single Folio Leaf.] London, Jennings, [180-]. [B.M.]

Perplexed Lovers (The): or, the History of Sir Edward Balchen, Bart. 3 vols., London, F. Noble; J. Noble, 1768. [B.M.: *Univ. Mag.*]

Perplexities of Love (The): A Novel. London, W. Lane, 1787. [T. D. Webster: Blakey.]

Perrault, Charles. Histories or tales of past times told by Mother Goose. With morals. Written in French by M. Perrault, and Englished by G. M., Gent. Salisbury, B. C. Collins, 1802. [B.M.]

Persian and Turkish Tales. 2 vols., 1767. [W. Brown.]

Persiana, The Nymph of the Sea. A Novel. London, William Lane, 1791. [Blakey.]

Pestalozzi, Johann Heinrich. Leonard and Gertrude. " A book for the poor." Translated from the German by Eliza Shepherd. Volume I [all published]. Geneva, 1824. [B.M.]

—— Leonard and Gertrude. A Popular Story, Written originally in German Translated into French, & now attempted in English; With the hope of its being useful to the Lower Orders of Society. Bath, S. Hazard; Cadell & Davies, London; Todd, York; Pennington, Kendal; Bulgin, Bristol. 1800. [Birrell & Garnett: Arthur Rogers.]

Pettigrew, Thomas Lettson. Lucien Greville. By a Cornet, In the Hon. East India Company's Service. With etchings by George Cruikshank. 3 vols., London, Saunders and Otley, 1833. [B.M.: New Monthly Mag.]

Phantasmagoria; or, the Development of Magical Deception. London, Tegg, [*c.* 1802.]. Stonehill.]

Phantoms of the Cloister; or, The mysterious manuscript. A novel. 3 vols., London, William Lane, 1795. [B.M.]

Pharisee Turned Publican; or, the History of Old Jenny. By the author of the Two Buckets. London, 1845. [B.M.]

Phelps, Mrs. J. T. The Good Aunt; Or, A Summer in the Country; A Moral Tale, for the Amusement and Instruction of Youth. With a view. London, W. Flint, 1811. [B.M.: Sotheran.]

Philamour and Philamena, or Genuine Memoirs of a Late Affecting Transaction. London, 1746. [Dobell.]

Philanthropist (The): Or, Selfishness and

Benevolence Illustrated: A Tale. By a lady. London, William Ball, 1836. [B.M.]

Philario & Eleanora. 2 vols., 1792. [*New Ann. Reg.*]

Philip Gray: a village story. Embodying the most popular evidences for the truth of Christianity. London, [1850]. [B.M.]

Philip Randolph; a tale of Virginia. By Mary Gertrude. London, Whittaker, 1844. [B.M.: *Eng. Cat.*]

Phillips, Lucius. Heaven's Best Gift; a Novel. 4 vols., 1797. [Allibone: Blakey.]

Phillips, Charles. The Loves of Celestine and St. Aubert; a Romantic Tale. 2 vols., 1811. [Allibone.]

Phillips, P. J. The Tournament of Chalons: a romance. 2 vols., London, 1832. [B.M.]

Phillips, Samuel. Caleb Stukely. 3 vols., Edinburgh, and London, William Blackwood, 1844. [B.M.: Wm. Brown: Elkin Mathews.]

Philosopher's Stone (The). A tale. By the author of " The Smuggler's Son." London, J. Harris, 1828. [B.M.]

Philosophical Quixote; or Memoirs of Mr. David Wilkins. In a Series of Letters. 2 vols., London, J. Johnson, 1782. [Dobell: Ingpen.]

Philosophy of Pleasure (The); Or, the History of a Young Lady, Of Luxurious Temperament and Prurient Imagination, who experiences repeatedly the Dangers of Seduction and whose escapes from the Snares of Love are truly wonderful, depicting many and various Luscious Scenes with her Lovers, and proving herself to be the Child of Nature Improved by chance. Freely translated from the original French. London, T. Becket, 1774. [Rochester Reprints.]

Phipps, E. The Fergusons; Or, Woman's Love and the World's Favour. 2 vols., London, Henry Colburn, 1839. [B.M.: James Glaisher.]

Phoebe; Or, The Miller's Maid, A Romance of Deep Interest. By the author of " Adeline." London, Lloyd, 1842. [B.M.: Ingpen.]

Physiognomist (The). A Novel. By the Author of " The Bachelor and the Married Man." 3 vols., London, Longman, Hurst, Rees, Orme, and Brown, 1818. [B.M.: McLeish: *New Monthly Mag.*]

Picard, Louis Benoît. The Gil Blas of the Revolution. 3 vols., London, Saunders and Otley; and Geo. B. Whittaker, 1825. [Blackwell: B.M.: Ingpen.]

—— The Novice; Or, The Man of Integrity. From the French of L. B. Picard. 3 vols., London, Baldwin, Cradock and Joy, 1825. [B.M.]

Picaroon (The), By the Author of " Makanna." 3 vols., London, Saunders and Otley, 1837. [B.M.]

Pichler, Karoline von. Greiner. Quentin Matsys, or the Blacksmith. From the German. London, Burns, [1845]. [B.M.]

—— Waldstein; or, The Swedes in Prague. From the German of Madame C. Pilcher, By J. D. Rosenthal [afterwards Haas.]. 2 vols., London, T. Rodwell, 1828. [B.M.: *Quarterly Review.*]

Pickard, M. Castel Roviego; a Romance. 4 vols., 1809. [Allibone.]

Picken, Andrew. The Black Watch. By the Author of " The Dominie's Legacy." 3 vols., London, Richard Bentley, 1834. [B.M.: Foyle: James Glaisher.]

—— The Club-Book: Being Original Tales, &c. By Various Authors. Edited by The Author of " The Dominie's Legacy." 3 vols., London, Cochrane and Pickersgill, 1831. [Allibone: B.M.: Pickering.]

—— The Dominie's Legacy. By the Author of " The Sectarian." 3 vols., London, William Kidd, 1830. [B.M.: Ingpen: Arthur Rogers.]

—— Mary Ogilvie: a tale of the Squire's experience. With 7 illustrations by R. Cruikshank. London, W. Kidd, [1840 ?] [B.M. (6th edn.).]

—— The Sectarian; or, The Church and the Meeting-House. 3 vols., London, Henry Colburn, 1829. [Allibone: B.M.]

—— Traditionary Stories Of Old Families, And Legendary Illustrations Of Family History. With notes, historical and biographical. 2 vols., London, Longman, Rees, Orme, Brown, Green, & Longman, 1833. [Allibone: B.M.]

—— Waltham; a Romance. 1832. [Allibone.]

Pickering, Ellen. Agnes Serle. By The Author of " The Heiress." 3 vols., London, Richard Bentley, 1835. [B.M.: Ingpen: Arthur Rogers.]

—— The Expectant, A Novel. 3 vols., London, T. C. Newby; and T. & W. Boone, 1842. [Allibone: B.M.]

—— Friend, Or Foe ? A Novel. 3 vols., London, T. C. Newby, 1843. [Allibone: B.M.]

—— The Fright. By the Author of " The Heiress" " The Merchant's Daughter " " The Prince and the Pedlar," " Nan Darrell," &c. 3 vols., London, T. & W. Boone, 1839. [B.M.: Ingpen: T. Thorp.]

—— The Grumbler; A Novel. 3 vols., London, T. C. Newby, 1843. [Allibone: B.M.: P. C. Cuttelle.]

—— The Heiress. A Novel. 3 vols., London, Richard Bentley, 1833. [Allibone: B.M.: Elkin Mathews.]

—— Kate Walsingham. By the author of " The Heiress." 3 vols., London, T. C. Newby, 1848. [Allibone: B.M.: *Eng. Cat.*]

—— The Marriage of The Favourite: Or, She Bred Him a Soldier. A Novel. By the Author of " The Heiress." 3

vols., London, G. B. Whittaker, 1826. [B.M.: *New Monthly Mag.*]

Pickering, Ellen. The Merchant's Daughter. By the Author of "The Heiress," "Agnes Serle," &c. 3 vols., London, Richard Bentley, 1836. [Allibone: B.M.: T. Thorp.]

—— Nan Darrell; Or, The Gipsy Mother. By the Author of "The Heiress," "The Merchant's Daughter," "The Squire," "The Prince and the Pedlar," &c. 3 vols., London, T. & W. Boone, 1839. [Allibone: B.M.: Ingpen.]

—— The Prince And The Pedlar; Or, The Siege of Bristol. By the Author of "The Heiress," "The Merchant's Daughter," etc. 3 vols., London, Richard Bentley, 1839. [Allibone: B.M.: Stonehill.]

—— The Quiet Husband. 3 vols., London, T. & W. Boone, 1840. [Allibone: B.M.: P. C. Cuttelle.]

—— The Secret Foe, An Historical Novel. 3 vols., London, T. and W. Boone, 1841. [Allibone: B.M.: Ingpen.]

—— Sir Michael Paulet, A Novel. 3 vols., London, T. C. Newby; and T. & W. Boone, 1842. [Allibone: B.M.]

—— The Squire. By the Author of "The Heiress," "The Merchant's Daughter," &c. 3 vols., London, Richard Bentley, 1837. [Allibone: B. M.: T. Thorp.]

—— Who Shall be Heir? 3 vols., London, T. & W. Boone, 1840. [Allibone: B.M.]

—— and **Youatt,** Elizabeth. The Grandfather. A novel. 3 vols., London, T.C. Newby, 1844. [B.M.]

Pickersgill, Mrs. Tales of the Harem. I. The Witch of Himlaya. II. The Cave of Gulistan. III. The Hetæria. IV. The Indian Maid. [In Prose & Verse.] London, Longman, Rees, Orme, Brown, & Green, 1827. [B.M.: Dobell.]

Pickersgill, Joshua. The Three Brothers; a Romance. 4 vols., London, 1803. [Allibone.]

Picnics from the Dublin Penny Journal, being a selection from the legends, tales and stories of Ireland, which have appeared in the published volumes of the Dublin Penny Journal. With 10 illustrations by B. Clayton Junr. Dublin, Philip Dixon Hardy, 1836. [*I. in F.*: G. Worthington.]

Picture of Society (A). London, T. Hookham, Junr. and E. T. Hookham, 1814. [*New Monthly Mag.*: Publisher's advert.]

Pictures in the Hermitage (The), or, the History of George Meadows. With 3 plates. London, J. Harris, 1808. [Dobell.]

Pie Voleuse (La). The Narrative of the Magpie; or, the Maid of Palaiseau. Being the History of The Maid and the Magpie. Founded upon the Circumstance Of an unfortunate Female having been Unjustly Sentenced to Death, on strong Presumptive Evidence. With a Preface, and curious Anecdotes. With

a vignette title. London, Printed by J. Swan, for William Hone, 1815. [Court Bk. Shop.]

Pienne, Duchess of. Italian Jealousy: or the History of Lady Georgina Cecil. 3 vols., London, 1803. [T. D. Webster.]

Piercy, S. H. Tales for Youth. 1809. [Allibone.]

Piers de Gaveston. By E. E. C. 2 vols., London, Whittaker, 1838. [B.M.]

Pigault-Lebrun (*see* LEBRUN).

Pigott, Harriet. The Private Correspondence Of a Woman of Fashion. 2 vols., London, Henry Colburn and Richard Bentley, 1832. [B.M.]

—— Records of Real Life in the Palace and the Cottage: Revised by the late J. Galt. 3 vols., London, Saunders and Otley, 1839. [B.M.: *Eng. Cat.*: T. D. Webster.]

—— The Three Springs of Beauty; a legend of the Cyclades. Dedicated to the Fair. London, Whittaker; Clarke, Bath, 1844. [B.M.: *Critic.*]

Piguenard, J. B. Zoflora; or, The Generous Negro Girl. A Colonial Story. From the French of J. B. Piguenard. 2 vols., London, Lackington, Allan, 1804. [J. C. Hardy: G. Worthington.]

Piguenit, C. D. The Arabian Nights Entertainments. Freely transcribed from the original translation. 1792. [B.M.]

Pile, Ann. Female Art: or, True and False. London, 1807. [Allibone: B.M.]

Pilgrimage to the Land of Burns (A); containing Anecdotes of the Bard, and of the Characters he immortalized, with numerous Pieces of Poetry, original and collected. London, Sherwood, 1823. [*Eng. Cat.*: *New Monthly Mag.*]

Pilkington, Mary. The Accusing Spirit, or De Courcy and Eglantine. A romance. By the author of Delia, Rosina, and The Subterranean Cavern. With a frontispiece. 4 vols., London, Printed at the Minerva Press, for Lane and Newman, 1802. [*Minerva Press Catalogue*: Blakey.]

—— The Asiatic Princess. 2 vols., London, Vernor and Hood; and E. Newbery, 1800. [B.M.: *Guardian of Education*: Arthur Rogers.]

—— Celebrity; Or, The Unfortunate Choice. A Novel. 3 vols., London, Printed at the Minerva Press, for A. K. Newman, 1815. [Allibone: B.M.: Publisher's advert.]

—— Crimes and Characters; or, the New Foundling. 3 vols., London, W. Earle, 1805. [Baker's Bookshop: B.M. Pickering.]

—— Delia, a pathetic and interesting tale. 4 vols., London, William Lane, 1790. [*Minerva Press Catalogue*: Blakey.]

—— The Disgraceful Effects of Falsehood, and the fruits of early indulgence; exemplified in the histories of Percival Pembroke and Augustus Fitzhue. London, J. Harris, 1807. [B.M.]

Pilkington, Mary. Edward Barnard; Or,

Merit Exalted; Containing The History of the Edgerton Family. With a frontispiece. London, E. Newbery, 1797. [Backus: B.M.]

Pilkington, Ellen, Heiress of the Castle. 3 vols., London, B. Crosby, 1807. [Arthur Rogers.]

—— Henry, Or the Foundling; To which are added the Prejudiced Parent, or the virtuous daughter: Tales calculated to improve the mind and morals of youth. With a frontispiece and a vignette-title. 1799. [Dobell.]

—— The Ill-Fated Mariner, or Richard Runaway. [Cawthorn's Catalogue, 1810.]

—— Marvellous Adventures, or The Vicissitudes of a Cat. London, Vernor and Hood, 1802. [*Camb. Hist. Eng. Lit.: Guardian of Education.*]

—— Mentorial Tales, for the Instruction of Young Ladies just leaving School, and entering upon the Theatre of Life. London, Harris, 1802. [B.M.: *Guardian of Education.*]

—— New Tales of the Castle; or, the Noble Emigrants, a story. London, J. Harris, 1803. [B.M. (2nd edn.).]

—— Obedience Rewarded, and Prejudice Conquered; or, the History of Mortimer Lascelles. London, 1797. [B.M.: *Camb. Hist Eng. Lit.*: McLeish.]

—— Parental Care Producing Practical Virtue; or, Youthful Errors conquered by Judicious Advice. Characteristic Incidents, drawn from Real Life; or, the History of the Rockinghams. London, 1810. [Block.]

—— A Reward for Attentive Studies; or, moral and entertaining stories. London, [1810 ?]. [B.M.]

—— Rosina: a novel. By the author of Delia, an interesting tale. 5 vols. London, Printed at the Minerva Press, for William Lane, 1793. [*Minerva Press Catalogue*: B.M.: Blakey.]

—— The Shipwreck, Or Misfortune the Inspirer of Virtuous Sentiments. With engravings. London, W. Darton, Junior, 1819. [B.M.: Arthur Rogers.]

—— Sinclair; or, The Mysterious Orphan. 4 vols., London, Minerva Press, 1809. [Cawthorn's Catalogue: Blakey.]

—— The Subterranean Cavern; by the Author of Delia & Rosina. 4 vols., London, William Lane, 1798. [*New Ann. Reg.*: Blakey.]

—— The Sorrows of Caesar; or, the Adventures of a Foundling Dog. London, G. & S. Robinson, 1813. [B.M.]

—— Tales of the Cottage, Or Stories, Moral and Amusing. For Young Persons. Written on the plan of that celebrated work, Les Veilles Du Chateau by Madam Genlis. London, Vernor and Hood, 1799. [B.M.: Arthur Rogers.]

—— Tales of the Hermitage. London, Vernor & Hood, 1798. [B.M.]

—— Violet Vale: or, Saturday Night. Dublin, 1805. [B.M.: T. D. Webster.]

Pilot (The). A Tale of the Sea. With a folding frontispiece. London, Duncombe [*c.* 1800]. [Stonehill.]

Pilpay—The Basiliade: or the Book of Truth and Nature; An Epic Poem, in 14 Cantos, in Prose. Translated from the Original Manuscript of the Celebrated Bramin and Philosopher, Pilpay. Found among the Treasures of Mohammed Shah, Emperor of the Mogul Tartars, at the Plunder of the City of Delhi, Capital of Hindostan, by the Nadir Shah, Thomas Khuli Khan. 2 vols., London, Hooper, 1761. [Ingpen.]

Pinchard, Mrs. The Blind Child; Or Anecdotes of the Wyndham Family, Written for the use of young people, by a Lady. With a frontispiece. London, 1791. [B.M.: *Eng. Lit. in Germany.*]

—— Family Affection, A Tale for Youth. With a frontispiece. Taunton, J. W. Marriott, 1816. [B.M.]

—— Mystery and Confidence: A Tale. By a Lady. 3 vols., London, Henry Colburn, 1814. [*New Monthly Mag.*: Pickering: Publisher's advert.]

—— The Two Cousins, A Moral Story, For the Use of Young Persons. In which is exemplified The necessity of moderation and justice To the attainment of happiness. By the Author of The Blind Child And Dramatic Dialogues. With a frontispiece. London, E. Newbery, 1794. [B.M.: Gumuchian: Sotheran.]

—— The Ward of Delamere, A Tale. 3 vols., London, Black, Parry, 1815. [B.M.: *New Monthly Mag.*]

—— The Young Countess: a tale for youth. By the authoress of the "Blind Child." London, C. Chapple, 1820. [G. Worthington.]

Pinkney, Jane Vaughan. Lady Granards Nieces. A Novel. 3 vols., London, Thomas Cautley Newby, 1848. [James Glaisher.]

Pious Cottager (The), or an account of the happy life and death of Mary Douglas. Northampton, 1821. [B.M.]

Pious Girl and her Swearing Father (The). [London], Religious Tract Society, [1830 ?]. [B.M.]

Pious Monks Peasant (The); or, the History of William Curphey. By the Author of "Little Pat, the Irish Chimney-Sweeper," &c. With a woodcut. London, Houlston, N.D. No. 17 of Houlston's Series of Tracts. [Block.]

Piper, John. The Life of Miss Fanny Brown (A Clergyman's Daughter), with the History and Remarkable Adventures of Mrs. Julen, an Apothecary's Wife. The Whole interspersed with a great Variety of Characters, Moral, Instructive and Entertaining. To which is added, A Description of the most elegant monuments in Westminster Abbey; the Curiosities in and about London; and Remarks on several Cathedrals. Birmingham, Printed for the Author, 1760. [W. Brown: G.

Worthington.]

Pirate of the Gulf (The), or, Lafitte. By the Author of "The South West." London, A. K. Newman, 1837. [B.M.: Elkin Mathews.]

Pirate's Doom (The); or, A Midshipman's First Voyage. By Trysail. With woodcuts. London, Hextall and Wall, 1843. [Stonehill.]

Pisani, Marianna. The Banker-Lord: A Novel. 3 vols., London, Henry Colburn, 1840. [B.M.]

—— Vandeleur; Or, Animal Magnetism. A Novel. 3 vols., London, Richard Bentley, 1836. [B.M.]

Piso, Lucius Manlius. Zenobia, Queen of the East; Or, Letters from Palmyra. 2 vols., London, Richard Bentley, 1838. [B.M.]

Piso and the Praefect: Or The Ancients off their Stilts. 3 vols., London, Smith, Elder, 1837. [B.M.: T. D. Webster.]

Pitman, Ambrose. Eugenio, or the Man of Sorrow. By a young gentleman of seventeen. 1780. [B.M.]

Pitt, George Dibden. The Sea-Fiend; or, the Abbot of St. Mark's. A Legendary Romance. With woodcuts. London, E. Lloyd, 1846. [B.M.: G. Meredith: B. Ono.]

—— The Wreck of the Heart; or, the Story of Agnes Primrose. A Domestic Tale. Upon which has been founded the two Popular Dramas produced at the City of London and Royal Victoria Theatres with unparalleled success. With woodcuts. London, E. Lloyd, 1842. [B.M.: B. Ono.]

Pity's Gift. A Collection of Interesting Tales to Excite the Compassion of Youth for the Animal Creation. Selected by A Lady. With vignettes. London, Longman & Newbery, 1798. [B. Halliday: Arthur Rogers.]

Plain Sense, A Novel. 3 vols., London, Printed for William Lane at the Minerva Press, 1795. [B.M.]

Plantagenet. 3 vols., London, John Macrone, 1835. [B.M.]

Planter's Daughter (The), And the Rector's Son; Or, Scenes at Richmond: In which is portrayed, A Gambler's Fate. An interesting domestic tale. London, Orlando Hodgson, N.D. [Court Bk. Shop.]

Planter's Daughter and Her Slave. By the author of "Early Lessons." London, A. K. Newman, [1820 ?]. [B.M.]

Pleasant and Delightful History of the Froliksome Courtier (The), and the Jovial Tinker. London, [1780 ?]. [B.M.]

Pleasant and Delightful History of Thomas Hickathrift (A). Whitehaven, [1780]. [B.M.]

Pleasant and Delightful History of the Unfortunate Daughter (The). [London], [1765 ?]. [B.M.]

Pleasant Dale, or the Happy Village. From the German. London, [1830 ?].

[B.M.]

Pleasant Tales for Little People. London, Dean, 1850. [B.M.: *Eng. Cat.*]

Pleasing Companion. London, William Lane, 1788.

Pleasing Instructor (The). [*Progress of Romance.*]

Pleasure Improved, or an account of Mrs. Wishwell's scholars performance, at their leaving school for the holidays. London, 1777. [B.M.]

Pleasures of Friendship (The). A Tale. London, G. and W. B. Whittaker, 1823. [B.M.: *New Monthly Mag.*]

Pleasures of Love (The). 1755. [*Cat. Lib. Prohib.*]

Pleasures of Want (The); or, in love and not in love; a novel. By a Popular Author. 3 vols., London, Fearman, 1819. [B.M.: *Eng. Cat.*]

Plebeians and Patricians. By The Author of "Old Maids," "Old Bachelors," &c. &c. 3 vols., London, Smith, Elder, 1836. [B.M.]

Pledge (The); or, the First Step to Fortune. A sequel to the "Bottle." London, [1848]. [B.M.]

Plessis (*see* Du Plessis).

Plot and a Peerage (A). London, William Tegg, 1848. [B.M.]

Plumtre, Annabella. Domestic Stories; from the German. [Allibone.]

—— Montgomery; or, Scenes in Wales. 2 vols., London, William Lane, 1796. [Allibone: *New Ann. Reg.*: Blakey.]

—— Stories for Children. 1804. [Allibone.]

—— The Western Mail; Being a Selection of Letters made from the Bag Taken from the Western Mail, when it was Robbed by George ——, in 17—. Mawman, 1801. [Stonehill.]

Plumptre, Anne. Antoinette; a Novel. 2 vols., [W. Lane], 1795. [Allibone: *New Ann. Reg.*: Blakey.]

—— The History of Myself and My Friend. A Novel. 4 vols., London, Henry Colburn, 1813. [Baker's Bookshop: B.M.: Pickering.]

—— The Rector's Son. 3 vols., London, Lee and Hurst, 1798. [B.M.: Mayhew: Arthur Rogers.]

—— Something New; Or, Adventures at Campbell-House. 3 vols., London, Printed by A. Strahan, for T. N. Longman and O. Rees, 1801. [B.M.: Elkin Mathews.]

—— and Annabella. Tales Of Wonder, of Humour, And Of Sentiment; Original and Translated. 3 vols., London, Henry Colburn, 1818. [Baker's Bookshop: B.M.: Stonehill.]

Pneumanee; Or, The Fairy Of the Nineteenth Century. 2 vols., London, J. Hatchard, 1814. [B.M.: Ingpen: McLeish.]

Poacher (The). London, W. J. Cleaver, 1850. [B.M.]

Poacher's Daughter (The): founded on fact. London, Religious Tract Society, [1830 ?]. [B.M.]

186

Poder De La Musica (El), The Power of Music; A Romance, by M. del R. Translated by R. R. B. 1827. [Dobell.]

Poet's Daughter (The). 3 vols., London, John Macrone, 1837. [B.M.]

Poisoned Goblet (The); or, The Knights of Castile. With a frontispiece. London, Duncombe, [c. 1800]. [Stonehill.]

Polack, Maria. Fiction without Romance, or, the Locket-Watch. 2 vols., London, Printed for the Author, 1830. [B.M.: *New Monthly Mag.*]

Police and Piety: or, the Agnews of Downing Street. A Satire. By the Hon. * * *. London, 1839. [B.M.]

Polidori, John William. Ernestus Berchtold; Or The Modern Oedipus. A Tale. London, Longman, Hurst, 1819. [B.M.: Dobell: Ingpen.]

—— The Vampyre. A Tale. London, Sherwood, Neely & Jones, 1819. [B.M.: Ingpen: Stonehill.]

Polish Chieftain (The). From the German of the Author of Abellino. London, J. F. Hughes. [Publisher's advert., 1806.]

Polite Amusements, Containing Select Histories Equally Instructive and Entertaining. Viz. The Platonic Lovers. The Fair Pilgrim, or Double Disguise. The Generous Lovers, or the fatal Effects of Jealousy. Translated from the French. London, M. Cooper, 1745. [B.M.: Pickering.]

Polite Lady (The): or, A Course of Female Education. In a Series of Letters, From a Mother to her Daughter. With a frontispiece. London, J. Newbery, 1760. [T. D. Webster.]

Polite Repository (The); or, Amusing companion for the year. Containing a selection of tales, histories, adventures, anecdotes, from the best modern publications. With a variety of originals, instructive and entertaining. With 7 engravings. [W. Lane, 1791]. [Blakey.]

Pollok, Robert. Helen of the Glen: a tale for youth. Glasgow, W. Collins, 1830 [B.M. (4th edn.).]

—— The Persecuted Family. A Narrative Of the Sufferings of the Presbyterians In the Reign of Charles II. With a frontispiece. Edinburgh, James Robertson; Maurice Ogle, Glasgow; Holdsworth & Ball, London, 1829. [B.M. (3rd edn.).]

—— Ralph Gemmell; a tale. With a biographical memoir of the author. Edinburgh, 1829. [B.M. (3rd edn.).]

—— Tales of the Covenanters. Edinburgh, 1833. [B.M.]

Polson, Thomas R. J. The Fortune-Teller's Intrigue; Or, Life in Ireland before the Union. A tale of Agrarian outrage. 3 vols. Dublin, James McGlashan; Wm. S. Orr, London, 1848. [B.M.]

Polydore and Julia: or the Libertine reclaim'd. A novel. London, S. Crowdes and H. Woodgate, 1756. [B.M.]

Ponsonby. 2 vols., London, John Richardson, 1817. [The Ingpen copy was entitled " Ponsonby. Italian Mothers."] [B.M.]

Ponsonby, Catherine. The Border Wardens. An Historical Romance. 3 vols., London, John Mortimer, 1844. [Allibone: B.M.]

—— The Desborough Family. 3 vols., London, John Mortimer, 1845. [Allibone: B.M.]

—— The Protégé. 3 vols., London, H. Hurst, [1847]. [Allibone: B.M.]

Ponsonby, Lady Emily. The Discipline of Life. 3 vols., London, Henry Colburn, 1848. [Block: B.M.]

—— Pride and Irresolution, A New Series of the Discipline of Life. 3 vols., London, Henry Colburn, 1850. [*Eng. Cat.*: Maggs: T. Thorp.]

—— The Two Brothers; Or, The Family that lived in the first Society. 2 vols., London, Richard Bentley, 1850. [B.M.: Brough: Elkin Mathews.]

Ponsonby. A tale of troublous times. 2 vols., London, Whittaker, 1850. [B.M.: *Eng. Cat.*: McLeish.]

Poole, John. Christmas Festivities; Tales, Sketches, and Characters, With Beauties of the Modern Drama in four specimens. With a portrait. London, Smith, Elder, 1845-1848. [Allibone: B.M.: *Eng. Cat.*]

—— Comic Sketches and Recollections. With a portrait. 2 vols., London, 1843. [T. Thorp.]

—— Little Pedlington and the Pedlingtonians. 2 vols., London, Henry Colburn, 1839. [B.M.: *Eng. Cat.*: R. S. Garnett.]

—— Phineas Quiddy; Or, Sheer Industry. 3 vols., London, Henry Colburn, 1843. [Allibone: B.M.: Chas. Hutt.]

Poor Child's Friend; consisting of narratives. London, 1825. [B.M.]

Poor Henry, or the little Pilgrim: a story for Christian Children. London, Rivington, 1847. [B.M.]

Poor Joseph; an authentic narrative. To which is added, An Account Of A Woman who was Providentially saved from Self-Murder. With a woodcut. London, Printed by Augustus Applegarth and Edward Cowper, for the Religious Tract Society, N.D. [Block.]

Poor Mary; or, the Love Engagement. A romance. London, [1847]. [B.M.]

Poor Sarah, or the Indian Woman. London, [1830 ?]. [B.M.]

Popular Tales and Romances of the Northern Nations. 3 vols., London, Simpkin, 1823. [Lowndes: *New Monthly Mag.*: *Quarterly Review.*]

Porter, Anna Maria. Artless Tales. 2 vols., London, 1793-1795. [Allibone: *Camb. Hist. Eng. Lit.*: *Eng. Lit. in Germany.*]

—— The Barony. 3 vols., London, Longman, Rees, Orme, Brown, and

Green, 1830. [Allibone: B.M.: Ingpen.]

Porter, Anna Maria. Don Sebastian, Or the House of Braganza. An Historical Romance. 4 vols., London, Longman, Hurst, Rees, and Orme, 1809. [B.M.: Marks: Arthur Rogers.]

—— The Fast of St. Magdalen, A Romance. 3 vols., London, Longman, Hurst, Rees, Orme, and Brown, 1818. [Allibone: B.M.: Ingpen.]

—— Honor O'Hara. A Novel. 3 vols., London, Longman, Rees, Orme, Brown, and Green, 1826. [Birrell & Garnett: B.M.: Ingpen.]

—— The Hungarian Brothers. 3 vols., London, Printed by C. Stower, for Longman, Hurst, Rees, and Orme, 1807. [Blackwell: B.M.: Pickering.]

—— The Knight of St. John. A Romance. 3 vols., London, Longman, Hurst, Rees, Orme, and Brown, 1817. [Ingpen: Pickering: Stonehill.]

—— The Lake of Killarney: A Novel. 3 vols., London, T. N. Longman and O. Rees, 1804. [*Camb. Hist. Eng. Lit.*: McLeish: Pickering.]

—— Octavia. 3 vols., 1798. [Allibone: *Camb. Hist. Eng. Lit.*: *New Ann. Reg.*]

—— The Recluse of Norway. 4 vols., London, Longman, Hurst, Rees, Orme, and Brown, 1814. [B.M.: Ingpen: T. D. Webster.]

—— Roche-Blanche; Or, the Hunters of the Pyrenees. A Romance. 3 vols., London, Longman, Hurst, Rees, Orme, and Brown, London, 1822. [Birrell & Garnett: B.M.: Ingpen.]

—— A Sailor's Friendship and A Soldier's Love. 2 vols., 1805. [Allibone: *Camb. Hist. Eng. Lit.*]

—— Tales of Pity, Intended to inculcate sentiments of Humanity. By A. M. P. London, [1814]. [Allibone: *Camb. Hist. Eng. Lit.*: *Quarterly Review.*]

—— The Village Of Mariendorpt. A Tale. 4 vols., London, Longman, Hurst, Rees, Orme, and Brown, 1821. [Birrell & Garnett: B.M.: Ingpen.]

—— Walsh Colville. 1797. [Allibone: *Camb. Hist. Eng. Lit.*]

Porter, Jane. Duke Christian Of Luneburg; Or, Tradition from the Hartz. 3 vols., London, Longman, Hurst, Rees, Orme, Brown, and Green. 1824. [B.M.: Court Bk. Shop: Ingpen.]

—— The Pastor's Fireside, A Novel. 3 vols., London, Longman, Hurst, Rees, Orme, and Brown, 1817. [B.M.: Arthur Rogers: Lyle H. Wright.]

—— The Scottish Chiefs, A Romance. 5 vols., London, Longman, Hurst, Rees & Orme, 1810 [B.M.: Ingpen: McLeish.]

—— Sir Edward Seaward's Narrative Of his Shipwreck, And consequent Discovery of Certain Islands in the Caribbean Sea: With a Detail of Many extraordinary and highly interesting events in his life, From the Year 1733 to 1749. As written in his own diary. Edited by Miss Jane Porter. 3 vols., London, Longman, Rees, Orme, Brown, and Green, 1831. [Block: B.M.]

Porter, Jane. Thaddeus of Warsaw. 4 vols., London, Longman, 1803. [Allibone: *Camb. Hist. Eng. Lit.*: Publisher's advert.]

—— The Two Princes of Persia. Addressed to Youth. With a frontispiece. London, Crosby and Sellerman, 1801. [Ingpen: Arthur Rogers.]

—— Young Hearts. A Novel By A Recluse. With a preface by Miss Jane Porter. 3 vols., London, Saunders & Otley, 1834. [Birrell & Garnett: B.M.]

—— and Anna Maria. Coming Out; And The Field of The Forty Footsteps. 3 vols., London, Longman, Rees, Orme, Brown, and Green, 1828. [Birrell & Garnett: B.M.: Publisher's advert.]

—— Tales Round a Winter Hearth. 2 vols., London, Longman, Rees, Orme, Brown, & Green, 1826. [Birrell & Garnett: B.M.: Maggs.]

Porter, Rippin. Love, Rashness, And Revenge; Or, Tales of Three Passions. 2 vols., London, Printed for W. Simpkin and R. Marshall, by J. Noble, Boston, 1816. [Allibone: B.M.: *New Monthly Mag.*]

Portrait of Life (The), or The Various Effects of Virtue and Vice Delineated; as they daily appear on the great Theatre of the World. In a Collection of Interesting Novels. 2 vols., London, J. Bell, 1770. [B.M.: T. D. Webster.]

Portraits of Fashionable Belles. London, 1814. [*New Monthly Mag.*]

Posthumous Papers of the Wonderful Discovery Club, formerly of Camden Town, established by Sir Peter Paton, edited by Poz. With a woodcut title & 11 illustrations by Point after Squib. London, William Mark Clark, 1838. [Marks.]

Pott, Joseph Holden. The Tour of Valentine. London, 1786. [B.M.: W. Brown: Arthur Rogers.]

Potter, John. The Curate of Coventry. A Tale. 2 vols., London, F. Newbery, 1771. [Pickering.]

—— The History of the Adventures of Arthur O'Bradley. 2 vols., London, 1769. [B.M.]

—— Olivia; or the Nymph of the Valley: a novel. 2 vols., London, W. Earle, 1813. [B.M.:*Quarterly Review.*]

—— The Virtuous Villagers, A Novel, In a Series of Letters. 2 vols., W. Cass, 1784. [Murrays: Stonehill.]

Potter, Matilda. Matilda; an Irish Tale. 1813. [Allibone.]

—— Mount Erin; an Irish Tale. 2 vols. [1810 ?]. [Allibone: *Quarterly Review.*]

Potter, Mr. Frederic; or, The libertine. Including memoirs of the family of Montague. 2 vols. [W. Lane, 1788]. [Blakey.]

Potter, T. Novelettes Moral and Sentimental, Partly Original and partly compiled by the late T. Potter, Surgeon at North Shields near Newcastle upon Tyne. [Edited by A. M. Potter.] With a portrait. London, Printed for the Editor, 1785. [B.M.: Pickering.]

—— The Moralist; or, portraits of the human mind exhibited in a series of novelettes, partly original, and partly compiled. 2 vols., London, 1785. [B.M.]

—— The Moralist, or tales of instruction and entertainment, partly original, and partly compiled. [Edited by A. M. Potter.] 2 vols., London, [1785 ?]. [Contents of vol. 2 are entirely different from preceding item]. [B.M.]

Power, Tyrone. The King's Secret. By the Author of " The Lost Heir." 3 vols., London, Edward Bull, 1831. [Allibone: B.M. (2nd edn.).]

—— The Lost Heir. And The Prediction. 3 vols., London, Edward Bull, 1830. [B.M.: Lib. of Congress: *New Monthly Mag.*]

Power of First Love (The) or Count Bertram and the Beautiful Imogine, of the Castle of St. Aldobrand. An Insteresting [*sic*] Tale. With a vignette and frontispiece. London, J. Bushnell, N.D. [Court Bk. Shop.]

Powis Castle, or Anecdotes of an antient family. 2 vols., London, W. Lane, 1788. [Blakey: T. D. Webster.]

Poynet, Quintin. The Wizard Priest And The Witch. A Romance. 3 vols., London, A. K. Newman, 1822. [B.M.: Stonehill.]

Prater (The). By Nicholas Babble. [Ingpen.]

Pratt, Mrs. John Burnett. Glen Tilloch: a tale. London, J. Lendrum, 1845. [B.M.]

Pratt, Samuel Jackson. Emma Corbet; Or, The Miseries of Civil War: Founded on some circumstances which happened in America. By the Author of " Liberal Opinions." 2 vols., Dublin, 1780. [Allibone: B.M.]

—— Family Secrets. 5 vols., London, T. N. Longman, 1797. [T. D. Webster.]

—— Liberal Opinions, upon Animals, Man, and Providence. In which are introduced Anecdotes of a Gentleman. By Courtney Melmoth (Benignus; written by himself). 6 vols., London, 1775-1777. [B.M.]

—— The Pupil of Pleasure; Or The New System Illustrated. Inscribed to Mrs. Eugenia Stanhope, Editor of Lord Chesterfield's Letters. By Courtney Melmoth. 2 vols., London, G. Robinson and J. Bew, 1776. [B.M.: *Cat. Lib. Prohib.*: Ingpen.]

—— Shenstone-Green; Or, The New Paradise Lost. Being a History of Human Nature, written by the Proprietor of the Green, The Editor Courtney Melmoth. 3 vols., London, Baldwin, 1779. [Allibone: B.M.: Ingpen.]

—— Travels for the Heart. Written in France, by Courtney Melmoth. 2 vols., London, John Wallis, 1777. [G. Worthington.]

Pratt, Samuel Jackson. Triumph of Benevolence; Or History of Francis Wills. 1772. [W. Brown.]

—— The Tutor of Truth. 2 vols., London. [Stonehill.]

Praying for the Living and the Dead; or the Story of Little Mary. London, [1849]. [B.M.]

Precept and Example; or, Midsummer Holidays. London, W. Darton, [1820 ?]. [B.M.]

Precipitate Choice (The); or, the History of Lord Ossory and Miss Rivers. A novel. By a Lady. 2 vols., London, 1772. [B.M.]

Predestined Wife: or Force of Prejudice; a Novel in a Series of Letters. By the Author of Edward and Sophia, Powis Castle, and Eliza Cleland. 2 vols., London, 1789. [T. D. Webster.]

Prediction, Or History of Miss Lucy Maxwell. 3 vols., 1771. [W. Brown.]

Present for a Little Boy (A). London, 1813. [B.M.]

Present for a Little Girl (A). With illustrations. London, 1797. [B.M.]

Present for Youth (A); or, a short and pleasing Account of the happy Effects of Divine Grace on the Minds of four young Persons; extracted, by permission, from Rictrie's Narrative of the Lives of Young Persons. London, Griffith. [*Guardian of Education.*]

Present for Youth (A): or, Tales from Life. By Rambler. London, [1800 ?]. [B.M.]

Present from my Teacher (A). London, 1826. [B.M.]

Present (The); Or, Child's Pleasing Companion. With woodcuts. Dundalk, Joseph Parks, [1800 ?]. [B.M.]

Present Times and Modern Manners; Or Tale of a Rector's Family. 4 vols., London, Printed by J. D. Dewick, for Appleyards, 1810. [B.M.: Stonehill.]

Prest, Thomas Peckett (Ascribed to). The Adventures of Valentine Vaux; or, The Tricks of a Ventriloquist. By Timothy Portwine. With woodcuts. London, E. Lloyd, 1840. [B. Ono.]

—— Agnes the Unknown, Or The Beggar's Secret. A Romance By the Author of " Ela, the Outcast," " Gipsy Boy," " The Royal Twins," " Evelina," " Blighted Heart," &c., &c. With illustrations, London, E. Lloyd, 1849. [B.M.: Stonehill.]

—— Almira's Curse; Or, The Black Tower of Bransdorf. A Romance. By the Author of " Ela, the Outcast," " The Old House of West Street," " The Robber's Foundling," " The Gipsy Boy," &c. With woodcuts. London, Edward Lloyd; and G. Purkess, [c. 1842]. [B.M.: Stonehill.]

—— Angelina; or, The Mystery of St.

Mark's Abbey. A Tale of Other Days. By the Author of " The Maniac Father; or, the Victim of Seduction," " Evelina," &c. &c. With woodcuts. London, E. Lloyd, [1849]. [B.M.: B. Ono.]

Prest, Thomas Peckett. Ben Bolt of the Perils of a Sailor. With woodcuts. London, G. Purkess, N.D. [B.M.]

—— The Black Mantle; or the Murder at the Old Ferry. London, E. Lloyd, 1846. [G. Meredith.]

—— Blanche Langdale The Outlaw's Bride. A Romance of Sherwood Forest. By the Author of " The Jew and the Foundling," " Hebrew Maiden," &c. London, E. Lloyd, 1847. [B.M.: B. Ono.]

—— The Blighted Heart; or, the Old Priory Ruins. A romance. London, 1840. [B.M.]

—— (Edited by)—The Calendar of Horrors: An Interesting collection of the Romantic, Wild, and Wonderful. With woodcuts. 2 vols., [1836]. [Bailey Bros.]

—— The Convict: a Romance. By the Author of " Kathleen," " Hebrew Maiden," &c. &c. With woodcuts. London, E. Lloyd, 1846. [B.M.: B. Ono.]

—— The Death Grasp, or, a Father's Curse, A Romance of Startling Interest. By the Author of " Ela, the Outcast," " Angelina," " Maniac Father," etc. etc. With woodcuts. London, E. Lloyd, [1844]. [B.M.: B. Ono: Stonehill.]

—— The Death Ship: or, The Pirate's Bride and the Maniac of the Deep. A Nautical Romance. With illustrations. London, Lloyd, [1846]. [B.M.: Stonehill.]

—— Ela, the Outcast; or, The Gipsy of Rosemary Dell. A Romance of Thrilling Interest. By the Author of " Angelina; or, the Mystery of St. Mark's Abbey," " Gallant Tom; or, the Perils of a Sailor Ashore and Afloat," " Ernnestine de Lacy; or, the Robbers' Foundling, "etc., etc. With woodcuts. London, E. Lloyd, [1841]. [Marks: Nattrass: Stonehill.]

—— Emily Fitzormond; or, the Deserted One. A tale of Mystery. By the Author of " Angelina," " Gallant Tom," " Ernnestine de Lacy," " The Death Grasp," " Mary Clifford," " Ela, the Outcast," " The Maniac Father," etc. etc. With woodcuts. London, E. Lloyd, [1842]. [B. Ono.]

—— Ernnestine de Lacy; or, The Robber's Foundling. An Old English Romance. With woodcuts. London, E. Lloyd, 1842. [B.M.: B. Ono: Stonehill.]

—— Ethelinde; or, the Fatal Vow. A Romance. By the author of " Ela the Outcast"; " Gipsy Boy"; " Evelina"; " Gallant Tom"; &c. &c. With illustrations. London, E. Lloyd, [1848]. [B.M.: Stonehill.]

—— Fatherless Fanny, or, A Young Lady's First Entrance into Life, being the Memoirs of a Little Mendicant, and Her Benefactors. By the author of the Old English Baron [Clara Reeve ?]. London, J. Tallis, 1819. [B.M.: Ingpen.]

Prest, Thomas Peckett. The First False Step. A novel. With illustrations. London, Edward Lloyd, 1846. [B.M.]

—— Gallant Tom: or, the Perils of a Sailor, ashore and afloat. An original nautical romance. By the Author of " The Smuggler King," " Death Ship," " Ela the Outcast." With woodcuts. London, E. Lloyd, 1844. [B.M.]

—— Geraldine; or, The Secret Assassins of The Old Stone Cross. With illustrations. London, Lloyd, [c. 1845]. [Stonehill.]

—— Gilbert Copley, the Reprobate. A Domestic Romance. By the Author of " The Hebrew Maiden; or, the Jew's Daughter," " Therese; or, the Orphan of Geneva," " Fatherless Fanny," " Kathleen; or, the Secret Marriage"; etc., etc., etc. With woodcuts. London, E. Lloyd, 1844. [B. Ono.]

—— Gilderoy; or, the Freebooter of Scotland. A Powerful Romance. By the Author of " Ela, the Outcast," " Evelina," &c. &c. With woodcuts. London, E. Lloyd, [c. 1845]. [B. Ono.]

—— The Gipsy Boy: a Romance of the Woods and the Wilds. With woodcuts. London, E. Lloyd, [1850]. [Marks: B. Ono.]

—— The Hebrew Maiden; or, The Lost Diamond. A Tale of Chivalry. By the Author of " Fatherless Fanny," " Tales of the Drama," &c. &c. With woodcuts. London, E. Lloyd, 1841. [B.M.: G. Meredith: B. Ono.]

—— The Highland Watch Tower; or, The Sons of Glenalvon. A Romance. By the Author of " Kathleen; or, the Secret Marriage," " The Hebrew Maiden; or, the Lost Diamond," " Fatherless Fanny," &c. &c. London, E. Lloyd, 1842. [B. Ono.]

—— Jack Junk; or, the Tar for all Weathers. A Romance of the Sea. With woodcuts. London, E. Lloyd, [c. 1849]. [B.M.: B. Ono: Stonehill.]

—— Jonathan Bradford; or, The Murder at the Road-Side Inn. A Romance. By the Author of " The Hebrew Maiden," " The Wife's Secret," &c., &c. With woodcuts. London, E. Lloyd, [c. 1845]. [B. Ono: Stonehill.]

—— Kathleen; Or the Secret Marriage. By the Author of The " Hebrew Maiden." With woodcuts. London, E. Lloyd, [1842]. [B.M.: Grafton: Stonehill.]

—— The Lady in Black, Or The Widow and the Wife. London, E. Lloyd, 1847. [B.M.: H. W. Fennell.]

—— A Lady in Search of a Husband. A Romance. With woodcuts. London,

E. Lloyd, [1847]. [B.M.: G. Meredith: Stonehill.]

Prest, Thomas Peckett. The Lone Cottage, or, Who's The Stranger? A Romance. With woodcuts. London, E. Lloyd, 1845. [B.M.: Stonehill.]

—— Love and Mystery; or, Married and Single. A Romance. London, Lloyd, 1849. [B. Ono.]

—— The Love Child: A Romance. With woodcuts. London, The Author, 1847. [B.M.: Arthur Rogers.]

—— The Maniac Father: or, The Victim of Seduction. A Romance of Deep Interest. With woodcuts. London, E. Lloyd, 1842. [Stonehill.]

—— Marianne, the Child of Charity. A domestic romance. By the author of " The Hebrew Maiden." London, 1845. [B.M.]

—— Martha Willis; or, the Maid, the Profligate, and the Felon. A Romance. By the Author of " Ela the Outcast," " Angelina"; " Rosalie; or, the Vagrant's Daughter;" " Florian the Dumb Boy," " Maniac Father," " Gallant Tom," " The Smuggler King"; " Florence; or, the Wild Mountain Maid"; " The Death Grasp," &c. &c. With woodcuts. London, E. Lloyd, 1844. [B.M.: B. Ono.]

—— Mary Clifford; or, the Foundling Apprentice girl. A tale. By the author of " Angelina," etc. London, [1842]. [B.M.]

—— May Grayson; or, Love and Treachery. A Romance. With woodcuts. London, Lloyd, 1842. [Stonehill.]

—— The Old House of West Street, or, London in the Last Century: A Romantic Tale. With woodcuts. London, E. Lloyd, 1846. [B.M.: B. Ono: Arthur Rogers.]

—— The Rivals; or, The Spectre of the Hall: A Romance. With woodcuts. London, Lloyd, [c. 1848]. [B.M.: Stonehill.]

—— The Royal Twins; or, The Sisters of Mystery. By the Author of " Ela the Outcast," " The Smuggler King," " The Old House of West Street," etc. With woodcuts. London, Printed by E. Lloyd; published by G. Purkess, [1848]. [B.M.: B. Ono.: Stonehill.]

—— The Smuggler King; or, the Foundling of the Wreck. A Nautico Domestic Romance. By the Author of " Gallant Tom"; " Ela, the Outcast"; " Angelina"; " Emily Fitzormond"; " Maniac Father"; " Martha Willis"; " Mary Clifford"; etc., etc. With cuts: London, E. Lloyd, 1844. [B. Ono.: Hollings.]

—— The String of Pearls; or, the Barber of Fleet Street. A domestic romance. With woodcuts. London, E. Lloyd, 1850. [H. W. Fennell: B. Ono.]

—— The Widow Mortimer; or, the Marriage in the Dark. A Romance. By the Author of " The String of Pearls,' &c. &c. With woodcuts. London, E. Lloyd, [1848 ?]. [B. Ono.]

Prettiest Book for Children (The); being the History of the Enchanted Castle situated in one of the Fortunate Isles, and governed by the Giant Instruction. By Stephano Bunyano. London, [1800 ?]. [B.M.]

Pretty Portress of Windsor Lodge (The); Or Filial Affection Rewarded. With 3 plates. London, William Darton, [1829].

Prévost D'Exiles, Abbé Antoine François. The Dean of Coleraine. A Moral History Founded On the Memoirs of an Illustrious Family in Ireland. Written in French, by the Author of A Man of Quality. And now done into English. 3 vols., London, C. Davis; C. Hitch and L. Hawes, 1752. [B.M.: *Guide to Best Fiction*: Arthur Rogers.]

—— The History of the Chevalier des Grieux. 2 vols., 1767. [Sotheby's.]

—— Manon Lescaut, from the French of the Abbé Prevost. [With a life of the author by the translator, D. C. Moylan.] With illustrations by Tony Johannot. London, 1841. [B.M.]

—— Translation of Manon L'Escaut from the French of the Abbé Prevost. [By Charlotte Turner Smith.] 1786. [Allibone: *Camb. Hist. Eng. Lit.*]

Prevot, Charles Victor (*see* D'ARLINCOURT, Vicomte).

Prickett, Miss. Warwick Castle, An Historical Novel. Dedicated To The Right Honourable The Countess of Clonmell. Containing, amongst other desultory Information, the Descent and Achievements of the Ancient Earls of Warwick, from the earliest Period of their Creation to the present Time. With some Account of Warwick, Birmingham, Lemmington, Kenilworth, Stratford-upon-Avon, &c. &c.; interspersed with Pieces of Local Poetry, Incidental Biography, and Authentic Anecdotes of English History. 3 vols., London, Baldwin, Cradock, and Joy, 1815. [Allibone: B.M.: *New Monthly Mag.*]

Priest (The). 3 vols., London, Baldwin, Cradock, and Joy, 1821. [B.M.]

Priestess (The). An Anglo-Saxon Tale, Of The Early Days of Christianity In Britain. By the Translator of " Margaret; or, The Gold Mine." London, J. Hatchard; Grant, Edinburgh, 1846. [B.M.]

Prince Fatal and Prince Fortune. A Fairy Tale. With woodcuts. Birmingham, T. Bloomer; and A. Carvalho, London, [1840]. [B.M.]

Prince of Orange (The). An Historical Romance Of the Dutch Protestant Revolution. 3 vols., London, Richard Bentley, 1845. [B.M.]

Prince (The), or the Royal Libertines.

3 vols., London, A. K. Newman, 1816. [*Eng. Cat.: New Monthly Mag.*]

Prince Riquet with the Tuft. London, J. L. Marks, [1830 ?]. [B.M.]

Princely History of Crispin and Crispianus (The); or, the gentle craft. London, [1750 ?]. [B.M.]

Princeps, Elizabeth Louisa Slater. Variety. A Novel. With Poetry. 3 vols., London, W. Fearman, 1820. [B.M.: *New Monthly Mag.*]

Principle and Passion. A Novel. 2 vols., Derby, 1819. [B.M.: *New Monthly Mag.*]

Principle and Practice; or, The Orphan Family. A Tale. With a frontispiece. Wellington, Salop: Houlston, 1827. [B.M.]

Principle: a tale. By the author of " Hadassah." London, Houlston, 1849. [B.M.: *Eng. Cat.*]

Prinsep, Augustus. The Baboo; And Other Tales Descriptive of Society in India. 2 vols., London, Smith, Elder, 1834. [B.M.]

Priory of St. Bernard; An old English Tale, Being the first literary production of a Young Lady. 2 vols., London, William Lane, [1790]. [Myers.]

Priscilla and Marcus. With 8 woodcuts. London, Houlston, [*c.* 1820]. [Gumuchian.]

Prison House; or, The World We Live in, by Mrs. Bridget Bluemantle. 4 vols., London, 1814. [T. Thorp.]

Privateer (The); A Tale. 2 vols., London, John Andrews, 1821. [B.M.]

Prize of Youthful Obedience (The). In two Parts. London, Darton and Harvey. [*Guardian of Education.*]

Proby, W. C. The Mysterious Seal; a Romance. 3 vols., 1799. [Allibone: *New Ann. Reg.*]

Procrastination; Or, The Vicar's Daughter. A Tale. With a frontispiece. London, Burton and Smith, 1824. [B.M.]

Proctor, George. The Lucubrations of Humphrey Ravelin, Esq., late Major in the ** Regiment of Infantry. London, G. & W. B. Whittaker, 1823. [B.M.: Dobell: *Quarterly Review.*]

Prodigal Youth (The); Disobedient Son, and Cruel Husband's Garland. In 3 parts. Newcastle [?], [1740 ?]. [B.M.]

Prodigious !!! Or, Childe Paddie in London. 3 vols., London, Printed for the Author, 1818. [Block: B.M.: Pickering.]

Profligate Mother, or Fatal Cabinet. 2 vols. [Cawthorn's Catalogue, 1810].

Profligate Prince (The); or, Court of Ethelred. A novel. London, Sherwood, Neely, 1812. [B.M.]

Progressive Tales for Little Children. In words of one and two syllables. Forming the sequel to " Very little Tales for very little children." Second Series. Edinburgh, Fraser, 1835. [B.M.]

Protector's Secret (The); or, The Puritan's Daughter. A Romance. With woodcuts. London, E. Lloyd, [*c.* 1849]. [B. Ono.: Stonehill.]

Protestant Rector (The), or a tale of other times in Ireland. By the author of " A Narrative of three years residence in Italy." London, Nesbit, 1830. [B.M.: *I. in F.*]

Proverbs of Little Solomon. Containing entertaining stories. Edinburgh, Oliver & Boyd, [1825 ?]. [B.M.]

Providential Care. A Tale, Founded on Facts. With a frontispiece. 1825.

Provincials (The), a country tale, dedicated to the intelligent reader in town and country. By the author of The Ramsay Family. 2 vols., London, [1818 ?]. [B.M.]

Prudence and Principle; a tale. By the author of " Rachel." London, Taylor and Hessey, 1821. [B.M.]

Pry, Paul. Oddities of London Life. 2 vols., London, R. Bentley, 1838. [B.M.]

—— Reminiscences, Mishaps, and Observations of Mr. Paul Pry, written by himself, and published by W. Smith. Edinburgh, 1833. [B.M.]

Psalmanazar, George. Memoirs of * * * *, commonly known by the name of George Psalmanazar, a reputed native of Formosa, written by himself, in order to be published after his death. London, R. Davis, 1764. [B.M.: McLeish.]

Pullan, Matilda Marian. Court-Partial of 18—: A Tale of Military Life. 2 vols., London, T. C. Newby, 1844. [Allibone: B.M.: T. Thorp.]

Pullin, Greg. Henry, The Recluse of Devon: Or, His first visit. A Tale from Life. 3 vols., London, John Bennett, 1835. [B.M.]

Punctuality, Sensibility, & Disappointment, Instructive and Entertaining Stories for Young People. With illustrations. London, Edward Lacey, N.D. [Block.]

Pupil of Adversity (The). An Oriental Tale. 1788. [*Eng. Lit. in Germany*: Blakey.]

Purbeck, The Misses. Honoria Sommerville: A Novel. 4 vols., London, G. G. J. and J. Robinson, 1789. [Block: *Eng. Lit. in Germany*: J. C. Hardy.]

—— Matilda and Elizabeth, A Novel By the Authors of Honoria Sommerville, Rainsford Park, The Benevolent Quixote, etc. 4 vols., London, Sampson Low, 1796. [*New Ann. Reg.*: Arthur Rogers.]

—— Neville Castle, or the Generous Cambrians, a Novel. By the Author of Raynsford Park. 4 vols., London, Dutton, 1802. [G. Worthington.]

—— Raynsford Park, A Novel. 4 vols., London, G. Kearsley, [1790]. [B.M.: *Eng. Lit. in Germany.*]

—— William Thornborough, the Benevolent Quixote. 4 vols., 1791. [W. Brown: T. D. Webster.]

Purcell, Mrs. The Orientalist; Or Electioneering in Ireland; A Tale, By Myself. 2 vols., London, Baldwin, Cradock, and Joy; J. Thomson, Edinburgh; William Gribbin, Dublin; Samuel Archer, Belfast, 1820. [B.M.: *New Monthly Mag.*]

Putney, Charlotte. The Brazen Mask. A Romance. 4 vols., London, A. K. Newman, 1826. [B.M.: *Edin. Mag.*: Stonehill.]

—— Cora, the Nabob's Granddaughter. London, 1824. [B.M.]

Puzzle for a Curious Girl (A). London, Tabart. [*Guardian of Education.*]

Pye, Henry James. The Democrat: interspersed with Anecdotes of well known Characters. 2 vols., London, Printed at the Minerva Press, for William Lane, 1795. [Allibone: *Eng. Lit. in Germany*: Arthur Rogers.]

Pye, Mrs. Hampden. Theodosius and Arabella. A novel. In a series of letters. 2 Vols. [W. Lane, 1786]. [Blakey.]

Pyne, William Henry. The Twenty-Ninth of May: Rare Doings At The Restoration. By Ephraim Hardcastle. Author of "Wine and Walnuts." 2 vols., London, Knight and Lacey, 1825. [B.M.: Ingpen: Lib. of Congress.]

—— Wine and Walnuts; Or, After Dinner Chit-Chat. By Ephraim Hardcastle, Citizen and Drysalter. 2 vols., London, Longman, Hurst, Rees, Orme, and Brown, 1823. [Bailey Bros.: B.M.: W. T. Spencer.]

Quaker (The). A novel, in a Series by a lady. 3 vols., London, William Lane, 1785. [Blakey.]

Queen's Lieges (The). 4 vols., London, T. C. Newby, 1846. [B.M.]

Quid (The); or tales of my messmates. Being a collection of yarns, ditties, quid-ditties and od-ditties. By a Steerage Passenger. London, W. Strange, 1832. [B.M.]

Quillinan, Edward. The Conspirators, Or the Romance of Military Life. 3 vols,. London, Henry Colburn, 1841. [Allibone: B.M.]

Quin, Michael Joseph. Nourmahal, An Oriental Romance. 3 vols., London, Henry Colburn, 1838. [Allibone: B.M.: T. D. Webster.]

Rabelais, Francis. Works. Formerly translated by Sir Thomas Urquart, and Explained by Mr. Motteux. Since carefully revised, and compared throughout with M. le du Chat's edition by Mr. Ozell. New edition, with improvements, and an entire new set of cuts. With a portrait, map and 26 plates. 5 vols., London, John Hurt for J. Brindley, 1750. [B.M.: Maggs.]

—— Works, translated from the French by Sir Thomas Urquhart and Motteux, with Explanatory Notes by Duchat, Ozell, and others. A New Edition, Revised and with Additional Notes. With 2 portraits. 2 vols., London, Bohn, 1849. [B.M.: Marks.]

Rachel Ashburn: a story of real life. By the author of "Harry and Walter." London, 1849. [B.M.]

—— : a tale. London, Houlston, 1817. [B.M.: *New Monthly Mag.*]

Radcliffe, Ann. The Castles of Athlin and Dunbayne. A Highland Story. London, Hookham, 1789. [*Camb. Hist. Eng. Lit.*: Stonehill.]

—— (?). The Fate of Velina de Guidova. A novel. 3 vols. [W. Lane, 1790]. [Blakey.]

—— Gaston de Blondeville, or The Court of Henry III. Keeping Festival in Ardenne, A Romance. St. Alban's Abbey, A Metrical Tale; With some Poetical Pieces. To which is Prefixed A Memoir of the Author, With Extracts from her Journals. 4 vols., London, Henry Colburn, 1826. [Block: B.M.: Arthur Rogers.]

—— The Italian, or the Confessional of the Black Penitents. A Romance. 3 vols., London, T. Cadell, Jun., and W. Davies, 1797. [Block: B.M.: Arthur Rogers.]

—— Manfrone; or, The one-handed monk. 4 vols. (1809). [*Cawthorn's Catalogue*: Blakey.]

—— The Mysteries of Udolpho, A Romance; Interspersed with some Pieces of Poetry. 4 vols., London, G. G. & J. Robinson, 1794. [Block: B.M.: Stonehill.]

—— The Romance of the Forest: Interspersed with some Pieces of Poetry. By the Authoress of "A Sicilian Romance." 3 vols., London, T. Hookham & J. Carpenter. 1791. [B.M.: Ingpen: Arthur Rogers.]

—— A Sicilian Romance. By the Authoress of the Castles of Athlin and Dunbayne. 2 vols., London, T. Hookham, MDCCLXC. [1790]. [B.M.: Lib. of Congress: Arthur Rogers.]

Rafter, Captain Michael. Savindroog; Or, The Queen of the Jungle. 3 vols., London, Longman, Brown, Green, and Longmans, 1848. [Allibone: B.M.]

Raikes, Harriet. The Marriage Contract. 2 vols., London, Richard Bentley, 1849. [B.M.]

Railway Passenger (A). London, Religious Tract Society, [1835 ?]. [B.M.]

Rainsford Villa: Or, Juvenile Independence. A Tale. London, J. Harris, 1823. [B.M.: Clarke-Hall: Elkin Mathews.]

Raithby, John. Delineations of the Heart, or, the History of Henry Bennet, a tragi-comi-satiric essay, attempted in the manner of Fielding. 2 vols., Dublin, 1792. [P. C. Cuttelle: *New Ann. Reg.*]

Rajah Kisna, An Indian Tale. 3 vols., London, 1786. [B.M.]

Rake of Taste (The), Or Adventures of

Tom Wildman. 2 vols., 1768. [W. Brown.]

Rake of Taste (The), or the Elegant Debauchee: a true story. London, P. Wicks, 1760. [B.M.]

Rambles of My Uncle (The). London, Baldwin, Cradock, and Joy, 1821. [B.M.]

Randall, Miss E. Adèle. A Tale of France. London, Relfe and Fletcher, 1838. [B.M.]

Rané (The). 3 vols., 1828. [T. Thorp.]

Rankin, Emily Elizabeth. Ellen Cameron, A Tale for Youth. With an engraved frontispiece. London, Baldwin and Cradock, 1829. [B.M.]

Rankin, F. Harrison. The Man Without a Soul. A Novel. 2 vols., London, Richard Bentley, 1838. [Allibone: B.M.]

Ranspach; or, Mysteries of a Castle: A Novel. 2 vols., Uttoxeter, Richards, 1797. [Stonehill.]

Raspe, Rudolf Eric. Baron Munchausen's Narrative of his Marvellous Travels and Campaigns in Russia. Humbly dedicated and Recommended to Country Gentlemen; and, if they please, to be repeated as their own, after a Hunt, at Horse Races, in Watering-Places, and other such polite assemblies; round the bottle and fire-side. Oxford, Printed for the Editor, 1786. [American Art Association.]

—— Sequel to the Adventures of Baron Munchausen. Humbly dedicated to Mr. Bruce, the Abyssinian Traveller. With 20 plates. 2 vols., London, H. D. Symonds, 1792. [B.M.: Marks.]

Ratcliffe, Elizabeth. The Mysterious Baron, or the Castle in the Forest, A Gothic Story. London, J. B. G. Vogel, 1808. [Stonehill.]

Rathbone, Hannah Mary. So much of the Diary of Lady Willoughby, as relating to her Domestic History and to the Reign of Charles I. London, Longman, Brown, Green & Longmans, 1844. [B.M.: Quaritch: Sotheran.]

—— Some further Portions of the Diary of Lady Willoughby which do relate to her Domestic History and to the Events of the latter Years of the Reign of King Charles the First, the Protectorate and the Restoration. London, Longman, Brown, Green, & Longmans, 1848. [Block: Quaritch.]

Ravensdale; A Tale By a Lady. 2 vols., Dublin, William Curry, Jun.; Longmans, Brown, 1845. [B.M.: Critic.]

Rayland Hall; Or, The Remarkable Adventures of Orlando Somerville. Front. London 1810. [Murray Hill.]

Raymond: A Tale of Truth. London, Saunders and Otley, 1843. [B.M.]

Rayner, W. H. Virtue and Vice. A Novel. 2 vols., London, 1806. [Allibone: B.M.]

Reach, Angus Bethune. Clement Lorimer; Or The Book with the Iron Clasps. A Romance. With 12 plates by George Cruikshank. London, David Bogue, 1849. [B.M.: Maggs: Pickering.]

Reach, Angus Bethune. Leonard Lindsay; or, The Story of a Buccaneer. 2 vols., London, D. Bogue, 1850. [Allibone: B.M.: Guide to Best Fiction.]

—— A Romance of a Mince-Pie; an incident in the Life of John Chirrup, of Forty-Winks, Pastrycook and Confectioner. With illustrations by " Phiz " [Hablot K. Browne]. London, H. D. Bogue, 1848. [B.M.: Pickering.]

Reading for Winter Evenings; A selection of Amusing and Instructive Stories. With a woodcut. Glasgow, Printed for the Booksellers, 1850. New and Improved Series. No. 22. [Court Bk. Shop.]

Reading Garland (The); or, Dick and Kate's happy marriage. Tewkesbury, [1790 ?]. [B.M.]

Real Life in Ireland; or, the Day and Night Scenes, Rovings and Sprees of Brian Boru, Esq. and his elegant friend Sir Shawn O'Doherty. By a Real Paddy. With plates. London, R. Bensley, 1821. [B.M.]

Reay Morden: A Novel. 3 vols., Edinburgh, 1829. [American Art Association.]

Rebecca, the Jewess. A tale, founded on the romance of Ivanhoe. London, J. & C. Evans, [1830 ?]. [B.M.]

Rebel (The): A Tale. 2 vols., London, Longman, Rees, Orme, Brown, & Green, 1826. [B.M.: Publisher's advert.: Quarterly Review.]

Rebel (The): a Tale of the Times. By a Lady. 2 vols., Southampton, 1799. [Baker's Bookshop: McLeish.]

Rebellion of the Beast (The); or, the Ass is Dead: Long Live the Ass! London, Hunt, 1826. [Eng. Cat.: New Monthly Mag.]

Rebou, Charles. The Widow's Walk. With 19 engravings. London, E. Appleyard, 1848. [Publisher's advert.]

Reclaimed Family (The), by the author of " Edwin and Mary." London, 1838. [B.M.]

Reclaimed Libertine (The), or The History of the Honourable Charles Belmont and Miss Melvill. In a Series of Letters. 2 vols., London, Francis & John Noble, 1769. [Arthur Rogers.]

Recluse (The). A Fragment. South Shields, 1787. [Robinson.]

Recluse of the Woods (The); or, The Generous Warrior. A Gothic Romance. With a frontispiece. London, Roe, 1809. [Stonehill.]

Recluse (The), or Old Briitsh [sic] Officer, and his faithful servant. With woodcuts. London, [1810 ?]. [B.M.]

Recluse (The), Or Old Father Green-Mantle, and Little Frank Miller, interspersed with passages from the Sacred History, calculated to improve and entertain The Juvenile Mind. With 3 plates. London, T. Knott, 1820.

Reconciled Sisters (The), or the Prudent Explanation. With 3 plates. London,

J. Harris, 1808. [Dobell.]

Reconciliation (The); or, The history of Miss Mortimer and Miss Fitzgerald. In a series of letters. An Hibernian novel. By an Irish lady. 2 vols. [W. Lane, 1783]. [Blakey.]

Rector and His Pupils (The): being a sequel to the Academy, or Picture of Youth. London, Harris, 1810. [B.M.: *Eng. Cat.*]

Rector of Overton (The), A Novel. 3 vols., London, Fisher, Son & Co., 1828. [B.M.: Martin A. McGoff: *Quarterly Review.*]

Red and White Roses (The), and other stories. London, Burns, [1843]. [B.M.]

Red Cross Warrior (The), or the Spirit of the Night. 1843. [H. W. Fennell.]

Red Tyger (The); or, Truth Will Out. 2 vols., London, Crosby, 1808. [B.M.: G. Worthington.]

Redbreast (The), and other tales, from the German. London, 1843. [B.M.]

Redding, Cyrus. Velasco. 3 vols., London, T. C. Newby, 1846. [Allibone: B.M.: *Critic.*]

Rede, William Leman. The Royal Rake, and the Adventures of Alfred Chesterton. With woodcuts. London, Printed for Private Circulation only. Chapman and Elcoate, 1842. [B.M.: B. Ono: Arthur Rogers.]

—— The Wedded Wanderer. With illustrations. London, G. Virtue, 1827.

Redwood, Charles. The Vale of Glamorgan: Scenes and Tales Among the Welsh. London, Saunders and Otley, 1839. [B.M.]

Reed, Andrew. Martha: A Memorial of an Only and Beloved Sister. 2 vols., London, Francis Westley, 1823. [Pickering.]

Reeve, Clara. The Champion of Virtue. A Gothic Story. By the Editor of the Phoenix. Colchester, 1777. [Title changed to *The Old English Baron* in later editions.] [Baker's Bookshop: B.M.: *Camb. Hist. Eng. Lit.*]

—— Destination, or Memoirs of a Private Family. 3 vols., 1799. [*New Ann. Reg.*: Salkeld.]

—— The Exiles; or, Memoirs of the Count de Cronstadt. 3 vols., London, Hookham, 1788. [Allibone: B.M.: Stonehill.]

—— Memoirs of Sir Roger de Clarendon, the Natural Son of Edward the Black Prince, commonly called the Black Prince; with anecdotes of many other eminent persons of the fourteenth century. 3 vols., London, Hookham and Carpenter, 1793. [B.M.: *Eng. Lit. in Germany: New Ann. Reg.*]

—— The Progress of Romance, Through Times, Countries and Manners; with Remarks on the good and bad effects of it, on them respectively in the course of Evening Conversations. By C. R., author of The English Baron. 2 vols.,

London, Printed for the Author, 1785. [B.M.: Ingpen.]

Reeve, Clara. The School for Widows. A Novel. 3 vols., London, Hookham, 1791. [Allibone: B.M.: Stonehill.]

—— The Two Mentors. A Modern Story. By the author of " The Old English Baron." 2 vols., London, 1783. [B.M.: W. Brown: *Eng. Lit. in Germany.*]

Reeve, Sophia. Cuthbert. A Novel. 3 vols., London, Sustenance and Stretch, 1828. [B.M.]

—— The Mysterious Wanderer; a Novel. 3 vols., London, 1807. [Allibone: T. Thorp.]

—— Stanmore; Or, The Monk, and The Merchant's Widow. 3 vols., London, G. and W. B. Whittaker, 1824. [Allibone: B.M.: Ingpen.]

Reformation: A Novel. 3 vols., London, Longman, Hurst, Rees, Orme, & Brown, 1822. [B.M.: *New Monthly Mag.*: Publisher's advert.]

Reformed Family (The). By an old officer. London, 1836. [B.M.]

Reformed Reprobate. A novel. 3 vols., London, 1804. [B.M.]

Reft Rob; or, the Witch of Scot-Muir, commonly called Madge the Snoover. A Scottish tale. By the author of Hardenbrass and Haverill. London, Sherwood, 1817. [B.M.: *Eng. Cat.: New Monthly Mag.*]

Refuge (The). By the author of " The Guide to Domestic Happiness." With a frontispiece. London, Button, 1805. [B.M. (5th edn.).]

Reginald du Bray: an historick tale. By a late Lord. Dublin, S. Colbert, 1779. [B.M.]

Reginald, or the House of Mirandola. By the author of Melbourne, etc. [Mrs. Martin]. 3 vols., London, Minerva Press, 1799. [B.M.: Blakey.]

Reid, Captain Thomas Mayne. The Rifle Rangers; or Adventures of an Officer in Southern Mexico. With plates. 2 vols., London, Shoberl, 1850. [Allibone: B.M.: Ingpen.]

Reinhold, Caroline. The Evening Bell; or the hour of relating entertaining anecdotes for dear young people. Translated from the German by C. S. Mangan. Dublin, Orr, 1848. [B.M.: *Eng. Cat.*]

Relapse (The). A novel. 2 vols., London, Lowndes, 1779. [B.M.]

Relapse; Or, True and False Morality. London, J. Hatchard, 1824. [B.M.]

Rellstab, Ludwig. Eighteen Hundred and Twelve: an historical romance. From the German by Mary Norman. 3 vols., London, Richard Bentley, 1849. [Block: B.M.: *Eng. Cat.*]

Remarkable History of Elizabeth Loveless, A faithful servant, and affectionate child, shewing How she was most amply rewarded. Very Interesting to all Young Persons. With a woodcut. London, Augustus Applegarth and

Edward Cowper, N.D. [Court Bk. Shop.]

Renneville, Madame de (*see* DE RENNE-VILLE).

Rennie,—. Saint Patrick: A National Tale Of the Fifth Century. By An Antiquary. 3 vols., Edinburgh, Archibald Constable; Longman, Hurst, Rees, Orme, and Brown; and Hurst, Robinson, London, 1819. [Allibone: B.M.: *I. in F.*]

Renou, Sarah. The Ionian; Or, Woman In the Nineteenth Century. 3 vols., London, Sherwood, Jones, 1824. [B.M.]

Renowned History of Giles Ginger-bread: A Little Boy who Lived upon Learning. London, T. Carnan, 1782. [Arthur Rogers.]

Renowned History of Prince Chery and Princess Fair-Star (The). Also the Story of the Pigeon and the Dove. London, Newbery, 1800. [Arthur Rogers.]

Renowned History of a White Cat (The), and other interesting Stories. London, Newbery, N.D. [*Guardian of Education.*]

Renwick, William. The Genuine Distresses of Damon and Celia. In a Series of Letters between the late General Crauford, Sir John Hussey Delaval, Sir Francis Blake Delaval and Two Unfortunate Lovers. 2 vols., Bath, 1771. [McLeish.]

—— The Solicitudes Of Absence. A Genuine Tale. London, Printed for the Author, 1788. [B.M.: Lyle H. Wright.]

Renzy, Captain Sparow de. Life, Love, and Politics; Or the Adventures of a Novice. A Tale. 2 vols., London, Knight and Lacey, 1825. [B.M.]

Requiescat in Pace; Or the poor widow. A True Story. With a vignette. London, James Burns, [1849]. [B.M.]

Requirer, A. J. The Old Sanctuary. A Romance of the Ashley. With woodcuts. London, Edward Lloyd, [1849 ?]. [B.M.: B. Ono.]

Retribution: A Novel, By the Author of the Gamesters, &c. 3 vols., 1788. [Martin A. McGoff.]

——; or, the Murder at the Old Dyke. London, Edward Lloyd, 1847. [B.M.]

—— or the Sicilian Vespers. 3 vols., 1809. [*Monthly Mag.*]

Return to England (The). A Tale Of the Fourth Year after the Battle of Waterloo. By a Friend of the Service. 2 vols., London, T. Cadell; W. Blackwood, Edinburgh, 1840. [B.M.]

Reuben, or the Suicide. 2 vols., London, 1787. [B.M.: W. Brown.]

Revealer of Secrets (The); Or The House that Jack built, A new story upon an old foundation. By the Author of Eversfield Abbey, Banks of the Wye, Aunt and Niece, Substance and Shadow, &c. &c. London, Printed at the Minerva Press for A. K. Newman, 1817. [Backus: B.M.: P. C. Cuttelle.]

Reveries of the Heart, in a Tour in England and France. 2 vols., 1781. [W. Brown.]

Reward of Virtue (The); or The History of Miss Polly Graham. Intermixed with several curious and Interesting Incidents in the lives of several Persons of both Sexes. Remarkable for the Singular Adventures which befell them. To which is added a Brief Description of Bounty Hall and its Inhabitants. London, J. Roson, 1769. [Pickering.]

Reynolds, Frederick Mansel. The Coquette. By the Author of " Miserrimus." 3 vols., London, Thomas Hookham, 1834. [Allibone: B.M.]

—— " Miserrimus." On a Gravestone in Worcester Cathedral Is this Emphatic Inscription, Miserrimus: With neither name nor date, comment nor text. Not Published, 1833. [B.M.]

—— The Parricide. A Domestic Romance. By the Author of " Miserrimus." 2 vols., London, Thomas Hookham, 1836. [B.M.: Pickering.]

Reynolds, George William Macarthur. Alfred; or the Adventures of a French Gentleman. London, Willoughby, [1840 ?]. [B.M.]

—— The Drunkard's Progress; a tale. London, G. Henderson, 1841. [B.M.]

—— Ellen Percy; or, The Memoirs of an Actress. With woodcuts. London, [*c*. 1845]. [Stonehill.]

—— Faust: a Romance of the Secret Tribunals. London, Vickers, [1847]. [Allibone: B.M.: *Eng. Cat.*]

—— Grace Darling; or, the Heroine of the Fern Islands. A Tale. London, G. Henderson, 1839. [Baker's Bookshop: *Eng. Cat.*: Arthur Rogers.]

—— (?). The Life and Adventures of Oliver Twiss The Workhouse Boy. By Bos. With woodcuts. London, E. Lloyd, [1839]. [B.M.: Huntington: B. Ono.]

—— Master Timothy's Book-case; or the Magic Lanthorn of the World. With illustrations. London, W. Emans, 1842. [B.M.]

—— The Mysteries Of the Court of London. With 52 illustrations by E. Hooper after Henry Anelay. 4 vols., London, John Dicks, 1849-50. [Lib. of Congress: Publisher's advert.]

—— The Mysteries of London. With illustrations by G. Stiff. 6 vols., [3rd Series by T. Miller. 4th Series by E. L. Blanchard.] London, George Vickers, 1846-50. [Block: B.M.]

—— (?). Nickelas Nickelbery. Containing the Adventures, Mis-Adventures, Chances, Mis-Chances, Fortunes, Mis-Fortunes, Mysteries, Mis-Eries, And Mis-Cellaneous Manoeuvres Of The Family of Nickelbery. By " Bos." With 42 engravings. London, E. Lloyl [*sic*] [1838 ?]. [B.M.: Huntingdon.]

—— The Parricide; Or, The Youth's Career of Crime. With 22 woodcuts by George Standfast. London, Printed for the Proprietor, by John Dicks, 1847. [This is a remodelled version of " The Youthful Impostor.".]. [Block.]

Reynolds, George William Macarthur. Pickwick Abroad; or, The Tour in France. With 41 etchings by Alfred Crowquill and John Phillips & 33 woodcuts by Bonner. London, Thomas Tegg, 1839. [Allibone: Marks.]

—— (?). Pickwick in America! Detailing All The Remarkable Adventures of Taat [*sic*] Illustrious Individual And His Learned Companions, In The United States; Extraordinary Jonathanisms, Collected by Mr. Snodgrass, And the Sayings, Doings And Mems, Of The Facetious Sam Weller, Edited by " Bos." With 46 engravings. London, E. Lloyd, N.D. [Huntington.]

—— The Pixy; Or, The Unbaptized Child. A Christmas Tale. With woodcuts. London, Published for the Proprietor, by John Dicks, 1848. [Block: Publisher's advert.]

—— (?). The Post-Humourous Notes Of the Pickwickian Club, Edited by " Bos." With 120 engravings. 2 vols., London, E. Lloyd, [1839 ?]. [B.M.: Huntington.]

—— Robert Macaire In England. With illustrations by Phiz [Hablot K. Browne]. 3 vols., London, Thomas Tegg, 1840. [Allibone; B.M.: Maggs.]

—— (?). The Sketch Book By " Bos," Containing A Great Number Of Highly Interesting And Original Tales, Sketches, &c. &c. With 17 engravings. London, E. Lloyd, [1836 ?]. [B.M.: Huntington.]

—— The Steam Packet, A Tale of the River and the Ocean. With illustrations. London, Willoughby, [1840]. [*Eng. Cat.*: H. M. Fletcher.]

—— Wagner: the Wehr-Wolf. With illustrations. London, Dicks, 1848. [Publisher's advert.]

—— The Youthful Impostor, A Novel. 3 vols., London, F. Coghlan, 1836. [Allibone: B.M.]

Reynolds, Susannah Frances. Gretna Green; or, All for Love. With illustrations. London, Dicks, 1848. [Publisher's advert.: Stonehill.]

—— Wealth and Poverty. With illustrations by George Standfast. London, Dicks, 1848. [Publisher's advert].

Rhoda. A Novel. By the Author of " Things by their right names," and " Plain Sense." 3 vols., London, Henry Colburn, and G. and S. Robinson, 1816. [Block: B.M.: *New Monthly Mag.*]

Rhoda; or, the Excellence of Charity. By the Author of " The Cottage on the Common." London, Grant, [1844]. [B.M.: *Eng. Cat.*]

Rhydisel: The Devil in Oxford. 2 vols., London, Sherwood, 1811. [Cleverdon: *Eng. Cat.*: *New Monthly Mag.*]

Riccoboni, Marie Jeanne. The History of the Marquis de Cressy. Translated from the French. London, 1765. [B.M.]

Riccoboni, Marie Jeanne. Letters from the Countess de Sancerre, to Count de Nancé, her friend. Translated from the French. 2 vols., London, 1767. [B.M.]

—— Letters from Elizabeth Sophia de Valiere to her Friend Louisa Hortensia de Canteleu. Translated from the French by Mr. Maceuen. 2 vols., London, Becket, 1772. [B.M.: Ingpen.]

—— Letters from Lady Juliet Catesby, To her Friend Lady Henrietta Campley. Translated from the French [of Mme. Riccoboni, by Frances Brooke]. London, R. and J. Dodsley. 1760. [MacManus: Pickering.]

Rice, Mrs. The Deserted Wife. A tale of much truth. 2 vols. [Minerva Press, 1803]. [Blakey: *Minerva Press Catalogue.*]

—— Henry, Or Secrets of the Ruins: A Moral Tale. With a frontispiece. Coventry, 1807. [Dobell.]

—— Monteith; a Novel founded on Scottish history. 2 vols., Minerva Press, 1805. [Allibone: Blakey.]

—— The Nabob: a moral tale. London, J. Harris, 1807. [B.M.]

Rich Young Country 'Squire (The), In a Series of Letters: A Novel, chiefly in the luscious taste. 1787. [Dobell.]

Richard Cœur de Lion. An Historical Romance. With woodcuts. London, Peirce, [1845]. [B.M.: Stonehill.]

Richard of York; Or, " The White Rose of England." 3 vols., London, Fisher, Son, and Jackson, 1832. [B.M.]

Richardson, Mrs. The Exile of Poland; Or, the Vow of Celibacy; A Novel, Translated from the French by Mrs. Richardson. 3 vols., London, W. Simpkin and R. Marshall; and C. Chapple, 1819. [B.M.: A. Filcek: *Quarterly Review.*]

Richardson, Charlotte Caroline. The Soldier's Child: or, Virtue Triumphant. A novel. 2 vols., London, J. Robinson, 1821. [Block: B.M.]

Richardson, Daniel. Trials and Triumphs; Comprising The Convict's Daughter, And The Convert's Daughter. With a frontispiece. London, Smith, Elder, 1834. [B.M.]

Richardson, John. Écarté; or, the Salons of Paris. 3 vols., London, Henry Colburn, 1829. [McLeish.]

Richardson, Moses A. The Borderer's Table-Book, Or Gatherings of the Local History and Romances of the English and Scottish Border. With woodcuts. 8 vols., Newcastle-upon-Tyne, 1846. [Sotheran.]

Richardson, Samuel. Clarissa; or, the History of a Young Lady: Comprehending the most Important Concerns of Private Life. And particularly shewing The Distresses that may attend the Misconduct both of Parents and Children in Relation to Marriage. Published by the Editor of Pamela. 7 vols., London, S. Richardson, 1748. [B.M.: Parker: Pickering.]

Richardson, Samuel. The History of Sir Charles Grandison In a Series of Letters Published from the Originals By the Editor of Pamela and Clarissa. 7 vols., London, S. Richardson, 1754. [B.M.: Ingpen: Arthur Rogers.]

—— Pamela: or, Virtue Rewarded. In a Series of Familiar Letters from a Beautiful Young Damsel to her Parents. 2 vols., London, C. Rivington, 1741-2. [*Camb. Hist. Eng. Lit.: Eng. Lit. in Germany*: Murray Hill.]

Richardson's Sunday-School Primer. With 24 woodcuts. Derby, T. Richardson, [c. 1810]. [B. Halliday.]

Richer, A. Great Events from Little Causes. Or, a Selection of Interesting and Entertaining Stories, Drawn from the Histories of different Nations. Wherein Certain Circumstances, seemingly inconsiderable, are discovered to have been apparently productive of very Extraordinary Incidents. Translated from the French of Monsieur A. Richer, by whom it was dedicated by Permission, to her most serene Highness the late Duchess of Orleans. London, F. Newbery, 1767. [Block: T. D. Webster.]

Richmond, Legh. The Dairyman's Daughter; an Authentic and Interesting Narrative in Five Parts. Communicated by a Clergyman of the Church of England. With a vignette title. Chelsea, The Religious Tract Society, [1810]. [B.M.: Court Bk. Shop.]

—— The Negro Servant; an authentic narrative of a young Negro. Edinburgh, [1804 ?]. [B.M.]

—— The Young Cottager; a narrative from real life. London, 1815. [B.M.]

Richter, Jean Paul Friedrich. Flower, Fruit and Thorn Pieces; or, the married life, death and wedding of the advocate of the poor, Firmian Stanislaus Siebenkäs, Parish Advocate in the Parish of Kuhschnappel. Translated by E. H. Noel. 2 vols., London, W. Smith, 1845. [B.M.: *Eng. Cat.*: Lib. of Congress.]

Ridley, James. The History of James Lovegrove, Esq.; in four books. 2 vols., London, 1761. [B.M.: *Eng. Cat.*]

—— The Tales of the Genii; or the Delightful Lessons of Horam, the Son of Asmar. Faithfully Translated from the Persian Manuscript By Sir Charles Morell. 2 vols., London, J. Wilkie, 1764. [B.M.: *Eng. Lit. in Germany*.]

Rigby, Elizabeth. The Jewess: A Tale From The Shores of the Baltic. With a portrait. London, John Murray. 1843. [B.M.]

—— Livonian Tales. The Disponent. The Wolves. The Jewess. By the Author of "Letters from the Baltic." London,

John Murray, 1846. [Allibone: B.M.: Lib. of Congress.]

Right and Wrong. Exhibited in the History of Rosa and Agnes. Written for her Children by a Mother. With a frontispiece. London, J. Harris, 1815. [B.M.: Gumuchian: Sotheran.]

Right and Wrong Way (The); or, the history of Mary Coleman and Jenny Green. By the author of " Jessie Barton," etc. London, 1850. [B.M.]

Rignall, Miss. Stories for the Fireside; or, Moral Improvement illustrated. London, Simpkin, 1839. [Allibone: B.M.: *Eng. Cat.*]

Ring and the Well (The); or, The Grecian Princess. A Romance. 4 vols., London, 1808. [T. D. Webster.]

Ring (The) in a Series of Letters By a Young Lady. London. J. Stockdale. 1784. 3 vols. [Murray Hill: *Eng. Lit. in Germany*.]

Ringbolt, C. Sailors' Life and Sailors' Yarns. London, 1847. [Allibone.]

Ringdove (The). A Romance. With woodcuts. London, E. Lloyd, [1848]. [B.M.: B. Ono.]

Rioters (The); Or, a Tale of Bad Times. With a frontispiece. Wellington, Salop, Houlston, 1827. [B.M.]

Ritchie, Leitch. The Game of Life. 2 vols., London, Edward Bull, 1830. [B.M.: *New Monthly Mag.*]

—— Head-Pieces and Tail-Pieces. By a Travelling Artist. With a frontispiece by H. Adlurd. London, Charles Tilt, 1826. [Allibone: *Blackwood's Edin. Mag.*: B.M.]

—— London Night Entertainments. [Allibone.]

—— The Magician. 3 vols., London, John Macrone, 1836. [B.M.]

—— The Romance of History. France. 3 vols., London, Edward Bull, 1831. [B.M.]

—— Schinderhannes, The Robber of the Rhine. London, 1833. [B.M.: Arthur Rogers.]

—— Tales and Confessions. London, Smith, Elder, 1829. [Allibone: B.M.]

Rival Mother or The History of the Countess de Salens and her two Daughters. 1755. [*Eng. Lit. in Germany*.]

Rival Pupils (The), Or A New Holiday Gift for a Boarding School. With plates. [1800]. [Combridges.]

Rob Roy; or, Days of Auld Lang Syne. With a frontispiece. London, Duncombe, [c. 1800]. [Stonehill.]

Robert, Clemence. The Tombs of St. Denis. 2 vols., London, 1845. [*Critic*.]

Robert and Adela: Or, The Rights of Women best maintained by the Sentiments of Nature. 3 vols., 1795. [*New Ann. Reg.*: T. D. Webster.]

Roberts, Mrs. Rose and Emily; or, Sketches of Youth. London, Longman & Hurst, 1812. [Baker's Bookshop: B.M.]

Roberts, Mrs. D. Delmore, or, Modern Friendship. A novel. 3 vols., London, B. Crosby, 1809. [B.M.]

Roberts, Lieut.-Col. David. The Adventures of Johnny Newcome in the Navy. With 20 plates. London, 1819. [T. Thorp.]

Roberts, George. Original Tales. Salisbury. 1805. [B.M.]

Roberts, Jane. Court Favourite; a Novel. 3 vols., London, Southgate, 1839. [Allibone: *Eng. Cat.*]

—— Löwenstein, King of The Forests: A Tale. 2 vols., London, Whittaker, 1836. [Allibone: B.M.]

Roberts, Margaret. Duty, A Novel. Interspersed with Poetry And preceded by a character of the Author. By Mrs. Opie. 3 vols., London, Longman, Hurst, Rees, Orme, and Brown, 1814. [B.M.: Publisher's advert.: *Quarterly Review.*]

Roberts, Mary, (?). Sister Mary's Tales in Natural History. London, Parker, 1834. [B.M.: *Eng. Cat.*]

Roberts, Miss R. Albert, Edward and Laura, and the Hermit of Priestland; three legendary tales. London, 1783. [B.M.]

—— Peruvian Tales. Translated from the French. 2 vols., London, 1774. [Arthur Rogers.]

Robertson, Mrs. Florence: or The Aspirant. A Novel. 3 vols., London, Whittaker, Treacher, 1829. [B.M.: McLeish.]

Robertson, J. P. Solomon Seesaw. With illustrations by Phiz [Hablot K. Browne]. 3 vols., London, Saunders and Otley, 1839 [B.M.: James Glaisher: T. Thorp.]

Robertson, Janet. Affinities of Foreigners. 2 vols., London, T. C. Newby, 1850. [B.M.]

Robin Goodfellow. A fairy tale. Written by a Fairy for the amusement of all the pretty little fairies. London, 1770. [B.M.]

Robin Hood; A Tale Of The Olden Time. 2 vols., Edinburgh, Oliver & Boyd; G. & W. B. Whittaker, London; and W. Turnbull, Glasgow, 1819. [B.M.: Sexton.]

Robin of Woodside Lodge (The): A True Tale, written for her Nieces, Anne and Kate, by Aunt E. With 9 lithographs. London, C. Haselden, 1850. [Sotheran.]

Robinson, Mr. Love Fragments. 1782. [W. Brown.]

Robinson, Emma. The Maid of Orleans. A Romantic Chronicle. 3 vols., London, 1849. [McLeish.]

—— Caesar Borgia: An Historical Romance. By the Author of " Whitefriars." 3 vols., London, Henry Colburn, 1848. [*Eng. Cat.:* Publisher's advert.]

—— Whitefriars, Or the Days of Charles the Second. An Historical Romance. 3 vols., London, Henry Colburn, 1844. [B.M.: Ingpen.]

—— Whitehall; Or, The Days of Charles I, An Historical Romance. By the Author of Whitefriars. 3 vols., London, John Mortimer, 1845. [B.M.: Lib. of Congress: Sexton.]

Robinson, Emma. Owen Tudor, An Historical Romance. 3 vols., London, Henry Colburn, 1849. [B.M.: Kyrle Fletcher: Holland.]

Robinson, John. Audley Fortescue; or, The victim of frailty. A novel. 2 vols. [W. Lane, 1795]. [Blakey: *New Ann. Reg.*]

Robinson, Mary. Angelina, A Novel. 3 vols., London, Hookham and Carpenter, 1796. [Blackwell: B.M.: Quaritch.]

—— The False Friend, a Domestic Story. 4 vols., London, 1799. [Allibone: *New Ann. Reg.*]

—— Hubert de Sevrac, a Romance of the eighteenth Century. 3 vols., London, 1796. [B.M.: *Eng. Lit. in Germany*: Quaritch.]

—— (attributed to). Julia St. Lawrence. 1789. [*Eng. Lit. in Germany.*]

—— The Natural Daughter, with Portraits of the Leadenhead Family. A Novel. 2 vols., London, 1799. [*New Ann. Reg.*: Quaritch.]

—— Sydney St. Aubyn. 2 vols., 1794. [*New Ann. Reg.*]

—— Vancenza, or, the Dangers of Credulity. 2 vols., London, Printed for the Authoress, 1792. [Arthur Rogers.]

—— Walsingham; Or, the Pupil of Nature. A Domestic Story. 4 vols., London, 1797. [Blackwell: *Eng. Lit. in Germany*: Quaritch.]

—— The Widow, Or a Picture of Modern Times. A Novel. In a Series of Letters. 2 vols., 1794. [*Eng. Lit. in Germany*: Marks: *New Ann. Reg.*]

Robinson, Mary Elizabeth. The Shrine of Bertha. A Novel. In a series of letters. 2 vols., London, W. Lane, 1794. [Allibone: *New Ann. Reg.*: Quaritch.]

Robson, Mary. The Orphan Girl. With plates. London, 1820. [*Monthly Mag.*]

Roby, John. Traditions of Lancashire. With engravings. 4 vols., Longman, 1829-1831. [B.M.: *Eng. Cat.*: T. Thorp.]

Roche, C. F. T. de la, (*see* DE LA ROCHE.)

Roche, J. Hamilton. A Suffolk Tale; or, the Perfidious Guardian. 2 vols., London, Printed for the Author, 1810. [B.M.: T. Thorp.]

Roche, Regina Maria. Alvondown Vicarage. A novel. 2 vols., London, Lane, Newman, 1807. [Blakey.]

—— Anna of Edinburgh. 2 vols., 1815. [*European Mag.*]

—— Bridal of Dunamore; and Lost and Won. Two Tales. 3 vols., London, Printed for A. K. Newman, 1823. [Allibone: B.M.: Pickering.]

—— The Castle Chapel. A Romantic Tale. 3 vols., London, A. K. Newman, 1825. [B.M.: *I. in F.*]

—— The Children of the Abbey, A Tale. With a frontispiece. 4 vols., London, Printed for William Lane, at the Minerva

Press, 1796. [Block : *Eng. Lit. in Germany : New Ann. Reg.*]

Roche, Regina Maria. Clermont, A Tale. With a frontispiece. 4 vols., London, William Lane, 1798. [Allibone : B.M. : Holden's Reprints.]

—— Contrast. 3 vols., London, A. K. Newman, 1828. [B.M. : *Quarterly Review :* Sotheran.]

—— The Discarded Son ; Or, Haunt of the Banditti. A tale. 5 vols., London, Printed at the Minerva Press, 1807. [B.M. : Arthur Rogers.]

—— The Houses of Osma and Almeria ; or, Convent of St. Ildefonso. A tale. 3 vols., London, A. K. Newman, 1810. [Allibone : B.M. : *Camb. Hist. Eng. Lit.*]

—— London Tales ; Or, Reflective Portraits. 2 vols., London, John Booth, 1814. [Allibone : B.M. : *Quarterly Review.*]

—— The Maid of the Hamlet. A Tale. 3 vols., 1794. [*New Ann. Reg.*]

—— The Monastery of St. Columb ; Or, The Atonement. A Novel. 5 vols., London, Printed at the Minerva Press for A. K. Newman, 1813. [Ingpen : Publisher's advert : Blakey.]

—— The Munster Cottage Boy. A Tale. 4 vols., London, Printed at the Minerva Press for A. K. Newman, 1820. [B.M. : *I. in F.*]

—— Nocturnal Visit. A tale. 4 vols., London, William Lane, 1800. *Camb. Hist. Eng. Lit.: Eng. Lit. in Germany. :* Blakey.]

—— The Nun's Picture. A Tale. 3 vols., London, A. K. Newman, 1836. [Allibone : B.M.]

—— The Tradition of the Castle ; Or, Scenes in the Emerald Isle. 4 vols., London, A. K. Newman, 1824. [Allibone : B.M. : *I. in F.*]

—— Trecothick Bower : or, The Lady of the West Country. A Tale. 3 vols., London, Printed at the Minerva Press, for A. K. Newman, 1814. [Allibone : Publisher's advert. : Blakey.]

—— The Vicar of Lansdowne ; Or, Country Quarters : A Tale. By Maria Regina Dalton. 2 vols., London, Printed for the Author, 1789. [B.M. : *Eng. Lit. in Germany :* W. R. Smyth.]

Rochester Castle ; Or, Gundulph's Tower. A Gothic Tale. With a frontispiece. London, J. Roe ; and Anne Lemoine, [1810]. [B.M. : Court Bk. Shop.]

Rock of Modrec (The), Or the Legend of Sir Eltram ; An Ethical Romance. Translated from an Ancient British Manuscript, Lately discovered among the ruins of an Abbey in North Wales. 2 vols., London, W. Bent, 1792. [B.M. : *New Ann. Reg.* : Pickering.]

Rodwell, George Herbert. The Memoirs of an Umbrella. With 68 engravings by Phiz [Hablot K. Browne]. London, E.

Mackenzie, 1845. [Allibone : B.M. : Arthur Rogers.]

Rodwell, George Herbert. Old London Bridge, a Romance of the Sixteenth Century. With plates by Alfred Ashley. London, Willoughby, [1848]. [B.M. : H. W. Fennell : W. T. Spencer.]

—— Woman's Love, a Romance of smiles and tears. With illustrations by Alfred Crowquill. London, Willoughby, [1846]. [B.M. : W. T. Spencer.]

Rogers. A. The History of Miss Temple, By a Young Lady. 2 vols., London, 1777. [*Eng. Lit. in Germany :* T. D. Webster.]

Roland Percie ; Or, The Elopement. A Novel. 2 vols., London, T. C. Newby, 1846. [B.M.]

Rolfe, Anne. Choice and No Choice ; Or, The First of May. 2 vols., London, Charles Frederick Cock, 1825. [Allibone : B.M.]

—— The Oath of Allegiance A Tale of the Times Of Philip the Second. With frontispiece by R. W. Buss. 2 vols., London, Saunders and Otley, 1847. [B.M. : King : Varda.]

Roman Catholic Priest (The). With an illustration by Kirkwood. Dublin, W. Curry, 1827. [B.M. : *I. in F.*]

Roman Lovers (The). A Tale. London, Edward Bull, 1839. [B.M.]

Roman Stories. Cambridge, 1827. [T. D. Webster.]

Romance of Ancient History (The). Egypt. 2 vols., London, Cochrane and M'Crone, 1834. [B.M.]

Romance of a Day (The) ; or, an adventure in Greenwich Park last Easter. With plates. London, I. Pottinger, 1760. [B.M.]

Romance of Irish History. 2 vols., London, Ridgway, 1832. [*Literary Gazette.*]

Romances and Tales for the Winter Fireside. 2 vols., London, 1827. [B.M.]

Romances Of Many Lands ; With Sketches of Life and Manners, Comic and Serious. 3 vols., London, Richard Bentley, 1835. [B.M.]

Romantic Facts ; Or Which is his Wife ? By the Author of Veronica, or the Mysterious Stranger. 4 vols., London, Printed at the Minerva Press, for A. K. Newman, 1816. [B.M. : *New Monthly Mag.*]

Romer, Isabella F. The Bird of Passage ; or Flying Glimpses of Many Lands. 3 vols., London, Richard Bentley, 1849. [Allibone : B.M. : T. D. Webster.]

—— Sturmer ; A Tale of Mesmerism. To which are added Other Sketches from Life. 3 vols., London, Richard Bentley, 1841. [B.M. : McLeish : Elkin Mathews.]

Rosa de Clifford ; Or La Coquetterie. 3 vols., 1838. [James Glaisher.]

Rosa in London, And Other Tales ; By the Author of The Young Mother, Or Albinia. 4 vols., London, Henry Colburn, 1809. [B.M. : *Monthly Mag. :* Bernard Whyte.]

Rosa, or Village Incidents. 2 vols., 1817. [*Monthly Mag.*]

Rosalie : or, the Castle of Montalabretti. 4 vols., 1811. [*Quarterly Review.*]

Rosalie ; or, The Victim of Infatuation. An Historical Fact. Translated from the French. With a frontispiece. London, Hurst, 1803. [Stonehill.]

Rosalind : or, an apology for the history of a Theatrical Lady. Dublin, 1759. [B.M.]

Rosamund, Countess of Clarenstein. 3 vols., London, A. J. Valpy, 1812. [B.M. : R. Walter Gibson : Pickering.]

Roscoe, Thomas. The German Novelists : Tales Selected from Ancient and Modern Authors in that Language : From the Earliest Period down to the Close of the Eighteenth Century. Translated from the Originals. With Critical and Biographical Notices. By Thomas Roscoe. 4 vols., London, Henry Colburn, 1826. [B.M. : Lib. of Congress : Publisher's advert.]

—— Italian Tales. Tales of Humour, Gallantry, and Romance, Selected and Translated [by Roscoe], from the Italian. With 16 etchings by George Cruikshank. London, Charles Baldwyn, 1824. [B.M. : Maggs.]

—— The Spanish Novelists : A Series of Tales, From The Earliest Period to the Close of the Seventeenth Century. Translated from the Originals, With Critical and Biographical Notices. 3 vols., London, Richard Bentley, 1832. [B.M. : Ernest Cooper : Lib. of Congress.]

Rose, Edward H. The Sea-Devil, or, Son of a Bellows-Mender. A tragi-comic romance of the present day. 2 vols., Plymouth-Dock, 1811. [B.M. : *Quarterly Review.*]

Rose Cecil. A Novel. 3 vols., London, Printed for William Lane, at the Minerva Press, 1797. [B.M. : *New Ann. Reg.*]

Rose of England, Or, The Adventures of a Prince. Dedicated to Her Royal Highness the Duchess of Kent. By the Author of Jane Shore, etc. With plates. London, Bennett, 1841. [Blackwell : Ingpen.]

Rose Sommerville, or, A Husband's Mystery and a Wife's Devotion. A romance. By Ellen T. London, Lloyd, 1847. [B.M. : Stonehill.]

Rose Talbot : A Tale. By the Author of "The Young Disciple ; " "Orphan's Choice ; " "Truant Scholar." With an engraving. London, Darton and Harvey, 1836. [B.M.]

Rosemary Lodge ; or domestic vicis-situdes. By a Lady. London, T. Harvey, [1800 ?]. [B.M.]

Rosenberg, Charles G. The Man of the People. 3 vols., London, T. C. Newby ; T. & W. Boone, 1843. [Allibone : B.M.]

Rosina ; Or, the Virtuous Country Maid : Being Memoirs of the Marchioness of Lemington. Written by herself ; To instruct her own sex by shewing the dangers Attending extraordinary beauty in females of humble rank, and the Security and Happiness imparted by Virtue. With plates. London, G. Virtue, Mackenzie and Dent, Newcastle upon Tyne, 1827. [Block (5th edn.)]

Ross, Mrs. The Bachelor and the Married Man, Or the Equilibrium of the "Balance of Comfort." 3 vols., London, Longman, Hurst, Rees, Orme, and Brown, 1817. [B.M. : *New Monthly Mag. :* Pickering.]

—— The Balance of Comfort ; Or The Old Maid and Married Woman. A Novel. 3 vols., London, Printed at the Minerva Press, for A. K. Newman, 1817. [B.M. : McLeish : *Quarterly Review.*]

—— The Cousins; or, a Woman's Promise and a Lover's Vow. A Novel. 3 vols., London, A. K. Newman, 1811. [*Eng. Cat. :* Marks : *Quarterly Review.*]

—— The Family Estate ; Or Lost and Won. A Novel. 3 vols., London, Printed at the Minerva Press, for A. K. Newman, 1815. [B.M. : Ingpen : Publisher's advert.]

—— The Governess ; Or, Politics in Private Life. By the Daughter of The Author of the "Balance of Comfort." London, Smith, Elder, 1836. [B.M.]

—— The Marchioness !!! or, The Matured Enchantress. By Lady ——. 3 vols., London, Printed at the Minerva Press, for A. K. Newman, 1813. [B.M. : Publisher's advert.: Blakcy.]

—— A Modern Calypso ; or, Widow's Captivation. A Novel. 4 vols., London, Printed at the Minerva Press, for A. K. Newman, 1813. [Pickering : Publisher's advert : *Quarterly Review.*]

—— Paired—Not Matched ; Or, Matrimony in the Nineteenth Century. A Novel. 4 vols., London, Printed at the Minerva Press, for A. K. Newman, 1815. [B.M. : Marks : Myers.]

—— The Strangers of Lindenfeldt ; Or, Who is my father ? A Novel. 3 vols., London, Printed at the Minerva Press, for A. K. Newman, 1813. [B.M. : Marks : Publisher's advert.]

Ross, Andrew. Mina ; a Tale of the Days of Nero. Perth, 1850. [Allibone.]

Rosse Castle ; or, the Vindictive Thane. To which is added, Secret Enemies. London, T. Hughes, 1814. [B.M.]

Rothwell, J. S. S. The Novelist. A collection of tales, translations, poems... particularly adapted as an aid to persons studying the English language. Magdeburgh, 1842. [B.M.]

Round Tower (The) ; or, A Tale of Mystery. A Romantic Tale. To which is added, The Nobel Genoese. A Tale. With a frontispiece. London, Printed by T. Maiden, For Ann Lemoine, And J. Roe, [1803]. [Block : Stonehill.]

Rousseau, Jean Jacques. Eloisa ; Or, a Series of Original Letters Collected and Published by J. J. Rousseau. Translated from the French. 4 vols., London, R. Griffiths ; and Becket and De Hondt, 1761. [Also an edition published in Dublin by James Hunter, 1761.] [B.M. : Court Bk. Shop : Ingpen.]

—— Letters of an Italian Nun and an English Gentleman. Translated from the French of Jean Jacques Rousseau. London, J. Bew, 1781. [Baker's Bookshop : W. Brown.]

Rouviere, Henrietta. The Heirs of Villeroy. A Romance. 3 vols., Minerva Press, 1805. [Blakey.]

—— Lussington Abbey. A Novel. 2 vols., [Minerva Press, 1804.] [Blakey.]

—— The Old Irish Baronet ; or, The Manners of My Country. 3 vols., London, Lane, Newman. 1807. [Publisher's advert : Blakey : B.M.]

Rover, Sir George. Coeleb's Suited, or The Opinions and Part of the Life of Caleb Coelebs, Esq. 1809. [*Monthly Mag.* : Cawthorn's Catalogue.]

Rowcroft, Charles. The Bushranger Of Van Diemen's Land. 3 vols., London, Smith, Elder, 1846. [Allibone : B.M. : *Critic.*]

—— Chronicles Of " The Fleet Prison." From the papers of the late Alfred Seedy, Esq. 3 vols., London, H. Hurst, 1847. [B.M. : McLeish.]

—— Evadne, or an Empire in its Fall. 3 vols., London, Boone, 1850. [Allibone ; B.M. : *Eng. Cat.*]

—— Fanny, the Little Milliner ; or, the Rich and the Poor. London, Smith, Elder, 1846. [B.M. : *Eng. Cat.*]

—— The Man Without a Profession. 3 vols., London, Saunders and Otley, 1844. [Block : B.M. : T. D. Webster.]

—— Tales of the Colonies : Or, The Adventures of an Emigrant. Edited by a Late Colonial Magistrate. 3 vols., London, Saunders & Otley, 1843. [Allibone : B.M.]

—— Tales of the Colonies : Or, The Adventures of an Emigrant. Edited by a Late Colonial Magistrate. Second Series. 3 vols., London, Smith, Elder, 1846. [Allibone : *Eng. Cat.*]

—— The Triumph of Woman ; a Christmas story. London, Parry, 1848. [B.M. : *Eng. Cat.*]

Rowlatt, R. The Lover's Grave ; or, the tragedy of Marshand. A domestic tale, founded on facts. 2 vols., London, 1840. [B.M.]

Rowson, Susanna Haswell. Charlotte, A Tale of Truth. 2 vols., London,

Printed for William Lane at the Minerva [Press], [1791]. [R. W. G. Vail.]

Rowson, Susanna Haswell. Charlotte's daughter : Or, The Three Orphans. A Sequel to Charlotte Temple. To which is prefixed, A Memoir of the Author. Boston : Richardson & Lord. J. H. A. Frost, Printer, 1828. [Later reprinted as *Lucy Temple.*] [R. W. G. Vail.]

—— The Inquisitor ; Or, Invisible Rambler. 3 vols., London, G. G. J. and J. Robinson, 1788. [B.M. : R. W. G. Vail.]

—— Mary, Or the Test of Honour. By a Lady. 2 vols., London, Abraham, 1789. [R. W. G. Vail.]

—— Mentoria ; Or the Young Lady's Friend. 2 vols., London, Printed for William Lane at the Minerva [Press], [1791]. [R. W. G. Vail.]

—— Rebecca, or the Fille de Chambre. London, 1792. [R. W. G. Vail.]

—— Reuben and Rachel ; Or Tales of Old Times. A Novel. 2 vols., Boston, Printed by Manning & Loring for David West, 1798. [*New Ann. Reg.* : R. W. G. Vail.]

—— Sarah, the Exemplary Wife. Boston, Charles Williams. Watson & Bangs, Printers, 1813. [B.M. : R. W. G. Vail.]

—— Trials of the Human Heart, A Novel. 4 vols., Philadelphia, Printed for the Author by Wrigley & Berriman, 1795. [R. W. G. Vail.]

—— Victoria. A Novel. The Characters taken from real Life, And calculated to improve the Morals of the Female Sex, By impressing them with a just Sense of The Merits of Filial Piety. By Susannah Haswell. 2 vols., London, Printed by J. P. Cooke for the Author, 1786. [W. Brown : R. W. G. Vail.]

Royal Legend (The). A tale. London, 1808. [B.M.]

Royal Wanderer (The), or The Exile of England ; a Tale. 3 vols., London, A. K. Newman, 1815. [*Bibliot. Brit.* : *Eng. Cat.* : *New Monthly Mag.*]

Rudolphi, F. I. **Hauff**, W., and **Grimm**, A. L. The King of the Swans, and other tales (from the German). London, Cundall, 1846. [B.M. : *Eng. Cat.*]

Rueful, Mrs. Prose and Poetry, on Religious, Moral, and Entertaining Subjects, with a brief, but authentic, and affecting History of Orenzo and Sarah, from 1793 to the Present Day. Bristol, Printed by George Routh for the Author, [c. 1800]. [Marks.]

Ruins of Selinunti (The) ; or the Val de Mazzara. Sicilian, Calabrian, and Neapolitan Sceneries, By A Late Rambler in these Countries. 3 vols., London, Printed at the Minerva Press, for A. K. Newman, 1813. [Block : Publisher's advert : Blakey.]

Ruling Passion (The). With frontispieces. 3 vols., London, T. C. Newby, 1845. [B.M. : *Critic.*]

Runaway's Return (The). London, Clowes, [1840 ?]. [B.M.]

Russell, Miss. A Sketch of Her Own Circle. 4 vols., London, A. K. Newman, 1823. [B.M. : *New Monthly Mag.*]

Russell, John. The Adventures of the Guildford Jack-Daw. Interspersed with Anecdotes of some Little Good and Bad Boys. For the use of children. With a frontispiece & 15 woodcuts. Guildford, J. Russell, [c. 1794]. [Gumuchian.]

Russell, John, Earl. The Nun of Arrouca, A Tale. London, John Murray, 1822. [B.M. : Ingpen : Stonehill.]

Ruth Pierce ; or the evil consequences of lying. London, [1830 ?]. [B.M.]

Rutledge, Jean Jacques. The Adventures of Monsieur Provence, Gentleman to Lord R—, The Hero of the Englishman's Fortnight at Paris. 2 vols., 1788. [Arthur Rogers.]

Ryan, Everhard. Reliques of Genius. London, Edward and Charles Dilly, 1777. [B.M. : Arthur Rogers.]

Ryley, Ann. Fanny Fitz-York, Heiress of Tremorne. 3 vols., London, Sherwood, Neely and Jones, 1818. [B.M. : Marks.]

Ryley, Samuel William. The Itinerant, or Memoirs of an Actor. 9 vols., London, Sherwood, Neely, and Jones, 1808-1827. [B.M.]

Rymer, James Malcolm. Ada, the Betrayed ; or, the Murder at the Old Smithy. A Romance of Passion. With woodcuts. London, E. Lloyd, N.D. [1847.] [B. Ono.]

—— The Black Monk, or the Secret of the Grey Turret. A Romance. By the Author of " Ada, the Betrayed ; " " Jane Brightwell ; " " Blanche, or the Mystery of the Doomed House ; " " The Miller's Maid ; " etc. etc. etc. With woodcuts. London, E. Lloyd, 1844. [B.M. : B. Ono : Stonehill.]

—— Grace Rivers ; or, The Merchant's Daughter. A tale. With woodcuts. London, E. Lloyd, 1844. [B. Ono. Hollings.]

—— Jane Brightwell ; or, the Beggar's Petition. A romance. London, [1848]. [B.M.]

—— Jane Shore ; or, London in the Reign of Edward the Fourth. An Historical Romance. By the Author of " The Black Monk," " Varney the Vampyre," &c. London, Lloyd, 1846. [B.M. : B. Ono.]

—— Miranda ; or, The Heiress of the Grange. A Romance, By the Author of " Ada the Betrayed," " Jane Brightwell," &c. &c. &c. With woodcuts. London, Edward Lloyd, [1848]. [B.M. : B. Ono.]

—— The Oath ; or, The Buried Treasure. By the Author of " Ada, the Betrayed," &c. With woodcuts. London, E. Lloyd, [1848 ?]. [B. Ono.]

Rymer, James Malcolm. Varney the Vampire : or, The Feast of Blood. A Romance. London, E. Lloyd, N.D. [G. Meredith : B. Ono : R. W. Hansen.]

Ryves, Elizabeth. The Hermit of Snowden ; Memoirs of Albert and Lavinia Faithfully taken from the Original Manuscript, found in the Hermitage. London, 1789. [McLeish.]

Sabbath-Breaker (The). A tale. By F.M.E. London, 1850. [B.M.]

Sa'di. The Gulistan, or Flower Garden, of Sheikh Sadi translated into English by J. Ross, from the Persian text of Gentius together with an essay on Sadi's life and genius. London, Richardson, 1823. [B.M. : *Eng. Cat. : Quarterly Review.*]

Sadoc and Miriam : a Jewish tale. London, Christian Knowledge Society, 1833. [B.M.]

Sailor's Bride : A Tale of Home. By the Author of " The Months of the Year," &c. &c. With a frontispiece. London, Charles Tilt, 1831. [B.M.]

Sailor-Boy (The). A novel. 2 vols., London, William Lane, 1800. [B.M. : Blakey.]

Saint-Aubain, Andreas Nicolai de. The Queen of Denmark, an Historical Novel. Edited by Mrs. Gore. 3 vols., London, Henry Colburn, 1846. [B.M. : *Critic : Denmark in Eng. & Amer. Lit.*]

Saint Aubin ; Or, The Infidel. 2 vols., Edinburgh, Oliver & Boyd. 1821. [B.M. : T. Thorp.]

St. Aubigné, Chevalier de. The Catastrophe ; a Tale Founded on Facts. From the French of the Chevalier de St. Aubigné. By J. Byerley. London, 1803. [McLeish.]

St. Aubyn, Rev. John Humphrey. The Elopement, Or the Deadly Struggle. 3 vols., London, Richard Bentley, 1838. [Allibone : B.M.]

—— Robert D'Artois Or The Heron Vow. A Romance. 3 vols., London, William Marsh, 1835. [B.M.]

St. Clair, Rosalia. The Banker's Daughter of Bristol ; Or, Compliance and Decision. A Novel. 3 vols., London, A. K. Newman, 1824. [B.M.]

—— Clavering Tower. A Novel. 4 vols., London, A. K. Newman, 1822. [B.M.]

—— Eleanor Ogilvie The Maid of the Tweed. A Romantic Legend. 3 vols., London, A. K. Newman, 1829. [B.M.]

—— Fashionables and Unfashionables. A Novel. 3 vols., London, A. K. Newman, 1827. [B.M.]

—— The First and Last Years of Wedded Life. A Novel. 4 vols., London, A. K. Newman, 1827. [B.M. : *New Monthly Mag.*]

—— The Highland Castle, And the

Lowland Cottage. A Novel. 4 vols., London, Printed at the Minerva Press, for A. K. Newman, 1820. [B.M.]

St. Clair, Rosalia. Marston : A Novel. By a Lady. 3 vols., London, Thomas Hookham, 1835. [B.M.]

—— The Pauper Boy ; Or, The ups and downs of life. A Novel. 3 vols., London, A. K. Newman, 1834. [B.M.]

—— The Sailor Boy ; Or, The Admiral and his Protegée. A Novel. 4 vols., London, A. K. Newman, 1830. [B.M. : *New Monthly Mag.*]

—— The Son of O'Donnel. A Novel. 3 vols., London, Printed at the Minerva Press for A. K. Newman, 1819. [B.M.]

—— Ulrica of Saxony. A Romantic Tale of the Fifteenth Century. 3 vols., London, A. K. Newman, 1828. [B.M.]

St. Clyde. A Novel. 3 vols., London, Gale, 1816. [B.M. : *Eng. Cat.*]

St. George, Catherine. Maria : a Domestic Tale. 3 vols., London, 1817. [Dobell: *Monthly Mag.*]

St. Hilaire, Bridget. The Priory of St. Mary. A Romance founded on Days of Old. 4 vols., London, 1810. [*Monthly Mag. :* T. D. Webster.]

Saint Hilary the Crusader. A Romantic Legend. 3 vols., London, 1808. [Ingpen.]

St. Hubert ; Or, The Trials of Angelina. A Novel. 3 vols., London, G. B. Whittaker, 1825. [B.M.]

St. John, Andrew. Tales of Former Times. With frontispieces. 2 vols., London, B. Crosby, 1808. [B.M. : Ingpen : G. Worthington.]

St. John, Bayle. The Eccentric Lover. A Novel. 3 vols., London, Richard Bentley, 1845. [Allibone : B.M.]

St. John, James Augustus. The Anatomy of Society. 2 vols., London, E. Bull, 1831. [B.M.]

—— Margaret Ravenscroft ; Or, Second Love. 3 vols., London, Longman, Rees, Orme, Brown, Green, & Longman, 1835. [Allibone : B.M.]

—— Sir Cosmo Digby. A Tale of The Monmouthshire Riots. 3 vols., London, Richard Bentley, 1843. [Allibone : B.M. : Arthur Rogers.]

—— Tales of the Ramad'han. 3 vols., London, Richard Bentley, 1835. [Allibone : B.M.]

St. John, Percy Bolingbroke. The Enchanted Rock ; a Comanche Legend. London, Hayward and Adam, 1846. [Publisher's advert.]

—— The Fireside, a domestic tale. London, H. K. Lewis, 1847. [B.M.]

—— Kentsea, or the Enchanted Rock. 1846. [Noel Broadbent.]

—— The King's Musketeer : an historical romance of old Paris and the Huguenots. Nos. 1 and 2 [all published]. London, 1848-1849. [Allibone : B.M.]

—— Paul Peabody. [Noel Broadbent.]

—— Three Days of the French Revolution. 1848. [Noel Broadbent.]

St. John, Percy Bolingbroke. The Trapper's Bride : a tale of the Rocky Mountains. With the Rose of Ouisconsin. Indian tales. London, 1845. [Allibone: B.M.]

—— Whitestone Canoe. 1846. [Noel Broadbent.]

Saint Julian's Abbey. A novel. In a series of letters. 2 vols., London, W. Lane 1788. [B.M. : Blakey.]

St. Leance ; or, the Castle of Rugosa : Giving an Account of the Invisible Band, that Long Infested the Pyrennean Mountains. And describing the Death of the Lovely Constance, the Earl of Rugosa's Daughter, Under the most dreadful Circumstances that can befall Human Nature. With a frontispiece. London, Bailey, 1821. [Stonehill.]

St. Leger, Francis Barry Boyle. Mr. Blount's MSS. Being Selections from the Papers of A Man of the World. By the Author Gilbert Earle. 2 vols., London, Charles Knight. 1826. [B.M. : Henry : *Quarterly Review.*]

—— Some Account of the Life of the Late Gilbert Earle, Esq. Written by Himself. London, Charles Knight, 1824. [Baker's Bookshop : B.M. : McLeish.]

—— Stories from Froissart. 3 vols., London, Henry Colburn, 1832. [Baker's Bookshop : Publisher's advert : Wm. Smyth.]

—— Tales of Passion : Lord Lovel's Daughter. The Bohemian—Second Love. By the Author of " Gilbert Earle." 3 vols., London, Henry Colburn, 1829. [Birrell & Garnett : B.M. : James Glaisher.]

Saint-Pierre, Jacques-Henri Bernardin de. The History of Paul and Virginia ; or, the Shipwreck. London, A. Lemoine, 1802. [B.M.]

—— The Indian Cottage. Translated from the French of Monsieur de St. Pierre, author of Etudes de la Nature. Paul et Virginie, etc. [by E. A. Kendall.] London, John Bew, 1791. [B.M. : Ingpen.]

—— The Indian Cottage ; or, A Search after Truth. From the French. London, William Lane, 1791 : [Blakey.]

—— Paul and Mary, An Indian Story. [A Translation by David Malthus, of *Paul and Virginia*.] 2 vols., London, J. Dodsley, 1789. [B.M. : Ingpen : Maggs.]

—— Paul and Virginia, from the French of S. Pierre, and Elizabeth, by Madame Cottin. New translations. With prefatory remarks by J. McDiarmid. Edinburgh, Oliver & Boyd, 1824. [B.M.]

—— Paul and Virginia, Translated by Henry Hunter. With a frontispiece. 1826. [Sotheran.]

—— Paul and Virginia. Translated from the French of Bernardin Saint-Pierre ; By Helen Maria Williams.

[No Publisher or Place of Publication], 1795. [Birrell & Garnett : B.M. : Gumuchian.]

Saint-Pierre, Jacques-Henri Bernadin de. Paul and Virginie. With a frontispiece, an engraved title and 4 plates by G. Barrett [3 after Moreau and 1 after Vernet]. London, 1788. [H.M. Fletcher : Murray Hill.]

St. Ruthin's Abbey. A Novel. 3 vols., London, Francis Noble, 1784. [J. C. Hardy.]

St. Venant, Madame de. Leopold de Circe, or, the Effects of Atheism. Translated by J[ohn] S[cott] Byerley. 2 vols., London, Chapple, 1807. [*Bibliot. Brit.* : B.M. : Stonehill.]

St. Victor, Helen. The Ruins of Rigonda ; Or, the Homicidal Father. A romance. 3 vols., London, 1808. [Blackwell : B.M.]

Sainte Foix, Philippe Auguste de. The Palace of Silence. Translated from the French by a Lady. London, 1775. [B.M. : W. Brown.]

Saintine, Joseph Xavier Boniface. Picciola, Or, Captivity. Captive. [Translated by Mrs. Gore ?] 2 vols., London, Henry Colburn, 1837. [B.M. : Publisher's advert.]

—— Picciola : a tale. Translated from the French. London, 1849. [B.M.]

Sally King. London, 1843. [B.M.]

Sam Belson, or a visit to the beach. A tale for young persons, etc. London, Simpkin, 1836. [B.M. : *Eng. Cat.*]

Samber, Robert. The Discreet Princess ; Or, the Adventures Of Finetta. A Novel. London, Printed in the year, 1755. [B.M.]

Samuel Sowerby ; or, Doings at Ravensdale Priory. By the author of " Captain Bolis." With 20 plates by " Phiz " [Hablot K. Browne]. London, Willoughby, [1843]. [B.M. : Pickering.]

Samuel : a story for choristers. London, Masters, 1850. [B.M. : *Eng. Cat.*]

Sand, George (*see* DUDEVANT, A. L. A. D.).

Sandeau, Léonard Silvain Jules. Madeleine ; a tale. With an analytical review of the style and writings of the author. By G. Planche. London, G. Slater. [1850]. [B.M.]

Sander, Meta. Dora Melder : A tale of Alsace. A Translation. Edited by the Rev. C. B. Tayler. With 2 illustrations. London, Longman, Brown, Green, and Longman, 1842. [B.M. : Publisher's advert.]

Sanders, Anna Maria. Helen ; Or, The Infant Prisoner of War : A Narrative. By Anna Maria. London, Partridge and Oakey, 1849. [B.M.]

Sanders, Charlotte Elizabeth. Edmund, a Tale for Children. By the Author of the Little Family. London, Mawman, 1802. [*Guardian of Education.*]

—— Holidays at Home. Written for the Amusement of Young Persons. With a frontispiece. London, 1803. [McLeish.]

Sanders, Charlotte Elizabeth. The Little Family Written for the Amusement and Instruction of Young Persons. 2 vols., Bath, R. Crutwell, 1797. [Allibone : B.M. : Arthur Rogers.]

Sandford, Lady Henrietta Cecilia. Stories from the History of Rome. Glasgow, R. Griffin, 1832. [Allibone : B.M.]

Sandham, Elizabeth. The Adopted Daughter. A Tale for Young Persons. With a frontispiece. London, J. Harris, 1815. [B.M. : Gumuchian : Ingpen.]

—— The Adventures Of a Bullfinch By the Author of " The Twin Sisters," " Poor Puss," &c. With a frontispiece. London, J. Harris, 1809. [B.M.]

—— The Adventures of Poor Puss. In Two Parts. With a frontispiece. London, J. Harris, 1809. [B.M. : Ingpen : Arthur Rogers.]

—— The Boys' School ; Or, Traits of Character In Early Life. A Moral Tale. With a frontispiece. London, John Souter, [1800 ?]. [B.M. (2nd edn.)]

—— The Grandfather ; Or, the Christmas Holidays. A Tale. London, Bowdery and Kerby, 1816. [B.M.]

—— The Happy Family at Eason House. Southampton, [1822 ?]. [B.M. : *Camb. Hist. Eng. Lit.*]

—— History of Britannicus and his Sister Octavia. With a frontispiece. London, Harris, 1819. [Allibone : *Eng. Cat.* : Sexton.]

—— The History of Elizabeth Woodville ; or, the Wars of the Houses of York and Lancaster. London, E. Wallis, 1822. [B.M. : *Camb. Hist. Eng. Lit. : Eng. Cat.*]

—— The History of William Selwyn. With a frontispiece. London, J. Harris, 1815. [Wm. Brown.]

—— Juliania ; or, the Affectionate Sisters. By the author of " The Happy Family at Eason House." London, 1800. [B.M.]

—— Lucilla ; or the reconciliation. By the author of " The Twin Sisters." 2 vols., London, Sherwood, 1819. [B.M. : *Eng. Cat. : New Monthly Mag.*]

—— The Orphan. Southampton, Privately Printed, 1808. [Algar.]

—— The School-fellows. A Moral Tale. By the author of " The Twin Sisters." London, J. Souter, 1818. [B.M. : *Camb. Hist. Eng. Lit. : Eng. Cat.*]

—— Sketches of Young People ; Or, A Visit to Brighton. By the Author of The Grandfather, Friendship, The Schoolfellows, &c. With a frontispiece. London, Harvey and Darton, 1822. [Block : B.M.]

Sarah and her Cousins, or, goodness better than knowledge. London, Hodson, 1833. [B.M. : *Eng. Cat.*]

205

Sarah and her Mistress, with hints on frugality and waste. London, [1849]. [B.M.]

Sargent, Jane Alice. Ringstead Abbey ; Or, The Stranger's Grave. With Other tales. London, Hurst, Chance, 1830. [B.M. : *New Monthly Mag.*]

—— Tales for Young Ladies, on their Entrance into Life. Consisting of " Ringstead Abbey," " Temptation," and " Consistency." London, Whittaker, Treacher, 1832. [Publisher's advert.]

Sarrazin, Adrien de. Bardouac ; Or, the Goat-herd of Mount Taurus : An Eastern Tale. Translated from the French of Adrien de Sarrazin. With a frontispiece. London, Sherwood, Neely, and Jones, 1815. [Ingpen.]

Serratt, John Henry. Koenigsmark The Robber, Or, The Terror of Bohemia ; In which is introduced, Stella, Or, The Maniac of the Wood, A Pathetick Tale. London, Tegg and Castleman, [1803]. [B.M. : T. D. Webster.]

Satchel (The) : or, amusing tales, for correcting rising errors in early youth. London, 1805. [B.M.]

Satiric Tales ; Consisting of a Voyage to the Moon ; All the Tailors, or, the Old Cloak ; and the Fat Witch of London. By Nicholas Lunatic. London, George Hughes and H. D. Symonds, 1808. [B.M. : Victorius.]

Saumery, P. L. The Devil Turn'd Hermit : or, The Adventures of Astaroth, Banish'd from Hell. A Satirical Romance. Exposing, with Great Variety of Humour, in a Series of Conversations between that Demon and the Author, The scandalous Frauds, lewd Amours and devout Mockery of the Monks and Nuns ; the Intrigues of Courts ; the Ambition, Avarice, and Cruelty of Ministers ; the Insincerity, Luxury, Prostitution, and Ingratitude of many private Characters ; with other Capital Vices of the present Age. Founded chiefly on real Facts, and interspersed with the Portraits and secret History of most of the considerable Persons that have lived in Europe within these thirty years past. Translated from the Original French of Mr. de M * * *. With a frontispiece. London, J. Hodges, 1741. [W. Brown : Mudie's : Pickering.]

Saurin, Bernard J. Mirza and Fatima, an Indian Tale, Translated from the French. London, T. Osborne, 1754. [W. Brown : Dobell : A. V. Turner.]

Savage, Miss. Trial And Self-Discipline. London, Simpkin, Marshall, 1835. [B.M.]

Savage, Marmion W. The Bachelor of the Albany. By the Author of " The Falcon Family." London, 1848. [Quaritch.]

—— The Falcon Family ; or, Young Ireland A Satirical Novel. London, Chapman and Hall, 1845. [B.M. : McLeish : Publisher's advert.]

Savage, Marmion W. My Uncle the Curate. A Novel. By the Author of " The Bachelor of the Albany," and " The Falcon Family." 3 vols., London, Chapman and Hall, 1849. [B.M. : R. Walter Gibson : *I. in F.*]

Savage (The), By Piomingo, a Headman and Warrior of the Muscogulgee Nation. 1811. [*Quarterly Review.*]

Savile, The Hon. Charles Stuart. Karah Kaplan ; Or, The Koordish Chief. A Tale of Persia and Koordistan. 3 vols., London, Richard Bentley, 1842. [Allibone : B.M. : Ingpen.]

—— Leonard Normandale ; or the Three Brothers. A novel. 3 vols., London, Henry Colburn, 1850. [B.M. : *Eng. Cat.*]

Saville, John Faucit. The Heads of the Headless. A Romance of the Reign of Henry Tudor. With woodcuts. London, E. Lloyd, [1847]. [B.M. : H. W. Fennell : B. Ono.]

Saxon and the Gael (The) ; or, The Northern Metropolis : Including A View of the Lowland and Highland Character. 4 vols., London, Thomas Tegg, 1814. [B.M. : Pickering : T. D. Webster.]

Sayers, Hon. Louisa Sarah. Henry Acton Or the Gold Smugglers And other tales. 3 vols., London, Saunders & Otley, 1839. [Allibone : B.M.]

Scargill, William Pitt. Atherton ; A Tale of the Last Century. By the Author of " Rank and Talent," &c. 3 vols., London, W. Simpkin & R. Marshall, 1831. [B.M. : Elkin Mathews.]

—— The Autobiography of a Dissenting Minister. London, Smith, Elder, 1834. [Geo. Bates : B.M.]

—— Blue-Stocking Hall ; a Work of Fiction, designed to inculcate the various Duties of Domestic Life. 3 vols., London, Henry Colburn and Richard Bentley, 1827. [The British Museum copy reads *Blue-Stocking Hall* [A quotation from *Love's Labour's Lost.*] 3 Volumes. London, Henry Colburn, 1827.] [B.M. : Ingpen : A. Margery.]

—— (Attributed to). Elizabeth Evanshaw. The Sequel of Truth. A Novel. 3 vols., London, Hunt and Clarke, 1827. [B.M. : Publisher's advert.]

—— Penelope : or, Love's Labour Lost. A Novel. 3 vols., London, Hunt & Clarke, 1828. [B.M. : Ingpen : *Quarterly Review.*]

—— Provincial Sketches. By the Author of " The Usurer's Daughter," " The Puritan's Grave," &c. &c. &c. London, Edward Churton, 1835. [B.M.]

—— The Puritan's Grave. By the Author of " The Usurer's Daughter."

3 vols., London, Saunders and Otley, 1833. [B.M. : Cleverdon.]

Scargill, William Pitt. Rank and Talent ; a Novel. By the Author of " Truckle-borough-Hall." 3 vols., London, Henry Colburn, 1829. [B.M.: McLeish : Elkin Mathews.]

—— Tales of a Briefless Barrister. 3 vols., London, Henry Colburn and Richard Bentley, 1829. [B.M. : Kyrle Fletcher.]

—— Tales of My Time. By the Author of Blue-Stocking Hall. 3 vols., London, Henry Colburn and Richard Bentley, 1829. [B.M. : Maggs.]

—— Truckleborough Hall ; A Novel. 3 vols., London, Henry Colburn, 1827. [B.M. : McLeish : A. Margery.]

—— Truth. A Novel By the Author of Nothing. 3 vols., London, Hunt, and Clarke, 1826. [B.M. : *Quarterly Review.*]

—— The Usurer's Daughter. By a Contributor to " Blackwood's Magazine." 3 vols., London, W. Simpkin and R. Marshall, 1832. [B.M. : McLeish : *Metropolitan Mag.*]

Scarlet Handerchief (The). A Novel. 3 vols., London, A. K. Newman, 1823. [*Eng. Cat. : New Monthly Mag.*]

Scarron, Paul. The comic Romance of Monsieur Scarron. Translated by Oliver Goldsmith. 2 vols., London, W. Griffin, 1775. [B.M. : Maggs : Iolo Williams.]

Scenes and Sketches of a Soldier's Life in Ireland. By the Author of ' Recollections of an Eventful Life.' London, Tait, 1826. [*Eng. Cat. : Quarterly Review.*]

Scenes in the Morea : Or, A Sketch of the Life Of Demetrius Argyri. London, Sherwood, Jones, 1824. [B.M.]

Sceptic (The). By a Lady. 2 vols., London, 1850. [B.M.]

Scheming ; A Novel. 3 vols., London, Henry Colburn, 1821. [B.M. : G. Worthington.]

Schiller, Johann Friedrich von. The Armenian ; or, the Ghost-Seer. A History founded on fact. Translated from the German of F. Schiller, Author of The Robbers, Don Carlos, etc. by the Rev. W. Render. 4 vols., London, H. D. Symonds, 1800. [Baker's Bookshop : B.M. : Pickering.]

—— The Ghost-Seer ; or The Apparitionist. An Interesting Fragment, Found among the Papers of Count O—, From the German of Schiller. [Translated by D. Boileau.] London, Vernor and Hood, 1795. [B.M. : Maggs : *New Ann. Reg.*]

Schmid, Johann Christoph von. The Cake, from the German. To which are added Titus and his Family ; the Forget-me-not [by A.G.], the Overseer of Mahlbourg, Bear-Hunt in the Pyrenees [by A.Y.Z.]. London, [1849]. [B.M.]

Schmid, Johann Christoph von. The Chapel of the Forest and the Robin Redbreast. Translated from the German of C. Schmid. Derby, 1845. [B.M.]

—— Christmas Eve, from the German of C. Schmid. London, 1843. [B.M.]

—— Clara ; or, the Dangers of Innocence, from the Tales for Youth, by C. de Schmid translated from German by Heliodora. Augsburg, 1843. [B.M.]

—— The Easter Eggs, a tale for children. By the author of Genovefa, translated from the German. London, Hamilton, 1929. [B.M. : *Eng. Cat.*]

—— Fifty Short Stories, translated into English from the Erzählungen of C. von Schmid, with introductory observations on pronunciation and accent. By H. J. Whitling. Nuremberg, 1846. [B.M.]

—— First Tales for Children. From the German. By Miss F. Johnstone. Bath, 1845. [B.M.]

—— Genevieve of Brabant : a legend of the Middle Ages. Translated from the German. Dublin, J. Duffy, 1835. [B.M.]

—— Genoveva of Brabant, a tale of old times (from the German of C. Schmid). London, Burns, [1843 ?]. [B.M.]

—— Henry of Eichenfels : or, How a child learned to know that there is a God. A tale translated from the German. Edinburgh, 1848. [B.M.]

—— The Hop Blossoms. Translated from the German of C. Schmid. Derby, 1845. [B.M.]

—— The Picture of the Virgin : Adapted from the German of Cristoph von Schmid, By Mary Howitt. With illustrations by John Absolon. London, Wm. S. Orr, 1844. [B.M.]

—— The Shepherd Boy And Other tales (From the German of Schmid). With a vignette. London, James Burns, [1849]. [B.M.]

—— Tales designed chiefly for the Young. Translated from the German. With illustrations. Dublin, Duffy, 1846. [B.M.]

School for Daughters, or the History of Miss Charlotte Sidney. 2 vols., 1775. [W. Brown : *Eng. Lit. in Germany.*]

School for Fashion (The). A Novel. 3 vols., London, Henry Colburn, 1829. [B.M.]

School for Fathers (The) ; Or, The Victim of a Curse, a novel, containing authentic memoirs and anecdotes, with historical parts. 3 vols., London, Robinson, 1788. [B.M. : Ingpen : T. Thorp.]

School for Husbands. Written by a Lady. 2 vols., 1774. [W. Brown : *Eng. Lit. in Germany.*]

School for Majesty ; or, The Sufferings of Zomelli. An Oriental History. London, W. Lane, 1783. [G. Worthington.]

School for Mothers (The) ; With the Politics of a Village. 3 vols., London, G. and W. B. Whittaker, 1823. [B.M. : *European Mag.* : *New Monthly Mag.*]

School for Sisters (The) ; Or, The Lesson of Experience. With a frontispiece. London, Longman, Hurst, Rees, Orme and Brown, 1823. [Block : B.M.]

School for Wives (The). In a series of letters. London, R. and J. Dodsley, 1763. [B.M.: W. Brown: T. D. Webster.]

School of Arts (The). By the author of " The Military Blacksmith." Edinburgh, William Oliphant, 1825. [Block.]

School of Fashion (The) : a Novel. 3 vols., London, Henry Colburn, 1829. [Elkin Mathews.]

School of Virtue (The). Consisting of Novels, Tales, Fables, Allegories, &c. &c. Moral and Entertaining ; In Prose and Verse. London, E. Sumpter, 1763. [Court Bk. Shop.]

School of Virtue (The). A Novel, on a New Plan, Inscribed to Her Majesty, by a Gentleman of the Temple. 2 vols., London, William Lane, 1787. [H. M. Fletcher : Blakey.]

School of Woman (The) : Or, Memoirs of Constantia. Address'd to the Duchess of * * * * *. By the Author of the School of Man, a Moral Work : Suppress'd at Paris, by Order of the King of France. Translated from the French. London, J. Robinson, 1753. [Block : Elkin Mathews : Pickering.]

Schoolfellows (The) ; or, the influence of character and connections displayed. By the author of " Sarah and her Husband." London, Roake & Varty, 1837. [B.M. (4th edn.)]

Schoolmistress (The) ; or, the true history of Jenny Hickling. London, Religious Tract Society, [1830]. [B.M.]

Scotch Betty : A True Story of a Poor Woman, who was run over by a Wagon, with A Particular Account of some interesting Conversation she had with a Physician who attended her. With a woodcut. London, Printed by A. Applegarth, for the Religious Tract Society, N.D. [Block.]

Scotch Marine (The) : or, Memoirs of the Life of Celestina ; A Young Lady, Who Secretly Deserting Her Family, Spent Two Year In Strict Amity, As A Man, With Her Beloved Castor. Containing a Relation of the various Fortunes she ran with him in that Time, without a Discovery or Suspicion of her Sex. Her Marriage afterwards with Cario, A North-Briton, in New-England ; her Voyage with that Gentleman to this Kingdom ; and their adventures here, till their Return to Scotland. Including a great Diversity of surprising Incidents. Printed from the Original Manuscript, for the Justification of her Character. 2 vols., Dublin, James Pott, 1761. [Pickering].

Scots Heiress (The). London, T. Hookham and J. Carpenter. [Publisher's advert. 1791.]

Scott, Caroline. Hermione ; or, The Defaulter. A Novel. 2 vols., London, Printed by the Minerva Press for A. K. Newman, 1816. [B.M. : *New Monthly Mag.*]

Scott, Lady Caroline Lucy. A Marriage in High Life. Edited by The Authoress of " Flirtation " [Lady Charlotte Maria Bury]. 2 vols., London, Henry Colburn, 1828. [B.M. : Clarke-Hall : *Quarterly Review.*]

—— Trevelyan. By the Author of " A Marriage in High Life." 3 vols., London, Richard Bentley, 1833. [P. C. Cuttelle : Sotheran : T. Thorp.]

Scott, Lady Harriet Anne. The Hen-Pecked Husband. A Novel, By The Author of " The M.P.'s Wife." 3 vols., London, Thomas Cautley Newby, 1847. [B.M.]

—— Hylton House and its inmates. By the author of " The Henpacked Husband." London, T. C. Newby, 1850. [B.M. : *Eng. Cat.*]

—— The M.P.'s Wife : And The Lady Geraldine. 2 vols., London, Edward Bull, 1838. [B.M.]

—— Percy Or The Old Love and the New By the Author of " The Henpecked Husband." 3 vols., London, Thomas Cautley Newby, 1848. [B.M.]

Scott, Helenus. The Adventures Of a Rupee. Wherein are interspersed Various Anecdotes Asiatic and European. London, J. Murray, 1782. [John Bligh : B.M. : Ingpen.]

Scott, Honoria. Amatory Tales of Spain, France, Switzerland, and the Mediterranean; containing The Fair Andalusian; Rosolia of Palermo ; and the Maltese Portrait : interspersed with pieces of original poetry. 4 vols., London, J. Dick, 1810. [B.M. : Pickering : *Quarterly Review.*]

—— The Castle of Strathmay ; or, Scenes in the North : illustrative of Scottish Manners and Society, a tale. By the author of " A Winter in Edinburgh." 2 vols., London, 1814. [B.M. (2nd edn.) : *New Monthly Mag.*]

—— The Vale of Clyde : a tale. 2 vols., London, 1810. [B.M.]

—— A Winter in Edinburgh ; or, the Russian Brothers ; a Novel. 3 vols., London, J. Dick, 1810. [Baker's Bookshop : B.M. : Pickering.]

Scott, Jonathan. The Arabian Nights Entertainments, Carefully Revised, and Occasionally Corrected From the Arabic. To which is added A Selection of New Tales, Now first translated from the Arabic Originals. Also, An Introduction and Notes, Illustrative of the Religion, Manners, and Customs, of the Mahummedans. By Jonathan Scott. With frontispieces after Smirke. 6 vols., London, Longman, Hurst, Rees, Orme, and Brown, 1811. [B.M. : Maggs : Marks.]

Scott, Jonathan. Tales, Anecdotes and Letters. Translated from the Arabic and Persian. Shrewsbury, Cadell, jun. and Davis, 1800. [Stonehill.]

Scott, Maria (Edited by). Winter Tales, or European Nights' Entertainments. With a frontispiece. London, 1825. [Lowndes.]

Scott, Michael. The Cruise of the Midge. By the Author of " Tom Cringle's Log." 2 vols., Edinburgh, William Blackwood ; and T. Cadell, London, 1836. [B.M. : Ingpen : Arthur Rogers.]

—— Tom Cringle's Log. 2 vols., Edinburgh, William Blackwood, 1833. [Ingpen : Marks : G. Worthington.]

Scott, Sarah. Agreeable Ugliness : Or, The Triumph of the Graces, Exemplified in the Real Life and Fortunes of a Young Lady of some Distinction. London, R. and J. Dodsley, 1754. [Huth : Maggs : Stonehill.]

—— The History of Cornelia. London, A. Millar, 1750. [Blackwell : B.M. : McLeish.]

—— The History of Sir George Ellison. 2 vols., London, A. Millar, 1766. [B.M.: Eng. Lit. in Germany : Ingpen.]

—— A Journey Through Every Stage of Life, Described in a Variety of Interesting Scenes, Drawn from Real Characters. By a Person of Quality. 2 vols., London, A Millar, 1754. [B.M. : Eng. Lit. in Germany : Ingpen.]

—— The Test of Filial Duty. In a Series of Letters between Miss Emilia Leonard, and Miss Charlotte Arlington. A Novel. 2 vols., London, Printed for the Author, 1772. [Huth.]

——, and Montagu, Lady Barbara. A Description of Millenium Hall, and the Country Adjacent. Together with the Characters and Inhabitants, and such historical Anecdotes and Reflections as may excite in the Reader proper Sentiments of Humanity, and lead the Mind to the Love of Virtue. By a Gentleman on his Travels. London, J. Newbery, 1762. [B.M. : W. T. Spencer : Stonehill.]

Scott, Sybil. Recollections Of a French Marchioness. 2 vols., London, T. C. Newby, 1846. [B.M.]

—— Rough and Smooth. A novel. By the author of " Recollections of a French Marchioness." 3 vols., London, Newby, 1849. [B.M. : Eng. Cat.]

Scott, Thomas. The Force of Truth : an authentic narrative. London, 1779. [B.M. : Eng. Lit. in Germany.]

Scott, Sir Walter. The Abbot. By the Author of " Waverley." 3 vols., Edinburgh, Printed for Longman, Hurst,

Rees, Orme, and Brown, London ; and Archibald Constable & John Ballantyne, Edinburgh, 1820. [Block : B.M. : Maggs.]

Scott, Sir Walter. Anne of Geierstein ; or The Maiden of the Mist. By The Author of " Waverley," &c. 3 vols., Edinburgh, Cadell ; and Simpkin and Marshall, London, 1829. [Block : B.M.: G. Worthington.]

—— The Antiquary. By the Author of " Waverley " and " Guy Mannering." 3 vols., Edinburgh, Printed by James Ballantyne for Archibald Constable ; Longman, Hurst, Rees, Orme and Browne, London, 1816. [Blackwell : Block : B.M.]

—— Chronicles Of The Canongate ; By The Author of " Waverley," &c. 2 vols., Edinburgh, Cadell ; and Simpkin and Marshall, London, 1827. [Block : B.M. : Maggs.]

—— Chronicles Of The Canongate. Second Series. By the Author of " Waverley," &c. 3 vols., Edinburgh, Cadell ; and Simpkin and Marshall, London, 1828. [Block : B.M. : Maggs.]

—— The Fortunes of Nigel. By the Author of " Waverley, Kenilworth," &c. 3 vols., Edinburgh, Archibald Constable ; and Hurst, Robinson, London, 1822. [Block : B.M. : Arthur Rogers.]

—— Guy Mannering ; or, The Astrologer. By the Author of " Waverley." 3 vols., Edinburgh, James Ballantyne for Longman, Hurst, Rees, Orme, and Brown, London ; and Archibald Constable, Edinburgh, 1815. [Block : B.M. : Pickering.]

—— Ivanhoe ; A Romance. By The Author of "Waverley." 3 vols., Edinburgh, Archibald Constable ; and Hurst, Robinson, London, 1820. [Block : B.M. : Pickering.]

—— Kenilworth : A Romance. By the Author of " Waverley," " Ivanhoe," &c. 3 vols., Edinburgh, Archibald Constable ; and John Ballantyne ; and Hurst, Robinson, London, 1821. [Block : B.M. : Arthur Rogers.]

—— The Monastery. A Romance ; By the Author of " Waverley." 3 vols. Edinburgh, Printed for Longman, Hurst, Rees, Orme, and Brown ; and Archibald Constable ; London ; and John Ballantyne, Edinburgh, 1820. [Block : B.M. : Maggs.]

—— Peveril of the Peak. By the Author of " Waverley, Kenilworth, " &c. 4 vols. Edinburgh, Archibald Constable ; and Hurst, Robinson, London, 1822. [Block : B.M. : Arthur Rogers.]

—— The Pirate. By the Author of " Waverley, Kenilworth," &c. 3 vols., Edinburgh, Archibald Constable ; & Hurst, Robinson, London, 1822. [Block : B.M. : Arthur Rogers.]

Scott, Sir Walter. Quentin Durward. By the Author of " Waverley, Peveril of the Peak," &c. 3 vols., Edinburgh, Archibald Constable ; and Hurst, Robinson, London, 1823. [Block : Ingpen : Arthur Rogers.]

—— Redgauntlet. A Tale of the Eighteenth Century. By the Author of " Waverley." 3 vols., Edinburgh, Archibald Constable ; and Hurst, Robinson, London, 1824. [Block : B.M. : Arthur Rogers.]

—— Rob Roy. By the Author of " Waverley," " Guy Mannering," and " The Antiquary." Edinburgh, James Ballantyne for Archibald Constable ; and Longman, Hurst, Rees, Orme, and Brown, London, 1818. [Block : B.M. : Arthur Rogers.]

—— St. Ronan's Well. By the Author of " Waverley, Quentin Durward," &c. 3 vols., Edinburgh, Archibald Constable ; and Hurst, Robinson, London, 1824. [Block : B.M. : Arthur Rogers.]

—— Tales of the Crusaders. By the Author of " Waverley, Quentin Durward," &c. 4 vols., Edinburgh, Archibald Constable ; and Hurst, Robinson, London, 1825. [Block : B.M. : Arthur Rogers.]

—— Tales of a Grandfather : Being Stories Taken from Scottish History. 3 vols., Edinburgh, Cadell, 1828. [Block : B.M. : Arthur Rogers.]

—— Tales of a Grandfather : Being Stories Taken from Scottish History. Second Series. 3 vols., Edinburgh, Cadell, 1829. [Block : B.M. : Ingpen.]

—— Tales of a Grandfather : Being Stories Taken from Scottish History. Third Series. 3 vols., Edinburgh, Cadell, 1830. [Block : B.M. : Arthur Rogers.]

—— Tales of My Landlord, Collected and Arranged by Jedediah Cleishbotham, Schoolmaster and Parish-Clerk of Gandercleugh. 4 vols., Edinburgh, William Blackwood ; and John Murray, London, 1816. [Block : *Quarterly Review* : Arthur Rogers.]

—— Tales of my Landlord, Second Series, Collected and Arranged by Jedediah Cleishbotham, Schoolmaster and Parish-Clerk of Gandercleugh. 4 vols., Edinburgh, Archibald Constable, 1818. [Block : B.M. : Arthur Rogers.]

—— Tales of my Landlord, Third Series, Collected and Arranged by Jedediah Cleishbotham, Schoolmaster and Parish-Clerk of Gandercleugh. 4 vols., Edinburgh, Archibald Constable ; and Longman, Hurst, Rees, Orme, and Brown ; and Hurst, Robinson, London, 1819. [Block : B.M. : Pickering.]

—— Tales of my Landlord, Fourth and Last Series, Collected and Arranged By Jedediah Cleishbotham, Schoolmaster and Parish-Clerk of Gandercleugh. 4 vols., Edinburgh, Robert Cadell ; and Whittaker, London, 1832. [Block : B.M. : Maggs.]

Scott, Sir Walter. Waverley ; or, 'Tis Sixty Years Since. 3 vols., Edinburgh, James Ballantyne and Archibald Constable ; and Longman, Hurst, Rees, Orme and Brown, London, 1814. [Block : B.M. : Maggs.]

—— Woodstock ; or, The Cavalier : A Tale of the Year Sixteen Hundred and Fifty-One. By the Author of " Waverley, Tales of the Crusaders," &c. 3 vols., Edinburgh, Archibald Constable ; and Longman, Rees, Orme, Brown, and Green, 1826. [Block : B.M. : Arthur Rogers.]

Scribe, Eugene. Piquillo Alliaga ; or the Moors under Philip the Third of Spain. With woodcuts. London, G. Pierce, 1846. [R. S. Frampton.]

Seally, John. Loves of Calisto and Emira ; or, The Fatal Legacy. London, 1776. [B.M. : W. Brown.]

—— Moral Tales, after the Eastern manner. 2 vols., London, [1780 ?]. [B.M.]

Sealy, Thomas Henry. The Porcelain Tower ; Or, Nine Stories of China, Compiled From Original Sources by " T.T.T." With etchings by John Leech. London, Richard Bentley, 1841. [B.M. : Pickering : T. Thorp.]

Sebright, Paul. Adèle ; or, The Tomb of My Mother. A Novel. 4 vols., London, A. K. Newman, 1824. [B.M.]

—— Coincidence ; Or, The Soothsayer. A Novel. 3 vols., London, Printed at the Minerva Press, for A. K. Newman, 1820. [B.M. : *New Monthly Mag.*]

Second Collection of Pathetic, Sentimental and Moral Narratives (The) ; selected from the best authors. With engravings. London, 1807. [B.M.]

Second Portraiture of Exclusive Society (A), or Foreign Exclusives in London. A satirical Novel. 3 vols., London, Henry Colburn, 1830. [*Eng. Cat.* : *New Monthly Mag.*]

Secrecy ; or, the Ruin on the Rock. By a Woman. 3 vols., London, Printed for the Author, [1795]. [Block : *New Ann. Reg.*]

Secret (The). A Christmas tale for the young. By the author of " Susan Carter." London, 1848. [B.M.]

Secret History and Misfortunes of Fatyma, and the history of Olympia, written by themselves. To which is added, Incle and Yarico, in verse. Banbury, [1820 ?]. [B.M.]

Secret History of Betty Ireland (The). London, S. Lee, [1750 ?]. [B.M.]

Secret History of a Devil in Petticoats, called the lovely Leonora, containing her life and adventures from the age of 14 till her death. London, 1848. [B.M.]

Secret History of Miss Blandy from her First Appearance at Bath to her

Execution at Oxford. 1752. [*Eng. Lit. in Germany.*]

Secret Oath (The) ; or, Blood-Stained Dagger. A Romance. With a frontispiece. London, Hurst, 1802. [Stonehill.]

Secret Tribunal (The) ; or, the Court of Winceslaus [*sic*]. A Mysterious Tale. With a frontispiece. London, Tegg and Castleman, [1803]. [Block.]

Secret Warning (The) ; or, The Fatal Hour. With woodcuts. [London] [c. 1840]. [Stonehill.]

Secretary (The) ; or, Circumstantial Evidence. With woodcuts. London, Lloyd, [c. 1845]. [Stonehill.]

Sedan (The). A Novel, in which many New and Entertaining Characters are Introduced. 2 vols., London, R. Baldwin, 1757. [B.M. : Arthur Rogers.]

Sedgwick, Miss. Home. London, Simpkin, Marshall, 1836. [B.M.]

Sedley, Sir Charles. Asmodeus ; or, the Devil in London : a Sketch. By the Author of " The Faro Table," etc. 3 vols., London, 1808. [B.M.]

—— The Barouche Driver and his Wife. A Tale for Haut-ton, Containing a Curious Biography of Living Characters, with Notes Explanatory. 2 vols., London, Hughes, 1807. [B.M. : Ingpen.]

—— The Faro Table, or The Gambling Mother. A Fashionable Fable. By the Author of The Barouche Driver and His Wife. 2 vols., London, Hughes, 1808. [B.M. : Ingpen : W. T. Spencer.]

—— A Winter in Dublin. A Descriptive Tale. 3 vols., London, Hughes, 1808. [B.M. : Ingpen : Arthur Rogers.]

Seducing Cardinal (The) ; Or Isabella Peto. London, Madam Le Duck [J. B. Brookes], 1830. [*Cat. Lib. Prohib.*]

Seduction ; or the perils of a woman's life. A romance. London, 1846. [B.M.]

Segrais (*see* DE SEGRAIS).

Seguin, James. Letters of Princess Zilia, to Prince Aza of Peru, Newly translated from the French original, by James Seguin. London, Printed for the Author, 1755. [B.M. : Woore.]

—— The English Nun. A Novel. 3 vols., London, William Lane, 1797. [Blakey : *Minerva Press Catalogue.*]

Selden, Catharine. Serena. A novel. 3 vols., London, William Lane, 1800. [B.M. : Blakey.]

—— Villa Nova ; or, The Ruined Castle. A romance. 2 vols., London, Lane, Newman, 1805. [B.M.]

—— Villasantelle ; or The Curious Impertinent. A Romance. London, A. K. Newman, 1817. [B.M. : *New Monthly Mag.*]

Select Collection of Oriental Tales (A). Edinburgh, 1776. [Stonehill.]

Selection of Eastern Tales (A) ; Partly from the French of Montesquieu. Edinburgh, Blair, 1817. [Stonehill.]

Selection of Stories (A) ; containing the history of the Two Sisters, The Fisherman, The King and Fairy Ring, and Honesty Rewarded. With illustrations. Glasgow, J. Lumsden, [1820 ?]. [B.M.]

Self-Delusion ; or, Adelaide d'Hauteroche : A Tale. By the Author of " Domestic Scenes." 2 vols., London, Longman, Hurst, Rees, Orme, and Brown, 1823. [B.M. : *New Monthly Mag. : Quarterly Review.*]

Self-Guidance : A Novel. 3 vols., London, Richard Bentley, 1832. [*Literary Gazette.*]

Self-Tormentor. 3 vols., 1789. [W. Brown.]

Sellon, Edward. Herbert Breakspear. A Legend of the Mahratta War. London, Whittaker, 1848. [*Cat. Lib. Prohib.*]

Selwyn, A. Montague Park ; or, Family Incidents. London, 1825. [B.M.]

—— A New Year's Gift ; or, Domestic Tales for Children. By the author of Eliza Delany. With 2 plates. London, William Cole, 1824. [B.M.]

—— Resignation ; or, Memoirs of the Dufane Family. London, J. Hatchard, 1824. [B.M.]

—— Tales of the Vicarage. With 4 plates. London, John Harris, 1824. [Gumuchian.]

—— Youth's Mirror ; or, tales adapted for the perusal of Children. London, [1830 ?]. [B.M.]

Semple, Robert. Charles Ellis : or, The Friends ; a Novel. 2 vols., 1806. [Allibone.]

Senate, E. Family Pride And Humble Merit. A Novel, Founded on Facts, And partly taken from the French. 3 vols., London, Sherwood, Neely, and Jones, 1810. [B.M. : *Monthly Mag. :* Pickering.]

Senior, Lt.-Col. Henry. Charles Vernon ; a Transatlantic Tale. 2 vols., London, Longman, 1849. [B.M. : *Eng. Cat.*]

Sentimental And Humorous Tales : viz. Sentimental : Death of Rousseau, Patriotic Clergyman, Victim of Dishonour. Humorous : The Absent Man. Epistle to Cunningham. Poetry : The Soldier's Dream. The Emigrant, &c. With a frontispiece. Newcastle, 1804. [T. D. Webster.]

Sentimental Connoisseur (The) : or, pleasing and entertaining novelist. London, 1778. [B.M.]

Sentimental Deceiver (The) : or History of Miss Hammond. A Novel, in a series of letters, by a lady. London, William Lane, 1784. [Blakey.]

Sentimental Excursions to Windsor and other Places. London, Walker, 1781. [Ingpen.]

Sentimental Fables design'd chiefly for the use of the ladies. Belfast, 1771. [B.M.]

Sentimental Journey (A) intended as a sequel to Mr. Sterne's. Through Italy, Switzerland, and France. By Mr. Shandy. 2 vols., Southampton, 1793. [B.M.]

Sentimental Lucubrations. By Peter Pennyless. London, Becket, 1770. [B.M. : Ingpen : W. T. Spencer.]

Sentimental Memoirs. By a Lady. 2 vols., London, Hookham, 1785. [B.M. : Stonehill.]

Sentimental Spy (The). A novel. 2 vols., London, 1773. [B.M.]

Sephora ; a Hebrew Tale descriptive of Palestine, and of the manners and customs of the ancient Israelites. 2 vols., London, Hatchard, 1826. [B.M. : *Eng. Cat. : Quarterly Review.*]

Sepoy's Daughter (The) ; A True Tale of the Indian War. By An Eye Witness. With woodcuts. London, Lea, [c.1845]. [Stonehill.]

Sequel to the Expedition of Humphrey Clinker. A Novel In One Volume, Being the Continuation of the Celebrated Novel written by the late Tobias Smollett, M.D. London, Printed by the Philanthropic Society, for Sherwood, Neely, 1810. [Ingpen.]

Sequel to Principle and Practice ; Or The Orphan Family. A Tale. London, Houlston, 1831. [B.M.]

Sergeant, Jane, Edward Travers : A Roman Catholic Story. By Adeline, Author of "Scenes in the West Indies;" "Ernald, or the Martyr of the Alps;" "Helen Leslie." "Missionary Lays ;" etc., etc. London, J. Mason, 1849. [B.M.]
—— Helen Leslie ; Or, Truth and Error. By Adeline, Author of "Scenes in the West Indies," "Ernald, or the Martyr of the Alps," And other Poems. London, J. Mason, 1848. [B.M.]

Serle, Thomas James. Eustace ; or, The Stage of Life. 3 vols., London, Henry Colburn, 1848. [Publisher's advert.]
—— Joan of Arc, The Maid of Orleans. 3 vols., London, Henry Colburn, 1841. [Allibone : B.M.]
—— The Players ; Or, The Stage of Life. 3 vols., London, Henry Colburn, 1847. [Allibone : B.M.]

Serres, Olivia Wilmot. Memoirs of a Princess ; or, First Love. An historical romance. By Olivia W. S——. 2 vols., London, John Maynard, 1812. [Baker's Bookshop : B.M. : *New Monthly Mag.*]
—— St. Julian. In a Series of Letters. London, Ridgway, 1805. [Stonehill.]

Servants Hall (The), a tale. Edited by a Clergyman. London, Rivington, 1849. [B.M. : *Eng. Cat.*]

Serviez, M. de. The Roman Empresses : or, the History of the Lives and secret Intrigues of the Wives of the XII.

Caesars ; with historical and critical Notes. Written originally in French, by Monsieur De Serviez, and translated by the Hon. Bysse Molesworth. 3 vols., London, Dodsley, 1752. [Kyrle Fletcher : Lowndes.]

Set Down at Court (A), including a Series of Anecdotes in High Life. 4 vols., 1812. [*Quarterly Review.*]

Setting Sun, or Devil among the Placemen. 3 vols., [Cawthorn's Catalogue, 1810.]

Seven Fairy Tales. London, 1848. [B.M.]

Seventy-Six. By the Author of "Logan." 3 vols., 1823. [*New Monthly Mag.*]

Severn, Emma. Anne Hathaway ; Or, Shakspeare in Love. 3 vols., London, Richard Bentley, 1845. [Allibone : B.M.]

Severn, John Percy. The Adventures of Ariston. By An Eton Boy. London, T. Cadell, 1830. [B.M. : *New Monthly Mag.*]

Sewell, Elizabeth Missing. The Affianced One. By the Author of " Gertrude." 3 vols., London, Edward Bull, 1832. [B.M.]
—— Amy Herbert, By a Lady. Edited by the Rev. William Sewell. 2 vols., London, Longman, Brown, Green and Longmans, 1844. [Allibone : B.M.]
—— The Earl's Daughter. By the Author of " Amy Herbert," " Gertrude." 2 vols., London, Longman, 1850. [Allibone : B.M. : *Eng. Cat.*]
—— Gertrude. By the author of Amy Herbert. Edited by W. Sewell. 2 vols., London, Longman, 1846. [B.M. (2nd. edn.)]
—— Laneton Parsonage : a tale for children on the practical use of a portion of the Church Catechism. By the author of " Amy Herbert." London, Longman, 1846-1847-1848. [Allibone : B.M. : *Eng. Cat.*]
—— Margaret Percival. By the author of " Amy Herbert." Edited by W. Sewell. 2 vols., London, Longman, 1847. [B.M. : *Eng. Cat. :* George's Sons.]
—— Margaret Percival in America : a tale. Being a sequel to Margaret Percival : a tale. London, 1850. [B.M.]
—— The Sketches : three tales. By the author of " Amy Herbert." London, Longman, 1848. [B.M. : *Eng. Cat.*]
—— Was it a Dream ? and—The New Churchyard. By the author of " Stories on the Lord's Prayer." London, 1849. [B.M.]

Sewell, William. Hawkstone, a Tale of and for England in 184-. 2 vols., London, John Murray, 1845. [B.M. : Brough : Sanders.]

Seymer, John Gunning. The Romance of Ancient Egypt : Second Series of the Romance of Ancient History. 2 vols., London, Whittaker, 1835. [B.M.]
—— The Romance of Ancient History,

Egypt. 2 vols., London, Cochrane & McCrone, 1834. [B.M.]

Seymour Castle ; or, the history of Julia and Cecilia, an entertaining and interesting novel. 2 vols., London, 1789. [B.M.]

Shafton, Pierce. Vagaries in Quest of the Wild and Whimsical. London, J. Andrews, 1827. [B.M. : Leonard Hyman : *Literary Gazette.*]

Shakspeare's Romances collected and arranged by Shakspeare II. 2 vols., London, Sherwood, 1825. [B.M. : *Eng. Cat. : Quarterly Review.*]

Sharp, T. [Edited by]. The Dream of Heaven, or, the Sister's Tale. Edited by T. Sharp. London, 1836. [B.M.]

Shaw, George. Experience : Tales. London, 1839. [Allibone.]

She is and She is not : a fragment of the true history of Miss C. de Grosberg. Dedicated to Mrs. M—t C—e R—dd. 1777. [B.M.]

She Thinks for Herself. 3 vols., London, Longman, Hirst, Rees, Orme, and Brown, 1813. [B.M.]

Shebbeare, John. The History of the Excellence and Decline of the Constitution, Religion, Laws, Manners, and Genius of the Sumatrans. And of the Restoration thereof in the reign of Amurath the Third. 2 vols., London, G. Kearsley, [1763]. [B.M.]

—— Lydia, Or Filial Piety. A Novel. By the Author of The Marriage-Act, a Novel. And Letters on the English Nation. 4 vols., London, J. Scott, 1755. [B.M. : Arthur Rogers : W. T. Spencer.]

—— The Marriage Act : A Novel, In which the Ruin of Female Honour, the Contempt of the Clergy, the Destruction of Private and Public Liberty, with other Fatal consequences, are Considered : In a Series of Interesting Adventures. 2 vols., London, Hodges, 1754. [B.M. : Maggs : Arthur Rogers.]

—— Matrimony. A Novel. Containing a series of interesting adventures. 2 vols., London, 1755. [B.M. (2nd edn.)]

Shee, Sir Martin Archer. Cecil Hyde. A Novel. 2 vols., London, Saunders and Otley, 1834. [B.M. : Publisher's advert.]

—— Harry Calverley. A Novel By the Author of " Cecil Hyde." 3 vols., London, Saunders and Otley, 1835. [Allibone : B.M. : Stonehill.]

—— Oldcourt ; A Novel. 3 vols., London, Henry Colburn, 1829. [Allibone : B.M.]

Sheild, Mary Jane. Holme Park, Or, The Reverses of Fortune, a tale of real life. London, Whittaker ; and R. Groombridge ; Grantham, S. Ridge. [1839.] [B.M.]

Shekleton, H. E. Lovett. Fitz-Edward,

and other tales. London, Simpkin, 1847. [B.M. : *Eng. Cat.*]

Shelley, Mary Wollstonecraft. Falkner, A Novel By The Author of " Frankenstein ; " " The Last Man," &c. 3 vols., London, Saunders and Otley, 1837. [*Ashley Lib :* B.M. : Ingpen.]

—— The Fortunes Of Perkin Warbeck, A Romance. By the Author of " Frankenstein." 3 vols., London, Henry Colburn and Richard Bentley, 1830. [B.M. : Ingpen : King.]

—— Frankenstein ; Or, The Modern Prometheus. 3 vols., London, Lackington, Hughes, Harding, Mavor & Jones, 1818. [*Ashley Lib. :* Block : B.M.]

—— The Last Man. By the Author of Frankenstein. 3 vols., London, Henry Colburn, 1826. [B.M. : Ingpen : Maggs.]

—— Lodore. By the Author of " Frankenstein." 3 vols., London, Richard Bentley, 1835. [Block : B.M. : Ingpen.]

—— Valperga : Or, The Life and Adventures Of Castruccio, Prince of Lucca. By the Author of " Frankenstein." 3 vols., London, G. & W. B. Whittaker, 1823. [*Ashley Lib. :* B.M. : Ingpen.]

Shelly, Percy Bysshe. St. Irvyne ; or, The Rosicrucian : A Romance. By A Gentleman of the University of Oxford. London, J. J. Stockdale. 1811. [Block : B.M. : Ingpen.]

—— Zastrozzi, A Romance. By P. B. S. London, G. Wilkie and J. Robinson, 1810. [Block : B.M. : *Monthly Mag.*]

Shepherd, Anne. Reality, and Ellen Seymour, or The Bud and the Flower. Bath, 1849. [Allibone.]

Shepherdess of the Alps (The) : A very Interesting, Pathetic, and Moral Tale. Published At the Request of several Ladies of Distinction. Manchester, Printed by A. Swindells, [c.1796-1799]. [Court Bk. Shop : *Lancs.*]

Shepherdess of Aranville (The). 1794. [*New Ann. Reg.*]

Shepherd's Cord (The) : or the history of Helen Grey. London, 1850. [B.M.]

Sherer, Colonel Joseph Moyle. The Broken Font. A Story of the Civil War. By the Author of " Tales of the Wars of Our Times," " Recollections of the Peninsula," &c &c. &c. 2 vols., London, Longman, Rees, Orme, Brown, Green, & Longman, 1836. [Allibone : B.M. : McLeish.]

—— The Story of a Life. By the Author of Scenes and Impressions in Egypt and Italy, Recollections of the Peninsula, &c. 2 vols., London, Longman, Rees, Orme, Brown, & Green, 1823. [B.M. (2nd. edn.)]

—— Tales of The Wars of our Times. By the Author of " Recollections of the Peninsula," &c. &c. &c. 2 vols., London,

Longman, Rees, Orme, Brown, and Green, 1829. [Allibone : B.M.]

Sheridan, Caroline Henrietta. Aims and Ends : And Oonagh Lynch : By the Author of " Carwell." 3 vols., London, Edward Bull, 1833. [B.M. : W. Brown.]

—— Carwell ; or, Crime and Sorrow. London, Henry Colburn, and Richard Bentley, 1830. [B.M. : T. D. Webster.]

Sheridan, Frances. Conclusion of the Memoirs of Miss Sydney Biddulph, as prepared for the Press by the late Editor of the former part. Dublin, 1767. [Arthur Rogers.]

—— The History of Nourjahad By the Editor of Sydney Bidulph. London, J. Dodsley, 1767. [B.M. : Arthur Rogers : Lyle H. Wright.]

—— Memoirs of Miss Sidney Bidulph, Extracted from her own Journal & now First Published. 3 vols., London, 1761. [Also Dublin, 1761.] [B.M. : Maggs : Arthur Rogers.]

Sheriffe, Sarah. Correlia, or the Mystic Tomb. A romance. By the author of Humbert Castle. 4 vols., London, Printed at the Minerva-Press, for Lane and Newman, 1802. [Allibone : *Eng. Lit. in Germany :* Blakey.]

—— The Forest of Hohenelbe, A Tale, By the Author of Humbert Castle and Correlia. 3 vols., London, Minerva Press, 1803. [Allibone : Stonehill.]

—— Humbert Castle, or The Romance of the Rhone. A novel. With a frontispiece. 4 vols., London, Printed at the Minerva Press, for William Lane, 1800. [Allibone : Blakey.]

Sherwood, Mary Martha. Arzoomund. With a frontispiece. Wellington, Houlston, 1829. [B.M. (2nd edn.)]

—— The Broken Hyacinth, or Ellen and Sophia. Revised by the Committe of Publication. Philadelphia, American Sunday School Union, 1832. [B.M.]

—— Caroline Mordaunt ; or, the Governess. London, Darton, [1845 ?]. [B.M. : *Eng. Cat.*]

—— The Children of the Hartz Mountains ; or the little Beggars. Revised by the Committee of Publication. Philadelphia, American Sunday School Union, [1830 ?]. [B.M.]

—— Clara Stephens ; or the White Rose. Revised by the Committee of Publication. Philadelphia, 1827. [B.M.]

—— The Convent of St. Clair. Berwick, 1833. [B.M.]

—— The Cottage in the Wood. Part I [and Part II]. With a woodcut. London, Houlston, N.D. No. 41 [and 42] of Houlston's Series of Tracts. [Block.]

—— A Drive in the Coach through the Streets of London : A Story founded on fact. Wellington, Houlston, 1819. [Dobell (4th edn.)]

—— The Dry Ground. Wellington, Houlston, 1827.[B.M.]

Sherwood, Mary Martha. Dudley Castle, London, W. Darton, [1820 ?]. [B.M.]

—— Emancipation. With a woodcut frontispiece and a vignette title. Wellington, Houlston, 1829. [Block : B.M. : Sotheran.]

—— Ermina ; or, the second part of Juliana Oakley. Philadelphia, American Sunday School Union, 1827. [B.M.]

—— The Errand-Boy. Revised by the Committee of Publication. Philadelphia, American Sunday School Union, 1830. [B.M.]

—— The Fairy Knoll. London, H. K. Lewis, 1848. [B.M. : *Eng. Cat.*]

—— The Father's Eye. Stereotype Edition. With a frontispiece. Berwick, Thomas Melrose, [1830]. [B.M.]

—— The Fawns. Wellington, Houlston, 1828. [B.M.]

—— The Flowers of the Forest. By the Author of " Little Henry and his Bearer." With a frontispiece. London, Printed for the Religious Tract Society, By J. Nisbet, 1834. [Court Bk. Shop.]

—— The Fountain of Living Waters. A vision. By the author of " Little Henry and his Bearer." [1825 ?]. [B.M.]

—— The Golden Clue. With a woodcut. London, W. Whittemore : Wightman and Cramp, [1820 ?]. [Block.]

—— Hard Times, 1831. [Marks.]

—— The Hedge Of Thorns. With a frontispiece. London, J. Hatchard, 1819. [B.M.]

—— The History of Emily and her Mother. With a frontispiece. Wellington, Salop, Houlston, 1825. [Gumuchian.]

—— The History of the Fairchild Family ; or, the Child's Manual ; being a collection of stories calculated to shew the importance and effects of a religious education. With frontispieces. 3 vols., London, J. Hatchard, 1818-47. [The 3rd part is by Mrs. Sherwood and Mrs. Streeten.] [Allibone : B.M. : *Camb. Hist. Eng. Lit.*]

—— The History of Henry Milner, A Little Boy, Who was not brought up according to the Fashions of this World. With a frontispiece. 4 vols., London, J. Hatchard, 1822-1837. [Block : B.M. : Elkin Mathews.]

—— The History of John Marten, a sequel to the Life of Henry Milner. London, Hatchard, 1844. [B.M. : *Eng. Cat.*]

—— The History of Little Henry and his Bearer. With a frontispiece. Wellington, F. Houlston, 1814. [Mollie Green.]

—— The History of Little Lucy and her Dhaye. Wellington, Houlston, 1825. [B.M. : (2nd edn.)]

—— The History of Lucy Clare. By the author of " Susan Gray," etc. Wellington, Houlston, 1815. [B.M. : *Eng. Cat.*]

—— The History of Mrs. Catherine

214

Crawley. Wellington, Houlston, 1824. [B.M.]

Sherwood, Mary Martha. The History of Susan Gray, as related by a Clergyman, for the Benefit of Young Women going to Service. Bath, Hazard ; Spragg, London, 1802. [*Guardian of Education.*]

—— The History of Theophilus and Sophia. Wellington, Houlston, 1822. [B.M. : (6th edn.)]

—— Home. Wellington, Houlston, 1828. [B.M.]

—— The Idiot Boy. Wellington, Houlston, 1828. [B.M.]

—— The Indian Pilgrim ; Or, The Progress of the Pilgrim Nazarene (formerly called Goonah Puriot, or the Slave of Sin) from the City of the Wrath of God to the City of Mount Zion. Delivered under the Similitude of a Dream. With a frontispiece. Wellington, Houlston, 1818. [Ingpen : McLeish : G. Worthington.]

—— The Infant's Progress from the Valley of Destruction to Everlasting Glory. 1821. [*Camb. Hist. Eng. Lit.*]

—— The Iron Cage. With a woodcut. London, W. Whittemore : Wightman and Cramp, [1820 ?]. [Block.]

—— Juliana Oakley. London, Houlston, 1825. [B.M. : *Eng. Cat.*]

—— Julietta de Lavenza. London, Hatchard, 1841. [B.M. : *Eng. Cat.*]

—— The Lady and her Ayah, an Indian Story. By the author of Little Henry and his Bearer. Dublin, 1816. [B.M.]

—— The Lady in the Arbour. Wellington, Houlston, 1827. [B.M.]

—— The Lady of the Manor. Being A Series of Conversations on the Subject of Confirmation. Intended for the Use of the Middle and Higher Ranks of Young Females. With frontispieces. 7 vols., Wellington, F. Houlston, 1823-1828. [T. C. Godfrey : Guntrip & Richardson : *Quarterly Review.*]

—— The Lambourne Bell. With a woodcut. London, W. Whittemore : Wightman and Cramp, [1820 ?]. [Block.]

—— The Little Girl's Keepsake. With a frontispiece and a vignette title. London, Darton, and Clarke, N.D. [Block.]

—— The Little Momière. With a frontispiece. London, J. Hatchard, 1833. [B.M.]

—— The Little Orphan. With a woodcut. London, W. Whittemore, 1829. [Block.]

—— Little Sally. With a woodcut. London, W. Whittemore, 1829. [Block.]

—— The Little Woodman and his Dog Caesar. London, Houlston. [*Camb. Hist. Eng. Lit. : Eng. Cat.*]

—— The Mail Coach ; and the Old Lady's Complaint. London, [1830 ?]. [B.M.]

Sherwood, Mary Martha. Margarita. By the author of The Traditions. 4 vols., [W. Lane, 1799.] [Blakey.]

—— Mary Anne. By the author of " Little Henry and his Bearer." London, Religious Tract Society, [1820 ?]. [B.M.]

—— The Monk of Cimiés. With a woodcut title and frontispiece. London, William Darton, [1837]. [B.M.]

—— My Aunt Kate. Wellington, Houlston, 1828. [B.M.]

—— My Three Uncles ; and the Swiss Cottage. London, [1825 ?]. [B.M.]

—— My Uncle Timothy : An Interesting Tale For Young Persons. With a frontispiece and vignette. London, Knight and Lacey ; and Harrison and Stephens, 1825. [B.M. : *Edin. Mag.*]

—— The Nun. London, Seeley, 1833. [B.M. : *Eng. Cat.*]

—— The Nursery Maid's Diary. With a woodcut. London, Printed for W. Whittemore : Wightman and Cramp, [1820 ?]. [Block : B.M.]

—— Obedience. With a frontispiece by W. H. Lizars. Berwick, Thomas Melrose, 1830. [Gumuchian.]

—— The Oddingley Murders. London, 1830. [B.M.]

—— The Orange Grove. Wellington, Houslton, 1829. [B.M.]

—— The Orphans of Normandy ; or Florentin and Lucie. London, Hatchard, 1825. [B.M. : *Eng. Cat.*]

—— The Parson's Case of Jewels. Berwick, Houlston, 1837. [B.M. : *Eng. Cat.*]

—— Procrastination ; or, the Evil of putting that off till to-morrow which ought to be done to-day. With a woodcut. London, W. Whittemore : Wightman and Cramp, [1820 ?]. [Block.]

—— The Rainbow. Wellington, Houlston, 1828. [B.M.]

—— The Red Book. By the author of " Little Henry and his Bearer." [1845 ?]. [B.M.]

—— Religious Fashion ; or the history of Anna. Philadelphia, American Sunday School Union, 1827. [B.M.]

—— Robert and Frederick. London, H. Bohn, 1842. [Allibone : *Eng. Cat.*]

—— Roxobel. With frontispieces. 3 vols., London, Houlston, 1830-1831. [B.M. : Ingpen : Arthur Rogers.]

—— Sea-side Stories. London, Darton, [1838 ?]. [Allibone : B.M. : *Eng. Cat.*]

—— Sequel to the Oddingley Murders. London, 1830. [B.M.]

—— Social Tales For the Young. London, Darton and Clark, [1841]. [Allibone : Block : *Eng. Cat.*]

—— Soffrona and her cat Muff. Wellington, Houlston, 1838. [B.M.]

—— Southstone's Rock. With a frontispiece and a vignette title. Wellington, Houlston, 1828. [B.M.]

Sherwood, Mary Martha. Stories Explanatory of the Church Catechism. With a frontispiece. Wellington, Houlston, 1829. [Henry Start.]

—— The Story Book of Wonders. London, Nelson, 1849. [Allibone : B.M. : *Eng. Cat.*]

—— Susannah ; or the Three Guardians. Revised by the Committee of Publication. Philadelphia, American Sunday School Union, 1829. [B.M.]

—— The Thunderstorm. Wellington, Houlston, 1828. [B.M.]

—— The Traditions. A Legendary Tale. Written by A Young Lady. 2 vols., London, Printed for William Lane, Minerva [Press], 1795. [Block : *New Ann. Reg. :* T. D. Webster.]

—— The two Sisters ; or, Ellen and Sophia, by the author of " Little Henry and his Bearer," " Mary Anne," &c. London, Religious Tract Society, 1827. [B.M. : Block.]

—— Victoria. With illustrations. London, J. Hatchard, 1833. [Block : Elkin Mathews : G. Worthington.]

—— Waste Not, Want Not. Part I. With a woodcut. London, W. Whittemore : Wightman and Cramp, [1824 ?]. [Block.]

—— Waste Not, Want Not. Part II. With a woodcut. London, W. Whittemore, 1824. [Block.]

—— Waste Not, Want Not. Part III. and IV. With 2 woodcuts. 2 vols., London, W. Whittemore : Wightman and Cramp [1824 ?]. [Block.]

—— The Welsh Cottage. Wellington, Houlston, 1820. [B.M.]

—— The Wish : or, Little Charles. Revised by the Committee of Publication. Philadelphia, American Sunday School Union, 1832. [B.M.]

—— The Young Mother. With a woodcut. London, W. Whittemore : Wightman and Cramp, [1820 ?] [Block.]

Sherwood, Mary Martha, & **Kelly,** Sophia. The De Cliffords : an historical tale. London, Darton, 1847. [Allibone : B.M. : *Eng. Cat.*]

Shipp, John. The Military Bijou ; Or The Contents of a Soldier's Knapsack : Being The Gleanings of Thirty-three Years' Active Service. 2 vols., London, Whittaker, Treacher, 1831. [B.M. : T. Thorp : T. D. Webster.]

Shipwreck (The) ; or Paul and Mary. 2 vols., London, W. Lane. [Publisher's advert, 1790].

Shipwrecked Sailor Boy (The); or the Reward of Hospitality. London, [1837 ?]. [B.M.]

Shoberl, Frederick, (Edited by). Tales of Woman. 2 vols., London, Henry Colburn, 1828. [B.M. : Pickering.]

Shopkeeper Turned Sailor (The), or the Folly of Going out of our Element. With woodcut titles. In 3 parts. London, Marshall, [179–]. [R. S. Frampton.]

Short, William Henry. De Merley, a legend of the Wansbeck. Morpeth, 1849. [B.M.]

Short But Tragical History of an Unfortunate Young Girl (A), who was seduced by a gentleman of fortune when she was only fifteen years of age. [London,] [1800 ?]. [B.M.]

Short Stories for Children. Part I. With plates. London, Darton, Harvey, and Darton, 1810. [B.M.]

Short Stories for Little Folks, or, Little Tales, calculated to excite juvenile minds to the love and practice of virtue. Stirling, [1820 ?]. [B.M.]

Short Stories from English History. With 12 plates and woodcuts. London, Society for Promoting Christian Knowledge, 1846. [Sotheran.]

Short Stories in Words of One Syllable. By the Author of Summer Rambles. With a frontispiece. London, E. Lloyd, 1801. [Gumuchian : *Nat. Mag. Co.*]

Short Stories, or Treasures of Truth, selected for Youthful Minds. With woodcuts. Banbury, [1810]. [King]

Short Story (A) : interspersed with Poetry. By a Young Lady. 2 vols., London, 1800. [B.M.]

Showes, Mrs. Agnes de Lilien. A novel from the German. 3 vols., [W. Lane. 1801.] [Blakey : *Minerva Press Catalogue.*]

—— The Restless Matron. A Legendary Tale. 3 vols., London, W. Lane, 1799. [*New Ann. Reg. :* Blakey.]

—— Statira ; or, The Mother. A Novel. By the Author of Interesting Tales. London, Minerva Press, for W. Lane, 1798. [B.M. : *New Ann. :* Blakey.]

Siamese Tales (The) : Being a Collection of Stories Told to the Son of the Mandarin Sam-Sib, For the Purpose of Engaging His Mind in the Love of Truth and Virtue. With an Historical Account of the Kingdom of Siam. To which is added : the principal maxims of the Talapoins. Translated from the Siamese. London, Vernor and Hood ; and Champante and Whitrow, 1796. [Birrell & Garnett : B.M. : Stonehill.]

Sicilian (The), by the Author of the Mysterious Wife. [Mrs. Meeke.] 4 vols., 1798. [*New Ann. Reg. :* Blakey.]

Sickelmore, Richard. Agnes and Leonora, A Novel. 2 vols., London. Minerva Press, 1799. [Blackwell.]

—— Edgar ; or, The phantom of the castle. A Novel. 2 vols., [W. Lane, 1798.] [Blakey.]

—— Mary-Jane. A novel. 2 vols., London, Author by William Lane, 1800. [Baker's Bookshop : Blakey.]

—— Osrick ; or Modern Horrors. A Romance. Interspersed with a few anecdotes, &c. that have their foundation in truth, and, which are occasionally pointed out to the reader. 3 vols.,

London, Lane, Newman, and Co. 1809. [Blakey.] 3 vols., 1809. [*Monthly Mag.*]

Sickelmore, Richard. Raymond, a Novel. Inscribed by permission to George Porter, Esq., M.P. 2 vols., London, Didier and Tebblett, 1801. [Baker's Bookshop : Marks : Pickering.]

—— Rashleigh Abbey, or Ruin on the Rock. 3 vols., London, Lane, Newman, 1805. [Publisher's advert : Blakey.]

Siddons, Henry. Leon. A Spartan Story. 2 vols., [W. Lane, 1791.] [*New Ann. Reg. :* Blakey.]

—— The Maid, Wife and Widow, A Tale. 3 vols., London, Richard Phillips 1806. [Blackwell : B.M. Publisher's advert.]

—— Reginald de Torbay and the twelve robbers. A romance. 2 vols., [*Minerva Press*, 1803]. [Blakey.]

—— Somerset, or The dangers of greatness, a tale, founded upon historic truths. 2 vols., London, William Lane, 1792. [Blakey.]

—— The Son of the Storm ; A tale. 4 vols., Richmond, 1809. [B.M. : *Monthly Mag.*]

—— Virtuous Poverty. 3 vols., London, Richard Phillips. [Publisher's advert, 1806.]

—— William Wallace : or, The Highland Hero. A tale founded on historical facts. 2 vols., London, 1791. [B.M. : *Eng. Lit. in Germany.*]

Sidney, Hon. Adela. Home And its influence. 3 vols., London, Richard Bentley, 1847. [Allibone : B.M.]

—— Sadness and Gladness. A Story of the present day. 3 vols., London, Richard Bentley, 1848. [Allibone : B.M. : McLeish.]

Sidney, Philip Francis. The Ruling Passion. A Comic Story, Of the Sixteenth Century. Revived, Revised and Edited, by Philip Francis Sidney. 3 vols., York, Printed for the Proprietors of the Hull Packet, Hull, 1821. [B.M.]

Sidney Castle ; or, The sorrows of De Courci. A novel. By the author of Edmund; or, The child of the castle. 2 vols., [W. Lane, 1792.] [Blakey.]

Sidney Place ; or, The bracelet. 2 vols., [W. Lane, 1788.] [Blakey.]

Siege of Belgrade (The) : An Historical Novel Translated From a German Manuscript. 4 vols., in 2, London, H.D. Symonds, 1741 [for 1791]. [B.M.]

Siege of Maynooth (The) ; Or, Romance in Ireland. 2 vols., London, James Ridgway, 1832. [B.M. : *I. in F.*]

Sigismar. By the author of " Villeroy." 3 vols., London, 1799. [B.M.]

Silvanella, or the Gypsey. A Novel. 4 vols., London, Minerva Press for A. K. Newman, 1812. [Murray Hill.]

Silwood, a novel. 2 vols., London, Richard Bentley, 1850. [B.M. : *Eng. Cat.*]

Simonde de Sismondi, Jean Charles Léonard. Julia Severa ; Or the Year Four Hundred and Ninety-two ; Translated from the French of J. C. L. Simonde de Sismondi. 2 vols., London, G. and W. B. Whittaker ; and Munday and Slatter, Oxford, 1822. [B.M. : T. D. Webster.]

Simple Memorials of an Irish Family. A Narrative of Facts. By a Clergyman. London, L. B. Seeley, 1824. [B.M.]

Simple Narrative (A) ; Or, A Visit to the Newton Family. 2 vols., London, Lane, Newman, Minerva Press, 1806. [Baker's Bookshop : B.M. : Stonehill.]

Simple Simon's Misfortunes And his Wife Margery's Cruelty. Which Began The very next morning after their Marriage. With woodcuts. London, Printed and Sold in Aldermary Church Yard, [1750 ?]. [B.M.]

Simple Stories for Cottage Children. London, 1831. [B.M.]

Simple Stories : a very easy reading-book. With illustrations. London, 1840. [B.M.]

Simple Tales for the Young. By the author of " The Gipsies and Fairy Birds." London, 1847. [B.M.]

Simpson, Captain John. Ricardo the Outlaw ; a Romance. 3 vols., London, J. Jones, 1823. [B.M. : *New Monthly Mag.*]

Simpson, John Palgrave. Gisella. By the author of " Second Love." 3 vols., London, Richard Bentley, 1847. [Allibone : B.M. : *Critic.*]

—— The Lily of Paris ; or, the King's Nurse. 3 vols., London, Richard Bentley, 1849. [B.M. : *Eng. Cat.*]

—— Second Love, And other tales, From the note-book of a traveller. 3 vols., London, Richard Bentley, 1846. [Allibone : B.M.]

Sims, H. C. Maria Anne Lais, the Courtezan ; or Certain Illustrations. A Romance. London, Rodwell, 1812. [*New Monthly Mag. :* Stonehill.]

Sin and Sorrow. A tale. 3 vols., London, Henry Colburn, 1850. [B.M. : *Eng. Cat.*]

Sin Forgiven ; or happy old Benjamin. London, [1850 ?]. [B.M.]

Sincerity : A Tale. By The Author of " Rachel," &c. With a frontispiece. London, Knight and Lacey, 1824. [D.M.]

Sinclair, Arthur. The Decameron of the West. A Series of Tales, &c. Edinburgh Printing & Publishing Company, 1839. [B.M.]

Sinclair, Catherine. Holiday House : a series of tales, etc. Edinburgh, W. Whyte, 1839. [B.M.]

—— Jane Bouverie ; or Prosperity and Adversity. Edinburgh, 1846. [B.M.]

—— Lord and Lady Harcourt : or, Country Hospitalities. London, Richard

Bentley, 1850. [B.M. : *Eng. Cat.* : G. Worthington.]

Sinclair, Catherine. Modern Accomplishments, or the March of Intellect. London, Longman, 1836. [B.M. : *Eng. Cat.* : H. H. Langley.]

—— Modern Flirtations ; Or, A Month at Harrowgate. 3 vols., Edinburgh, William Whyte ; Longman, Brown ; Simpkin, Marshall ; Hamilton, Adams ; Whittaker ; Duncan and Malcom, London ; W. Curry, Jun., Dublin ; William Collins, Glasgow, 1841. [B.M. : Lib. of Congress : G. Worthington.]

—— Modern Society ; or the March of Intellect. The conclusion of Modern Accomplishments. London, Longman, 1837. [B.M. : *Eng. Cat.* : H. H. Langley.]

—— Sir Edward Graham : or, Railway Speculators. 3 vols., London, Longman, 1849. [B.M. : *Eng. Cat.*]

Sinclair, Harvey. A Peep at the World ; or, the Children of Providence. A Novel. 3 vols., London, Parsons, 1804. [Allibone : Baker's Bookshop : Pickering.]

Sinclair, William. The Dying Soldier ; a Tale, founded on facts. London, Hatchard, 1838. [Allibone : B.M. : *Eng. Cat.*]

Singers of the Sanctuary (The), and the Missionary. Two tales, by the author of " Angels' Work." London, J. H. Parker, 1850. [B.M. : *Eng. Cat.*]

Singular Adventures of Sir Gawin (The) : and the Enchanted Castle. A fairy tale. Glasgow, 1802. [B.M.]

Singular Tale (A), or, the Adventures of Edward Dillon, a Young Irishman. Interspersed with Pathetic and Comical Stories. Written by Himself. With a frontispiece. London, [1807]. [McLeish.]

Singularity, Patriotism, and Artifice, Instructive and Entertaining Stories for Young People. With illustrations. London, Edward Lacey, N.D. [Block.]

Sinner's Redemption (The), or the Conversion of Joshua Tuckfield, who said he had seen Heaven and Hell, and some persons therein he had known when on earth. With woodcuts. Nottingham, [1815]. [Pickering.]

Sinnett, Mrs. Percy. A Story about a Christmas in the Seventeenth Century. With 2 plates. London, Chapman and Hall, 1846. [B.M. : Dobell : Gumuchian.]

Sir Andrew Sagittarius ; Or, The Perils of Astrology. A Novel. 3 vols., London, James Haldane, 1824. [B.M.]

Sir Arthur Wilmot : A Tale Of The Seventeenth Century. 2 vols., London, James Cochrane, 1835. [B.M.]

Sir Bevis of Lancaster, or The Murdered Knight, a Terrific Romance. With a plate. London, Kemmish, and Stevens, [1820]. [Pickering.]

Sir Patrick Hume's Daughter. [London], Religious Tract Society, [1830 ?]. [B.M.]

Sister's Care. By the author of " Michael the Chorister." London, 1849. [B.M.]

Sister's Gift. (The) ; or the Bad Boy reformed. York, 1826. [B.M.]

Sisters (The) : A Novel. 4 vols., London, Baldwin, Cradock and Joy, 1821. [B.M.]

Sisters of Ashdale (The) ; an Affecting Narrative of Peggy and Patty Summers ; Who, after experiencing various Vicissitudes in High Life, are Reduced to Extreme Distress. Their Brother's Return from India ; And his overhearing in a Coffee-House Capt. Jackall Giving an Account to an Associate (in Guilt), how he personated their brother to entrap them ; His Encounter with Him, and being Wounded. The End of Capt. Jackall by his own hand. after a lapse of fruitless inquiries, finds his sisters in a miserable garret Patty just Expiring, and Peggy Died in his Arms. With a frontispiece. London, T. Hughes, N.D. [Court Bk. Shop.]

Sisters of Nansfield (The). A Tale for Young Women. By the Author of " The Stories of Old Daniel," &c. 2 vols., London, Longman, Hurst, Rees, Orme, Brown and Green, 1824. [B.M. : T. D. Webster.]

Sisters (The) ; or Character exemplified. A simple tale. London, Simpkin, 1848. [B.M. : *Eng. Cat.*]

Sisters (The) ; or, England and France. A Romance. London, Little, 1844. [*Eng. Cat.* : Lib. of Congress.]

Sisters (The) ; or, Virtue Triumphant. Being the history of Sophia and Charlotte Melford. Written by one of the sisters. London, Hodgson, [1830 ?]. [B.M.]

Six Stories for the Nursery : in Words of One or Two Syllables. By a Mother. London, Godwin, 1819. [*Nat. Mag. Co.*]

Six Stories, in English and French. By the authoress of Stories by a Mother, etc. London, 1812. [B.M.]

Six Weeks in Paris. 3 vols., London, Johnston, 1817. [*Eng. Cat.* : *New Monthly Mag.*]

Sketch Book Of The South. London, Edward Churton, 1835. [B.M.]

Sketch of the Life and Transactions of Peter Brown (A), an English Sailor. Glasgow, [1815 ?]. [B.M.]

Sketch of the Times or The History of Lord Derville. 1780. [*Eng. Lit. in Germany.*]

Sketches of Character, Or Specimens of Real Life. A Novel. 3 vols., London, Printed for Longman, Hurst, Rees, and Orme ; B. Crosby ; and J. Landsdown, Bristol, by Mills, Bristol, 1808. [B.M. : Ingpen.]

Sketches of Life and Character. By E. P. London, Thomas Hurst ; Thomas Richardson, Derby, 1835. [B.M.]

Sketches of Wales and the Welsh. By Amy. With a vignette title. London, Hamilton, Adams, 1847. [B.M.]

Sketches, Scenes and Characters. Chiefly of a Religious Tendency. By An Officer of the Line. Dublin, James Marshall Leckie; W. Whyte, W. Oliphant, and Brown and Wardlaw, Edinburgh; W. Collins, Glasgow; James Duncan, James Nisbet, & Houlston, London, 1828. [B.M.]

Skinn, Mrs. The Old Maid; Or, History of Miss Ravensworth, In a Series of Letters. 3 vols., London, 1771. [B.M.: W. Brown: Stephen Hunt.]

Skyrack; a fairy tale. London, 1849. [B.M.]

Slade, J. Alice Glynn: A Tale, From the Diary of a Physician. With a frontispiece. London, Whittaker, 1845. [B.M.]

Sleath, Eleanor. The Bristol Heiress; Or, the Errors of Education, A Tale. 5 vols., London, Printed at the Minerva Press, for Lane, Newman, 1809. [Court Bk. Shop: Stonehill.]

—— The Nocturnal Minstrel; or, the Spirit of the Wood. A romance. 2 vols., London, A. K. Newman, 1810. [B.M.: Blakey.]

—— The Orphan of the Rhine. A Romance. 4 vols., London, Minerva Press, 1798. [Allibone: Holden's Reprints: Blakey.]

—— Pyrenean Banditti. A Romance. 3 vols., London, Printed at the Minerva Press, for A. K. Newman, 1811. [Publisher's advert: Blakey: Murray Hill.]

—— Who's the Murderer? or The mystery of the forest. A novel. 4 vols., London, Minerva Press, 1802. [Allibone: Publishers advert: Blakey.]

Sleeping Beauty in the Wood (The): an entertaining tale. To which is added, the Story of the envious man, and him that he envied. Glasgow, R. Hutchison, 1817. [B.M.]

Sleeping Beauty in the Wood (The). A Tale. With woodcuts. London, Printed and Sold in Aldermary Church Yard, [1790?] [B.M.]

Sleeping Beauty in the Wood (The). A tale. Birmingham, S. & T. Martin, [1820?]. [B.M.]

Sleeping Beauty in the Wood (The). A tale. To which is added Paddy and the Bear, a true story. Glasgow, Printed for the Booksellers, [1850?]. [B.M.]

Slingsby, Henry. My Grandmother's Guests and Their Tales. 2 vols., London, James Robins; and Joseph Robins, Dublin, 1825. [Allibone: B.M.: Publisher's advert.]

Sloane, Edward. Essays, Tales, and Sketches. Halifax, Leyland, 1849. [B.M.]

Sloven (The): To which is added The Proud Gentleman His own Shoeblack.

With 15 woodcuts. London, T. Hughes, [1820?]. [B.M.]

Small-Talker (The), A Series of Letters from A Lady in the West of England to Lady Anne D—— abroad. London, Johnson & Payne, 1769. [Stonehill.]

Smallwood, Edward. The Czar A Romance of History. By the Author of " Manuella, the Executioner's Daughter, a Story of Madrid; " " Antonio Foscarini," &c. 3 vols., London, Edward Smallwood, 1840. [B.M.]

—— Manuella, The Executioner's Daughter. A Story of Madrid. With frontispieces by A. Hervieu. 3 vols., London, Richard Bentley, 1837. [B.M.]

Smart, Thomas. The Prisoner: Or, Cruelty Unmasked. In Letters to a Friend. Huddersfield, Sikes, [1797]. [B.M.]

Smedley, Francis Edward. Frank Fairlegh, or Scenes from the Life of a Private Pupil. With illustrations by George Cruikshank. London, Arthur Hall, Virtue, 1850. [B.M.: Brough: Maggs.]

—— Seven Tales by Seven Authors. Edited by the author of " Frank Fairlegh." London, George Hoby, 1849. [Block: B.M.]

Smedley, Menella Bute. The Maiden Aunt, written by a Lady. 3 vols., London, J. Bew, 1776. [E. Hector.]

Smeeton, George. Doings in London; or Day and Night Scenes of the Frauds, Frolics, Manners and Depravities of the Metropolis. Southwark, G. Smeeton, 1828. [B.M.]

Smiles and Tears: Comprising Maria Darlington, A Sketch from Real Life; and Sixteen Other Sketches and Tales. With a frontispiece and vignettes from posthumous designs of Thurston. London, William Charlton Wright, 1825. [B.M.]

Smith, A. R. Herne, The Hunter. A Legend of Windsor Forest. By A. K. S. With a frontispiece. London, Dean and Munday, N.D. [Court Bk. Shop.]

Smith, Albert. The Adventures of Jack Holyday: With something about His Sister. With illustrations. London, Wm. S. Orr, 1844. [B.M.]

—— The Adventures of Mr. Ledbury And His Friend Jack Johnson. With illustrations by John Leech. 3 vols., London, Richard Bentley, 1844. [Blackwell: B.M.: Noel Broadbent.]

—— The Fortunes Of the Scattergood Family. With illustrations by John Leech. 3 vols., London, Richard Bentley, 1845. [Allibone: B.M.: Kyrle Fletcher.]

—— The Marchioness de Brinvilliers, the poisoner of the seventeenth century. A romance of old Paris. With a frontispiece by John Leech. London, Richard Bentley, 1846. [B.M.: Noel Broadbent.]

Smith, Albert. Marguerite de Bourgogne, A Tradition of Ancient Paris. Privately Printed, 1845. [Noel Broadbent.]

—— The Pottleton Legacy : a Story of Town and Country Life. With illustrations by Hablot K. Browne. London, David Bogue, 1849. [B.M. : Noel Broadbent : Marks.]

—— The Struggles and Adventures of Christopher Tadpole At Home and Abroad. With a portrait and plates by John Leech. London, Richard Bentley, 1848. [Birrell & Garnett : B.M. : Maggs.]

—— The Wassail-Bowl. A Series of Humorous Tales and Sketches. With illustrations by John Leech. 2 vols., London, Richard Bentley, 1843. [Block : B.M. : Maggs.]

Smith, Anna White. Caroline, and Zelite ; or, Transatlantic Tales, Taken from Real Life. London, Charles Frederick Cock, 1824. [B.M.]

Smith, Catherine. Barozzi ; Or The Venetian Sorceress. A Romance of the Sixteenth Century. 2 vols., London, Printed at the Minerva Press for A. K. Newman, 1815. [B.M. : Publisher's advert.]

—— The Caledonian Bandit ; or The Heir of Duncaethal. A Romance of the thirteenth century. 2 vols., London, A. K. Newman 1811. [Allibone : *Quarterly Review :* Blakey.]

—— The Castle of Arragon, or the Banditti of the Forest ; a Romance. 4 vols., 1809. [*Monthly Mag.*]

—— The Misanthrope Father ; or, the Guarded Secret. A novel. 3 vols., London, 1807. [B.M.]

Smith, Charlotte. The Banished Man. A Novel. 4 vols., London, T. Cadell, Jun. and W. Davies, 1794. [B.M. : Huth : Ingpen.]

—— Celestina. A Novel. 4 vols., London, T. Cadell, 1791. [B.M. : Maggs : T. Thorp.]

—— D'Arcy. A Novel. Dublin, 1793. [T. D. Webster.]

—— The Deserted Daughter. With a vignette on the title. London, J. Roe, [c. 1825]. [Marks.]

—— Desmond. A Novel. 3 vols., London, G. G. J. & J. Robinson, 1792. [B.M. : *New Ann. Reg. :* Arthur Rogers.]

—— Emmeline, The Orphan of the Castle. 4 vols., London, T. Cadell, 1788. [Allibone : B.M. : Pickering.]

—— Ethelinde, or the Recluse of the Lake. 5 vols., London, T. Cadell, 1789. [Ingpen : Arthur Rogers : Stonehill.]

—— The Letters of a Solitary Wanderer. 3 vols., 1800. [Arthur Rogers.]

—— Marchmont : A Novel. 4 vols., London, Sampson Low, 1796. [Birrell and Garnett : B.M. : Court Bk. Shop].

—— Minor Morals, interspersed with Sketches of Natural History, historical anecdotes, and Original Stories. 2 vols., London, Crosby, 1798. [B.M. : *Guardian of Education :* Lowndes.]

Smith, Charlotte. Montalbert. A Novel. 3 vols., London, 1795. [*Eng. Lit. in Germany :* Lowndes : T. D. Webster.]

—— The Old Manor House. A Novel. 4 vols., London, J. Bell, 1793. [Blackwell : B.M. : F. R. Hockliffe.]

—— Rambles Farther : A Continuation Of Rural Walks : In Dialogues. Intended For the use of young persons. 2 vols., London, T. Cadell, Jun. and W. Davies, 1796. [B.M.]

—— The Republican's Mistress. A novel. 3 vols., London, W. Wright, 1821. [B.M.]

—— The Romance of Real Life. 3 vols., London, T. Cadell, 1787. [B.M. : Arthur Rogers : T. D. Webster.]

—— Rural Walks : in dialogues for young persons. 2 vols., London, 1795. [B.M.]

—— The Wanderings of Warwick. London, J. Bell, 1794. [Blackwell : B.M. : Maggs.]

—— The Young Philosopher : A Novel. 4 vols., London, T. Cadell, Jun. and W. Davies, 1798. [Allibone : Blackwell : B.M.]

Smith, Charlotte Ann. The Companion. A tale of Domestic life. Cheltenham, [1849]. [B.M.]

Smith, Mrs. E. Emmeline ; or Good Humour. London, 1847. [B.M.]

Smith, Elizabeth Elton. Clarendon ; a Tale of Recent Times. London, Dolman, 1848. [Allibone : B.M. : *Eng. Cat.*]

—— The First False Step. London, 1848. [B.M.]

—— The Three Eras Of Woman's Life. 3 vols., London, Richard Bentley, 1836. [B.M.]

Smith, Hannah. The History of Rosano and Amanda, and the confessor Raldino. With a frontispiece, engraved title, and 3 plates. Birmingham, William Evans, [1830]. [Tregaskis.]

Smith, Horatio. Adam Brown, The Merchant. By the Author of Brambletye House, &c. 3 vols., London, Henry Colburn, 1843. [Block : B.M. : Lib. of Congress.]

—— Arthur Arundel, A Tale of The English Revolution. By the Author of " Brambletye House," &c. 3 vols., London, Henry Colburn, 1844. [B.M. : Cleverdon : Lib. of Congress.]

—— Brambletye House ; or, Cavaliers & Roundheads. A Novel. By One of the Authors of " Rejected Addresses." 3 vols., London, Henry Colburn, 1826. [B.M. : Ingpen : Pickering.]

—— Gaieties and Gravities ; A Series of Essays, Comic Tales, and Fugitive Vagaries Now First Collected. By One

of the Authors of "Rejected Addresses."
3 vols., London, Henry Colburn, 1825.
[B.M. : McLeish : Marks.]

Smith, Horatio. Gale Middleton. A
Story of the Present Day. By the
Author of "Brambletye House," &c.
3 vols., London, Richard Bentley, 1833.
[Allibone : B.M. : Lib. of Congress.]

—— Jane Lomax ; Or, A Mother's
Crime, By the Author of " Brambletye
House," " Reuben Apsley," &c. 3 vols.,
London, Henry Colburn, 1838. [Block :
B.M. : Lib. of Congress.]

—— Love and Mesmerism. 3 vols.,
London, Henry Colburn, 1845. [Alli-
bone : B.M. : Lib. of Congress.]

—— Massaniello ; An Historical Romance. 3 vols., London, Henry Colburn,
1842. [B.M. : Kyrle Fletcher : Ingpen.]

—— The Midsummer Medley for 1830.
A Series of Comic Tales, Sketches, and
Fugitive Vagaries, in Prose and Verse.
By the Author of " Brambletye House,"
&c. &c. 2 vols., London, Henry
Colburn & Richard Bentley, 1830.
[Block : B.M. : Lib. of Congress.]

—— The Moneyed Man, Or, The Lesson
of a Life. 3 vols., London, Henry Colburn, 1841. [B.M. : Lib. of Congress :
Arthur Rogers.]

—— The New Forest. A Novel. By the
Author of " Brambletye House," &c.
3 vols., London, Henry Colburn, 1829.
[Birrell & Garnett : B.M. : Ingpen.]

—— Oliver Cromwell : an Historical
Romance. 3 vols., London, Henry
Colburn, 1840. [Baker's Bookshop :
Eng. Cat. : Elkin Mathews.]

—— Reuben Apsley. By the Author of
Brambletye House, The Tor Hill, &c.
3 vols., London, Henry Colburn, 1827.
[B.M. : F. Chambers : A. Margery.]

—— Romance of the Early Ages. By
the Author of " Brambletye House,"
&c. 3 vols., London, Henry Colburn and
Richard Bentley, 1832.

—— The Runaway ; Or, The Seat of
Benevolence. A Novel. 4 vols., London,
Crosby and Letterman, 1800. [B.M. :
Court Bk. Shop.]

—— Tales Of The Early Ages. By the
Author of " Brambletye House,"
" Zillah," &c. 3 vols., London, Henry
Colburn and Richard Bentley, 1832.
[Block : B.M. : Lib. of Congress.]

—— The Tor Hill, By The Author of
" Brambletye House," " Gaieties and
Gravities," &c. &c. 3 vols., London,
Henry Colburn, 1826. [Block : B.M. :
Ingpen.]

—— Trevanion ; or Matrimonial Errors,
a Novel. 4 vols., London, 1801. [B.M.]

—— Walter Colyton ; A Tale of 1688.
By the Author of " Brambletye House,"
&c. &c. 3 vols., London, Henry Colburn
& Richard Bentley, 1830. [Birrell &
Garnett : B.M. : Ingpen.]

Smith, Horatio. Zillah ; A Tale of The
Holy City. By the Author of " Bram-
bletye House," " The Tor Hill,"
" Reuben Apsley," &c. 4 vols., London,
Henry Colburn, 1828. [B.M. :
Lowndes : Arthur Rogers.]

Smith, John Frederick. The Prelate. A
Novel. 2 vols., London, T. & W. Boone,
1840. [B.M.]

—— Stanfield Hall. A Romance. In
Two Chronicles. With woodcuts. London, Lloyd, [c. 1840]. [Stonehill.]

Smith, Julia. The Old School. 2 vols.,
London, Booth, 1813. [B.M. : *Eng.
Cat. :* B. Halliday.]

—— The Prison of Montauban, or Times
of Terror : a Reflective Tale by the
Editor of Letters of the Swedish Court.
London, Cradock, 1810. [G. Worthington.]

Smith, Maria Lavinia. The Fugitive of
the Forest. A Romance. 2 vols., London, William Lane, 1801. [Ingpen.]

Smith, Thomas. A Shepherd's Son ; or,
the Wish accomplished. A moral Tale.
Interspersed with poetical Effusions,
designed for the Improvement of Youth.
London, Newbery, 1800. [B.M. :
Guardian of Education.]

Smith, William Henry. Ernesto : A
Philosophical Romance. London, Smith,
Elder, 1835. [B.M. : Arthur Rogers.]

Smollett, Tobias. The Adventures of
Ferdinand Count Fathom. By the
Author of Roderick Random. 2 vols.,
London, W. Johnston, 1753. [B.M. :
King : Maggs.]

—— The Adventures of Peregrine Pickle.
In which are included, Memoirs of a
Lady of Quality. 4 vols., London,
Printed for the Author, 1751. [B.M. :
Ingpen : Maggs.]

—— The Adventures of Roderick Random. 2 vols., London, J. Osborn, 1748.
[B.M. : Quaritch : Arthur Rogers.]

—— The Adventures of Sir Launcelot
Greaves. By the Author of Roderick
Random. 2 vols., London, J. Coote,
1762. [B.M. : *Eng. Lit. in Germany :*
Pickering.]

—— The Expedition of Humphrey
Clinker. By the Author of Roderick
Random. 3 vols., London, W. Johnston
& B. Collins, 1771. [Vol. I. misdated
1671.] [B.M. : Ingpen : Quaritch.]

—— A Faithful Narrative Of the Base
and inhuman Arts That were lately
practised upon the Brain of Habbakkuk
Hilding, Justice, Dealer, and Chapman,
Who now lies at his House in *Covent
Garden*, in a deplorable State of Lunacy ;
a dreadful Monument of *false Friendship*
and *Delusion*. By Drawcansir Alexander,
Fencing-Master and *Philomath*. London,
J. Sharp, 1752. [Ashley Lib. : B.M.]

—— The History and Adventures of an
Atom. 2 vols., London, Robinson and

Roberts, 1749 [really 1769]. [Block : B.M. : Lowndes.]

Smuggler's Son (The) ; or Sherwood Quarry. A tale. By the author of " the Philosopher's Stone." London, [1830 ?]. [B.M.]

Smugglers (The), a tale descriptive of the sea-coast manners of Scotland. 3 vols., Edinburgh, 1820. [B.M. : Storey.]

Smyth, E. The History of Tabby, a favourite cat. London, Didier & Tebbett, 1809. [B.M.]

Smythe, Elizabeth Anne. The History of Mary the Beggar Girl. (The Rival Dogs). With woodcuts. London, Knevett, Arliss and Baker, [1820 ?]. [B.M. : Arthur Rogers.]

Smythies, Harriet Maria Yorick. The Breach of Promise. A Novel. By the Author of " The Jilt ; " " Cousin Geoffrey ; " " The Marrying Man ; " " The Matchmaker ; " &c. &c. 3 vols., London, T. C. Newby, 1845. [B.M. : Critic.]

—— Cousin Geoffrey, The Old Bachelor A Novel. To which is added Claude Stocq. Edited by Theodore Hook. With a portrait. 3 vols., London, Richard Bentley, 1840. [B.M. : Chas. Hutt.]

—— Fitz-herbert ; Or, Lovers and Fortune-Hunters. By The Authoress of " The Bride of Siena." 3 vols., London, Saunders and Otley, 1838. [B.M.]

—— The Jilt. A Novel. By the Author of " Cousin Geoffrey," " The Marrying Man," &c. 3 vols., London, Richard Bentley, 1844. [B.M.]

—— The Life of a Beauty. A Novel. By the Author of " The Jilt," " The Breach of Promise," " Cousin Geoffrey," " The Marrying Man," " The Matchmaker," &c. &c. 3 vols., London, T. C. Newby, 1846. [B.M.]

—— The Marrying Man. A Novel. By the Author of " Cousin Geoffrey." 3 vols., London, Richard Bentley, 1841. [H. Bates : B.M.]

—— The Matchmaker. A Novel. By the Author of " Cousin Geoffrey," and " The Marrying Man." 3 vols., London, Henry Colburn, 1842. [B.M.]

—— A Warning to Wives ; or, the Platonic Lover. A novel. By the author of " Cousin Geoffrey," etc. 3 vols., London, T. C. Newby, 1847. [B.M. : Eng. Cat.]

Soane, George. Eve of St. Marco ; a Novel. 3 vols., London, 1812. [Allibone.]

—— The Frolics of Puck. 3 vols., London, Bull and Churton, 1834. [Block : B.M. : Pickering.]

—— January Eve ; a Tale of the Times. London, Churton, 1847. [B.M. : Eng. Cat.]

—— The Last Ball ; And Other Tales. 3 vols., London, Edward Churton, 1843. [Allibone : B.M.]

Soane, George. Specimens of German Romance. Selected and Translated from Various Authors. With frontispieces by George Cruikshank. 3 vols., London, Geo. B. Whittaker, 1826. [B.M. : Pickering : Quarterly Review.]

Soave, Francesco. Moral Tales ; from the Italian of Francesco Soave. Translated by P. R. Rota. London, Wingrave, 1802. [Guardian of Education.]

Sobieski, John, and **Stuart,** Charles Edward (see ALLAN, John Hay, and STUART, Charles.)

Social Influences : Or Villiers. 3 vols., London, T. C. Newby, 1846. [B.M. : Critic.]

Society in India. By An Indian Officer. 2 vols., London, Henry Colburn, 1841. [B.M.]

Society ; Or, The Spring in Town. 3 vols., London, Saunders and Otley, 1831. [B.M.]

Soldier Boy (The). A novel. By the author of The Sailor Boy. 3 vols., London, William Lane, 1801. [B.M. : Blakey.]

Soldier of Pennaflor. 5 vols., London, Printed at the Minerva Press, for A. K. Newman, 1811. [Publisher's advert.]

Soldiers of Venezuela (The) : A Tale. 2 vols., London, T. Egerton, 1818. [B.M. : New Monthly Mag.]

Soldier's Tale (The), extracted from the Village Association : with two or three words of advice, By Old Hubert. London, [1793 ?]. [B.M. (2nd. edn.]

Solicitudes of Absence. 1788. [W. Brown.]

Solle, Henri François de la, (see DE LA SOLLE).

Some Account of the Cunningham Family. Designed for The Amusement and Instruction of Youth. By Cornelia. London, John Hatchard, 1824. [B.M.]

Some New Thoughts For the New Year. With a woodcut. London, J. Marshall and R. White. [1794 ?]. Cheap Repository. Sunday Reading. [Court Bk. Shop.]

Somers, E. C. Little Stories for my Pretty Little People. London, 1847. [Allibone.]

—— Tales for my Children. 1847. [Allibone.]

Somers, Walter. Stradella ; or, The Power of Song. An Italian Romance. With woodcuts. London, Dipple, 1848. [Stonehill.]

Somerset, Henry. All Sorts of Lovers, or Indiscretion, Truth, and Perfidy. 3 vols., London, Printed at the Minerva Press, by A. K. Newman, 1811. [Publisher's advert.]

Somerville, Elizabeth. Aurora and Maria ; or, The Advantages of Adversity. Brentford, 1809. [Camb. Hist. Eng. Lit.]

—— The Birth-day ; or, Moral Dialogues and Stories for the Instruction and

Amusement of Juvenile Readers. London, B. Crosby, 1802. [B.M. : *Camb. Hist. Eng. Lit.*]

Somerville, Elizabeth, Flora ; or, the deserted Child. London, Longman. [*Guardian of Education.*]

—— The New Children in the Wood or the Welch Cottagers. A Tale. With a frontispiece. London, B. Crosby, 1802. [*Guardian of Education* : Gumuchian.]

—— The Village Maid : or, Dame Burton's Moral Stories for the instruction and amusement of Youth. With a frontispiece. London, Vernor and Hood, 1801. [B.M. : Gumuchian.]

Something Strange. By Gabrielli [Mrs. Meeke]. 4 vols., London, Lane, Newman, 1806. [Publisher's advert : Blakey.]

Son of Duplicity (The). London, J. Ridgway ; and Simpkin, Marshall, 1836. [B.M.]

Sophia : Or, The Dangerous Indiscretion. A Tale, Founded on Facts. 3 vols., London, Longman, Hurst, Rees, Orme, and Brown, 1818. [B.M. : *New Monthly Mag.*]

Sophia, or The Embarrassed Wife, containing the History of Mira, The New Foundling. A Novel. By a Lady. Being her First Literary Attempt. Dedicated by permission to Her Grace the Duchess of Devonshire. 2 vols., London, Allen, [Ingpen.]

Sophronia ; or, Letters to the Ladies. London, Printed for William Johnston, 1761. [Block : B.M.]

Sorrowful Sam ; Or, the Two Blacksmiths. With a woodcut. London, J. Marshall, [1800 ?]. Cheap Repository. [Block : B.M.]

Sorrows of Gustavus (The), or The History of a Young Swede. 2 vols., London, Henry Colburn, 1808. [Pickering.]

Sorrows of Selfishness (The) ; Or, The history Of Miss Richmore. By Prudentia Homespun. With a frontispiece. London, T. N. Longman and O. Rees ; and J. Harris, 1802. [B.M. : *Guardian of Education.*]

South Sea Fortune (The), or The Chaplain advanced to the Saddle. Containing the Genuine Private Memoirs of a Worthy Family in Gloucestershire from the fatal year 1720, to the Year 1748. Written by Mrs. Richwould, one of the most interested Parties. 2 vols., London, J. Wren, 1758. [Pickering.]

Southern, George. Conversion of Cleora ; a Tale of Truth. London, Longman, 1848. [Allibone : *Eng. Cat.*]

Southern Tower (The) ; Or, Conjugal Sacrifice, and Retribution. London, T. Hurst, [1802]. [B.M. : Stonehill.]

Southey, Caroline. Chapters on Churchyards. By the Authoress of Ellen Fitzarthur, Widow's Tale, Solitary Hours, etc. 2 vols., Edinburgh, William Black-

wood : and T. Cadell, 1829. [Block : George's Sons : Arthur Rogers.]

Southey, Caroline. Probation, And Other Tales. By the Author of" Selwyn in search of a Daughter," " Tales of the Moors," &c. Edinburgh, Black, London, Longman, 1832. [*Metropolitan Mag.*]

—— Selwyn In search of a daughter And Other tales. By the Author of " Tales of the Moors," " Probation," " Olympia Morata," &c. 3 vols., London, Saunders and Otley, 1835. [B.M. : Stonehill.]

—— Tales of the Factories, by the authoress of Ellen Fitzarthur. London, 1833. [B.M.]

—— Tales of the Moors : or, Rainy Days in Ross-shire. By the Author of Selwyn in Search of a Daughter. Edinburgh, William Blackwood ; and T. Cadell, London, 1828. [B.M. : Ingpen : G. Worthington.]

Southey, Robert. The Doctor, &c. With a frontispiece to Volume 7. 7 vols., [Vols. I–V] London, Longman, Rees, Orme, Brown, Green and Longman, 1834–1838. [Vols. VI and VII] London, Longman, Brown, Green, and Longmans, 1847–1848. [B.M. : Lowndes : Publisher's advert.]

Southwood, T. Dilworth ; a Novel. 3 vols., 1808. [Allibone.]

Soutter, Miss E. A. The Work-Table, Or Evening Conversations, Designed for The Improvement and Instruction of Young Persons. With a frontispiece. 2 vols., London, W. Simpkin and R. Marshall, 1823. [B.M.]

Souza, Adelaide Marie de (*see* DE SOUZA-BOTELHO).

Spalding, Thomas. Ann ; or, The Conflict and Triumph of Faith : with an Introduction by the Rev. Henry Townley. London, Sunday School Union Depository, 1841. [Allibone : Publisher's advert.]

Spectre (The). With a frontispiece. 2 vols., London, John Stockdale, 1789. [B.M. : T. D. Webster.]

Spectre Mother (The), or the Haunted Tower, by the Author of Midnight Horrors, Female Pilgrim, &c. With a frontispiece and vignette. London, Dean and Munday, [1810.] [B.M. : Court Bk. Shop : Ingpen.]

Spectre of the Mountain of Granada (The). 3 vols., London, Minerva Press, 1811. [*Quarterly Review :* Blakey.]

Speculation. Oxford and London, 1850. [B.M.]

Spence, Elizabeth Isabella. Dame Rebecca Berry, or, Court Scenes in the Reign of Charles the Second. 3 vols., London, Longman, Rees, Orme, Brown, & Green, 1827. [*Blackwood's Edin. Mag.* : B.M. : Publisher's advert.]

—— How to be Rid of a Wife, and The Lily of Annandale : Tales. 2 vols.,

London, Longman, Rees, Orme, Brown, & Green, 1823. [Baker's Bookshop : B.M. : Arthur Rogers.]

Spence, Elizabeth Isabella. Memoirs of the Danby Family : designed chiefly for the Entertainment and Improvement of Young Persons, By a Lady. With a frontispiece after Thurston. London, E. Newbery, 1799. [B.M. : Sotheran.]

—— Old Stories. 2 vols., London, Longman, Hurst, Rees, Orme, & Brown, 1822. [B.M. : Ingpen.]

—— A Traveller's Tale Of The last Century. 3 vols., London, Printed by Strahan and Spottiswoode, for Longman, Hurst, Rees, Orme, and Brown, 1819. [B.M. : Publisher's advert.]

Spencer, Arthur. Iskander ; Or, The Hero of Epirus. A Romance. 3 vols., London, Printed at the Minerva Press for A. K. Newman, 1819. [B.M.]

Spencer, Edmund. The Prophet of the Caucasus ; An Historical Romance of Krim-Tatary. 3 vols., London, Whittaker, 1840. [B.M.]

Spiess, Christian Heinrich. The Fallen Minister, and other Tales. From the German of Spiess by William B. Hewetson. 2 vols., London, Minerva Press 1809. [Blakey : B.M. : *Monthly Mag.*]

—— The Mountain Cottager : or, Wonders upon Wonder, a tale from the German [of C. H. Spiess by Annabella Plumptre]. London, W. Lane, 1798. [Allibone : *New Ann. Reg.* : Blakey.]

Spindler, Carl. The Jesuit. 3 vols., London, Saunders & Otley, 1832. [B.M. : Elkin Mathews : T. D. Webster.]

—— The Jew. 3 vols., London, Edward Bull, 1832. [B.M. : Elkin Mathews : *New Monthly Mag.*]

—— The Natural Son. A German Tale, Descriptive of the age of the Emperor Rudolph II. Translated from Spindler, By Lord Albert Conyngham. 3 vols., London, John Mitchell, 1835. [B.M.]

Spirit in Armour (The) ; Or Fall of Ambition. A Romance. With a frontispiece. London, Printed by J. D. Dewick for T. and R. Hughes, [1808]. [Court Bk. Shop.]

Spirit of Buncle (The) ; Or The Surprising Adventures of that original and extraordinary character John Buncle, Esq. London, Charles Stocking, 1823. [Lyle H. Wright.]

Spirit of Elbe (The), a Romance. 3 vols., London, 1799. [*New Ann. Reg.*]

Spirits of the Past (The). Coblenz, 1850. [B.M.]

Splendid Follies, A Novel founded on Facts, By the Author of the " Observant Pedestrian," " Montrose," etc. 3 vols., London, Hughes, 1810. [B.M. : *Monthly Mag.* : Stonehill.]

Spy Glass (The) ; or, Truths brought home to the Mind's Eye. London, Houlston, 1823. [*Quarterly Review.*]

Squire, Miss. The Beggar and his Benefactor. [Cawthorn's Catalogue. 1810.]

Staël-Holstein, Madame A. L. G. Necker de (*see* DE STAËL-HOLSTEIN).

Stage Coach (The) : containing the Character of Mr. Manly and the History of his Fellow Travellers. 2 vols., London, T. Osborne, 1753. [B.M. : *Eng. Lit. in Germany.*]

Stanford, Jane Kinderley. A Lady's Gift, Or Woman as she ought to be. London, Smith, Elder, 1835. [B.M.]

—— The Stoic ; or, Memoirs of Eurysthenes the Athenian. London, Smith, Elder, 1834. [B.M. : *Eng. Cat.*]

Stanhope, Louisa Sidney. The Age We Live In. A Novel. 3 vols., London, A. K. Newman, 1809. [B.M. : *Monthly Mag.* : Pickering.]

—— The Bandit's Bride ; Or, The Maid of Saxony. A Romance. By the Author of Montbrasil Abbey, &c. 4 vols., London, Printed at the Minerva Press, 1807. [Blakey.]

—— The Confessional of Valombre. A Romance. 4 vols., London, Printed at the Minerva Press, for A. K. Newman, 1812. [B.M. : Publisher's advert : *Quarterly Review.*]

—— The Corsair's Bride. A Legend Of the Sixteenth Century. 3 vols., London, A. K. Newman, 1830. [B.M. : *New Monthly Mag.*]

—— The Crusaders. An Historical Romance, Of the Twelfth Century. 5 vols., London, Printed at the Minerva Press for A. K. Newman, 1820. [B.M. : *New Monthly Mag.* : Blakey.]

—— Di Montranzo ; Or, The Novice of Corpus Domini. A Romance. 4 vols., London, Printed at the Minerva Press, for A. K. Newman, 1810. [B.M. : Pickering : Publisher's advert.]

—— The Festival of Mora. An Historical Romance. 4 vols., London, John Richardson, 1821. [Baker's Bookshop : B.M.]

—— Madelina. A Tale founded on facts. 4 vols., London, Printed at the Minerva Press, for A. K. Newman, 1814. [Publisher's advert : *Quarterly Review* : Blakey.]

—— Montbrasil Abbey ; or, Maternal trials. A tale. 2 vols., London, Printed at the Minerva Press, for Lane, Newman, and Co., 1806. [Blakey.]

—— The Nun of Santa Maria di Tindaro. A Tale. 3 vols., London, Printed at the Minerva Press for A. K. Newman, 1818. [B.M.]

—— Runnemede. An Ancient Legend. 3 vols., London, A. K. Newman, 1825. [B.M.]

—— The Seer of Tiviotdale. A Romance. 4 vols., London, A. K. Newman, 1827.

[*Blackwood's Edin. Mag.* : B.M. : Publisher's advert.]

Stanhope, Louisa Sidney. The Siege of Kenilworth. A Historical Romance. 4 vols., London, A. K. Newman, 1824. [B.M.]

—— Striking Likenesses ; Or The Votaries of Fashion. A Novel. 4 vols., London, J. F. Hughes, 1808. [B.M. : Pickering.]

—— Sydney Beresford. A Tale of the Day. By the author of The Bandit's Bride, &c. 3 vols., London, Sherwood, Gilbert, and Piper, 1835. [B.M.]

—— Treachery ; Or, The Grave of Antoinette. A Romance, Interspersed with Poetry. 4 vols., London, Printed at the Minerva Press for A. K. Newman, 1815. [B.M. : *New Monthly Mag.* : Publisher's advert.]

Stanley, Louisa. Children taught by Experience. Stories for the nursery. London, E. Lacey, [1835 ?]. [B.M.]

—— The Juvenile Story-Book. With 30 wood engravings. London, 1840. [B.M.]

—— Original Tales for Boys and Girls. With illustrations. London, R. A. Charlton, [1840 ?]. [B.M.]

—— Sidney Tales ; a Pleasing Collection of Instructive Tales and Narratives. Arranged by Louisa Stanley. With plates. London, John Reynolds, N.D. [Court Bk. Shop.]

Stanly. A Tale Of the Fifteenth Century. 3 vols., London, Chapman, and Hall, 1835. [B.M. : G. Worthington.]

Stapleton, Miles. Paynell ; Or, the Disappointed Man. 2 vols., London, John Richardson, 1837. [B.M.]

Stark, Catherine. Lucy Belleville : a tale for little girls. Brighton, 1849. [B.M.]

Steamers v. Stages, Or Andrew and his Spouse : An Aquatic Excursion by Steam. With woodcuts by Robert Cruikshank. London, 1830. [Chas. Hutt.]

Steele, Sir Robert. The Marine Officer ; or, sketches of service. 2 vols., London, Henry Colburn, 1840. [B.M. : *Eng. Cat.*]

Stellins ; or, The new Werter. 2 vols., London, Printed at the Minerva Press, for William Lane, 1793. [Blakey.]

Step-Brothers (The). A tale. By the Author of The Young Emigrants, etc. London, 1828. [B.M.]

Stephen, Sir George. Adventures Of An Attorney In Search of a Practice. London, Saunders and Otley, 1839. [Allibone : B.M.]

—— The Jesuit At Cambridge. 2 vols., London, Henry Colburn, 1847. [B.M. : James Glaisher : Publisher's advert.]

Stephens, George. The Manuscripts of Erdély. A Romance. 3 vols., London, Smith, Elder, 1835. [B.M.]

—— Père La Chaise ; Or, The Confessor : A Tale of the Times. Edited by George Stephens. 3 vols., London, Whittaker, 1840. [Allibone : B.M.]

Stephens, Nella. De Mowbray ; Or, The Stranger Knight. A Romance. 4 vols., London, A. K. Newman, 1823. [B.M.]

—— The Robber Chieftain ; Or, Dinas Linn. A Romance. 4 vols., London, A. K. Newman, 1825. [B.M.]

Stepney, Catherine, Lady. The Courtier's Daughter. 3 vols., London, Henry Colburn, 1838. [B.M. : Ingpen.]

—— The Heir Presumptive. 3 vols., London, Richard Bentley, 1835. [B.M.]

—— The Lords of Erith, a romance. 3 vols., London, 1809. [B.M. : *Monthly Mag.*]

—— The New Road to Ruin. A Novel. 3 vols., London, Richard Bentley, 1833. [B.M. : Ingpen.]

—— The Three Peers. 3 vols., London, Richard Bentley, 1841. [B.M.]

Sterling, John. Arthur Coningsby. 3 vols., London, Effingham Wilson, 1833. [B.M.]

—— Fitzgeorge ; a novel. 3 vols., London, Effingham Wilson, 1832. [B. M. : Cleverdon : Pickering.]

Sterling, Rev. Joseph. The History of the Chevalier Bayard. Dublin, Luke White, 1781. [B.M. : G. Worthington.]

Sterne, Miss G. M. Tales For an English Home. Bristol, George Davey ; London, Longman, Rees, Orme, Brown, Green, & Longman, 1833. [Allibone : B.M.]

Sterne, Laurence. The Life and Opinions of Tristram Shandy Gentleman. 9 vols., [Volumes I. & II.] [York], 1760. [Volumes III. & IV.] London, Dodsley, 1761. [Volumes V. & VI.] London, T. Becket & P. A. de Hondt, 1762. [Volumes VII. & VIII.] London, T. Becket & P. A. de Hondt, 1765. [Volume IX.] London, T. Becket & P. A. de Hondt, 1767. [Sterne's signature appears in volumes 5, 7, & 9.] [B.M. : Maggs : "Sunday Times" Book Exhibition.]

—— A Political Romance addressed to ——, Esq. of York. [The History of a good Warm Watch Coat.] Addressed to —— Esq. of York. London, [J. Murdoch ?], 1769. [B.M. : Maggs.]

—— A Sentimental Journey Through France and Italy. By Mr. Yorick. 2 vols., London, T. Becket & P. A. de Hondt. 1768. [B.M. : Maggs : Arthur Rogers.]

Stevens, A. Tales from the Parsonage. London, 1850. [B.M.]

Stevens, George Alexander. The Adventures of a Speculist. Or a Journey through London. Compiled from papers written by George Alexander Stevens (Author of ' A Lecture Upon Heads '), with his Life, a Preface, Corrections and Notes by the Editor. Exhibiting a Picture of the Manners, Fashions, Amusements, etc., of the Metropolis at the Middle of the Eighteenth Century ;

and including several Fugitive Pieces of Humour, by the same Author, now first collected and published. 2 vols., London, Printed for the Editor, 1788. [B.M. : W. Brown : *Cat. Lib. Prohib.*]

Stevens, George Alexander. The History of Tom Fool. 2 vols., London T. Waller, 1760. [B.M. : W. Brown : Tregaskis.]

Stevens, Grace Buchanan. Llewellen, Or, The Vale of Phlinlimmon : A Novel. 3 vols., Edinburgh, Printed by John Moir, for Mecredie, Skelly ; and T. & G. Underwood, London, 1818. [B.M. : *New Monthly Mag.*]

Stevens, John. The Modern Wife. A Novel. 2 vols., London, T. Lowndes, 1769. [Pickering : Stonehill.]

Steward, Mrs. T. F. The Interdict, A Novel. 3 vols., London, T. & W. Boone, 1840. [Allibone : B.M.]

—— The Mascarenhas A Legend of The Portuguese in India By The Author of " The Prediction," &c. 3 vols., London, Smith, Elder, 1836. [B.M.]

—— The Prediction. 3 vols., London, Saunders and Otley, 1834. [B.M.]

Stewart, Agnes M. Brotherly Love : or, the Sisters. London, 1848. [B.M.]

—— Chastity ; or, the Sister of Charity. London, 1848. [B.M.]

—— Diligence ; or, Ethel Villiers and her slothful friend. London, 1848. [B.M.]

—— Humility ; or, Blanche Neville and the Fancy Fair. London, 1848. [B.M.]

—— Liberality ; or the Benevolent Merchant. London, 1848. [B.M.]

—— Meekness ; or, Emily Herbert and the Victim of Passion. London, 1848. [B.M.]

—— Stories of the Seven Virtues. In 7 parts. London, Dolman, 1848. [B.M.]

—— Temperance ; or, Edward Ashton. London, 1848. [B.M.]

—— Stories About Alfred the Great, for the Amusement and Instruction Of Children. By A.M.S. Dublin, J. Browne, [1840 ?]. [B.M.]

Stewart, Alexander. Stories from the History of Scotland. London, Simpkin, Marshall. [Allibone : *Eng. Cat.*]

Stewart, D. The Life and Surprising Exploits of Rob Roy Macgregor ; With an Historical Sketch of the Celebrated Clan MacGregor. Newcastle, Mackenzie & Dent, [c. 1820.] [Stonehill.]

Stewart, Elizabeth, M. Fitz Alwyn, the first Lord Mayor, and the Queens' Knights. A tale of the Drapers' Company. London, 1848. [B.M.]

—— Githa of the Forest. By the Author of " Lord Dacre of Gilsland," " Rodenhurst," &c. 3 vols., London, E. Churton, 1845. [B.M. : *Critic* : McLeish.]

—— Lord Dacre Of Gilsland. A Novel. 3 vols., London, T. C. Newby, 1843. [Allibone : B.M.]

—— Rodenhurst : Or, The Church and

the Manor. By E.M.S. 3 vols., London, John Mortimer, 1845. [Allibone : B.M. : *Critic.*]

Stewart, Harriet. The Tuscan Vase ; a moral tale. London, 1840. [B.M.]

Stewart, Rev. John. The Killarney Poor Scholar. Swaffham, 1830. [B.M.]

Stewarton, Mr. The Secret History of the Court and Cabinet of St. Cloud : In a Series of Letters from a Gentleman at Paris to a Nobleman in London, Written during the months of August, September, and October, 1805. 3 vols., London, John Murray, 1806. [Block : B.M. : Stonehill.]

Stickney, Sarah (*see* ELLIS, Sarah Stickney).

Stingy Farmer's Dream (The) ; or the history of Thomas Howman. London, [1800 ?]. [B.M.]

Stiven, Alexander. Love and War, A Historical Romance. 2 vols., London, Printed for the Author, 1814. [*New Monthly Mag.* : Stonehill.]

Stockdale, Mary R. The Life of a Boy. By the Author of the Panorama of Youth. 2 vols., London, G. & W. B. Whittaker, 1821. [B.M. : Ingpen : Pickering.]

Stocqueler, J. H. Alfred the Great, a Romance. 1849. [Noel Broadbent.]

Stoddart, Lady. The Eskdale Herd-Boy ; A Scottish Tale, for the Instruction and Amusement of Young Persons. With a frontispiece. London, Grant and Griffith, 1850. [Block.]

Stone, Anne. Features of the youthful mind ; or, tales for juvenile readers. Margate, 1802. [B.M.]

Stone, Elizabeth. Miss Pen and her Niece ; Or, The Old Maid and the Young One. 3 vols., London, Richard Bentley, 1843. [Allibone : B.M. : John Smith.]

—— Mr. Dalton's Legatee, a very nice Woman. 3 vols., London, T. C. Newby, 1850. [Allibone : B.M.]

—— William Langshawe, the Cotton Lord. 2 vols., London, Richard Bentley, 1842. [B.M.]

—— The Young Milliner. London, Cunningham and Mortimer, 1843 [Allibone : B.M. : Publisher's advert.]

Stone-Pickers (The), and other stories. Yarmouth, 1833. [B.M.]

Stories about many Things. Founded on Facts. With a frontispiece. London, Harvey and Darton, 1833. [B.M.]

Stories and Sketches for the amusement of leisure moments. London, Burns, 1846. [B.M.]

Stories by a Mother, for the use of her own children. London, 1820. [B.M.]

Stories for the Christmas Week. 2 vols., London, Howell, 1826. [*Eng. Cat.*: *Quarterly Review.*]

Stories for Summer Days and Winter Nights. First Series. In 12 numbers

[London, Groombridge, 1849-1850.] [B.M. : *Eng. Cat.*]

Stories for Summer Days and Winter Nights. Second Series. 8 vols., London, Groombridge, 1850-1853. [B.M. : *Eng. Cat.*]

Stories from Fly Land, Bee Land, Bird Land and Mouse Land. By C.D.B. London, 1848. [B.M. (2nd. edn.)]

Stories from the History of Wales. By the Author of " The History of Wales arranged as a Catechism." Shrewsbury, 1833. [B.M.]

Stories from Old Chroniclers : With a Prefatory Essay and Historical Notes. With illustrations. 3 vols., London, Charles Knight, 1825. [Publisher's advt.]

Stories from Roman History. By a Lady. With illustrations. London, Harvey and Darton, 1823. [B.M. : Dobell : J. D. Miller.]

Stories of Chivalry and Romance. London, Longman, Rees, Orme, Brown, & Green, 1827. [*Blackwood's Edin. Mag.* : B.M. : G. Worthington.]

Stories of Edward and his little friends. London, 1837. [B.M.]

Stories of the Elements. Containing the Old Man and his four Servants. Volcanoes and Earthquakes. And the Volcanic Island and the Indian Family. London, 1848. [B.M.]

Stories of the Head and Heart ; for the Young : from the German. By the authoress of " What is an Egg worth " (S.T.). London, [1842 ?]. [B.M.]

Stories of Old Daniel, or Tales Of Wonder and Delight containing Narratives of Foreign countries and manners, and designed for the introduction to the study of voyages, travels, and history in general. With a frontispiece. London, Printed for M. J. Goodwin, by B. McMillan, 1810. [B.M. (2nd. edn.)]

Stories of School Boys. London, Tract Society, [1849]. [B.M. : *Eng. Cat.*]

Stories, Old and New. London, 1840. [B.M.]

Stories Selected from the History of France for Children. London, Harris, 1819. [Dobell.]

Story for Christmas (A). London, [1850]. [B.M.]

Story of Anna (The), by a Lady. London. [B.M.]

Story of the Caravan (The) ; or, the Driver and his Dog. London, [1800 ?]. [B.M.]

Story of Clarissa (The), In Two Parts. London, Printed for the Author, 1817. [B.M. : *New Monthly Mag.*]

Story of Fatima (The), by a Lady. London, 1844. [B.M.]

Story of George Panton ; Or, Mischievous Effects arising from Children being too fond of Talking. With woodcuts. London, James Wallis, [1840 ?]. [B.M.]

Story of the Girl and Her Basket of Eggs (The). With woodcuts. Birmingham, T. Bloomer ; and A. Carvalho, London, [1840 ?] [B.M.]

Story of the Methodist (The) ; or, the injur'd husband's revenge : a true history. London, [1770 ?]. [B.M.]

Story of the Rat with a Bell (The). With woodcuts. Birmingham, T. Bloomer ; and A. Carvalho, London, [1840.] [B.M.]

Story of Sinful Sally (The), The Hampshire Tragedy, the Bad Bargain, and Robert and Richard. London, Howard and Evans, J. Hatchard, [18--]. [J. D. Miller.]

Story on which the New Tragedy, call'd The Brothers [by Edward Young], now acting at the Theatre Royal in Drury Lane, is founded. Dedicated to the author of the play. London, 1853. [B.M.]

Story on which the New Tragedy (The) called Virginia is founded. London, 1754. [B.M.]

Story without a Name And The Leys of Tytcheley Or Records of a Family By ANΓKH. Frankfort, Printed for the Author, 1844. [B.M.]

Storys of the Bewitched Fiddler, Perilous Situation, and John Hetherington's Dream. Glasgow, [1850 ?]. [B.M.]

Storys of Prince Lupin, Yellow Dwarf, and the Three Wishes. Glasgow, Printed for the booksellers, [1850 ?]. [B.M.]

Story-Teller (The). A Collection of Tales, Original, Translated, and Selected. With plates. 2 vols., London, James Robins, 1830. [B.M.]

Stover, Karl. The Curate's Favorite Pupil : After the German of Karl Stover. By Mary Howitt. With illustrations by John Absolon. London, Wm. S. Orr, 1844. [B.M.]

Straella, Leonora des. The English Baronet. A Novel. 3 vols., London, A. K. Newman, 1826. [B.M. : *Quarterly Review.*]

Strange Adventures of Mons. de Jardin (The). To which is added an anecdote of Frederick the Great. Penrith, [1805 ?] [B.M.]

Stranger Chieftain (The) ; Or, Lara and his Page. A Tale. 2 vols., London, A. K. Newman, 1834. [B.M.]

Stranger (The) ; or, The Llewellyn Family. A Cambrian Tale. 2 vols., [W. Lane.] 1798. [*New Ann. Reg.* : Blakey.]

Strawberries (The), translated from the French. To which is added, Neglect of Prayer, the Christian Servant, the Infidel's death-bed. In 4 parts. Derby, Catholic Book Society, 1846. [B.M]

Stray Child (The). With woodcuts. London, Religious Tract Society, [1830]. [B.M.]

Street, Miss. The Lake of Winder-mere. A novel. By the editor of *Maria*. 2 vols., [*Minerva Press Catalogue*: Blakey.]

—— The Recluse of the Appenines, a tale. By the author of The lake of Windermere, London, William Lane, 1792. [*Minerva Press Catalogue*: Blakey.]

—— Theodore : a domestic tale. 2 vols., London, William Lane, 1792. [*Minerva Press Catalogue*: Blakey.]

Streeten, Mrs. The Fortescue Family, A Tale For Young Persons, In which The principle of Christian Charity is familiarly Illustrated and Explained. London, Houlston, 1840. [Allibone : B.M.]

Streit, Friedrich Wilhelm. The Memoirs of the Count of P——; a novel, trans-lated from the German by F.W.S. 1767. [B.M.]

Strickland, Agnes. Historical Tales Of Illustrious British Children. With a frontispiece. London, N. Hailes, 1833. [B.M.]

—— The Juvenile Forget me Not ; Or, Cabinet Of Entertainment and instruc-tion. By the author of " The Rival Crusoes," " The Young Emigrant," etc. etc. With plates. London, N. Hailes, 1827. [Block : B.M.]

—— The Moss-House : In which many of the Works of Nature are rendered as a source of Amusement to Children. London, W. Darton, 1822. [Arthur Rogers.]

—— The Pilgrims of Walsingham Or Tales of the Middle Ages An Historical Romance. 3 vols., London, Saunders and Otley, 1835. [Allibone : B.M. : W. T. Spencer.]

—— Prejudice Reproved, or the History of the Negro Toy seller. By the author of the " Tell-Tale." London, 1826. [B.M.]

—— Tales and Stories From History. With illustrations. 2 vols., London, John W. Parker, 1836. [Allibone : B.M.]

—— Tales of the School-Room, By the Editor of " The Parting Gift," &c., &c. With a frontispiece. London, William Darton, [1830]. [Gumuchian : Arthur Rogers.]

—— The Tell-Tale. An Original Collec-tion of Moral and Amusing Stories. With 12 engravings. London, Harris, 1823. [Gumuchian.]

—— The Young Emigrant. 1826. [*Camb. Hist. Eng. Lit.*]

Strickland, Agnes and Elizabeth. The Rival Crusoes. London, Harris, 1826. [Allibone : *Camb. Hist. Eng. Lit.*]

Strickland, Catherine Parr. Reforma-tion Or The Cousins. With a vignette and an engraving. London, James Woodhouse, 1819. [B.M.]

Strickland, Jane. Edward Evelyn : a tale of the rebellion of Prince Charles Edward. London, H. Bohn, 1843. [B.M. : *Eng. Cat.*]

—— Ellen Cleveland ; or, the young Samaritan. A tale of the pestilence. London, Dean, [1834]. [B.M. : *Eng. Cat.*]

—— The Orphan Captive, or, Christian Endurance. A tale of the shipwreck and slavery of an Ambassador's daughter London, Dean, [1848]. [B.M. : *Eng. Cat.*]

—— The Spanish Conscript and his Family ; a Tale of Napoleon's Cam-paign in Russia. London, Clarke, 1846. [B.M. : *Critic.*]

String of British Pearls (A) : a moral Tale. 3 vols., London, 1813. [*New Monthly Mag.*]

Strolling Player (The) ; or, life and adventures of William Templeton. 3 vols., London, 1802. [B.M. : Sotheby's]

Strutt, Mrs. Genevieve ; Or, The Or-phan's Visit. A Novel. 3 vols., London, Printed at the Minerva Press for A. K. Newman, 1818. [B.M. : *New Monthly Mag.*]

Strutt, Elizabeth. Chances and Changes A Domestic Story By The Author of " Six Weeks on the Loire." 3 vols., London, Saunders and Otley, 1835. [Allibone : B.M. : T. D. Webster.]

Strutt, Joseph. Queenhoo-Hall, A Ro-mance : and Ancient Times, A Drama. [Edited by Sir Walter Scott.] 4 vols., London, John Murray, 1808. [Ingpen : Pickering : Arthur Rogers.]

Stuart, Augusta Amelia. Cave of Toledo ; or, the Gothic Princess. An historical romance. 5 vols., London, Printed at the Minerva Press, for A. K. Newman, 1812. [Allibone : Publisher's advert. : *Quarterly Review.*]

—— Exile of Portugal. 2 vols., 1809. [Allibone : *Monthly Mag.*]

—— Ludovicus ; a Tale. 4 vols., 1810. [Allibone.]

Stuart, E. Royalists and Roundheads. 3 vols., London, Shoberl, 1850. [Baker's Bookshop : *Eng. Cat.*]

Student of Salamanca (The). A Tale. Edinburgh, Blackwood, 1847. [*Critic.*]

Submission Exemplified ; or, The Ami-able Stranger, a Narrative. London, 1818. [*New Monthly Mag.*]

Submissions of Dependence (The). A Novel. 1797. [*New Ann. Reg.*: T. D. Webster.]

Substance and Shadow ; or, The Fisher-man's Daughters of Brighton. A patch-work story. By the Author of " Light-and Shade," etc. 4 vols., London, Printed at the Minerva Press, for A. K. Newman, 1812. [B.M. : *New Monthly Mag.* : Publisher's advert.]

Such Follies Are : a novel. 3 vols., London, William Lane, 1795. [B.M. : *New Ann. Reg.* : Blakey.]

Such is the World. 3 vols., London, G. and W. B. Whittaker, 1821. [B.M.]

Sue, Maria Joseph Eugène. Arthur, or the Journal of an unknown. London, [1846]. [B.M.]

—— The Commander of Malta ; also, Atar-Gull ; or, The Slave's Revenge ; and, Paula Monti, by the same author. With woodcuts. London, Appleyard, 1847. [Stonehill.]

—— The Commander of Malta. Translated from the French by Adelbert D'Orsy. Belfast, Simms and M'Intyre, 1846. [*Critic.*]

—— De Rohan, or The Court Conspirator. An Historical Romance. 3 vols., London, Henry Colburn, 1845. [B.M. : Kyrle Fletcher : Publisher's advert.]

—— The Duchesse de Bracciano, translated from the French. And original tales. By Elizabeth O'Hara. London, Smith, Elder, 1850. [B.M. : *Eng. Cat.*]

—— The Female Bluebeard : or, The Adventurer. To which is added : The Abbey of St. Quentin, an epilogue to the Female Bluebeard. With 34 woodcuts by Walmsley. London, Strange, 1845. [B.M. : Stonehill : G. Worthington.]

—— Martin the Foundling, Or The Adventureres of a Valct dc Chambrc. With a portrait & illustrations. London, E. Appleyard, 1847. [B.M. : Lib. of Congress : Publisher's advert.]

—— Matilda : Or, The Misfortunes of Virtue. Translated by Charles Rochford. With 21 plates by G. Standfast. London, Daly, 1845. [B.M. : *Eng. Cat.* : Lib. of Congress.]

—— The Mysteries of Paris, Adapted to the English Reader. With illustrations by H Valentin. 3 vols., London, Chapman and Hall, 1845. [B.M. : Lib. of Congress : Sotheran.]

—— The Mysteries of Paris. From the French. With illustrations. London, 1844. [B.M.]

—— The Mysteries of Paris ; from the French, by J. D. Smith. With engravings By T. Onwhyn. 3 vols., London, 1844. [B.M.]

—— The Mysteries of Paris. Translated with explanatory notes by H. D. Miles. London, [1846]. [B.M.]

—— The Orphan ; or Memoirs of Matilda. By Eugene Sue, Author of " The Mysteries of Paris." Translated by the Hon. D. G. Osborne. With plates by Robert Cruikshank. 2 vols., London, T. C. Newby, [1845]. [Critic : Marks.]

—— Paula Monti : Or, the Hôtel Lambert. From the French By The Translator of the " Mysteries of Paris," and the " Wandering Jew." With 20 woodcut plates. London, Chapman and Hall, 1845. [Block : B.M. : Marks.]

Sue, Maria Joseph Eugène. The Protestant Leader, a Novel. 3 vols., London, T. C. Newby, 1849. [B.M.]

—— The Salamander, or The Midshipman. Kernok the Corsair. With a frontispiece. London, A. K. Newman, 1846. [Arthur Rogers.]

—— The Temptation ; or The Watch Tower of Koat-Vën. A Romantic Tale ; also, Therese Dunoyer ; or, The Manor House of Treff-Hartlog. Translated from the French. London, Vickers 1845. [B.M. : Stonehill.]

—— Therese Dunoyer ; or, the prediction of Gwene Hlan. A novel. New edition translated from the French. London, 1845. [B.M.]

—— The Wandering Jew. With woodcuts. 3 vols., London, Chapman and Hall, 1844. [B.M. : Ingpen : Marks.]

—— The Wandering Jew ; a Tale of the Jesuits. By Eugene Sue. Translated from the French, by D. M. Aird. London, Bruce and Wyld, 1845. [*Critic.*]

—— The Wandering Jew : a tale of the Jesuits. Translated with explanatory notes, by H. D. Miles. London, 1846. [B.M.]

Sufferings of Ouang (The) : or, Artful Villainy Discovered. A Chinese Tale. With a frontispiece and vignette. London, S. Carvalho, N.D. [Court Bk. Shop.]

Sullivan, Mrs. Frederick. Memoirs of a Chaperone Edited by Lady Dacre. 3 vols., London, Richard Bentley, 1832. [Block.]

—— Tales of the Peerage and the Peasantry. Edited by Lady Dacre. 3 vols., London, Richard Bentley, 1835. [B.M. : Ingpen : Elkin Mathews.]

Sullivan, Mary Ann. Owen Castle, Or, Which is the Heroine ? A Novel. Dedicated by Permission to the Right Honourable Lady Combermere. 4 vols., London, Simpkin and Marshall, 1816. [Allibone : B.M. : *New Monthly Mag.*]

Sullivan, Robert. Flittings of Fancy. By Robert Sulivan. 2 vols., London, Henry Colburn, 1837. [B.M. : Publisher's advert.]

—— Raff Hall. By Robert Sullivan. 3 vols., London, Henry Colburn, 1838. [B.M.]

Sullivan, William Francis. The History of Mr. Rightway and his Pupils ; An entertaining and instructive Lesson for Young Gentlemen. With a frontispiece. London, William Darton, Junr., 1816. [Sotheran.]

—— The Young Liar ! ! a Tale of Truth and Caution, for the Benefit of the Rising Generation. With 2 plates. London, A. K. Newman, 1818. [Marks.]

—— The Young Truants. An instructive and entertaining lesson for both Sexes. With illustrations. London, Dean and Munday, 1817. [Arthur Rogers.]

—— Young Wilfrid ; or, The Punish-

ment of Falsehood. A Tale of Truth and
Caution. With illustrations. London,
Dean and Munday, 1821. [J. D. Miller.]

Summer by the Sea (A). A novel. By
Orlando. 2 vols., London, Lane, Newman, 1807. [B.M. : Blakey.]

Summer's Walk (The) ; or, Make Hay
while the Sun Shines. With a woodcut.
London, Houlston, N.D. No. 12 of
Houlston's Series of Tracts. [Block.]

Summersett, Henry. Aberford, A Novel ;
Or What You Will. London, J. Hatchard, 1796. [Birrell & Garnet.]

—— All Sort of Lovers ; or, Indiscretion,
truth and Perfidy. 3 vols., [Minerva
Press, 1805]. [Blakey.]

—— The Fate of Sedley. A Novel. By
the author of The offspring of Russell.
2 vols., [W. Lane, 1795.] [*Minerva Press
Cat.* : Stonehill : Blakey.]

—— Leopold Warndorf. A novel. 2 vols.,
London, William Lane, 1800. [B.M. :
Blakey.]

—— The Mad Man of the Mountain. A
Tale. 2 vols., London, William Lane,
1799. [*New Ann. Reg.* : Blakey.]

—— The Offspring of Russell. A novel.
2 vols., London, William Lane, 1794.
[*New Ann. Reg.* : *Minerva Press
Catalogue* : Blakey.]

—— Probable Incidents : or, Scenes in
life, a novel, 2 vols., London, William
Lane, 1797. [Blakey.]

**Supplement to Baron Munchausen's
Travels,** containing his ascent to the
Dog-star. London, J. Mawman, 1802.
[B.M.]

**Supplement to the Life and Opinions
of Tristram Shandy** (A) serving to
elucidate that work. By the author of
Yorick's Meditations. London, 1760.
[B.M.]

Supposed Daughter (The) ; or Innocent
Impostor. 3 vols., London, F. and J.
Noble, 1773. [B.M. (New edn.)]

Surprising Adventures of Bigenio
(The), An Hermaphrodite, containing a
true Account of its Birth, Education, and
subsequent Seduction by its Tutor,
Eloping from Home, turning Thief,
Intrigues at Bath, &c. With a frontispiece. 1824. [Sawyer.]

**Surprising Adventures of Captain
Winterfield.** With a frontispiece.
Glasgow, [1800]. [Combridges.]

**Surprising Life and Adventures of the
Gentleman-Robber** (The), Redmond
O'Hanlon. Glasgow, Printed for the
Booksellers, [1840 ?]. [B.M.]

Surprising Life of Richard Turpin
(The), a Notorious Highwayman ; Containing a True and Detailed account of
his Many Escapades, etc. To which is
added The Life of Sawney Beane, The
Man-Eater. London, Dean and Munday, [c. 1808]. [Stonehill.]

Surr, Thomas Skinner. Consequences :
or, Adventures at Wraxall Castle, A
Novel. By a Gentleman. 2 vols., 1796.

[*Eng. Lit. in Germany* : *New Ann.
Reg.* : T. D. Webster.]

Surr, Thomas Skinner. George Barnwell.
A Novel. 3 vols., London, Symonds,
1798. [Ingpen : *New Ann. Reg.* :
Sotheby's].

—— The Magic of Wealth. A Novel.
3 vols., London, Printed for T. Cadell
& W. Davies, by G. Sidney, 1815.
[Baker's Bookshop : B.M. : Pickering.]

—— The Mask of Fashion. 2 vols., 1807.
[Sotheby's].

—— Richmond ; Or, Scenes in the Life
of a Bow Street Officer, Drawn up from
his Private Memoranda. 3 vols., London,
Henry Colburn, 1827. [B.M. : Pickering : Victorius.]

—— Splendid Misery, A Novel. 3 vols.,
London, Hurst, 1801. [*Eng. Lit. in
Germany* : Stonehill.]

—— A Winter in London, Or, Sketches
of Fashion ; A Novel. 3 vols., London,
Richard Phillips, 1806. [Arthur Rogers :
Stonehill : T. D. Webster.]

Surtees, Robert Smith. Handley Cross ;
Or, The Spa Hunt. A Sporting Tale.
By the Author of " Jorrocks' Jaunts and
Jollities," &c. 3 vols., London, Henry
Colburn, 1843. [Bailey Bros. : B.M. :
Guide to Best Fiction.]

—— Hawbuck Grange ; or The Sporting
Adventures of Thomas Scott, Esq.
With 8 etchings by " Phiz " [Hablot K.
Browne]. London, Longman, Brown,
Green, and Longmans. 1847. [B.M. :
Maggs : Marks.]

—— Hillingdon Hall ; Or, The Cockney
Squire ; A Tale of Country Life. By the
Author of " Handley Cross," &c. 3
vols., London, Henry Colburn, 1845.
[B.M. : *Guide to Best Fiction* : Rose-
bery.]

—— Jorrock's Jaunts and Jollities, or the
Hunting, Shooting, Racing, Driving,
Sailing, Eating, Eccentric, and Extrava-
gant Exploits of that Renowned Sporting Citizen, Mr. John Jorrocks. With 12
plates by " Phiz " [Hablot K. Browne].
London, Spiers, 1838. [Marks.]

Susan and Magdalene : or, a fortnight's
visit. By the author of " Harriet and
her Cousin." Edinburgh, 1834. [B.M.]

Susan Harvey. Confirmation. London,
1843. [B.M.]

Susan, a novel. 2 vols., [Cawthorn's
Catalogue, 1810.]

Susan Palmer, the plain looking child.
London, 1848. [B.M.]

Suspicion, or the Benevolent Recluse, by
Lady ——. 2 vols., London, Printed at
the Minerva Press, for A. K. Newman,
1814. [Publisher's advert.]

Suspicious Lovers, By the Author of
Woodbury. 1777. [*Eng. Lit. in Germany.*]

Sutherland, Lieut. Alexander. Macrimmon. A Highland Tale. By the Author
of Redmond the Rebel, Cospatrick of
Raymondsholm, St. Kathleen, &c.

4 vols., London, A. K. Newman, 1823.
[B.M. : *New Monthly Mag. : Quarterly Review.*]

Sutherland, Lieut. Alexander. Redmond the Rebel ; Or, They met at Waterloo. A Novel. 3 vols., London, Printed at the Minerva Press for A. K. Newman, 1819. [B.M. : R. Walter Gibson : *I. in F.*]

—— St. Kathleen ; Or, The Rock of Dunnismoyle. A Novel. By the Author of Redmond the Rebel. 4 vols., London, Printed at the Minerva Press for A. K. Newman, 1820. [B.M. : *I. in F. : New Monthly Mag.*]

—— Tales of a Pilgrim. By the Author of " A Summer Ramble in the North Highlands." Edinburgh, William Hunter ; and James Duncan, 1827. [B.M. : *Literary Gazette.*]

Sutton Abbey a Novel. In a Series of Letters, founded on Facts. 2 vols., 1779. [*Eng. Lit. in Germany :* T. D. Webster.]

Swan, Rev. Charles. Gesta Romanorum, or Entertaining Moral Stories, invented by the Monks as a Fire-Side Recreation whence the most Celebrated Poets, from the Earliest Times, have extracted their Plots, translated from the Latin, with Preliminary Observations and Notes, by the Rev. Charles Swan. 2 vols., London, 1824. [B.M. : Marks.]

Sweep, Soot O ! or some account of Little Jem. [1797 ?]. Cheap Repository. [B.M.]

Sweepstone, W. H. The Two Widows ; Or Matrimonial Jumbles. With engravings by Alfred Ashley. London, T. C. Newby, [1830]. [Ingpen.]

Sweetser, Mrs. M. L. The Double Courtship. A Romance of Deep Interest. With woodcuts. London, Lloyd, 1847. [B.M. : Stonehill.]

Sybil (The), a Novel. 1769. [*Eng. Lit. in Germany.*]

Sydney Morcom. 2 vols., London, Edward Moxon, 1844. [B.M.]

Sykes, Mrs. S. Margiana ; or, Widdrington Tower. A tale of the fifteenth century. 5 vols., London, Lane, Newman, 1808. [Blakey : Stonehill.]

—— Sir William Dorien. A Domestic Story. By the Author of Margiana ; or, Widdrington Towers. 3 vols., London, Printed at the Minerva Press, for A. K. Newman, 1812. [B.M. : Publisher's advert : *Quarterly Review.*]

—— Stories of the Four Nations, Containing Montargis, a French Story ; My aunt Patty, an English Story ; Lillias de Lara, a Spanish Story ; The Calabrian, an Italian Story. By the Author of Margiana ; Sir William Dorien, &c. &c. With a frontispiece. London, Printed at the Minerva Press for A. K. Newman, 1813. [B.M. : *New Monthly Mag. :* Publisher's advert.]

Sylvanella, or the Gypsey. 4 vols., 1812. [*New Monthly Mag.*]

Symmons, Caroline. The Cottage of the Var, A Tale. 3 vols., London, Samuel Tipper, 1809. [B.M.]

Tabart, Benjamin. Popular Fairy Tales ; or, a Liliputian Library ; containing twenty-six choice pieces of Fancy and Fiction, by those renowned personages King Oberon, Queen Mab, Mother Goose, Mother Bunch, Master Puck, and other distinguished personages at the Court of the Fairies. Now first collected and revised by Benjamin Tabart. With 26 engravings. London, Sir, R. Phillips, [1818]. [B.M. : Court Bk. Shop : Arthur Rogers.]

—— Tarbart's Collection of Popular Stories for the Nursery, From the French, Italian and old English Writers, Newly translated and revised. With plates. 4 vols., London, Tabart, 1804-9. [Dobell : T. C. Godfrey.]

Taciturna and Jocunda ; Or, Genius Alaciel's Journey through those two Islands : A Satirical Work. Translated from the French. London, R. Withy ; and J. Cook, 1760. [B.M. : W. Brown : G. Worthington.]

Talbot, H. Fox. Legendary Tales in Verse and Prose. Collected by H. F. Talbot, Esq. London, Ridgway, 1830. [*Eng. Cat. : New Monthly Mag.*]

Tale (A), For Gentle and Simple. London, Rowland Hunter, 1815. [B.M. : *New Monthly Mag.*]

Tale of the Last Century (A). The Secret Memoirs of H. Pumpkin, etc. [1825.] [B.M.]

Tale of a Looking Glass. From " the Bee." With woodcuts. London, [1810 ?] [B.M.]

Tale of Middle Life (A), and other sketches in prose and verse. By the author of " Some Passages in the life of a Mofussilite." Calcutta, W. Thacker, [1850 ?]. [B.M.]

Tale of Mystery (A) ; Or the Castle of Solitude. Containing The Dreadful Imprisonment Of Count L. and the Countess Harmina, His Lady. London, Thomas Tegg ; T. Hurst ; T. Brown, Edinburgh ; and B. Dugdale, Dublin, [1803]. [B.M. : Stonehill.]

Tale of the Olden Time (A). By A Harrow Boy. London, John Andrews, 1821. [B.M. : Stonehill.]

Tale of the Rebellion of 1745 (A), Or, the Broken Heart. To which is added The Three Wishes, And the Adventures of Two Tee-Totallers. With a woodcut vignette. Glasgow, Printed for the Booksellers, [1840 ?]. [B.M.]

Tale of a Sixpence (A). London, 1849. [B.M.]

Tale without an End (The). London, 1847. [B.M.]

Tales and Incidents of Childhood. By a

Mother. London, E. Lacey, [1840 ?]. [B.M.]

Tales and Legends of Ireland. 2 vols., Cork, Bolster, 1831. [*I. in F.*]

Tales and Poetry. By Alpha. Wakefield, Nichols, [1849]. [B.M.]

Tales by an Unwilling Author. 2 vols., Dublin, R. Milliken, 1822. [B.M. : *Edin. Mag.*]

Tales, Entertaining and Sympathetic, inscribed to the heart. 2 vols., [W. Lane, 1788.] [Blakey.]

Tales for the British People. By Candida. London, James Ridgway, 1834. [B.M.]

Tales for Infant Minds. By a Mother. London, 1834. [B.M.]

Tales for my Grandchildren. London, Hatchard, 1841. [B.M. : *Eng. Cat.*]

Tales for Youth ; or, The high road to renown, through the paths of pleasure ; being a collection of tales illustrative of an alphabetical arrangement of subjects, the observance of which will enable young men to arrive with respectability at the pinnacle of fame. [W. Lane, 1798.] [Blakey.]

Tales from the Eastern Land ; being a second series of Eastern Romance. London, [1845 ?]. [B.M.]

Tales from the German. By a Lady. With lithographs. London, George Anderson, 1827. [Publisher's advert.]

Tales Moral and Amusing. For the instruction of children, etc. Edinburgh, Oliver & Boyd, [1830 ?]. [B.M.]

Tales of the Academy. With illustrations. 2 vols., London, A. K. Newman, 1820. [B.M. : *Eng. Cat.* : Arthur Rogers.]

Tales of Adventure by Sea and Land. With illustrations. London, Burns, 1847. [B.M. : *Eng. Cat.* : Arthur Rogers.]

Tales of all Nations. London, Thomas Hurst, 1827. [B.M.]

Tales of Chivalry ; or, Perils by Flood and Field. With illustrations by S. Williams. 2 vols., London, Berger, [c. 1840]. [B.M. : *Eng. Cat.*]

Tales of the Classics. A New Delineation of the most Popular Fables, Legends, and allegories, commemorated in the works of Poets, painters and sculptors. Selected and written by a Lady for the amusement and instruction of her own daughters. Dedicated to Princess [afterwards Queen] Victoria. 3 vols., London, Colburn, and Bentley, 1830. [R. Hall : Leonard Hyman : Lib. of Congress.]

Tales of Early Piety. By two sisters. London, Hatchard, 1836. [B.M. : *Eng. Cat.*]

Tales of Elam (The). 2 vols., London, William Lane, 1794. [Blakey.]

Tales of the Fancy, containing Fitzallen and Glenarvon. With a frontispiece. London, G. Cowie, 1823. [W. Brown.]

Tales of the Fire-Side. 3 vols., London, Baldwin, 1817. [*New Monthly Mag.*]

Tales of Flood and Field. Comprising " The Adventures of a Young Rifleman," " The Adventures of the Rifleman's Comrade," " The Adventures of a French Sergeant." 3 vols., London, 1833. [McLeish.]

Tales of Four Nations. 3 vols., London, Whitaker, Treacher, and Arnot, 1829. [B.M.]

Tales of Humble Life. London, Charles Knight, 1824. [B.M. : Publisher's advt.]

Tales of Humour, Gallantry, and Romance, Selected and Translated from the Italian. With plates by George Cruikshank. London, Baldwyn, 1824. [B.M. : F. Harvey : Chas. Hutt.]

Tales of the Imagination. By The Author of The Bachelor and the Married Man, The Physiognomist, and Hesitation. 3 vols., London, Longman, Hurst, Rees, Orme, and Brown, 1820. [Baker's Bookshop : B.M. : Publisher's advert.]

Tales of a Lay-Brother. First Series. Neville's Cross. 3 vols., London, Saunders and Otley, 1844. [B.M.]

Tales of Lowanvale. By the Author of " Charles Primrose." [*Literary Annalist.*]

Tales of my Aunt Martha ; containing : 1. The Laird. 2. The Sisters. 3. The Château in La Vendée. 3 vols., London, W. Fearman, 1822. [B.M.]

Tales of my Father, and My Friends. London, Printed for the Author, 1823. [B.M.]

Tales of my Landlady. Edited by Peregrine Puzzlebrain, assistant to the Schoolmaster at Gandercleugh. 3 vols., London, Iley, 1818. [B.M. : *Eng. Cat.* : *New Monthly Mag.*]

Tales of my Landlord, New Series, containing the Fair Witch of Glas Llyn. 3 vols., London, W. Fearman, 1820. [B.M. : W. T. Spencer.]

Tales of my Landlord. New Series. Containing Pontefract Castle. 3 vols., London, W. Fearman, 1820. [Baker's Bookshop : B.M.]

Tales Of Old Mr. Jefferson, Of Gray's Inn. Collected by Young Mr. Jefferson, of Lyon's Inn. The First Series. 2 vols., London, G. and W. B. Whittaker, 1823. [Backus : B.M. : *Quarterly Review.*]

Tales of Other Realms, selected during a late Tour through Europe. By a Traveller. 2 vols., 1809. [*Monthly Mag.* : T. D. Webster.]

Tales of our Counties ; Or, Provincial Portraits. 3 vols., London, William Marsh & Alfred Miller ; and Constable, Edinburgh, 1830. [B.M. : Elkin Mathews : *New Monthly Mag.*]

Tales of Perplexity. The Rendezvous. The Disinherited. Cross Purposes.

London, Sampson, Low, 1829. [B.M.]

Tales of the Pirates ; or, Lives of Smugglers and Buccaneers. With woodcuts. London, 1847. [Stonehill.]

Tales of a Rambler. With illustrations by H. C. Selous. London, Smith, Elder, 1836. [B.M.]

Tales of the Stanley Family. London, Whittaker, 1830. [*Eng. Cat. : New Monthly Mag.*]

Tales of Switzerland. With a frontispiece. 2 vols., London, Francis Westley and L. B. Seeley, 1822-1823. [B.M.]

Tales of Terror ! or More Ghosts. Forming a complete phantasmagoria. London, 1802. [B.M.]

Tales of the Tombs : A Scries of Anecdotes Illustrative of the Affections. By G—— M——. Dublin, W. F. Wakeman ; Simpkin & Marshall, and R. Groombridge, London, 1833. [B.M.]

Tales of Welsh Society and Scenery. 2 vols., London, Longman, Rees, Orme, Brown, and Green, 1827. [*Blackwood's Edin. Mag. :* B.M. : Kyrle Fletcher.]

Tales of Yore. 3 vols., [Cawthorn's Catalogue, 1810.]

Tales Original and Translated from the Spanish. By a Lady. With 8 woodcuts. London, J. J. Stockdale. 1810. [B.M. : Dobell : Lib. of Congress.]

Tales, Romances, Apologues, Anecdotes, and Novels. From the French. 2 vols., 1786. [W. Brown.]

Talfourd, Sir Thomas Noon. Salvador, The Guerilla. By the Author of " The Castilian," &c. 3 vols., London, Richard Bentley, 1834. [B.M.]

Talisman (The) : a rich and rare collection of original and select Magic Tales, &c. of the most intense interest, being highly calculated to amuse both old and young. With folding plates. London, G. Cowie, N.D. [T. Thorp.]

Tallant, Anne. Octavia Elphinstone, A Manx Story. And Lois, A Drama, Founded on a Legend in The Noble Family of ——. 2 vols., London, J. Hatchard, 1834. [B.M.]

Tautphoeus, Baroness Jemima von. The Initials : a Novel. 3 vols., London, Richard Bentley, 1850. [Allibone : B.M. : *Guide to Best Fiction.*]

Tayler, Charles Benjamin. Edward ; or, Almost an Owenite. London, 1840. [B.M.]

—— A Fireside Book, Or The Account of a Christmas Spent at Old Court. By the Author of May You Like It. With a frontispiece by George Cruikshank. London, J. A. Hessey, 1828. [B.M. : Ingpen : Sotheran.]

—— Lady Mary ; or, Not of the World. London, Longman, 1845. [B.M. : *Eng. Cat.*]

—— Margaret ; or, the Pearl. London, Longman, 1844. [B.M. : *Eng. Cat.*]

Tayler, Charles Benjamin. Mark Wilton, the Merchant's Clerk. London, Chapman and Hall, 1848. [B.M. : *Eng. Cat.*]

—— May You Like It : by a Country Curate. 2 vols., London, T. Boys, 1823. [James Glaisher : Sexton.]

Taylor, Mr. The Rose of Melville ; or, The Deserted Infant. A tale for youth of both sexes. London, 1822. [B.M.]

Taylor, B. Fortitude ; or, Euphemia : A Novel. 2 vols., London, W. Simpkin and R. Marshall, 1816. [B.M.]

Taylor, Eliza. Education ; Or, Elizabeth, her Lover and Husband. A Tale for 1817. 3 vols., London, Printed at the Minerva Press, for A. K. Newman, 1817. [B.M.]

—— The Heiress of Avonmore. 3 vols., [Minerva Press, 1804.] [Blakey : *Minerva Press Catalogue.*]

—— Josephine. A novel. By an incognita. with a frontispiece. 2 vols., London, Printed at the Minerva Press, for William Lane, 1799. [*Minerva Press Catalogue :* Blakey.]

—— The Nobleman and his Steward ; or, Memoirs of the Albany Family. 3 vols., [Minerva Press, 1802]. [Blakey : *Minerva Press Catalogue.*]

—— Rosalind. A novel. By the author of Josephine. 2 vols., London, Printed at the Minerva Press, for William Lane, 1799. [*Minerva Press Catalogue :* Blakey.]

Taylor, Emily. Tales of the English. William de Albini, Of Buckenham Castle. London, Darton and Harvey, 1833. [B.M.]

—— Tales Of The Saxons. With a frontispiece and engraved title. London, Harvey and Darton, 1832. [B.M.]

Taylor, Emily Fortescue. Geronimo and Leonora, an Italian tale. London, 1850. [D.M.]

Taylor, Isaac. The Temple of Melekartha. 3 vols., London, Holdsworth and Ball, 1831. [B.M. : T. D. Webster.]

Taylor, Mrs. Isaac. The Family Mansion. A Tale. With a frontispiece. London, Taylor & Hessey, 1819. [Allibone : Ingpen : Lowndes.]

—— Retrospection. A Tale. With a frontispiece. London, Taylor and Hessey, 1821. [B.M. : T. D. Webster.]

Taylor, Jane. Display. A Tale for Young People. London, Taylor and Hessey, 1815. [B.M. : *Camb. Hist. Eng. Lit. :* Lowndes.]

Taylor, Jefferys. Cottage Traditions ; or, the Peasant's Tale of Ancestry. London, Cundall, 1842. [B.M. : *Eng. Cat.*]

—— Harry's Holiday ; Or, The Doings of One Who Had Nothing to Do. With a Preface by Jane Taylor. With a frontispiece. London, Rest Fenner, 1818. [B.M. : Gumuchian : Arthur Rogers.]

—— The Little Historians : a new

chronicle of the affairs of England in Church and State ; by Lewis and Paul, etc. 3 vols., London, Baldwin, 1824. [B.M. : *Camb. Hist. Eng. Lit.*]

Taylor, Jefferys. Ralph Richards. The Miser. With a frontispiece by the Author. London, Baldwin, Cradock and Joy, 1821. [B.M. : Gumuchian.]

—— Tales and Dialogues in Prose and Verse. London, Holdsworth, 1822. [Allibone : Lowndes.]

—— The Young Islanders. A Tale of the Last Century. London, Bogue, 1842. [B.M. : Arthur Rogers.]

Taylor, Joseph. Apparitions ; or the mystery of Ghosts, Hobgoblins, and Haunted Houses, developed. Being a collection of entertaining stories, founded on fact. Second edition, enlarged. London, Lackington & Allen, 1815. [B.M.]

Taylor, Colonel Philip Meadows. Confessions Of A Thug. 3 vols., London, Richard Bentley, 1839. [B.M. : Ingpen : Lib. of Congress.]

—— Tippoo Sultaun ; A Tale of The Mysore War. 3 vols., London, Richard Bentley, 1840. [Allibone : B.M.]

Taylor, William. Tales of Yore (translated [by William Taylor, of Norwich] from different foreign languages). 3 vols., London, 1810. [B.M.]

Teachers Tales. No. 1-4. London, 1833-1840. [B.M.]

Temper ; or the story of Susan and Betsy. London, The Religious Tract Society, [1830 ?]. [B.M.]

Tempest, Basil. The Vallies ; or, Scenes and Thoughts from Secluded Life. 2 vols., London, Longman, Rees, Orme, Brown, & Green, 1827. [B.M. : Publisher's advert.]

Temple, Edmond. The Life of Pill Garlick ; Rather a Whimsical Sort of Fellow. 2 vols., London, Printed for the Author, 1813-1816 [B.M.; F. S. Read.]

Temple, Mrs. Ferdinand Fitzormond ; or, The Fool of Nature ; a Novel. 5 vols., London, Richard Phillips, 1805. [Allibone : Publisher's advert.]

Temple Beau (The) : or, the Town Coquets. A novel. London, 1754. [B.M.]

Temptation ; or, the Mysterious Casket. By the author of " Luke Somerton," etc. Pages 1-40 [no more published]. London, [1845]. [B.M.]

Temugin ; afterwards surnamed Genghiskar. An Historical Romance. By the Author of " Amram," &c. 3 vols., London, Spence, 1846. [*Critic*.]

Tenants of the Wild (The) ; and A Legend of 1711-12. Mauritius, E. Baker, 1842. [B.M.]

Tender Father (The). A Novel. 2 vols., London, Riley, 1775. [Stonehill.]

Tendrils Cherished ; or, Home Sketches. By E. B. London, Houlston, 1844. [B.M. : *Eng. Cat.*]

Terentia, A Novel. By the Author of The Platonic Guardian, etc. 2 vols., London, T. Hookham and J. Carpenter, 1791. [B.M. : *New Ann. Reg. :* T. D. Webster.]

Thackeray, William Makepeace. The Book of Snobs. With illustrations. London, Bradbury and Evans, 1848. [*Eng. Cat. :* Ingpen.]

—— Comic Tales and Sketches, edited and illustrated by Mr. Michael Angelo Titmarsh, Author of " The Paris Sketch Book," etc. With 12 plates by the Author. 2 vols., London, Hugh Cunningham, 1841. [Blackwell : B.M. : F. Harvey.]

—— Doctor Birch and his Young Friends, by Mr. M. A. Titmarsh. With 16 plates by the Author. London, Chapman & Hall, 1849. [Block : B.M. : Maggs.]

—— The History of Pendennis. His Fortunes and Misfortunes, his friends and his greatest enemy. With 48 illustrations by the Author. 2 vols., London, Bradbury and Evans, 1849-1850. [Block : B.M. : Maggs.]

—— The History of Samuel Titmarsh and the Great Hoggarty Diamond. With an engraved title and 9 plates by the Author. London, Bradbury and Evans, 1849. [B.M. : Maggs : Arthur Rogers.]

—— An Interesting Event. By M. A. Titmarsh. London, David Bogue, 1849.

—— The Kickleburys on the Rhine. By Mr. M. A. Titmarsh. With 15 illustrations. London, Smith, Elder, 1850. [Block : Maggs.]

—— Mrs. Perkin's Ball. By M. A. Titmarsh. With illustrations by the Author. London, Chapman and Hall, [1847]. [Block : B.M. : Maggs.]

—— Our Street. By Mr. M. A. Titmarsh. With a vignette and 15 plates. London, Chapman and Hall, 1848. [Block : B.M. : Maggs.]

—— Rebecca and Rowena. A Romance upon Romance. By Mr. M. A. Titmarsh. With a vignette and 8 plates by Richard Doyle. London, Chapman & Hall, 1850. [B.M. : Maggs : Sotheran.]

—— The Second Funeral of Napoleon : In Three Letters to Miss Smith, of London. And the Chronicle of the Drum. By Mr. M. A. Titmarsh. With a frontispiece. London, Hugh Cunningham, 1841. [Block : B.M.]

—— Vanity Fair. A Novel without a Hero. With illustrations by the Author. London, Bradbury and Evans, 1848. [Block ; B.M. : Maggs.]

Tharmott, Maria. Sans Souci Park ; a Novel. 3 vols., 1806. [Allibone.]

Theatre of Love (The) ; or Collection of Novels, none of which were ever printed before. London, 1759. [B.M.]

Thelamont ; or, Perfect Generosity. A novel. By the editor of Clidanor and Cecilia. London, 1744. [B.M.]

Thelwall, John. The Daughter of Adoption : A Tale of Modern Times. By John Beaufort. 4 vols., London, R. Phillips, 1801. [B.M. : Stonehill.]

Themidore and Rozette, Or Authentic Anecdotes of A Parisian Counsellor and Courtisan, Translated from the last Paris edition by a Citizen of the World. London, T. Hookham, 1782. [Mudie's.]

Theodore, or the Enthusiast. 4 vols., London, Longman, 1807. [Baker's Bookshop : B.M.]

Theopha, or Memoirs of a Greek Slave. 2 vols., 1798. [*New Ann. Reg.*]

There is Poison in the Packet. With a woodcut. London, Houlston, N.D. No. 70 of Houlston's Series of Tracts. [Block.]

Theresa ; Or, The Wizard's Fate. A Romance. By A Member of the Inner Temple. 4 vols., London, Printed at the Minerva Press, for A. K. Newman, 1815. [B.M. : *New Monthly Mag.* : Publisher's advert.]

Thicknesse, Mrs. The School of Fashion. 2 vols., London, 1800. [P. C. Cuttelle : T. Thorp.]

Things by Their Right Names : A Novel. By a Person Without a Name. 2 vols., London, Robinson, 1812. [Baker's Bookshop ; B.M. : Ingpen.]

Thistlethwaite, James. The Child of Misfortune, or the History of Mrs. Gilbert. 2 vols., London, 1777. [E. M. Lawson.]

—— The Man of Experience ; or, the Adventures of Honorius. 2 vols., London, J. Boosey, 1778. [B.M.]

Thom, Robert. Wang Keaou-Lwan Piu Nëen Han ; or, The Lasting Resentment of Miss Keaou Lwan Wang : a Chinese Tale, founded on Fact ; Translated from the Original by Sloth. Canton, 1839. [Allibone.]

Thomas, Ann. Adolphus De Biron. A Novel founded on The French Revolution. 2 vols., Plymouth, Printed for the Authoress, [1795]. [Baker's Bookshop : Arthur Rogers.]

Thomas, Elizabeth. Purity of Heart, Or the Ancient Costume, A Tale, Addressed to the Author of Glenarvon. By An Old Wife of Twenty Years. London, W. Simpkin and R. Marshall, 1816. [B.M. : *New Monthly Mag.* : *Quarterly Review.*]

Thomas, Francis Tracy. Monkwood Priory ; a Novel. 2 vols., London, 1799. [Allibone.]

Thomas Shaw, or the Baby's Baptism. By the author of " The Military Blacksmith " etc etc. Edinburgh, William Oliphant, 1825. [Block.]

Thomas Steady and John Wild. In 2 parts. London, The Religious Tract Society, [1830 ?]. [B.M.]

Thompson. Mrs. A. M. Ellen of Dingle. A narrative of facts. London, 1850. [B.M.]

Thompson, B. The Ring, or the Merry Wives of Madrid, translated by B. Thompson. 1799. [*New Ann. Reg.*]

Thompson, Benjamin. The Florentines, or Secret Memoirs of the noble family De C**. London, J. F. Hughes, 1808. [B.M.]

Thompson, Edward. The Rector of Auburn. 2 vols., London, Simpkin and Marshall ; R. B. Seeley and W. Burnside ; and J. Mitchell, 1837. [B.M.]

Thompson, R. The Atalantis Reviv'd : being, A Select Collection of Novels, of Illustrious Persons of both Sexes. 2 vols., London, 1745-1748. [Stonehill.]

Thoms, William John, (Edited by). A Collection of early Prose Romances. Edited by W. J. Thoms. 3 vols., London, Pickering, 1827-1828. [B.M. : Lowndes.]

—— Gammer Gurton's Pleasant Stories of Patient Grissel, Princess Rosetta and Robin Goodfellow : and Ballads, etc. Newly revised and amended by Ambrose Merton, Gent. With 6 plates by John Franklin and John Absolon. London, Chapman and Hall, [1846]. [*Eng. Cat.* : Arthur Rogers.]

Thomson, Mrs. Excessive Sensibility ; Or, The History of Lady St. Laurence. 2 vols., London, Robinson, 1787. [Allibone : W. Brown.]

Thomson, Mrs. Fatal Follies, or, the History of the Countess of Stanmore. 4 vols., London, 1788. [Allibone : Baker's Bookshop : B.M.]

—— Labyrinths of Life. 4 vols., 1791. [Allibone : W. Brown.]

—— The Pride of Ancestry ; or, who is she ? A Novel. 4 vols., London, 1804. [Allibone : B.M.]

—— Laurette ; or, The Caprices of Fortune. 3 vols., London, Lane, Newman ; 1807. [Publisher's advert : Blakey.]

Thomson, Mrs. A. T. [*see* THOMSON, Katharine).

Thomson, Rev. James. The Denial ; or, the Happy Retreat. A novel. 3 vols., London, J. Sewell, 1790. [Allibone : B.M.]

—— The History of Major Piper ; or The Adventures of a Musical Drone. A Novel. 5 vols., 1793. [Allibone : *New Ann. Reg.* : T. D. Webster.]

—— Winifred, a tale of wonder. 2 vols., London, 1803. [B.M.]

Thomson, Katharine. Anne Boleyn. An Historical Romance. By Mrs. A. T. Thomson. 3 vols., London, Henry Colburn, 1842. [B.M. : Ingpen : Lowndes.]

—— The Chevalier. A Romance of The Rebellion of 1745. 3 vols., London, Richard Bentley, 1844. [Allibone : B.M. : Lowndes.]

—— Constance. A Novel. 3 vols., London, Richard Bentley, 1833. [B.M. : Glen : McLeish.]

Thomson, Katherine. The Lady Annabetta. A Novel. By The Authoress of " Constance " & " Rosabel." 3 vols., London, Saunders and Otley, 1837. [B.M. : Lowndes.]

—— The Lady of Milan ; Or, Fidelity unto Death. 3 vols., London, Richard Bentley, 1845. [Allibone : B.M. : Lowndes.]

—— Ragland Castle : A Tale Of the Great Rebellion. 3 vols., London, Richard Bentley, 1843. [Allibone : B.M. : Lowndes.]

—— Rosabel, A Novel. By the Authoress of Constance. 3 vols., London, Longman, Rees, Orme, Brown, Green and Longman, 1835. [B.M. : Lowndes.]

—— Tracey ; Or, The Apparition. A Tale of the last century. 3 vols., London, Richard Bentley, 1847. [Allibone : B.M. : Lowndes.]

—— The White Mask. 3 vols., London, Richard Bentley, 1844. [Allibone : B.M. : Lowndes.]

—— Widows And Widowers. A Romance of Real Life. 3 vols., London, Richard Bentley, 1842. [Allibone : B.M. : Lowndes.]

Thomson, Richard. Tales of an Antiquary : chiefly illustrative of the Manners, Traditions, and Remarkable Localities of Ancient London, 3 vols., London, Henry Colburn, 1828. [B.M. : Pickering : Stonehill.]

Thomson, Dr. William. Mammoth ; a Novel. 2 vols., 1789. [Allibone.]

—— The Man in the Moon ; Or, Travels Into the Lunar Regions, By the Man of the People. 2 vols., London, J. Murray, 1783. [B.M. : Maggs.]

Thornley, Herbert. Life in London. A romance. London, E. Dipple, 1846. [B.M.]

Thornton, Elizabeth. The Marchioness, A Strange but True Tale. 2 vols., London, Simpkin, Marshall, 1842. [Allibone : B.M.]

—— Truth and Falsehood. A Romance. 3 vols., London, Chapman and Hall ; William Tait, Edinburgh, 1847. [Allibone : B.M.]

Thornton, Henry John. Paul Fitz-Henry ; or, A Few Weeks in Paris. A Narrative. London, Mitchell, 1846. [*Critic.*]

Thornton, Rev. John. Jessamine Cottage ; a Domestic Narrative of the Happy Death of a Mother and Four Children. London, Thomas Ward, 1842. [Publisher's advert.]

Thorp, Ann. Aunt Kate's Story, about the Vicar and his Family. Bristol, J. Martin, 1846. [B.M.]

Three Advices (The), An Irish Tale ; To which is added The Silent Man. With a Variety of Anecdotes. With a woodcut. Glasgow, W. & R. Inglis, [c. 1835]. [B.M.]

Three Birth-Days (The) ; Or A Cure for Ill-temper. With 4 plates. London, J. Wallis. 1812. [Gumuchian.]

Three Germans (The), Mysteries exemplified in the Life of Holstein of Lutztein, A German Romance. 3 vols., 1807. [Blackwell.]

Three Ghosts of the Forest (The) ; A Tale of Horror. An Original Romance. London, J. Ker, N.D. [Court Book Shop.]

Three Little Beggars (The). With 8 woodcuts. London, Houlston, [c. 1820]. [Gumuchian.]

Three Nights in a Lifetime, And Inishairlach : Domestic Tales. Edinburgh, Machlachlan & Stewart ; Baldwin and Cradock, London, 1832. [B.M.]

Three Old Maids of the House of Penruddock. By Bridget Bluemantle. 3 vols., Minerva Press, 1806. [Blakey.]

Three Patriarchs (The) : a series of Scripture Stories. By Margaretta. Llandovery, 1850. [B.M.]

Three Poets (The). A Tale Of Domestic Life And Poetry : By Alpha. Wakefield, George Nichols, [1830 ?]. [B.M.]

Three Sisters and Their Three Pennies (The). London, Religious Tract Society, [1830 ?]. [B.M.]

Three True and Remarkable Stories. The awful Death of a murderer. The Power of Conscience. And, the terrors of a Guilty Conscience. Lancaster, C. Clark, N.D. [Court Book Shop.]

Three Weeks at Fladong's. A novel. By a late visitant. 3 vols., London, Iley, 1817. [B.M. : *Eng. Cat.*]

" Thy Kingdom Come." With a woodcut. London, Houlston, N.D. No. 45 of Houlston's Series of Tracts. [Block.]

Ticken, William. Santos de Montenos ; Or, Annals Of a Patriot Family. Founded on recent facts. 3 vols., London, N. L. Pannier, 1811. [B.M. : McLeish : Pickering.]

Tieck, Ludwig. Fermer, the Genius, a novel. Translated into English with philological notes, and an essay on the author by F. Marckwort. Brunswick, 1837. [B.M.]

—— The Old Man of the Mountain ; The Love Charm ; and Pietro of Albano. Tales from the German Tieck. By Julius Charles Hare. London, Edward Moxon, 1831. [Lowndes : Elkin Mathews.]

—— The Pictures ; the Betrothing ; Novels Translated from the German [by Cannop Thirwall]. London, Whittaker, 1825. [G. Worthington.]

—— The Rebellion in the Cevennes, an Historical Novel. By Ludwig Tieck. Translated from the German, by Madame Burette. 2 vols., London, Nutt, 1845. [B.M. : *Critic.*]

—— The Roman Matron ; or, Vittoria Accorombona. A Novel, Translated from the German of Ludwig Tieck. 3 vols., London, T. C. Newby, 1845. [B.M. : *Critic*.]

Tieck, Ludwig. Tales from the " Phantasus," etc. of L. Tieck. London, J. Burns, 1845. [B.M.]

Tighe, Henry. Passion : A Tale. By Henry Tighe, Written during his presence at Eton. Oxford, W. Baxter for J. Vincent, 1822. [Elkin Mathews : *Univ. Mag.*]

Tilley, Cecilia Frances. Chollerton ; a tale of our own times. By a Lady. London, Ollivier, 1846. [B.M. : *Eng. Cat.*]

Timbs, John. Cameleon Sketches. By the Author of " A Picturesque Promenade Round Dorking." London, For the Author, 1828. [B.M. : Ingpen.]

Timbury, Jane. The Male-Coquette ; or, The History of the Hon. Edward Astell, 1770. [B.M.]

—— The Philanthropic Rambler. In 2 parts. London, Printed for the Author, 1790-1791. [B.M.]

Times (The). 2 vols., London, Printed at the Minerva Press, for A. K. Newman, 1811. [T. D. Webster.]

Times Past. A Romantic Melange. 3 vols., London, Lane, Newman, 1805. [Publisher's advert : Blakey.]

Timon, But Not of Athens. 2 vols., London, Saunders and Otley, 1840. [B.M.]

Timothy Grub : His Life and Opinions. Wild Thoughts Tamed : Poems. 2 vols., London, [No publisher's name], 1828. [Block.]

Tinsley, Mrs. Charles. The Priest of the Nile. A Tale of Ancient Egypt. 2 vols., London, Whittaker, 1841. [B.M.]

Tkin Shen. The Rambles of the Emperor Ching Tih. A Chinese Tale. Translated by Tkin-Shen, Student of the Anglo-Chinese College, Malacca. With a Preface by James Legge. London, Longman, Brown, Green, and Longmans, 1843. [B.M. : Publisher's advert.]

Toads and Diamonds. London, [1840 ?]. [B.M.]

Todd, Elizabeth. The History Of Lady Caroline Rivers, In a Series of Letters. 2 vols., London, Printed for the Author, 1788. [B.M.]

Toepffer, Rodolphe. The Parsonage, A Tale. And Eliza and Widmer, A Tale. (Originally published in Geneva). London, Cookes and Ollivier, 1836. [B.M.]

Token of Remembrance (A), from a Mother to her absent children, comprising simple tales, dialogues and easy poetry. London, Simpkin, Marshall, 1822. [B.M. : *Eng. Cat.*]

Tom Gay's Comical Jester, or the Wit's Merry Medley, being a new and most beautiful Collection of Brilliant Jests, Funny Jokes, Merry Stories, Humorous Adventures, Pleasant Tales, Smart Repartees, Witty Quibbles, and Irish Bulls, etc., etc., to which is added, **A** Curious Collection of New Conundrums, Rebusses and Riddles, Sharp Epigrams, Droll Epitaphs, Amorous Poems, Songs, Fables, etc., the whole being entirely freed from that Dulness which infests most other Jest Books, and is calculated to kill Care, banish Sorrow, promote Mirth, crack the Sides, chear the Heart, and prove an Everlasting Cordial for Low Spirits. With a frontispiece. London, J. Cooke, [1760]. [Pickering.]

Tom Racquet, and his three maiden aunts ; with a word or two about " The Whittleburys." With illustrations by Robert Cruikshank. London, 1844. [B.M.]

Tom Thumb. His Travels over England and Wales, Interspersed with Adventures that happened to him in the Course of his Journey. With a folding map. 1746. [Chas. Hutt.]

Tomlins, Elizabeth Sophia. Baroness D'Alunton ; a Novel. [Allibone.]

—— Rosalind de Tracy ; a Novel. 3 vols., 1798. [Allibone : *New Ann. Reg.*]

To-morrow. By M—— B——. Wellington, Houlston, 1817. [B.M.]

Tonna, Charlotte Elizabeth. Consistency. By Charlotte Elizabeth. Author of " Osric," " Rachel," &c. London, J. Hatchard, 1826. [B.M.]

—— Dangers and Duties : or, Disregard for Truth.

—— Derry, A Tale of the Revolution. By Charlotte Elizabeth, Authoress of Osric, The Rockite, The System, &c. &c. London, James Nisbet, 1833. [B.M. : T. D. Webster.]

—— The Deserter, By Charlotte Elizabeth. Dublin, Religious Tract and Book Society for Ireland ; and J. Nisbet, London ; Waugh and Innes, Edinburgh ; G. Gallic, Glasgow, 1836. [B.M.]

—— Perseverance ; Or, Walter and his Little School. By Charlotte Elizabeth, Author of " Osric," " Zadoc," " Izram," &c &c. London, James Nisbet, 1826. [B.M.]

—— The Rockite, An Irish Story. By Charlotte Elizabeth, Author of Osric, The System, Consistency, &c. &c. London, James Nisbet, 1829. [B.M. : T. D. Webster.]

—— The Shepherd Boy and The Deluge. By Charlotte Elizabeth. With 6 vignettes. London, Francis Westley, 1823.

—— The System ; A Tale of the West Indies. By Charlotte Elizabeth. London, Frederick Westley, and A. H. Davis, 1827. [B.M. : T. D. Webster.]

—— Tales and Illustrations, chiefly intended for Young Persons. By Charlotte Elizabeth. 2 vols., Dublin, The Religious Tract and Book Society for Ireland, 1829. [G. Worthington.]

Tooke, William. The Loves of Othniel and Achsah. Translated from the Chaldee. [Actually written by Tooke.] 2 vols., London, W. Tooke for J. Wilkie, 1769. [B.M. : Dobell : Arthur Rogers.]

Torini ; A Tale Of Italy. London, P. Rolandi, 1831. [B.M.]

Torr, John Berry. The Uncle's Legacy. A Novel. 3 vols., London, T. C. Newby, 1849. [Allibone : B.M. : *Eng. Cat.*]

Torrens, Henry Whitelock. The Book Of The Thousand Nights And One Night. From the Arabic of the Aegyptian M.S. as edited by Wm. Hay Macnaghten, Esq. B.C.S. Done into English By Henry Torrens. Calcutta, W. Thacker, 1838. [B.M.]

—— Madame de Malguet. A Tale of 1820. 3 vols., London, Longman, Brown, Green, and Longmans, 1848. [B.M. : Arthur Rogers : G. Worthington.]

Torrens, Robert. Cœlibia choosing a Husband ; a modern novel. 2 vols., London, 1809. [B.M. : *Monthly Mag.*]

—— The Victim of Intolerance : or, the Hermit of Killarney. 3 vols., Dublin, Gale, Curtis and Fenner, 1814. [*I. in F.*]

Torrenwald. A Romance. By Scriblerus Secundus, *Sometime Instructor of Youth, Vulgo Grinder.* 4 vols., London, A. K. Newman, 1824. [B.M.]

Tory Baronet (The) ; Or, Tories, Whigs, and Radicals. By One who knows them. 3 vols., London, Richard Bentley, 1841. [B.M.]

Tourte - Cherbuliez, Marie. Annette Gervais : from the French. London, Hamilton, 1843. [B.M. : *Eng. Cat.*]

Towers, Isabella Jane. The Children's Fireside, being a series of tales for winter evenings. London, 1828. [B.M.]

—— Perils in the Woods, or, the Emigrant Family's Return ; a Tale. With plates. London E. Wilson, 1835 [Block : B.M.]

Towers of Lothian (The) ; Or, The Banks of Carron : A Scottish Legend. By the Author of the " Two Pilgrims." 4 vols., London, Printed by M. Allen, for Holmes and Whitterton, 1809. [B.M.]

Tracey, Rev. Thomas. Undine ; or, The Spirit of the Waters. A Miniature Romance. London, Cunningham, 1840. [Ingpen.]

Tracey the Poet. A Sketch from the Life. 3 vols., London, A. K. Newman, 1823. [B.M. : *New Monthly Mag.*]

Traits and Trials : A Novel. 2 vols., London, James Cawthorn, 1821. [B.M.]

Traits of Scottish Life, And Pictures Of Scenes and Character. 3 vols., London, Whittaker, Treacher, 1830. [B.M. : *New Monthly Mag.*]

Transition. London, Published for the Author by E. Churton, 1837. [B.M.]

Translation of the Fragment of an Arabic Manuscript. While opening the earth for the erection of a gate to a famous city, the workmen came upon an urn of burnt clay, containing a large roll of very fine parchment covered with writing in Arabic characters. Time has destroyed a great part of the writing— that on the inner portion of the roll only being legible. We have had the fragment transcribed, and now offer a translation of it to the Public. As it appeared in the Observer of Friday, Sept. 23, 1842. Edinburgh, W. and H. Robinson, 1842. [B.M.]

Trapp, Joseph, (?). The Sprite of the Nunnery ; a tale, from the Spanish. By the author of the Life of Linnaeus. 2 vols., London, 1796. [B.M.]

Traveller (The) ; or, Adventures on the Continent. 3 vols., 1826. [*Quarterly Review.*]

Travels and Adventures of James Massey. London, J. Watts, 1743. [Publisher's advert.]

Travels and Adventures of Mdlle. De Richelieu (The), Who made the Tour of Europe, dressed in Men's Cloaths, attended her Maid Lucy as her Valet de Chambre. 3 vols., London 1744. [T. D. Webster.]

Travels and Surprising Adventures of Mademoiselle de Leurich (The), who travelled over Europe, dressed in Mans Apparel. 3 vols., London, 1851. [McLeish.]

Travels before the Flood, from the Arabic. 2 vols., 1796. [*New Ann. Reg.*]

Travels into France and Italy. In a Series of Letters to a Lady. 2 vols., London, Becket and De Hondt, 1771. [Stonehill.]

Travels of Mons. le Post-Chaise. Written by Himself, London, J. Swan, 1753. [Halliday.]

Travels of Polycletes, Translated from the French. London, Souter, 1826. [*Eng. Cat. : Quarterly Review.*]

Travel of Zoroaster (The), King of the Bactrians. Composed chiefly for the Instruction of a Young Prince. 3 vols., London, J. Fuller, 1753. [G. Worthington.]

Tre Giuli of Casti (The) : translated from the Italian. London, 1826. [*New Monthly Mag.*]

Trefusis, Elizabeth. Poems and Tales. 2 vols., London, 1808. [Allibone : B.M.]

Trelawney, Anne. Characters at Brighton. A Novel. 4 vols., London, 1808. [B.M.]

Trelawny, Captain Edward John. Adventures of a Younger Son. 3 vols., London, Henry Colburn & Richard Bentley, 1831. [*Ashley Lib. :* B.M. : King.]

Trevor : or the new Saint Francis. A tale for the times. London, Longman, 1847. [B.M.]

Treyssac de Vergy, Pierre Henri. Henrietta, Countess of Benvor. A sentimental novel, In a series of letters to Lady Susannah Fitzroy. 2 vols., London, J. Roson, 1770. [Publisher's advert.]

Treyssac de Vergy, Pierre Henri. The Lovers : or the Memoirs of Lady Sarah B— and the Countess P—. Published [or rather written] by M. Treyssac de Vergy. London, 1769-1772. [Volume II. reads " The Lovers : or The Memoirs of Lady Mary Sc . . . . . ," etc.] [B.M.]

—— The Palinode : Or, The Triumphs of Virtue over Love : A Sentimental Novel. In which are painted to the Life the Characters and Manners of some of the most celebrated beauties in England. 2 vols., London, G. Woodfall, [17--]. [Danielson.]

Trial of Betty the Cook Maid (The), before the worshipful Justice Feeler, for laying a bed in the morning. London, 1795. [B.M.]

Trial of an Ox (The), for Killing a Man, With The Examination of the Witnesses, Before Judge Lion, At Quadruped Court, near Beast Park. With woodcuts. Banbury, J. G. Rusher, [1835 ?]. [B.M.]

Trial (The), or The History of Charles Horton, Esq. 1791. [*Eng. Lit. in Germany.*]

Trimmer, Jane. Miscellaneous Stories for Children. Collected by J. Trimmer, etc. London, E. Lacey, [1820 ?]. [B.M.]

Trimmer, Sarah. Fabulous Histories. The History of the Robins. For the Instruction of Children on their Treatment of Animals. With a frontispiece. London, Griffith and Farran, [1786]. [Block : *Camb. Hist. Eng. Lit.*]

—— Instructive Tales. London, Christian Knowledge Society, 1855. [B.M. (New edn.)]

—— The Servant's Friend, an exemplary tale. London, 1787. [B.M. (2nd edn.)]

—— The Silver Thimble. By the author of " Instructive Tales," etc. London, E. Newbery, 1801. [B.M.]

—— The Two Farmers, An Exemplary Tale, etc. London, 1787. [B.M. : *Camb. Hist. Eng. Lit.*]

Trinket (The) ; A Novel. By a Lady. London, 1774. [Blackwell : B.M.]

Trip to Weymouth (A). A novel. 2 vols., London, W. Lane, 1790. [B.M. : Blakey.]

Triumph of Good Nature (The). Exhibited in the history of Master Harry Fairborn and Master Trueworth. With woodcuts. London, Newbery, [1810 ?]. [B.M. : *Guardian of Education.*]

Triumphs of Fortitude (The) : A Novel, In a Series of Letters. 2 vols., London, Richardson, 1789. [Stonehill.]

Trollope, Anthony. The Kellys And The O'Kellys ; Or, Landlords and Tenants. A Tale of Irish Life. 3 vols., London, Henry Colburn, 1848. [B.M. : *I. in F.* : Sadleir.]

Trollope, Anthony. La Vendee : An Historical Romance. 3 vols., London, Henry Colburn, 1850. [Sadleir.]

—— The Macdermots Of Ballycloran. 3 vols., London, Thomas Cautley Newby, 1847. [B.M. : Sadleir.]

Trollope, Frances. The Abbess, A Romance. By the Author of the " Domestic Manners of the Americans," &c. 3 vols., London, Whittaker, Treacher, 1833. [Allibone : B.M. : Holland.]

—— The Attractive Man. A Novel. 3 vols., London, Henry Colburn, 1846. [Allibone : B.M. : Lowndes.]

—— The Barnabys in America ; Or, Adventures Of the Widow Wedded. With 9 etchings by John Leech. 3 vols., London, Henry Colburn, 1843. [Allibone : B.M. : Lowndes.]

—— The Blue Belles of England. 3 vols., London, Saunders & Otley, 1842. [B.M. : Ingpen.]

—— Charles Chesterfield ; Or, The Adventures Of a Youth of Genius. With plates by Phiz [Hablot K. Browne]. 3 vols., London, Henry Colburn, 1841. [B.M. : Ingpen : Parker's & Son.]

—— Father Eustace : A Tale of the Jesuits. 3 vols., London, Henry Colburn, 1847. [Backus : B.M. : Ingpen.]

—— Hargrave ; Or, The adventures Of A Man of Fashion. 3 vols., London, Henry Colburn, 1843. [Allibone : B.M.]

—— Jessie Phillips, A Tale of the Present Day. With a portrait by Brown and 11 etchings by John Leech. 3 vols., London, Henry Colburn, 1843. [B.M. : Lowndes : Pickering.]

—— The Laurringtons ; Or Superior People. 3 vols., London, Longman, Brown, Green, and Longmans, 1844. [Allibone : B.M. : Publisher's advert.]

—— The Life and Adventures Of Jonathan Jefferson Whitlaw ; Or, Scenes on the Mississippi. With 15 engravings by A. Hervieu. 3 vols., London, Richard Bentley, 1836. [B.M. : Ingpen : Lowndes.]

—— Life and Adventures of Michael Armstrong, The Factory Boy. With 24 plates by Onwhyn, R. W. Buss and Hervieu. London, Henry Colburn, 1840. [Block : B.M. : Ingpen.]

—— The Lottery of Marriage. A Novel. 3 vols., London, Henry Colburn, 1849. [Allibone : Baker's Bookshop : Ingpen.]

—— The Old World and the New. A Novel. 3 vols., London, Henry Colburn, 1849. [Baker's Bookshop : B.M. : Ingpen.]

—— One Fault. A Novel. 3 vols., London, Richard Bentley, 1840. [Block : B.M.]

—— Petticoat Government. A novel. 3 vols., London, Henry Colburn, 1850. [B.M.]

Trollope, Frances. The Regugee in America. A Novel. 3 vols., London, Whittaker, Treacher, 1832. [B.M. : Ingpen : McLeish.]

—— The Robertses On Their Travels. 3 vols., London, Henry Colburn, 1846. [Allibone : B.M. : G. Worthington.]

—— A Romance of Vienna. 3 vols., London, Richard Bentley, 1838. [Allibone : B.M. : McLeish.]

—— The Three Cousins. A Novel. 3 vols., London, Henry Colburn, 1847. [B.M. : Lowndes : Publisher's advert.]

—— Town and Country : A Novel. 3 vols., London, Henry Colburn, 1848. [B.M. : Publisher's advert.]

—— Tremondyn Cliff. 3 vols., London, Richard Bentley, 1835. [Birrell & Garnett : B.M. : Ingpen.]

—— The Vicar of Wrexhill. With etchings by A. Hervieu. 3 vols., London, Richard Bentley, 1837. [Block : B.M. : Ingpen.]

—— The Ward of Thorpe-Combe. 3 vols., London, Richard Bentley, 1842. [Allibone : B.M. : McLeish.]

—— The Widow Barnaby. 3 vols., London, Richard Bentley, 1839. [B.M. : Clarke-Hall : Ingpen.]

—— The Widow Married ; A Sequel to " The Widow Barnaby." With 21 etchings by R. W. Buss. 3 vols., London, Henry Colburn, 1840. [Block : B.M. : Ingpen.]

—— The Young Countess ; Or, Love and Jealousy. 3 vols., London, Henry Colburn. 1848. [*Eng. Cat. :* Arthur Rogers.]

—— Young Love ; a Novel. 3 vols., London, Henry Colburn, 1844. [*Critic : Eng. Cat. :* Publisher's advert.]

Trotter, John Bernard. Stories for Calumniators. 2 vols., Dublin, Fitzpatrick, 1809. [B.M. : *I. in F.*]

—— Travels in Phrenologasto by Gio. Battista Balscopo. London, Saunders and Otley. 1829. [Arthur Rogers : Norman.]

Trotter, Robert. Lowran Castle, Or The Wild Boar of Curridoo. With Other Tales, Illustrative of the Superstitions, Manners, and Customs of Galloway. Dumfries, 1822. [Ingpen.]

Troubles Arising from being Too Late (The) ; The History of Two Sisters. With 19 woodcuts. London, Thomas Dean, [1850]. [B.M. : Gumuchian.]

Troubles of a Good Husband (The). Northampton, 1818. [Norman.]

Troubles of Life (The) ; being a familiar description of the troubles of the poor laborer, the little shopkeeper, the great tradesman, the sickly man, the disappointed lover, the unhappy husband, the widower, and lastly, the child of sorrow. To which is added the story of the Guinea and the Shilling, etc. London, [1800 ?]. [B.M.]

Truant Scholar (The) ; Kate Rivers ; and The Blind Girl and her Teacher. By the author of " The Orphan's Choice," etc. London, Harvey, 1836. [B.M.]

True Charity ; Or, A Tale of the Year 1800. With a frontispiece. London, Poole, 1827. [B.M.]

True Delicacy ; or, the history of Lady Frances Tylney and Henry Cecil. (A sentimental story.) 2 vols., London, W. Adlard, 1769. [B.M.]

True Heroism and Other Stories. With a frontispiece. Edinburgh, William and Robert Chambers, 1849. [Block.]

True History of Henrietta de Bellgrave (The), a Woman born only for Calamities. [London, 1750 ?]. [B.M.]

True History of a Little Old Woman who found a Silver Penny. With 12 plates. London, Tabart, 1805. [Maggs.]

True History of Zoa (The), The Beautiful Indian, Daughter of Henrietta de Belgrave ; and of Rodomond, an East India Merchant, whom Zoa releases from Confinement, and intended Death, and with him Escapes to England. To which is added, the affecting history of Lisette and Login, a Russian Tale. London, Dean and Munday, [1820 ?]. [B.M. : Court Bk. Shop.]

True Stories of Cottagers. London, 1849-1850. [B.M.]

True Stories : Or, Interesting Anecdotes of Children ; Designed through the Medium of Example to inculcate Principles of Virtue and Piety. With a frontispiece after Corbould. York, 1820. [Sotheran.]

True Warnings. With a woodcut. London, Houlston, N.D. No. 58 of Houlston's Series of Tracts. [Block.]

Trueba y Cozio, Don Telesforo de. The Castilian. 3 vols., London, Henry Colburn, 1829. [B.M. : McLeish : Elkin Mathews.]

—— The Exquisities. 3 vols., London, Henry Colburn. [Allibone : *Eng. Cat.*]

—— Gomez Arias ; or, The Moors of the Alpujarras. A Spanish Historical Romance. 3 vols., London, Hurst, Chance. 1828. [Allibone : B.M. : *Quarterly Review.*]

—— The Incognito ; Or, Sins and Peccadillos. 3 vols., London, Whittaker, Treacher, 1831. [Allibone : B.M.]

—— Paris and London. A Novel. By the Author of " The Castilian," " The Exquisites," &c. 3 vols., London, Henry Colburn and Richard Bentley, 1831. [B.M. : Pickering : T. D. Webster.]

—— The Romance of History. Spain. By Don T. de Trueba. 3 vols., London, Edward Bull, 1830. [B.M.]

—— Salvador. By the author of " The Castilian," etc. London, 1834. [B.M.]

Trusler, John. Life ; Or, The Adventures Of William Ramble, Esq. With three frontispieces, Designed by Ibbetson, Highly engraved [missing from the B.M. copy], And Two new and Beautiful Songs, With the music By Pleyel and Sterkel. By the Author of Modern Times ; Or, the Adventures of Gabriel Outcast. 3 vols., London, Dr. Trusler, 1793. [Vols. II and III : Life ; Or, The Adventures of William Ramble, Esq. By the Author of Modern Times ; Or the Adventures of Gabriel Outcast, London, Dr. Trusler, 1793.] [B.M. : *New Ann. Reg.*]

Trusler, John. Modern Times, or, the Adventures Of Gabriel Outcast. Supposed to have been written by himself in imitation of Gil Blas. 3 vols., London, Logographic Press, 1785. [Blackwell : B.M. : McLeish.]

Truth and Falsehood, exemplified in the true history of Jane and Lucy. London, Religious Tract Society, [1830 ?]. [B.M.]

Truth and Fashion ; a Sketch. By F. R——n. 2 vols., London, Whittaker, 1825. [*Edin. Mag.*]

Truth ; by the Author of Nothing. 3 vols., London, Hunt, 1826. [*New Monthly Mag.*]

Truth in the Garb of Fiction, or Sketches from Real Life. 4 vols., [Cawthorn's Catalogue, 1810.]

Tschink, Cajetan. The Victim of Magical Delusion ; or, The Mystery of the Revolution of P——L : a Magico-Political Tale. Founded on Historical Facts, and Translated from the German of Cajetan Tschink. By [Rev.] P[eter]. Will. 3 vols., London, G. G. and J. Robinson, 1795. [B.M. : *New Ann. Reg.* : Stonehill.]

Tucker, Colonel John Montmorency. Tales Of the Camp and Cabinet. 2 vols., London, T. C. Newby, 1844. [Allibone : Baker's Bookshop : B.M.]

Tucker, T. R. Vaults of Lepanto, a Romance. 3 vols., London Printed at the Minerva Press, for A. K. Newman, 1814. [Publisher's advert.]

Tuckett, T. R. Urbino ; or, The Vaults of Lepanto. A Romance. 3 vols., London, Minerva Press, 1814. [Blakey.]

Tuckey, Mary B. Creation ; or a Morning Walk with Anna. By the Author of " The Great Exemplar." Dublin, 1845. [B.M.]

Tudor Sisters (The) ; A Story of National Sacrilege. 3 vols., London, Thomas Cautley Newby, 1846. [B.M.]

Tuite, Lady Eliza Dorothea. Edwin and Mary. London, Simpkin Marshall, 1838. [B.M. : *Eng. Cat.*]

Tupper, Martin Farquhar. The Crock of Gold : A Rural Novel. London, Richard Bentley, 1844. [Block : B.M.]
—— Heart : A Social Novel, Etc. London, Richard Bentley, 1844. [Baker's Bookshop : B.M.]
—— The Twins : A Domestic Novel. &c. London, Richard Bentley, 1844. [Baker's Bookshop : B.M.]

Turf (The). A Satirical Novel. 2 vols., London, Henry Colburn and Richard Bentley, 1831. [B.M. : Ingpen : Pickering.]

Turner, Margaret. Infatuation ; or Sketches from Nature. 2 vols., London, 1810. [Allibone : B.M. : *Monthly Mag.*]

Turnerelli, Edward P. Tales of the Rhenish Chivalry. Founded on the Records of History and Tradition. With 2 lithographs. London, William Marsh, 1835. [B.M.]

Turn-Out (The) ; Or, Patience the best Policy. By the Author of " Principle and Practice." With a frontispiece. Wellington, Houlston, 1829. [B.M.]

'Twas Right to Marry Him : or, the History of Miss Petworth. 2 vols., London, 1774. [B.M.]

'Twas Wrong to Marry Him or The History of Lady Dursley. 1773. [*Eng. Lit. in Germany.*]

Twelve Nights Entertainments ; or tales of various lands. London, Burns, 1845. [B.M. : *Critic.*]

Twenty Four Tales of the English Church. London, Houlston, 1832. [B.M. : *Eng. Cat.*]

Twin Brothers (The) ; or Virtue and Vice contrasted. London, T. Hurst, 1802. [B.M.]

Twin Sisters (The) ; Or, The Effects of Education, a Novel, In a Series of Letters, By a Lady. 3 vols., London, T. Hookham, 1788. [Allibone : Ingpen : T. Thorp.]

Twin Sisters (The) ; or, Two Girls of Nineteen. Being the Interesting Adventures of Sophia and Charlotte Melford. An affecting narrative. Written by Charlotte, one of the sisters. With a frontispiece. London, Dean and Munday, N.D. [Court Bk. Shop.]

Two Bogies (The), the Real Bogie and the Unreal Bogie, a tale of Conscience. With a frontispiece. London Darton, 1830. [Adrian Hammond.]

Two Brothers (The) ; a narrative exhibiting the effects of education. London, Groombridge, 1837. [B.M. : *Eng. Cat.*]

Two Calmuck Youths. London, Religious Tract Society, [1830 ?]. [B.M.]

Two Clerks of Oxenford (The), and Where can it be ? 1819. [*New Monthly Mag.*]

Two Cottagers (The), as related by an old Gentleman. London, [1848]. [B.M.]

Two Cousins (The). London, Religious Tract Society, [1843 ?]. [B.M.]

Two Cousins (The) ; or Spare the rod and spoil the child. London, [1797 ?]. Cheap Repository. [B.M.]

Two Delightful Novels : or, the Unlucky Fair One. Being the Amours of Milistrate and Prazimene Translated from the French by a Person of Quality. London, [1750 ?]. [B.M.]

Two Doves (The), and other tales. London, Burns, 1845. [B.M. : *Eng. Cat.*]

Two Girls (The). [London,] Religious Tract Society, [1830 ?]. [B.M.]

Two Girls of Eighteen (The). 2 vols., 1810. [*Monthly Mag.*]

Two Heroes : a Story of the Battle of the Nile. London, 1849. [B.M.]

Two Orphans, or John and Mary ; a moral tale, by A. G. Cirencester, [1838]. [B.M.]

Two Pilgrims (The). A Romance. 2 vols., London, Printed at the Minerva Press, for Lane, Newman, 1805. [Court Book Shop.]

Two Soldiers (The). With a woodcut. Bath, J. Marshall, [1795]. Cheap Repository. [Block : B.M.]

Two Sunday School Boys (The) ; or, The History of Thomas and Joseph. By a Sunday School Teacher. London, Printed for the Author, [1820 ?]. [B.M.]

Two Wealthy Farmers (The), With the sad Adventures of Miss Bragwell. Part V. With a woodcut. London, J. Marshall ; and R. White, [1796]. Cheap Repository. [B.M. : Court Book Shop.]

Tyburn Tree ; Or, The Mysteries of the Past. London, Vickers, 1847. [H. W. Fennell.]

Tyranny of Love (The) ; or, Memoirs of the Marchioness D'Aremberg. 2 vols., London, C. Elliot & T. Kay, [1800 ?]. [B.M.]

Tytler, Ann Fraser. Leila in England ; A continuation of Leila, or the Island. London, J. Hatchard, 1842. [B.M. : Arthur Rogers.]

—— Leila ; Or, The Island. With a frontispiece. London, J. Hatchard, 1839. [B.M. : Ingpen.]

—— Mary and Florence ; Or, Grave and Gay. By A.F.T. London, J. Hatchard, 1835. [B.M. : T. D. Webster.]

—— Mary and Florence At Sixteen. A Continuation of Grave and Gay. With a frontispiece. London, J. Hatchard. 1838. [B.M. : T. D. Webster.]

Tytler, Margaret Fraser. Tales of Good and Great Kings. Edinburgh, 1845. [Allibone : B.M.]

—— Tales of the Great and Brave. London, Harvey, 1838. [Allibone : B.M.]

—— Tales of the Great and Brave. Second Series London, Hatchard, 1843. [Allibone : B.M. : *Eng. Cat.*]

—— Tales of Many Lands. By the Author of " Tales of the Great and Brave." London, Harvey and Darton, 1839. [Allibone : B.M.]

—— The Wonder Seeker ; or, the History of Charles Douglas. With a frontispiece. London, Grant, 1846. [B.M. : *Eng. Cat. :* Arthur Rogers.]

Ulpius, V. Ferrandino, a German Ro-

mance. Translated by Henry G. Bohn. 2 vols., London, Printed at the Minerva Press, for A. K. Newman, 1814. [Elkin Mathews : Publisher's advert.]

Ulpius, V. The History of Rinaldo Rinaldini, Captain of Banditti. Translated from the German of Vulpius. By I. Hinckley. 3 vols., London, Strahan, 1800. [Stonehill.]

Ulric and Gustavus, Or, The Unhappy Swedes ; A Finland Tale. With a frontispiece. London, Tegg, [1803]. [Ingpen.]

Ulric and Ilvina : the Scandinavian Tale. 2 vols., London, Allen and West, 1797. [B.M.]

Una and Arthur, An Allegorical History : The Incidents from Spencer. 2 vols., Cambridge, Printed for the Author by Fletcher and Co., 1779. [Arthur Rogers.]

Unbaptised Sceptic (The). A true story. By a Clergyman. London, 1843. [B.M.]

Uncle Barnaby ; or Recollections of his character and opinions. London, Religious Tract Society, [1843]. [B.M.]

Uncle Buncle's Story Book. London, [1841]. [B.M.]

Uncle Oliver and his Nephew. London, 1840. [B.M.]

Uncle Peter's Fairy Tales. The First Story containing the History and Adventures of Little Mary, Queen of the Great Island of Brakarakakaka. By Uncle Peter, F.R.L.M.M.T.T.F.A.S.Q. Q.X.Y.Z., etc. London, Longman, Brown, Green, & Longmans, 1844. [B.M. : Publisher's advert.]

Uncle Tweazy And his Quizzical Neighbours : A Comi-Satiric Novel. By The Author of the " Observant Pedestrian," &c. &c. &c. 3 vols., London, W. Simpkin and R. Marshall, 1816. [B.M. : *New Monthly Mag.*]

Unexpected Wedding (The), In a Series of Letters. London, T. Becket and P. A. De Hondt, 1768. [Ingpen : Myers : Pickering.]

Unfortunate and at Last Happy Lady (The), or, the Reward of Virtue and Innocence, being the history of Clarissa Moore. London, 1780. [B.M.]

Unfortunate Beauty ; Or Memoirs of Miss Anna Maria Soames and several others. A Narrative founded on known Facts, interspersed with several uncommon characters, and exemplified in many instances that befel them during the course of many years' courtship and unsuccessful love. London, J. Scott, 1757. [Ingpen.]

Unfortunate Caledonian in England (The) ; or, genuine memoirs of an impressed young gentleman in the year 1779. Written by himself. London, 1781. [B.M.]

Unfortunate Officer (The) ; or the history of M. Bertin Marquis de Fratteaux, etc. London, [1753 ?]. [B.M.]

Unfortunate Russian (The). London, Ellerton and Henderson for J. Hatchard 1822. [B.M.]

Unfortunate Sensibility ; or, The Life of Mrs L******. Written by Herself. In a Series of Sentimental Letters. Dedicated to Mr. Yorick in the Elysian Fields. 2 vols., London, Richardson, 1784. [W. Brown : Arthur Rogers : Stonehill.]

Unfortunate Sisters (The), or the Distressed Ladies ; being a history founded upon real truths. London, 1756. [B.M.]

Unfortunate Union ; Or The Test of Virtue. A Story founded on Facts and Calculated to Promote the Cause of Virtue in Younger Minds. Written by a Lady. 2 vols., London, Richardson and Urquhart, 1778. [*Eng. Lit. in Germany* : Ingpen.]

Unfortunate Young Nobleman (The) ; a tale of sympathy, founded on fact. London, R. Harrild, [1820 ?]. [B.M.]

Unhappy Bride (The) ; or the Grave of the Profligate. A domestic tragedy. London, [1847]. [B.M.]

Unhappy Mistake (The), Or the Fatal Effects of Jealousy : An entertaining and diverting history, founded on facts of a gentleman in France ; to which is added the Lover's Generosity. London, J. Miller, 1773. [Dobell.]

United Irishman (The) : or, The Fatal Effects of Credulity. 2 vols., Dublin, 1819. [*I. in F.*]

Unknown Warrior : Or, The Secret Band. A Romance of the Eleventh Century. With woodcuts. London, G. Purkess, [c. 1840]. [B. Ono : Stonehill.]

Unnatural Mother (The), and The Rural Wedding. London, Otley, [1820]. [Arthur Rogers.]

Unnatural Mother and Ungrateful Wife (The), a narrative : founded on true and very interesting facts. Contain'd in three letters, from a Lady in the Country to her Friend, a Lady of Distinction in Town. London, J. Jefferies ; Mrs. Dodd ; and Mrs. Windbush, [1750 ?]. [Block : B.M.]

Upham, Edward. Karmath. An Arabian Tale. By the Author of " Rameses," An Egyptian Tale, etc. etc. London, Charles Frederick Cock, 1827. [B.M.]

—— Rameses ; An Egyptian Tale : With Historical Notes, of the Era of the Pharaohs. 3 vols., London, G. B. Whittaker, 1824. [B.M. : Ingpen : McLeish.]

Urquhart, William. Sir John May Mead, the London Merchant. A tale. London, J. D. Darling, 1848. [Allibone : B.M. : *Eng. Cat.*]

Usbeck and Fatima ; An Eastern Tale, etc. With a frontispiece. Sold by all the Booksellers in Town and Country, 1814. [B.M. : Elkin Mathews : T. Thorp.]

Usborne, T. H. Tales of the Braganza ;

With Scenes and Sketches. London, Cradock, 1842. [Allibone : B.M.]

Use and Abuse, a tale. By the author of " Wayfaring sketches among the Greeks and Turks." London, Rivington, 1848. [B.M. : *Eng. Cat.*]

Use of Sight (The) : Or, I Wish I Were Julia. Intended for the Amusement and Instruction of Children. By the Author of the " Moss-House." &c. With plates. London, William Darton, [1824]. [Block.]

Utterson, Mrs. Tales of the Dead ; Principally Translated from the French. London, 1813. [B.M. : McLeish : *Quarterly Review.*]

Vagras ; a Tale of Spain. 3 vols., 1822. [*Europes Mag.*]

Vain Cottager (The), or History of Lucy Franklin. 1814. [*New Monthly Mag.*]

Valentine. A Novel. 2 vols., London, W. Lane, 1790. [B.M.]

Valombroso, or the Venetian Nun. 2 vols., London, [Minerva Press, 1804.] [Publisher's advert : Blakey.]

Van Dyk, Henry Stoe. The Gondola. London, Lupton Relfe, 1827. [*Blackwood's Edin. Mag.* : B.M. : Ingpen.]

Van Lennep, J. The Adopted Son ; A historical novel. Translated from the Dutch by E. W. Hoskin. 1847. [B.M.]

Varieties in Woman. A Novel. 3 vols., London, Baldwin, Cradock, and Joy, 1819. [B.M.]

Varieties of Life ; Or, Conduct and Consequences. A Novel. By the Author Of " Sketches of Character." 3 vols., London, Longman, Hurst, Rees, Orme, and Brown, 1815. [B.M. : Ingpen : *New Monthly Mag.*]

Variety ; or, Stories for Children from the age of seven years to twelve. London, John Harris, 1825. [B.M. (2nd edn.)]

Various Recollections of Domestic Scenes, and Little Love Affairs which occured in my family. Compiled and written for my dearly beloved husband at Martinique. By Madam Marie de T****. Maints Souvenirs, Domestique et d'Amourettes qui se Passerent dans ma Famille. Rédigés et Ecrits à mon cher Mari à Martinique. Par Madame Marie de T****. 3 vols., 1748. [*Cat. Lib. Prohib.*]

" Vater Unser " : a tale for children, Translated freely from the German, by a Lady. London, Whittaker, 1844. [B.M.]

Vaughan, Thomas. Fashionable Follies. A Novel. Containing the History of a Parisian Family. With a frontispiece. 2 vols., London, J. Dodsley, 1781. [B.M. : Pickering : Arthur Rogers.]

Vaux, Frances Boyer. The Dew Drop or the Summer Morning's Walk, 1818 [*Camb. Hist. Eng. Lit.*]

—— The Disappointment. [*Camb. Hist. Eng. Lit.*]

Vaux, Frances Boyer. Domestic Pleasures ; or, The Happy Fireside : Illustrated by Interesting Conversations. London, Harvey, 1816. [B.M. : *Camb. Hist. Eng. Lit.* : *Eng. Cat.*]

—— Henry : a story for little boys, etc. London, 1825. [B.M.]

Vaux, James Hardy. Memoirs of the first thirty-two Years of the Life of James Hardy Vaux, a Swindler and Pickpocket ; now transported for the second Time and for Life, to New South Wales. Written by himself. [Edited by Barron Field.] 2 vols., London, W. Clowes, 1819. [Allibone : B.M. : Lowndes.]

Veiled Picture (The) : Or, the Mysteries of Gorgono, The Appennine Castle Of Signor Androssi. A Romance of the Sixteenth Century. London, Thomas Tegg ; T. Hurst ; T. Brown, Edinburgh ; and B. Dugdale, Dublin, [1802]. [B.M. : Stonehill.]

Velde, Carl Franz Vander. Arwed Gyllensterna, A Tale of the Early Part of the Eighteenth Century ; From the German of C. F. Vander Velde. 2 vols., London, E. Lloyd, 1827. [B.M. : *Literary Gazette.*]

Ventum, Harriet. Amiable Tutoress ; of, the History of Mary and Jane Hornsby. A Tale for Young Persons. London, Hurst, 1801. [Allibone : *Guardian of Education.*]

—— Charles Leeson, Or the Soldier. With a frontispiece. 1810. [Arthur Rogers.]

—— The Holiday Reward Or Tales to instruct and amuse good children, during Christmas and Midsummer vacations. With a frontispiece. London, J. Harris, 1814. [Gumuchian.]

—— Justina ; or, The History of a Young Lady. 4 vols., London, Badcock, 1801. [Stonehill.]

—— Selima ; or the Village Tale. A novel, in a series of letters by the authoress of Fanny. 6 vols., London, T. Hookham, [1798]. [B.M. : G. David.]

—— Tales for Domestic Instruction. Containing the Histories of Ben Hallyard ; Hannah Jenkins, etc. With a frontispiece. London, J. Harris, 1806. [B.M. : Gumuchian : Arthur Rogers.]

Vere, Horace. Guiscard ; or, The Mysterious Accusation. A Romance. 2 vols., London, A. K. Newman, 1809. [Allibone : *Monthly Mag.* : Blakey.]

Vere, Marquis de. (*see* DE VERE, Marquis.)

Vergy, Treyssac de (*see* TREYSSAC DE VERGY.)

Veronica ; or, the Mysterious Stranger. A novel. By Lister. 2 vols., London, 1798. [B.M.]

Verri, Count Alessandro. The Roman Nights At The Tomb of The Scipios. Translated from the Italian of Verri. 2 vols., Edinburgh, Constable, 1825. [Baker's Bookshop : B.M. : Stonehill.]

Very Little Tales for Very Little Children. First [and second] series. In 2 parts. Edinburgh, Fraser, 1835. [B.M. (4th edn.)]

Vesuvia ; or, Anglesea Manor. By the Author of Valombrosa. 3 vols., London, Minerva Press, 1807. [Blakey.]

Vicar of Bray (The). A Tale. 2 vols., London, Baldwin, 1771. [W. Brown : Ingpen : Henry Start.]

Vicissitudes in Genteel Life. 4 vols., 1794. [*New Ann. Reg.*]

Victim (The), in Five Letters to Adolphus. With a frontispiece. London, 1800. [McLeish.]

Victim of Deception (The). 2 vols., [Blakey.]

Victim of Passion (The), or Memoirs of the Comte de Saint Julien. London. Lane, 1795. 3 vols., 1794. [Blakey. *New Ann. Reg.*]

Victor, Benjamin. The Widow of the Wood. London, C. Corbett, 1755. [Blackwell : Ingpen : Arthur Rogers.]

Victor, M. Therese ; or, The Orphan of Geneva. An interesting Romance. Translated from the French of the celebrated M. Victor by Sarah S. Wilkinson. On this story are founded No Less than Five Melo-Dramas. London, Dean and Munday, [c. 1810]. [Stonehill.]

Victoria, or The Male Coquette and the Dupe. 3 vols., London, J. Robins, 1828. [B.M.]

Victorious Champion (The). Or The Most Wonderful Adventures of Sebastian. With a frontispiece. Halesworth, W. Harper, N.D. [Court Book Shop.]

Vidal, Mrs. Francis. Cabramatta, and Woodleigh Farm. London, Rivington, 1850. [B.M. : *Eng. Cat.*]

—— Esther Merle, and other Tales. London, J. Hughes, 1847. [Allibone ; B.M. : *Eng. Cat.*]

—— Tales for the Bush. Originally published in Australia. London, Rivington, 1846. [B.M. : *Eng. Cat.*]

—— Winterton ; a Tale. London, Rivington, 1846. [Allibone : B.M. : *Eng. Cat.*]

Vidocq, Eugène François. Life in Paris ; Or the Adventures of a Marquis : A New Historical Romance. With woodcuts. London, E. Appleyard, 1848. [Block : G. Worthington.]

Vidyapati. The Pooroos-Purikhya, or Collection of Moral Tales translated from the original Sungskit into English, by Muha Rajah Kalee Krishun Bahadoor. Serampore, 1830. [B.M.]

Vieusseux, André. Anselmo : A Tale of Italy. 2 vols., London, Charles Knight, 1825. [B.M. : McLeish : Maggs.]

View of the Lancashire Dialect (A) ; By way of Dialogue ; Between Tummus o' William's, o' Margit o' Roaf's, And Meary o' Dick's, o' Tummy o' Peggy's. Containing The Adventures & Misfortunes Of A Lancashire Clown. Leeds,

J. Binns ; and N. Binns, Preston, 1787. [B.M.]

View of the Village of Hampton (A). With the original Lancashire Collier Girl. London, 1797. [B.M.]

Vigny, Alfred Victor, Comte de. Cinq Mars ; Or, A Conspiracy under Louis XIII. An Historical Romance, By Count Alfred de Vigny. Translated by William Hazlitt. With a frontispiece. London, David Bogue, 1847. [B.M. : *Eng. Cat. :* Arthur Rogers.]

Vigny, Alfred Victor, Comte de. and **Blaze**, E. Lights and Shades of Military Life. From the French By M. Shoberl. Edited by Sir C. Napier. 2 vols., London, Henry Colburn, 1840. [B.M. : Lib. of Congress.]

Village Association ; or, the Politics of Edley. Containing the Soldier's Tale ; The Headborough's Mistake ; the Sailor's Tale ; the Curate's Quotations ; and Old Hubert's Advice. London, 1793. [B.M.]

Village Coquette (The) ; A Novel. By the Author of " Such is the World." 3 vols., London, G. and W. B. Whittaker, 1822. [B.M.]

Village Curate and his daughter Julia (The), describing her journey to London. A tale. London, 1797. [B.M.]

Village Incidents : Or, Religious Influence in Domestic Scenes. By a Lady. London, J. Hatchard, 1828. [B.M.]

Village Maid (The) ; or, The Interesting Adventures of Montsirant. With a frontispiece. London, Roe and Lemoine, 1804. [Stonehill.]

Village Memoirs, Containing Susan Turner. Friendly Visits. The Good Wife. The Village Fair. London, C. and J. Rivington, 1825. [B.M.]

Village School (The) ; or, Memoirs of Mrs. Propriety and her little scholars. By O. M. Wellington, Houlston, 1817. [B.M.]

Village School-Girls (The). A tale. By Eilza T*****, author of the " Orphan's Choice," etc. London, Darton & Harvey, 1835. [B.M.]

Village Tale (The) ; or Memoirs of Little Anna, the Woodcutter's Daughter. With 4 plates. [181–]. [Salkeld.]

Village Tales, moral and religious, for children. By the author of " Jane Brooks," etc. London, Wertheim, 1850. [B.M.]

Village Walks. By the Author of " Emma de Lissau." [Amelia Bristow.] London, Thomas Ward, 1837. [Publisher's advert.]

Villeroi Or Religion Founded on Principle, not on Excitement. By the Author of " The Valley of the Clusone," Etc. Etc. Dublin, William Curry, Jun. : Simpkin and Marshall, London ; Fraser, Edinburgh, 1835. [B.M.]

Villette, De la (*see* DE LA VILLETTE).

Villiers Cornelius. Vargas : A Tale of Spain. 3 vols., London, Baldwin, Cradock, & Joy, 1822. [B.M. : Ingpen : Elkin Mathews.]

Villiers, Henry. The Stranger's Grave. London, Longman, Hurst, Rees, Orme, Brown, & Green, 1823. [B.M. : Publisher's advert.]

Villiers : A Tale Of The Last Century. 3 vols., London, Whittaker, 1835. [B.M.]

Vincent, Sir Francis. Arundel, A Tale of the French Revolution. 3 vols., London, Saunders and Otley, 1840. [Allibone : B.M.]

Vincent, Henry. The Irish Assassin ; or, The Misfortunes of the Family of O'Donnell. An Original Tale. With a frontispiece and vignette by T. Rowlandson. London, Tegg, [c. 1800]. [Stonehill : Murray Hill.]

Virgin Bride (The). A Romance. With woodcuts. London, Edward Lloyd, [c. 1840]. [Stonehill.]

Virginia, or the Peace of Amiens. 4 vols., 1811. [*Quarterly Review.*]

Virtue and Vice : or, the history of Charles Careful and Harry Headless. With woodcuts. London, Harris, 1815. [B.M. : F. Harvey.]

Virtue in a Cottage ; or, a Mirror for Children in humble Life. [*Guardian of Education.*]

Virtue Rewarded : Exemplified in The Following Narrative, Founded on Fact. Published as a Warning to Youth of both Sexes, To guard them against the Specious appearance of friendship, and the Dangerous Delusions of Vice. London, G. and W. B. Whittaker, 1823. [B.M.]

Virtue Triumphant. 2 vols., London. Cooper, 1753.

Virtue Triumphant ; or the history of Queen Esther. London, [1797 ?]. [B.M.]

Virtue's Friend ; Being Tales of Instruction. Containing Affecting, Religious, and Entertaining Stories. Calculated, To excite juvenile minds To the Love and Practice of Virtue. Printed by A. Swindells, N.D. [Block.]

Vishnusarman The Heetopades of Veeshnoo-Sarma in a Series of connected Fables, interspersed with moral, prudential, and political Maxims ; translated from an ancient Manuscript in the Sanskreet Language, with explanatory Notes, by Charles Wilkins. Bath, 1787. [Allibone : B.M. : Lowndes.]

—— Hitopadesa, or Salutary Counsels of Vishnusarman In a Series of connected Fables, translated literally by Francis Johnson, London, Allen, 1848. [Bailey Bros. : B.M. : *Eng. Cat.*]

—— The Hitopadesha : a collection of fables and tales in Sanscrit by V. with the Bengali and the English translations revised. Edited by Lakshami Narayan Nyalankar. [Here follow native characters.] Calcutta, 1830. [B.M.]

Visit (The). With an engraved title-page. London, Hamilton, 1832. [B.M. : *Eng. Cat.*]

Visit to the Castle of Truth (A). Written by a Lady. Bath, 1828. [B.M.]

Visit to Clarina (The) ; or, the effects of revenge. An Irish story. London, 1842. [B.M.]

Visit to Grove Cottage for the Entertainment and Instruction of Children. With an engraved title and illustrations. 1823. [Arthur Rogers.]

Visit to the Manor House ; Or, the Twelve Days at Christmas : With Hints For Improvement. By a Lady. Brentford, P. Norbury, 1819. [Baker's Bookshop : B.M.]

Visiting Day : A Novel. 2 vols., London, T. Lowndes, 1768. [B.M. : Ingpen.]

Visits of Tommy Lovebook (The) to his Neighbouring Little Misses and Masters. With woodcuts. London, J. Harris, 1804. [Marks.]

Vladimir, or the Career of Falsehood ; a Tale for Youth. London, J. Harris, 1821. [Publisher's advert.]

Voltaire, François Marie Arouet de. Babouc ; or, The World as it Goes. By Monsieur de Voltaire. To which are added, Letters Concerning his Disgrace at the Prussian Court : With his Letter to his Niece on that Occasion. Also, The Force of Friendship, or, Innocence Distress'd. A Novel. London, W. Owen, 1754. [B.M. : W. T. Spencer : Tregaskis.]

—— Candid, Or, All for the Best. London, 1759. [B.M. : W. Brown : *Guide to Best Fiction.*]

—— The Hermit ; an Oriental Tale. Newly translated from the French of M. de Voltaire. London, 1779. [B.M.]

—— Micromegas : A Comic Romance Being A Severe Satire upon the Philosophy, Ignorance, and Self-Conceit of Mankind. Together with a Detail of the Crusades : And a new Plan for the History of the Human Mind Translated from the French of M. de Voltaire. London, D. Wilson and T. Durham, 1753. [Birrell & Garnett : Ingpen : Arthur Rogers.]

—— Pupil of Nature. London, 1771. [W. Brown.]

—— Romances, Tales, and Smaller Pieces. 2 vols., London, 1794. [B.M. : Lib. of Congress.]

—— The White Bull ; an Oriental History, from an ancient Syriac Manuscript, communicated by Mr. Voltaire. Cum notis editoris et variorum : sc. clarissimm : Philoterasti Pantophagi, etc. The whole faithfully done into English [by J. Bentham]. 2 vols., 1774. [B.M.]

—— The Works of M. de Voltaire. Translated from the French. With notes, historical, and Critical. By T. Smollett, T. Francklin and others.

Volume the eighteenth [contains the translation of " Candide "]. London, J. Newbery, 1762. [Baker's Bookshop.]

Voltaire, François Marie Arouet de. Young James, or the Sage and the Atheist an English Story, from the French of M. de Voltaire. London, Murray, 1776. [Baker's Bookshop (2nd edn.)]

—— Zadig : Or the Book of Fate, An Oriental History. With a frontispiece. London, John Brindley, 1749. [Tregaskis.]

Voltmann, Caroline von. The White Lady, a romance from the German of C. Von Woltmann. Translated by J. D. Haas. London, Burns, 1845. [B.M. : *Critic.*]

—— The White Lady (translated from the German of C. von Woltmann), and Undine (translated from the German of La Motte Fouqué). Tales from the German. [Translated by the Hon. C. L. Lyttelton.] In 2 parts. London, Pickering, 1844. [B.M. : *Eng. Cat.*]

Voluptuarian Museum (The) : Or History Of Sir Henry Loveall. In a tour through England, Ireland, Scotland & Wales. With 6 illustrations. Paris [London], Printed for the Proprietors, [1825 ?]. [Ashbee Collection.]

Von Grosse (*see* GROSSE).

Von Haller (*see* HALLER).

Von Knorring, Baroness Sofia Margareta, The Peasant and his Landlord. Translated by Mary Howitt. 2 vols., London, Richard Bentley, 1848. [B.M. : Sweden Year Book.]

Von Kotzebue (*see* KOTZEBUE).

Von Kuiegge (*see* KUIEGGE).

Von Miltie (*see* MILTIE).

Von Paalzow, Henriette. Godway Castle. By Madame Palzow : translated by Frances Kinderley Barnard. London, 1846. [B.M.]

—— St. Roche. A Romance from the German. Edited by James Morier. 3 vols., London, Richard Bentley, 1847. [Hodgson : Ingpen : T. D. Webster.]

Von Voltmann (*see* VOLTMANN).

Voyage through Hell (A), by the invincible Man of War, Capt. Single-eye, Commander. London 1770. [B.M.]

Voyage to Immanuel's Land, in the Ship Hopewell ; With an Account of Many Remarkable Deliverances from Danger. A Description of the Countries Visited, Their Laws, Manners, and Habits ; and a Statement and view of the advantages of the Celestial Country. London, James Nisbet, 1826. [B.M.]

Voyage to Lethe (A), By Capt. Samuel Cock, sometime Commander of the good ship the Charming Sally ; dedicated to the Rt. Worshipful Adam Cock, Esq., of Black-Mary's-Hole, Coney-Skin Merchant. London, J. Conybeare, 1741. [Pickering.]

Voyage to the Moon (A), Strongly Recommended To All Lovers Of Real Freedom. London, Printed for the Author, 1793. [B.M.]

Voyage to the World in the Centre of the Earth. Giving an Account of the Customs . . . of the Inhabitants in which is introduced The History of an Inhabitant of the Air written by himself. With some Account of the Planetary Worlds. 1755. [Arthur Rogers.]

Voyages and Adventures of Edward Teach (The) commonly called Black Beard, the notorious pirate. To which is added, The Two Princes. Newcastle, [1800 ?]. [B.M.]

Waddington, Julia Rattray. Janet Or Glances at Human Nature. The Second of a Series of Tales on the Passions : By The Author of " Misrepresentation." 3 vols., London, Saunders and Otley, 1839. [Allibone : B.M.]

—— Misrepresentation Or Scenes in Real Life. One of a Series of Tales on the Passions. 3 vols., London, Saunders and Otley, 1838. [Allibone : B.M. : Kyrle Fletcher.]

—— The Monk And The Married Man. 3 vols., London, Saunders and Otley, 1840. [B.M. : Ingpen.]

—— Newstoke Priors. 3 vols., London, Richard Bentley, 1842. [Allibone : B.M.]

Wailly, Armand François Léon de. Stella and Vanessa : a romance from the French, by Lady [Lucie] Duff Gordon. 2 vols., London, Richard Bentley, 1850. [B.M.]

Wainewright, Harriet (*see* STEWART, Harriet).

Wakefield, Priscilla. Juvenile Anecdotes, founded on facts. 2 vols., London, 1795-1798. [B.M.]

—— Sketches of human manners, delineated in stories. London, Harvey, 1814. [B.M. (4th edn.) : *Eng. Cat.*]

Waldeck Abbey. A novel. By the author of The Weird Sisters, &c. 2 vols., London, William Lane, 1795. [*New Ann. Reg.* : Blakey.]

Waldegrave, A Novel. 3 vols., London, Henry Colburn, 1829. [B.M.]

Waldgrove ; or the Fortunes of Bertram ; a Tale of 1746. 2 vols., London, Whittaker, 1845. [*Critic.*]

Walker, ——. Common Events. A Continuation of Rich and Poor. Edinburgh, William Blackwood ; and T. Cadell, London, 1825. [B.M.]

—— Rich and Poor. Edinburgh, William Blackwood ; and T. Cadell, London, 1823. [B.M. : Ingpen : *Quarterly Review.*]

Walker, Mrs. Cousin George, And Other Tales. 3 vols., London, T. C. Newby, 1845. [B.M. : G. Sexton.]

Walker, George. Cinthella, or a Woman of Ten Thousand. 4 vols., 1797. [*New Ann. Reg.*]

—— Don Raphael, a Romance. 3 vols., London, Walker, 1803. [Maggs : Stonehill.]

—— The Haunted Castle, A Norman Romance. 2 vols., London, Printed for William Lane at the Minerva Press, 1794. [Arthur Rogers : Blakey.]

—— The House of Tynian. A novel, 4 vols., London, W. Lane, 1795. [*New Ann. Reg.* : Blakey.]

—— The Romance of the Cavern ; or, The history of Fitz Henry and James. 2 vols., London, William Lane, 1792. [Blakey.]

—— Theodore Cyphon ; Or, The Benevolent Jew. A Novel. 3 vols., London, 1796. [*Eng. Lit. in Germany : New Ann. Reg.* : T. D. Webster.]

—— Surprising Travels and Adventures of Sylvester Tramper, through the Interior of South Africa. With a frontispiece. London, [c. 1816]. [Francis Edwards.]

—— The Three Spaniards, A Romance. 3 vols., London, G. Walker, 1800. [Ingpen.]

—— The Vagabond. 2 vols., 1798. [*New Ann. Reg.*]

Walker, Mary. Memoirs of the Marchioness de Louvois. In Letters. By a Lady. 3 vols., London, Robson, 1777. [*Eng. Lit. in Germany :* Pickering.]

Walks and Talks ; or Aunt Ida's Tales for young persons. By a Lady. London, John Murray, 1850. [B.M.]

Wall, Anton. Amatonda. A Tale, From the German of Anton Wall. [By Henry Crabb Robinson.] London, Longman, Hurst, Rees, Orme, and Brown, 1811. [B.M. : Ingpen.]

Wallace, Ellen. The Clandestine Marriage, And The Sisters. 3 vols., London, Richard Bentley, 1840. [Allibone : B.M.]

—— Constance D'Oyley. A Tale. By the Author of " The Clandestine Marriage." 3 vols., London, Richard Bentley. 1844. [B.M.]

—— Margaret Capel. A Novel. By the Author of " The Clandestine Marriage." 3 vols., London, Richard Bentley, 1846. [B.M. : *Critic :* Publisher's advert.]

—— Mr. Warrenne, The Medical Practitioner. A Novel. By the Author of " Constance D'Oyley," " Margaret Capel," &c. 3 vols., London, Richard Bentley, 1848. [B.M. : Martin. A. McGoff.]

Wallace, Captain R. G. Forty Years in the World ; or, Sketches and Tales of a Soldier's Life. 3 vols., London, Whittaker, 1825. [*Edin. Mag. : Eng. Cat. :* Arthur Rogers.]

Walpole, Horace. The Castle of Otranto. A Story Translated by William Marshall, Gent. From the Original Italian of Onuphrio Muralto, Canon of the Church of St. Nicholas at Otranto. London, Tho. Lownds, 1765. [B.M. : Maggs : Quaritch.]

Walpole, Horace. Hieroglyphic Tales. Strawberry Hill Press, 1785. [B.M. : *Library :* Lowndes.]

Walter Deverell. A Domestic Tale. 3 vols., London, Saunders and Otley, 1838. [B.M.]

Walter O'Neil : or, The Pleasure of Doing Good. London, Darton & Harvey, 1838. [*I. in F.*]

Waltzburg : A Tale Of the Sixteenth Century. 3 vols., London, Whittaker, Treacher, 1833. [B.M.]

Wanderer of the Alps (The): or, Alphonso. A romance. 2 vols., London, William Lane, 1796. [By Mr. Stinger.] [*Minerva Press Catalogue.*] [Blakey.]

Wanderer, Or the Surprizing Escape. A Narrative founded on true facts. 1747. [*Camb. Hist. Eng. Lit.*]

Wandering Spirit (The) ; or, Memoirs of the House of Morno. With a frontispiece. London, Hurst, 1802. [Stonehill.]

Waning Church (The). London, Nisbet, 1832. [B.M.]

Wanley Penson. 3 vols., 1791. [W. Brown.]

Wanted ! A Wife !! London, 1849. [B.M.]

Wanton Tom ; Or, the Merry History of Tom Stitch, the Taylor. In 2 Parts. London, Printed and Sold in Aldermary Church Yard, [1750]. [B.M. : Maggs.]

Warbroke Legend (The) ; a Tale of the Dead. 2 vols., London, 1820. [*New Monthly Mag.*]

Warburton, Eliot Bartholomew George, Reginald Hastings ; a Tale of the Troubles in 164—. 3 vols., London, Hurst and Blackett, 1850. [Allibone : *Eng. Cat. :* T. D. Webster.]

Warburton, Sydney. Twelve Years Ago. A Tale, by the Author of Letters to My Unknown Friends. London, Longman, Brown, Green, & Longmans, 1847. [B.M. : Publisher's advert. : G. Worthington.]

Ward, Catharine George. Alice Gray. A Domestic Novel. By Catherine Mason (Late C. Ward). 3 vols., London, A.K. Newman, 1833. [B.M.]

—— The Bachelor's Heiress, or a Tale without Mystery, a Novel. 3 vols., London, 1814. [*Quarterly Review.*]

—— The Cottage on the Cliff. A Seaside Story. With plates. London, Printed by C. Baynes for George Virtue, 1823. [Block : B.M. : A. H. Dawson.]

—— The Daughter of St. Omar. A novel. 2 vols., London, Printed at the Minerva Press, for A. K. Newman and Co., 1810. [Blakey.]

—— The Eve of St. Agnes. A Novel. By Mrs. Catherine Mason, (Late C. Ward). 4 vols., London, A. K. Newman, 1831. [B.M. : Norman.]

Ward, Catherine George. Family Portraits, Or, Descendants of Trelawney. With plates. London, George Virtue, 1824. [H. W. Fennell : Ingpen : Arthur Rogers.]

—— The Fisher's Daughter ; Or, The Wanderings of Wolf, And the Fortunes of Alfred. Being the sequel to that so greatly admired and popular Work, entitled The Cottage on the Cliff. With plates. London, G. Virtue, 1824. [Ingpen : Marks : Pickering.]

—— The Knight of the White Banner ; or, The Secrets of the Castle. With illustrations. London, Virtue, 1827. [W. T. Spencer : Stonehill.]

—— My Native Land : or, The Test of Heroism. A novel. London, Printed at the Minerva Press, for A. K. Newman, 1813. [Allibone : Publisher's advert : Blakey.]

—— The Mysteries of St. Clair, Or Mariette Mouline. With an engraved title & a frontispiece. London, J. Jaques ; and Wright, 1824. [Marks : Mudie's : Stonehill.]

—— The Mysterious Marriage ; Or, The Will of my Father. With plates. London, J. Tallis, 1820. [McLeish : Elkin Mathews.]

—— *Founded on Facts.* The Orphan Boy, Or Test of Innocence. With engravings. London, G. Virtue ; W. & S. Couchman ; and J. S. Wellington, 1821, [B.M.]

—— Robertina ; Or, The Sacred Deposit. A Novel. 2 vols., London, Printed at the Minerva Press for A. K. Newman, 1818. [B.M. : *Monthly Mag.*]

—— The Rose of Claremont, Or Daughter, Wife and Mother. With illustrations. 2 vols., London, J. Tallis, [1820]. [Baker's Bookshop : B.M. : Stonehill].

—— The Son and the Nephew, or more Secrets than One. 3 vols., London, 1815. [Allibone : *New Monthly Mag.*]

Ward, Harriet. Helen Charteris. A Novel. 3 vols., London, Richard Bentley, 1848. [Allibone : B.M.]

Ward, Robert Plumer. De Clifford ; Or, The Constant Man. By the Author of " Tremaine," " De Vere," &c. 4 vols., London, Henry Colburn, 1841. [B.M. : Ingpen : John Smith.]

—— De Vere ; or, The Man of Independence. By The Author of Tremaine. 4 vols., London, Henry Colburn, 1827. [B.M. : Ingpen : Arthur Rogers.]

—— Illustrations Of Human Life. By the Author of " Tremaine " and " De Vere." 3 vols., London, Henry Colburn, 1837. [B.M. : James Glaisher : Arthur Rogers.]

—— Pictures Of The World At Home and Abroad ; By The Author of " Tremaine," " De Vere," " Human Life," &c. &c. 3 vols., London, Henry Colburn, 1839. [Baker's Bookshop : B.M. : Ingpen.]

Ward, Robert Plumer. The Three Vows. 3 vols., 1845. [James Glaisher.]

—— Tremaine, Or, the Man of Refinement. With a frontispiece. 3 vols., London, Henry Colburn, 1825. [B.M. : Ingpen : McLeish.]

Waring, George. The Light-House, and other Tales. London, R. Clarke, 1848. [Allibone : *Eng. Cat.*]

Warner, Miss, (of Bath). Herbert Lodge. A New Forest Story. 3 vols., Bath, Cruttwell, 1808. [Baker's Bookshop : Ingpen : T. D. Webster.]

Warner, Richard. Bath Characters : or Sketches from Life. By Peter Paul Pallet. London, G. Wilkie & J. Robinson, 1807. [Elkin Mathews.]

—— Netley Abbey, a Gothic Story. Southampton, T. Skelton, 1795. [*Eng. Lit. in Germany :* Blakey. : T. D. Webster.]

Warning (The) ; a tale, etc. London, 1850. [B.M.]

Warren, Caroline Matilda. Conrade ; or, the Gamesters. A novel, founded on facts, 2 vols., London, Lane, Newman, 1806. [Allibone : *Miss Berry's Journal* : B.M.]

Warren, Samuel. Now and Then. Through a Glass, Darkly. Edinburgh, Wm. Blackwood, 1848. [Brough : Cleverdon : Ingpen.]

—— Passages from the Diary of a Late Physician. With Notes and illustrations by the Editor. 3 vols., Edinburgh, Blackwood, 1832-1838. [B.M. : *Camb. Hist. Eng. Lit. :* W. T. Spencer.]

—— Ten Thousand a Year. 3 vols., Edinburgh and London, William Blackwood, 1841. [B.M. : Ingpen : Arthur Rogers.]

Warren Family (The) : or, Scenes at home. By S.W. London, James & Bain, 1813. [B.M.]

Warton, Joseph. Ranelagh House : A Satire in Prose, in the manner of Monsieur Le Sage. London, 1747. [B.M. : Dulau.]

Water Fairy's Gifts (The), And Other tales. A Story Book for Holiday Hours. With 4 plates. London, Joseph Cundall, 1846. [B.M. : Court Book Shop.]

Watkins, Lucy. Cavigni of Tuscany. A Terrific Romance. With a vignette and a frontispiece. London, Dean and Munday, N.D. [Court Book Shop.]

—— Helen Beresford, or the Child of Misfortune, an Original & Pathetic Narrative. With a vignette and a frontispiece. London, Dean & Munday, N.D. [Court Book Shop.]

—— The Miser, or interesting Memoirs of Harry Pemberton, Esq. A true story. London, Dean & Munday, [1810 ?]. [B.M.]

Watson, William Davy. Trevethlan : A Cornish Story. 3 vols., London, Smith, Elder, 1848. [Allibone : B.M.]

Watts, Miss. Wonderful Travels of Prince Fan-Feredin. 1794. [*New Ann. Reg.*]

Watts, Alaric Alexander. Scenes of Life And Shades of Character. Edited by Alaric A. Watts. 2 vols., London, Henry Colburn and Richard Bentley, 1831. [Allibone : B.M.]

Waverley ; a tale. Founded on the Rebellion in the year 1745. London, J. & C. Evans, 1822. [B.M.]

Way to be Happy (The) ; or, the History of the Family at Smiledale to which is added The Story of Little George. With 16 woodcuts. Glasgow, J. Lumsden, 1819. [Pickering.]

Way to Lose Him (The), or The History of Miss Wyndham. 1772. [*Eng. Lit. in Germany.*]

Way to Make Home Comfortable (The) : the history of Mary Barker. London, Darton and Clark, [1850 ?]. [B.M.]

Way to Please Him (The), or The History of Lady Sedley, By the Author of The Way to Lose Him. 1772. [*Eng. Lit. in Germany.*]

Way to Plenty (The) ; Or, the Second Part of Tom White. With a woodcut. London, J. Marshall. [Block.]

Ways of Pleasantness, and Paths of Peace : a series of instructive tales, in prose and verse, etc. London, Hodgson, [1830 ?]. [B.M.]

Webb, Mrs. J. B. Julamerk ; a Tale of the Nestorians. 3 vols., London, Simpkin, Marshall, 1848. [Allibone : *Eng. Cat.*]

—— Julio Arnouf ; a Tale of the Vaudois. London, Darton, 1842. [Allibone : *Eng. Cat.*]

—— Travels and Adventures of Charles Durand. London, Darton, 1847. [Allibone : *Eng. Cat.*]

Weber, Henry. Tales of the East : Comprising The most popular romances Of Oriental origin ; And the best imitations by European Authors : With new translations, and additional tales, never before published. To which is prefixed An Introductory Dissertation, Containing an account of each work, and of its Author, Or Translator, By Henry Weber. 3 vols., Edinburgh, Printed by James Ballantyne, for John Ballantyne, Sylvester Doig and Andrew Stirling ; Longman, Hurst, Rees, Orme, and Brown, London, 1812. [B.M. : Stephen Hunt : Arthur Rogers.]

Weber, Veit. The Black Valley, a Tale, from the German of Weber. And Albert de Nordenshill, translated from the German. 2 vols., 1796. [*New Ann. Reg.*]

—— The Sorcerer, a Tale, from the German of Veit Weber. [Translated by Robert Huish.] London, J. Johnson, 1795. [B.M. : Pickering : Arthur Rogers.]

—— Woman's Revenge, Or The Tribunal

249

of Blood. London, Clements, Romancist and Novelists' Library, 1841. [Ingpen : Arthur Rogers.]

Webster, Grace. The Disputed Inheritance. A Novel. 3 vols., London, Richard Bentley, 1845. [Allibone : B.M. : Arthur Rogers.]

—— Ingliston. Edinburgh, William Tait ; Simpkin, Marshall, London ; and John Cumming, Dublin, 1840. [Allibone : B.M.]

—— Raymond Revilloyd. 2 vols., London, Richard Bentley, 1850. [Allibone : *Eng. Cat.*]

Wedded Life in the Upper Ranks. The Wife and Friends, And The Married Man. 2 vols., London, Henry Colburn and Richard Bentley, 1831. [Backus : B.M. : Publisher's advert.]

Wedding Ring (The) ; Or, History of Miss Sidney in a Series of Letters. 3 vols., 1779. [*Eng. Lit. in Germany :* T. Thorp.]

Weeks, Harriett Waller. Memoirs of the Villars Family ; Or, The Philanthropist : A Novel. 3 vols., London, Printed for the Author, and published by C. Chapple, 1815. [B.M. : *New Monthly Mag.*]

Weight of a Feather (The) ; and, The Value of Five Minutes ! A moral tale. (Horrible Revenge. A tale.) London, E. Thomas, 1820. [B.M.]

Weill, Alexandre. Village Tales from Alsatia. Translated from the German by Sir Alexander [Cornewall] Duff-Gordon, Bart. London, Bogue, 1848. [B.M. : *Eng. Cat.*]

Weimar, Miss. Alzylia, A Novel. 4 vols., London, Printed for the Author, by T. Collins, and Published by C. Chapple, 1808. [B.M.]

Weird Sisters (The). A novel. 3 vols., London, W. Lane, 1794. [*New Ann. Reg.* : Publisher's advert : Blakey.]

Wells, Charles Jeremiah. Stories after Nature. London, T. and J. Allman ; and C. and J. Ollier, 1822. [B.M. : *European Mag.*]

Wells, Helena. Constantia Neville ; Or, The West Indian. A Novel. 3 vols., London, Printed by C. Whittingham for T. Cadell and W. Davies ; and W. Creech, Edinburgh, 1800. [B.M. : *Eng. Lit. in Germany :* McLeish.]

—— The Step-Mother. A Domestic Tale from Real Life, By a Lady. 2 vols., London, T. N. Longman, 1798. [Allibone : *New Ann. Reg.* : Arthur Rogers.]

Wells, Sarah Wilmot. Tales ; Mournful, Mirthful and Marvellous. 3 vols., London, Longman, Rees, Orme, Brown, & Green ; and J. Denne, Margate, 1827. [Allibone : B.M.]

Wentworth, Zara. De Santillana ; Or, The Force of Bigotry. A Romantic Tale. 4 vols., London, A. K. Newman, 1825. [B.M.]

Wentworth, Zara. The Hermit's Cave ; Or, The Fugitive's Retreat. A Romance. 4 vols., London, A. K. Newman, 1821. [B.M.]

—— The Recluse of Albyn Hall. A Novel. 3 vols., London, Printed at the Minerva Press, for A. K. Newman, 1819. [Allibone : B.M. : *New Monthly Mag.*]

—— The Uncles ; Or, Selfishness and Liberality. A Novel. 3 vols., London, A. K. Newman, 1822. [Allibone : B.M. : *New Monthly Mag.*]

West, Edward. Chronicles of the Careworn ; or, Walks and Wanderings. London, Cunningham and Mortimer, [1843]. [B.M. : Publisher's advert.]

West, George. The Chieftain of the Vale. 1820. [*New Monthly Mag.*]

West, Jane. The Advantages of Education, Or the History of Maria Williams. A tale for misses and their mammas, by Prudentia Homespun. 2 vols., London, William Lane, 1793. [B.M. : Blakey.]

—— Alicia de Lacy, An Historical Romance, by the Author of " The Loyalist." 4 vols., London, Longman, 1814. [Blackwell : Ingpen : *Quarterly Review.*]

—— The Church of Saint Siffrid. By the Author of Ned Evans. 4 vols., 1797. [*New Ann. Reg.*]

—— A Gossip's Story, And A Legendary Tale. By the Author of Advantages of Education. 2 vols., London, T. N. Longman, and O. Rees, 1796. [Blackwell : Ingpen : Stonehill.]

—— The History of Ned Evans : A Tale of the Times. 4 vols., Dublin, 1796. [Stephen Hunt : *I. in F.* : *New Ann. Reg.*]

—— The Infidel Father ; by the author of " A tale of the times." 3 vols., London, Strahan, 1802. [Blackwell : B.M. : Ingpen.]

—— The Loyalists : An Historical Novel. By the Author of " Letters to a Young Man," " A Tale of the Times," &c. 3 vols., London, Longman, Hurst, Rees, Orme, & Brown, 1812. [B.M. : Ingpen : McLeish.]

—— The Refusal. By the Author of the " Tale of the Times," " Infidel Father," &c. 3 vols., London, Longman, Hurst, Rees, and Orme, 1810. [B.M. : Pickering. : Varda.]

—— Ringrove ; or, Old Fashioned Notions. By the Author of " Letters to a Young Man," " A Tale of the Times," &c. &c. 2 vols., London, Longman, Rees, Orme, Brown, & Green, 1827. [Allibone : B.M. : Publisher's advert.]

—— A Tale of the Times. By the Author of " A Gossip's Story." Dedicated by Permission to Mrs. Carter. 3 vols., London, T. N. Longman, and O. Rees, 1799. [B.M. : Ingpen : McLeish.]

West Indian (The) : Or, The Happy Effects of Diligence and Self-Control ; exemplified in The History of Philip

Montague. With a frontispiece. Wellington, F. Houlston, 1827. [B.M.]

Westbrook Village, a Novel. 2 vols., 1799. [*New Ann. Reg.*]

Westerton, a tale for the young. By a Lady. London, Simpkin, Marshall, 1850. [B.M.]

Westmacott, Charles Molloy. The English Spy: an Original Work, Characteristic, Satirical, and Humorous, comprising Scenes and Sketches in every Rank of Society, being Portraits of the Illustrious, Eminent, Eccentric, and Notorious, drawn from Life by Bernard Blackmantle. With plates by Robert Cruikshank, Thomas Rowlandson, T. Wageman and G. M. Brightly, and woodcuts. 2 vols., London, [Volume I] Sherwood Jones, 1825. [Volume II] Sherwood Gilbert and Piper, 1826. [Block : Maggs : Myers.]

—— Fitzalleyne of Berkeley. A Romance of the Present Time. By Bernard Blackmantle, Author of the English Spy. With a woodcut on the titles. 2 vols., London, Sherwood, 1825. [Block : B.M. : T. D. Webster.]

Weston, Anna Maria. Pleasure and Pain, or the Fate of Ellen ; a novel. 3 vols., London, T. Tegg, 1814. [B.M. : *New Monthly Mag. :* Salkeld.]

Weston, Louisa. The Cambrian Excursion. With a frontispiece. London, Baldwin, 1826. [*Eng. Cat. :* Arthur Rogers.]

Weston, Stephen. Fan-hy-Cheu : a tale in Chinese and English : with notes and a short Grammar of the Chinese language, by S. Weston. London, 1814. [B.M. : Lowndes.]

What Has Been. A novel. 2 vols., [W. Lane, 1801.] [Blakey.]

What May I Learn? or, Sketches of School-Girls. By Cousin Kate. Edinburgh, Hamilton, 1849. [B.M.]

What Will Your Neighbour Grinaway Say? With a woodcut. London, Houlston, N.D. No. 59 of Houlston's Series of Tracts. [Block.]

What You Please ; or, Memoirs of modern characters ; a novel. By the author of " Tourville." 4 vols., Bristol, J. Lansdown, 1804. [B.M.]

Whately, Elizabeth. Reverses ; Or, Memoirs Of the Fairfax Family. By the Author of " Conversations on the Life of Christ," And the " First Preaching of the Gospel by the Apostles." London, B. Fellowes, 1833. [B.M.]

Which is Best? being stories about the five divisions of the world, and stories of the five senses. London, Dean, [1849]. [B.M. : *Eng. Cat.*]

Which is the Heroine? 2 vols., London, Robins, 1826. [Blackwell : *Eng. Cat.*]

Whim (The), or the Mutual Impressions. 2 vols., London, T. Hookham and J. Carpenter, [Publisher's advert, 1791.]

White, Charles. The Adventures of a King's Page. By the Author of " Almack's Revisited." 3 vols., London, Henry Colburn, 1829. [B.M. : McLeish : Elkin Mathews.]

—— Almack's Revisited. 3 vols., London, Saunders & Otley, 1828. [B.M. : Ingpen : Salkeld.]

—— The Cashmere Shawl. An Eastern Fiction. 3 vols., London, Henry Colburn, 1840. [Allibone : B.M.]

—— Herbert Milton ; a Novel. 3 vols., London, Saunders, 1827. [Allibone : *Eng. Cat.*]

—— The Married Unmarried. By the Author of " Almack's Revisited." 3 vols., London, Saunders and Otley, 1837. [B.M.]

White, E. H. The Plebeian, and other Tales. London, Strange, 1848. [Allibone : *Eng. Cat.*]

White, Eliza. Gertrude ; or, thoughtlessness and inattention corrected. A tale. London, 1823. [B.M.]

White, James. The Adventures of John of Gaunt, Duke of Lancaster. 3 vols., London, Robinson, 1790. [*Eng. Lit. in Germany : Guide to Best Fiction :* Ingpen.]

—— The Adventures of King Richard Coeur-de-Lion. To which is added, The Death of Lord Falkland : a poem. 3 vols., London, 1791. [B.M. : W. Brown : *Guide to Best Fiction.*]

—— The Adventures Of Sir Frizzle Pumpkin ; Nights at Mess ; And Other Tales. With 8 illustrations by George Cruikshank. Edinburgh, William Blackwood ; and T. Cadell, London, 1836. [B.M. : Marks : Pickering.]

—— Earl Strongbow ; or, the History of Richard de Clare and the Beautiful Geralda. 2 vols., London, 1789. [B.M. : *Eng. Lit. in Germany :* Marks.]

White, Joseph Blanco. Second travels of an Irish Gentleman in search of a religion. With notes and illustrations, not by the editor of " Captain Rock's Memoirs." 2 vols., London, 1833. [B.M.]

White, Mary. Beatrice ; Or, The Wycherley Family. A Novel. 4 vols., London, A. K. Newman, 1824. [B.M.]

White Slave (The). A romance for the nineteenth century. By the author of " Ada," etc. London, 1844. [B.M.]

Whitehead, Charles. The Earl of Essex. A Romance. 3 vols., London, Richard Bentley, 1843. [Allibone : B.M.]

—— Richard Savage. A Romance of Real Life. With 17 etchings by John Leech. 3 vols., London, Richard Bentley, 1842. [Allibone : B.M.]

—— Smiles and Tears : Or The Romance of Life. 3 vols., London, Richard Bentley, 1848. [*Eng. Cat. :* James Glaisher.]

Whitehead, Emma. Pierce Falcon, The Outcast. A Novel. 3 vols., London, Richard Bentley, 1835. [Allibone : B.M.]

Whitelaw, Alexander. The Casket of Literary Gems. Second Series. Edited by Alex. Whitelaw. With plates. 2 vols., Glasgow, Blackie, Fullarton ; A. Fullarton, Edinburgh ; J. M. Leckie, Dublin ; James Duncan, & Simpkin & Marshall, London, 1829. [B.M.]

Whitfield, Henry. A Picture from Life, or the History of Emma Tankerville and Sir Henry Moreton. 2 vols., London, 1804. [Baker's Bookshop.]

—— Villeroy ; or, The fatal moment. By a lady, 3 vols., London, W. Lane, 1791. [Blakey.]

Whiting, Sydney. Affection, Its Flowers and Fruits. A Tale of the Times. 3 vols., London, T. C. Newby, 1848. [B.M.]

Whitmore, W. Modern Gulliver's Travels. Lilliput : Being a New Journey to that Celebrated Island. Containing a Faithful Account of those Famous Little People from the year 1702 to 1796. By Lemuel Gulliver, Jun. London, T. Chapman, 1796. [B.M. : Arthur Rogers.]

Whitty, Michael James. Tales of Irish Life, Illustrative of the Manners, Customs, and Condition of the People. With 6 woodcuts by George Cruikshank. 2 vols., London, J. Robins, 1824. [B.M. : I. in F. : Sotheran.]

Who Can He Be ; or, Who is his Father ? A novel. By the author of two popular works lately published. 3 vols., London, 1810. [B.M.]

Whole Life and Death of Long Meg of Westminster (The). With woodcuts. London, Printed and Sold in Aldermary Church Yard, [1750 ?]. [B.M.]

Whole Pleasures of Matrimony (The), interwoven with sundry comical stories. London, [1750 ?]. [B.M.]

Who'll Buy ? or, The Best Bargain. With a woodcut. London, Houlston, N.D. No. 37 of Houlston's Series of Tracts. [Block.]

Whyte, Alexander. Velina. A Moral Tale. 2 vols., London, William Miller, 1812. [Allibone : B.M. : *Quarterly Review.*]

Wickenden, W. S. Count Glarus, Of Switzerland. Interspersed with some pieces of poetry. Dedicated, by permission, To Edward Jenner, Esq. M.D. F.R.S. Gloucester, J. Roberts, [1819]. [B.M.]

Widow and the Fatherless (The), a simple tale. London, Rivington, [1848]. [B.M. : *Eng. Cat.*]

Widow of Kent (The) ; or, the history of Mrs. Rowley. A novel. 2 vols., London, 1788. [B.M.]

Widow of Zarephath (The). London, [1796 ?]. Cheap Repository. [B.M.]

Widow O'Leary (The) ; a story of the present famine. Cork, 1847. [B.M.]

Wieland, Christoph Martin. Araspes and Panthea ; Or, The Effects of Love. London, 1775. [Lib. of Congress.]

—— Confessions in Elysium ; or, the Adventures of a Platonic Philosopher Taken from the German of C. M. Wieland by John Battersby Elrington. 3 vols., London, Minerva Press, 1804. [B.M. : Pickering : Blakey.]

—— Crates and Hipparchia. A tale, in a series of letters, translated from the German by C. R. Coke. London, Longman, 1823. [B.M.]

—— The History of Agathon. Translated from the German Original, with a Preface by the Translator. With a frontispiece. 4 vols., London, T. Cadell, 1773. [Blackwell : B.M. : *Guide to Best Fiction.*]

—— Private History of Peregrinus Proteus, The Philosopher. Translated from the German. 2 vols., London, Johnson, 1796. [Ingpen : *New Ann. Reg. :* Arthur Rogers.]

—— Reason Triumphant over Fancy ; Exemplified in the Singular Adventures of Don Sylvio de Rosalva : A History in which every Marvellous Event occurs naturally. Translated from the German Original of Mr. C. M. Wieland. 3 vols., London, J. Wilkie, 1773. [*Guide to Best Fiction :* Pickering.]

—— Select Fairy Tales, from the German of Wieland. 2 vols., London, 1796. [Lowndes : *New Ann. Reg.*]

—— Socrates out of his senses ; or Dialogues of Diogenes of Sinope. Translated out of the German of Wieland, by Mr. Wintersted. 2 vols., London, T. Davies, 1771. [B.M. : Ingpen.]

Wieman, Miss. Abzylia, or The Trial of Virtue ; a Novel. 4 vols., 1808. [Allibone.]

Wife, a Model for Women. 3 vols., [Cawthorn's Catalogue, 1810.]

Wightwick, George. The Life and Remains Of Wilmot Warwick. Edited by his friend Henry Vernon. 2 vols., London, James Ridgway, 1828. [B.M. : McLeish : Elkin Mathews.]

Wigley, Sarah. Glencarron : A Scottish Tale. 3 vols., London, Henry Colburn, 1811. [Allibone : Ingpen : Pickering.]

Wilberforce, Robert Isaac. Rutilius and Lucius ; or Stories of the Third Age. London, J. Hughes, 1842. [Allibone : B.M. : *Eng. Cat.*]

Wilberforce, Samuel. Agathos, and other Sunday Stories. By a Clergyman. London, R. B. Seeley and W. Burnside, 1839 [Block.]

—— Note-Book of a Country Clergyman. London, Seeley, 1833. [Allibone.]

Wild Roses : or, Cottage Tales. With engravings. 2 vols., London, Ann Lemoine, and J. Roe, [c. 1790]. [B.M. : Ingpen : Sexton.]

Wilkins, George. Body and Soul. 2 vols., London, Longman, Rees, Orme, Brown, and Green, 1822-1823. [Allibone : Publisher's advert.]

—— The Convert. By the Author of " The Two Rectors." London, Longman, Rees, Orme, Brown, & Green, 1826. [Block : B.M. : *Literary Gazette.*]

—— The Two Rectors. London, Longman, Hurst, Rees, Orme, Brown and Green, 1824. [B.M.]

—— The Village Pastor. By one of the authors of Body and Soul. London, Longman, 1825. [B.M. : *Eng. Cat.*]

Wilkinson, James. Hau Kiou Choaan, Or The Pleasant History. A Translation from the Chinese Language. To which are added, I. The Argument or Story of a Chinese Play, II. A Collection of Chinese Proverbs, and III. Fragments of Chinese Poetry. With Notes [by Bishop Percy]. With frontispieces. 4 vols., London, R. & J. Dodsley, 1761. [B.M. : Ingpen : Arthur Rogers.]

Wilkinson, Janet W. Hands, not Hearts ; a Novel. 3 vols., London, Richard Bentley, 1849. [Allibone : *Eng. Cat.*]

Wilkinson, Sarah S. The Castle of Montabino, Or The Orphan Sister. With a frontispiece. [1809.] [Arthur Rogers.]

—— The Castle Spectre ; an ancient baronial romance, founded on the original drama of M.G.L. London, [1820 ?]. [B.M.]

—— Convents of Grey Penitents. 2 vols., 1810. [Allibone.]

—— The Deformed Mendicant ; or, English Exiles ; Being the History of Sir Everard Mortimer, and his Daughter Margaret. An Historical Legend of the Seventeenth Century. With a frontispiece. London, Harrild, [c. 1810]. [Stonehill : Murray Hill.]

—— Fugitive Countess. 4 vols., 1807. [Allibone.]

—— The History of Crazy Jane. With copper-plate frontispiece & 3 woodcuts by Bewick. Alnwick, W. Davison, 1818. [Gumuchian : Arthur Rogers.]

—— The Mysteries of the Castle Del Carino. Frontispiece. London, N.D. [Murray Hill.]

—— New Tales. 3 vols., London, Iley, 1819. [Blackwell : *Eng. Cat.*]

—— Priory of St. Clair ; or, Spectre of the Murdered Nun. A Gothic Tale. With a frontispiece. London, Harrild, 1811. [Stonehill.]

—— The Ruffian Boy ; or, Castle of Waldemar. A Venetian Tale. On which is founded the interesting and popular Melo Drama now performing at The Surrey Theatre. Taken from Mrs. Opie's celebrated tale of that name. With a frontispiece. London, J. Bailey, N.D. [Court Book Shop.]

—— The Spectres ; or Lord Oswald and Lady Rosa, inclding [*sic*] an Account of the Marchioness of Civetti, Who was basely consigned to a Dungeon beneath her Castle. By her eldest Son, whose cruel Avarice plunged him into the Commission of the worst of Crimes, that stain the Anuals [*sic*] of the Human Race. An Original Romantic Tale. With a frontispiece. London, Langley, [1814]. [Court Book Shop : R. S. Frampton.]

Wilkinson, Sarah S. Thatched Cottage. 2 vols., 1805. [Allibone.]

—— The Wife of Two Husbands ; or, Fritz, The Outlaw. With a frontispiece. London, Roe and Lemoine, 1804. [Stonehill.]

—— The Woodland Cousins ; or Agnes and Ellinor : a Rustic Tale ; in which is exemplified Traits of Disposition and Temper of Two Females ; affording a striking example of the effects of envy. With a frontispiece. London, J. Bailey, [c. 1820]. [Marks.]

Will Waver, Or Radical Principles. A Tale. Part the First. Oxford, Printed by W. Baxter, for J. Parker ; and F. C. and J. Rivington, 1821. [B.M.]

Will Without Wit. With a woodcut. London, Houlston, N.D. No. 87 of Houlston's Series of Tracts. [Block.]

William and Azubah ; or the Alpine Recess, a Novel. 2 vols., 1812. [*New Monthly Mag.*]

William and Charles, or the Bold Adventurers. By the Author of Lord Winworth, Maria Harcourt, Phoebe, etc., 2 vols., London, C. Stalker, 1789. [J. C. Hardy.]

William Sedley ; Or, the Evil Day Deferred. With a frontispiece. London, John Marshall, [1783]. [B.M.]

Williams, Catherine M. Alice Russell, and Other Tales. London, Bull, 1841. [Allibone : *Eng. Cat.*]

Williams, Helen Maria. The History of Perourou ; or the Bellows-Mender. Dublin, 1801. [B.M.]

—— Julia, a Novel ; Interspersed with Some Poetical Pieces. 2 vols., London, T. Cadell, 1790. [Allibone : B.M. : W. Brown.]

Williams, John. The Curate Of Elmwood. A Tale. Edited by Anthony Pasquin, Esq. London, Martin and Bain, 1795. [B.M.]

Williams, Mitchell. Feudal Days ; Or, the Freebooter's Castle. A Romance. 3 vols., London, Mitchell Williams, 1826. [B.M.]

Williams, Robert Folkestone. Eureka : A Prophecy of the Future. By the Author Of " Mephistopheles in England." 3 vols., London, Longman, Rees, Orme, Brown, Green, & Longman, 1837. [B.M.]

—— The Luttrells ; or the Two Marriages. 3 vols., London, Henry Colburn, 1850. [B.M. : *Eng. Cat.*]

Williams, Robert Folkestone. Maids of Honour : A Tale Of The Court of George I. 3 vols., London, Henry Colburn, 1845. [B.M. : Holland : Publisher's advert.]

—— Mephistopheles in England ; Or, The Confessions Of A Prime Minister. 3 vols., London, Longman, Rees, Orme, Brown, Green, & Longman, 1835. [B.M.]

—— The Secret Passion. By the Author of " Shakspeare and his Friends," " The Youth of Shakspeare," &c. 3 vols., London, Henry Colburn, 1844. [Allibone : B.M.]

—— Shakspeare and His Friends ; Or, " The Golden Age " of Merry England. 3 vols., London, Henry Colburn, 1838. [Allibone : Block : B.M.]

—— Sir Roger de Coverley, A Tale of the Court of Charles the Second. By the Author of " Maids of Honour." 3 vols., London, Henry Colburn, 1846. [B.M. : Critic.]

—— Strawberry Hill ; An Historical Novel. By the Author of " Shakspeare and his friends," "Maids of Honour," " Sir Roger de Coverley," &c. 3 vols., London, Henry Colburn, 1847. [Allibone : B.M. : Publisher's advert.]

—— The Youth of Shakspeare. By the Author of " Shakspeare and his Friends." 3 vols., London, Henry Colburn, 1839. [B.M. : T. D. Webster.]

Williams, William Frederic. Fitzmaurice ; a Novel. 2 vols., London, 1800. [Allibone : Baker's Bookshop.]

—— Sketches of Modern Life ; or Man as he ought not to be. A novel. 2 vols., London, 1799. [B.M. : New Ann. Reg.]

—— Tales of an Exile. 2 vols., London, Printed at the Minerva Press, for Lane, Newman & Co., 1803. [Blakey.]

—— The Witcheries of Craig Isaf ; a Novel. 2 vols., London, 1804. [Allibone : Blakey.]

—— The World We Live In. A novel, 3 vols., London, Lane, Newman & Co., 1804. [Allibone : Blakey.]

—— The Young Father. 3 vols., London, Lane, Newman, 1805. [Allibone : Blakey.]

Williamson, Captain F. The Dominican ; a Romance. 3 vols., London, 1809. [Allibone.]

Willyams, Jane Louisa. Chillon ; Or, Protestants of the Sixteenth Century : An Historical Tale. 2 vols., London, J. Hatchard, 1845. [B.M. : James Glaisher : Wm. Smith.]

Wilmot, R. Ardent ; A Tale of Windsor Forest, In the Nineteenth Century. Dedicated to the Memory of His Most Gracious Majesty, George the Fourth. 4 vols., London, Chappel ; Moreton, Windsor ; and Ingalton, Eton, 1832. [B.M. : Literary Gazette : Pickering.]

Wilmot, R. H. Scenes in Feudal Times ;

a Romance. 4 vols., London, 1809. [Allibone : B.M.]

Wilmot ; or The pupil of folly. 4 vols., London, William Lane, 1782. [Blakey.]

Wilson, Alexander. Alice Allan. The Country Town. Et Cet. London, Geo. B. Whittaker, 1825. [B.M.]

Wilson, Charles Henry. The Wandering Islander, or The History of Mr. Charles North, 2 vols., 1792. [New Ann. Reg. : Arthur Rogers.]

Wilson, Mrs Cornewell Baron. Chronicles of Life. 3 vols., London, T. & W. Boone, 1840. [Allibone : B.M.]

—— Popularity ; And The Destinies of Woman : (Tales of the World.) 2 vols., London, Hugh Cunningham, 1842. [Allibone : B.M. : Publisher's advert.]

Wilson, Edward. Deodatus, or Martyr of Carthage ; a Tale. London, Burns, 1845. [Allibone : Eng. Cat.]

Wilson, Harriette. Clara Gazul, Or Honi Soit Qui Mal Y Pense. 3 vols., London, Printed for the Author, 1830. [Allibone : Block : B.M.]

—— Paris Lions and London Tigers. With 12 plates. London, J. J. Stockdale. 1825. [Pickering.]

Wilson, James. The Fire-Eater. Edinburgh, John Anderson, Jun., 1823. [B.M. : Pickering : Sexton.]

—— Tournay ; Or Alaster of Kempencairn. By the Author of the Fire-Eater. Edinburgh, John Anderson, Jun., 1824. [B.M.]

Wilson, John. The Foresters. By the Author of Lights and Shadows of Scottish Life ; and the Trials of Margaret Lyndsay. Edinburgh, William Blackwood ; and T. Cadell, London, 1825. [Allibone : B.M. : Ingpen.]

—— Lights and Shadows of Scottish Life. A Selection from the Papers of the Late Arthur Austin. Edinburgh, William Blackwood, 1822. [Guide to Best Fiction,: Ingpen : Pickering.]

—— The Trials of Margaret Lyndsay. By the Author of Lights and Shadows of Scottish Life. Edinburgh, William Blackwood ; and T. Cadell, London, 1823. [B.M. : Ingpen : Myers.]

Wilson, Plumpton. Protestant Truth and Roman Catholic Errors ; a Tale. 1830. [Allibone.]

Wilson, Mrs. W. C. Little Stories for Children. By the author of " Children's Stories in Children's words." London, [1846 ?]. [B.M.]

—— A Mother's Stories for Children. By the author of " Children's Stories in Children's Words." London, Seeley, [1849]. [B.M. : Eng. Cat.]

—— Pleasant Stories for Children. By the author of " Children's Stories in Children's Words." London, 1846. [B.M.]

—— Pretty Stories for Children. By the Author of " Children's Stories in

Children's words." London, [1847]. [B.M.]

Wilson, Mrs. W. C. Simple Stories for Children. By the author of " Children's Stories in children's words. " London, [1843]. [B.M.]

—— A Sister's Stories for Children. By the author of " Children's Stories in Children's Words." London, [1849]. [B.M.]

—— True Stories for Children. By the Author of " Children's Stories in Children's Words." London, [1847]. [B.M.]

—— Useful Stories for children. By the author of " Children's Stories in Children's words." London, [1848]. [B.M.]

Wiltshire Beau or Adventures of Ben Barnard. 1765. [*Eng. Lit. in Germany.*]

Windsor Tales : or, the amours of a Gentleman and Lady ; with some Court-Intrigues ; a genuine history. London, [1755 ?]. [B.M.]

Wingrove, Ann. The Spinster's Tale ; in which is introduced Langbridge Fort, a romance. 3 vols., London, 1801. [B.M.]

Winter, A. Michaelo and the Twins ; A Tale of the Lazzaroni in Naples. With plates. Bath, [184–]. [R. Hall.]

Winter, L. F. Castle Harcourt ; Or, The Days of King Richard the Third. A Tale of 1483. 3 vols., London, A. K. Newman, 1825. [B.M.]

Winter, Mary. Alton Park ; Or, Conversations On Religious and Moral Subjects ; Chiefly designed For the Amusement and Instruction Of Young Ladies. 2 vols., London, Printed and Published for the Author, By Keating and Brown, 1830. [B.M.]

Winter Evenings Companion (The). Being a new collection of diverting Essays, Merry Stories &c. To which are added, A choice collection of Songs . . . also, the Jocular Companion : Or, a curious collection of Jests, etc. London, [1750 ?]. [B.M.]

Winter in Paris (A) ; or, Memoirs of Madame de C**** : written by herself. 3 vols., London, Henry Colburn, 1811. [B.M. : Publisher's advert.]

Wise Men of Gosmanthorpe (The). A tale. London, 1801. [B.M.]

Wise-Ones Bubbled, Or Lovers Triumphant. 2 vols., 1760. [W. Brown.]

Wishwell, Rhoda. The Pleasures of Benevolence ; or, the History of Miss Goodwill. By a lady. London, 1809. [B.M.]

Witch and the Maid of Honour (The). 2 vols., London, Longman, 1799. [B.M. : Ingpen : *New Ann. Reg.*]

Witch of the Woodlands (The) ; Or the Cobbler's New Translation. Here Robin the Cobler for his former Evils, Is punished bad as Faustus with his Devils. With woodcuts, London, Printed and Sold in Aldermary Church Yard, [1750 ?]. [B.M.]

Wit's Miscellany (The), or A Companion for the Choice Spirits, consisting of a Great Variety of Odd and Uncommon Epigrams, Facetious Drolleries, Whimsical Mottoes, Merry Tales, Fables, etc., all calculated for the Entertainment and Diversion of Good Company, and to pass a Winter Evening in Mirth and Good Humour. With a frontispiece. London, Printed for the Author, and sold to any Body that will buy it, by H. Serjeant, 1774. [B.M. : Pickering.]

Wizard of Windshaw (The). A Tale of the Seventeenth Century. 3 vols., London, J. W. Southgate, 1839. [B.M. : H. M. Fletcher.]

Wocklow, M. Radzivil, a Romance. Translated from the Russ of the celebrated M. Wocklow. 3 vols., London, W. Lane, 1790. [J. C. Hardy.]

Wolfstein ; or the Mysterious Bandit : a Terrific Romance ; to which is added the Bronze Statue : a Pathetic Tale. With a frontispiece. London, J. Bailey, [c. 1820]. [Marks.]

Wollaston, George. The Life and History of a Pilgrim, a Narrative founded on Fact. By G—— W——. Dublin, Oli. Nelson, 1753. [Dobell : Norman : Arthur Rogers.]

Woltmann, Caroline von (*see* VOLTMANN).

Woman : As she is, And As she should be. 2 vols., London, James Cochrane, 1835. [B.M.]

Woman of Fashion (The) : or, The History of Lady Diana Dormer. 2 vols., London, J. Wilkie, 1767. [Blackwell : Henry Start : Murray Hill.]

Woman of Genius (The). 3 vols., London, Longman, Hurst, Rees, Orme & Brown, 1821-2. [Block : B.M. : Ingpen.]

Woman of Honor (The). 3 vols., London, 1768. [W. Brown : Stonehill.]

Woman of Quality (The) ; or, The history of Lady Adelinda Bellamont. In a series of letters. [W. Lane, 1795.] [Blakey.]

Woman, Or, Minor Maxims. A Sketch. 2 vols., London, Printed at the Minerva Press, for A. K. Newman, 1818. [B.M. : *New Monthly Mag.* : T. Thorp.]

Wonderful Adventures of Mr. O'Flynn, in search of old Mother Clifton. [London, 1850 ?]. [A single sheet.] [B.M.]

Wonderful Tour of Little Peter Paganini. London, [1841]. [B.M.]

Wonders of Home (The). In eleven stories, by Grandfather Grey. With illustrations. London, Grant and Griffiths, 1850. [B.M.]

Wood, Captain George. The Rambles of Redbury Rook ; or, a Caution to his own Species how they embrace the Profession of Arms, by the Author of the Subaltern Officer. London, Wood, 1826. [Baker's Bookshop : B.M.]

Wood, Captain George. The Subaltern Officer. A Narrative. London, 1825. [B.M.]

Wood, Sara. The Tests of Time : a story of social life. London, J. Chapman, 1843. [Allibone : B.M. : *Eng. Cat.*]

Wood Nymph (The). 3 vols., London, A. K. Newman, [Publisher's advert, 1812.]

Woodbury or The Memoirs of William Marchmont and Miss Walbrook. 1773. [*Eng. Lit. in Germany.*]

Woodbury Papers (The) ; With Notes, Critical and Explanatory. 3 vols., Edinburgh, 1840. [Allibone : Ingpen.]

Woodfall, Sophia. Frederick Montravers ; or, The Adopted Son. A Novel. 2 vols., 1803. [B.M.]

—— Rosa ; or, The Child of the Abbey ; a Novel. 4 vols., 1804. [Allibone.]

Woodfin, Mrs. A. The Discovery : or, Memoirs of Miss Marianne Middleton. 2 vols., London, 1764. [Allibone : B.M.

—— History of Miss Harriet Watson. 2 vols., London, 1763. [Allibone.]

—— The History of Miss Sally Sable. By the author of Memoirs of a Scotch Family. 2 vols., London, [1770 ?]. [B.M.]

—— Northern Memoirs, Or the History of a Scotch Family. Written by a Lady. 2 vols., London, Noble, [1757]. [Ingpen.]

Woodland, Miss M. Bear and Forbear ; or, the history of Julia Marchmont, intended for the use of Young Ladies. A moral tale. With a frontispiece, 1823. [B.M. : Holland.]

—— Histories of Four Young Ladies. 2 vols., London, Baldwin. [Allibone : *Eng. Cat.*]

—— Matilda Mortimer ; or, False Pride : A Moral Tale. With a frontispiece. London, Tabart, 1809. [Block.]

—— A Tale of Warning ; Or, The Victims of Indolence. Intended for the use of Young Ladies. With a frontispiece. London, B. Tabart, 1809. [Arthur Rogers.]

—— Tales for Mothers and Daughters. 4 vols., 1807. [Allibone.]

Woodland Cottage (The). A novel. 2 vols., London, 1796. [B.M.]

Woodroofe, Anne. Michael, The Married Man ; or, The Sequel to The History of Michael Kemp. By the Author of " Shades of Character," " History of Michael Kemp," &c. &c. With a frontispiece. In 2 Parts. London, John Hatchard, 1827. [B.M. : H. M. Fletcher.]

—— Shades of Character ; Or, The Infant Pilgrim. By the Author of " The History of Michael Kemp." 3 vols., Bath, Printed for the Author, 1824. [B.M.]

Woodthorpe, Augusta Maria. The Hour of Two : a Novel. 3 vols., London, 1809. [Allibone : B.M. : P. C. Cuttelle.]

Woodville : or, The Interesting Memoirs of a Beggar Girl. With a frontispiece, London, 1809. [Murray Hill.]

Woolrych, Humphry William. Our Island : Comprising Forgery, a Tale ; And The Lunatic, a Tale. 3 vols., London, Edward Bull, 1832. [B.M. : McLeish : Elkin Mathews.]

Worboise, Emma Jane. Alice Cunningham By Emma Jane. London, Wertheim 1846. [Allibone : *Eng. Cat.*]

Words of Truth. By the Author of " The Well-spent Hour," and " The Warning." London, Simpkin & Marshall, 1833. [B.M. : *Literary Annalist.*]

Work-Box (The) ; or, Grand-papa's present. London, 1828. [B.M.]

Wormeley, Mary Elizabeth. Forest Hill ; A tale of social life In 1830-1831. 3 vols., London, Richard Bentley, 1846. [B.M. : *Critic.*]

Wray, Leopold. The Quarrelsome Dog. Translated freely from the German by Leopold Wray. With 12 plates. [1850]. [Arthur Rogers.]

Wreck Ashore (The) ; or, A Bridegroom from the Sea. With a frontispiece. London, Duncombe, [c. 1800]. [Stonehill.]

Wren (The) ; or, the fairy of the greenhouse : put together for little boys. London, 1843. [B.M.]

Wrench, Matilda. The Charcoal Burners ; or, The Grateful Artist. Translated from the German, by Miss Matilda Wrench. London, Burns, 1845. [B.M. : *Critic.*]

—— The Highland Glen ; or, Plenty and Famine. London, 1847. [B.M. (3rd edn.)]

Wright, John. Alma Mater, Or Seven Years at the University of Cambridge, By a Trinity-Man. 2 vols., 1827. [B.M. : Francis Edwards : Arthur Rogers.]

Wright, Rev. John. The Last of the Corbes, Or, the Macmahons' Country : A Legend connected with Irish History in 1641. London, John Macrone, 1835. [Allibone : B.M. : *I. in F.*]

Wright, T. Solyman and Fatima ; Or, The Sceptic Convinced. An Eastern Tale. 2 vols., London, John Bew, 1791. [B.M.]

Writer's Clerk (The) : or, The Humours Of The Scottish Metropolis. 3 vols., London, G. B. Whittaker, 1825. [B.M. : Ingpen : Pickering.]

Wyss, Johann David Rudolf. The Family Robinson Crusoe : or, Journal of a Father shipwrecked, with his wife and children, on an Uninhabited island. Translated from the German of M. Wiss. 2 vols., With 4 illustrations by H. Corbould. London, M. J. Godwin, 1814. [B.M. : Sotheby's]

—— The Swiss Family Robinson ; Or, Adventures on a Desert Island. Forming a Second Series or Continuation of the

Work already Published under that Title. With engravings. London, Simpkin, Marshall, 1849. [*Eng. Cat. :* Arthur Rogers.]

Yamboo ; or, The North American Slave. A Tale. By the Author of The Bravo of Bohemia. 3 vols., London, Printed at the Minerva–Press, 1812. [Blakey : Murray Hill.]

Yamhaska ; or, Memoirs of the Goodwin Family, Edinburgh, 1826. [B.M.]

Yanzee, Maria. Fate ; or, Spong Castle. London, Parsons, 1803. [Blackwell : Stonehill.]

Year at Hartlebury (A), Or The Election. By Cherry and Fair Star. 2 vols., London, Saunders and Otley, 1834. [B.M. : Publisher's advert.]

Yearsley, Ann. The Royal Captives : A Fragment of Secret History. Copied from an old manuscript. 2 vols., London, G. G. and J. Robinson, 1795. [Allibone : B.M. : *New Ann. Reg.*]

Yeates, Mrs. Eliza, A Novel. 2 vols., Lambeth, S. Tibson, 1800. [Allibone : B.M.]

Yin Seaou Low or the lost child. A Chinese tale. [Abstracted from the Chinese original by S. Birch.] From the Asiatic Journal, May, 1841. London, [1841]. [B.M.]

Yonge, Charlotte Mary. Abbeychurch, Or Self Control and Self Conceit. With a frontispiece. London, James Burns ; and Henry Mozley, Derby, 1844. [Allibone : B.M. : Ingpen.]

—— Henrietta's Wish : or Domineering. A tale. London, Masters, 1850. [B.M. : *Eng. Cat.*]

—— Kenneth, or the Rear Guard of the Grand Army. By the author of Scenes and Characters. Oxford and London, J. H. Parker, 1850. [B.M.]

—— Scenes and Characters ; or, Eighteen months at Beechcroft. By the Author of " Abbeychurch, or Self control and Self conceit." London, James Burns, 1847. [B.M.]

Yorick's Sentimental Journey, Continued. To which is prefixed, some Account of the Life and Writings of Mr. Sterne. 2 vols., London, [17 – –]. [Lowndes.]

York Dialogue (A), between Ned and Harry : or, Ned giving Harry an account of his courtship and marriage state. To which is added two excellent new songs. [Newcastle ? 1790 ?]. [B.M.]

Yorke, Mrs. My Master's Secret ; or, the Troublesome Stranger. 2 vols., Minerva Press, 1804. [Allibone : Blakey.]

—— Valley of Collares, or The Cavern of Horrors. A romance. Translated from the Portuguese. 3 vols., London, Author at the Minerva Press, 1800. [Blakey.]

Yorkshire Beauty (The), or distressed lady made happy. Warrington, [1815 ?]. [B.M.]

Youatt, Elizabeth. The Price of Fame, A Novel. 3 vols., London, T. and W. Boone, 1842. [Allibone : B.M.]

Young, Mary Julia. The East Indian, Or Clifford Priory. A Novel. 4 vols., London, Earle and Hemet, 1799. [Ingpen.]

—— The Family Party. 3 vols., London, William Lane, 1791. [B.M. : Blakey : *Minerva Press Catalogue.*]

—— The Heir of Drumcondra ; or, Family Young. 3 vols., London, Printed at the Minerva Press, for A. K. Newman, 1810. [Publisher's advert.]

—— Moss Cliff Abbey. 4 vols., London, J. F. Hughes. [Publisher's advert., 1806.]

—— The Mother and Daughter. A pathetic tale. 3 vols., London, 1804. [B.M.]

—— Right and Wrong ; or, the Kinsmen of Naples. A romantic story. 4 vols., London, 1803. [B.M.]

—— Rose-Mount Castle ; or, False report. A novel. 3 vols., London, William Lane, 1798. [Blakey.]

—— A Summer At Brighton. A Modern Novel. 3 vols., London, Printed by D. N. Shury for J. F. Hughes, 1807. [B.M.]

Young Baronet (The), or the Broken Leg. London, Harvey and Darton, 1830. [B.M.]

Young Drummer (The), or the affectionate Son. A tale of the Russian campaign. London [Leeds], 1847. [B.M.]

Young Duellists (The) ; or, the affair of honor. London, Simpkin and Marshall, 1837. [B.M.]

Young Fisherman's Narrative : a true story. London, Religious Tract Society, [1830 ?] [B.M.]

Young Forester (The), a narrative of the early life of a Christian Missionary. [London ?], Privately Printed, 1840. [B.M.]

Young Hearts. A Novel By A Recluse. With a preface By Miss Jane Porter. 3 vols., London, Saunders and Otley, 1834. [B.M.]

Young Hocus ; or, the History of John Bull during the years 1783, 1784, 1785, 1786, 1787, 1788, 1789. A novel. By Sir W—— L——, K——. With notes, critical and explanatory. Volume I. [No more published.] London, [1789 ?]. [B.M.]

Young Infidel : A Fire-side Reverie. By a Friend to Truth. Colchester, Swinborne and Walter, 1821. [B.M.]

Young Jewess and Her Christian Schoolfellows (The). By the Author of " Rhoda," &c. With a frontispiece by J. Gilbert. London, Grant and Griffith, 1848. [Publisher's advert.]

Young Mother (The) ; or, Albinia. 3 vols., London, Lane, Newman, 1808. [Publisher's advert : Blakey.]

Young Philosopher (The) : or, instructive entertainer. Huddersfield, Brook & Lancashire, [1790 ?]. [B.M.]

Young Protestant (The). By a Clergyman. London, Seeley, 1848. Tales for the Times. No. 1. [B.M.]

Young Queen : A Tale. 3 vols., London, James Cochrane, 1835. [B.M.]

Young Rifleman's Comrade (The) : A Narrative of Military Adventures. London, Henry Colburn, 1826. [B.M. : *Eng. Cat. :* F. Harvey.]

Young Servants (The) ; or Aunt Susan and her nieces. London, The Religious Tract Society, 1838. [B.M.]

Young Wanderer's Cave (The), And Other Tales. By the Author of " The Children's Fireside." London, Whittaker, Treacher, 1830. [B.M. : *New Monthly Mag.*]

Younger Brother (The), a tale. 2 vols., London, 1770-72. [B.M. : Sotheby's].

Youthful Jester (The) ; or, Repository of Wit and Innocent Amusement, containing Moral and Humorous Tales, Merry Jests, Laughable Anecdotes, and Smart Repartees, the whole being as innocent as it is entertaining. With woodcuts. London, Printed for J. Harris, by J. Crowder, 1804. [Pickering.]

Youth's Monitor (The) ; containing Moral and Instructive Tales. London Hurst, 1801. [*Guardian of Education.*]

Zélie in the Desert. Or the Female Crusoe. Translated from the French. London, C. Forster, 1789. [W. Brown : J. C. Hardy.]

Zeluca ; Or, Educated and Uneducated Woman. A Novel. 3 vols., Brighton, Printed for the Author, by J. Forbes, 1815. [Blackwell : B.M.]

Ziegenhirt, Sophia F. The Orphan Of Tintern Abbey. A Novel. 3 vols., London, Printed at the Minerva Press, for A. K. Newman, 1816. [B.M. : *New Monthly Mag.*]

—— Seabrook Village and its Inhabitants, or The History of Mrs. Worthy and Her Family. Written for Young People. London, Henry Colburn, 1811. [B.M. : Publisher's advert. : Arthur Rogers.]

Zornlin, Rosina Maria. The Solar Eclipse ; Or, the Two Almanacks : Containing More enquiries in astronomy. With a frontispiece. London, James Ridgway, 1836. [Block : B.M.]

Zschokke, Johannes Heinrich Daniel. The Bravo of Venice. A Romance. Translated from the German by M. G. Lewis. London, Printed by D. N. Shury for J. F. Hughes, 1805. [Birrell & Garnett : B.M. : Ingpen.]

—— Goldenthal : A Tale. By Zschokke. London, Whittaker, 1833. [B.M.]

—— The Goldmakers' Village ; or a History of the manner in which two and thirty men sold themselves to the Devil. Translated from the German. London, Burns, 1845. [B.M. : *Eng. Cat.*]

—— The Lover's Stratagem, And Other Tales. With illustrations by Linton. London, John and Daniel A. Darling, [1848]. [Block : B.M. : Lib. of Congress.]

—— Tales from the German. Translated by P. Godwin. 1846. [*Guide to Best Fiction.*]

—— Veronica ; or, The Free Court of Aarau. Translated by S. Spring. 1846. [*Guide to Best Fiction.*]

INDEX TO TITLES

* * * * *see* Memoirs of . . .
* * * * * * * * * * * * * *
see Memoirs of a . . .

Abbess of St. Hilda.
—— of Valtiera, by Agnes Lancaster.
——. A Romance, by Samuel William Henry Ireland.
——. A Romance, by Frances Trollope.
Abbey Church, by Charlotte Mary Yonge.
—— of Clugny, by Mary Meeks.
—— of Innismoyle, by Selina Bunbury.
—— of St. Asaph, by Isabella Kelly.
Abbey of Weyhill.
Abbot, by Sir Walter Scott.
—— of Montserrat, by William Child Green.
Abbotsmere.
Abdeker, by A. Le Camus.
Abdiel.
Abduction, or the Adventures of Major Sarney.
Abel Allnut, by James Justinian Morier.
Abelard and Heloise, *see* History of the lives of . . .
Aben–Hamet, by François René Vicomte de Chateaubriand.
Aberford, A Novel, by Henry Summersett.
Abissinian Reformer, by Charles Lucas.
Abomilech, *see* Chronicle of . . .
Abou Casem, *see* History of . . .
Absent Man.
Absentee, by Maria Edgeworth.
Absenteeism, by Sydney Lady Morgan.
Abstract.
Abzylia, by Miss Wieman.
Academy, or a Picture of Youth.
Acceptance.
Accomplish'd woman, by Jacques du Bosc.
Accomplished Hypocrite.
—— Rake, by Mary Davys.
—— Whore, by Pietro Aretino.
—— Woman, *see* Accomplish'd.
Account of Barbarossa.
Accusing Spirit, by Mary Pilkington.
Actress of the present day.
Ada the betrayed, by James Malcolm Rymer.
—— Grenville, by Peter Leicester.
—— Reis, by Lady Caroline Lamb.
—— A Tale, by Camilla Needham.
Adam Bell, by Pierce Egan the younger.
—— Blair, *see* Some passages in the life of Mr. . . .
—— Brown, by Horatio Smith.
—— the Gardener, by Charles Cowden Clarke.

Adela Northington, by Mrs. Burke.
Adelaide and Theodore, by the Comtesse de Genlis.
—— de Narbonne.
—— Lindsay, by Anne Marsh.
——, or the Chateau de St. Pierre, by Mrs. Edgeworth.
——, or conjugal affection.
——, or the Countercharm, by Catherine Cuthbertson.
——, or the intrepid daughter, by Barbara Hofland.
—— ; A Story of Modern Life, by Miss Cathcart.
Adelaide's gift, by Macauslane.
Adèle, or the Tomb of my Mother, by Paul Sebright.
—— : A Tale of France, by Miss E. Randall.
Adelfrida.
Adeline Mowbray, by Amelia Opie.
——, or the grave of the forsaken.
—— ; or the Orphan.
—— St.. Julian, by Ann Kerr.
Adolphe and Blanche, by Etienne François de Lantier.
—— and Selanie, by Henri L. Dubois.
——: an anecdote, by Henri Benjamin Constant de Rebecque.
Adolphus de Biron, by Ann Thomas.
Adonia.
Adopted Daughter, by Elizabeth Sandham.
—— son, by J. van Lennep.
Adra, or the Peruvians, by George Payne Rainsford James.
Adrastus and Olinda, by W. R. Chetwood.
Adultress, or Anecdotes of Two Noble Families.
Advantages of Education, by Jane West.
Adventure of Captain Greenland, by W. Goodall.
—— of the Hunchback.
Adventurers, or Scenes in Ireland.
Adventures in Borneo.
—— in the Moon.
——, intrigues, and amours of a Lady's maid.
—— of an Aide-de-Camp, by James Grant.
—— of Alonzo.
—— of Anthony Varnish, by Charles Johnstone.
—— of Ariston, by John Percy Severn.
—— of an Atom, *see* History and . . .
—— of an Attorney, by Sir George Stephen.
—— of an Author.

259

Adventures of a Bank-Note, by Thomas Bridges.
—— of Barney Mahoney, by Thomas Crofton Croker.
—— of a Bedstead, *see* Curious and diverting history and . . .
—— of Bilberry Thurland, by Charles Hooton.
—— of a Black Coat.
—— of a Bullfinch, by Elizabeth Sandham.
—— of a cat, *see* Life and . . .
—— of the celebrated little Thomas Dellow.
—— of Charles Villars.
—— of a Colonist.
—— of Congo.
—— of a Corkskrew.
—— of David Simple, by Sarah Fielding.
—— of Dick Distich, by George Daniel.
—— of Dick Hazard.
—— of a doll, by Mary Mister.
—— of a Donkey, by Arabella Argus.
—— of a dramatist, by Benjamin Frere.
—— of Emmera.
—— of Felix and Rosarito, by John Corry.
—— of Ferdinand Count Fathom, by Tobias Smollett.
—— of a flea, *see* Memoirs and . . . .
—— of a Fly.
—— of Frank Hammond.
—— of Gabriel Tangent.
—— of George Maitland.
—— of Gil Blas, by Alan Rene le Sage.
—— of a gold-finder.
—— of a gold-headed cane.
—— of the Gooroo Paramartan, by Constantinus Josephus Beschius.
—— of Grimmalkin.
—— of a guardsman, by Charles Cozens.
—— of the Guildford Jack-Daw, by John Russell.
—— of a Hackney Coach, by Dorothy Kilner.
—— of Hajji Baba of Ispahan, by James Justinian Morier.
—— of Hajji Baba of Ispahan in England, by James Justinian Morier.
—— of a halfpenny.
—— of Hatim Taï, by Duncan Forbes.
—— of Henry Fitzherbert.
—— of Hugh Trevor, by Thomas Holcroft.
—— of an Irish gentleman, by John Gideon Millingen.
—— of an Irish Smock.
—— of Jack Holyday, by Albert Smith.
—— of Jack Smart.
—— of John Le-Brun, by R. Cross.
—— of John of Gaunt, by James White.
—— of Johnny Newcome in the Navy, by Lieut.-Col. David Roberts.
—— of a Kidnapped Orphan.
—— of King Richard, by James White.
—— of a King's Page, by Charles White.
—— of the little girl in the wood.
—— of Madiboo.

Adventures of Marmaduke Midge.
—— of Master Headstrong.
—— of a medical student, by Robert Douglas.
—— of Michailow.
—— of Miss Beverly.
—— of Miss Lucy Watson.
—— of Monsieur Provence, by Jean Jacques Rutledge.
—— of Mr. George Edwards, by " Sir " John Hill.
—— of Mr. Ledbury, by Albert Smith.
—— of Mr. Loveill.
—— of Musul.
—— of Naufragus.
—— of Newcome in the Navy, by Lieut.-Col. David Roberts.
—— of an ostrich feather of quality.
—— of Patrick O'Donnell.
—— of Peregrine Pickle, by Tobias Smollett.
—— of Philip Quarll.
—— of a pincushion, by Dorothy Kilner.
—— of a poor beggar.
—— of Poor Puss, by Elizabeth Sandham.
—— of a post captain.
—— of a Rake, by Robert Lewis.
—— of Ralph Reybridge, by William Linley.
—— of Robert Chevalier, by Alan René Le Sage.
—— of Roderick Random, by Tobias Smollett.
—— of a Rupee, by Helenus Scott.
—— of a school-boy.
—— of a sergeant in the French army.
—— of a Seven-shilling Piece, by Ann Hamilton.
—— of a silver penny.
—— of a silver threepence.
—— of Sir Frizzle Pumpkin, by James White.
—— of Sir Launcelot Greaves, by Tobias Smollett.
—— of the six princesses of Babylon, by Lucy Peacock.
—— of a soldier.
—— of a Speculist, by George Alexander Stevens.
—— of Susan Hopley, by Catherine Crowe.
—— of Sylvia Hughes.
—— of Telemachus, by François de Salignac de la Mothe Fénelon.
—— of Theagenes and Chariclea, by Heliodorus.
—— of Thomas Eustace.
—— of Thomas Two-shoes, by Mary Elliott.
—— of a Turk.
—— of Ulysses, by Charles Lamb.
—— of a vagabond.
—— of Valentine Vaux, by Thomas Peckett Prest.
—— of a Valet.
—— of Victor Allen, by Sophia King.
—— of a watch.

Adventures of a whipping-top.
—— of a young rifleman.
—— of a younger son, by Captain Edward James Trelawny.
Advertisement for a husband.
—— : or Twenty Years Ago, by Eliza Clarke.
Asop's Fables.
Affecting history of the Duchess of C****.
—— history of an Inn-keeper in Normandy.
—— history of Louisa, the wandering maniac.
—— history of Tom Bragwell.
—— history of two young gentlewomen.
Affection, its flowers & fruits, by Sydney Whiting.
Affectionate Brothers, by Barbara Hofland.
—— orphans.
Affianced One, by Elizabeth Missing Sewell.
Affinities of Foreigners, by Janet Robinson.
Agatha, or a Narrative of Recent Events.
Agathon, see History of . . .
Agathonia, by Catherine Grace Frances Gore.
Agathos, and other Sunday Stories, by Samuel Wilberforce.
Age and youth, by August Heinrich Julius La Fontaine.
—— of Chivalry, by Comtesse de Genlis.
—— we live in.
—— we live in, by Louisa Sidney Stanhope.
Agent and his natural son.
Agincourt, by George Payne Rainsford James.
Agitation, or Memoirs of George Woodford.
Agnes and Leonora, by Richard Sickelmore.
—— de Courci, by Agnes Maria Bennett.
—— de Lilien, by Mrs. Showes.
—— de Mansfeldt, by Thomas Colley Grattan.
—— de Tracy, by John Mason Neale.
—— Grey, see Wuthering Heights.
—— Morton.
——, a novel.
—— Serle, by Ellen Pickering.
——, a tale founded on facts.
—— the unknown, by Thomas Peckett Prest.
Agreeable Ugliness, by Sarah Scott.
Ailzie Grierson.
Aims and Ends, by Caroline Henrietta Sheridan.
Al Kalomeric, by Mohammed Abou Ali, Ben Ali, Ben Hassan Ebn Moclah.
Al Raoui, see Story of . . .
Aladdin.
Alan Fitz-Osborne, by Anne Fuller.
—— Gilbert's last birthday.
Albani, or the Murderer of his Child.
Albany : A Novel.

Albatross, by William Henry Giles Kingston.
Albert de Nordenshild.
——, Edward and Laura, by Miss R. Roberts.
—— Lunel, by Henry, Baron Brougham and Vaux.
——, or the Wilds of Strathnavern, by Elizabeth Helme.
Albigenses, by Charles Robert Maturin.
Albina.
Alchemist, by Mary Hughes.
Alcon Malanzore, by Mrs. Esme Steuart Erskine.
Alderman and Peer.
Alexander Alexander, see Life of . . .
Alexandrians, An Egyptian Tale.
Alexena.
Alexis : or The Young Adventurer, by Baron Lansdowne.
——, the tyrant of the East.
Alf von Deulman, by Miss A. E. Booth.
Alfred, by Mary Elizabeth Parker.
—— and Cassandra.
—— and Galba, by Rev. John Campbell.
—— and Thomas, see History of . . .
—— Dudley.
—— the Great, by J. H. Stocqueler.
—— of Normandy, by Caroline Maxwell.
——, or the adventures of a French gentleman, by George William Macarthur Reynolds.
——, or, the effects of true repentance.
Algerines, by William Child Green.
Alibeg the Tempter, by William Child Green.
Alice Allan, by Alexander Wilson.
—— Cunningham, by Emma Jane Worboise.
—— Franklin, by Mary Howitt.
—— Glynn, by J. Slade.
—— Grant.
—— Gray, by Catherine George Ward.
—— Home.
—— Leighton.
—— Lemington, by Rose Ellen Hendriks.
—— of Infidelity, by Grace Stuart Hume.
—— or the Mysteries, by Edward Bulwer, Lord Lytton.
—— Paulet, by W. Massie.
—— Russell, by Catherine M. Williams.
—— Seymour, by Catherine Maria Grey.
Alicia and her Aunt.
—— de Lacy, by Jane West.
—— Grey, by Catherine Grace Godwin.
—— Montague, see History of . . .
Alidia and Cloridan.
Alinda, or the child of mercy, by Emma de Lisle.
Aline, an old friend's story, by Catherine Maria Grey.
Alithea Woodley.
All classes, by Hannah D. Burdon.
—— for Love, or the World well lost.
—— is not fable.
—— sorts of lovers, by Henry Summersett.
Alla Giornata, by Lady Charlotte Susan Maria Bury.

Allan Breck, by George Robert Gleig.
—— M'Dougal.
—— of Olway, by John Bethune.
Allanston, by Lady Georgina Chatterton.
Allee Neemroo, by James Baillie Fraser.
All's right at last, by Frances Moore.
Allwin and Theodore, by Friedrich C. W. Jacobs.
Alma Mater, by John Wright.
Almack's, by Mrs. Hudson.
—— Revisited, by Charles White.
Almagro & Claude.
Almeria Belmore, by E. O'Connor.
—— D'Aveiro, by Mrs. Mackenzie.
Almira.
Almira's Curse, by Thomas Peckett Prest.
Almoner.
Almoran and Hamet, by John Hawkesworth.
Alphonsine, by Comtesse de Genlis.
Alphonso and Eleonora, by Sir John Talbot Dillon.
—— and Elinor.
—— Blas de Lirias, see History and adventures of Don . . .
——, or the natural son, by Comtesse de Genlis.
Alpine Tale.
Alpine Wanderers, by A. Brown.
Altham and his Wife, By Charles Ollier.
Altoban.
Alton Locke, by Charles Kingsley.
—— Park, by Mary Winter.
Altrive tales, by James Hogg.
Alvar and Seraphina, by John Canton.
Alve, or infidelity.
Alvondown Vicarage, by Regina Maria Roche.
Always happy.
Alwyn, or the Gentleman Comedian, by Thomas Holcroft.
Alzylia, by Miss Weimar.
Amabel, or Memoirs of a Woman of Fashion, by Eliza Hervey.
Amadis of Gaul, by Vasco de Lobeira.
Amanda, see History of . . .
Amantes, by George Hutton.
Amatonda, by Anton Wall.
Amatory tales of Spain, France, Switzerland, and the Mediterranean, by Honoria Scott.
Amazement, by Mary Meeke.
Ambassador's Secretary, by Jane Harvey.
—— Wife, by Catherine Grace Frances Gore.
Ambition, by Miss M. G. Lewes.
Ambrose and Eleanor, by Lucy Peacock.
—— Ward.
Ambrosio, or The Monk, see The Monk, a Romance.
Amelia, by Henry Fielding.
—— Harcourt, see History of . . .
—— Mansfield, by Sophie Cottin.
——, or the distress'd Wife.
American savage, by Mrs. Barnby.
Amiable tutoress, by Harriet Ventum.
—— Willie, by Ann Jane Morgan.
Amicable Quixote.

Amilec, by C. F. T. de la Roche.
Amintor and Teresa, see History of . . .
Ammorvin and Zallida, by Mary Charlton.
Amnesty, by Charles F. Ellerman.
Amoroso, by F. Dudley.
Amorous Intrigues and Adventures of Don Ferdinand & Donna Marie.
—— Letters between Miss Loveman and Miss Longfart.
—— Merchant, by Mrs. Barry.
—— Quaker.
—— Tale of the Chaste Loves of Peter the Long, by Thomas Holcroft.
Amos Armfield, by George Mogridge.
Amours and Adventures of Charles Careless.
—— and Adventures of Miss Kitty N . . .
—— of Lais.
Amram.
Amurath.
Amusement in High Life.
Amusements in High Life.
Amusing stories.
Amy Harrington, by C. G. Hamilton.
—— Herbert, by Elizabeth Missing Sewell.
——, or love and madness.
—— Ray.
Amymone, by Eliza Lynn Linton.
Amyotts' Home.
Anastasius, by Thomas Hope.
Anatomy of Society, by James Augustus St. John.
Ancient Highland story of the robbers of the forest.
—— Records, by T. J. Horsley Curties.
—— Régime, by George Payne Rainsford James.
Andre, by A. L. A. D. Dudevant.
Andrew of Padua, by Francisco Furbo.
—— Stuart, by Mary Ann Hanway.
—— Winpenny, see Memoirs of . . .
Andronica, or the fugitive bride, by Mary Charlton.
Anecdotes for good children.
—— of Altamont Family, by Mary Meeke.
—— of a Boarding-School, by Dorothy Kilner.
—— of the Clairville family, by Mrs. C. Mathews.
—— of a Convent.
—— of a Croat.
—— of the Delborough Family, by Susannah Gunning.
—— of kings.
—— of a Little Family.
—— of Mary.
—— of two well-known families. By Eliza Parsons.
Angela, a novel, by Anne Marsh.
Angelica's Ladies Library.
Angelicus and Fergusia.
Angelina, by Callou.
——, A Novel, by Mary Robinson.
——, or the mystery of St. Marks, by Thomas Peckett Prest.

Angelina, or mystic Captives, by Henry Guy.

Angeline, or Sketches from Nature.

Angelion, or the wizard of Elis, by Maria Geisweiler.

Angelo Guicciardini.

——, a novel, by Edward Henry Iliff.

Angel's Form and a Devil's Heart, by Selina Davenport.

—— work.

Anglo-Irish of the Nineteenth Century, by John Banim.

Anglo-Saxon Version of the story of Apollonius of Tyre.

Anglo-Saxons, by Leslie Armstrong.

Animated skeleton.

Ankerwick Castle, by Mrs. Croffts.

Ann and Ellen and the little Kitten.

—— and her eleven sisters, *see* History of . . .

——, or the conflict and triumph of faith, by Thomas Spalding.

—— Dale.

—— Melville.

—— Sheldon, *see* Authentic and interesting memoirs of Miss . . .

Anna, *see* Story of . . .

—— of Edinburgh, by Regina Maria Roche.

——, or Memoirs of a Welch Heiress, by Agnes Maria Bennett.

—— Ross, by Grace Kennedy.

—— St. Ives, by Thomas Holcroft.

Annaline, by Laetitia Matilda Hawkins.

Annals of administration.

—— of the Family of M'Roy, by Martha Blackford.

—— of Humble Life.

—— of Orlingbury.

—— of the Parish, by John Galt.

Anne Boleyn, by Katherine Thomson.

—— Dysart, by Christiana Jane Douglas.

—— Gray, a novel, by Lady Harriet Cradock.

—— Groves, by Agnes Carey.

—— Hathaway, by Emma Severn.

—— of Brittany.

—— of Geierstein, by Sir Walter Scott.

Annette.

—— Gervais, by Marie Tourte-Cher-buliez.

—— of Yverdon.

Annie Gray, by Sidney O. Moore.

—— Sherwood.

—— Walton.

Anonymous Letters.

Another Traveller, by Samuel Paterson.

Anschar, by Richard John King.

Anselmo, or the day of trial, by Mary Hill.

——, a tale of Italy, by André Vieusseux.

Anston Park, by James Edmeston.

Antar, a Bedouin Romance, by Terrick Hamilton.

Anthony Leger, *see* Life and adventures of . . .

—— Traugott, by James D. Haas.

—— Varnish, *see* Adventuers of . . .

Anti-Coningsby, by William North.

Anti-Delphine, by Mrs. Byron.

Antidote to the Miseries of Human Life, by Harriet Corp.

Anti-Gallican, by Edward Long.

Anti-Pamela.

Antipathy, by John Ainslie.

Anti-Punch, by William North.

Antiquary, by Sir Walter Scott.

Antoinette, a novel, by Anne Plumptre.

Antonina or the Fall of Rome, by William Wilkie Collins.

Ants, The A Rhapsody.

Anzoletta Zadoski, by Mrs. Howell.

Apollonius of Tyre, *see* Anglo-Saxon version of the story of . . .

Apology for the Life of Bampfylde-Moore Carew, by Robert Goadby.

—— for the life of Mrs. Shamela Andrews, by Henry Fielding.

Apostate's Progress.

Apparition, a romance.

Apparitions, by Joseph Taylor.

Appeal of Madame La T – – –

Appearance and Principle.

Appointed hour.

Apprentice turned Master.

Aquileia and Berwick, *see* The History of the Sieges of . . .

Arabella Bolton, *see* Memoirs of Miss . . .

—— Stuart, by George Payne Rainsford James.

Arabian Letters.

—— nights, by Rev. Edward Forster.

—— Nights Entertainments.

—— nights' entertainments, by George Moir Bussey.

—— Nights Entertainments, by M. Galland.

—— Nights entertainments, by C. D. Piguenit.

—— Nights' Entertainments, by Jonathan Scott.

—— nights' entertainments, *see also Thousand and One Nights.*

—— Tale, by William Beckford.

—— Tales, by Dom Chavis and Jacques Cazotte.

Arabin, By Thomas MacCombie.

Arabs in Spain, by James Cavanagh Murphy.

Araspes and Panthea, by Christoph Martin Wieland.

Arborleigh.

Arden of Faversham, *see* History of . . .

Ardent, by R. Wilmot.

Arethusa, by Frederick Chamier.

Argal, or the silver devil, by George Hadley.

Argentine : An Autobiography.

Argentum.

Argus : The House-Day at Eadlip.

Ariana and Maud, by Marian Moore.

Ariel, or the Invisible Monitor.

Aristocrat.

Aristomenes

Arley.

Arlington, by Thomas Henry Lister.

Armata, by Thomas Baron Erskine.

Armenian, by Johann Friedrich Schiller.

Armenians, by Charles Macfarlane.

Arminius, or Germania Freed, by Baron Cronzeck.

Armourer's Daughter.

Arnold, or a Trait.

—— Zulig.

Arpasia, or the wanderer.

Arrah Neil, by George Payne Rainsford James.

Arrival at a new home, by Henrietta Louisa Farrer.

Arrivals from India, by Henrietta Rouviere Mosse.

Arsaces, see History of . . .

Art. Maguire, by William Carleton.

Arthur Arundel, by Horation Smith.

—— Benson.

—— Coningsby, by John Sterling.

—— Fitz-Albini, by Sir Samuel Egerton Brydges.

—— Frankland.

—— Montague, by Admiral Edward Hawker.

—— Monteith, by Martha Blackford.

—— O'Bradley, see History of the adventures of . . .

—— of Britanny, by Peter Leicester.

—— O'Leary, Charles James Lever.

——, or the journal of an unknown, by Marie Joseph Eugéne Sue.

—— Seymour.

Artless Lovers.

—— Tales, by Anna Maria Porter.

Arulia.

Arundel, by Richard Cumberland.

——: a tale of the French Revolution, by Sir Francis Vincent.

Arvendel, or sketches in Italy and Switzerland.

Arville Castle.

Arwed Gyllensterna, by Carl Franz Vander Velde.

Arzoomund, by Mary Martha Sherwood.

Ashford Rectory, by Anna Brownell Jameson.

Ashton Hall, by Mrs. A. Montgomery.

Asiatic Princess, by Mary S. Pilkington.

Asmodeus, by Alan Rene Le Sage.

——, by Sir Chalres Sedley.

Aspasia.

Assassin of St. Glenroy, by Anthony Frederick Holstein.

Assembly of Birds.

Asteria and Tamerlain.

Astolfo's journey to the kingdom of the Moon.

Astonishing history and adventures of Betsey Warwick.

Astonishment, by Francis Lathom.

Astraea's return, by Harriot Augusta Freeman.

Astrologer : a legend of the Black Forest.

——, or the Eve of San Sebastian, by J. M. H. Hales.

Astrologer's daughter, by Rose Ellen Hendriks.

At Home, by Mrs. C. D. Burdett.

—— Home and Abroad, by Charlotte Eaton.

Atala, or the Amours of two Indians, by François René Vicomte de Chateaubriand.

Atlantis reviv'd, by R. Thompson.

Atherton, by William Pitt Scargill.

Atrocities of a convent.

Attic fragments, by Elizabeth Helme.

Attila. A Romance, by George Payne Rainsford James.

Attorney, or the contrast, by Trevor Lloyd Ashe.

Attractive Man, by Frances Trollope.

Auberry Stanhope, by Jane Harvey.

Aubid, by James Atkinson.

Aubrey, by Anne Marsh.

—— A Novel, by R. C. Dallas.

—— Stanhope, see Auberry Stanhope.

Auction : a modern Novel.

Audley Fortescue, by John Robinson.

Augusta, by Dr. Andrews.

Augusta Denbigh.

—— Fitzherbert.

—— ; or the Dependent Niece.

Augustus & Adelina, by Miss C. D. Haynes.

—— and Mary, by William Mudford.

—— Fitz-George.

—— : or the Ambitious Student.

Aunt and Niece.

—— Atta, by Henrietta Louisa Farrer.

—— Dorothy's Tale, by Lady Georgiana Chatterton.

—— Harding's keepsake.

—— Henry's Stories.

—— Kate's story, by Ann Thorp.

—— Martha. ...

—— Mary's Tales, by Mary Hughes.

—— Upton and her nephews and nieces, by George Mogridge.

Aureus, by Peregrine Oakley.

Auriol, by William Harrison Ainsworth.

Aurora and Maria, by Elizabeth Somerville.

——, or the Mysterious Beauty, by Camilla Dufour.

Aurungzebe, by John Ainslie.

Austenburn Castle.

Authentic and interesting history of Miss Moreton.

—— and interesting memoirs of Miss Ann Sheldon.

——and interesting history of Miss Moreton.

—— memoirs of the little man and the little maid.

Authoress : a tale.

Autobiography of a Dissenting Minister, by William Pitt Scargill.

—— of a Footman.

—— of an Irish Traveller.

—— of Rose Allen.

Autumn in Cheltenham, by J. P. Hurstone.

Avenger, or the Sicilian Vespers.

Ayesha, the Maid of Kars, by James Justinian Morier.

Aylmers, by Nathaniel Thomas Haynes Bayly.

Ayrshire, Legatees, by John Galt.

Ayton Priory, by John Mason Neale.
Azalias and Aimar.
Azemia, by William Beckford.
Azeth the Egyptian, by Eliza Lynn Linton.

Babay.
Baboo, by Augustus Prinsep.
Babouc, by François Maire Arouet de Voltaire.
Babylon the great.
Babylonian princess, see Memoirs of a . . .
Baby's baptism, by Henrietta Louisa Farrer.
Bachelor and the Married Man, by Mrs. Ross.
—— keeper, see Batchelor keeper.
——, a novel, by Thomas George Moore.
—— of the Albany, by Marmion W. Savage.
—— of Salamanca, by Alan Rene Le Sage.
Bachelor's heiress, by Catherine George Ward.
—— Journal, by Medora Gordon Byron.
—— Miseries.
Backslider.
Bad boy reformed by kindness.
Bagnio Miscellany.
Bahar-Danush, by Inatula.
Bakhtyar Nameh, by Sir William Ouseley.
Balance of Comfort, by Mrs. Ross.
Balbe Berton, see Life and heroic actions of . . .
Baldwin, or A Miser's Heir, by Richard H. Newell.
Ballad Singer, by Mrs. Edgeworth.
Balloon, or Aerostatic Spy.
Bandit Chief.
Bandit's Bride, by Louisa Sidney Stanhope.
Banditti of Monte Baldo.
Banished, by Wilhelm Hauff.
—— Man, by Charlotte Smith.
Banker-Lord, by Marianna Pisani.
Banker's Daughters of Bristol, by Rosalia St. Clair.
—— Wife, by Catherine Grace Frances Gore.
Banks of the Carron.
—— of the Douro, by Emily Clarke.
—— of the Wye, by J. H. James.
Bannockburn, A Novel.
Banquet of Dun Na nGedh, by John O'Donovan.
Barbara Markham.
Barbarossa, see Account of . . .
—— and Pollyana, see History of . . .
Barber of Paris, by Paul de Kock.
Bard of the West, by Frances Peck.
Bardouac, by Adrien de Sarrazin.
Bards, by Evan Jones.
Barford Abbey, by Susannah Gunning.
Barham Downs, by Robert Bage.
Barnabas Hill.
Barnaby Boulton, see History of . . .
—— Rudge, see Master Humphrey's Clock.

Barnabys in America, by Frances Trollope.
Barnadiston.
Barney Branagan, see Misfortunes of . . .
—— Mahoney, see Adventures of . . .
Baron de Courcy.
—— de Falkenheim.
—— de Fleming, by August La Fontaine.
—— Munchausen's Narrative, by Rudolf Eric Raspe.
—— of Falconberg, by Mrs. Bridget.
—— of Lauderbrooke, by William Holloway.
—— of Manstow.
Baroness d'Alunton, by Elizabeth Sophia Tomlins.
—— de Beaumont.
Baronet, a novel.
——, ou l'amant malgré lui, by Julia Corner.
Baronet's family, by Anne Beale.
Baron's daughter, by Isabella Kelly.
Baron's Little Daughter, by Mrs. Cecil Francis Alexander.
Barons of Felsheim, by Pigault Lebrun.
Barony, by Anna Maria Porter.
Barouche Driver, by Sir Charles Sedley.
Barozzi, by Catherine Smith.
Bar-Sinister, by Hon. Camden Elizabeth Lambert.
Bartholomew Fair.
Base-Born.
Bashaw Count Bonneval, see Memoirs of the . . .
Basil Harlow, by Catherine Grace Godwin.
Basiliade, by Pilpay.
Basket maker.
Bastard of Normandy.
Bastile, or History of Charles Townly.
Batchelor keeper.
Bateman's Tragedy.
Bath and London.
—— Characters, by Richard Warner.
——, Satirical Novel, by Thomas Brown, the Elder.
Baths of Bagnole.
Bathurst, by William Henry De Merle.
Battle Cross, by John Brent.
—— of the Horn-books.
—— of Life. A Love Story, by Charles Dickens.
Battledore for Miss in her Teens.
Battleridge.
Bay wreath.
Beacon Priory.
Bear and forbear, by Miss M. Woodland.
—— ye one another's burthens.
Bearn and the Pyrenees, by Louisa Stuart Costello.
Beatrice Chesterford.
——, or the inconstant.
——, or the Wycherley Family, by Mary White.
——, A Tale founded on Facts, by Barbara Hofland.
Beau monde.
—— Ogleby, see Comical adventures of . . .

265

k

Beauchamp, or the Error, by George Payne Rainsford James.
—— : or the wheel of fortune, by James Holroyd Fielding.
Beauford, by H. Card.
Beau-Philosopher.
Beautiful page.
Beauty and the beast.
—— of the British Alps, by Mary Leman Grimstone.
Bechuana girl.
Before and after.
Beggar and his Benefactor, by Miss Squire.
—— boy, by Thomas Bellamy.
—— Girl and her Benefactors, by Agnes Maria Bennett.
Beggarly boy.
Belford Regis, by Mary Russell Mitford.
Belinda, by Maria Edgeworth.
Belinda, or the Fair Fugutive.
Belisarius, by Jean François Marmontel.
——, an Historical Romance, by Comtesse de Genlis.
Bellah, by Anne Marsh.
Belle Marianne, by Thomas Frognal Dibdin.
—— Of the Family, by Catherine Maria Grey.
—— Sauvage, by M. Lyttelton.
Bellegarde.
Belleville Lodge.
Bellgrove Castle.
Belmont Grove.
—— Lodge, by Harriet Jones.
Belmont's Daughter, by Miss E. H. Macleod.
Belmour. A Novel, by Hon. Anne Seymour Damer.
Ben Bolt, by Thomas Peckett Prest.
—— Brace, by Frederick Chamier.
—— Bradshaw.
—— Howard.
—— the soldier, see History and adventures of . . .
Benedicta.
Benevola.
Benevolent Eccentric, by Henry Haverard Hall.
—— Man.
—— merchant.
—— monk, by Theodore Melville.
—— Quixote.
—— recluse, by Lady Dunn.
Benignity.
Beningbrough Hall.
Benjamin St. Martin, see History of . . .
Benson Powlet.
Berkeley Castle, by Hon. George Charles Grantley Fitzhardinge Berkeley.
—— Hall.
Berkshire Shepherd, by Lucy Lyttelton Cameron.
Bernard Leslie, by Rev. William Gresley.
Bertha's Visit to her Uncle, by Jane Mercet.
Bertrand, or memoirs of a Northumbrian nobleman.
Bessy Grey.

Betrothed cousins, by Emma Hamilton.
—— Lovers, by Allesandro Manzoni.
Betsy Warwick, see Astonishing history and adventures of . . .
—— Green, see History of . . .
—— Thoughtless, see History of Miss . . .
Betty Barnes, see History of . . .
—— Brown.
—— the cookmaid, see Trial of . . .
—— Gillis.
—— Ireland, see Secret History of . . .
Bevis of Southampton, see History of the life and death of that noble Knight . . .
Bianca Capello, by Rosina Lady Lytton.
Bigenio, see Surprising adventures of . . .
Bigotry, or The Warning Voice.
Bijoux Indiscrets, by Denis Diderot.
Bilberry Thurland, see Adventures of . . .
Billow and the rock, by Harriet Martineau.
Biography of a Spaniel.
Biondetta.
Bird of passage, by Isabella F. Romer.
Bird's nest.
Birmingham Counterfeit.
Birth, life, and death of John Franks.
Birth-Day, by Elizabeth Somerville.
Birthday, a tale for the young, by Lady Harriet Howard.
—— ; with other Tales, by Elizabeth Frances Dagley.
Birthright, by Catherine Grace Frances Gore.
Births, Deaths, and Marriages, by Theordore Edward Hook.
Bishop's daughter, by Erskine Neale.
Bit o'Writin, by John Banim.
Bivouac, by William Hamilton Maxwell.
Black Banner.
—— Castle, by C. F. Barrett.
—— Convent.
—— Giles the Poacher.
—— Gown Papers, by L. Mariotti.
—— Mantle, by Thomas Peckett Prest.
—— mask, by Thomas Frost.
—— monk, by James Malcolm Rymer.
—— pirate.
—— Prophet, by William Carleton.
—— Robber, by Edward Ball.
—— Rock House.
—— valley, by Veit Weber.
—— vulture.
—— Watch, by Andrew Picken.
—— William's grave.
Blackbird's nest.
Black-eyed Susan, by E. F. Marriott.
Blacklegs and Whitefeet.
Blanch and Rosalinda.
Blanche and Carlos.
—— Cressingham.
—— Langdale, by Thomas Peckett Prest.
—— Leslie.
Blandfords, by Henrietta Rouviere Mosse.
Blank book of a small colleger, by Erskine Neale.
Blansay, by J. C. Gorgy.
Bleeding Nun.
Blenheim Lodge.

Blighted Ambition, by R. Carr.
—— heart, by Thomas Peckett Prest.
Blind Beggar, by François Guillaume Ducray Dumenil.
—— beggar of Bethanl Green, *see* The history of the . . .
—— beggar of Bethnal Green and Pretty Bessy.
—— Betsy.
—— Child, by Mrs. Pinchard.
—— clergyman and his little guide, by Selina Bunbury.
—— Man and his Son.
—— Soldier.
Blood-stained mantle.
Blossoms of morality, by Arnaud Berquin.
—— of Peace.
Blue beard.
—— Belles of England, by Frances Trollope.
—— -eyed Patty, *see* Life and surprising adventures of . . .
—— Mountains.
—— -Stocking Hall, by William Pitt Scargill.
Boarding School, or Familiar Conversations.
Boatman's daughter, by Alfred Barrett.
Bob Norberry, by — Levey.
Body and soul, by George Wilkins.
Bogle Corbet, by John Galt.
Boldon Delaval, by Robert Bigsby.
Bondmaid, by Frederika Bremer.
Bondman, a Story of the times of Wat Tyler, by Mrs. O'Neill.
Bonze, by Mons. d'Alenson.
Book for the cottage.
—— of the Boudoir, by Sydney Lady Morgan.
—— of nursery tales.
—— of Oddities.
—— of the Passions, by George Payne Rainsford James.
—— of Snobs, by William Makepeace Thackeray.
—— of stories for young people.
——, or Procrastinated Memoirs.
—— without a name, by Sydney Lady and Sir Thomas Charles Morgan.
Boon, by Captain Manners.
Border Chieftains, by Mary Houghton.
—— Wardens, by Catherine Ponsonby.
Borderers, by Mrs. Byron.
Borderer's Table-Book, by Moses A. Richardson.
Bosc, *see* du Bosc.
Bosom friend, by Catherine Maria Grey.
Bosworth Field, by Peter Leceister.
Bottle, or drunkard's career, by Gabriel Alexander.
——, or the first step to crime.
Bouverie, or the pupil of the world, by Anthony Frederick Holstein.
Boyne Water, by John and Michael Banim.
Boy's own book of stories from history, by Mary Bennett.
Boys' School, by Elizabeth Sandham.

Bracelet, by E. Guichard.
Brambleton Hall.
Brambletye House, by Horatio Smith.
Brampton Rectory, by Mary Matilda Howard.
Bravo of Bohemia.
—— of Venice, by Johannes Heinrich Daniel Zschokke.
Bravo's son, by William Farrow.
Brazen Mask, by Charlotte Putney.
Breach of Promise, by Harriet Maria Yorick Smythies.
Brick Bolding, by Pigault Lebrun.
Bridal of Dunamore, by Regina Maria Roche.
Bride and no wife, by Henrietta R. Mosse.
—— of Obeyda.
Brief account of Little William.
Brighton in an Uproar, by Henrietta Maria Moriarty.
——, or the Steyne, by Thomas Brown.
Brinboc, *see* Memoirs of M. de . . .
Bristol Heiress, by Eleanor Sleath.
Britannicus and his sister Octavia, *see* History of . . .
British admiral.
—— Don Juan, by Henry Coates.
—— Knight Errant.
—— Oak.
Broken Font, by Colonel Joseph Moyle Sherer.
—— Heart.
—— heart, by Mary Bennett.
—— hyacinth, by Mary Martha Sherwood.
Brother, a Novel.
Brother Tragedians, by Isabel Hill.
Brotherly love, by Agnes M. Stewart.
Brothers.
——, *see* Story on which the new tragedy, call'd the . . .
—— and sisters, by Frederika Bremer.
—— in High Life, by Mrs. D. Johnson.
—— A Novel for Children.
——, or consequences.
Brougham Castle, by Jane Harvey.
Brownie of Bodsbeck, by James Hogg.
Bruce's voyage.
Bruja, *see* La Bruja.
Bryan Perdue, *see* Memoirs of . . .
Buccaneer, A Tale, by Anna Maria Hall.
Budget of the Bubble Family, by Rosina Lady Lytton.
Bungay Castle, by Elizabeth Bonhote.
Burford Cottage, by Edward Augustus Kendall.
Burgomaster of Berlin, by Georg Wilhelm Heinrich Häring.
Burman slave girl.
Burton, a Novel, by Ronald Mac-Chronicle.
——, or the bright halfpenny, by Clara Moore.
—— Wood, by Mrs. Cox.
Bushranger of Van Diemen's Land, by Charles Rowcroft.
Busy-Bodies, by the Misses Corbett.

Busy-Body, a novel.

——, or successful spy, by Charles de Fieux, Chevalier de Mouhy.

But how to spend the Evening ?

Butler's diary.

Buxton Diamonds.

Bytal Pucheesee, by Captain W. Hollings.

—— -Puchisi, by Rajah Kalee-Krishen Behadur.

Cabal. A Tale of the Reign of William the Fourth.

Cabin Conversation, by Selina Bunbury.

Cabinet Minister, by Catherine Grace Frances Gore.

—— of Amorous Curiosities.

—— of instruction and amusement.

—— of Lilliput.

—— of Momus.

Cabramatta Store, by Mrs. Francis Vidal.

Cabronazos.

Cæsar Borgia, by Jane Robinson.

Cagliostro, *see* Count . . .

Cake, from the German, by Johann Christoph von Schmid.

Calaf, by Mrs. M. Holford.

Caleb Kniverton, by Francis Edward Paget.

—— Stukely, by Samuel Phillips.

Caledonia, by Kate Montalbion.

Caledonian Bandit, by Catherine Smith.

—— bards, *see* Works of the . . .

Calendar of Horrors, by Thomas Peckett Prest.

Calista, by Anna Maria Johnson.

Calisto and Emira, *see* Loves of . . .

Callistus and Sophronius.

——, or the Man of Fashion, by Thomas Mulso.

Calthorpe, or the Fallen Fortunes, by Thomas Gaspey.

Camarúpa and Cámalata, *see* Loves of . . .

Cambrian Excursion, by Louisa Weston.

—— Pictures, by Ann Hatton.

Cameleon Sketches, by John Timbs.

Cameron. A Novel.

Camilla, or a Picture of Youth, by Madame D'Arblay.

—— Toulmin, by Mrs, Newton Crosland.

Camillo.

Camisard, by Frances Clare Adeline Coxe.

Camp of the Crusaders, by L. N. Musnicki.

—— of Refuge, by Charles Macfarlane.

Campbell ; or the Scottish Probationer, by Alexander Balfour.

Canadian girl.

Canary Bird, by Edward Augustus Kendall.

—— Bird, by Alicia Catherine Mant.

Candid, or, All for the Best, by François Marie Arouet de Voltaire.

Canterbury Tales.

—— tales for the year 1797, by Harriet Lee.

Capacity and Extent of the Human Understanding, by John Kirkby.

Capful of Moonshine, by John Mills.

Caprice : or Anecdotes of the Listowel Family.

Capricious father.

—— mother.

Captain and Miss Rivers, *see* History of . . .

—— Cobler, by Thomas Cooper.

—— Greenland, *see* Adventures of . . .

—— John Avery, *see* Famous adventures of . . .

—— O'Sullivan, by William Hamilton Maxwell.

—— Popanila, *see* Voyage of . . .

—— Rock, *see* Memoirs of . . .

—— Winterfield, *see* Surprising adventures of . . .

Captain's Wife, by William Johnson Neale.

Captive Fair.

—— maiden.

—— of Valence.

——, of the history of Mr. Clifford.

—— A Tale of the War of Guienne.

Captives in India, by Barbara Hofland.

——, or the history of Charles Arlington.

Captive's vow, by Charity Bachelor.

Carbonaro, by Duke de Levis.

Card, by Rev. John Kidgell.

Cardinal de Retz, by Mrs. Jenkins.

—— virtues, by Harriette Campbell.

Cardinal's Daughter, by Robert Mac-kenzie Daniel.

Cardiphonia, by Rev. John Newton.

Cards Spiritualized.

Carite and Polydorus, by L'Abbé Jean Jacques Barthélemy.

Caroline.

—— and Zelite, by Anna White Smith.

—— de Montmorency.

—— Lismore, by Alicia Catherine Mant.

Caroline Merton.

—— Mordaunt, by Mary Martha Sherwood.

—— of Lichtfield, by Jeanne Isabelle Bottens, Baroness de Montolieu.

——, or the diversities of fortune, by Anne Hughes.

—— Ormsby.

Carpenter's Daughter of Derham Down.

Carriage, by Maria Benson.

Carry and Milly, by Henrietta Louisa Farrer.

Carthusian Friar, by Sarah Green.

Cartouche the celebrated French robber, by Richard Brinsley Peake.

Carwell, or Crime and Sorrow, by Caroline Henrietta Sheridan.

Cashmere Shawl, by Charles White.

Casket of Literary Gems, by Alexander Whitelaw.

——, or the orphan's portion.

Caskets, by Lucy Lyttelton Cameron.

Cassidy, Grace, by Marguerite Countess of Blessington.

Castel Roviego. by M. Pickard.

Castelneau, by George Payne Rainsford James.

Castilian, by Don Telestoro de Trueba y Cozio.

Castle and hovel, by Selina Bunbury.

—— Baynard, by Charles Robert Forrester.

—— Chapel, by Regina Maria Roche.

—— de Albani.

—— fiend.

—— Harcourt, by L. F. Winter.

—— martyr.

—— of Arragon, by Catherine Smith.

—— of Beeston, by John Broster.

—— of Berry Pomeroy, by Edward Montague.

—— of Bucktholme.

—— of Caithness.

—— of Ehrenstein, by George Payne Rainsford James.

—— of Eridan, by G. A. Graglia.

—— of Hardayne, by John Bird.

—— of Inchvally, by Stephen Cullen.

—— of Kolmeras, by Comtesse de Genlis.

—— of Lindenberg, by Mathew Gregory Lewis.

—— of Montabino, by Sarah S. Wilkinson.

—— of Mowbray, by Mrs. Harley.

——of Ollada, by Francis Lathom.

—— of Otranto, by Horace Walpole,

—— of Probation.

—— of the Pyrenees.

—— of St. Bernard.

—— of St. Caranza.

—— of St. Donats.

—— of St. Vallery.

—— of Santa Fe.

—— of Strathmay, by Honoria Scott.

—— Tariffa.

—— of Tynemouth, by Jane Harvey.

—— of Villa-Flora.

—— of Vivaldi, by Caroline Horwood.

—— of Walforth and Monteagle, by Mrs. Dogherty.

—— of Wolfenbach, by Eliza Parsons.

—— on the rock.

—— Rackrent, by Maria Edgeworth.

—— Spectre, by Sarah S. Wilkinson.

—— Zittaw.

—— -builders.

Castles in the air. A Novel, by Catherine Grace Frances Gore.

—— in the Air, or the whims of my aunt.

—— of Athlin and Dunbayne, by Ann Radcliffe.

—— of Marsange and Nuger.

—— of Montreuil and Barre.

—— of Wolfnorth and Mont Eagle.

Casualties. A Novel, by Mary Goldsmith.

Catalina, by William Hillyard.

Catastrophe, by Chevalier de St. Aubigné.

Catharine Crawley, see History of Mrs. . . .

—— Howell.

Catherine de Medicis.

—— Howard.

Catherine, or the wood of Llewellyn, by Mr. Nicholson.

—— Waters.

Cathluna.

Cato.

Cavalier, a Romance, by William Bennett.

Cave of Consenza, by Eliza Bromly.

—— of St. Sidwell.

—— of Toledo, by Augusta Amelia Stuart.

Cavendish. Or, The Patrician at Sea, by William Johnson Neale.

Cavern in the Wicklow mountains.

—— of Astolpho.

—— of Death.

—— of Horrors.

—— of Roseville, by Madame de Herbster.

—— of Strozzi.

——, or the two sisters, by Madame de Herbster.

Cavigni of Tuscany, by Lucy Watkins.

Caxtons, a Family Picture, by Edward Bulwer, Lord Lytton.

Cecil Hyde, by Sir Martin Archer Shee.

——, or the Adventures of a Coxcomb, by Catherine Grace Frances Gore.

——, a Peer, by Catherine Grace Frances Gore.

Cecilia, or the Eastern Lovers.

——, or Memoirs of an Heiress, by Madame d'Arblay.

Cecily Fitz-Owen.

Celebrated Nanny Goose, see History of the . . .

Celebrity, or the Unfortunate Choice, by Mary S. Pilkington.

Celensis, or the history of Hyempsal.

Celestina. A Novel, by Charlotte Smith.

Celestine and St. Aubert, see Loves of . . .

Celia in Search of a Husband, by Medora Gordon Byron.

—— suited.

Celts Paradise, by John Banim.

Cephas.

Ceraline, by Jane Harvey.

Cesario Rosalba, by Ann Hatton.

Chæreas and Callirrhoe, see Loves of . . .

Chamber of Death.

Champion of Virtue, by Clara Reeve.

Chances and Changes, by Elizabeth Strutt.

——; or nothing of the New School.

Changeling, by Miss Martin.

—— of Fortune, by Clara Percy.

Chantilly.

Chapel of the forest, by Johann Christoph von Schmid.

Chapters of Churchyards, by Caroline Southey.

Character, or Jew and Gentile, by Mary Leman Grimstone.

Characters and opinions.

—— at Brighton, by Anne Trelawney.

Charcoal burners, by Matilda Wrench.

Charenton, by M. de Lourdoueix.

Charicles, by Wilhelm Adolf Becker.

Charite and Polydorus, by L'Abbe Jean Jacques Barthelemy.

Charity, a moral tale, by Caroline Conway Bailey.

Charles and Charlotte.

—— and Eugenia, by Madame de Renneville.

—— and Lisette, *see* Laughable adventures of . . .

—— the bold, by Charles Victor Prevot, Vicomte d'Arlincourt.

—— Careless, *see* Amours and Adventures of . . .

—— Chesterfield, by Frances Trollope.

—— Durand, *see* Travels and adventures of . . .

—— Ellis, by Robert Semple.

—— Falkland, *see* History of . . .

—— Fitzgerald and Miss Sarah Stapleton, *see* History of Mr . . .

—— Harcourt, by Georgina C. Munro.

—— Henly, by Sarah Green.

—— Jones, *see* History of . . .

—— Leeson, by Harriet Ventum.

—— Mandeville, *see* History of . . .

—— Mowbray.

—— Munson, *see* History of . . .

—— O'Malley, by Charles James Lever.

—— Ross.

—— Tyrrell, by George Payne Rainsford James.

—— Vernon, by Lt.-Col. Henry Senior.

—— Villers, *see* Adventures of . . .

—— Wentworth, *see* History of . . .

Charles's sum, by Henrietta Louisa Farrer.

Charley Chalk.

—— Crofts, *see* Memoirs of . . .

Charlie Seymour.

Charlotte Corday, by Rose Ellen Hendriks.

—— Summers, *see* History of . . .

——, a tale of truth, by Susanna Haswell Rowson.

Charlotte's Daughter, by Susanna Haswell Rowson.

Charlton, or Scenes in the North of Ireland, by John Gamble.

Charmed scarf, by A. Morton.

Charms of Dandyism, by Olivia Moreland.

Chartley the Fatalist, by James Dalton.

Chaste loves of Peter the Long, by Thomas Holcroft.

Chastity, or the Sisters of Charity, by Agnes M. Stewart.

Chateau de Myrell.

—— d'If, by Alexandre Dumas.

—— of Leaspach.

Chatsworth, the patrician, by Peter George Patmore.

Cheapside Apprentice, by Sarah More.

Chelsea Hospital, by George Robert Gleig.

—— Pensioners, by George Robert Gleig.

Cherries.

Chevalier Bayard, *see* History of the . . .

—— Bayard, *see* Right joyous and pleasant history of the feats, gests and prowesses of the . . .

—— de Faublas, *see* Life and adventures of the . . .

—— de Versenai, by Sophie Cottin.

——: a romance of the Rebellion of 1745, by Katharine Thomson.

Cheveley, by Rosina Lady Lytton.

Chieftain of the Vale, by George West.

Child and the Hermit.

—— of the Atlantic, by Charlotte Adams.

—— of disobedience.

—— of misfortune, by James Thistlethwaite.

—— of Mystery, by Hannah Maria Lowndes.

—— of Nature, by Claude Adrien Helvetius.

—— of Providence, by William Gardiner.

—— of Providence, a novel.

—— of two fathers.

—— of Woe, by Elizabeth Norman.

Childe Harolde, *see* Wanderings of . . .

Childhood of Mary Leeson, by Mary Howitt.

Childhood's duties, by Mary Ann Serrett Barber.

Children as they are.

—— in the wood, by Clara English.

—— in the Wood, *see* The History of the . . .

—— of the Abbey, by Regina Maria Roche.

—— of the Hartz Mountains, by Mary Martha Sherwood.

—— of the Manse, by Mrs. J. C. Lundie.

—— of the New Forest, by Captain Frederick Marryat.

—— taught by experience, by Louisa Stanley.

Children's fireside, by Isabella Jane Towers.

—— Friend, by Arnaud Berquin.

—— Miscellany, by Thomas Day.

—— year, by Mary Howitt.

Child's vision.

Chillon ; or the Protestants of the sixteenth Century, by Jane Louisa Willyams.

Chimes, a Goblin Story, by Charles Dickens.

Chinese Novels, by Sir John Francis Davis.

—— spy, by Ange de Goudar.

—— tales, by Thomas Simon Guellette.

Ching Tih In Keang, *see* Rambles of the Emperor . . .

Chiron, by Charles Caraccioli.

Chit-Chat, or natural characters.

——, or short tales in short words.

Chivalry of Scotland, by James Jackson.

Choice and no Choice, by Anne Rolfe.

—— gift.

—— tales.

Chollerton, by Cecilia Frances Tilley.

Christabelle, the Maid of Rouen, by Mary Ann Hanway.

Christian drummer.
—— Physiologist, by Gerald Griffin.
—— tales, by Edward Godwin.
—— trials.
Christina, or memoirs of a German princess, by Jeanne Isabelle Bottens, Baroness de Montolieu.
Christmas box.
—— Carol in prose, by Charles Dickens.
—— dinner.
—— Eve, by Johann Christoph von Schmid.
—— Eve and Christmas Matins, by Frederika Bremer.
—— Festivities, by John Poole.
—— Greeting to my English Friends, Hans Christian Andersen.
—— Holidays or the Young Visitants.
—— log.
—— Roses, by Wilhelm Hauff.
—— shadows.
—— Stories. Containing John Wildgoose, by Edward Berens.
—— Tales.
—— tales for the amusement of young ladies and gentlemen.
—— Tales, Historical and Domestic, by W. H. Harrison.
—— Week in the Country.
Christopher Tadpole, see Struggles and Adventures of . . .
—— Wagstaff, see Life, travels and adventures of . . .
Chronicle of Abomilech.
—— of the Cid.
—— of the City of the Seven Hills.
Chronicles and history of England, see Stories and studies from the . . .
—— of the Bastile, by Louis Alexis Chamcrovzow.
—— of the Canongate, by Sir Walter Scott.
—— of the careworn, by Edward West.
—— of Clovernook, by William Douglas Jerrold.
—— of the Fleet Prison, by Charles Rowcroft.
—— of Gretna Green, by P. O. Hutchinson.
—— of an Illustrious House, by Ann Hatton.
—— of the Kirk, by John Anderson.
—— of Life, by Mrs. Cornewell Baron Wilson.
—— of the Ton, by Henry Mordaunt.
—— of Waltham, by George Robert Gleig.
Chrysal, by Charles Johnstone.
Church of Saint Siffrid, by Jane West.
Cicely and Agnes.
——, or the power of honesty.
——, or the Rose of Raby, by Agnes Musgrave.
Cid, see Chronicle of the . . .
Cigar, by William Clarke.
Cinderella, by Mrs. Cuthbert Orlebar.
Cinq Mars, a Conspiracy, by Alfred Victor, Comte de Vigny.
Cinthelia, by George Walker.

Circassian Chief, by William Henry Giles Kingston.
Citizen : a novel, by Mrs. A. Gomersall.
—— of Prague, by Mary Howitt.
—— of the World, by Oliver Goldsmith.
—— of the world, by John Lovett.
Citizen's daughter.
City Cousins.
—— jilt.
—— nobility.
—— of the Jugglers, by William North.
—— of the Seven Hills, see Chronicle of the . . .
Civil Wars of Granada, by G. P. de Hita.
Clairville family, see Anecdotes of the . . .
Clan Albin, by Mrs. Christian Isobel Johnstone.
Clandestine Marriage, by Ellen Wallace.
Clara, by Sophie Cottin.
—— and Antonia, see Letters between . . .
—— and Emma, by Mary Anne Bourne.
—— and Emmeline, by Elizabeth Helme.
—— de Montfier, by Elizabeth Anne Le Noir.
—— Duplessis, by August Heinrich Julius La Fontaine.
—— Fane, by Louisa Stuart Costello.
—— Gazul, by Harriette Wilson.
—— Lennox, by Margaret Lee.
——, or the dangers of innocence, by Johann Christoph von Schmid.
—— Stephens, by Mary Martha Sherwood.
——, a Tale.
—— Webster.
Clarendon, a tale, by Elizabeth Elton Smith.
Clarentine, a Novel, by Sarah Harriet Burney.
Claret cup, by James Hannay.
Clarinda Cathcart, see History of Miss . . .
——, or a genuine narrative of all that befell a lady.
Clarissa, see The Story of . . .
——, or the History of a Young Lady, by Samuel Richardson.
Clarisse.
Classical Tales and Legends, by Rev. William Balmbro' Flower.
Claude du Val, by Henry Downes Miles.
——, or the double sacrifice, by Mary Molesworth.
Claudine Mignot, by Mary Ann Hartley.
—— : or Pertinacity, by Mrs. Bridget.
——, or the Savoyarde, by Jean Pierre Clavis de Florian.
——, a Swiss tale.
Clavering Tower, by Rosalia St. Clair.
Clematis cottage.
Clement Lorimer, by Angus Bethune Reach.
Clementine Bedford, by Maria Geertruida de Cambon.
Cleone, a Tale of Married Life, by Mary Leman Grimstone.
Cleopatra and Octavia, see The Lives of . . .
Clergyman's widow, see History of a . . .

Clerimont, by C. W. Briscoe.

Clermont, by Regina Maria Roche.

Cleveland, a tale of the Catholic church, by Mrs. Murray Gartshore.

Clio : or a Secret History of the Life and Amours of the late celebrated Mrs. S—n—m.

—— or Secret Memoirs of Mrs. S—N—M

Clongibbon, by James French.

Cloudesley, by William Godwin.

Club-Book, Edited by Andrew Picken.

Coalition, or Family Anecdotes, by Mrs. S. Boys.

Cobbler ! Stick to your last.

Coberley Hall, by Robert Hughes.

Cock and Anchor, by Joseph Sheridan Lefanu.

—— Robin, see Death and burial of . . .

Cock-Fighter.

Cockney Adventures, by Renton Nicholson.

—— in Scotland, by Capt. F. H. T. Bellew.

Coelebs, see Sequel to . . .

—— deceived, by Harriet Corp.

—— in search of a mistress.

—— in Search of a Wife, by Hannah More.

—— Married.

——, a novel, by James Hakewill.

—— suited, by Sir George Rover.

Cœlibia choosing a husband, by Robert Torrens.

Coincidence, or the Soothsayer, by Paul Sebright.

Cola Monti, by Dinah Maria Craik.

Colin Clink, by Charles Hooton.

Collection of early prose romances, by William John Thoms.

College, Chums, by Charles Lister.

—— Life, by Edward Bradley.

—— Life, by Joseph Thomas Hewlett.

College recollections.

Collegians, by Gerald Griffin.

Collier's wedding, see Comical history of the . . .

Collin St. Clyde.

Colonel Berkley and his friends.

—— Ormsby.

—— Torlogh O'Brien, see Fortunes of . . .

Columbus, by Joachim Heinrich Campe.

Columella, by Richard Graves.

Comforts of Arabella.

Comic novel.

—— Romance, by Paul Scarron.

—— sketches and recollections, by John Poole.

—— Tales and Sketches, by William Makepeace Thackeray.

Comical adventures, at sea and on shore of Jacko the baboon.

—— Adventures of Beau Ogleby.

—— and diverting courtship.

—— courtship between a Leith carter and a fish woman.

—— fellow.

—— history of the collier's wedding, by Edward Chicken.

Comical history of Simple John and his twelve misfortunes.

Coming Out, by Jane and Anna Maria Porter.

Commander of Malta, by Marie Joseph Eugène Sue.

Commissioner, or De Lunatico Inquirendo, by George Payne Rainsford James.

Commodore and his Daughter.

Commodore's daughter, by B. Barker.

Common Events, by-Walker.

—— Life.

—— Sense, see Life and adventure of . . .

Companion, by Charlotte Ann Smith.

Compensation, and by whom received, by Frederic Montagu.

Complete picture of human life.

Compton Audley, by Lord William Pitt Lennox.

—— Merivale, by Mary Matilda Howard.

Con Cregan, see Confessions of . . .

Concealment. A Novel.

——, or the cascade of Llantwarryhn, by Mrs, E. M. Foster.

Conclusion of the Memoirs of Miss Sydney Biddulph, by Frances Sheridan.

Conduct.

—— is Fate, by Lady Charlotte Susan Maria Bury.

—— of married life, by " Sir " John Hill.

Confederates. A Story.

Confession of Count de Harcourt.

Confessional of Valombre, by Louisa Sidney Stanhope.

Confessions in Elysium, by Christoph Martin Wieland.

—— of a beauty.

—— of Con Cregan, by Charles James Lever.

—— of a Coquet.

—— of an Elderly Gentleman, **by** Marguerite, Countess of Blessington.

—— of an Elderly Lady, by Marguerite, Countess of Blessington.

—— of a gamester.

—— of Harry Lorrequer, by Charles James Lever.

—— of an homeopathist.

—— of Honor Delany, by Rev. George Brittaine.

—— of Jean Baptiste Couteau, **by** Robert Jephson.

—— of an old Bachelor, by E. Carrington.

—— of an Old Maid, by E. Carrington.

—— of an Oxonian, by Thomas Moore.

—— of a pretty woman, by Julia Pardoe.

—— of Sir Henry Longueville, by Robert Pierce Gillies.

—— of a Thug, by Colonel Philip Meadows Taylor.

—— of a Whitefoot, by H. G. Curran.

Confidential Memoirs, by Mary Elliott.

Conflict, a sentimental tale, by M. Heron.

——, or the history of Miss Sophia Fanbrook.

Conformists, by John Banim.
Congal and Fenella, by J. Jamieson.
Coningsby, or the New Generation, by Earl of Beaconsfield.
——, a tragic tale, by Sir Samuel Egerton Brydges.
Conirdan.
Coniston Hall, by Rev. William Gresley.
Connaught, a tale of 1798, by Matthew Archdeacon.
Conquests of the Heart.
Conrad Blessington.
Conrade, or the gamesters, by Caroline Matilda Warren.
Conscience, by Mary Meeke.
—— duplicity.
Conscript, by John Scott Byerley.
Consequences, or adventures at Wraxall Castle, by Thomas Skinner Surr.
Consider well what you are about.
Consistency, by Charlotte Elizabeth Tonna.
Conspiracy, a Venetian Romance.
Conspirators, or the Romance of Military Life, by Edward Quillinan.
Constance de Lindensdorf, by Sophia Frances.
—— D'Oyley, by Ellen Wallace.
—— Lyndsay, by C. G. Hamilton.
——, a novel.
——, a Novel, by Katharine Thomson.
——, or the star of the ballet, by John Henry Mancur.
—— A Tale.
Constancy and Contrition.
——, a moral tale.
Constant Lover, by Augustus von Kotzebue.
Constantia Beauchamp.
—— Neville, by Helena Wells.
——, or a true picture of human life.
Constantine Castriot, by Ann Catherine Holbrook.
Consuelo, by A. L. A. D. Dudevant.
Contarini Fleming, by the Earl of Beaconsfield.
Contemplation, cowardice, & Vicissitude, by Emily Ospringe.
Contemplative Man, by Herbert Lawrence.
Contested Election, by Alicia Margaret Ennis.
Conti the Discarded, by Henry Fothergill Chorley.
Continental Adventures. A Novel, by Charlotte Anne Eaton.
Continuation of Early lessons, by Maria Edgeworth.
—— of Don Quixote, *see* Continuation of the history and adventures of the renowned Don Quixote.
—— of the History and adventures of the renowned Don Quixote, by Fernandez De Avellaneda.
—— of Vivian Grey.
Contract, by Elizabeth Sarah Villa-Real Gooch.
Contradiction, by Rev. William Cole.

Contradictions, or who could have thought it ? by John Hemet.
Contrast, by Constantine Henry Phipps, Marquis of Normanby.
——, by Regina Maria Roche.
——, or the history of James and Thomas.
——, or how to be happy, by Mary Elliott.
——, or the opposite consequences of good and evil habits.
——, or poverty and Riches.
——, or Scotland in 1745 and 1825.
——, a tale.
Convent, a narrative founded on fact, by Rachel MacCrindell.
—— of Grey Penitents.
—— of St. Clair, by Mary Martha Sherwood.
—— of St. Ursula.
—— : Or the History of Julia.
—— : or, the history of Sophia Nelson, by Anne Fuller.
—— Spectre.
—— Tales by Ann Adams.
Convents of grey penitents, by Sarah S. Wilkinson.
Conversation, or Shades of Difference, by Mrs. Heron.
Conversations and amusing tales, by Harriet English.
Conversion of Cleora, by George Southern.
Convert, by George Wilkins.
——, and Hester Marten.
Convict, or Navy lieutenant, by Eliza Parsons.
——, a romance, by Thomas Peckett Prest.
——, a Tale, by George Payne Rainsford James.
Conviction, or Is she innocent, by Ann Hatton.
Coombe Wood.
Coombe Abbey, by Selina Bunbury.
Coquette, by Frederick Mansel Reynolds.
Coquetterie, La, *see* la Coquetterie.
Cora, the Nabob's granddaughter, by Charlotte Putney.
Coraly.
Corasmin, by Hugh Murray.
Cordelia, by Mrs. Fortnum.
Corfe Castle, by John Fitzgerald Pennie.
Corinna of England, by J. H. James.
——, or Italy, by A. L. G. Necker de Stael-Holstein.
Corrected temper.
Correction. A Novel, by Anne Raikes Harding.
Correlia, or the mystic tomb, by Sarah Sheriffe.
Correspondence of two lovers.
Correspondents, by Miss Berry (?)
Corsair, by Harry Hazel.
Corsair's Bride, by Louisa Sidney Stanhope.
Corse de Leon, by George Payne Rainsford James.
Cospatrick of Raymondsholm.

273

Cottage, by Susannah & Margaret Minifies.
—— among the mountains.
—— dialogues among the Irish Peasantry, by Mary Leadbetter.
—— Fire-Side.
—— fireside, or the Parish schoolmaster, by Rev. Henry Duncan.
—— girl, by Mary Bennett.
—— in the Chalk Pit, by Alicia Catherine Mant.
—— in Kent.
—— in the Wood.
—— in the Wood, by Mary Martha Sherwood.
—— of the Appenines, by Marianne Kenley.
—— of Merlin Vale, by Isabella Morrington.
—— of the Var, by Caroline Symmons.
—— on the Cliff, by Catherine George Ward.
—— on the Common.
—— sketches.
—— tales.
—— traditions, by Jefferys Taylor.
Cottager's assistant.
—— daughter, or the Sorrows of Rosa.
—— daughter, a tale founded on facts, by Margaret Mackintosh.
—— daughter, a tale of the nineteenth century.
Cottagers of Glenburnie, by Elizabeth Hamilton.
Cotter's tale-book for the winter evenings, by James Leslie.
Cotton-Tree, by Theodora Elizabeth Lynch.
Counselling the doubtful.
Count Bertram, *see* History of . . .
—— Cagliostro, by Thomas Andrew James.
—— de Harcourt, *see* Confession of . . .
—— de Poland, by Susannah Gunning.
—— de Rethel.
—— de Santerre.
—— de Valmont, by L'Abbé Louis Phillipe Gérard.
—— di Novini.
—— Donamar.
—— Eugenio, by Harriet Butler.
—— Fathom, *see* Adventures of Ferdinand . . .
—— Glarus, by W. S. Wickenden.
—— Gleichen, *see* History of . . .
—— Königsmark, by Frederick Chamier.
—— of Hoensdern.
—— of Monte Christo, by Alexandre Dumas.
—— of P——, *see* Memoirs of the . . .
——, of sublunary life.
—— Roderic's Castle.
—— St. Blancard, by Mary Meeke.
Countess and Gertrude, by Laetitia Matilda Hawkins.
—— Faustina, by Ida, Countess Hahn-Hahn.
—— of Berci, *see* Memoirs of the . . .
—— of Bressol, *see* Memoirs of the . . .

Countess of Delwyn, *see* History of the . .
—— of G., *see* Life of . . .
—— of Hennebon, by Mrs. Harley.
—— of Salisbury.
Country and London.
—— Belles, by Agnes Anne Barber.
—— cousins.
—— Curate, by George Robert Gleig.
—— curate, or Pastor's fireside.
—— Houses.
—— neighbours, by Sarah Harriet Burney.
——, or Old Michael and Young Maurice.
—— Quarters, by Marguerite Countess of Blessington.
—— Stories, by Mary Russell Mitford.
Course of Gallantries, by Du Clos.
—— of a revolution.
Court and Cabinet of St. Cloud, *see* Secret history of the . . .
—— favourite, by Jane Roberts.
—— intrigue, or the victim of constancy.
—— intrigues, a novel, by William Peake.
—— intrigues, or the secret history of Ardelisa.
—— jester.
—— of Holyrood.
—— of Oberon, by Countess of Hardwicke.
—— of Sigismund Augustus, by Alexander Bronikowski.
—— -Partial of 18——, by Matilda Marian Pullan.
—— Secret, by George, Lord Lyttleton.
Courtenay of Walreddon, by Anna Eliza Bray.
Courtezan, by George Moore.
Courtier of the Days of Charles the Second, by Catherine Grace Frances Gore.
Courtier's Daughter, by Catherine, Lady Stepney.
Courtly Annals, by Richard Matthew.
Cousin Elizabeth.
—— Geoffrey, by Harriet Maria Yorick Smythies.
—— George, by Mrs. Walker.
—— Gertrude.
—— Kate, by Catherine Grace Godwin.
—— Natalia's tales.
—— Rachel's visit.
Cousins, by Mrs. Mitford.
—— of Schiras, by John Brereton Birch.
——, or quality before quantity, by Mary Elliott.
——, or a woman's promise, by Mrs Ross.
Coxheath Camp.
Craigh-Melrose Priory, by Henrietta Rouviere Mosse.
Cranmer, by Thomas Frognall Dibdin.
Crates and Hipparchia, by Christoph Martin Wieland.
Craven Derby, or the Lordship by Tenure, by Deale.
Crayford, or the force of influence.
Crazy Jane, *see* The History of . . .
—— Wright.

Creation, or a morning walk, by Mary B. Tuckey.
Creolana, by J. W. Orderson.
Creole, by Samuel James Arnold.
Cressingham, or the Missionary, by C. P. Adams.
Crestyphon, by John Hefford.
Crichton, by William Harrison Ainsworth.
Cricket on the Hearth, by Charles Dickens.
Crim. Con., by Henrietta Maria Moriarty.
Crimes and characters, by Mary S. Pilkington.
Cripple.
—— of Rothenstein.
Crispin and Crispianus, see Princely history of . . .
Crock of Gold, by Martin Farquhar Tupper.
Crockfords, see Life in the West.
Crohoore of the Billhook, by Michael Banim.
Cromwell Doolan, by Sir Richard George Augustus Levinge.
—— in Ireland.
Crooked paths, by Lucy Lyttelton Cameron.
Croppy, by John and Michael Banim.
Crotchet Castle, by Thomas Love Peacock.
Cruel husband and suffering wife.
—— Husband, or Devonshire tragedy.
Cruise of the Midge, by Michael Scott.
Crusade of Fidelis.
Crusaders : An Historical Romance, by Louisa Sidney Stanhope.
Crusoe Richard Davis, see Life and surprizing adventures of . . .
Cry. A New Dramatic Fable, by Sarah Fielding and Jane Collier.
Cumal and Lina, by C. F. Lossius.
Cumberland Cottager, by Miss Broderick.
Cunningham Family, see Some Account of the . . .
Cupid and Hymen.
—— and Psyche, by Lucius Apuleius.
—— and Psyche, see Fable of the . . .
—— and Psyche, see Loves of . . .
Curate of Coventry, by John Potter.
—— of Craman, see History of the . . .
—— of Elmdale, by Henry P. Linton.
—— of Elmwood, by John Williams.
—— of Linwood, by C. G. Hamilton.
—— of Steinhollt, by James Flamank.
—— of Wildmere, by Julia Addison.
Curate's Daughter, by Mary Mullion.
—— daughters, by Hannah Maria Lowndes.
—— favorite pupil, by Karl Stover.
Cure of the Gout.
Curiosity, a Novel, by Joan de Luce.
Curious and Diverting History and adventures of a Bedstead.
Curse of Sentiment.
—— of Ulrica.
Cuthbert, a Novel, by Sophia Reeve.
Cypher, by P. Littlejohn.
Cypriots.

Cyril Thornton, see Youth and manhood of . . .
Czar : a romance of history, by Edward Smallwood.
Czarina : an historical Romance of the Court of Russia, by Barbara Hofland.

Dacre, a Novel, by Maria Theresa Lister.
Dacresfield.
Daemon of Sicily, by Edward Montague.
—— of Venice.
Dagger, by Marquis von Grosse.
Dairyman's daughter, by Legh Richmond.
Dalinda.
Dame Partlet's farm.
—— Rebecca Berry, by Elizabeth Isabella Spence.
—— Truelove's tales.
Damon and Celia, see Genuine distresses of . . .
Dan and Jane, by Hannah More.
Danby Family, see Memoirs of the . . .
Danebury.
Danger of the Passions.
Dangerous Connections, by P. A. F. Choderlos de Laclos.
—— Errors.
—— Secrets.
Dangers and duties, by Charlotte Elizabeth Tonna.
—— of coquetry, by Amelia Opie.
—— of Dutch-Land.
—— of infidelity.
—— through Life, by Elizabeth Gunning.
Daniel Dennison, by Barbara Hofland.
—— O'Rourke, by Thomas Crofton Croker.
Danish Fairy Legends and Tales, by Hans Christian Andersen.
—— Story-Book, by Hans Christian Andersen.
Daphnis and Chloe, by Longus.
D'Arcy, by Charlotte Turner Smith.
Dark Falcon, by James Baillie Fraser.
—— lady of Doona, by William Hamilton Maxwell.
—— Scenes of History, by George Payne Rainsford James.
Darnley, or the Field of the Cloth of Gold, by George Payne Rainsford James.
—— Vale, by Elizabeth Bonhote.
Dasa Kumara Charita, by Dandin.
Daughter.
—— of Adoption, by John Beaufort.
—— of a Genius, by Barbara Hofland.
—— of St. Omar, by Catherine George Ward.
——, or the history of Miss Emilia Royston, by Maria Susanna Cooper.
Daughter-in-Law, her father, and family.
Daughters, a novel, by Catherine Maria Grey.
—— of Isenberg, by Alicia Tyndal Palmer.
Davenant, or the Escape.
Davenels.
Davenport Family, see History of the . . .

D'Aveyro, by F. L. C. Mountjoye.

David Copperfield, *see* Personal history of . . .

—— Ranger, *see* Juvenile Adventures of . . .

—— Simple, *see* Adventures of . . .

Davy Dreamy, *see* Memoirs of . . .

Dawn Island, by Harriet Martineau.

Day in Stowe Gardens, by Mary Sabilla Novello.

—— in the Woods, by Thomas Miller.

—— of rest.

Days of Bruce, by Grace Aguilar.

—— of Chivalry.

—— of Queen Mary.

—— when we had tails on us, by Lieut.-Col. J. J. Hort.

Dead Man's Hollow.

Deaf and dumb boy, by Rev. W. Fletcher.

Dealings with the Firm of Dombey and Son, by Charles Dickens.

Dean of Coleraine, by Abbé Antoine François Prévost d'Exiles.

Death and burial of Cock Robin.

—— grasp, by Thomas Peckett Prest.

—— of Cain, by Mary Collyer.

—— ship, by Thomas Peckett Prest.

Death-Bed repentance.

—— Repentance, by Ann Jane Morgan.

Death's a friend.

Debauchee rewarded.

De Beauvoir.,

De Brinboc, *see* Memoirs of M. . . .

Débutante ; or the London Season, by Catherine Grace Frances Gore.

Decameron, by Giovanni Boccaccio.

—— of the West, by Arthur Sinclair.

Deceitfulness of pleasure.

December Tales, by William Harrison Ainsworth.

Deception.

Decided Preference.

Decision, by Barbara Hofland.

—— and Indecision, by Mrs. Parker.

—— : a Tale, by Anne Raikes Harding.

De Clifford, by Mrs. Kennedy.

—— or the Constant Man, by Robest Plumer Ward.

——, or Passion more powerful than Reason.

De Cliffords, by Mary Martha Sherwood and Sophia Kelly.

De Courville, *see* Gothic story of . . .

Deeds of faith, by John Mason Neale.

—— of the Olden Time, by Ann Hatton.

Deerbrook, by Harriet Martineau.

De Foix, by Anna Eliza Bray.

Deformed Mendicant, by Sarah S. Wilkinson.

Deirdri, by Theophilus O' Flanagan.

De Lacy, or passion's slave.

De La Macy, by J. R. W. Lomas.

De La Mark and Constantia.

De la Sarre, *see* Life and adventures of M . . .

Delaval.

Delaware, by George Payne Rainsford James.

Delborough Family, *see* Anecdotes of the . . .

De Leurich, *see* Travels and surprising adventures of Mademoiselle.

Delia, A pathetic and interesting tale, by Mary Pilkington.

Delicate distress, by Elizabeth and Richard Griffith.

Delicate embarrassment.

Delicate objection.

Delineations of the heart, by John Raithby.

De Lisle, by Hon. Mrs. Grey.

Dellingborough Castle.

Delmore, or modern friendship, by Mrs. D. Roberts.

Deloraine, by William Godwin.

Deloraine, by Mrs. Martin.

De L'Orme, by George Payne Rainsford James.

Delphine, by A. L. G. Necker de Stael-Holstein.

Delusion. A Novel.

Delves, by Susannah Gunning.

De Merley, by William Henry Short.

Demetrius, a Russian romance.

Demi-Rep of Fashion, *see* Memoirs of a . . .

Democrat, by Henry James Pye.

——, a Tale.

De Montfort.

De Mowbray, by Nella Stephens.

Denial, by Rev. James Thomson.

Dennis Neale, *see* Memoirs of the life and remarkable exploits of . . .

Denouement.

Denounced, by John Banim.

Denton Hall.

Deodatus, by Edward Wilson.

Dependence.

D'Erbine.

De Renzey, by R. N. Kelly.

De Rohan, by Marie Joseph Eugene Sue.

Derry, a tale of the Revolution, by Charlotte Elizabeth Tonna.

Derwent Priory, by A. Kendall.

Derwentwater, by Edward Duros.

De Santillana, by Zara Wentworth.

Desborough Family, by Catherine Ponsonby.

Description of Millenium Hall, by Sarah Scott and Lady Barbara Montagu.

Deserted daughter, by Charlotte Turner Smith.

—— wife, by Mrs. Rice.

Deserter, by Charlotte Elizabeth Tonna.

——, a Novel, by Amelia Beauclerc.

Des Grieux, *see* History of the Chevalier . . .

Desmond. A Novel, by Charlotte Turner Smith.

Destination, by Clara Reeve.

Destiny, or the Chief's Daughter, by Susan Edmondstone Ferrier.

——, or Family Occurrences.

Desultory Man, by George Payne Rainsford James.

—— Sketches.

Detraction Displayed, by Amelia Opie.

De Valcourt, by Agnes Maria Bennett.

De Vasacour, by Charles John Gardiner, Earl of Blessington.

De Vere: or the man of independence, by Robert Plumer Ward.

Devereux. A Tale, by Edward Bulwer, Lord Lytton.

Devil and Tom Walker.

—— in love, by Jacques Cazotte.

—— in petticoats, see Secret history of a . . .

—— turn'd Hermit, by P. L. Saumery.

—— upon Crutches, by Alan Rene Le Sage.

—— upon Crutches in England.

—— upon two Sticks in England, by William Combe.

Devil's Elixir, by Ernst Theodor Amadeus Hoffmann.

Devoted, by Lady Charlotte Susan Maria Bury.

—— One, by Amelia Fitzallen.

Dew Drop, by Frances Boyer Vaux.

De Willenberg, by J. M. H. Hales.

D'Horsay, by John Mills.

Di Montranzo, by Louisa Sidney Stanhope.

Diable Boiteux, by Alan Rene le Sage.

Dialogue between John Smith and Thomas Brown.

—— between Scipio and Bergansa, by Miguel de Cervantes.

—— of courtship between Jockey and Maggy.

Dialogues between a Woman and a Virgin.

—— of a Christian and a Jewess.

—— of a Married Lady and Maid.

—— of a Quaker and his Maid.

Diamond and the Pearl, by Catherine Grace Frances Gore.

Diamonds and Toads.

Diary and notes of Horace Templeton, by Charles James Lever.

——, and Strife and Peace, by Frederika Bremer.

—— of a Blase, by Captain Frederick Marryat.

—— of a Desennuyee, by Catherine Grace Frances Gore.

—— of a Little Dog.

—— of a Nun.

—— of a physician, see Manuscripts from the . . .

Dick the day scholar.

—— Distich, see Adventures of . . .

—— Field.

——, the little pony, see Memoirs of . . .

—— Turpin, by Henry Downes Miles.

—— Whittington, see Life and times of Whittington.

Did you ever see such damned stuff ?

Dilemmas of Pride, by Margracia Loudon.

Diligence, or Ethel Villiers, by Agnes M. Stewart.

Diligent Dick, see History of . . .

Dilworth, by T. Southwood.

Dinan, by Arthur Johnson.

Dinarbas, by Ellis Cornelia Knight.

Disappointed Heir, by Mrs. A. Gomersall.

Disappointment, by Frances Boyer Vaux.

Disasters of a frolicsome pig.

Discarded daughter, by Eugenia de Acton.

—— Son, by Regina Maria Roche.

Discipline, a Novel, by Mary Brunton.

—— of life, by Lady Emily Ponsonby.

Discontented Man, by Anthony Frederick Holstein.

Discovery of the Island Frivola.

——, or the Memoirs of Miss Marianne Middleton, by Mrs. A. Woodfin.

——, or the Mysterious separation of Hugh Doherty, by Hugh Doherty.

Discreet Princess, by Robert Samber.

Disgrace to the Family, by W. Blanchard Jerrold.

Disgraceful effects of falsehood, by Mary S. Pilkington.

Disinherited, by Lady Charlotte Susan Maria Bury.

Disinterested Love.

—— marriage.

—— Nobob.

Disobedience, a Novel.

Disobedient Joseph, by Mrs. Mitford.

Disorder and Order, by Amelia Beauclerc.

Disowned, by Edward Bulwer, Lord Lytton.

Display, by Jane Taylor.

Disputed inheritance, by Grace Webster.

Disruption, by W. Cross.

Dissenting Minister, see Autobiography of a . . .

Dissipation, by Anne Raikes Harding.

Distant Hills, by Rev. William Adams.

Distinction, a tale.

Distressed Lady.

—— lady's garland.

—— lovers.

—— Orphan.

—— virtue.

Diurnal Events.

Diversions of Hollycot, by Mrs. Christian Isobel Johnstone.

Diverting history of Number Nip, by Johann Karl August Musaeus.

Divorced, by Lady Charlotte Susan Maria Bury.

Doctor Birch and his young friends, by William Makepeace Thackeray.

——, &c., by Robert Southey.

Dr. Faustus, see The History of Dr. John Faustus.

—— Faustus, see Life and adventures of the celebrated . . .

Doctor Hookwell, by Robert Armitage.

—— John Faustus, see History of . . .

Doctor's little daughter, by Eliza Meteyard.

Dog of Knowledge.

Doings in London, by George Smeeton.

Dolgorucki and Menzikof, by August Heinrich Julius Lafontaine.

Dombey and Son, *see* Dealings with the Firm of . . .

Domestic Anecdotes.

—— comforts, by Francis Kelly.

—— contrasts.

—— Misery.

—— Pleasures, by Frances Boyer Vaux.

—— Scenes, a Novel.

—— scenes, or the adventures of a doll.

—— scenes, a tale for the times.

—— stories from the German, by Annabella Plumptre.

—— Tales, by Mary Johnston.

Dominican, by Captain F. Williamson.

Dominie's Legacy, by Andrew Picken.

Dominique the resolute.

Don Alphonso Blas de Lirias, *see* History and Adventures of . . .

—— Antonio de Trezzanio, *see* Life and surpirzing adventures of . . .

—— Esteban, by Valentin Llanos Gutierrez.

—— Ferdinand and Donna Marie, *see* Amorous Intrigues of . . .

—— Juan de las Sierras, by Alicia Lefanu.

—— Juan van Halen, *see* Memoirs of . . .

—— Pedro Antos, *see* Manœuvres of . . .

—— Quixote, by Miguel de Cervantes.

—— Raphael, by George Walker.

—— Sebastian, by Anna Maria Porter.

Donald Monteith, by Selina Davenport.

Donalda, or the Witches of Glensheill.

Doncaster Races, by Alexander Bicknell.

Don't despair, by William Beck.

—— stake a pound to raise a crown.

Doom of Giallo, by James Boaden.

Doomed, by Alexander Hamilton.

Dora Melder, by Meta Sander.

Dorando, a Spanish Tale, by James Boswell.

Dorinda Catsby, *see* History of Miss . . .

—— Grafton, by J. P. Hurstone.

Dorothea, or a ray of the new light.

Double courtship, by Mrs. M. L. Sweetser.

—— Disappointment.

—— marriage.

—— Oath, by Baroness de Calabrella.

—— surprise.

—— Trial.

Douglas and MacDonald.

—— D'Arcy, by William Hayley.

——, or the Highlander, by Robert Bisset.

——, a narrative.

Dovedell Hall, by William Holloway.

Doveton, by Sir John William Kaye.

Dowager, by Catherine Grace Frances Gore.

Dramatic scenes from real life, by Sydney Lady Morgan.

Dramatic Stories, by Thomas Arnold.

—— Tales. by James Hogg.

—— tales. The Zingaro girl.

Drawing-Room tales, by Caroline Horwood.

Dreadful fire.

Dream, by Robert Evans.

Dream of Alicbiades.

—— of fate.

—— of Heaven, by T. Sharp.

—— of life.

—— of the Lily Bell, by Henry Morley.

—— of Little Tuk, by Hans Christian Andersen.

Drelincourt and Rodalvi, by Mrs. Byron.

Drive in the Coach through the streets of London, by Mary Martha Sherwood.

Drop in the Ocean.

Druidess.

Drunkard's progress, by George William Macarthur Reynolds.

Dry ground, by Mary Martha Sherwood.

Duchenier, by John Mason Neale.

Duchess de la Vallière, by Comtesse de Genlis.

—— de la Vallière, by Charles Lennox.

—— of C., *see* Affecting history of the . . .

—— of York.

——, or woman's love and woman's hate, by A. Boyd.

Duchesse de Bracciano, by Marie Joseph Eugène Sue.

Dudley, by Adelaide O'Keefe.

—— Castle, by Mary Martha Sherwood.

—— Cranbourne.

Duellists, or men of Honour, by William Lucas.

Duke Christian of Luneburg, by Jane Porter.

—— ; A Novel, by Catherine Maria Grey.

—— of Clarence, by Mrs. E. M. Foster.

—— of Exeter, by Robert Bage.

—— of Lauzun, by Comtesse de Genlis.

—— of Monmouth, by Gerald Griffin.

Dun NanGedh, *see* Banquet of . . .

Dunallan, by Grace Kennedy.

Duncan and Peggy, by Elizabeth Helme.

Dunethvin.

Dunleith Abbey.

Dunsany.

Dunster Castle, by Joseph Thomas Hewlett.

Duodecimo, or the Scribbler's Progress.

Duped guardian, by Mrs. H. Cartwright.

Du Plessis's Memoirs.

Durval and Adelaide, by Catherine Lara.

Dusseldorf, by Anna Maria Mackenzie.

Dutch in the Medway, by Charles Macfarlane.

Duty and Inclination, by Letitia Elizabeth Landon.

——, a Novel, by Margaret Roberts.

Dying soldier, by William Sinclair.

Each sex in their humour.

Eardley Hall.

Earl of Desmond, by Caroline Maxwell.

—— of Douglas, by Marie Catherine le Jumel de Berneville, Comtesse d' Aulnois.

—— of Essex, by Charles Whitehead.

—— Osric, by Mrs. Isaacs.

—— Strongbow, by James White.

Earldom Restored, by Edward Lakeby.

Earl's daughter, by Elizabeth Missing Sewell.
Early Feuds.
—— love.
—— prose romances, see Collection of . . .
Earthquake, a tale, by John Galt.
East India Sketch-Book.
—— Indian, by Mary Julia Young.
Easter eggs, by Johann Christoph von Schmid.
—— gift.
—— Offering, by Frederika Bremer.
Eastern romance.
—— Tales or Moral Allegories.
Easy Stories for the Amusement and Information of Children.
—— tales for little children.
Eben Erskine, by John Galt.
Écarté, by John Richardson.
Eccentric Lover, by Bayle St. John.
—— Tales, by W. F. Von Kosewitz.
—— Traveller.
Eccentricity: a Novel, by Louisa Macnally.
Eda Morton and her cousins.
Edelfrida, A Novel.
Eden Vale, by Catherine Parry.
Edgar. A National Tale, by Elizabeth Appleton.
——, or the phantom of the castle, by R. Sickelmore.
Edinburgh: A Satirical Novel.
—— tales, by Mrs. Christian Isobel Johnstone.
Edington, by Richard Hey.
Edith Leslie.
—— of Glammis, by Alexander Hamilton.
Edith's lesson.
Edmond of Lateragh.
Edmund and Eleonora, by Edmund Marshall.
—— Fitzaubrey.
—— of Erin, see Life and acts of the renowned and chivalrous . . .
—— of the forest.
—— O'Hara.
—— Oliver, by Charles Lloyd, Junior.
——, or the child of the castle.
——, a tale for children, by Charlotte Elizabeth Sanders.
Edric the Forester, by Ann Kerr.
Edrick the Saxon, by Arthur Stanley Bride.
Education: or Elizabeth, her lover and Husband, by Eliza Taylor.
Edward and Anna, by Rev. John Bristed.
—— and Annette, by August Heinrich Julius Lafontaine.
—— and Frances, by Leonardo Nuñes.
—— and George.
—— and Harriet.
—— and Julia.
—— and Laura.
—— and Sophia.
—— Bernard, by Mary S. Pilkington.
—— Beaumont.
——, the Crusader's Son, by Louisa Mary Barwell.

Edward de Courcy.
—— Evelyn, by Jane Strickland.
—— Fitz-York, by C. Janson.
—— Lascelles, see Scenes from the Life of . . .
—— Neville.
——, a novel.
——, or almost an Owenite, by Charles Benjamin Tayler.
——, or the Pursuit of Happiness.
——, or sorrows from Separation.
—— Orland.
—— the orphan, by Dorothy Kilner.
—— Teach, see Voyages and adventures of . . .
——. Translated from the French, by Claire L. R. Bonne, Duchesse de Duras.
—— Travers, by Jane Sergeant.
——. Various Views of Human Nature, by Dr. John Moore.
—— Westley, by William Gardiner.
—— Wortley.
Edwardina, by Catherine Harris.
Edward's Cross, by W. E. Ennersley.
Edwin and Anna.
—— and Henry, by Robert Huish.
—— and Julia, see Interesting story of . . .
—— and Mary, by Lady Eliza Dorothea Tuite.
——, or the Heir of Aella.
——; or the Motherless Boy, by Bourne Hall Draper.
——, or the wandering fugitive.
Edwy and Bertha, by John Corry.
—— and Elgiva, by John Agg.
——, son of Ethelred the Second.
Effects and adventures of Raby Rattler, by Thomas Hall.
—— of groundless hatred.
—— of tyranny.
Effingham Hazard.
Effusions of friendship and fancy, by John Langhorne.
Egbert, or the monk of Penmon.
Eglantine, or, the family of Fortescue, by Charlotte Nooth.
——, or the flower that never fades.
Eight historical tales.
Eighteen hundred and fifteen, by John Agg.
—— hundred and twelve, by Ludwig Rellstab.
El Buscapié, by Adolphe de Castro.
El Poder, see Poder.
Ela, or the delusions of the heart, by Mrs. Burke.
—— the outcast, by Thomas Peckett Prest.
Elder brother.
Eldest son, by Rev. Caesar Henri Abraham Malan.
Eleanor, by Selina Bunbury.
—— Ogilvie, by Rosalia St. Clair.
——, or the Spectre of St. Michael's, by Miss C. D. Haynes.
Eleanora, a Novel, by Mrs. A. Gomersall.
Eleazer and Naphtaly, by Jean Pierre Clavis de Florian.

Election, by Rev. George Brittaine.
Elements of Tuition.
Elfrida, heiress of Belgrove, by Emma Parker.
——, or Paternal Ambition.
Elidure and Ella, by William Gibson.
Eliezer.
Elisa Powell, by Edward Davies.
Eliza Beaumont and Harriet Osborne, by Indiana Brooke.
—— Cleland.
—— Grimwood.
—— Harding, by Esther Hewlett.
—— : a novel, by Mrs. Yeates.
——, or the pious village girl.
—— Warwick, see History of . . .
Elizabeth and her three beggars, by Barbara Hofland.
—— de Bruce, by Mrs. Christian Isobel Johnstone.
—— de Mowbray.
—— Evanshaw, by William Pitt Scargill.
—— Loveless, see Remarkable History of . . .
——, a novel, by Mrs. Carver.
——, or the Exiles of Siberia, by Sophie Cottin.
—— Percy.
—— Williams, see Letters from . . .
—— Wisebourn, see Life of the late celebrated Mrs. . . .
—— Woodville, see History of . . .
Ella, the Ballet girl, by Rose Ellen Hendriks.
——, or the Emperor's Son, by Honble. Camden Elizabeth Lambert.
——, or he's always in the way, by Maria Hunter.
—— Rosenberg, by William Herbert.
—— St. Lawrence, by Mrs. Isaacs.
Ellen, by Eliza Paget.
—— and Julia by Eliza Parsons.
—— Braye, by Miss Blackwell.
—— Cameron, by Emily Elizabeth Rankin.
—— Cleveland, by Jane Strickland.
——, Countess of Castle Howel, by Agnes Maria Bennett.
—— Harding.
——, Heiress of the Castle, by Mary S. Pilkington.
—— Middleton, by Lady Georgiana Fullerton.
—— of Dingle, by Mrs. A. M. Thompson.
——, or the Naughty Girl Reclaimed.
—— or the Young Godmother, by Alicia Catherine Mant.
—— Percy, by George William Macarthur Reynolds.
—— Ramsay, by Hannah W. Moore.
—— Rushford.
——, a tale of Ireland, by Miss Johnston.
——, the teacher, by Barbara Hofland.
—— Walsingham.
—— Woodley, by Elizabeth Bonhote.
Ellen's Dream.
Ellesmere Family.
——, a novel, by Mary Meeke.

Ellie Forestere, by John Brent.
Ellinor, by Mary Ann Hanway.
Elliott, by Mrs. Burke.
Ellmer Castle.
Elmina, a tale.
Elnathan.
Eloisa de Clairville.
——, or a Series of Original Letters, by Jean Jacques Rousseau.
Eloise de Montblanc.
Elopement, or the Deadly Struggle, by Rev. John Humphrey St. Aubyn.
——, or the imprudent connexion, by John Corry.
Elphinstone, by Alfred Butler.
Elsmere and Rosa, see The History of . . .
Eton.
Elvina.
Elvington, by Eliza Nathan.
Emancipation, by Mary Martha Sherwood.
Embarrassed lovers.
Embassy, by Louis Alexis Chamerovzow.
Emerance to Lucy, see Letters from . . .
Emigrant family, by Alexander Harris.
—— orphans.
——, a tale of Australia, by W. H. Leigh.
Emigrants, a gallant tale.
—— of Ahadarra, by William Carleton.
Emilia and Alphonsus.
—— Wyndham, by Anne Marsh.
Emily and her Cousins, by M. Baker.
—— and her Mother, see History of . . .
—— de Varmont, by Jean Baptiste Louvet de Couvray.
—— Fitzormond, by Thomas Peckett Prest.
—— Grey.
—— Montague, see History of . . .
——, a moral tale, by Rev. Henry Kett.
—— Moreland, by Hannah Maria Lowndes.
——, a Novel.
—— of Lucerne, by Mrs. E. M. Foster.
—— of Santraile, see Family of Santraile.
——, or the Countess of Rosendale, by Honble. Catherine Charlotte Maberly.
——, or the history of a natural daughter.
——, or the test of sincerity, by Lucy Peacock.
—— or Traits of Principle.
——, or the Wife's first error, by Elizabeth Bennett.
—— Percy.
——, a tale for young persons.
—— Trevor.
Emily's reward, by Barbara Hofland.
Emir Malek, by John Henry Barrow.
Emma and her nurse, see Memoirs of . . .
—— and the little Silk-Makers.
—— Corbett, by Samuel Jackson Pratt.
—— Courtney, see Memoirs of . . .
—— de Lissau, by Amelia Bristow.
—— Dorvill.
——. A Novel, by Jane Austen.
——, or the child of sorrow.
——, or the Foundling of the Wood, by Charlotte Brooke.

Emma, or the unfortunate attachment, by Georgiana Cavendish, Duchess of Devonshire.

Emmeline, or good humour, by Mrs. E. Smith.

——, or the Orphan of the Castle, by Charlotte Turner Smith.

—— with Some Other Pieces, by Mary Brunton.

Emperor Manalay, *see* History of the . . .

Empire of the Nairs, by James Lawrence.

Employment, the true source of happiness, by Diana Bayley.

Empress, a Novel, by G. Bennett.

Empronia.

Enamoured spirit, by Jacques Cazotte.

Enchanted Doll, by Mark Lemon.

—— knights, by Johann Karl August Musaeus.

—— lake, by A. L. A. D. Dudevant.

—— mirror.

—— ring, by C. M. Littleton.

—— rock, by Percy Bolingbroke St. John.

Enchantress.

Encourager, by George Mogridge.

Endless entertainment, by J. Mark.

Energy : a tale, by Barbara Hofland.

Engagement : A Novel.

English at home, by Constantine Henry, Phipps, Marquis of Normanby.

—— Baronet, by Leonora des Straella.

—— Boy at the Cape, by Edward Augustus Kendall.

—— Brothers.

—— exposé, by Medora Gordon Byron.

—— Fashionables Abroad, by Mrs. C. D. Burdett.

—— Fireside, by John Mills.

—— Gill Blas, by John Canton.

—— governess, by Rachel MacCrindell.

—— Hermit.

—— in France, by Constantine Henry Phipps, Marquis of Normanby.

—— in India, by Thomas Henry Ottley.

—— in India, and other Sketches.

—— in Italy, by Constantine Henry Phipps. Marquis of Normanby.

—— Life.

—— merchant, by T. Bolas.

—— Night's Entertainments.

—— Nun, by Catharine Selden.

—— Princess.

—— spy, by Charles Molloy Westmacott.

—— Stories, by Maria Hack.

—— Struwelpeter, by Heinrich Hoffmann.

—— Woman, by Medora Gordon Byron.

Englishman in Paris.

——, a novel, by Medora Gordon Byron.

Englishman's Fortnight in Paris.

Entail : or the Lairds of Guppy, by John Galt.

Entanglement.

Entertainer.

Entertaining and instructive tales.

—— history of little Goody Goosecap.

—— History of Old Robin Gray.

—— history of Palidor and Fidele.

Entertaining juggler.

—— Novelist.

—— novels, by Jane Barker.

—— story-teller.

Enthusiasm not religion.

Entire new collection of romances and novels.

Entretien des Beaux Esprits, by Eliza Haywood.

Ephraim Tristram Bates, *see* Life and Memoirs of Mr . . .

Epicurean, a tale, by Thomas Moore.

Ereston, by Charles Courtenay.

Ermina, by Mary Martha Sherwood.

—— Montrose, by Emily Clarke.

Ernest Campbell, by John Ainslie.

—— Maltravers, by Edward Bulwer, Lord Lytton.

—— Singleton, by Robert Armitage.

Ernestina, *see* History of . . .

——, a novel, by Esther Holstein.

Ernestine : or the child of mystery, by Miss Blackwell.

Ernesto, by William Henry Smith.

Ernestus Berchtold, by John William Polidori.

Ernnestine de Lacy, by Thomas Peckett Prest.

Errand boy, by Mary Martha Sherwood.

Erratics, by a Sailor.

Errors and their Consequences.

—— of education, by Eliza Parsons.

—— of Innocence, by Harriet Lee.

—— of sensibility.

Escapes, Wanderings and Preservation of a Hare.

Eskdale herd-boy, by Lady Stoddart.

Esquimaux ; or, Fidelity, by Emily Clarke.

Essay of three tales.

Essays and tales.

—— and tales, by M. E. Engel.

——, tales, and poems, by T. S. Norgate.

——, tales and sketches, by Edward Sloane.

Estelle, by Jean Pierre Clavis de Florian.

Esther Merle, by Mrs. Francis Vidal.

——, or the two Mothers.

Ethel Churchill, by Letitia Elizabeth Landon.

Ethelbert, by Catherine Cuthbertson.

Ethelia, by Jane Harvey.

Ethelinda, or the fair maid of the Inn.

Ethelinde, or the fatal vow, by Thomas Peckett Prest.

——, or the Recluse of the Lake, by Charlotte Turner Smith.

Ethelwina, by T. J. Horsley Curties.

Etonian, by Charlotte Adams.

Eudoxia, by Don Pedro Montengon.

Eugene and Eugenia by Choudard Desforges.

—— Aram, by Edward Bulwer, Lord Lytton.

Eugenia and Adelaide.

Eugenio, or the man of sorrow, by Ambrose Pitman.

Eugenius, or Anecdotes of the Golden Vale, by Richard Graves, the Younger.

Euphemia, by Charlotte Lennox.
Euphemia's little scholars, see History of . . .
Euphronia, by Mrs. Norris.
Eura and Zedepyra, by David Booth.
Eureka : A Prophecy of the Future, by Robert Folkestone Williams.
Eustace Conway, by John Frederick Denison Maurice.
—— Fitz-Richard.
——, or the stage of life, by Thomas James Serle.
Euston Hall, by J. A. Boddy.
——, a novel.
Eva, a novel, by Isabella Kelly.
—— of Cambria, by Emma de Lisle.
——, or the bridal spectre.
—— St. Clair, by George Payne Rainsford James.
Evadne, by Charles Rowcroft.
Eve of All-Hallows, by Mathew Weld Hartstonge.
—— of St. Agnes, by Catherine George Ward.
—— of St. Marco, by George Soane.
—— of San-Pietro.
—— San Marco.
Evelina, or a young lady's entrance into the world, by Madame d'Arblay.
Evelyn, by Selina Bunbury.
—— Harcourt, by Mrs, M. A. Gascoigne.
—— Howard.
—— Mountjoy, by Mrs. Robert Moore.
—— Stuart, by Anne Kent.
Evening amusement.
—— amusement for the ladies.
—— bell, by Caroline Reinhold.
—— Brush.
—— recreations.
—— visit, by Lucy Lyttelton Cameron.
—— walk.
Evenings Abroad, by Frances Maclellan.
—— at Haddon Hall, edited by the Baroness of Calabrella.
—— at home, by Dr. John Aikin and Mrs. Barbauld.
—— at Sackville College, by John Mason Neale.
—— in the Pyrenees, by Selina Bunbury.
—— with the old story-tellers.
Eventful epoch, by Nicholas Mitchell.
Everard, an Irish tale, by Matthew Archdeacon.
Eversfield Abbey.
Every Day Occurrences.
Evil eye.
Example, or family scenes.
——, or history of Lucy Cleveland.
Excessive Sensibility, by Mrs. Thomson.
Exclusives, by Lady Charlotte Susan Maria Bury.
Excursion, by Charlotte Brooke.
—— into the Planets, see Fantastical . . .
—— of Osman.
Exemplary Mother, by Maria Susanna Cooper.
—— novels, by Miguel de Cervantes.

Exertion, or children of the forest, by Mary Anne Bourne.
Exhibitions of the Heart, by Miss A. A. Hutchinson.
Exile of Erin, by William Frederick Deacon.
—— of Erin, by Elizabeth Gunning.
—— of Poland, by Mrs. Richardson.
—— of Portugal, by Augusta Amelia Stuart.
——, or Matilda of the Castle.
Exiles of Palastine, by John Carne.
——, or Memoirs of the Count de Cronstadt, by Clara Reeve.
Expatriated, by George Jones.
Expectant : a Novel, by Ellen Pickering.
Expedition of Humphrey Clinker, by Tobias Smollett.
—— of Little Pickle.
Experience, a tale for all ages, by Anne Raikes Harding.
—— : tales, by George Shaw.
Experiences of a Gaol Chaplain, by Erskine Neale.
Explanation, or agreeable surprise.
Exploits of Don Quixote, by Miguel de Cervantes.
Express, a novel, by Frances d'Aubigne.
Exquisite : A collection of tales, Histories, and Essays.
Exquisites, by Don Telesforo de Trueba y Cozio.

F. Reveep, see Life and surprising adventures of . . .
Fable of Cupid and Psyche, by Lucius Apuleius.
Fables ancient and modern.
—— and tales for the ladies.
—— calculated for the amusement and instruction of youth.
—— in Monosyllables, by Eleanor, Lady Fenn.
—— originales, by John Kidgell.
Fabulous Histories, by Sarah Trimmer.
Faces in the Fire, by George Frederick Pardon.
Facts and Fancies, by George Godwin.
—— and fictions from Italy, by Francis Sylvester Mahony.
Fair Adulteress.
—— Adultress.
—— Cambrians.
—— Circassian, by Alexandre Marie Anne de Lavaissiere de Lavergne.
—— Hiberbian.
—— impostor.
—— maid of Wyoming, by Gabriel Alexander.
—— of May Fair, by Catherine Grace Frances Gore.
—— Rosamond, by Thomas Miller.
—— Rosamond, see Life and death of . . .
—— Rosamund, by Pierce Egan, the Younger.
—— Syrian, by Robert Bage.
—— wanderer.

Fairchild Family, see History of the . . .
Fairy birds from fancy islet.
—— bower, by Harriet Mozley.
—— Favours and other tales, by Elizabeth Frances Dagley.
—— Knoll, by Mary Martha Sherwood.
—— of misfortune, by Edward Dubois.
—— ring.
—— Spectator, by Eleanor, Lady Fenn.
—— stories.
—— Tales for youth.
—— tales from all Nations, by Anthony R. Montalba.
—— tales, selected from the best authors.
—— Tales translated from the German.
Faith and Fiction, by Elizabeth Bennett.
Faithful Narrative, by Tobias Smollett.
Faithless sea captain.
Fakeer, a tale, by Richard Owen Cambridge.
Falcon family, by Marmion W. Savage.
Falconbridge Abbey, by Mary Ann Hanway.
Falkland, by Edward Bulwer, Lord Lyfton.
Falkner, a Novel, by Mary Wollstonecraft Shelley.
Fall of the Nan Soung, by A. L. Lymbunner.
Fallen minister, by Christian Heinrich Spiess.
False appearances.
—— friend, by Mary Robinson.
—— gratitude.
—— Hair, by George Payne Rainsford James.
—— Step and The Sisters, by Miss Jones.
Familiar Letters between the principal characters in David Simple, by Sarah Fielding.
—— tales for young children.
Families of Owen and De Montfort.
Family Affection, by Mrs. Pinchard.
—— annals, or the sisters, by Mary Hays.
—— annals, or worldly wisdom, by Rachel Hunter.
—— at Heatherdale.
—— at Smiledale, see History of the . . .
—— Book, by Arnaud Berquin.
—— Estate, by Mrs. Ross.
—— failings, by Miss Fisher.
—— Legends and Traditions of the South of Ireland, by Thomas Crofton Croker.
—— Mansion, by Mrs. Isaac Taylor.
—— of Halden, by August Heinrich Julius La Fontaine.
—— of Kinkvervankotsdarsprakengotschderns, see Modern Anecdote of the . . .
—— of M'Roy, see Annals of the . . .
—— of St. Richard the Saxon.
—— of Santraile, by Harriet Jones.
—— party, by Mary Julia Young.
—— Picture, by Thomas Holcroft.
—— Picture Gallery.
—— Pictures, by Susannah Gunning.

Family Portraits, by Catherine George Ward.
—— Pride and Humble Merit, by E. Senate.
—— quarrels, by August Heinrich Julius Lafontaine.
—— Records, by Lady Charlotte Susan Maria Bury.
—— Robinson Crusoe, by Johann David Rudolf Wyss.
—— Secrets, Literary and domestic, by Samuel Jackson Pratt.
—— Secrets, or hints to those who would make a home happy, by Sarah Stickney Ellis.
—— secrets, or a page from life's volume.
—— Sepulchre, by Theodora Elizabeth Lynch.
—— sketches.
—— Suppers, by Julie de Lafaye-Bréhier.
Famous adventures of Captain John Avery.
—— history of the seven wise masters of Rome.
—— history of the seven wise mistresses of Rome.
—— history of the unfortunate lovers Hero and Leander.
Fancied events, by Elizabeth Sarah Villa-Real Gooch.
Fancy Fair.
Fan-Hy-Cheu, by Stephen Weston.
Fanny, the Amours of a West Country Young Lady.
—— and her mamma, by Caroline Leicester.
—— and her mother.
—— Brown, see Life of Miss . . .
—— Fitz-York, by Ann Ryley.
—— Hill, see Memoirs of a * * * * *
* * * * * * * * * *
—— the little milliner, by Charles Rowcroft.
—— Mason, see History of . . .
—— Meadows, see History of . . .
—— Mills, see History of . . .
——, a novel.
——, or the deserted daughter.
——, or the happy repentance, by François Marie de Baculard D'Arnaud.
—— Seymour, see History of . . .
Fantastical excursion into the Planets.
Fardorougha the Miser, by William Carleton.
Farewell tales, by Barbara Hofland.
Farmer of Inglewood Forest, by Elizabeth Helme.
Farmer's Boy, by Elizabeth Gunning.
—— Daughter, by Lucy Lyttelton Cameron.
—— daughter of Essex, by James Penn.
Farmers, or tales of the times.
Farmer's son of Kent.
Farmers Three Daughters, by Alexander Balfour.
Faro Table, by Sir Charles Sedley.
Fascination, by Catherine Grace Frances Gore.

Fashion and its Votaries, by Honble. Catherine Charlotte Maberly.
Fashionable Follies, by Thomas Vaughan.
—— friend, by Elizabeth Bonhote.
—— Infidelity.
—— Mysteries, by Francis Lathom.
—— swindler.
Fashionables and Unfashionables, by Rosalia St. Clair.
Fast of St. Magdalen, by Anna Maria Porter.
Fatal Ambition, by A. V. Forster.
—— effects of deception.
—— Effects of Inconstancy, by C. J. Dorat.
—— effects, or letters of the Marchioness de Syrcé.
—— follies, by Mrs. Thomson.
—— friendship.
—— indifference.
—— Interview, by Isaac Hurlstone.
—— love.
—— marriage.
—— obedience.
—— Revenge, by Charles Robert Maturin.
—— Scarf, by Madame Leinstein.
—— Secret : or Unknown Warrior, by Sophia King.
—— Step, or the history of Mrs. Brudenel.
—— Vow, by Francis Lathom.
Fatalist, by Nicholas Mitchell.
Fatalists, by Mrs. Kelly.
Fatality.
Fate of beauty.
—— of Graysdale.
—— of Sedley, by Henry Summersett.
—— of Velina de Guidova, by Mary Ann Radcliffe.
—— ; or Spong Castle, by Maria Yanzee.
Father and Daughter, by Amelia Opie.
—— and son, or Claremont.
—— and Son, a tale.
—— as he should be, by Barbara Hofland.
—— Butler and the Lough Derg Pilgrim, by William Carleton.
—— Clayton, by Grace Kennedy.
—— Connell, by John Banim.
—— Darcy, by Anne Marsh.
—— Eustace, by Frances Trollope.
—— Felix, by C. J. Cannon.
—— Innocent.
—— John.
—— Oswald.
Fatherless Fanny.
—— Fanny, by Thomas Peckett Prest.
—— Rosa, by Robert Huish.
Father's advice to his daughter, by Jean Nicolas Bouilly.
Fathers and sons, by Theodore Edward Hook.
Father's Curse, by Anna Eliza Bray.
—— Eye, by Mary Martha Sherwood.
—— instruction, by Thomas Percival.
—— Love and a Woman's Friendship, by Henrietta Rouviere Mosse.

Father's tales to his daughter, by Jean Nicolas Bouilly.
Fatima, see Story of . . .
Faulconstein Forest.
Fault was all his own, by Elizabeth Eyton.
Faust, by Johann Wolfgang Goethe.
——, a romance of the Secret Tribunals, by George William Macarthur Reynolds.
Faustus, by Johann Wolfgang Goethe.
——, see History of Dr. John . . .
—— see Life and adventures of the celebrated Dr. . . .
Faux Pas.
Favourite of nature, by Mary Ann Kelty.
—— of Venus, by Theresa Berkley.
Favourites, beauties, and amours, of Henry of Windsor.
—— of Felicity.
Fawn of Sertorius, by Robert Eyres Landor.
—— of Spring-Vale, by William Carleton.
Fawns, by Mary Martha Sherwood.
Fears and Cares, by E. D. Carr.
Feats on the Fiord, by Harriet Martineau.
Features from Life, by Elizabeth Blower.
—— of the youthful mind, by Anne Stone.
Feelings of the Heart.
Felicia to Charlotte, by Mary Collyer.
Felician Alphery, by Hewson Clarke.
Felissa or the life and opinions of a Kitten, Attributed to Charles Lamb.
Felix Alvarez, by Robert Charles Dallas.
—— and Rosarito, see The Adventures of . . .
—— de Lisle, by Anne Flinders.
Fellow Commoner, by John Hobart Caunter.
Female adventurers.
—— American.
—— art, by Ann Pile.
—— Banishment, by Charles de Fieux, Chevalier de Mouhy.
—— Bluebeard, by Marie Joseph Eugène Sue.
—— Confessions, by W. Hall.
—— Constancy.
—— Favourites, see The History of . . .
—— Foundling.
—— Freemasons.
—— friendship.
—— Intrepidity.
—— Pilgrim, by John Mitchell.
—— pilgrim, or deserted wife.
—— politician.
—— Quixote, by Charlotte Lennox.
—— Sensibility.
—— Soldier.
—— Stability, by Charlotte Palmer.
—— Werter.
Ferdinand and Ordella, by Hon. Mary Ann Cavendish Bradshaw.
—— Count Fathom, see Adventures of . . .
—— Fitzormond, by Mrs. Temple.
—— Franck.
Fergusons, or Woman's Love, by E. Phipps.
Fermer the genius, by Ludwig Tieck.

Fernando, or the hero of the times, by
Miss A. Bransby.
Ferrandino, by V. Ulpius.
Ferrers : A romance of the Reign of
George the Second, by Charles Ollier.
Festival of Mora, by Louisa Sidney Stan-
hope.
—— of the Passions.
—— of St. Jago.
Fetches, by John Banim.
Feudal Days, by Mitchell Williams.
—— Tyrants, by Matthew Gregory Lewis.
Feuds of Luna and Perollo.
Fiction without romance, by Maria
Polack.
Fiddle-Faddle's sentimental tour.
Fidelia, or the prevalence of fashion.
Fidelis and Harriot, see Memoirs of . . .
Field of Normandy.
Fiesco, by M. Lyttleton.
Fifty short stories, by Johann Christoph
von Schmid.
Fight of the Fiddlers, by George Payne
Rainsford James.
Filchum Cantum, see History of . . .
Fille de chambre, see Rebecca, or the
Fille de chambre.
Fine Lady, by Sophia Briscoe.
Finesse.
Finger-Post.
Finish to the Adventures of Tom, Jerry
and Logic, by Pierce Egan.
Fire-Eater, by James Wilson.
Fire, or never despair.
Fireside Book, by Charles Benjamin
Tayler.
—— companion.
——, a domestic tale, by Percy Boling-
broke St. John.
—— philosophy, by Mary Ann Kelty.
—— Scenes.
—— stories.
—— Stories by Mrs. Leslie.
—— Tales for the Young, by Sarah
Stickney Ellis.
First and Last Years of Wedded Life, by
Rosalia St. Clair.
—— collection of pathetic, sentimental
and moral narratives.
—— false step, by Thomas Peckett
Prest.
—— false step, by Elizabeth Elton
Smith.
—— Impressions, by Margaret Hodson.
—— love.
—— love, by Margracia Loudon.
—— night of my wedding, by Pigault
Lebrun.
—— tales for children, by Johann
Christoph von Schmid.
—— voyage of Rodolph the voyager.
Fish and the ring.
Fisherman.
Fisherman's children.
—— daughter.
—— hut.
Fishermen.
Fisher's Daughter, by Catherine George
Ward.

Fitz Alwyn, by Elizabeth M. Stewart.
Fitz of Fitz-Ford, by Anna Eliza Bray.
Fitz-Albini, Arthur, by Sir Samuel
Egerton Brydges.
Fitzallan, by Robert Huish.
Fitzalleyne of Berkeley, by Charles
Molloy Westmacott.
Fitz-Edward, by Emma de Lisle.
——, and other tales, by H. E. Lovett
Shekleton.
Fitzgeorge, by John Sterling.
Fitzherbert, or Lovers and Fortune-
Hunters, by Harriet Maria Yorick
Smythies.
Fitzmaurice, by William Frederic
Williams.
Fitzroy, or impulse of the moment, by
Maria Hunter.
Fitzwalters, by James Norris Brewer.
Fitzwiggins, by W. Massie.
Five Nights of St. Alban's by William
Mudford.
—— Years of Youth, by Harriet
Martineau.
Flatterer, or false friendship, by Mary
Ann Hedge.
Fleetwood, by William Godwin.
Flies in amber, by Julia S. H. Pardoe.
Flight of the Camisards, by Rev. Christian
Gottlob Barth.
Flights of Inflatus.
Flim-Flams, by Isaac D'Israeli.
Flirtation, a Novel, by Lady Charlotte
Susan Maria Bury.
Flittings of Fancy, by Robert Sullivan.
Floods.
Flora and her children.
——, the Beauty of the Scottish Border.
—— Mortimer, by Mrs. Edmonds.
——, or the deserted child, by Elizabeth
Somerville.
Florence Graham, by Malcolm Graham.
—— Macarthy, by Sydney, Lady
Morgan.
——, or the Aspirant, by Mrs. Robertson.
Florentine tales.
Florentines, by Benjamin Thompson.
Florestan, or the New Lord of the Manor,
by Thomas Dolby.
Flower basket.
——, Fruit, and Thorn Pieces, by Jean
Paul Friedrich Richter.
Flowers, of the forest, by Mary Martha
Sherwood.
Flying Dutchman, by William Johnson
Neale.
Follies of fashion, by M. Lyttleton.
—— of St. James's Street.
Folly and mischief of prejudices &
obstinacy, by Sarah Maria Lloyd.
—— of finery.
Fool of Quality, by Henry Brooke.
Fool's pence.
Forbidden apartments, by William
Linley.
Force of blood, by Miguel de Cervantes.
—— of Example.
—— of Love, by John Dent.
—— of nature.

Force of truth, by Thomas Scott.
Ford Family in Ireland.
Foreign exclusives in London.
—— Tales and Traditions, by George Godfrey Cunningham.
Forest and the fortress, by Laura Jewry.
—— and game law tales, by Harriet Martineau.
—— Days, by George Payne Rainsford James.
—— Hill, by Mary Elizabeth Wormeley.
—— of Comalva, by Mary Hill.
—— of Hohenelbe, by Sarah Sheriffe.
—— of Montalbano, by Catherine Cuthbertson.
Forester, Le, see Le Forester.
——, a Tale of 1688, by Hon. Mary Louisa Boyle.
Foresters, by John Wilson.
Forester's Daughter, by Hannah D. Burdon.
Foresters : a Novel, by Susannah Gunning.
Forged Note, by Hannah Maria Lowndes.
Forgery, or Best Intentions, by George Payne Rainsford James.
Forlorn hope, by Anna Maria Hall.
Forman, a tale.
Forms of Pride, by Lucy Lyttelton Cameron.
Forrester.
Forresti, or the Italian cousins.
Forsaken ; a Tale.
Fortescue Family, by Mrs. Streeten.
——, a Novel, by James Sheridan Knowles.
——, or the soldier's reward.
Fortitude and Frailty, by Fanny Holcroft.
——, or Euphemia, by B. Taylor.
——, A Tale, by Barbara Hofland.
Fortnight's ramble through London.
—— visit, by William Gardiner.
Fortress : an historical tale of the fifteenth century, by Amelia Lane.
Fortunate Country Maid, by Charles de Fieux, Chevalier de Mouhy.
—— Employ.
—— foundlings, by Eliza Haywood.
—— lovers, by John Breues.
—— Man.
—— Orphan, by Charles de Fieux, Chevalier de Mouhy.
—— transport.
Fortunatus, see History of . . .
Fortune and fortitude, by Thomas Miller.
Fortune-Hunting, by Margracia Loudon.
Fortunes and Adventures of Raby Rattler, by Thomas Hall.
—— frolic.
—— of Colonel Torlogh O'Brien, by Joseph Sheridan Lefanu.
—— Of the Falconars, by Mrs. Gordon.
—— of Francesco Novello Da Carrara, by Galeazzo Gatari.
—— of Frank Fairchild, by Matthew Henry Barker.
—— of Hector O'Halloran, by William Hamilton Maxwell.

Fortunes of Nigel.
—— of Nigel, by Sir Walter Scott.
—— of Perkin Warbeck, by Mary Wollstonecraft Shelley.
—— of Roger De Flor.
—— of the Scattergood Family, by Albert Smith.
—— of woman, by Martha Macdonald Lamont.
—— reverses, by Julie de Lafaye-Bréhier.
Fortune-Teller.
Fortune-Teller in the Old Bailey, see History of the . . .
Fortune-Tellers' Intrigue, by Thomas R. J. Polson.
Fortunio, by Marie Catherine le Jumel de Berneville, Comtesse d'Aulnois.
Forty Years in the World, by Captain R. G. Wallace.
Foscari.
Foscarini.
Foster-Brother, by Thorton Hunt.
Foundling of Cordova, by John Henry.
—— of Devonshire, by Miss C. D. Haynes.
—— of Glenthorn, by Alexander Balfour.
——, or the History of Lucius Stanhope.
——, or the school of life, by Carl Gustav Nieritz.
Fountain of Arethusa, by Robert Eyres Landor.
—— of living waters, by Mary Martha Sherwood.
Four interesting tales.
—— Seasons.
—— young ladies, see Histories of . . .
Fragment.
Fragments in the manner of Sterne, by Isaac Brandon.
Frances, or the Two Mothers.
Francesca Carrara, by Letitia Elizabeth Landon.
Francis and Josepha, by V. A. Hubber.
—— Clive, see Life and adventures of Mr. . . .
—— the first, by Alexandre Dumas.
—— Lever.
—— the Philanthropist.
Frank and George.
—— and his Christmas gift, by Mrs. Mitford.
——, being the sixth part of Early Lessons, by Maria Edgeworth.
—— Fiarchild, see Fortunes of . . .
—— Fairlegh, by Francis Edward Smedley.
—— Hammond, see Adventures of . . .
—— Orby.
Frankenstein, by Mary Wollstonecraft Shelley.
Frascati's.
Freaks of fortune.
Frederic and Caroline.
—— and Louisa, by Osborn T. W. Heighway.
—— and Pharamond, by John Langhorne.

Frederic Latimer, by Count Xavier De Maistre.
—— or the libertine, by Mr. Potter.
Frederica, or the memoirs of a young lady.
—— Risberg.
Frederick.
—— de Montford, by E. Goulbourne.
—— Dornton, by R. N. Kelly.
—— Montravers, by Sophia Woodfall.
—— Morland, by David Carey.
——, or Incidents Illustrative of the beauties and Graces of vital piety.
—— St. Clair.
—— Wilding.
Free grace.
—— Lance, by Daniel M'Carthy.
Freebooter of the Alps, by James Griffin.
Freebooter's Bride.
Freida the Jongleur, by Barbara Hemphill.
Freischütz, see The Original Legend of . . . by A. Apel.
French Adventurer, by Robert Martin Lesuire.
—— dagger, see History of a . . .
—— Gil Blas, by Henri Le Maire.
—— Protestant.
Freston Tower, by Richard Cobbold.
Friar Hidalgo, by E. Martin.
Friar's Tale, by Luke Aylmer Conolly.
Friend of Virtue, by Gaspar Moise de Fontanieu.
—— or foe, by Ellen Pickering.
Friendly champions.
—— Labours, by Lucy Peacock.
Friends and fortune, by Anna Harriet Drury.
—— and lovers.
—— of Fontainbleu, by Hannah D. Burdon.
——, or the contrast between Virtue and Vice, by Elizabeth Griffin.
——, or the history of Billy Freeman and Tommy Truelove.
——, or the Influence of Religion, by A. E. M. Hansard.
——, Or Original Letters of a Person Deceased.
——, or the triumph of innocence over false charges.
——, a sentimental history, by William Guthrie.
—— ; a true tale of Woe.
—— unmasked, by Miss A. A. Hutchinson.
Friendship in a Nunnery.
Fright, by Ellen Pickering.
Frolicksome courtier, see History of the . . .
Frolics of Puck, by George Soane.
Froliksome courtier, see Pleasant and delightful history of the . . .
From Oxford to Rome.
Frugal the wild bee, see The history of . . .
Fruit Shop.
Fruitless repentance.
Fruits of Education, by Lucy Lyttelton Cameron.

Fruits of Instruction.
Fugitive countess, by Sarah S. Wilkinson.
—— of Folly.
—— of the Forest, by Maria Lavinia Smith.
——, or family incidents, by Sarah Green.
Fugitives, or a Trip to Canada, by Edward Lane.
Fun for the parlour.
—— upon fun.
Funeral of the dairyman's daughter.
Further advantages of Jemmy Donkey, by Arabella Argus.

Gabriel Tangent see Adventures of . . .
Gabrielle and Augustina, by Miss S. Fletcher.
—— de Vergy.
——: or Pictures of a Reign, by Louisa Stuart Costello.
Gaieties and Gravities, by Horatio Smith.
Gainsayer Silenced.
Galatea, by Jean Pierre Clavis de Florian.
Gale Middleton, by Horatio Smith.
Galfred and Julietta, by Thomas Brerewood.
Gallant Tom, by Thomas Peckett Prest.
Galloway, Legends of, by J. Denniston.
Gallus, by Wilhelm Adolf Becker.
Gambler's Dream.
Gamblers, or the treacherous friend, by Hannah Maria Lowndes.
Gambler's wife, or murder will out by John Duncan (?)
Game of Life, by Leitch Ritchie.
Gamester.
——, a true story.
Gamesters, by Anna Maria Mackenzie.
Gammer Gurton's pleasant stories, by William John Thoms.
Gap of Barnesmore, by Isaac Butt.
Garry Owen, by Maria Edgeworth.
Garters and ruffles, by Arnaud Berquin.
Gaston de Blondeville, by Ann Radcliffe.
—— de Foix, by George Payne Rainsford James.
Gathered rose.
Gathering of the West, by John Galt.
General entertainer.
—— Lover.
Generosity, a novel.
—— of an Arabian Prince.
Generous Attachment.
—— Briton.
—— guardian.
—— lover, by Abbé Pietro Chiari.
—— man.
—— sister, by Mrs. H. Cartwright.
Genevieve of Brabant, by Johann Christoph von Schmid.
——, or the history of a servant-girl, by Marie Louis Alphonse de Lamartine de Prat.
——, or the Orphan's Visit, by Mrs. Strutt.
Genevive, a tale, by Frances Susanna Carr.
Genii, by Girard.
Genius, by Marquis von Grosse.

Genoveva of Brabant, by Johann Christoph von Schmid.

Gentle moralist.

Gentleman in Black, by James Dalton.

—— in debt, by William J. O'Neill Daunt.

—— Jack, A Naval Story, by William Johnson Neale.

—— Jack ; or life on the road.

—— of the Old School, by George Payne Rainsford James.

Genuine copies of all the love letters and cards which passed between an illustrious personage and a noble lady.

—— distresses of Damon and Celia, by William Renwick.

—— Letters from a gentleman to a young lady, by Thomas Hull.

—— memoirs of Miss Faulkner.

—— memoirs of Miss Harriet Melvin.

George and Eliza.

—— Barnwell, Life of . . .

—— Barnwell, a Novel, by Thomas Skinner Surr.

—— Bateman, by Elizabeth Blower.

—— Desmond, see History of . . .

—— Edwards, see Adventures of Mr. . . .

—— Godfrey, see History of . . .

—— Lovell, by James Sheridan Knowles.

—— Maitland, see Adventures of . . .

—— Mason, see History of . . .

—— , or the planter of the Isle of France, by Alexandre Dumas.

—— Panton, see Story of . . .

—— St. George, by Henry Cockton.

—— the Third, by Edward Mangin.

Georgiana and her father.

Georgie and Lizzie.

Georgina Hammond, by Mrs. Robert Mackenzie Daniel.

—— Neville, see History of . . .

—— , a novel, by Mrs. Howell.

—— , or Memoirs of the Bellmour Family, by Georgina Bouverie.

Gerald Fitzgerald, by Ann Hatton.

—— : a tale of conscience, by G. Lowther.

Geraldina, a novel.

Geraldine Fauconberg, by Sarah Harriet Burney.

—— Hamilton, by Lady Isabella Mohn.

—— Murray, by Miss E. H. Macleod.

—— of Desmond, by Miss Crumpe.

—— , or Modes of Faith and Practice, by Mary Jane Mackenzie.

—— , or the secret assassins of the Old Stone Cross, by Thomas Peckett Prest.

—— , a tale of conscience, by Eleanor C. Agnew.

Geraldwood.

German Christmas Eve, by Apolline Flohr.

—— Gil Blas, by Baron Adolf Franz Friedrich Ludwig von Kuiegge.

—— novelists, by Thomas Roscoe.

—— Popular Stories, by Jakob Ludwig Karl and Wilhelm Grimm.

—— Romance, by Thomas Carlyle.

—— sorceress, by M. Lyttleton.

—— Stories, by Robert Pierce Gillies.

Geronimo and Leonora, by Emily Fortescue Taylor.

Gertrude, by Elizabeth Missing Sewell.

——. Agnes and Melite.

—— de Wart, by Appenzeller.

—— , or thoughtlessness and inattention corrected, by Eliza White.

—— , A Tale of the Sixteenth Century.

Gesta Romanorum, by Rev. Charles Swan.

Gethsemane, by Marie Louis Alphonse de Lamartine de Prat.

Ghost of the rock.

—— Stories.

Ghost-Hunter and his family, by John and Michael Banim.

Ghost of Harcourt.

Ghost-Seer, By Johann Friedrich von Schiller.

Gideon Giles, by Thomas Miller.

Gil Blas, see Adventures of . . .

—— Blas Corrected, by J. S. Osmond.

—— Blas of the Revolution, by Louis Benoît Picard.

Gilbert Copley, by Thomas Peckett Prest.

—— Earle, see Some account of the life of the late. . .

—— Gurney, by Theodore, Edward Hook.

Gilderoy, by Thomas Peckett Prest.

Giles Gingerbread, see The renowned history of . . .

Gilmour, or the last Lockinge.

Giovanni Sbogarro, by Percival Gordon.

Gipsey Bride.

—— Chief, by Hannah Maria Lowndes.

—— Countess, by Susannah Gunning.

—— Girl, by Hannah Maria Lowndes.

Gipsey's warning, by H. J. Copson.

Gipsies.

Gipsy boy, by Thomas Peckett Prest.

—— daughter, by Mrs. Kentish.

—— mother, by Hannah Maria Lowndes.

—— , a tale, by George Payne Rainsford James.

Girl and her basket of eggs.

—— of the Mountains, by Eliza Parsons.

Girls in their Teens, by Julia Corner.

Gisella, by John Palgrave Simpson.

Gitana, a tale, by Sophia Briggs.

Githa of the Forest, by Elizabeth M. Stewart.

Giuseppe, the Italian boy, by M. Fison.

Gladiator, a tale of the Roman Empire, by Martha Macdonald Lamont.

Gladwin's Persian Moonshee, see Pleasant stories from . . .

Glanville Family.

Glen Tilloch, by Mrs. John Burnett Pratt.

Glenarvon, by Lady Caroline Lamb.

Glencarron, by Sarah Wigley.

Glencore Tower.

Glendearg Cottage, by Jane Christmas.

Glenfell.

Glenfergus, by Robert Mudie.

Glenlonely, by William Henry De Merle.

Glenmore Abbey by Mrs. Isaacs.

Glenullyn.

Glory, a tale of morals, by George Gaspey.
Goals and guerdons.
Godfrey de Hastings.
—— Malvern, by Thomas Miller.
Godmother's tales.
—— Tales, by Barbara Hofland.
Godolphin, by Edward Bulwer, Lord Lytton.
Godway Castle, by Henriette von Paalzow.
Goethe's Novel, by Johann Wolfgang Goethe.
Going too far.
Gold Worshipper, by Mrs. Mark Hurdlestone Moodie.
Golden clue, by Mary Martha Sherwood.
—— Legends.
—— marriage.
Goldenthal, by Johannes Heinrich Daniel Zschokke.
Gold-Finder, see Adventures of a . . .
Gold-Headed Cane, see Adventures of a . . .
Goldmakers' village, by Johann Heinrich Daniel Zschokke.
Goldsmith's widow.
Gomerock Castle, by Arthur Howe Holdsworth.
Gomez and Eleonora.
—— Arias, by Don Telesforo de Trueba y Cozio.
Gondola, by Henry Stoe Van Dyk.
Gonzalo de Baldivia, by Ann Hatton.
Gonzalva de Cordova, by Jean Pierre Clavis de Florian.
Good Aunt, by Mrs. J. T. Phelps.
—— Boy Henry, by Nicholaas Anslijn.
—— boys, or examine yourselves, by Rev. Caesar Henri Abraham Malan.
—— effects of sincere and constant prayer.
—— Farmer.
—— Father.
—— Genius, by Augustus Septimus and Henry Mayhew.
—— Grandmother, by Barbara Hofland.
—— humour.
—— Match, by Lady Georgiana Chatterton.
—— men of modern date, by Sarah Green.
—— Mother's Legacy.
—— news in bad times.
—— our of evil, or, the history of Adjai, by Miss A. F. Childe.
—— out of evil, a tale of a cellar, by John Johns.
—— shepherd and his little lambs.
Good-Humour, or my uncle the General.
Good-Nature, or Sensibility, by Miss Aimwell.
Good-Natured bear, by Richard Hengist Horne.
—— boy and the ill-natured boy, see Histories of the . . .
Goody Two Shoes, see Modern . . .
Gooroo Paramartan, see Adventures of the . . .
Gorey cup of Condor's Well.
Gospel Stories.

Gossip's Story, by Jane West.
—— Week, by Mary Boddington.
Gotha.
Gothic legends.
—— story of De Courville.
Governess, by Marguerite Countess of Blessington.
——, or Courtland Abbey.
——, or evening amusements at a boarding school.
——, or little female academy, by Sarah Fielding.
——, or Politics in Private Life, by Mrs. Ross.
Gowrie, or the King's Plot, by George Payne Rainsford James.
Grace Darling, by George William Macarthur Reynolds.
—— Dermott.
—— Rivers, by James Malcolm Rymer.
—— Snodgrass, see History and Character of . . .
Graham Hamilton, by Lady Caroline Lamb.
Granby, by Thomas Henry Lister.
Grand Assizes.
Grandeur and Meanness, by Mary Charlton.
Grandfather, by Ellen Pickering and Elizabeth Youatt.
——: or the Christmas Holidays, by Elizabeth Sandham.
Grandpapa's drawer opened.
Grantley Manor, by Lady Georgiana Fullerton.
Grasville Abbey, by George Moore.
Grateful tributes, by Mary Elliott.
Gratitude and other tales, by Henrietta Rouviere Mosse.
——, or the juvenile writers.
Grave Digger, by Robert Mackenzie Daniel.
Great Bear's story.
—— events from little causes, by A. Richer.
—— Tom of Oxford, by Joseph Thomas Hewlett.
—— wheel.
Greatest Plague of Life, by Augustus Septimus and Henry Maydew.
Grecian Stories, by Maria Hack.
Green bushes.
Green's first tales for little children.
Greenwich Hospital, by Matthew Henry Barker.
—— Pensioners, by Lieut. Hatchway.
Gregory Krau, by Rev. Christian Gottlob Barth.
Gretna Green, see Chronicles of . . .
—— Green Marriages, by Sarah Green.
—— Green, or all for love, by Susannah Frances Reynolds.
—— Green, or the elopement of Miss D——, by Hannah Maria Lowndes.
Greville, or a Season in Paris, by Catherine Grace Frances Gore.
Grey Friar, by John English.
Griffith Abbey, by Mrs. C. Mathews.
Grimmalkin, see Adventures of . . .

Grove Cottage, by Sarah Atkins.
Grubthorpe Family, see History of the ...
Grumbler ; A Novel, by Ellen Pickering.
Guardian Angel, by Augustus von Kotzebue.
Guards ; a novel.
Guerilla chiefs, by Emma Parker.
Guiding star, by Frances S. Parker.
Guildford Jack-Daw, see Adventures of the Guildford Jack-Daw.
Guilty or not guilty, by Ann Hatton.
—— tongue.
Guiscard, by Horace Vere.
Gulistan, by Sa'di.
Gulliver's last voyage.
Gulzara.
Gumal and Lina, by J. L. A. Dumas.
Gurney Married, by Theodore Edward Hook.
Gustavus : or the Macaw.
Guy Fawkes, by William Harrison Ainsworth.
—— Mannering, by Sir Walter Scott.
Guzman d'Alfarache, see Life and adventures of ...
Gwelygordd, by Charles Lucas.

H—— Family, by Frederika Bremer.
Hackney-Coachman.
Hadassah.
Hadleigh Grove.
Hajji Baba of Ispahan, see The Adventures of ...
Half-Pay Officer, by John Heriot.
Half-Sisters, by Geraldine Endsor Jewsbury.
Hall and the Hamlet, by William Howitt.
—— and the Manor House.
—— of Hellingsley, by Sir Samuel Egerton Brydges.
Hamel the Obeah Man.
Hamilton King, by Matthew Henry Barker.
—— Murray, see Life and real adventures of ...
Hamiltons, by Catherine Grace Frances Gore.
Hamlain.
Hampstead murder.
Hampton Court.
Handley Cross, by Robert Smith Surtees.
Hands, not hearts, by Janet W. Wilkinson.
Handy Andy, by Samuel Lover.
Hannah Hewit, by Charles Dibdin.
Hans the Miser.
—— of Iceland, by Victor Hugo.
—— Sloane, by John Brownlow.
Happiness and misery.
—— : a tale for the grave and the gay.
Happy bride.
—— change.
—— cottagers.
—— Discovery.
—— faces, by Amelia Opie.
—— Family at Eason House, by Elizabeth Sandham.
—— family, or memoirs of Mr. & Mrs. Norton.

Happy home, by James Hamilton.
—— Orphans, by Claude Prosper Jolyot de Crebillon.
—— restorations.
—— Sequel.
—— spinster.
—— Waterman.
Harcourt, a novel, by Mary Meeke.
Hard times, by Mary Martha Sherwood.
Harden Hall.
Hardenbrass and Haver ill.
Hardness : or the Uncle, by Captain Charles H. Knox.
Hare.
Hargrave, or the adventures of a man of fashion, by Frances Trollope.
Harlequin, see History and comical adventures of ...
Harley Beckford.
—— Radington, by Miss D. P. Campbell.
Harold the Exile.
——, the last of the Saxon Kings, by Edward Bulwer, Lord Lytton.
Harriet and her cousin.
—— and Mary Bond, by Henrietta Louisa Farrer.
—— Watson, see History of Miss ...
Harriett, or the Innocent Adultress.
Harrington : A Tale, by Maria Edgeworth.
Harriot and Charlotte Meanwell, see Memoirs of ...
—— Fitzroy, see History of Miss ...
—— Stuart, see Life of ...
Harriott Fairfax, see History of Miss ...
Harry and Archie.
—— and his mother, by William Parr.
—— and Lucy Concluded, by Maria Edgeworth.
—— and William.
—— Beaufoy, by Maria Hack.
—— Calverley, by Sir Martin Archer Shee.
—— Lorrequer, see Confessions of ...
—— Mowbray, by Capt. Charles H. Knox.
Harry's Holiday, by Jeffreys Taylor.
Hartlebourn Castle.
Hartley House.
Harvest Home.
Haslan Gheray, by William Allan.
Hatim Taï, see Adventures of ...
Hatred, or the Vindictive Father.
Hau Kiou Choaan, by James Wilkinson.
Haughty duchess.
Haunted Castle, by George Walker.
—— cavern, by John Palmer.
—— fire of Uller.
—— Man, by Charles Dickens.
—— Priory, by Stephen Cullen.
—— tower.
—— tower, by Charles Giberne.
—— woman.
Haverhill, by James Athearn Jones.
Hawbuck Grange, by Robert Smith Surtees.
Hawkstone, by William Sewell.
Hawkwood.
Hawthorn Cottage, by John Jones.

He deceives himself, by Marianne Chambers.
—— is found at last.
Headlong Hall, by Thomas Love Peacock.
Head-Pieces and Tail-Pieces, by Leitch Ritchie.
Heads of the headless, by John Faucit Saville.
Heart and the fancy, by Elizabeth Ogilvy Benger.
——, a social novel, by Martin Farquhar Tupper.
Hearts are trumps, by James Hannay.
—— of steel.
—— *versus* Heads, by Innes Hoole.
Heaven's best gift, by Lucius Phillips.
Hebrew Maiden, by Thomas Peckett Prest.
—— tales.
—— talisman.
Hector O'Halloran, *see* Fortunes of . . .
——, Prince of Troy, *see* History of . . .
Hedge of Thorns, by Mary Martha Sherwood.
Hedin, by Hon. William Herbert.
Heerfort and Clara.
Heetopades, by Vishnusarman.
Heidelberg. A Romance, by George Payne Rainsford James.
Heir of Drumcondra, by Mary Julia Young.
—— of Montague.
—— of Mordaunt, by Miss Cathcart.
—— of Selwood, by Catherine Grace Francis Gore.
—— Presumptive, by Catherine, Lady Stepney.
Heiress and her Suitors.
—— di Montalde, by Ann Kerr.
——, a Novel, by Ellen Pickering.
—— of Avonmore, by Eliza Taylor.
—— of Bruges, by Thomas Colley Grattan.
—— of the Castle of Morlina.
——, a tale, by William Champion Eaton.
—— : a tale, founded on facts.
Heirs of Villeroy, by Henrietta Rouviere.
Helen Beresford, by Lucy Watkins.
—— Charteris, by Harriet Ward.
—— de Tournon, by Adelaide Marie Emilie de Souza-Botelho.
—— Halsey.
—— Leslie, by Jane Sergeant.
—— Monteagle, by Alicia Lefanu.
—— of the Glen, by Robert Pollok.
—— of Glenross, by H. Martin.
——, or the Infant Prisoner of War, by Anna Maria Sanders.
—— Porter.
—— Sinclair.
—— Stanley, by Matilda M. Hays.
—— ; a tale, by Maria Edgeworth.
Helena : a Novel.
Heliodora, or the Grecian Minstrel, by Johann Wolfgang Goethe.
Heloise : or the Siege of Rhodes, by George Monck Berkeley.
Hen-Pecked Husband, by Lady Harriet Ann-Scott.

Hennebon.
Henri Quatre, by John Henry Mancur.
Henrietta, by Charlotte Lennox.
—— and her cousins.
—— Bellmann, by August Heinrich Julius Lafontaine.
——, Countess of Benvor, by Pierre Henri Treyssac de Vergy.
—— de Bellgrave, *see* True history of . . .
—— of Gerstenfeld.
—— Temple, by Earl of Beaconsfield.
Henrietta's wish, by Charlotte Mary Yonge.
Henry, by Richard Cumberland.
—— Acton, by Honble. Louisa Sarah Sayers.
—— and Edward.
—— and Isabella, or the Reverses of Fortune.
—— and Isabella, or a traite through Life, by Anne Hughes.
—— and James.
—— Bennet, *see* Delineations of the heart.
—— Count of Kolinski, by Mrs. Murray.
—— de Beauvais.
—— de Pomeroy, by Anna Eliza Bray.
—— Domville.
—— Fitzherbert, *see* Adventures of . . .
—— Fitzosmond.
—— Fitzroy.
—— the Fourth of France, by Alicia Lefanu.
—— Freemantle.
—— Masterton, by George Payne Rainsford James.
—— Milner, *see* History of . . .
—— a novel, by P. Littlejohn.
—— of Eichenfels, by Johann Christoph von Schmid.
—— of Guise, by George Payne Rainsford James.
—— of Monmouth, by Nicholas Michel.
—— of Northumberland, by Helen Craik.
—— : or the foundling, by Mary S. Pilkington.
——, or secrets of the ruins, by Mrs. Rice.
—— the Recluse, by Greg Pullin.
—— Sinclair, by Miss Healey.
—— Somerville.
——, a story for little boys, by Frances Bowyer Vaux.
—— Stukely, by William Helme.
——, a tale.
—— Willoughby.
Henwick Tales, by Mrs. Marshall.
Heraline, by Laetitia Matilda Hawkins.
Herbert Breakspear, by Edward Sellon.
—— Lacy, by Thomas Henry Lister.
—— Lodge, by Miss Warner.
—— Milton, by Charles White.
Herberts, by Alfred Butler.
Hercules of Greece, *see* History of the life and glorious actions of the mighty . . .
Heretic, by Lajetchnikoff.
Herman of Unna, by Professor Kramer.

Hermann and Emilia, by August Heinrich Julius Lafontaine.

Hermione ; or the Defaulter, by Caroline Scott.

——, or the Orphan sisters, by Charlotte Lennox.

Hermit Abroad, by Captain Felix Macdonough.

—— and the Wandering Infants.

—— in the Country, by Captain Felix Macdonough.

—— in Edinburgh, by Captain Felix Macdonough.

—— in Italy, by Victor Joseph Etienne de Jouy.

—— in London, by Captain Felix Macdonough.

—— in Prison, by Victor Joseph Etienne de Jouy and Antoine Jay.

——, a novel, by Lady Atkins.

—— of Caucasus, by Joseph Moser.

—— of Glenconella, by Eneas Macdonnell.

—— of the grove.

—— of Mount Dragon.

—— of the rock.

—— of Snowden, by Elizabeth Ryves.

——, or adventures of Philip Quarll, by Peter Longueville.

——, an Oriental tale, by François Marie Arouet de Voltaire.

Hermitage, a British story.

——, a novel, by Joshua Bridges Fisher.

Hermit's Cave, by Zara Wentworth.

Hermsprong, by Robert Bage.

Herne the hunter, by A. R. Smith.

Hero and Leander, *see* The famous history of the unfortunate Lovers . . .

——, or the adventures of a night.

Heroic life and exploits of Siegfried the Dragon slayer.

—— virtue.

Heroick Princes.

Heroine of the Peninsula, by Captain Felix Macdonough.

——, or adventures of a fair romance reader, by Eaton Stannard Barrett.

Herwald de Wake, by Hewson Clarke.

Hesitation.

Hester Wilmot, *see* History of . . .

Hide and Seek.

Hieroglyphic Tales, by Horace Walpole.

High Life.

Highest Castle and the Lowest Cave, by Rebecca Edridge.

Highland Castle, by Rosalia St. Clair.

—— Cottage.

—— glen, by Matilda Wrench.

—— Inn.

—— Mary, by Alexander Balfour.

—— Rambles, by Sir Thomas Dick Lauder.

—— Smugglers, by James Baillie Fraser.

—— Watch Tower, by Thomas Peckett Prest.

Highlander, or a Tale of my Landlord.

Highlanders, a Tale, by Captain Felix Macdonough.

High-Ways and By-Ways, by Thomas Colley Grattan.

Hilaria.

Hildebrand.

Hillingdon Hall, by Robert Smith Surtees.

Hints towards forming a Character of a Young Princess, by Hannah More.

Historical tales of illustrious British children, by Agnes Strickland.

—— Tales of the Southern Counties.

Histories of four young ladies, by Miss M. Woodland.

—— of the Good-Natured Boy & the Ill-Natured Boy.

—— of Lady Frances S—— and Lady Caroline S——, by Miss S. and Margaret Minifies.

—— of some of the Penitents in the Magdalen House.

—— or tales of past times, by Charles Perrault.

Historiettes, by Constantine Henry Phipps Marquis of Normanby.

History and Adventures of an Atom, by Tobias Smollett.

—— and adventures of Ben the soldier.

—— and adventures of Don Alfonso Blas de Lirias.

—— and Adventures of Frank Hammond.

—— and Adventures of Joseph Andrews, by Henry Fielding.

—— and character of Grace Snodgrass.

—— and comical adventures of Harlequin.

—— and comical transactions of Lothian Tom.

—— of Abou Casem.

—— of the adventures of Arthur O' Bradley, by John Potter.

—— of Agathon, by Christoph Martin Wieland.

—— of Alfred and Thomas.

—— of Alicia Montague, by Jean Marishall.

—— of all real and threatened invasions.

—— of Amanda.

—— of Amelia Harcourt.

—— of Amintor and Teresa.

—— of the Amours of Napoleon Bonaparte, by Charles Doris.

—— of Ann and her Eleven Sisters.

—— of Arden of Faversham, by John Chilton.

—— of Arsaces, by Charles Johnstone.

—— of Automathes.

—— of a Banbury Cake.

—— of Barbarossa and Pollyana.

—— of Barnaby Boulton.

—— of the Basket Maker.

—— of Benjamin St. Martin.

—— of Betsy Green.

—— of Betty Barnes.

—— of the blind beggar of Bethnal Green.

—— of Britannicus and his sister Octavia, by Elizabeth Sandham.

—— of Buckhaven.

—— of Captain and Miss Rivers.

—— of the celebrated Nanny Goose.

History of Charles Falkland.
—— of Charles Jones.
—— of Charles Mandeville, by Frances Moore.
—— of Charles Munson.
—— of Charles Wentworth, by Edward Bancroft.
—— of Charlotte Summers.
—— of the Chevalier Bayard, by Rev. Joseph Sterling.
—— of the Chevalier des Grieux, by Abbé Antoine François Prévost D'Exiles.
—— of the Children in the Wood.
—— of Cleanthes of Celemene.
—— of a Clergyman's Widow, by Barbara Hofland.
—— of Clorana.
—— of Cornelia, by Sarah Scott.
—— of Count Bertram.
—— of Count Gleichen, by François Marie de Baculard D'Arnaud.
—— of the Countess of Delwyn, by Sarah Fielding.
—— of Crazy Jane, by Sarah S. Wilkinson.
—— of Croesus, by Walter Anderson.
—— of the Curate of Craman.
—— of the Davenport Family.
—— of Diligent Dick.
—— of Dr. John Faustus.
—— of a dog, by Pigault Lebrun.
—— of Eliza.
—— of Eliza Musgrove.
—— of Eliza Warwick.
—— of Elizabeth Woodville, by Elizabeth Sandham.
—— of Ellen.
—— of Elsmere and Rosa, by George Colman, the Younger.
—— of Emily and her mother, by Mary Martha Sherwood.
—— of Emily Montague, by Frances Moore.
—— of Emma.
—— of the Emperor Manalay.
—— of Euphemia's little scholars.
—— of the excellence and decline of the Constitution, religions, laws, manners and genius of the Sumatrans, by John Shebbeare.
—— of the Fairchild Family, by Mary Martha Sherwood.
—— of the Family at Smiledale.
—— of Fanny Mason.
—— of Fanny Meadows, by Maria Susanna Cooper.
—— of Fanny Mills.
—— of Fanny Seymour.
—— of Female Favourites, by Mlle. de Laroche-Guilhem.
—— of Filchum Cantum.
—— of a flirt, by Lady Charlotte Susan Maria Bury.
—— of Fortunatus.
—— of the fortune-teller in the Old Bailey.
—— of four Kings.

History of four young ladies, by Miss M. Woodland.
—— of a French dagger, by Henri L. Dubois.
—— of the Frolicksome Courtier.
—— of Frugal the wild bee, by Mr. Frankly.
—— of George Desmond, by Mary Martha Sherwood.
—— of George Godfrey, by Thomas Gaspey.
—— of George Mason.
—— of Georgina Neville.
—— of the Grubthorpe Family, by Rachel Hunter.
—— of Hector, Prince of Troy.
—— of Henry Earl of Moreland, by Henry Brooke.
—— of Henry Milner, by Mary Martha Sherwood.
—— of Hester Wilmot, by Hannah More.
—— of the Hon. Mrs. Rosemont and Sir Henry Cardigan, by Miss Elliott.
—— of Honest Peter.
—— of Honoria.
—— of the Honourable Edward Mortimer, by Albinia Gwynn.
—— of the human heart.
—— of Hypolitus, by Marie Catherine le Jumel de Berneville, Comtesse d' Aulnois.
—— of Idle Jack Brown.
—— of Israel Jobson.
—— of Jack and the giants.
—— of Jack Connor, by William Chaigneau.
—— of Jack of Newbury.
—— of Jack Sheppard.
—— of James Lovegrove, by James Ridley.
—— of Jane Price.
—— of Jane Shore.
—— of Jemmy and Jenny Jessamy, by Eliza Haywood.
—— of Jim Crow, by John Briggs.
—— of John Juniper, by Charles Johnstone.
—— of John Milner, by Mary Martha Sherwood.
—— of John Steady and Edward Careless.
—— of John Wise.
—— of Johnny Armstrong.
—— of Joshua Trueman.
—— of Judith Potts.
—— of Julius Fitz-John.
—— of the King and the cobler.
—— of La Riviere.
—— of Lady Anne Neville, by Alexander Bicknell.
—— of Lady Barton, by Elizabeth Griffith.
—— of Lady Bettesworth and Captain Hastings.
—— of Lady Caroline Rivers, by Elizabeth Todd.
—— of Lady Emma Melcombe.

History of Lady Julia Mandeville, by Frances Moore.
—— of Lady Louisa Stroud.
—— of Lady Lucy Fenton.
—— of Lady Sophie Sternheim, by Marie Sophie von Laroche.
—— of Lawrence Lazy.
—— of the Life and Adventures of Mr. Anderson.
—— of the life and death of that Noble Knight Bevis of Southampton.
—— of the life and glorious actions of the mighty Hercules.
—— of the life of the Squire Marcos de Obregon, by Vincente Espinel.
—— of Little Ann.
—— of little Henry and his bearer, by Mary Martha Sherwood.
—— of little King Skilful.
—— of little Lucy, by Mary Martha Sherwood.
—— of the lives of Abelard and Heloise, by Joseph Berington.
—— of Lord Aimworth.
—— of Lord Ashborn.
—— of Lord Belford.
—— of Lord Clayton.
—— of Lort Stanton.
—— of Lucy Clare, by Mary Martha Sherwood.
—— of Lucy Wellers.
—— of Major Bromley and Miss Clifford.
—— of Major Piper, by Rev. James Thomson.
—— of Margaret Catchpole, by Rev. Richard Cobbold.
—— of Margaret, sister to John Bull.
—— of Margaret Whyte, by Lucy Lyttelton Cameron.
—— of the Marquis de Cressy, by Marie Jeanne Riccoboni.
—— of the Marquis de Roselle, by Madame Elie de Beaumont.
—— of Martin and James.
—— of Mary the Beggar Girl, by Elizabeth Anne Smythe.
—— of Mary, the maid of the inn.
—— of Mary Prince.
—— of Mary Wood.
—— of Master Jackey.
—— of the Matrimonial adventures of a banker's clerk.
—— of Matthew Wald, by John Gibson Lockhart.
—— of May Flower, by Count Anthony Hamilton.
—— of Michael Kemp.
—— of the Miss Baltimores.
—— of Miss Betsy Thoughtless, by Eliza Haywood.
—— of Miss Clarinda Cathcart, by Jean Marishall.
—— of Miss Dorinda Catsby.
—— of Miss Emilia Beville.
—— of Miss Greville, by Mrs. James Keir.
—— of Miss Hariot Fitzroy.
—— of Miss Harriet Watson, by Mrs. A. Woodfin.

History of Miss Harriott Fairfax.
—— of Miss Indiana Danby.
—— of Miss Katty N . . .
—— of Miss Lucinda Courtney.
—— of Miss Maria Barlowe.
—— of Miss Meredith, by Eliza Parsons.
—— of Miss Pamela Howard.
—— of Miss Pittborough.
—— of Miss Sally Sable, by Mrs. A. Woodfin.
—— of Miss Sommerville.
—— of Miss Temple, by A. Rogers.
—— of Montellion.
—— of Mother Bunch.
—— of Mother Shipton.
—— of Mr. Bragwell.
—— of Mr. Charles Fitzgerald and Miss Sarah Stapleton, by David Marley.
—— of Mr. John de Castro, by George Colman the Younger.
—— of Mr. Rightway and his pupils, by William Francis Sullivan.
—— of Mr. Stanley and Miss Temple.
—— of Mrs. Catharine Crawley, by Mary Martha Sherwood.
—— of my father, by Augustus von Kotzebue.
—— of myself and my friend, by Anne Plumptre.
—— of Ned Evans, by Jane West.
—— of Netterville.
—— of Nicolas Pedrosa.
—— of the noble Marquis of Salus.
—— of Nourjahad, by Frances Sheridan.
—— of Numa Pompilius, by Jean Pierre Clavis de Florian.
—— of an officer's widow, by Barbara Hofland.
—— of Old Hardy.
—— of an old lady and her family.
—— of Ophelia, by Sarah Fielding.
—— of Pendennis, by William Makepeace Thackeray.
—— of Perourou, by Helen Maria Williams.
—— of a pin.
—— of Polly Willis.
—— of Pompey the Little, by Francis Coventry.
—— of Primrose Prettyface.
—— of Prince Fatal.
—— of the proceedings in the case of Margaret, by Adam Fergusson.
—— of Reynard the Fox.
—— of Rhedi, by W. Duff.
—— of Rinaldo Rinaldini, by V. Ulpius.
—— of Robin Hood.
—— of the robins, *see* Fabulous Histories.
—— of Rory O'More.
—— of Rosano and Amanda, by Hannah Smith.
—— of Samuel Thomson, by Lucy Lyttelton Cameron.
—— of Samuel Titmarsh, by William Makepeace Thackeray.
—— of a Sandalwood box, by Mrs. Henry Glassford Bell.
—— of Sandford and Merton, by Thomas Day.

History of a Savage girl.
—— of Sawney Beane.
—— of a school boy.
—— of Sidney and Volsan.
—— of the Sieges of Aquileia and Berwick.
—— of Sir Charles Beaufort.
—— of Sir Charles Dormer and Miss Harriet Villers.
—— of Sir Charles Grandison, by Samuel Richardson.
—— of Sir Geoffry Restless.
—— of Sir George Ellison, by Sarah Scott.
—— of Sir George Warrington, by Charlotte Lennox.
—— of Sir Harry Herald and Sir Edward Haunch, by Henry Fielding.
—— of Sir Henry Clarendon.
—— of Sir Roger and his son Joe.
—— of Sir William Harrington, by Thomas Hull.
—— of the sleeping beauty in the wood.
—— of Sophia Shakespear.
—— of Sophron and Tigranes.
—— of Susan Gray, by Mary Martha Sherwood.
—— of Tabby, by E. Smyth.
—— of the tales of the fairies, by Marie-Catherine le Jumel de Berneville Comtesse D'Aulnois..
—— of a tame robin.
—— of that celebrated Lady Ally Croaker.
—— of Theophilus and Sophia, by Mary Martha Sherwood.
—— of Thomas Martin.
—— of Tom Fool, by George Alexander Stevens.
—— of Tom Jones, the foundling in his married state.
—— of Tom Jones, by Henry Fielding.
—— of Tom Long.
—— of Tom Rigby, by John Chater.
—— of Tom Weston, by George Brewer.
—— of Tom White.
—— of Tommy Playlove.
—— of Tommy Titmouse.
—— of two modern adventurers.
—— of two orphans.
—— of the two wealthy farmers.
—— of Valentine and Orson.
—— of Vanillo Gonzales, by Alan Rene Le Sage.
—— of Victoria Mortimer, by Mrs. Helena Berkenhout.
—— of white cat.
—— of Whittington.
—— of Wilhelmina Susannah Dormer.
—— of Will Brown, the poacher.
—— of Will Ramble.
—— of William Selwyn, by Elizabeth Sandham.
—— of a woman of quality, by " Sir " John Hill.
—— of the Yellow dwarf.
—— of Young Edwin.
—— of a young lady of distinction, by Elie de Beaumont.

Hitopadesa, by Vishnusarman.
Hitopadesha, by Vishnusarman.
Hoel Morvan, by William Shergold Browning.
Hofer, the patriot of the Tyrol, by J. H. Newton.
—— the Tyrolese.
Holiday House, by Catherine Sinclair.
—— present.
—— Reward, by Harriet Ventum.
—— visit.
Holidays at Brighton.
Holland tide, by Gerald Griffin.
Holme Park, by Mary Jane Shield.
Home, by Miss Sedgwick.
——, by Mary Martha Sherwood.
—— among strangers, by Maria Hutchins Callott.
—— and its influence, by Honble, Adela Sidney.
—— for the holdiays.
—— Happiness
—— Influence, by Grace Aguilar.
—— mission.
——, a Novel, by Margaret Cullen.
——, or family cares, by Frederika Bremer.
—— or the Iron Rule, by Sarah Stickney Ellis.
Homicide, by Mary Charlton.
Hon. Miss Rosemont and Sir Henry Cardigan, *see* History of the . . .
Honest London spy.
—— penny is worth a silver shilling, by Lucy Lyttleton Cameron.
—— Roger, *see* History of . . .
Honesty the best policy.
Honey-Stew of the Countess Bertha, by Alexandre Dumas.
Honor Delafont.
—— Delany, *see* Confessions of . . .
—— O'Hara, by Anna Maria Porter.
—— ; or the story of the brave Caspar and the fair Annerl, by Clemens Brentano.
Honoria, *see* History of . . .
——, or the infatuated child, by James Barton.
—— Sommerville, by The Misses Purbeck.
Honorine d'Userchi, by Madame de Charriere.
Honour and Shame.
—— ! A Tale, by Eliza Peake.
Honourable Edward Mortimer, *see* History of the . . .
Hop blossoms, by Johann Christoph von Schmid.
Hope
—— of the Katzekopfs, by Francis Edward Paget.
—— on, hope ever, by Mary Howitt.
——, or judge without prejudice, by Miriam Malden.
Horace Templeton, *see* Diary and notes of . . .
Horrible revenge.
Horrid Mysteries, by Marquis of Grosse.
Horrors of Oakendale Abbey.

Horse Guards, by Lieut.-Col. J. J. Hort.

Hortorian miscellany, by W. Adkins.

Hougue Bie de Hambie, by James Bulkeley.

Hour and the Man, by Harriet Martineau.

—— of trial, by Mary Anne Neri.

—— of two, by Augusta Woodthorpe.

Hours of affluence, by Medora Gordon Byron.

House of Clarendon, see Memoirs of the ancient . . .

—— of Lancaster.

—— of Marley.

—— of Ravenspur, by Anna Brownell Jameson.

—— of Tynian, by George Walker.

—— that Jack built.

Houses of Osma and Almeria, by Regina Maria Roche.

How to be happy, by Mrs. Kentish.

—— to be Rid of a Wife, by Elizabeth Isabella Spence.

Howard, by John Gamble.

—— Castle.

Hubbub, or the history of Farmer Russel.

Hubert de Sevrac, by Mary Robinson.

——, or the orphans of St. Madelaine, by Miss F. L. Bingham.

Hugh Talbot, by William J. O'Neill Daunt.

—— Trevor, see Adventures of . . .

Hugenot: A tale of the French Revolution, by George Payne Rainsford James.

Hulme Abbey, by Mrs. Frederick Layton.

Human Beings, by Francis Lathom.

—— frailties.

—— Heart.

—— Heart, see The History of the . . .

—— Life, with Variations, by Caroline Herbert.

—— nature.

—— vicissitudes.

Humbert Castle, by Sarah Sheriffe.

Humility, or Blanche Neville, by Agnes M. Stewart.

—— : A Tale, by Barbara Hofland.

Humorous adventures of Jump Jim Crow.

Humour and pathos, by George R. Wythen Baxter.

Humourist.

Humphrey Clinker, see Expedition of . . .

—— Humbug, see Life & confessions of . . .

—— Ravelin, see Lucubrations of . . .

Hundred Years Hence.

Hungarian Brothers, by Anna Maria Porter.

—— Castle, by Julia S. H. Pardoe.

—— Tales, by Catherine Grace Frances Gore.

Hurstwood: A Tale of the Year 1715, by Rev. John Henry Ashworth.

Husband and the lover, by Alicia Tyndal Palmer.

Husband and wife.

—— forced to be jealous.

—— Hunter, by John O'Brien Grant.

—— Hunters.

Husband hunting.

——, in answer to the wife, by Eliza Haywood.

Husband's Resentment.

Hussar, and George Robert Gleig.

Hut and the Castle, by Catherine Cuthbertson.

——, or Alzendorf.

Hyacinth O'Gara, see Recollections of . . .

Hyacinthe, by Catherine Maria Grey.

Hyde Marston, by William Carleton.

—— Nugent.

Hylton House, by Lady Caroline Lucy Scott.

Hypocrite, or the modern Janus, by Selina Davenport.

Hyppolitus.

I can do without it.

—— can't afford it, by Emma Hamilton.

—— heard it said so.

—— Says, Says I, by Edward Nares.

Ianthe, by Emily Clarke.

Iberian tales and novels.

Ida of Austria.

Idalia.

Idiot boy, by Mary Martha Sherwood.

—— Heiress.

—— A Novel, by Miss H. Boswell.

Idle Ann, by Mary Elliott.

—— Jack Brown, see History of . . .

Idler reformed, by Rose Ellen Hendriks.

Idolatry of the Heart.

Ildegerte, by Augustus von Kotzbue.

Iliad of Homer, by James Macpherson.

I'll consider of it.

Ill effects of a rash vow.

Ill-fated mariner, by Mary Pilkington.

Illusions of Sentiment.

Illustrations of Human Life, by Robert Plumer Ward.

—— of Lying, by Amelia Opie.

—— of Political Economy, by Harriet Martineau.

—— of taxation, by Harriet Martineau.

I'm afloat, I'm afloat.

Image boys, by Rev. Caesar Henri Abraham Malan.

—— of his father, by Augustus Septimus and Henry Mayhew.

Imaginary adultress.

—— Biography, by Sir Samuel Egerton Brydges.

Immelina.

Imogen.

Impartial History of the Life, Amours, Travels and Transactions of Mr. John Barker.

Impenetrable secret, by Francis Lathom.

Impertinent wife, by Comtesse de Genlis.

Impetuous lover.

Important trifles.

Impostor, or born without a conscience, by William North.

Improving tales.

Improvisatore, by Hans Christian Anderson.

In School and out of School.

—— what manner Little Henry came to the knowledge of God.

Incidents of youthful life, by William Beloe.

Incognita, or Emily Villars.

Incognito, The, by Don Telesforo Trueba y Cozio.

Incredulous Boy.

Independence, by Mary Meeke.

Independent. A Novel, by George Monck Berkeley.

Indian adventurer.

—— Cottage, by Jacques-Henri Bernardin de Saint-Pierre.

—— juggler.

—— Life, by Mary Ann Hartley.

—— Pilgrim, by Mary Martha Sherwood.

—— voyage, by Alicia Lefanu.

Indiana, see The Life and Adventures of . . .

——, by A. L. A. D. Dudevant.

—— Danby, see History of Miss . . .

Indiscreet Marriage.

Industry and Idleness, by Mary Elliott.

—— : A tale of real life.

Insella, by Charles Ollier.

Infant stories.

Infantile tales.

Infantine Stories, by Mrs. E. Fenwick.

Infant's Progress, by Mary Martha Sherwood.

Infatuation, by Margaret Turner.

Infernal Conference, by John Macgowan.

—— Quixote, by Charles Lucas.

Infidel Father, by Jane West.

Influence and Example.

—— : A Moral Tale, by Charlotte Anley.

Ingliston, by Grace Webster.

Ingoldsby legends, by Richard Harris Barham.

Inhabitants of the earth, by Anthony Frederick Holstein.

Inheritance, by Susan Edmondstone Ferrier.

Inhuman stepmother.

—— uncle, by W. R. Chetwood.

Initials, by Baroness Jemima von Tautphoeus.

Injured Innocence.

Inklings of Adventure.

Innisfoyle Abbey, by John O'Brien Grant.

Inn-Keeper in Normandy, see Affecting history of an . . .

Inn-Keeper's album, by William Frederick Deacon.

Innocence betrayed.

Inquisition.

Inquisitor, by Susanna Haswell Rowson.

Insinuating bawd.

Instructions to young ladies, by Jeanne Marie le Prince de Beaumont.

Instructive and entertaining novels, by Miguel de Cervantes.

—— rambles, by Elizabeth Helme.

—— tales, by Sarah Trimmer.

Integrity, or the artist Stanton.

——, or the history of Sophia Francourt.

—— : A tale, by Barbara Hofland.

Intellectual Family, by Emma Ackfield.

Interdict, by Mrs. T. F. Steward.

Interesting adventures of a little white mouse.

—— Event, by William Makepeace Thackeray.

—— memoirs, by Mrs. James Keir.

—— story of Edwin and Julia.

—— Tales, consisting of Isidore.

—— Tales selected and translated from the German.

Intriguante, by Anthony Frederick Holstein.

Intrigue a la Mode.

Intriguing beauty.

Introspection, or a peep at real characters.

Inundation, by Catherine Grace Frances Gore.

Inutility of Virtue.

Invasion, by Gerald Griffin.

——, or what might have been.

Invisible enemy, by Thomas Pike Lathy.

—— Gentleman, by James Dalton.

—— hand, by W. Clayton.

—— Man.

—— Spy, by Eliza Haywood.

Involuntary Inconstant.

Ionian, by Sarah Renou.

Iphigenia.

Ireland, a tale, by Harriet Martineau.

Irish Assassin, by Henry Vincent.

—— Chieftain and his family, by Theodore Melville.

—— chieftain, or the Isles of Life and Death, by Edward Maturin.

—— Coquette.

—— Dick, by Ann Jane Morgan.

—— drove, by Margaret Percival.

—— Excursion, by Mrs. Colpoys.

—— girl.

—— guardian, or errors of eccentricity, by Anna Maria Mackenzie.

—— guardian, a pathetic story.

—— heiress, by Mrs. F. C. Patrick.

—— Life, by Isaac Butt.

—— Necromancer, by Thomas Henry Marshal.

—— pearl.

—— Peasant.

—— priest.

—— priests and English landlords, by Rev. George Brittaine.

—— recluse, by Sarah Isdell.

—— schoolboy.

—— widow.

Irishman at home.

——, a military-political novel.

——, or the favourite of fortune.

Irishmen by Lieut. Arnold.

—— and Irishwomen, by Rev. George Brittaine.

Irishwoman in London, by Ann Hamilton.

Iron cage, by Mary Martha Sherwood.

—— Shroud.

Irrelagh, by Miss E. Colthurst.

Isaac Jenkins, *see* History of . . .
Isabel de Barsas.
——, or influence.
—— or the orphan of Valdarno, by M. Lyttleton.
—— St. Albe, by Miss Crumpe.
——: A Tale, by Charles Lloyd, Junr.
Isabella : A Novel.
——, or the memoirs of a coquette.
——: or the rewards of good-nature, by Arthur Murphy.
Isabinda, by Mrs. Courtney.
Isadora of Milan, by Anthony Frederick Holstein.
Isidora of Gallicia, by Mrs. Hugill.
——; or the Adventures of a Neapolitan, by John Richard Digby Best.
Iskander, by Arthur Spenser.
Island on the Mere, by R. W. Essington.
Ismene and Ismenias, by Eustathius.
Isn't it odd ?
Israel Jobson, *see* History of . . .
It was me.
Italian Banditti, by Isaac Crookenden.
—— Convert.
—— jealousy, by, the Duchess of Pienne.
—— Letters, by William Godwin.
—— Marauders.
—— Mysteries, by Francis Lathom.
——: or the Confessional of the Black Penitents, by Ann Radcliffe.
—— stories, by Margaret Hodson.
—— Tales, by Thomas Roscoe.
—— Vengeance, by Selina Davenport.
Itanoka.
Itinerant, by Samuel William Ryley.
Iu-Kiao-Li, by M. Abel-Remusat.
Ivan Clarowitz, by Catherine II., Empress of Russia.
—— Vejeeghen, by Thaddeus Bulgáran.
Ivanhoe, by Sir Walter Scott.
Ivy Castle.
Ivo and Verena, by Mary Ann Dyson.

Jack Adams, by Frederick Chamier.
—— and the Giants, *see* History of . . .
—— and Gill and old Dame Gill.
—— Ariel, by John Dix.
—— Ashore, by Lieut. the Honble. Edward Granville George Howard.
—— Brag, by Theodore Edward Hook.
—— Brown in Prison, by Hannah More.
—— Cade, by James Cooke.
—— Connor, *see* History of . . .
—— Hinton, by Charles James Lever.
—— Holyday, *see* Adventures of . . .
—— Hornet, by John Gideon Millingen.
—— Junk, by Thomas Peckett Prest.
—— of the Mill, *see* Life and Adventures of . . .
—— of Newbury, *see* The History of . . .
—— Rann, *see* Life and adventures of . . .
—— Sheppard, *see* Life and surprising adventures of Jack Shepperd, *also see* History of . . .
—— Shepphkerd, *see* Life and surprising adventures of . . .

Jack Shepperd, by William Harrison Ainsworth.
—— Smart, *see* Adventures of . . .
—— Tench.
Jacko the baboon, *see* Comical adventures at sea and on shore of . . .
Jacob Faithful, by Captain Frederick Marryat.
Jacqueline of Holland, by Thomas Colley Grattan.
Jacquerie, by George Payne Rainsford James.
Jacques, by A. L. A. D. Dudevant.
James Dowell.
—— the fatalist, by Denis Diderot.
—— Forbes.
—— Hardy Vaux, *see* Memoirs of the first thirty-two years of the life of . . .
—— Hatfield.
—— Jarvis.
—— Lovegrove, *see* History of . . .
—— Manners, by Elizabeth Helme.
—— Massey, *see* Travels and Adventures of . . .
—— the Second, Edited by William Harrison Ainsworth.
—— Wallace, by Robert Bage.
Jane Bouverie, by Catherine Sinclair.
—— Brightwell, by James Malcolm Rymer.
—— de Dunstanville, by Isabella Kelly.
—— Eyre, by Charlotte Bronte.
—— Hudson, the American girl.
—— Lomax, by Horatio Smith.
—— Martin, *see* Memoir of . . .
—— of France, by Comtesse de Genlis.
—— Price, *see* History of . . .
—— Shore, by James Malcolm Rymer.
—— Shore, *see* History of . . .
Janet and Harry.
——, or Glances at Human Nature, by Julia Rattray Waddington.
January Eve, by George Soane.
Japhet in Search of a Father, by Captain Frederick Marryat.
Jaquelina of Hainault.
Jaqueline of Olzeburg.
Jealousy, and Revenge, by Eliza Peake.
—— a novel, by R. N. Hutton.
—— or the dreadful mistake.
Jean Baptiste Couteau, *see* Confessions of . . .
Jeannette and Jeannot.
—— Isabelle, by George Valentine Cox.
—— a novel, by Mrs. Martin.
Jem Bunt, by Matthew Henry Barker.
—— Gudgeon.
Jemima : A Novel, by Annie Hughes.
—— Placid, by Dorothy Kilner.
Jemmy and Jenny Jessamy, *see* The History of . . .
—— Twitcher, *see* Life, adventures, Intrigues and Amours of the celebrated . . .
Jennet Gill
Jenny Lind, by Rose Ellen Hendriks.
Jephthah, or the Maid of Gilead.
Jeremiah Parkes, by Mrs. Robert Mackenzie Daniel.

Jerningham, by Sir John William Kaye.
Jerry Allan, by Grace Kennedy.
Jessamine Cottage, by Rev. John Thornton.
Jessico Mandeville, by Miriam Malden.
Jessie Barton.
—— Phillips, by Frances Trollope.
Jessy, or the bridal day.
——, or the Rose of Donald's Cottage.
Jesuit, by Carl Spindler.
——, or, the history of Antony Babington, by Mrs. F. C. Patrick.
—— at Cambridge, by Sir George Stephen.
Jesuitism and Methodism.
Jew, by Carl Spindler.
—— and the foundling.
Jewels, or Michael Ashdell's trial.
Jewess : a tale from the shores of the Baltic, by Elizabeth Rigby.
Jewish captivity, see Tale of the . . .
—— maiden, by Miss M. G. Lewis.
Jilt : a novel, by Harriet Maria Yorick Smythies.
Jim Crow, see The History of . . .
Jireh.
Joan : A Novel, by Matilda Fitz-John.
—— of Arc, by Thomas James Serle.
Joanna, or the Female Slave.
Jocelyn, by Marie Louis Alphonse de Lamartine de Prat.
Joe Oxford.
—— Thompson, see Life and adventures of . . .
John and Henry.
—— Avery, see Famous adventures of Captain . . .
—— Bull, see Memoirs of . . .
—— Bull and his wonderful lamp.
—— Buncle, see Life of . . .
—— Buncle, Junior, by Thomas Cogan.
—— Daniel, see Life and astonishing adventures of . . .
—— de Castro, see The history of Mr. . . .
—— de Lancaster, by Richard Cumberland.
—— Doe, by John Banim.
—— Franks, see The birth, life, and death of . . .
—— Jones's Tales, by George Payne Rainsford James.
—— Juniper, see History of . . .
—— Le-Brun, see Adventures of . . .
—— Manesty, by William Maginn and Charles Ollier.
—— Marston, Hall, see Life and adventures of . . .
—— Milner, see History of . . .
—— Nicol, see Life and adventures of . . .
—— of England, by Captain Henry Curling.
—— of Gaunt, see Adventures of . . .
—— Steady and Edward Careless, see History of . . .
—— Wise, see History of . . .
Johnny Armstrong, see History of . . .
—— Derrivan's Travels, by Rev. George Brittaine.

Johnny Newcome, see Military adventures of . . . See Adventures of . . .
Jolly sailor's jester.
Jonathan Bradford, by Thomas Peckett Prest.
—— Jefferson Whitlaw, see Life and adventures of . . .
Jones the foundling, see History of Jones the foundling in his married state.
Jorrocks' Jaunts and Jollities, by Robert Smith Surtees.
Joscelina, by Isabella Kelly.
Joseph, by Paul Jeremiah Bitaubé.
—— Andrews, see History and adventures of . . .
—— Benson, by J. T. Bell.
—— Jenkins, by James Grant.
—— Rushbrook, by Captain Frederick Marryat.
Josephine, or early trials, by Catherine Grace Godwin.
—— a novel, by Eliza Taylor.
Joshua Trueman, see History of . . .
Journal of an Exile, by Thomas Alexander Boswell.
—— of a Governess.
—— of the Heart, by Lady Charlotte Susan Maria Bury.
—— of Llewellin Penrose, by John Eagles.
—— of Penrose.
Journey round my chamber, by Count Xavier de Maistre.
—— round my room, by Count Xavier de Maistre.
—— through every stage of life, by Sarah Scott.
—— to London.
—— to the Moon.
—— to the World Underground, by Ludwig Baron Holberg.
Journeyman Joiner, by A. L. A. D. Dudevant.
Judith, a novel, by Mrs. E. M. Foster.
—— or, the Prophetess of Bethulia.
—— Potts, see History of . . .
Julamerk, by Mrs. J. B. Webb.
Julia the Curate's Daughter.
—— de Gramont, by Cassandra Lady Hawke.
—— de Roubigné, by Henry Mackenzie.
—— de St. Pierre, by Helen Craik.
—— Fitz-Clarence.
—— Howard, by Mary Letitia Martin.
—— Mandeville, see History of Lady . . .
—— : A Novel, by Helen Maria Williams.
—— of Ardenfield.
—— ; or the Adventures of the daughter of a Village Curate, by Mr. M'Millan.
—— Ormond.
—— St. Lawrence, by Mary Robinson.
—— St. Pierre.
—— Severa, by Jean Charles Léonard Simonde de Sismondi.
Julian of Osnaberg.
Juliana, a novel.
—— Oakley, by Mary Martha Sherwood.
—— Ormeston.
Juliania, by Elizabeth Sandham.
Julien, by F. G. Ducray Dumenil.

Juliet.
—— Grenville, by Henry Brooke.
Julietta, by William Parnell.
—— di Lavenza, by Mary Martha Sherwood.
Julio Arnouf, by Mrs. J. B. Webb.
Julius Fitz-John, *see* History of . . .
——, or the deaf and dumb orphan.
Jumelles, *see* Les . . .
Jump Jim Crow, *see* Humorous adventures of . . .
Justina, or the history of a young lady, by Harriet Ventum.
—— or, Religion pure and undefiled.
Juvenile adventures of David Ranger.
—— Adventures of Miss Kitty F . . r
—— Album, by Sarah Bowdich.
—— Amulet.
—— Anecdotes, by Priscilla Wakefield.
—— artist, by Rev. Christian Gottlob Barth.
—— budget, by Ann Maria Hall.
—— Christmas Tales.
—— culprits, by George Mogridge.
—— emigrants.
—— Fabulist.
—— forget me not, by Agnes Strickland.
—— gleaner, by William Alexander.
—— Indiscretions, by Agnes Maria Bennett.
—— Journal, by Mrs. Cockle.
—— library.
—— memoirs.
—— moralists, by George Mogridge.
—— Olio.
—— sketch book.
—— Spectator, by Arabella Argus.
—— stories and dialogues.
—— story-book, by Louisa Stanley.
—— tales.
—— Tatler, by Eleanor, Lady Fenn.

Kanor.
Kanousky.
Karah Kaplan, by the Honble. Charles Stuart Savile.
Karmath, by Edward Upham.
Kate Walsingham, by Ellen Pickering.
Katherine, a tale, by Barbara Hofland.
Kathleen, or the secret marriage, by Thomas Peckett Prest.
Katty N . . ., *see* History of Miss . . .
Keeper's Travels, by Edward Augustus Kendall.
Kellys and the O'Kellys, by Anthony Trollope.
Kenilworth, by Sir Walter Scott.
Kenneth, or the Rear Guard of the Grand Army, by Charlotte Mary Yonge.
Kentsea, by Percy Bolingbroke St. John.
Kept Mistress.
Kerwald Castle, by Mrs. Barnby.
Key to the drama.
Khan's Tale, by James Baillie Fraser.
Kickleburys on the Rhine, by William Makepeace Thackeray.
Killarney poor scholar, by Rev. John Stewart.

Killinchy, by James Meikle.
Kilverstone Castle.
Kindness in Women, by Nathaniel Thomas Haynes Bayly.
King and the cobler, *see* History of the . . .
—— and the Countess, by Stephen Watson Fullom.
—— can do no wrong.
—— Dobbs, by James Hannay.
—— Henry IV.
—— Henry the Fourth.
—— Lear, by Charles Lamb.
—— of the Peak, by William Bennett.
—— of the swans, by F. J. Rudolphi, W. Hauff, and A. L. Grimm.
—— Richard, *see* Adventures of . . .
King's daughter.
—— Highway, by George Payne Rainsford James.
—— Musketeer, by Percy Bolingbroke St. John.
Kings of England, *see* Tales of the . . .
King's Own, by Captain Frederick Marryat.
—— page, *see* Adventures of a . . .
—— Secret, by Tyrone Power.
—— Son, by Barbara Hofland.
Kingsconnell, by Mrs. Gordon.
Kinsman of Mahomet.
Kirkbeck, *see* Tales of . . .
Kirkholme Priory, by Laura Jewry.
Kit Bam's Adventures, by Mary Cowden Clarke.
Kitty N——, *see* Amours and adventures of Miss . . .
Kitty's Atlantis.
Klosterheim, by Thomas De Quincey.
Knight of the Glen.
—— of Gwynne, by Charles James Lever.
—— of Newbrough.
—— of the rose, by Lucy Peacock.
—— of St. John, by Anna Maria Porter.
—— of the White Banner, by Catherine George Ward.
Knights, by Robert Charles Dallas.
—— of the Swan, by Comtesse de Genlis.
——, or sketches of the heroic age.
Koenigsmark, the Robber, by H. J. Sarratt.
—— the Robber, by Matthew Gregory Lewis.
Koromantyn Slaves.
Kruitzner, by Harriet Lee.

La Bruja, by Thomas Parker.
Labours of Idleness, by George Darley.
Labyrinths of Life, by Mrs. Thomson.
La Coquetterie.
Ladder of gold, by Robert Bell.
Ladies miscellany.
Lady Alice, or the new Una, by Jedediah Vincent Huntington.
—— Ally Croaker, *see* History of that celebrated. . . .
—— and her Ayah, by Mary Martha Sherwood.
—— Annabetta, by Katharine Thomson.

Lady Anne, *see* Life and adventures of . . .

—— Anne Granard, by Letitia Elizabeth Landon.

—— Anne Neville, *see* History of . . .

—— Barton, *see* History of . . .

—— Bettesworth and Captain Hastings, *see* History of . . .

—— Caroline Rivers, *see* History of . . .

—— Celia Farrencourt, by Henry Milton.

—— Durnevor, by Anthony Frederick Holstein.

—— Eliza Audley, *see* Memoirs of . . .

—— Emma Melcombe, *see* History of . . .

—— Godiva.

—— Granard's Nieces, by Jane Vaughan Pinkney.

—— Hamilton.

—— Harriot Butler, *see* Memoirs of . . .

—— in the arbour, by Mary Martha Sherwood.

—— in Black, by Thomas Peckett Prest.

—— in Search of a Husband, by Thomas Peckett Prest.

—— Jane Grey.

—— Jane Grey, by Thomas Miller.

—— Jane's Pocket.

—— Julia Mandeville, *see* History of . . .

—— Juliana Harley, *see* Story of . . .

—— Louisa Stroud, *see* History of . . .

—— Lucy Fenton, *see* History of . . .

—— McLairn, by Maria Hunter.

—— Mary, by Charles Benjamin Tayler.

—— of the bedchamber, by Mrs. A. Crawford.

—— of the Cave, by H. H. Hasworth.

—— of the Manor, by Mary Martha Sherwood.

—— of Martendyke.

—— of Milan, by Katharine Thomson.

—— Singleton, by Thomas Medwin.

—— Sophie Sternheim, *see* History of . . .

—— Willoughby's Diary, *see* So much of the Diary of Lady Willoughby. *Also see* Some further portions of the Diary of Lady Willoughby.

Lady's Drawing-Room.

—— Gift, by Jane Kinderley Stanford.

—— revenge.

—— Tale.

Lairds of Fife.

—— of Glenfern, by Mary Johnston.

Lake of Killarney, by Anna Maria Porter.

—— of Winander mere, by Miss Street.

Lambourne bell, by Mary Martha Sherwood.

Lamia : A Confession, by Mrs. Robert Cartwright.

Lamp of the Sanctuary.

Lancashire Collier Girl.

—— Witches, by William Harrison Ainsworth.

Land and Sea Tales, by Matthew Henry Barker.

—— Sharks and Sea Gulls, by Captain William Nugent Glascock.

Lane's annual novelist.

Laneton Parsonage, by Elizabeth Missing Sewell.

Langreath, by Eliza Nathan.

La Riviere, *see* History of . . .

Lascelles, by Marian Moore.

Lascivious Hypocrite.

La Soubrette.

Last Aldini, by A. L. A. D. Dudevant.

—— Ball, by George Soane.

—— Days of Aurelian, by William Ware.

—— Days of a Condemned, by Victor Hugo.

—— days of Mary Stuart, by Emily Finch.

—— Days of Pompeii, by Edward Bulwer, Lord Lytton.

—— King of Ulster, by Edmund Getty.

—— Man, by Mary Wollstonecraft Shelley.

—— man, or Omegarus and Syderia.

—— of the Barons, by Edward Bulwer, Lord Lytton.

—— of the Corbes, by Rev. John Wright.

—— of the Fairies, by George Payne Rainsford James.

—— of the Lairds, by John Galt.

—— of the O'Mahonys.

—— of the Plantagenets, by William Heseltine.

Lasting Impressions, by Joanna Carey.

Laugh and be Fat.

Laughable adventures of Charles and Lisette.

Laughton Priory, by Mary Meeke.

Launcelot Wedge, by Charles Hooton.

Laura and Augustus.

—— Blundell.

—— : a Novel, by Andrew Macdonald.

——, or original letters.

——, or the Orphan, by Anne Burton.

—— Valcheret.

—— Valmont.

Laurentia.

Laurette, by Mrs. Thomson.

Laurringtons, by Frances Trollope.

Laval, Rosine, by R. Smith.

La Vendee, by Anthony Trollope.

Lavinia Fitz-Aubyn.

Lawrence Lazy, *see* History of . . .

Lawrie Todd, by John Galt.

Lawyers in love, by William Johnson Neale.

Le Forester, by Sir Samuel Egerton Brydges.

Leap Year, by Selina Davenport.

Learning at a Loss.

—— better than house and land, by Joanna Carey.

Legacy.

Legend and Romance, by Richard John.

—— of Argyle, by David Carey.

—— of Cloth Fair.

—— of M'Donnell, by Archibald M'Sparran.

—— of Reading Abbey, by Charles Macfarlane.

—— of the Tower of London, by J. H. Hainsforth.

Legendary tales in verse and prose, by H. Fox Talbot.
—— Tales of the Highlands, by Sir Thomas Dick Lauder.
Legends and stories of Ireland, by Samuel Lover.
—— and traditionary stories.
—— of Connaught, by Matthew Archdeacon.
—— of Galloway, by James Denniston.
—— of the Lakes, by Thomas Crofton Croker.
—— of the Library at Lilies, by George Grenville, Lord Nugent.
—— of a Nunnery, by Edward Montague.
—— of the Rhine, by Thomas Colley Grattan.
—— of Scotland, by Ronald Mac Chronicle.
—— of terror.
——, tales, and stories of Ireland, by Philip Dixon Hardy.
Leicestershire tales, by Mary Linwood.
Leila in England, by Ann Fraser Tytler.
——, or the Island, by Ann Fraser Tytler.
——, or the Siege of Granada, by Edward Bulwer, Lord Lytton.
Lemira of Lorraine.
Lennox family.
Leolin Abbey, by Alicia Lefanu.
Leon, a Spartan story, by Henry Siddons.
Leonard and Gertrude, by Johann Heinrich Pestalozzi.
—— Lindsay, by Angus Bethune Reach.
—— Normandale, by The Honble. Charles Stuart Savile.
Leonora, by Maria Edgeworth.
——, a Love story, by Lady Boothby.
——: or characters drawn from real life.
——, or the Presentation at Court, by Elizabeth Lachlan.
Leontine, by Honble. Catherine Charlotte Maberly.
Leopold de Circe, by Madame de St. Venant.
—— Warndorf, by Henry Summersett.
Leper of the City of Aoste, by Count Xavier De Maistre.
Lermos and Rosa.
Lesson for Lovers.
Lessons of a governess, by Comtesse de Genlis.
Letitia and Laura.
—— or the castle without a Spectre, by Rachel Hunter.
Letters between Amelia in London and her Mother in the Country, by William Combe.
—— between Clara and Antonia.
—— between Emilia and Harriet.
—— between an English Lady and her friend at Paris.
—— between Master Tommy and Miss Nancy Goodwill.
—— between two lovers and their friends, by William Combe.

Letters from Altamont, by Rev. Charles Jenner.
—— from Cockney lands.
—— from the Countess de Sancerre, by Marie Jeanne Riccoboni.
—— from Elizabeth Sophia de Valiere, by Marie Jeanne Riccoboni.
—— from Elizabeth Williams.
—— from Emerance to Lucy, by Jeanne Marie le Prince de Beaumont.
—— from Henrietta to Morvina.
—— from Lady Juliet Catesby, by Marie Jeanne Riccoboni.
—— from the Inspector to a Lady, by " Sir " John Hill.
—— from Lothario to Penelope, by Rev. Charles Jenner.
—— from the mountains, by Anne Grant.
—— from Mrs. Palmerstone, by Rachel Hunter.
—— from a Portuguese nun, by Marianna Alcoforado.
—— from Sophia to Mira.
—— of Charlotte.
—— of a Hindoo Rajah, *see* Translation of the . . .
—— of an Italian Nun, by Jean Jacques Rousseau.
—— of a Mameluke, by Joseph Lavallée.
—— of Miss Riversdale.
—— from Ortis to Lorenzo.
—— of a Peruvian Princess, by Madame F. d'I. de H. Grafigny.
—— of Princess Zilia, by James Seguin.
—— of a solitary wanderer, by Charlotte Smith.
—— of a village governess, by Elizabeth Bond.
—— on different Subjects, by Lady Sarah Pennington.
—— supposed to have been written by Yorick and Eliza, by William Combe.
—— that passed between Theodosius and Constantia, by John Langhorne.
—— to little Henry.
—— to my sisters.
—— written by a Peruvian princess, by Madame F. d'I. de H. Grafigny.
—— written from Lausanne.
Lettice Arnold, by Anne Marsh.
Lettre de Cachet, by Catherine Grace Frances Gore.
Levi and Sarah, by Julius Ursinus Niemcewicz.
Levite, by Elizabeth H. F. Murphy.
Levity and Sorrow, by Michal Angelo Bianchi.
Lewis de Boncoeur, by Catherine Lara.
—— Tyrrell.
Libbie Marsh's Three Eras, by Elizabeth Cleghorn Gaskell.
Liber Amoris, by William Hazlitt.
Liberal American.
—— critic, by Captain Thomas Ashe.
—— Opinions, by Samuel Jackson Pratt.
Liberality and Prejudice, by Eliza A. Coxe.

Liberality, or the benevolent merchant, by Agnes M. Stewart.

Libertine, by Mrs. Byrne.

—— husband, by A. L. G. Necker de Stael-Holstein.

—— husband reclaimed.

Libertines.

Library of Fiction.

—— of French Romance.

Lichtenstein, by Wilhelm Hauff.

Lidora : An Ancient Chronicle, by Jean Claude Gorgy.

Liesli, by Carl Gottlieb Samuel Heun.

Lieutenant, and the Crooked Midshipman, by Augustus Collingridge.

Life, adventures and amours of Sir R[ichard] P[errot].

——, adventures, intrigues and amours of the celebrated Jemmy Twitcher.

—— and acts of the renowned and chivalrous Edmund of Erin, by Frances Peck.

—— and adventures of Anthony Leger.

—— and adventures of a cat.

—— and adventures of the celebrated Dr. Faustus.

—— and adventures of the Chevalier de Faublas, by Jean Baptiste Louvet de Couvray.

—— and adventures of Common Sense, by Herbert Lawrence.

—— and adventures of an eccentric traveller, by Charles Atkinson.

—— and adventures of a fly, by Stephen Jones.

—— and adventures of Guzman d' Alfarache, by Mateo Alemán.

—— and adventures of Indiana, by Pierre Carlet de Chamblain de Marivaux.

—— and adventures of Jack of the Mill, by William Howitt.

—— and adventures of Jack Rann, by James Lindridge.

—— and adventures of Joe Thompson, by Edward Kimber.

—— and adventures of John Marston Hall, by George Payne Rainsford James.

—— and adventures of John Nicol.

—— and adventures of Jonathan Jefferson Whitlaw, by Frances Trollope.

—— and Adventures of Lady Anne.

—— and adventures of a limb of the Law, by Michael Fagg.

—— and adventures of M. de la Sarre, by Thomas Crowley.

—— and adventures of Martin Chuzzlewit, by Charles Dickens.

—— and adventures of Mathew Bishop.

—— and Adventures of Michael Armstrong, by Frances Trollope.

—— and adventures of Mr. Anderson, *see* History of the . . .

—— and adventures of Mr. Francis Clive, by Phoebe Gibbes.

—— and adventures of Mr. Pig and Miss Crane.

—— and adventures of Nicholas Nickleby, by Charles Dickens.

Life and adventures of Oliver Twiss, by George William Macarthur Reynolds.

—— and adventures of Paul Plaintive.

—— and adventures of Peter Wilkins, by Robert Paltock.

—— and adventures of the Prince of Salerno, by Marquis de Vere.

—— and adventures of Sir Bartholomew Sapskull.

—— and adventures of Toby.

—— and adventures of Valentine Vox, by Henry Cockton.

—— and astonishing adventures of John Daniel.

—— and confessions of Humphrey Humbug.

—— and death of Fair Rosamond.

—— and death of a monkey.

—— and death of St. George.

—— and exploits of the ingenious gentleman Don Quixote, by Miguel de Cervantes.

—— and extraordinary adventures of James Molesworth Hobart, by N. Collard.

—— and extraordinary adventures of Lucy Amelia Gordon.

—— and extraordinary adventures, the perils and critical escapes, of Timothy Ginnadrake, by Francis Fleming.

—— and heroic actions of Balbe Berton.

—— and history of a pilgrim, by George Wollaston.

—— and memoirs of Mr. Ephraim Tristram Bates.

—— and opinions of Miss Sukey Shandy.

—— and opinions of Sebaldus Nothanker, by Friedrich Nicholai.

—— and opinions of Sir Richard Maltravers, by Henry Augustus Dillon-Lee, Viscount Dillon.

—— and opinions of Tristram Shandy, by Laurence Sterne.

—— and opinions of Tristram Shandy, by John Carr.

—— and perambulation of a mouse, by Dorothy Kilner.

—— and real adventures of Hamilton Murray.

—— and remains of Wilmot Warwick, by George Wightwick.

—— and singular memoirs of Matilda Countess de Lausanne, by Miss Guion.

—— and surprising adventures of blue-eyed Patty.

—— and surprising adventures of Jack Shepperd.

—— and surprising exploits of Rob Roy Macgregor, by D. Stewart.

—— and surprizing adventures of Crusoe Richard Davis.

—— and surprizing adventures of Don Antonio de Trezzanio.

—— and surprizing adventures of F. Reveep.

—— and times of Dick Whittington.

—— as it is.

—— as it is : a Second Series of tales, by Mrs. Paxton.

Little fables for little folks, by John Henry Brady.

—— Fadette, by A. L. A. D. Dudevant.

—— Family, by Charlotte Elizabeth Sanders.

—— Forget-me-not.

—— Foundling, by Lydia Falconer Miller.

—— Frank and other tales.

—— girl and her Bible.

—— Girl in the Wood, *see* Adventures of the . . .

—— girl's keepsake, by Mary Martha Sherwood.

—— Goody Goosecap, *see* Entertaining history of . . .

—— grey mouse.

—— Henry and his bearer, *see* the History of . . .

—— Hermitage, by L. F. Jauffret.

—— historians, by Jefferys Taylor.

—— Italians.

—— Jack, *see* History of . . .

—— Jem, the rag merchant, by J. T. Bell.

—— Juba.

—— King Skilful, *see* History of . . .

—— lessons for little folks, by Mary Elliott.

—— Lucy, *see* History of . . .

—— man and the little maid, *see* Authentic Memoirs of the . . .

—— Martin.

—— Mary.

—— Mary, a tale for children.

—— Maurice and his uncle.

—— Momière, by Mary Martha Sherwood.

—— Moralists.

—— Mountaineers of Auvergne.

—— orphan, by Mary Martha Sherwood.

—— peace-maker.

—— Pedlington, by John Poole.

—— Peter Paganini, *see* Wonderful Tour of . . .

—— Pickle, *see* Expedition of . . .

—— prisoner, or passion and patience.

—— prisoner, or a visit to the Island of Malta.

—— Robinson.

—— Sally, by Mary Matha Sherwood.

—— savage, by Captain Frederick Marryat.

—— Savoyard.

—— Selina.

—— stories for children, by Mrs. W. C. Wilson.

—— stories for little children.

—— stories for my pretty little people, by E. C. Somers.

—— stories of one and two syllables for little children.

—— stranger, by Captain Frederick Marryat.

—— Susan and her lamb.

—— tales for the nursery, by Eleanor Lady Fenn.

—— Thomas Dellow, *see* Adventures of the celebrated . . .

Little traveller, by Henrietta Louisa Farrer.

—— wanderers.

—— warbler.

—— white mouse, *see* Interesting Adventures of a . . .

—— Wife, by Catherine Marie Grey.

—— William, *see* Brief account of . . .

—— Willie, the lame boy, by William Balmbro' Flower.

—— woodman and his dog Caesar, by Mary Martha Sherwood.

Live and Learn, by Francis Lathom.

Lives, Amours, and surprising adventures of Daphnis and Chloe, by Longus.

—— of Cleopatra and Octavia, by Sarah Fielding.

Living waters by the Pilgrim's path.

Livonian Tales, by Elizabeth Rigby.

Lizzie Leigh, by Elizabeth Cleghorn Gaskell.

Llewellen, or the Vale of Phlinlimmon, by Grace Buchanan Stevens.

Llewellin Penrose, *see* Journal of . . .

——, a tale, by Adelaide O'Keefe.

Llewelyn's Heir.

Lobenstein Village, by August Lafontaine.

Lochandhu, by Sir Thomas Dick Lauder.

Lochiel, or the Field of Culloden, by David Carey.

Lodore, by Mary Wollstonecraft Shelley.

Lofoden, by Edward Wilson Landor.

Logan.

Log-Cabin, by H. F. Lee.

Lollards, by Thomas Gaspey.

London courtship.

—— Doll, *see* Memoirs of a . . .

—— in the Olden Time, by Miss H. Laurence.

—— jingles.

—— Legends, by John Yonge Akerman.

—— Night Entertainments, by Leitch Ritchie.

—— : or a Month at Stevens's.

—— ; or truth without treason, by Francis Lathom.

—— Tales, by Regina Maria Roche.

Lone Cottage, by Thomas Peckett Prest.

Long engagements.

—— lost found.

—— Meg, *see* The whole life and death of . . .

—— pack.

Longbeard, by Charles Mackay.

Longest day.

Longsword, Earl of Salisbury, by Rev. Thomas Leland.

Look to the end, by Sarah Stickney Ellis.

Looking-Glass for the Mind, by Arnaud Berquin.

Lord Aimworth and Charles Hartford, *see* History of . . .

—— and Lady Harcourt, by Catherine Sinclair.

—— Ashborn, *see* History of . . .

—— Belford, *see* History of . . .

—— Clayton, *see* History of . . .

—— Dacre of Gilsland, by Elizabeth M. Stewart.

Lord Fitzhenry, by Elizabeth Gunning.
—— Morcar of Hereward, by Julia S. H. Pardoe.
—— of Hardivyle.
—— of the manor, by Thomas Hall.
—— Roldan, by Allan Cunningham.
—— Stanton, *see* History of . . .
—— Viscount Cherington, *see* Memoirs of the Right Honourable . . .
—— Walford, by L. Lewis.
Lords of Erith, by Catherine, Lady Stepney.
Lorenz Stark, by J. J. Engel.
Lorimer, a tale, by Miss Aiken.
Lorimon, by François Marie de Baculard D'Arnaud.
Loss and Gain, by John Henry, Cardinal Newman.
Lost and won, by Henrietta Camilla Jenkins.
—— Brooch, by Harriet Mozley.
—— Evidence, by Hannah D. Burdon.
—— Happiness, by Lady Georgiana Chatterton.
—— Heir, by Tyrone Power.
—— manuscripts of a Blue Jacket.
—— Ship, by William Johnson Neale.
Lothian Tom, *see* History and comical transactions of . . .
Lottery of Life, by Marguerite Countess of Blessington.
—— of life, by M. Lyttleton.
—— of Marriage, by Frances Trollope.
Louis and Nina, by J. C. Gorgy.
Louisa Egerton, by Mary Leman Grimstone.
—— Forrester.
—— Matthews.
—— : A Narrative of Facts, by George Henry Glasse.
——, or the bride, by Harriet Mozley.
——, or the cottage on the Moor, by Elizabeth Helme.
——, or the reward of an affectionate daughter.
—— : Or Virtue in Distress.
——, or the virtuous villager.
—— Selby, *see* Life of Miss . . .
—— Seymour, by Catherine Grace Godwin.
—— Stroud, *see* History of Lady . . .
——, a tale, by Rev. Charles Jenner.
——, the wandering maniac, *see* Affecting history of . . .
—— Wharton.
Love, by Lady Charlotte Susan Maria Bury.
—— and avarice.
—— and crime.
—— and friendship.
—— and gratitude, by August Heinrich Julius Lafontaine.
—— and horror.
—— and madness, by Rev. Sir Herbert Croft.
—— and Mesmerism, by Horatio Smith.
—— and money, by Mary Howitt.
—— and mystery, by Thomas Peckett Prest.

Love and Pride, by Theodore Edward Hook.
—— and satire, by George Colman.
—— and State Intrigues of the Court of H——, *see* Memoirs of the . . .
—— and war, by Alexander Stiven.
—— as it may be, by Mrs. Bayfield.
—— at first sight, by Susannah Gunning.
—— at first sight, or the history of Miss Caroline Stanhope.
—— at first sight, or the history of Miss Lydia Harmwood.
—— Child, by Thomas Peckett Prest.
—— Fragments, by Mr. Robinson.
—— in a barn.
—— in high life.
—— in a tub.
—— Letters and cards which passed between an illustrious personage and a noble lady, *see* Genuine copies of all the . . .
—— lost.
—— match, by Henry Cockton.
—— -Match, by Honble. Catherine Charlotte Maberly.
——, mystery, and misery, by Anthony Frederick Holstein.
—— of Eveline for Lord Armond.
——, Rashness and Revenge, by Rippin Porter.
—— story.
—— token, by Hannah Maria Lowndes.
——, War and adventure, by Hugh Harkness.
Lovel Castle.
Lover and the Husband, by Charles de Bernard.
Lovers, by Isaac Disraeli.
—— and Friends, by Ann Hatton.
Lover's grave, by R. Rowlatt.
Lovers' labours.
Lovers, or the memoirs of Lady Sarah B—, by Pierre Henri Treyssac de Vergy.
Lover's quarrel.
—— Stratagem, by Johannes Heinrich Daniel Zschokke.
Love's Exchange, by Charles John Boyle.
Loves of Calisto and Emira, by John Sheally.
—— of Camarúpa and Cámalatà, by William Franklin.
—— of Celestine and St. Aubert, by Charles Phillips.
—— of Chœreas and Callirrhoë, by Chariton.
—— of Cupid and Psyche, and Lucius Apuleius.
—— of Mejnoun and Leila, by Isaac Disraeli.
—— of Mirtil.
—— of Othniel and Achsah, by William Tooke.
—— of Paris, by Paul Henri-Corentin Feval.
—— of Peter the Long, *see* Amorous Tale of the Chaste . . .
—— of the Saints.

306

Love's perils
—— pilgrimage.
Löwenstein, by Jane Roberts.
Lowran Castle, by Robert Trotter.
Loyalists, by Jane West.
Lubin and Rosetta.
Lucelle.
Lucien Greville, by Thomas Lettson Pettigrew.
Lucilla, or the reconciliation, by Elizabeth Sandham.
Lucille Belmont, by Alexander Baillie Cochrane.
Lucinda Courtney, see History of Miss . . .
—— Hartley.
——, or the angry father.
Lucius Carey, by H. J. Coates.
—— and unlucky.
Lucky escapes.
Lucretia, or the children of night, by Edward Bulwer, Lord Lytton.
——, or virtue the best dowry.
Lucubrations of Humphrey Ravelin, by George Proctor.
Lucy Ashbourne.
—— Belleville, by Catherine Stark.
—— Clare, see History of . . .
—— Fenton, see History of Lady . . .
—— Maxwell, see Prediction, or History of Miss . . .
—— Morley.
—— Neal.
——. A novel, by Eliza Parsons.
——, or I will not be naughty again, Papa.
—— Seymour, by Harriet Drummond.
—— Temple, see Charlotte's Daughter.
—— Unwin.
—— Wellers, see History of . . .
Lucy's pilgrimage.
Ludovicus, a tale, by Augusta Amelia Stuart.
Luke Somerton.
Lumley House.
Lusignan, or the Abbaye of La Trappe.
Lussington Abbey, by Henrietta Rouviere.
Lustful Turk.
Luttrells, by Robert Folkestone Williams.
Lydia, or Filial Piety, by John Shebbeare.
—— Tongue-pad, see Memoirs of . . .
Lynn Haverhill.

M. de Brinboc, see Memoirs of . . .
M. de la Sarre, see Life and adventures of . . .
M.D.'s Daughter.
M. Knowles, see Surprising Life and adventures of . . .
M.P.'s Wife, by Lady Harriet Anne Scott.
Mabel Carrington.
——, or the child of the battle-field, by Miss Barry.
Mabinogian, by Lady Charlotte Guest.
Macdermot, by John Agg.
Macdermots, of Ballycloran, by Anthony Trollope.

MacDonald, or the great mistake.
MacGrigor and Clarendon, by Alexander Gordon.
MacNeil, or the Scottish orphans.
Macrimmon, by Lieut. Alexander Sutherland.
M'Roy, see Annals of the family of . . .
Mad pranks of Tom Tram.
Madame Barneveldt, see Memoirs of . . .
—— de Guizot's tales for youth, by Elizabeth Charlotte Pauline de Meulan.
—— de Maintenon, by Comtesse de Genlis.
—— de Malguet, by Henry Whitelock Torrens.
Madeleine, by Léonard Silvain Jules Sandeau.
——, a tale of Auvergne, by Julia Kavanagh.
Madelina, by Louisa Sidney Stanhope.
Madeline, a Tale, by Amelia Opie.
——, or the Castle of Montgomery, by Isabella Kelly.
Mdlle. de Richelieu, see Travels and adventures of . . .
Madge Blarney.
Madiboo, see Adventures of . . .
Madman of the mountain, by Henry Summersett.
Madness the Rage.
Magdalen and other tales, by James Sheridan Knowles.
——, or the penitent of Godstow.
Magi and the star.
Magic and Mesmerism.
—— Lantern, by Marguerite Countess of Blessington.
—— of Kindness, by Augustus Septimus and Henry Mayhew.
—— of Wealth, by Thomas Skinner Surr.
—— Ring, by Friedrich Heinrich Baron de la Motte Fouqué.
—— spell, by William Gardiner.
Magician, by Leitch Ritchie.
—— and robbers.
Magnanimous Amazon.
Mahmoud.
Maid Marian, by Thomas Love Peacock.
—— of Avon, by Frances Peck.
—— of the Hallig, by Johann Christoph Biernatzki.
—— of the Hamlet, by Regina Maria Roche.
—— of Kent.
—— of Killarney, by Rev. Patrick Brontë.
—— of Moscow, by Barbara Hofland.
—— of the Mountain.
—— of Orleans, by Emma Robinson.
—— of Padua, by Miss C. D. Haynes.
—— of quality.
—— of the village, By Mrs. Kentish.
——, Wife and Widow, by Henry Siddons.
Maiden and married life of Mary Powell, by Anne Manning.
—— aunt, by Menella Bute Smedley.
—— Monarch.
—— wife, or the heiress De Courcy, by Ann Hamilton.

307

Maids as they are, by Martha Homely.
—— Husband, by Henrietta Camilla Jenkins.
—— of Honour, by Robert Folkestone Williams.
Mail coach, by Mary Martha Sherwood.
Maitre Jacques, see Memoirs of . . .
Majolo, by John Galt.
Major Bromely and Miss Cliffer, see History of . . .
—— Piper, see History of . . .
Makanna.
Malcolm Douglas.
Male-Coquette, by Jane Timbury.
Malpas, by William Bennett.
Malvagna, by Edward Cheney.
Malvina, by Sophie Cottin.
Mamma and her child.
—— and Mary, by Mary Ann Kelty.
Mamma's absence.
—— Stories.
Mammon in London.
Mammoth, by Dr. William Thomson.
Man, by Mary Ann Hedge.
—— as he is, by Robert Bage.
—— -at-Arms, by George Payne Rainsford James.
—— in the Moon, by Dr. William Thomson.
—— Made of Money, by William Douglas Jerrold.
—— of Benevolence.
—— of Experience, by James Thistlethwaite.
—— of Failing.
—— of fashion, see Memoirs of a . . .
—— of Feeling, by Henry Mackenzie.
—— of Fortune, by Catherine Grace Frances Gore.
—— of Honour, by Henry Mackenzie.
—— of honour, see Memoirs of . . .
—— of Nature, by James Burne.
—— of nature, or nature and love, by August Heinrich Julius Lafontaine.
—— of the People, by Charles G. Rosenberg.
—— of pleasure in Paris.
—— of Sensibility.
—— of snow, by Lydia Falconer Miller.
—— of sorrow, by Theodore Edward Hook.
—— of Two Lives, by James Boaden.
—— of the World, by Henry Mackenzie.
—— who eloped with his own Wife, by Lieut.-Col. J. J. Hort.
—— without a Profession, by Charles Rowcroft.
—— Without a Soul, by F. Harrison Rankin.
Manalay, see History of the Emperor . . .
Manasseh.
Manderville, or the Hibernian Chiliarch, by Francis S. Higginson.
Mandeville : or the last words of a Maniac.
——, or the Lynmouth Visitors.
——, a Tale, by William Godwin.
Manfredi.
Manfredi, by Sarah Lansdell.

Manfrone, by Mary Ann Radcliffe.
Maniac, by Amelia Bristow.
—— Father, by Thomas Peckett Prest.
Manners : a Novel, by Frances Moore.
—— of the day.
Manœuvres of Don Pedro Antos.
Manoeuvring Mother, by Lady Charlotte Susan Maria Bury.
Manon Lescaut, by Abbé Antoine François Prévost-d'Exiles.
—— Lescaut, see Translation of . . .
Manor of Glenmore, by Dennis Burrowes Kelly.
Man-O'-War's Man.
Mansfield Park, by Jane Austen.
Mansie Wauch, see Life of . . .
Mansion-House.
Manstein family, see Memoirs of the . . .
Manuella, by Edward Smallwood.
Manuscripts from the diary of a physician.
—— of Erdély, by George Stephens.
Many-Coloured life, by Thomas Gaspey.
Maple Vale.
Marcella, or the Missionary Abroad and At Home.
Marchioness de Brinvilliers, by Albert Smith.
—— de Louvois, see Memoirs of the . . .
——, or the matured enchantress, by Mrs. Ross.
—— ; a strange but true tale, by Elizabeth Thornton.
Marchmont, a Novel, by Charlotte Turner Smith.
Marco Visconti, by Tommaso Grossi.
Marcos de Obregon, see History of the life of the Squire . . .
Marcus Flaminius, by Ellis Cornelia Knight.
Mardens and the Daventrys, by Julia S. H. Pardoe.
Margam Abbey.
Margaret at home.
—— Capel, by Ellen Wallace.
—— Catchpole, see History of . . .
—— Coryton, by Leigh Cliffe.
—— Graham, by George Payne Rainsford James.
—— Lyndsay, see Trials of . . .
—— Maitland, see Passages in the life of Mrs. . . .
—— Melville, by Alicia Catherine Mant.
—— Oliphant, see Passages in the life of Mrs. . . .
——, or the pearl, by Charles Benjamin Tayler.
—— Percival, by Elizabeth Missing Sewell.
—— Percival in America, by Elizabeth Missing Sewell.
—— Ravenscroft, by James Augustus St. John.
—— Russell.
—— sister to John Bull, see History of . . .
—— Waldegrave, by C. G. Hamilton.
—— Whyte, see History of . . .
Margaretta.

Margarita, by Mary Martha Sherwood.

Margiana, by Mrs. S. Sykes.

Marguerite de Bourgogne, by Albert Smith.

—— de Valois, by Alexandre Dumas.

Maria, by Elizabeth Blower.

—— * * *, *see* Memoir of . . .

—— Barlowe, *see* History of Miss . . .

—— Cecilia.

—— : a Domestic Tale, by Catherine St. George.

—— : the Genuine Memoirs of an Admired Lady of Rank, by Edward Kimber.

—— Harcourt.

—— Menzikoff.

——, or the Hollanders, by Louis Buonaparte.

——, or a Shandean Voyage.

——, or the Vicarage.

——, a Persian Slave, *see* Memoirs of . . .

Mariamne, an historical novel, by Nathaniel Ogle.

——, or Irish anecdotes.

Marian.

—— de Brittoon, by S. S. Derenzy.

—— ; or a young maid's fortunes, by Ann Maria Hall.

Marianne, by Pierre Carlet de Chamblain De Marivaux.

——, the child of charity, by Thomas Peckett Prest.

Maria's Reward.

Marie Anne Lais, by H. C. Sims.

—— Antoinette, by Alexandre Dumas.

—— Louise, by Emilie Carlén.

Marina and Amelia, by Eliza Jeary.

Marine officer, by Sir Robert Steele.

Mark Wilton, by Charles Benjamin Tayler.

Marly, or a Planter's Life in Jamaica.

Marmaduke Herbert, by Marguerite, Countess of Blessington.

—— Lorrimer, by Joseph Middleton.

—— Midge, *see* Adventures of . . .

Marmontel's Tales, by Jean François Marmontel.

Marquis de Cressy, *see* History of the . . .

—— de Roselle, *see* History of the Noble . . .

—— de St. Forlaix, *see* Memoirs of the . . .

—— de Villebon, *see* Memoirs of the . . .

—— of Salus, *see* History of the noble . . .

Marriage Act, by John Shebbeare.

—— Contract, by Harriet Raikes.

—— in High Life, by Lady Caroline Lucy Scott.

——, a Novel, by Susan Edmondstone Ferrier.

——, A novel, by Thomas Marten.

—— of the Favourite, by Ellen Pickering.

—— of St. Pierre.

—— Present.

Married life, by Miss Howard.

—— Man, by George Moore.

—— Unmarried, by Charles White.

Marrying Man, by Harriet Maria Yorick Smythies.

Marston. A Novel, by Rosalia St. Clair.

——, or the Soldier and the Statesman, by Rev. George Croly.

Marten and his Scholars, by Lucy Lyttelton Cameron.

Martha, a memorial of an only and beloved sister, by Andrew Reed.

—— Willis, by Thomas Peckett Prest.

Martin and James, *see* History of . . .

—— and Mansfeldt, by Anna Maria Mackenzie.

—— Chuzzlewit, *see* The Life and adventures of . . .

—— the Foundling, by Marie Joseph Eugene Sue.

—— Toutround, by James Justinian Morier.

Martyria, by William Mountford.

Marvellous Adventures, by Mary S. Pilkington.

—— magazine.

—— pleasant love story.

Mary and Fanny.

—— and Florence, by Ann Fraser Tytler.

—— and Florence at Sixteen by Ann Fraser Tytler.

—— and her Cat, by Mrs. E. Fenwick.

—— Anne, by Mary Martha Sherwood.

—— Anne Wellington, by Revd. Richard Cobbold.

—— Ashley, by Frederic Montagu.

—— Aston.

—— Atkins.

—— Barton. An historical tale, by Count Henryk Krasinski.

—— Barton, A Tale of Manchester, by Elizabeth Gaskell.

—— the beggar girl, *see* History of . . .

—— Burton.

—— Campbell, by Harriet Martineau.

—— Clifford, by Thomas Peckett Prest.

—— de Clifford, by Sir Samuel Egerton-Brydges.

—— Elliot, by Catherine Douglas Bell.

——, a fiction, by Mary Wollstonecraft Godwin.

—— Gray.

—— Harland.

—— Jane, by Richard Sickelmore.

—— Jones, or the soldier's daughter.

—— Leeson, *see* Childhood of . . .

——, the maid of the inn, *see* History of . . .

—— of Burgundy, by George Payne Rainsford James.

—— Oglivie, by Andrew Picken.

——, or the test of honour, by Susanna Haswell, Rowson.

—— Parker.

—— Phillips.

—— Powell, *see* Maiden and married life of . . .

—— Price.

—— Prince, *see* History of . . .

—— Queen of Scots, by C. F. Barrett.

—— Raymond, by Catherine Grace Frances Gore.

Mary Schweidler, by Wilhelm Meinhold.
—— Spencer, by Anne Howard.
—— Wood, *see* History of . . .
Mary's grammar, by Jane Marcet.
Masaniello, the fisherman King of Naples.
Mascarenhas, by Mrs. T. F. Steward.
Mask of fashion, by Thomas Skinner Surr.
Masqued weddings, by Miss Elliott.
Masquerades, or what you will.
Massaniello, by Horatio Smith.
Massenburg, by Cecilia Mary Cadell.
Massouf.
Master Headstrong, *see* Adventures of . . .
—— Humphrey's Clock, by Charles Dickens.
—— Jackey, *see* History of . . .
—— Mosaic Workers, by A. L. A. D. Dudevant.
—— Passion, by Thomas Colley Grattan.
—— Timothy's Book-Case, by George William Macarthur Reynolds.
—— Tommy and Miss Nancy Goodwill, *see* Letters between . . .
Masterman Ready, by Captain Frederick Marryat.
Matchmaker, by Harriet Maria Yorick Smythies.
Maternal love, by Margracia Loudon.
Mathew Bishop, *see* Life and adventures of . . .
Matilda, *see* Life and singular memoirs of . . .
—— and Elizabeth, by The Misses Purbeck.
—— and Fanny.
—— and Malek Adhel, by Sophie Cottin.
——, Countess de Lausanne, *see* Life and singular memoirs of . . .
—— ; an Irish Tale, by Matilda Potter.
—— Montfort, by Peter Peregrine.
—— Mortimer, by Miss M. Woodland.
——, or the Adventures of an Orphan.
——, or the Barbadoes Girl, by Barbara Hofland.
—— or the efforts of virtue.
——, or the Misfortunes of Virtue, by Marie Joseph Eugene Sue.
—— St. Aubin.
—— : a tale of the day, by Constantine Henry Phipps, Marquis of Normanby.
Matrimonial Adventures of a Banker's Clerk, *see* History of the . . .
Matrimony, the height of bliss, by Mary Meeke.
——, a novel, by John Shebbeare.
Matron of Erin, by Mrs. Kelly.
Matrons, by Thomas Percy.
Matthew Wald, *see* History of . . .
Maude Effingham, by Theodora Elizabeth Lynch.
Mauprat, by A. L. A. D. Dudevant.
Maurice and Berghetta, by William Parnell.
—— : the Elector of Saxony, by Mrs. Colquhoun.
—— Powell.
Max Wentworth.
Maxwell, by Theodore Edward Hook.

May day.
—— Flower, *see* History of . . .
—— Grayson, by Thomas Peckett Prest.
—— you like it, by Charles Benjamin Tayler.
Mayor of Wind-Cap and Canvassing, by John and Michael Banim.
Mazeppa ; or the Wild Horse of the Ukraine.
Medallion, by S. Pearson.
Medley.
Meekness, or Emily Herbert, by Agnes M. Stewart.
Mehaled and Sedli, by Baron de Dalberg.
Melanthe, by Honble. Catherine Charlotte Maberly.
Melbourne.
Melcombe Lodge.
Melincourt, by Thomas Love Peacock.
Melissa and Marcia, by Eliza Hervey.
Melmoth House, by Mrs. J. Jenner.
—— the Wanderer, by Charles Robert Maturin.
Melton de Mowbray, by William Henry De Merle.
Melwin Dale.
Member, an Autobiography, by John Galt.
Memoir of Jane Martin.
—— of Maria ***.
—— of Valentine de T., by Mrs. M. C. Best.
Memoirs and adventures of a Flea.
—— and Opinions of Mr. Blenfield.
—— for the history of Madame de Maintenon, by Charlotte Lennox.
—— of****, by George Psalmanazar.
—— of a * * * * * ** * * * * * * **, by John Cleland.
—— of the ancient House of Clarendon.
—— of Andrew Winpenny, by Francis Glasse.
—— of Antonina.
—— of an author, by Jane Harvey.
—— of a Babylonian Princess.
—— of a Baroness.
—— of the Bashaw Count Bonneval.
—— of a Brahmin, by William Browne Hockley.
—— of Bryan Perdue, by Thomas Holcroft.
—— of Captain Rock, by Thomas Moore.
—— of Captain Shelburne.
—— of a Chaperone, by Mrs. Frederick Sullivan.
—— of Charley Crofts.
—— of the Chevalier Pierpoint.
—— of a Coquet.
—— of Count du Beauval, by J. B. de Boyer, Marquis D'Argens.
—— of the Count of P——, by Friedrich Wilhelm Streit.
—— of the Countess of Berci, by Charlotte Lennox.
—— of the Countess of Bressol, by Pierre Carlet de Chamblain De Marivaux.
—— of a Coxcomb, by John Cleland.

Memoir of the Danby Family, by Elizabeth Isabella Specne.
—— of Davy Dreamy.
—— of a Demi-rep of Fashion, by Amelia Gunnersbury.
—— of Dick the little pony.
—— of Don van Halen, by Valentin Llanos Guttierez.
—— of Emma and her nurse, by Lucy Lyttelton Cameron.
—— of Emma Courtney, by Mary Hays.
—— of a family in Swisserland, by Anne Ormsby.
—— of Female Philosophers.
—— of a Femme de Chambre, by Marguerite Countess of Blessington.
—— of Fidelis and Harriot.
—— of the first thirty-two years of the life of James Hardy Vaux, by James Hardy Vaux.
—— of a French lady of pleasure.
—— of a gentlewoman of the old school, by Anne McTaggart.
—— of a Griffin, by Captain F. H. T. Bellew.
—— of Harriot and Charlotte Meanwell.
—— of John Bull.
—— of Lady Eliza Audley, by Mrs. H. Cartwright.
—— of Lady Harriot Butler.
—— of the Life and Adventures of Sobrina.
—— the life and gallant exploits of the old Highlander.
—— of the life and remarkable exploits of Dennis Neale.
—— of the life of Parnese, by Robert Paltock.
—— of the life, sufferings, and surprising adventures of a noble Foreigner at * * * * * * *.
—— of the little man and the little maid.
—— of a London Doll.
—— of the love and State intrigues of the Court of H——.
—— of Lydia Tongue-pad.
—— of M. de Brinboc.
—— of Madame Barneveldt, by Susannah Gunning.
—— of a Magdalen, by Hugh Kelly.
—— of Maitre Jacques.
—— of a Malayan Family, by William Marsden.
—— of a man of fashion.
—— of a man of honour.
—— of a man of pleasure, by Henri François de la Solle.
—— of the Manstein Family.
—— of the Marchioness de Louvois, by Mary Walker.
—— of Maria, a Persian slave.
—— of the Marquis de St. Forlaix, by Nicolas Étienne Framery.
—— of the Marquis de Villebon.
—— of Mary, by Susannah Gunning.
—— of Miss Arabella Bolton.
—— of Miss D'Arville.

Memoir of Miss Faulkner, *see* Genuine . . .
—— of Miss Sydney Biddulph, by Frances Sheridan.
—— of modern philosophers, by Elizabeth Hamilton.
—— of the Montague Family.
—— of a Muscovite, by Rosina, Lady Lytton.
—— of myself.
—— of the Nutrebian Court.
—— of an old wig, by Richard Fenton.
—— of Oliver Cromwell and his children.
—— of an Oxford scholar.
—— of a peeress, by Catherine Grace Frances Gore.
—— of a peg-top, by Dorothy Kilner.
—— of a physician, by Alexandre Dumas.
—— of a picture, by William Collins.
—— of Planetes, by Thomas Northmore.
—— of Prince Alexy Haimatoff, by Thomas Jefferson Hogg.
—— of Prince Menzikoff, by M. de la Harpe.
—— of a princess, by Olivia Wilmot Serres.
—— of the Princess of Zell, by Sarah Draper.
—— of a Printer's Devil.
—— of a Protestant, by Oliver Goldsmith.
—— of the remarkable life and surprising adventures of Miss Jenny Cameron, by Archibald Arbuthnot.
—— of the Right Honourable Lord Viscount Cherington, by Captain Richard Muller.
—— of a Schoolmaster.
—— of a Scots Heiress.
—— of Sir Charles Belville.
—— of Sir Charles Goodville.
—— of Sir Roger Clarendon, by Clara Reeve.
—— of a social monster.
—— of a swindler and thief, by James Hardy Vaux.
—— of Thule.
—— of two beloved pupils.
—— of two young gentlemen.
—— of an umbrella, by George Herbert Rodwell.
—— of an unfortunate young nobleman, by James Annesley.
—— of the Villars family, by Harriet Waller Weeks.
—— of the Year Two Thousand Five Hundred, by Louis Sebastien Mercier.
—— of a young lady of family.
—— of a young lady of quality.
Memory.
Mems. of America, by Thomas Archer.
Men and manners, by Francis Lathom.
—— and women : a novel.
—— and women, or manorial rights, by Catherine Crowe.
—— of Capital, by Catherine Grace Frances Gore.
—— of Character, by William Douglas Jerrold.

Mental improvement for a young lady, by Sarah Green.
—— Novelist, by Alex. Kellet.
—— recreations, by Anthony Anderson.
—— Triumph.
—— wanderings.
Mentoria, by Susanna Haswell Rowson.
Mentorial tales, by Mary S. Pilkington.
Mephistopheles in England, by Robert Folkestone Williams.
Mercenary marriage.
Merchant of Venice, by Mary Lamb.
—— of Venice, *see* Novel from which the play of the . . .
Merchant's Daughter, by Ellen Pickering.
—— widow, by Barbara Hofland.
Mercy at Marsden Rocks, by Richard Charles Coxe.
Meredith, by Marguerite Countess of Blessington.
Merelina.
Merkland, by Margaret Oliphant.
Merlin Vale, *see* Cottage of . . .
Merrie England in the Olden Time, by George Daniel.
Merry frolick.
—— medley.
—— tales.
Merrye Englaunde.
Merryland, *see* New Description of . . .
Metamorphoses, or Effects of Education, by Mary Hughes.
Metamorphosis of Sona, by John Dudley.
——, or Golden Ass, by Lucius Apuleius.
Methodist lady, *see* Story of the . . .
Metropolis.
—— by Eaton Stannard Barrett.
Michael Armstrong, *see* Life and adventures of . . .
—— Cassidy, by Elizabeth Hardy.
—— Kemp, *see* History of . . .
—— the Married Man, by Anne Woodroofe.
Michaelo and the twins, by A. Winter.
Michailow, *see* Adventures of . . .
Mick and Nick, by Rev. Christian Gottlob Barth.
Micromegas, by François Marie Arouet de Voltaire.
Midnight Assassin.
—— Bell, by Francis Lathom.
—— groan.
—— horrors.
—— hour.
—— ramble.
—— rambler.
—— the Signal.
—— Sun, by Frederika Bremer.
—— Wanderer, by Margaret Campbell.
—— weddings, by Mary Meeke.
Midshipman Easy, *see* Mr. . . .
Midsummer Eve, by Alfred Butter.
—— Eve, by Anne Maria Hall.
—— Holydays.
—— Medley, by Horatio Smith.
—— Night's Dream, by Mary Lamb.
Mildred Vernon, by Hamilton Murray.
—— Winnerley.

Milesian Chief, by Charles Robert Maturin.
Milford House, by George Loftus.
Milistina.
Military adventures of Johnny Newcome.
—— Bijou, by John Shipp.
Mill, by Francis, Earl of Ellesmere.
Millener's girl.
Millenium Hall, *see* Description of . . .
Miller of Angibault, by A. L. A. D. Dudevant.
Milliner's girl, *see* Millener's Girl.
Millman's Tales.
Mina, by Andrew Ross.
Minerva Castle, by Jane Harvey.
Minor, The.
—— morals, by Charlotte Turner Smith.
—— Morals for young people, by Sir John Bowring.
Minstrel Love, by Friedrich Heinrich Karl Baron de la Motte Fouqué.
——, or, Anecdotes of Distinguished Personages.
Miranda, or the heiress of the Grange, by James Malcolm Rymer.
——, or three steps.
Miriam and Rosette, by Amelia Bristow.
——, a novel.
—— Coffin.
——, a Jewish tale.
——; or the Power of Truth, by Charlotte Anley.
Mirror of the months, by Peter George Patmore.
—— seduction.
Mirth and Morality, by George Mogridge.
Mirza, by James Justinian Morier.
—— and Fatima, by Bernard J. Saurin.
Misanthropic father, by Catherine Smith.
Miscellaneous pieces, by Charles Secondat, Baron de Montesquieu.
—— stories, by Jane Trimmer.
Miscellanies, by William Beloe.
——, by Henry Fielding.
Miscellany of Eastern Learning, by Denis Dominique Cardonne.
Miser married, by Catherine Hutton.
——, or interesting memoirs of Henry Pemberton, by Lucy Watkins.
Miseries and Pleasures of Matrimony.
—— of an heiress, by Anthony Frederick Holstein.
—— of Human Life, by James Beresford.
—— of poor simple innocent silly Tam.
Miserrimus, by Frederick Mansel Reynolds.
Miser's Daughter, by William Harrison Ainsworth.
—— fate, by P. O'Shaughnessy.
—— secret.
Misfortunes of Barney Branagan, by William Carleton.
—— of Elphin, by Thomas Love Peacock.
—— of love.
Misogug, by Michael de Palmzeaux.
Misrepresentation, by Julia Rattray Waddington.
Miss Aylmer.

Miss Baltimores, *see* History of the . . .
—— Beverly, *see* Adventures of . . .
—— Blandy, *see* Secret History of . . .
—— C——y's Cabinet of Curiosities.
—— D'Arville, *see* Memoirs of . . .
—— Emilia Beville, *see* History of . . .
—— Greville, *see* History of . . .
—— Harriot Fitzroy *see* History of . . .
—— Indiana Danby, *see* History of . . .
—— Jenny Cameron, *see* Memoirs of the remarkable life and surprising adventures of . . .
—— Kitty N——, *see* Amours and adventures of . . .
—— Lovely de Macclesfield, by Madame de Renneville.
—— Loveman and Miss Longfart, *see* Amorous Letters between . . .
—— Lucinda Courtney, *see* History of . . .
—— Lucy Watson, *see* Adventures of . . .
—— Melmoth, by Sophia Briscoe.
—— Meredith, *see* History of . . .
—— Moreton, *see* Authentic and interesting history of . . .
—— Pamela Howard, *see* History of . . .
—— Pen and her niece, by Elizabeth Stone.
—— Pittborough, *see* History of . . .
—— Sally Sable, *see* History of . . .
—— Sommerville, *see* History of . . .
—— Sydney Biddulph, *see* Memoirs of . . .
—— Temple, *see* History of . . .
Mission, or Scenes in South Africa, by Captain Frederick Marryat.
Missionary ; an Indian Tale, by Sydney, Lady Morgan.
—— stories.
—— tales, by Mary Ann Serrett Barber.
Missions at Home, by Rev. Caesar Henri Abraham Malan.
Miss-led general, by Eaton Stannard Barrett.
Mistake, a novel, by P. Littlejohn.
Mistaken Evil.
Mister Humfries' Clock.
Mistletoe.
Mistress of Royalty.
Mock-Monarchs.
Moderation : a Tale, by Barbara Hofland.
Modern Accomplishments, by Catherine Sinclair.
—— amours.
—— anecdote of the family of Kinkvervankotsdarsprakengotschderns, by Elizabeth Craven.
—— antique.
—— Atalantis.
—— Calypso, by Mrs. Ross.
—— Characters, by Eliza Haywood.
—— Characters, by Edward Montague.
—— Chivalry, by Catherine Grace Frances Gore.
—— Cymon, by Paul de Kock.
—— fine gentleman.
—— Flirtations, by Catherine Sinclair.
—— French Life, by Catherine Grace Frances Gore.

Modern Goody Two Shoes, by Mary Elliott.
—— Griselda, by Maria Edgeworth.
—— Gulliver's Travels, by W. Whitmore.
—— hero in the kingdom of Cathai, by Benjamin Frere.
—— Husband, by Hookham.
—— incident in domestic life, by Isabella Kelly.
—— Kate, by Anthony Frederick Holstein.
—— Literature, by Robert Bisset.
—— Lovers.
—— Manners.
—— Martyr, by Timothy East.
—— miniature.
—— Novel Writing, by William Beckford.
—— Pythagorean, by Robert Macnish.
—— Rake.
—— society, by Catherine Sinclair.
—— times, by Elizabeth Helme.
—— times, by John Trusler.
—— times, or anecdotes of the English family.
—— unbeliever, by Emma Newton.
—— Villa, by Medora Gordon Byron.
—— wife, by John Stevens.
Modes of Life.
Molly Gay.
Momus's Cabinet of amusement.
Monastery, by Sir Walter Scott.
Monastery of St. Columb, by Regina Maria Roche.
—— of St. Mary, by Emilia Grossett.
Monastic ruins.
Money-Lender, by Catherine Grace Frances Gore.
Moneyed Man, by Horatio Smith.
Monimia.
Monitress.
Monk and the Married Man, by Julia Rattray Waddington.
—— and the vine-dresser.
—— of Cimiés, by Mary Martha Sherwood.
—— of the Grotto.
—— of Udolpho, by T. J. Horsley Curties.
——— : a Romance, by Matthew Gregory Lewis.
——— : a romance By R. S. Esq.
Monkey man.
Monks and the robbers.
Monk's daughter.
Monks of St. Andrews.
Monkwood Priory, by Francis Tracy Thomas.
Monmouth, a tale, by Anna Maria Johnson.
Mons. de Jardin, *see* Strange adventures of . . .
Monsieur Botte, by Pigault Lebrun.
—— Provence, *see* Adventures of . . .
—— Violet, *see* Narrative of the travels and adventures of . . .
Montague family, *see* Memoirs of the . . .

Montague Newburgh, by Alicia Catherine Mant.
—— Park, by A. Selwyn.
Montalbert, a Novel, by Charlotte Turner Smith.
Montalde.
Montauban, by George Fitz-George.
Montbrasil Abbey, by Louisa Sidney Stanhope.
Monte Christo, *see* Count of . . .
—— Video, by Mrs. Bridget.
Monteith, by Mrs. Rice.
Montellion, *see* History of . . .
Montford Castle.
Montgomery, or Scenes in Wales, by Annabella Plumptre.
——, or the West Indian adventurer.
Month at Brussels, by John Agg.
—— in Town, by John Agg.
Montoni, by Edward Mortimer.
Montreithe.
Montrose, or the Gothic Ruin.
Montville.
Moor of Venice, *see* Story of the . . .
Moorland Cottage, by Elizabeth Cleghorn Gaskell.
Moorlands. Tales, by Robert Charles Dallas.
Moral Amusement.
—— Budget.
—— courage.
—— Legacy.
—— paralysis, by Mrs. Barber.
—— Stories for Children, by Mrs. C. Napier.
—— tales.
—— tales, by Mrs. Cooper.
—— tales, by Joseph Moser.
—— Tales, by Jeannie Marie Le Prince de Beaumont.
—— tales, by Francesco Soave.
—— tales after the Eastern manner, by John Seally.
—— tales and histories, by Rev. John Adams.
—— tales, by a father.
—— Tales for Young People, by Maria Edgeworth.
—— tales for young people, by Mrs. Hurry.
Moralist, by T. Potter.
Morduant Hall, by Anne Marsh.
——: sketches of life, by Dr. John Moore.
More ghosts, by Mrs. F. C. Patrick.
——minor morals.
—— miseries, by James Beresford.
—— short stories, by Edward Mangin.
—— short stories in words of two syllables.
Moreton.
Morlands, by Robert Charles Dallas.
Morley Ernstein, by George Payne Rainsford James.
Morni, by Richard Benson.
Mornings at Matlock, by R. Shelton Mackenzie.
Mornton, by Margaret Cullen.
Mortimer Delmar.

Mortimer Hall, by Mrs. Bridget.
Mortimers.
Mosaic workers, by A. L. A. D. Dudevant.
Moscow, or the Grandsire, by Mrs. M. Mainwaring.
Moss Cliff Abbey, by Mary Julia Young.
Moss-House, by Agnes Strickland.
Moss-Troopers.
Mother and, daughter, or La Marana, by Honoré de Balzac.
—— and daughter, a pathetic tale, by Mary Julia Young.
—— Bunch, *see* History of . . .
—— Bunch's closet newly broke open.
—— Bunch's Fairy Tales.
—— Grim, *see* Noted history of . . .
——, or the happy distress, by William Guthrie.
—— Shipton, *see* History of . . .
Mother-in-Law: or the Innocent Sufferer.
Motherless Mary.
Mothers and Daughters, by Catherine Grace Frances Gore.
—— and sons, by Rev. George Brittaine.
Mother's Gift.
—— jewels, by Mrs. M. C. Best.
—— Recompense, by Grace Aguilar.
—— stories for children, by Mrs. W. C. Wilson.
Motto, by George Brewer.
Mount Erin, by Matilda Potter.
—— Henneth, by Robert Bage.
—— Pausillipo, by F. L. C. Mountjoye.
—— Pelham, by Ann Hilditch.
—— Sorel, by Ann Marsh.
Mountain chief.
—— cottager, by Christian Heinrich Spiess.
—— Decameron, by Joseph Downes.
—— hermit.
—— peasants, by Rev. Caesar Henri Abraham Malan.
Mountalyth, by Jane Harvey.
Mourtray Family, by Eliza Hervey.
Mouse-Trap.
Mr. and Mrs. Wilson, *see* Story of . . .
—— Anderson, *see* History of the life and adventures of . . .
—— Baker, *see* Impartial history of the life, amours, travels and transactions of . . .
—— Bentley, Rural Philosopher, by Henry Man.
—— Blount's MSS., by Francis Barry Boyle St. Leger.
—— Bragwell, *see* History of . . .
—— Dalton's Legatee, by Elizabeth Stone.
—— Ledbury, *see* Adventures of . . .
—— Midshipman Easy, by Captian Frederick Marryat.
—— O'Flynn, *see* Wonderful adventures of . . .
—— Pig and Miss Crane, *see* Life and adventures of . . .
—— Rightway and his pupils, *see* History of . . .

Mr. St. George.
—— Stanley and Miss Temple, *see* History of . . .
—— Warenne, by Ellen Wallace.
Mrs. Armytage, by Catherine Grace Frances Gore.
—— Cleveland and the St. Clairs.
—— Gooch, *see* Life of . . .
—— Leicester's School, by Charles and Mary Lamb.
—— Leslie and her grandchildren, by Mrs. Hamerton.
—— Lovechild's golden present, by Eleanor, Lady Fenn.
—— Maberly.
—— Perkins Ball, by William Makepeace Thackeray.
—— Shamela Andrews, *see* Apology for the life of . . .
—— Wilberforce.
Much to Blame.
Mujnoon.
Mummy : A Tale of the Twenty-Second Century, by Jane C. Loudon.
Munchausen at Walcheren.
Mungo the little traveller, by Mary Mister.
Munster Abbey, by Sir Samuel Egerton Leigh.
—— Cottage Boy, by Regina Maria Roche.
Murder in the wood.
Murdered Bride.
Murderer, by J. Bounden.
Murray House, by Eliza Parsons.
Musical travels through England, by T. L. Bicknell.
Mussulman, by Richard Robert Madden.
Mutability of human life.
Mutual attachment.
My aunt Kate, by Mary Martha Sherwood.
—— Aunt Pontypool by George Payne Rainsford James.
—— Bible and my calling, by Lucy Lyttelton Cameron.
—— bird and my dog.
—— Children's Diary.
—— Cousin Nicholas, *see* Some account of . . .
—— father, *see* History of . . .
—— foster brother, by Selina Bunbury.
—— grandfather Gregory.
—— Grandfather's Farm.
—— Grandmother's Guests, by Henry Slingsby.
—— Life, by William Hamilton Maxwell.
—— Master's Secret, by Mrs. Yorke.
—— native land, by Catherine George Ward.
—— Old Cousin.
—— old portfolio, by Henry Glassford Bell.
—— own story.
—— own times.
—— sister Minnie, by Mrs. Robert Mackenzie Daniel.
—— three uncles, by Mary Martha Sherwood.

My uncle the clockmaker, by Mary Howitt.
—— Uncle the Curate, by Marmion W. Savage.
—— Uncle Thomas, by Pigault Lebrun.
—— Uncle Timothy, by Mary Martha Sherwood.
—— Village versus " Our Village," by Thomas Crofton Croker.
Myrtle.
Myself and my friend, *see* History of . . .
Mysteries elucidated, by Mrs. A. M. Mackenzie.
—— of the Castle Del Carino, by Sarah Wilkinson.
—— of the Court of London, by George William Macarthur Reynolds.
—— of Ferney Castle, by George Lambe.
—— of the forest, by Mary Houghton.
—— of Hungary, by Edward Moore.
—— of London, by George William Macarthur Reynolds.
—— of London. Fourth Series, by Edward Lytton Blanchard.
—— of the old castles of France, by A. Bailly.
—— of Oronza.
—— of Paris, by Marie Joseph Eugene Sue.
—— of St. Clair, by Catherine George Ward.
—— of Udolpho, by Ann Radcliffe.
Mysterious Baron, by Elizabeth Ratcliffe.
—— Count, by Anne Lerr.
—— dagger.
—— Father.
—— Florentine.
—— foundling.
—— Freebooter, by Francis Lathom.
—— Gentleman Farmer, by John Corry.
—— Hand, by A. J. Crandolph.
—— Husband, by Mary Meeke.
—— Man.
—— Marriage, by Catherine George Ward.
—— Monk, by C. A. Bolen.
—— Novice.
—— omen.
—— penitent.
—— pilgrim.
—— seal, by W. C. Proby.
—— sisters.
—— Visit, A Novel, by Mrs. Eliza Parson.
—— Visitor, or May, by Henry Montague Cecil.
—— voice, by Elizabeth Leon.
—— wanderer, by Sophia Reeve.
—— Warning, by Eliza Parsons.
—— wife, by Mary Meeke.
Mystery and confidence, by Mrs. Pinchard.
—— Developed, by Martin M'Dermot.
—— of the Black Tower, by John Palmer.
——, or Forty years ago, by Thomas Gaspey.
—— Revealed, by Oliver Goldsmith.
—— upon mystery.

Mystic Castle.
—— Cottager of Chamouny.
—— Events, by Francis Lathom.
—— Sepulchre, by John Palmer.
—— tower.

Nabob by Mrs. Rice.
—— at Home, by Mrs. Monkland.
—— a novel.
Nabob's Wife, by Mrs. Monkland.
Nan Darrell, by Ellen Pickiering.
Nannie and Jane.
Nanny Goose, *see* The History of the celebrated . . .
Napoleon, *see* History of the Amours of . . .
—— : or the mysteries of the hundred days, by Frances Peck.
Narrative of the extraordinary adventures of four Russian sailors, *also see* Narritive . . .
—— of the Magpie, *see* Pie Voleuse.
—— of the residence of the Persian Princes, by James Baillie Fraser.
—— of the travels and adventures of Monsieur Violet, by Captain Frederick Marryat.
Narratives for the young, by Rev. Caesar Henri Abraham Malan.
—— of a parent, by Mrs. Everest.
Narritive of the extraordinary adventures of four Russian sailors, *also see* Narrative of . . .
Natchez, by François René Vicomte Chateaubriand.
Nathalie, by Julia Kavanagh.
National feeling.
—— romances, by Jean Pierre Clavis de Florian.
—— Tales, by Thomas Hood.
Natural Daughter, by Mary Robinson.
—— Son, by Denis Diderot.
—— Son, by Carl Spindler.
Nature and Art, by Elizabeth Inchbald.
——, a Novel.
——, or a picture of the Passions, by John Scott Byerley.
Naval Club, by Matthew Henry Barker.
—— Officer, by Captain Frederick Marryat.
—— Sketch-Book, by Captain William Nugent Glascock.
—— Surgeon, by William Johnson Neale.
Navy at home.
Neapolitan.
Necromancer, or the Tale of the Black Forest, by Lawrence Flammenberg.
Ned Allen, by David Hannay.
—— Bently, by William Amphlett.
—— Clinton, by Francis Glasse.
—— Delaney.
—— Evans, *see* History of . . .
Negro servant, by Legh Richmond.
—— slave, by W. Naish.
Neighbours, by Frederika Bremer.
Neotetaeria.
Netley Abbey, by Richard Warner.
Net-Maker of Bagdad.

Network.
Never wrong.
Neville Castle, by the Misses Purbeck.
—— Family, by M. Despaurrins.
New Aera, by Comtesse de Genlis.
—— amusements of the German Spa, by Jean Philippe de Limbourg.
—— Arabian Nights' Entertainments, by Joseph Von Hammer.
—— Atalantis.
—— British Universal jester.
—— Canterbury tales, by Oliver Outline.
—— Care-killer.
—— Children in the Wood, by Elizabeth Somerville.
—— Clarissa, by Madame Elie de Beaumont.
—— Collection of fairy tales, by Henry Brooke.
—— collection of Gothic stories.
—— description of Merryland.
—— entertaining novelist.
—— Forest, by Horatio Smith.
—— Gil Blas, by Henry David Inglis.
—— gleaner.
—— happy week, by Miss M. Corbett.
—— juvenile scrap-book, by Mrs. Charles Cecil.
—— Landlord's Tale.
—— lodger.
—— modern story teller.
—— monk.
—— road to ruin, by Catherine, Lady Stepney.
—— Robinson Crusoe, by Joachim Heinrich Campe.
—— sketches of everyday life, by Frederika Bremer.
—— sylph.
—— tales, by Jean Pierre Clavis de Florian.
—— Tales, by Amelia Opie.
—— Tales, by Sarah S. Wilkinson.
—— tales of the castle, by Mary S. Pilkington.
—— Tom Thumb.
—— Year's day, by Catherine Frances Gore.
—— Year's Gift, by A. Selwyn.
Newcome in the Navy, The Adventures of, by Lieut.-Col. David Roberts.
Newgate, a Romance.
Newminster Abbey.
Newspaper Wedding.
Newstoke Priors, by Julia Rattray Waddington.
Newton Forster, by Captain Frederick Marryat.
Nice Distinctions.
Nicholas Nickleby, *see* Life and adventures of . . .
Nickelas Nickebery, by George William Macarthur Reynolds.
Nickleby married.
Nicolas Pedrosa, *see* History of . . .
Night adventurer.
—— and Morning, by Edward Bulwer, Lord Lytton.
—— Hag.

Night near Windsor, by Augustus Collingridge.
—— Side of Nature, by Catherine Crowe.
—— Watch.
Nightingale and other Tales, by Hans Christian Andersen.
Nightmare Abbey, by Thomas Love Peacock.
Nights of the Round Table, by Mrs. Christian Isobel Johnstone.
Nina, by Frederika Bremer.
——, an Icelandic tale.
Nine days wonder, by Mary Meeke.
No Enthusiasm.
—— Sense like Common Sense, by Mary Howitt.
—— virtue without struggle.
Nobility run mad.
Noble Cornutos.
—— enthusiast.
—— exile, by F. Laech.
—— family, by Mrs. Austin.
—— rival, by Victor Hugo.
—— wanderers.
Nobleman and his steward, by Eliza Taylor.
Nocturnal minstrel, by Eleanor Sleath.
—— Revels.
—— Visit, by Regina Maria Roche.
Nominal husband.
Norah Dalrymple.
—— Toole.
Norman Abbey.
—— Banditti, by Felix Ellia.
—— Leslie, by C. G. Hamilton.
Norman's Bridge, by Anne Marsh.
Norrington.
Northanger Abbey, by Jane Austen.
Nothern cottage.
—— Irish tales, by John Gamble.
—— Memoirs, by Mrs. A. Woodfin.
Norval and Julia.
Note-Book of a country clergyman, by Samuel Wilberforce.
Noted history of Mother Grim.
Notoriety.
Notre-Dame, by Victor Hugo.
Noureddin, by Catherine I. Finch.
Nourjahad, see History of . . .
Nourmahal, by Michael Joseph Quin.
Novel adventures of Tom Thumb, by Louisa Mary Barwell.
—— from which the play of the Merchant of Venice is taken, by G. Fiorentino.
Novelist, by J. S. S. Rothwell.
Novellettes, by Augustus von Kotzebue.
—— moral and sentimental, by T. Potter.
Novels for Grown Gentlemen and Ladies, by Madame Elie de Beaumont.
—— of Nature, by Mrs. Chadwick.
——, tales and stories, by Queen Margaret of Navarre.
November Nights, by William Frederick Deacon.
Novice, by Lucy Lyttelton Cameron.
—— of Saint Dominick, by Sydney, Lady Morgan.
—— of St. Ursula, by F. G. D. Dumenil

Novels, or the Heir of Montgomery Castle, by Matthew Moral.
——, or the Man of Integrity, by Louis Benoit Picard.
Now and Then, by Samuel Warren.
Nubilia in search of a husband, by William Mudford.
Numa Pompilus, see The History of . . .
Number Nip, see Diverting History of . . .
—— one, by Anna Maria Hall.
Nun, by Denis Diderot.
——, by Mary Martha Sherwood.
—— and her daughter.
—— of Arrouca, by John, Earl Russell.
—— of Gnadenzell, by Robert Huish.
—— of Miserecordia, by Sophia Frances.
—— of St. Agatha.
—— of Santa Maria di Tindaro, by Louisa Sidney Stanhope.
——, or the adventures of the Marchioness of Beauville.
——, or memoirs of Angelique.
Nuneham Park, by Harriot Rebecca King.
Nunnery, by Edward Jerningham.
—— for coquettes.
Nuns of the Desert, by Eugenia de Acton.
Nun's Picture, by Regina Maria Roche.
Nurse M'Vourneen, by Rev. George Brittaine.
Nursery governess, by Elizabeth Napier.
—— maid's diary, by Mary Martha Sherwood.
—— tales.
Nutrebian Court, see Memoirs of the . . .

Oakcliffe Hall.
Oakdale Cottage, by Harriot Rebecca King.
Oakleigh, by W. M. Holmes.
Oakwood Hall, by Catherine Hutton.
Oath of Allegiance, by Anne Rolfe.
——, or the buried treasure, by James Malcolm Rymer.
Obedience, by Mary Martha Sherwood.
—— Rewarded, by Mary S. Pilkington.
O'Briens and the O'Flahertys, by Sydney, Lady Morgan.
Observant pedestrian.
Obstinancy : a tale, by Mrs. Anna Maria Hall.
Oby Sedgwick.
Ocean Child.
Octavia, by Anna Maria Porter.
—— Elphinstone, by Anne Tallant.
Odd enough, to be sure, by August Heinrich Julius Lafontaine.
—— Moments.
—— Sketches, by William Anderson.
—— Volume, by the Misses Corbett.
Oddest of all oddities.
Oddingley murders, by Mary Martha Sherwood.
Oddities of London Life, by Paul Pry.
Odious comparisions, by John Richard Digby Best.
O'Donnel : a National tale, by Sydney, Lady Morgan.

O'Donoghue, by Charles James Lever.
Ofelia, by Dôna Francisca Pazos.
Officer's daughter.
—— daughters.
—— widow, *see* History of an . . .
Offspring of fancy.
—— of Russell, by Henry Summersett.
Ogilvies, by Dinah Maria Craik.
O'Halloran.
O'Hara family, *see* Tales by the . . .
——, or 1798, by William Hamilton Maxwell.
Old Arm-Chair, by John Holland.
—— bachelor in the old Scottish village, by Thomas Aird.
—— Betty and the ragged money, by Ann Jane Morgan.
—— castle.
—— Commodore, by Lieut, the Honble. Edward Howard.
—— country house, by Catherine Marie Grey.
—— Curiosity shop, *see* Master Humphrey's Clock.
—— Daddy Gander's Fiary Tales.
—— Dame Walder, by Henry Fearon.
—— Daniel, *see* Stories of . . .
—— Dower House, by Catherine Maria Grey.
—— Earl and his young wife.
—— English Baron, *see* Champion of Virtue.
—— English gentleman, by John Mills.
—— Family Legend, by James Norris Brewer.
—— Farm House, by John Close.
—— Flanders, by Octave Delepierre.
—— friend with a new face, by Eliza Parsons.
—— Hall, by John Mills.
—— Hardy, *see* History of . . .
—— Heads upon Young Shoulders.
—— Highlander, *see* Memoirs of the life and gallant exploits of the . . .
—— house of West Street, by Thomas Peckett Prest.
—— Irish baronet, by Henrietta Rouviere.
—— Irish Knight, by Margaret Graves Derenzy.
—— lady and her family, *see* History of an . . .
—— London Bridge, by George Herbert Rodwell.
—— Maid : or history of Miss Ravensworth, by Mrs. Skinn.
—— Maiden's Talisman, by James Dalton.
—— Man and his Granddaughter, by James Harrington Evans.
—— man of the mountain, by Ludwig Tieck.
—— Manor House, by Charlotte Turner Smith.
—— man's head, by Esther Hewlett.
—— Mr. Jefferson, *see* Tales of . . .
—— Nick, by Edward Dubois.
—— oak chest.
—— Oak Chest, by George Payne Rainsford James.

Old Robin Gray, *see* Entertaining history of . . .
—— Roger Bond.
—— sailor's Jolly Boat, by Matthew Henry Barker.
—— St. Paul's, by William Harrison Ainsworth.
—— Sanctuary, by A. J. Requirer.
—— school, by Julia Smith.
—— Stories, by Elizabeth Isabella Spence.
—— Tapestry, by M. W. Maskell.
—— times and new.
—— times revived.
—— travelling woman.
—— wife and young husband, by Mary Meeke.
—— Wives' Tales.
—— woman, by Mrs. Carver.
—— Word and the new, by Frances Trollope.
Oldcourt, by Sir Martin Archer Shee.
Olive, a novel, by Dinah Maria Craik.
Oliver Cromwell, by Horatio Smith.
—— Cromwell and his children, *see* Memoirs of . . .
—— Twiss, *see* Life and adventures of . . .
—— Twist, by Charles Dickens.
Olivia, or deserted bride, by Elizabeth Bonhote.
——, or the Nymph of the valley, by John Potter.
——, or the orphan.
Olla Podrida, by Captain Frederick Marryat.
Omen, by John Galt.
——, or Memoirs of Sir Henry Melville and Julia Eastbrook, by Arthur Gifford.
One fault, by Frances Trollope.
—— in a Thousand, by George Payne Rainsford James.
One-Pound Note, by Francis Lathom.
Onesimus.
Only child.
—— Daughter, by Harriette Campbell.
—— a Fiddler, by Hans Christian Andersen.
—— Son, by William Kennedy.
Opera, by Catherine Grace Frances Gore.
Oppressed Captive.
Ora and Juliet, by Emma de Lisle.
Orange girl of Venice.
—— grove, by Mary Martha Sherwood.
Ordeal.
—— by touch, by John Duncan (?)
Order and Disorder.
Oriental Anecdotes, by M. A. de Fauques.
—— Tale, by James Justinian Morier.
—— tales.
—— tales, *see* Select collection of . . .
—— Wanderings.
Orientalist, by Thomas Bacon.
——, or electioneering in Ireland, by Mrs. Purcell.
Original anecdotes : or the history of Haroun Alrachid.
—— Fables, by John Kidgell.

Original legend of Der Freischütz, by A. Apel.
—— moral tales for children, by Caroline Horwood.
—— of the Miniature, by Selina Davenport.
—— stories and anecdotes.
—— Stories from Real Life, by Mary Wollstonecraft Godwin.
—— Tales, by Richard Cumberland.
—— tales, by George Roberts.
—— tales for boys and girls, by Louisa Stanley.
—— tales for children.
—— tales, histories, essays and translations.
—— tales of my landlord's school, by William Gardiner.
—— tales, or true stories.
Orlandino, by Maria Edgeworth.
Orlando and Seraphina, by Mr. Nicholson
Ormond, by Sophia Lee.
Ornaments Discovered, by Mary Hughes.
O'Rourke, Daniel, by Thomas Crofton Croker.
Orphan, by Elizabeth Sandham.
—— Boy, by Mary Elliott.
—— Boy, by Catherine George Ward.
—— captive, by Jane Strickland.
—— Girl, by Mary Hughes.
—— girl, by Mary Robson.
—— heiress of Sir Gregory.
—— of Bollenbach.
—— of Nepaul.
—— of the Rhine, by Eleanor Sleath.
—— of Tintern Abbey, by Sophia F. Ziegenhirt.
—— of Waterloo, by Martha Blackford.
——, or the entertaining history of little Goody Goosecap.
——, or memoirs of Matilda, by Marie Joseph Eugene Sue.
——, a romance.
—— sisters, a tale founded on facts.
Orphans choice.
—— of Lissau, by Amelia Bristow.
—— of Llangloed.
—— of Normandy, by Mary Martha Sherwood.
—— of Snowdon, by Elizabeth Gunning.
O'Ruarc.
Orwell, Manor, by Mary Elizabeth Parker.
Osborne, or the Country Gentleman, by Rev. Joseph Jones.
O'Shaughnessy, Denis, by William Carleton.
Osier bed at Camberwell.
Osmond, A Tale, by Mary Ann Kelty.
Osmyn the unknown.
Osrick, or modern horrors, by Richard Sickelmore.
Ostentation and Liberality, by Arabella Argus.
Oswald Castle.
Oswick, the bold outlaw.
Othello, by Charles Lamb.
Other times, by Thomas Gaspey.
Othniel and Achsah, *see* Loves of . . .
Ottawah.

Otterbourne, by Edward Duros.
Our grandpapa's chest, by Robert Huish.
—— guardian, by Mrs. Robert Mackenzie Daniel.
—— Island, by Humphrey William Woolrych.
—— own times.
—— Street, by William Makepeace Thackeray.
—— Town, by Mrs. Fitzatherley.
—— Village, by Mary Russell Mitford.
Ouranoulogos, by John Galt.
Out of Town.
Outalissi, by Christopher Edward Leroy.
Outcast, a story of the modern reformation.
Outcasts : A Romance, by Friedrich Heinrich Karl, Baron de la Motte Fouqué.
Outlaw, by Anna Maria Hall.
Outlaw's Bride, by Hannah Maria Lowndes.
Outlines of truth.
Outsiders of Society.
Outward Bound, by Lieut, the Honble. Edward Granville George Howard.
Overbury, by John Edward Nassau Molesworth.
Overturned chaise, by Mrs. Mitford.
Owain Goch, by William Bennett.
Owen and De Montfort, *see* The Families of . . .
—— Castle, by Mary Ann Sullivan.
—— Glendower and other tales, by Anthony Frederick Holstein.
—— Glendower, An Historical Romance by Miss Hardy.
—— Tudor, by Jane Robinson.
Owlet of Owlestone Edge, by Francis Edward Paget.
Oxford scholar, *see* Memoirs of an . . .
—— to Rome, *see* From . . .
Oxonians : A glance at Society, by Samuel Beazley.

Pacha of many tales, by Captain Frederick Marryat.
**** packet broke-open.
Packet, a Novel, by Elizabeth Gunning.
Paddiana, by Sir William Gregory.
Paddy and Thomas.
Paddy-Go-Easy, by William Carleton.
Pageant, by F. E. Paget.
Paired—not matched, by Mrs. Ross.
Palace of Enchantment.
—— of Silence, by Philippe Auguste de Sainte Foix.
Palais Royal.
Palidor and Fidele, *see* Entertaining history of . . .
Palinode, by Pierre Henri Treyssac de Vergy.
Palmario, by Robert Pierce Gillies.
Palmerin, of England, by Francisco de Moraes.
Palmira and Ermance, by Mary Meeke.

Pamela Howard, *see* History of Miss . . .
—— in high life.
——, or Virtue Rewarded, by Samuel Richardson.
Pandurang Hari, by William Browne Hockley.
Panthea, by Robert Hunt.
Pantika, by William Howitt.
Papa Brick, by Pigault Lebrun.
Paraclete, by Thomas Pike Lathy.
Parasite
Parental Care, by Mary Pilkington.
—— duplicity.
—— monitor, by Elizabeth Bonhote.
—— present of pretty stories, by Miss A. L. M. Hitchon.
—— stories.
Parents and Wives, by Sarah Green.
Parent's assistant, by Maria Edgeworth.
—— monitor, by David Barker.
—— Offspring, by Caroline Barnard.
Paris and London, by Don Telesforo Trueba y Cozio.
—— Chit-Chat.
—— lions and London tigers, by Hariette Wilson.
Parish clerk.
—— Clerk, by Joseph Thomas Hewlett.
—— election.
—— priest in Ireland, by Joseph Hillary.
Parisian, by Mary Charlton.
Parmenides, Prince of Macedonia, by Joshua Dinsdale.
Parnese, *see* Memoirs of . . .
Parricide, a domestic romance, by Frederick Mansel Reynolds.
——, or the youth's career of crime, by George William MacArthur Reynolds.
Parricide's Grave, by Grenville Fletcher.
Parsonage House, by Elizabeth Blower.
——, a Tale, by Rodolphe Toepffer.
Parsons and Widows, by Joseph Thomas Hewlett.
Parson's case of jewels, by Mary Martha Sherwood.
—— Daughter, by Theodore Edward Hook.
—— wife.
Parthenissa, by Roger Boyle, the Earl of Orrery.
Partings and Meetings.
Partners for Life, by Mrs. Newton Crosland.
Pascal Bruno, by Alexandre Dumas.
Passages from the Diary of a late Phsician, by Samuel Warren.
—— from the life of a daughter at home.
—— in the life of Mrs. Margaret Maitland, by Margaret Oliphant.
Passion and Principle, by Frederic Chamier.
—— and Reason, by Elizabeth Cullen Brown.
—— : a tale, by Henry Tighe.
Passions, by Mrs. Byrne.
Past Events, by Mary Charlton.
Pastimes of a Convent.
Pastor Chief.
Pastoral annals, by Rev. James Spencer

Knox.
Pastorals in prose.
Pastor's daughter, by J. A. James.
—— Family, by Marianne Parrott.
—— Fire-Side, by Jane Porter.
Patchwork, by Captain Basil Hall.
Pathetic, sentimental and moral narratives, *see* First collection of . . ., *also see* Second collection of . . .
—— tales, poems, by Joshua Bridges Fisher.
Patience and Perseverance, by Barbara Hofland.
Patient Griselda, by Giovanni Boccaccio.
Patriarchal Times, by Adelaide O'Keefe.
Patriotic Sketches of Ireland, by Sydney, Lady Morgan.
Patronage, by Maria Edgeworth.
Patty Primrose.
Paul and Mary, by Jacques-Henri Bernadin de Saint-Pierre.
—— and Virginia, by Jacques-Henri Bernardin de Saint-Pierre.
—— and Virginie, by Jacques-Henri Bernardin de Saint-Pierre.
—— Clifford, by Edward Bulwer, Lord Lord Lytton.
—— Ferrol, by Caroline Clive.
—— Fitz-Henry, by Henry John Thornton.
—— Jones, the Pirate, by Pierce Egan, the younger.
—— Jones : a romance, by Allan Cunningham.
—— Peabody, by Percy Bolingbroke St. John.
—— Periwinkle, by William Johnson Neale.
—— Plaintive, *see* Life and adventures of . . .
—— the Poacher, by Thomas Frost.
—— the Reckless.
—— Swanston, *see* Memoirs of Sergeant . . .
Paula Monti, by Marie Joseph Eugene Sue.
Pauline, a tale of Normandy, by Alexandre Dumas.
——, or the victim of the heart, by Contant d'Orville.
Pauper Boy, by Rosalia St. Clair.
Pavilion : a novel, by Mrs. Crespigny.
——, or a month in Brighton, by John Agg.
Paynell, by Miles Stapleton.
Peace Campaigns of a Cornet, by Lieut.-Col. North Ludlow Beamish.
Peaceful Villa.
Pearl fisher of St. Domingo.
—— necklace and the scarlet frock.
Peasant and his landlord, by Baroness Sofia Margareta Von Knorring.
——, or female philosopher, by Mrs. Fell.
Pedantry, superstition, & temperance.
Pedlars.
Peep at our Ancestors, by Henrietta R. Mosse.
—— at the theatres.
—— at the world, by Harvey Sinclair.
Peer and the blacksmith, by R. Bedingfield.

Peers and Parvenus, by Catherine Grace Frances Gore.
Peer's Daughters, by Rosina Lady Lytton.
Peggy and her Mammy, by Mary Elliott.
—— and Patty.
—— Lum, by Caroline Fry.
Pelham, or the adventures of a Gentleman, by Edward Bulwer, Lord Lytton.
Pemberton Family, see Tales of the . . .
Pen Owen, by James Hook.
—— Tamar, by Mrs. H. M. Bowdler.
Pendennis, see History of . . .
Penelope : or Love's Labour Lost, by William Pitt Scargill.
—— Wedgebone, by Lieut.-Col. J. J. Hort.
Penitent : A Domestic Story of the Nineteenth Century.
—— father.
Penitents in the Magdalen House, see Histories of some of the . . .
Penruddock.
Penscellwood Papers, by Robert Armitage.
Pentamerone, or the Story of Stories, by Giovanni Battista Basile.
Percival Keene, by Captain Frederick Marryat.
——, or Nature Vindicated, by Robert Charles Dallas.
Percy Mallory, by James Hook.
——, or the friends.
—— or the old love and the new, by Lady Lydia Scott.
Pere La Chaise, edited by George Stephens.
Peregrine Bunce, by Theodore Edward Hook.
——, or the fool of fortune, by M. Lyttleton.
—— Pickle, see Adventures of . . .
—— Pultuney, by Sir John William Kaye.
—— Scramble, by Sir Henry Veel Huntley.
Peregrinus Proteus, see Private History of . . .
Perfidy detected.
Pericles and Aspasia, by Walter Savage Landor.
——, a tale of Athens, by C. F. Cornwallis.
Peril of Beauty, by Frederick Chamier.
Perils in the Woods, by Isabelle J. Towers.
Perjured lover.
Perkin Warbeck, by Alexander Campbell.
Perourou, see History of . . .
Perpetual Almanack.
Perplexed lovers.
Perplexities of Love.
——, or the fortunate elopement, by Mrs. Matthews.
Persecuted Family, by Robert Pollok.
Perseverance, or God helps them, by Charles Cowden Clarke.
—— or Walter, by Charlotte Elizabeth Tonna.
Persian Adventurer, by James Baillie Fraser.

Persian and Turkish Tales.
—— fables, by Rev. H. G. Keene.
—— Moonshee, see Pleasant stories from Gladwin's . . .
Persiana.
Persiles and Sigismunda, by Miguel de Cervantes.
Personal History of David Copperfield, by Charles Dickens.
Personation, by Selina Davenport.
Peruvian Princess, see Letters written by a . . .
—— Tales, by Miss R. Roberts.
Peter Bayssière.
—— Brown, see Sketch of the life and transactions of . . .
—— the Long, see Amorous Tale of the Chaste Loves of . . .
—— of the Castle, by John Banim.
—— Priggins, by Joseph Thomas Hewlett.
—— Schlemihl, by Adelbert von Chamisso, and see Wonderful history of . . .
—— Simple, by Captain Frederick Marryat.
—— Wilkins, see Life and adventures of . . .
Peter's Letters to his Kinsfolk, by Peter Morris.
Petrarch and Laura, by Comtesse de Genlis.
Petrel, by Admiral William Fisher.
Petticoat government, by Frances Trollope.
—— tales, by The Misses Corbett.
Peveril of the Peak, by Sir Walter Scott.
Phantasmagoria, of fun, by Charles Robert Forrester.
—— or the development of magical deception.
——, or sketches of life and literature, by Maria Jane Jewsbury.
Phantasmion, by Sara Coleridge.
Phantasus, see Tales from the . . .
Phantom, or Mysteries of the Castle, by Mrs. Mathews.
—— Ship, by Captain Frederick Marryat.
Phantoms of the Cloister.
——, or the adventures of a gold-headed cane, by Theophilus Johnson.
Pharisee turned publican.
Pharsamond, by de Marivaux.
Phedora, by Mary Charlton.
Philamour and Philamena.
Philanthropic Rambler, by Jane Timbury.
Philanthropist, or Selfishness and Benevolence Illustrated.
Philario & Eleanora.
Philip Augustus, by George Payne Rainsford James.
—— Colville, by Grace Kennedy.
—— Gray.
—— Quarll, see Adventures of . . .
—— Randolph.
Philosopher's stone.
Philosophic Kidnapper, by Mary Charlton.

Philosophical Quixote.
—— wanderers, by John Bigland.
Philosophy in Sport, by John Ayrton Paris.
—— of pleasure.
Phineas Quiddy, by John Poole.
Phoebe ; Or, The Miller's Maid.
Phoenix, or History of Polyarchus and Argenis, by John Barclay.
Phrosyne, by H. Gally Knight.
Physiognomical travels, by Johann Karl August Musaeus.
Physiognomist.
Pic Nic Papers, Edited by Charles Dickens.
Picaroon.
Picciola, by Joseph Xavier Boniface Saintine.
Pickwick Abroad, by George William Macarthur Reynolds.
—— in America, by George William Macarthur Reynolds.
—— Papers, see Posthumous Papers of the Pickwick Club.
Pickwickian Club, see Post-humourous notes of the . . .
Picnics from the Dublin Penny Journal.
Picture, and the Prosperous Man, by John George Hamilton Bourne.
—— from life, by Henry Whitfield.
—— : a novel, by Miss S. and Margaret Minifies.
—— of society.
—— of the Virgin, by Johann Christoph von Schmid.
Pictures, by Ludwig Tieck.
—— in the Hermitage.
—— of the heart, by John Murdoch.
—— of Private life, by Sarah Stickney Ellis.
—— of the World, by Robert Plumer Ward.
Pie voleuse.
Piece of family biography, by Edward Dubois.
Piedmontese envoy, by Prothesia S. Goss.
Pierce Falcon, by Emma Whitehead.
Pierre and Adeline, by D. F. Haynes.
—— and his family, by Miss Grierson.
—— Viaud, see Shipwreck and adventures of Monsieur . . .
Piers de Gaveston.
Pigou, see Story of . . .
Pilgrim of the Cross, by Elizabeth Helme.
——, or a picture of life, by Charles Johnstone.
Pilgrimage to the land of Burns.
Pilgrims of the Rhine, by Edward Bulwer, Lord Lytton.
—— of the Thames, by Pierce Egan.
—— of Walsingham, by Agnes Strickland.
Pill Garlick, see Life of . . .
Pilot, a tale of the sea.
Pin Money, by Catherine Grace Frances Gore.
Pine Tree Dell, by Euphrasia Fanny Haworth.

Pink tippet, by Lucy Lyttelton Cameron.
Pious cottager.
—— girl and her swearing father.
—— Manks Peasant.
Pippie's warning, by Catherine Crowe.
Pique, by Sarah Stickney Ellis.
Piquillo Alliaga, by Eugene Scribe.
Pirate, by Sir Walter Scott.
—— and the three Cutters, by Captain Frederick Marryat.
—— of Bofine, by F. W. Dunne.
—— of the gulf.
—— of Naples, by Mary Charleton.
Pirate's doom.
Piso and the Prefect.
Pity's gift.
Pixy, or the unbaptized child, by George William Macarthur Reynolds.
Pizarro, by Elizabeth Helme.
——, by Joachim Heinrich Campe.
Placid Man, by Rev. Charles Jenner.
Placide, by Comtesse de Genlis.
Plain sense.
—— story, by Mrs. Leslie.
Planetes, see Memoirs of . . .
Plantagenet.
——, a tale of the twelfth century, by Anna Millikin.
Planter of the Isle of France, by Alexandre Dumas.
Planter's daughter & her slave.
—— daughter and the rector's son.
Platonic guardian, by Anna Maria Johnson.
—— Marriage, by Mrs. H. Cartwright.
Play hours, by George Mogridge.
Players, or the stage of life, by Thomas James Serle.
Playfair Papers, by Paul Patterson.
Playfellow, by Harriet Martineau.
Pleasant adventures of Gusman, by Mateo Alemán.
—— and delightful history of the froliksome courtier.
—— and delightful history of Thomas Hickathrift.
—— and delightful history of the unfortunate daughter.
—— Dale.
—— stories from Gladwin's Persian Moonshee, by T. V. Moodelliar.
—— stories for children, by Mrs. W. C. Wilson.
—— tales for little people.
Pleasing and instructive stories for young children, by Mary Hughes.
—— Companion.
—— Instructor.
Pleasure and pain, by Anna Maria Weston.
—— improved.
Pleasures of benevolence, by Rhoda Wishwell.
—— of Friendship.
—— of Love.
—— of matrimony, see Whole . . .
—— of Retirement, by Duclos.
—— of want.
Plebeian, by E. H. White.

Plebeians and Patricians.
Pledge, or the first step to fortune.
Plexippus, by Richard Graves.
Plot and a peerage.
Pneumanee.
Poacher.
Poacher's daughter.
—— wife, by Charlton Carew.
Poder de la Musica.
Poems and tales, by Elizabeth Trefusis.
Poet's Daughter.
Poisoned goblet.
Polanders, by Pigault Lebrun.
Poles in the Seventeenth Century, by Count Kenry K. Krasinski.
Police and piety.
Polish Bandit, by Francis Lathom.
—— chieftain.
—— tale, by Mrs. Murray.
—— Tales, by Catherine Grace Frances Gore.
Polite Amusements.
—— lady.
—— repository.
Political fame, by Rose Ellen Hendriks.
—— Quixote, by G. Buston.
—— Romance, by Laurence Sterne.
Polly Willis, see History of . . .
Polydore and Julia.
Pomfret, by Henry Fothergill Chorley.
Pompey the Little, see History of . . .
Ponsonby.
——, A tale of troublous times.
Poor child's friend.
—— Cousin, by Robert Mackenzie Daniel.
—— Henry, by Rev. Christian Gottlob Barth.
—— Henry, or the little pilgrim.
—— Jack, by Captain Frederick Marryat.
—— Joseph.
—— laws and paupers illustrated, by Harriet Martineau.
—— Mary, or the love engagement.
—— Puss, see Adventures of . . .
—— Sarah.
—— soldier, by Mrs. Champion de Crespigny.
—— watchmaker of Geneva, by Rev. Caesar Henri Abraham Malan.
Pooroos-Purikhya, by Vidyapati.
Pope and the Actor, by Hannah D. Burdon.
—— : a novel, by John Richard Digby Best.
Poplar Grove, by H. Gardener.
—— Grove, by Esther Hewlett.
Popular Fairy Tales, by Benjamin Tabart.
—— Member, by Catherine Grace Frances Gore.
—— moral tales, by Rev. John Adams.
—— Tales and legends of the Irish Peasantry, by Samuel Lover.
—— tales and romances of the Northern nations.
—— tales for young people, by Maria Edgeworth.
—— Tales of the Germans, by Johann Karl August Musaeus.

Popularity and the Destinies of Woman, by Mrs. Cornewell Baron-Wilson.
Porcelain Tower, by Thomas Henry Sealy.
Port-Admiral, by William Johnson Neale,
Portrait, a novel, by Miss Elliott.
—— of Life.
Portraits of fashionable belles.
Post Captain, by Dr. John Moore.
—— captain, see Adventures of a . . .
Post-Humourous Notes of the Pickwickian Club, by George William Macarthur Reynolds.
Posthumous papers of the Pickwick Club, by Charles Dickens.
—— papers of the wonderful Discovery Club.
—— Records of a London Clergyman, by John Hobart Caunter.
Pottleton Legacy, by Albert Smith.
Poverty and the Baronet's family, by Henry Digby Beste.
Power of first Love.
Powis Castle.
Prairie-Bird, by Honble. Charles Augustus Murray.
Prater.
Praying for the living and the dead.
Precept and example.
Precepts and Practice, by Theodore Edward Hook.
Precipitance, by Mrs. John Smythe Memis.
Precipitate choice.
Predestined wife.
Prediction, by Mrs. T. F. Steward.
——, or History of Miss Lucy Maxwell.
Preference : a novel, by Selina Davenport.
Preferment : or my Uncle the Earl, by Catherine Grace Frances Gore.
Prejudice, by Azilé d'Arcy.
—— reproved, by Agnes Strickland.
Prelate : a novel, by John Frederick Smith.
Premier, by William Mudford.
Present for a little boy.
—— for a little girl.
—— for youth.
—— from my teacher.
——, or Child's pleasing Companion.
—— times and modern manners.
President's Daughter, by Frederika Bremer.
Prettiest book for children.
Pretty Portress of Windsor Lodge.
—— stories for children, by Mrs. W. C. Wilson.
—— tales for pretty people, by James Leslie Armstrong.
Price of Fame, by Elizabeth Youatt.
Pride and Irresolution, by Lady Emily Ponsonby.
—— and Prejudice, by Jane Austen.
—— of ancestry, by Mrs. Thomson.
—— of the Village, by Hannah Maria Lowndes.
Priest, The.
—— of the Nile, by Mrs. Charles Tinsley.

Priestess, an Anglo-Saxon tale.
Prima Donna, by Richard Becke.
Prime Minister, by William Henry Giles Kingston.
Primrose Prettyface, see History of . . .
Prince Alexy Haimatoff, see Memoirs of . . .
—— and the Pedlar, by Ellen Pickering.
—— Arthur, by Alexander Bicknell.
—— Chery, see Renowned History of . . .
——, Duke and the Page, by Rosina, Lady Lytton.
—— Fan-Feredin, see Wonderful travels of . . .
—— Fatal, Also see History of . . .
—— Lupin, see Storys of . . .
—— Menzikoff, see Memoirs of . . .
—— of Abissinia, by Samuel Johnson.
—— of Orange.
—— of Salerno, see Life and adventures of the . . .
——, or the Royal Libertines.
—— Riquet with the tuft.
Princely history of Crispin and Crispianus.
Princess Narina, by Charles Cowden Clarke.
—— of Cleves, by Elizabeth Griffith.
—— of Zell, see Memoirs of the . . .
——, or the Beguine, by Sydney, Lady Morgan.
Principle ! by Miss E. H. Macleod.
—— and passion.
—— and Practice.
——, a tale.
Printer's devil, see Memoirs of a . . .
Priot claim, by Mrs. Iliff.
Priors of Prague, by William Johnson Neale.
Priory of St. Bernard.
—— of St. Clair, by Sarah S. Wilkinson.
—— of St. Mary, by Bridget St. Hilaire.
Priscilla and Marcus.
Prison House.
—— of Montauban, by Julia Smith.
Prisoner of If, by Alexandre Dumas.
—— : or cruelty unmasked, by Thomas Smart.
Prisoners of Australia, by Charlotte Anley.
Prison-House, by Mrs. Bridget.
Private Correspondence of a Woman of Fashion, by Harriet Pigott.
—— history of Peregrinus Proteus, by Christoph M. Wieland.
—— Life, by Mary Jane Mackenzie.
—— Memoirs and Confessions of a justified sinner, by James Hogg.
Privateer ; a tale.
Privateers-Man, by Captain Frederick Marryat.
Prize in the lottery, by Abbé Pietro Chiari.
—— of youthful obedience.
—— : or the Lacemakers of Missenden, by Caroline Barnard.
Probable incidents, by Henry Summersett.

Probation and other tales, by Caroline Southey.
Procrastination, or the evil of putting off till tomorrow, by Mary Martha Sherwood.
——, or the Vicar's Daughter.
Prodigal youth.
Prodigious ! ! !
Profligate mother.
—— Prince.
Progress of crime, by Robert Huish.
—— of the Pilgrim Good-Intent, by Mary Ann Burges.
—— of romance, by Clara Reeve.
Progressive tales for little children.
Promessi Sposi, by Alessandro Manzoni.
Proper Spirit, by Lucy Lyttelton Cameron.
Prophet of the Caucasus, by Edmund Spencer.
—— of St. Paul's, by Constantine Henry Phipps, Marquis of Normanby.
Prophetess : A Tale of the last century in Italy, by Alexander Brodie.
Prose and poetry, by Mrs. Rueful.
—— and verse, by Jane C. Loudon.
Protector's secret.
Ptotégé, by Catherine Ponsonby.
Protestant, by Anna Eliza Bray.
—— leader, by Marie Joseph Eugène Sue.
—— rector.
—— truth and Roman Catholic Errors, by Plumpton Wilson.
Proverbs of Little Solomon.
Providential Care.
Provincial Sketches, by William Pitt Scargill.
Provincials, a country tale.
Provost, The, by John Galt.
—— of Paris, by William Shergold Browning.
Prudence and principle.
Pryings of a Postman, by Edward Capern.
Punch's letters to his son, by William Douglas Jerrold.
Punctuality, sensibility, & disappointment.
Pupil of adversity.
—— of Nature, by François Marie Arouet de Voltaire.
—— of Pleasure, by Samuel Jackson Pratt.
Puritan's Grave, by William Pitt Scargill.
Purity of Heart, by Elizabeth Thomas.
Puzzle for a curious girl.
Puzzled and Pleased, by Francis Lathom.
Pyrenean Banditti, by Eleanor Sleath.

Quaker.
Quakers : a tale, by Elizabeth B. Lester.
Quarrelsome Dog, by Leopold Wray.
Quarterclift, by Hugh Harkin.
Quarter-Deck, by Matthew Henry Barker.

Queen Mab, by Marie-Catherine le Jumel de Berneville, Comtesse d' Aulnois.
—— mother, by Louisa Stuart Costello.
—— of Denmark, by Andreas Nicolai de Saint-Aubain.
Queenhoo-Hall, by Joseph Strutt.
Queen's Lieges.
—— Page, by Selina Davenport.
—— Poisoner, by Louisa Stuart Costello.
Quentin Durward, by Sir Walter Scott.
—— Matsys, by Karoline von Greiner Pichler.
Question, Who is Anna ? by Miss M. S. Croker.
Quid, or tales of my messmates.
Quiet Husband, by Ellen Pickering.
Quintin Matsys, by Pierce Egan, the younger.
Quintus Servinton, by Mary Leman Grimstone.

Raby Rattler, see Effects and adventures of . . .
Rachel Ashburn.
—— Cohen, by Mrs. Kemp.
——, a tale.
Radama, by Mary Ann Hedge.
Radical : an autobiography, by John Galt.
Radzivil, by M. Wocklow.
Raff Hall, by Robert Sullivan.
Ragland Castle, by Katharine Thomson.
Railway passenger.
Rainbow, by Mary Martha Sherwood.
Rainsford Villa.
Rajah Kishna.
Rake and the Misanthrope, by August Heinrich Julius La Fontaine.
—— of taste.
——, or Adventures of Tom Wildman.
Ralph Gemmell, by Robert Pollok.
—— Reybridge, see Adventures of . . .
—— Richards, by Jefferys Taylor.
Ramble of Philo, by Captain Nixon.
—— or more paths than one, by Mary Elliott.
Rambler of Fortune, by Captain Thomas McCormick.
Rambles Farther, by Charlotte Turner Smith.
—— of the Emperor Ching Tih In Këang Nan, by Tkin Shen.
—— of Fancy, by Lucy Peacock.
—— of Mr. Frankly, by Elizabeth Bonhote.
—— of my uncle.
—— of Redbury Rook, by Captain George Wood.
Rameses : An Egyptian tale, by Edward Upham.
Rané.
Ranelagh House, by Joseph Warton.
Ranger of the Tomb, by Wilhelmina Johnson.
Rank and fashion, by Benjamin Frere.
—— and Talent, by William Pitt Scargill.

Ransom : a tale of the thirteenth century, by Laura Jewry.
Ranspach.
Ranthorpe, by George Henry Lewes.
Ranuph de Rohais, by Robert Pierce Gillies.
Raphael, or peaceful life, by August Heinrich Julius Lafontaine.
Rash vows, by Comtesse de Genlis.
Rashleigh Abbey, by Richard Sickelmore.
Rasselas, see Prince of Abissinia.
Rat with a Bell, see Story of the . . .
Rational Amusements for leisure hours, by Mrs. Ives Hurry.
—— Brutes, by Dorothy Kilner.
Rattlin' the Reefer, by Lieut. the Honble. Edward Granville George Howard.
Raven and the dove, by Lucy Lyttelton Cameron.
Raven's Feather, by Rev. Christian Gottlob Barth.
Ravensdale.
Rayland Hall.
Raymond and other tales, by Mary Gore.
——, a novel, by Richard Sickelmore.
—— Revilloyd, by Grace Webster.
—— : A tale of truth.
Raynsford Park, by the Misses Purbeck.
Read and give it a name, by Mrs. Llewellin.
Reading for winter evenings.
—— garland.
Real life in Ireland.
—— life in London, by Pierce Egan.
—— Pearls in a false setting, by Count Henry de la Pasture.
Realities and Ellen Seymour, by Anne Shepherd.
—— and reflections, by Ann Catherine Holbrook.
—— : Not a novel, by Anne Raikes Harding.
Reason triumphant over fancy, by Christoph Martin Wieland.
Reay Morden.
Rebecca and Rowena, by William Makepeace Thackeray.
—— the Jewess.
——, a novel, by Mrs. E. M. Foster.
——, or the fille de chambre, by Susanna Haswell Rowson.
Rebel : a tale.
——, a tale of the times.
Rebellion in the Cevennes, by Ludwig Tieck.
—— of the beast.
Rebellious school-girl, by Mary Hughes.
Recess, by Sophia Lee.
Reclaimed family.
—— libertine.
Recluse : A Fragment.
—— of Albyn Hall, by Zara Wentworth.
—— of the Appenines, by Miss Street.
—— of Norway, by Anna Maria Porter.
—— of the Woods.
——, or History of Lady Gertrude Lesly, by Esther Finglass.
——, or old Briitsh [sic] officer.
—— : or Old Father Green-Mantle.

Recluse : A translation of "Le Solitaire," by Charles Victor Prevot, Vicomte d'Arlincourt.
Recollections of a Chaperon, by Charlotte Dacre.
—— of a French Marchioness, by Sybil Scott.
—— of Hyacinth O'Gara, by Rev. George Brittaine.
—— of a pedestrian, by Thomas Alexander Boswell.
Reconciled sisters.
Reconciliation.
Records of Israel, by Grace Aguilar.
—— of a noble family, by Jane Harvey.
—— of real life, by Harriet Pigott.
Rector and his Pupils.
—— of Auburn, by Edward Thompson.
—— of Overton.
Rector's Memorandum Book, by Frances Elizabeth King.
—— son, by Anne Plumptre.
Rectory guest, by Catherine Maria Grey.
—— of Valehead, by Rev. Robert Wilson Evans.
Red and white roses.
—— barn, by William Maginn.
—— book, by Mary Martha Sherwood.
—— Cross Warrior.
—— Tyger.
Redbreast and other tales.
Redgauntlet, by Sir Walter Scott.
Redmond O'Hanlon, see Surprising life and adventures of . . .
—— the Rebel, by Lieut. Alexander Sutherland.
Reflection : a tale, by Barbara Hofland.
Reformation : a novel.
—— : or the Cousins, by Catharine Parr Strickland.
Reform'd Coquet, by Mary Davys.
Reformed family.
—— reprobate.
Reformer, by Cecilia Mary Cadell.
Reformist ! ! ! by Sarah Green.
Reft Rob.
Refuge.
Refugee in America, by Frances Trollope.
Refugees : an Irish tale, by Anne Raikes Harding.
Refusal, by Jane West.
Regent's daughter, By Alexandre Dumas.
Reginald Dalton, by John Gibson Lockhart.
—— de Torby, by Henry Siddons.
—— Du Bray.
—— Hastings, by Eliot Bartholomew George Warburton.
——, or the House of Mirandola.
—— Trevor, by Edward Trevor Anwyl.
Reine Canziani, by C. Godwin.
Relapse : a novel.
—— : or true and false morality.
Religious fashion, by Mary Martha Sherwood.
Reliques of Genius, by Everhard Ryan.
Remarkable history of Elizabeth Loveless.
Reminiscences, mishaps, by Paul Pry.

Remorseless assassin, by James Barton
Rencontre, by Albinia Gwynn.
Rene, a tale, by François René, Vicomte de Chateaubriand.
Renegade, by Charles Victor Prevot, Vicomte D'Arlincourt.
Renowned history of Giles Gingerbread.
—— History of Prince Chery.
—— history of a white cat.
Repealers, by Marguerite, Countess of Blessington.
Reprobate, a novel, by August Heinrich Julius Lafontaine.
Republican's mistress, by Charlotte Smith.
Requiescat in Pace.
Rescued fragments of Cabin Memorandums, by Lieut. L. Butcher Halloran.
Residence of the Persian princes, see Narrative of the . . .
Resignation ; or Memoirs of the Dufane Family, by A. Selwyn.
Restalrig, by Eliza Logan.
Restless matron, by Mrs. Showes.
Retaliation, or the history of Sir Edward Oswald, by Mrs. H. Cartwright.
Retreat : or sketches from nature, by Mary Ann Hedge.
Retribution : a novel.
——, or the murder at the Old Dyke.
——, or the Sicilian Vespers.
Retrospection, by Mrs. Isaac Taylor.
Retrospections, by Selina Bunbury.
Return of the Fairies, by Comtesse de Choiseul.
—— to England.
Reuben and Rachel, by Susanna Haswell Rowson.
—— Apsley, by Horatio Smith.
——, or the Suicide.
Revealer of Secrets.
Revelations of the Dead-Alive, by John Banim.
Revengeful Turk, see Romantic Tales.
Reverie, by Charles Johnstone.
Reveries of the Heart.
Reverses, or Memoirs of the Fairfax Family, by Elizabeth Whately.
Review of three days pleasure, by Dorothy Kilner.
Revolt of the bees, by J. M. Morgan.
Reward for attentive studies, by Mary S. Pilkington.
—— of virtue.
Reynard the Fox, see History of . . .
—— the fox, see Most delectable history of . . .
Rhedi, see History of . . .
Rhoda, a Novel.
——, or the excellence of charity.
Rhodomaldi, by Grenville Fletcher.
Rhydisel.
Ricardo the outlaw, by Captain John Simpson.
Rich and Poor, by Walker.
—— Boys and Poor Boys, by Barbara Hofland.
—— young country squire.
Richard Coeur de Lion.

Richard of England, by Thomas Archer.
—— of York.
—— Savage, by Charles Whitehead.
—— Turpin, *see* Surprising Life of . . .
Richardson's Sunday-School Primer.
Richelieu, by George Payne Rainsford James.
——, or the broken heart, by L. F. A. Du Plessis.
Riches and poverty, by P. Barrell.
Richmond : or scenes in the life of a Bow-Street Officer, by Thomas Skinner Surr.
Ridley Seldom, by Anne Howard.
Rienzi, by Edward Bulwer, Lord Lytton.
Rifle Rangers, by Captain Thomas Mayne Reid.
Right and Wrong, exhibited in the history of Rosa and Agnes.
—— and wrong, or the kinsmen of Naples, by Mary Julia Young.
—— and wrong way.
—— joyous and pleasant history of the feats, gests and prowesses of the Chevalier Bayard, by Jacques de Mailles.
Rinaldo Rinaldini, *see* History of . . .
Ring and the well.
——, in a series of letters.
——, or the merry wives of Madrid, by B. Thompson.
Ringdove.
Ringhan Gilhaize, by John Galt.
Ringrove, by Jane West.
Ringstead Abbey, by Jane Alice Sargant.
Rioters.
Riquet with the tuft, *see* Prince . . .
Rising Sun, by Eaton Stannard Barrett.
Rival Beauties, by Julia S. H. Pardoe.
—— chiefs, by Anna Millikin.
—— Crusoes, by Agnes and Elizabeth Strickland.
—— mother.
—— Mothers, by Madame de Genlis.
—— Pupils.
Rivalry, by Henry Milton.
Rivals, or the spectre of the Hall, by Thomas Peckett Prest.
——: Tracy's ambition, by Gerald Griffin.
Rob Roy, by Sir Walter Scott.
—— Roy Macgregor, *see* Life and surprising exploits of . . .
—— Roy, or days of Auld Lang Syne.
Robber, by James Dalton.
—— Chief, by Malcolm Graham.
—— Chieftain, by Nella Stephens.
—— A Tale, by George Payne Rainsford James.
Robbers of the forest, *see* Ancient Highland Story of the . . .
Robert and Adela; or, The Rights of Women.
—— and Frederick, by Mary Martha Sherwood.
—— Bruce, by Gabriel Alexander.
—— Chevalier, *see* Adventures of . . .
—— d'Artois, by Rev. John Humphrey St. Aubyn.

Robert Macaire in England, by George William Macarthur Reynolds.
—— Melville, by Richard Cope.
Robertina, by Catherine George Ward.
Robertses on their travels, by Frances Trollope.
Robin Goodfellow.
—— Goodfellow, who was nobody's enemy but his own, by Edward Berens.
—— Hood, *see* History of . . .
—— Hood and his merry foresters, by Stephen Percy.
—— Hood and Little John, by Pierce Egan, the younger.
—— Hood : a tale of the Olden Time.
—— of Woodside Lodge.
Roche-Blanche, by Anna Maria Porter.
Rochester Castle.
Rock of Modrec.
——: or Alfred and Anna, by Mrs. Barnaby.
Rockhaven, by E. H. St. Pierre Jones.
Rockite, by Charlotte Elizabeth Tonna.
Rodenhurst, by Elizabeth M. Stewart.
Roderick Dhu, by Thomas Archer.
—— Random, *see* Adventures of . . .
Rodolph the voyager, *see* First voyage of . . . .
Rodolphus of Werdenberg, by August Heinrich Julius Lafontaine.
Rody the Rover, by William Carleton.
Roger de Clarendon, *see* Memoirs of Sir . . .
Roland Bradshaw, by Thomas Hall.
—— Cashel, by Charles James Lever.
—— Percie.
Roman Catholic priest.
—— Empresses, by M. de Serviez.
—— Lovers.
—— matron, by Ludwig Tieck.
—— nights, by Alessandro, Count Verri.
—— stories.
Romance and Reality, by Letitia Elizabeth Landon.
—— of Ancient Egypt, by John Gunning Seymer.
—— of Ancient history, Egypt, by John Gunning Seymer.
—— of the Castle, by Jane Elson.
—— of the Cavern, by George Walker.
—— of a day.
—— of the early ages, by Horatio Smith.
—— of the Forest, by Ann Radcliffe.
—— of the Harem, by Julia S. H. Pardoe.
—— of the Hebrides, by Francis Lathom.
—— of the Highlands, by Peter Middleton Darling.
—— of History, England, by Henry Neele.
—— of History, France, by Leitch Ritchie.
—— of History, India, by John Hobart Caunter.
—— of History, Italy, by Charles Macfarlane.
—— of History, Spain, by Don Telesforo de Trueba y Cozio.
—— of Irish history.

Romance of Jewish History, by Misses C. and M. Moss.

—— of a mince pie, by Angus Bethune Reach.

—— of Private life, by Sarah Harriet Burney.

—— of the Pyrenees, by Catherine Cuthbertson.

—— of Real Life, by Charlotte Turner Smith.

—— of Vienna, by Frances Trollope.

—— of War, by James Grant.

—— readers and romance writers, by Sarah Green.

Romances, by Isaac Disraeli.

—— and tales for the winter fireside.

—— of the Chivalric Ages, by H. Cope.

—— of Many Lands.

—— of Real Life, by Catherine Grace Frances Gore.

—— Tales, and Smaller Pieces, by François Marie Arouet de Voltaire.

Romantic Facts.

—— fiction, by Friedrich Heinrich Karl, Baron de la Motte Fouqué.

—— Tales, by Isaac Crookenden.

—— tales, by Matthew Gregory Lewis.

Rome and the Abbey, by Eleanor C. Agnew.

Romeo and Juliet, by Charles Lamb.

Romulus: a tale of Ancient times, by August Heinrich Julius La Fontaine.

Ronaldsha, by Mrs. Dogherty.

Rookwood, by William Harrison Ainsworth.

Rory O'More, by Samuel Lover.

—— O'More, *see* History of . . .

Rosa de Clifford.

—— de Montmorien, by Ann Hilditch.

—— in London.

——, or the child of the Abbey, by Sophia Woodfall.

——, or village incidents.

——, the work-girl, by Margaret Percival.

Rosabel, a Novel, by Katharine Thomson.

Rosabella: or a Mother's Marriage, by Catherine Cuthbertson.

Rosalie: or the Castle of Montalabretti.

——, or the victim of infatuation.

Rosalind de Tracy, by Elizabeth Sophia Tomlins.

——, a novel, by Eliza Taylor.

——, or an apology for the history of a theatrical lady.

Rosaline de Vera, by Henry Augustus Dillon-Lee Viscount Dillon.

—— Woodbridge, by Hannah Maria Lowndes.

Rosalviva: or the Demon dwarf, by Grenville Fletcher.

Rosamond: a sequel to Early Lessons, by Maria Edgeworth.

Rosamund, Countess of Clarenstein.

—— Gray, *see* A Tale of . . .

Rosanna, or a Father's Legacy, by Laetitia Matilda Hawkins.

Rosano and Amanda, *see* The History of . . .

Rosara, or the adventures of an actress, by Pietro Chiari.

Rosaura di Viralva, by Mary Charlton.

Rose Allen, *see* Autobiography of . . .

—— and Emily, by Mrs. Roberts.

——, Blanche and Violet, by George Henry Lewes.

—— Cecil.

—— d'Albret, by George Payne Rainsford James.

—— Eglington, by William Balmbro' Flower.

—— of Claremont, by Catherine George Ward.

—— of England.

—— of Melville, by Mr. Taylor.

—— of Tistelön, by Emilie Carlén.

—— of Woodlee, by Maria Bainbridge.

—— Sommerville.

—— Talbot.

Rosella: or modern occurrences, by Mary Charlton.

Rosemary Lodge.

Rose-Mount Castle, by Mary Julia Young.

Rosenberg, by Mrs. Howell.

Rosina: a novel, by Miss Pilkington.

——, or the village maid, by Louisa Jones.

——: or the Virtuous Country Maid.

Rosse Castle.

Rotchfords, by Dorothy Kilner.

Rothelan: a romance, by John Galt.

Roué, By Samuel Beazley.

Rough and smooth, by Sybil Scott.

—— Recollections of Rambles Abroad and at home, by Calder Campbell.

Round tower.

Roxobel, by Mary Martha Sherwood.

Roxolana, by L. N. Musnicki.

Royal Captives, by Ann Yearsley.

—— exile, by Sarah Green.

—— legend.

—— Rake, by William Leman Rede.

—— Sufferer, by John Agg.

—— twins, by Thomas Peckett Prest.

—— wanderer, or the exile of England.

—— Wanderer, or secret memoirs of Caroline, by E. Barron.

Royalists and Roundheads, by E. Stuart.

Royston Gower, by Thomas Miller.

Rudolph & Adelaide, by M. A. Marchant.

Ruffian boy, by Sarah S. Wilkinson.

Rufus, or the Red King, by James Gregor Grant.

Ruins of Avondale Priory, by Isabella Kelly.

—— of Rigonda, by Helen St. Victor.

—— of Ruthvale Abbey, by Miss C. D. Haynes.

—— of Selinunti.

—— of Tivoli, by Frances Clifford.

Ruling Passion.

—— Passion, a Comic Story, by Philip Francis Sidney.

Runaway, by Horatio Smith.

Runaway's return.

Runnemede: an ancient legend, by Louisa Sidney Stanhope.

Rural love, by Francis Douglas.
—— walks, by Charlotte Turner Smith.
Russell. A Tale of the Reign of Charles the Second, by George Payne Rainsford James.
Russian tales, by Nikolai Mikhailovich Karamzin.
Rustum Khan, by Thomas Henry Ottley.
Ruth Pierce.
Ruthinglenne, by Isobella Kelly.
Rutilius and Lucius, by Robert Isaac Wilberforce.
Rybrent de Cruce, by Miss Head.

Sabbath breaker.
Sadaski, by Thomas Bellamy.
Sadness and gladness, by Honble. Adela Sidney.
Sadoc and Miriam.
Sailor-boy.
—— Boy, by Rosalia St. Clair.
Sailors and Saints, by Captain William Nugent Glascock.
Sailor's Bride.
—— Friendship, by Anna Maria Porter.
—— life and sailors' yarns, by C. Ringbolt.
Sainclair, by Comtesse de Genlis.
St. Alma, by J. C. Gorgy.
St. Antholin's, by Francis Edward Paget.
Saint Aubin.
—— Bernard's Priory, by Mrs. Harley.
—— Botolph's Priory, by T. J. Horsley Curties.
—— Clair of the Isles, by Elizabeth Helme.
—— Clair : or the heiress of Desmond, by Sydney, Lady Morgan.
—— Clyde.
—— Etienne, by Miss Martin.
—— George, *see* Life and death of . . .
—— Godwin, by Edward Dubois.
—— Hilary the crusader.
—— Hubert.
—— Irvyne, by Percy Bysshe Shelley.
—— James's, or the Court of Queen Anne, by William Harrison Ainsworth.
—— James's, or a peep at delusion, by Eliza Best.
—— Johnstoun, by Eliza Logan.
—— Julian, by Oliver Wilmot Serres.
—— Julian's Abbey.
—— Julien, by August Heinrich Julius La Fontaine.
—— Justin, by Sophia Bouverie.
—— Kathleen, by Lieut. Alexander Sutherland.
—— Leance.
—— Leger, by Richard B. Kimball.
—— Leon : a tale of the Sixteenth Century, by William Godwin.
—— Leon : A tale of the Sixteenth, Seventeenth and Eighteenth Centuries, by Edward Dubois.
—— Leonard's Forest, by William Henry Hitchener.
—— Margaret's Cave, by Elizabeth Helme.

Saint Otsburg, by Caroline Horwood.
—— Patrick, by Rennie.
—— Patrick's Eve, by Charles James Lever.
—— Roche, by Henriette von Paalzow.
—— Ronan's Well, by Sir Walter Scott.
—— Ruthin's Abbey.
Salamander, by Marie Joseph Eugène Sue.
Salathiel, by Rev. George Croly.
Sally King.
—— Sable, *see* History of Miss . . .
Salvador, by Don Telesforo de Trueba y Cozio.
—— the Guerilla, by Sir Thomas Noon Talfourd.
——, or Baron de Montbelliard, by Mrs. Croffts.
Sam Belson.
Samboe, by Mary Ann Hedge.
Samuel Sowerby.
——, a story for choristers.
—— Thomson, *see* History of . . .
—— Titmarsh, *see* History of . . .
Sancho, by John W. Cunningham.
Sand and Canvas, by Samuel Bevan.
Sandford and Merton, *see* History of . . .
Sandoval : or the Freemason, by Valentin Llanos Guttierez.
Sandron Hall, by the Hon. George Charles Grantley Fitzhardinge Berkeley.
Sans Souci Park, by Maria Tharmott.
Santa Maria, by J. Fox.
Santo Sebastiano, by Catherine Cutherson.
Santos de Montenos, by William Ticken.
San-Yu-Low, by Sir John Francis Davis.
Sappho, by J. Nott.
Saragossa, by E. A. Archer.
Sarah and her cousins.
—— and her mistress.
——, the exemplary wife, by Susanna Haswell Rowson.
Sarsfield, by John Gamble.
Satchel, or amusing tales.
Satiric tales.
Saucy Arethusa, by Frederick Chamier.
—— Jack, by Lieut. Charles Peake.
Savage.
—— girl, *see* History of a . . .
Savindroog, by Captain Michael Rafter.
Savoyard boy and his sister, by Hermann Kletke.
Sawney Beane, *see* History of . . .
Saxon and the Gael.
Sayings and Doings, by Theodore Edward Hook.
Says she to her neighbour, What ? by Barbara Hofland.
Scarlet handkerchief.
Scattergood family, *see* Adventures of the . . .
Scenes and characters, by Charlotte Mary Yonge.
—— and sketches of a soldier's life in Ireland.
—— and Stories, by Frederick William Naylor Bayley.

329

Scenes and tales of country life, by Edward Jesse.
—— at Brighton, by Innes Hoole.
—— in Craven, by James Leslie Armstrong.
—— for the Young, by Isaac Day.
—— from the life of Edward Lascelles, by Henry David Inglis.
—— in Feudal times, by R. H. Wilmot.
—— in the Morea.
—— in Our Parish, by Elizabeth Holmes.
—— of life, by Mrs. Barber.
—— of Life, by Alaric Alexander Watts.
—— of 1792, by George Delgarno Hill.
Sceptic.
Scheming : a novel.
——, a tale, by Catherine Grace Godwin.
Schinderhannes, by Leitch Ritchie.
School boy, see History of a . . .
—— for Daughters.
—— for Fashion.
—— for Fathers.
—— for Husbands.
—— for Majesty.
—— for Mothers.
—— for parents, by A. Kendall.
—— for Sisters.
—— for Widows, by Clara Reeve.
—— for Wives.
—— for Wives, by Mrs. M. A. Gascoigne.
—— of Arts.
—— of fashion.
—— of fashion, by Mrs. Thicknesse.
—— of Virtue.
—— of Woman.
School-Fellows, by Elizabeth Sandham.
Schoolfellows : or a by-way to fame, by Richard Johns.
——, or the influence of character and connections displayed.
School-Girl in France, by Rachel Mac-Crindell.
Schoolmistress, a moral tale for young ladies, by Rachel Hunter.
——, or the true history of Jenny Hickling.
Scotch Betty.
—— Marine.
—— Novel Reading, by Sarah Green.
—— parents, by John Carter.
Scotchwoman, by Anthony Frederick Holstein.
Scots heiress.
Scott, Sir Michael, by Allan Cunningham.
Scottish adventurers, by Hector Macneil.
—— Cavalier, by James Grant.
—— Chiefs, by Jane Porter.
—— chieftains, by Hannah Maria Lowndes.
—— Heiress, by Robert Mackenzie Daniel.
—— legend, by T. J. Horsley Curties.
—— orphans, by Martha Blackford.
—— Peasant's Fireside, by Alexander Bethune.
Scrinium, by Rebecca Edridge.
Sea devil, by Edward H. Rose.
—— Fiend, by George Dibden Pitt.

Seabrook Village, by Sophia F. Ziegenhirt.
Sea-Kings, in England, by Edwin Atherstone.
Seaside stories, by Mary Martha Sherwood.
Seasons : stories for very young children, by Jane Marcet.
Sea-Wolf, by John Brent.
Sebaldus Nothanker, see Life and opinions of . . .
Sebastian and Isabel, by – Loney.
—— and Zeila, by John Corry.
Secluded man, by Rev. Mr. Holder.
Second collection of pathetic, sentimental and moral narratives.
—— Love, and other tales, by John Palgrave Simpson.
—— Love, or Way to be happy, by Mrs. Norris.
—— portraiture of exclusive society.
—— travels of an Irish gentleman, by Joseph Blanco White.
—— voyage of Rodolph the voyager, see First voyage of Rodolph the voyager.
Secrecy, or the ruin on the rock.
Secresy, by Mrs. E. Fenwick.
Secret Avengers, by Ann Hatton.
——. A Christmas tale for the young.
—— Foe, by Ellen Pickering.
—— history and misfortunes of Fatyma.
—— history of Betty Ireland.
—— history of the Court and Cabinet of St. Cloud, by Mr. Stewarton.
—— history of a devil in petticoats.
—— history of Miss Blandy.
—— machinations, by Sarah Ann Hook.
—— memoirs of an illustrious Princess, by John Agg.
—— a Novel, by Isabella Kelly.
—— oath.
—— of the Cavern, by Mrs. Burke.
—— Passion, by Robert Folkestone Williams.
—— tribunal.
—— warning.
Secretary, a novel, by Lieut.-Col. J. J. Hort.
——, or circumstantial evidence.
Secrets in every Mansion, by Ann Hatton.
—— made public, by James Norris Brewer.
—— of the Castle, by David Carey.
Sectarian, by Andrew Picken.
Sedan : a novel.
Seducing Cardinal.
Seduction, or the perils of a woman's life.
Seer of Tiviotdale, by Louisa Sidney Stanhope.
Select collection of Oriental tales.
—— fairy tales, by Crhistoph Martin Wieland.
—— moral tales, by Jean Francis Marmontel.
—— Novels, by Madeleine Angelique De Gomez.

Select Stories for the instruction and entertainment of Children, by Arnaud Berquin.
—— tales and fables, by Benjamin Cole.
—— Tales of Count Hamilton, by Count Anthony Hamilton.
Selection of Eastern Tales.
—— of stories.
Self, by Catherine Grace Frances Gore.
—— -Condemned, by Thomas Gaspey.
—— -Control : a novel, by Mary Brunton.
—— -Deception, by Emma Parker.
—— -Delusion.
—— -Denial, by Barbara Hofland.
—— -Dependence, by Eliza Paget.
—— -Devotion, or the history of Katherine Randolph, by Harriette Campbell.
—— -Devotion, or the Prussians at Hochkirch, by Emilie Friederike Sophie Lohmann.
—— -Guidance.
—— -Indulgence, by Lady Charlotte Campbell.
—— -Sacrifice, by Erskine Neale.
—— -Seeker, by Lucy Lyttelton Cameron.
—— -Tormentor.
Selima, or the Village tale, by Harriet Ventum.
Selwyn in search of a Daughter, by Caroline Southey.
Sense and Sensibility, by Jane Austen.
Sentiment Not Principle, by Mrs. M. de Haviland.
Sentimental and humorous tales.
—— connoisseur.
—— deceiver.
—— excursions to Windsor and other places.
—— fables.
—— Journey, by Laurence Sterne, *Also see* Continuation of Yorick's . . .
—— Journey, continued, *see* Yorick's . . . .
—— journey intended as a sequel to Mr. Sterne's.
—— Lucubrations.
—— memoirs.
—— spy.
—— tablets of the good Pamphile, by Jean Claude Gorgy.
Separation, by Lady Charlotte Susan Maria Bury.
Sephora.
Sepoy's daughter.
Sequel to Adventures of Baron Munchausen, by Rudolf Eric Raspe.
—— to the Antidote to the Miseries of Human Life, by Harriet Corp.
—— to Coelebs, by F. Barlow, Junr.
—— to the Expedition of Humphrey Clinker.
—— to the Oddingley murders, by Mary Martha Sherwood.
—— to Principle and practice.
Seraphina : or a Winter in Town, by Caroline Burney.
Serena, a novel, by Catherine Selden.

Sergeant in the French army, *see* Adventures of a . . .
Series of Genuine Letters between Henry and Frances, by Elizabeth and Richard Griffith.
—— of tales from the German, by Adlerjung.
Servant's friend, by Sarah Trimmer.
—— hall.
Set about it at once, by Catherine Douglas Bell.
—— down at court.
Setma, the Turkish girl, by Rev. Christian Gottlob Barth.
Setting Sun.
Settlers in Canada, by Captain Frederick Marryat.
Seven fairy tales.
—— tales by seven authors, by Francis Edward Smedley.
—— temptations, by Mary Howitt.
—— wise masters of Rome, *see* The famous history of the . . .
—— wise mistresses of Rome, *see* The famous history of the . . .
Seventy-Six.
Sexton's Hero, by Elizabeth Cleghorn Gaskell.
Seymour Castle.
—— of Sudley, by Hannah D. Burdon.
Shades of Character, by Anne Woodroofe.
Shadow of the Cross, by Rev. William Adams.
Shadows and sunshine, by Isabel Goldsmid.
—— of the clouds, by James Anthony Froude.
Shakspeare and his friends, by Robert Folkestone Williams.
Shakspeare's romances.
Shakspere, the Poet, the Lover, the Actor, the Man, by Captain Henry Curling.
Shamela Andrews, *see* Apology for the life of Mrs.
Shawn Na Soggarth, by Matthew Archdeacon.
She is and she is not.
—— lives in hopes, by Miss Hatfield.
—— thinks for herself.
—— would be a Heroine, by Sophia Griffith.
Shenstone-Green, by Samuel Taylor Pratt.
Sheperdess of Aranville.
Shepherd Boy, by Johann Christoph von Schmid.
—— Boy and the Deluge, by Charlotte Elizabeth Tonna.
—— Boy of Snowden, by William Gardiner.
—— brothers, by Clara Hall.
—— of Salisbury Plain, by Hannah More.
Shepherdess of the Alps.
—— of Aranville, *see* Sheperdess of Aranville.

331

Shepherd's Calendar, by James Hogg.
—— cord.
—— son, by Thomas Smith.
Shepperton Manor, by John Mason Neale.
Sherwood Forest, by Elizabeth Sarah Villa-Real Gooch.
Ship of Glass, by Hargrave Jennings.
Shipwreck and Adventures of Monsieur Pierre Viaud, by J. G. Dubois-Fontanelle.
——, or memoirs of an Irish Officer, by Theodore Edgeworth.
——, or Misfortune the Inspirer of Virtuous sentiments, by Mary S. Pilkington.
——, or Paul and Mary.
Shipwrecked sailor boy.
Shipwrecks, *see* Tales of . . .
Shirley : a tale, by Charlotte Brontë.
Shoes of Fortune, by Hans Christian Andersen.
Shopkeeper turned sailor.
Short but tragical history of an unfortunate young girl.
—— Stories for Children.
—— stories for little folks.
—— stories from English history.
—— Stories in words of one syllable.
—— stories, or treasures of truth.
—— story.
Shrine of Bertha, by Mary Elizabeth Robinson.
Shrovetide child, by Pigault Lebrun.
Siamese Tales.
Siberian Anecdotes, by Thomas Haweis.
Sibyl's warning, by Edward Ball.
Sicilian.
—— mysteries, by Ann Hatton.
—— romance, by Ann Radcliffe.
——, a romance, by J. T. Benett.
Sidney and Volsan, *see* History of . . .
—— Castle.
—— Place.
—— tales, by Louisa Stanley.
Siege of Aubigny, by M. D'Uffreux.
—— of Belgrade.
—— of Florence, by Daniel M'Carthy.
—— of Kenilworth, by Louisa Sidney Stanhope.
—— of Lichfield, by Rev. William Gresley.
—— of Maynooth.
—— of Rochelle, by Comtesse de Genlis.
Sieges of Aquileia and Berwick, *see* History of the . . .
Siegfried the Dragon slayer, *see* Heroic life and exploits of . . .
Siegwart, by Johann Martin Miller.
Sigevart, by Johann Martin Miller.
Sigismar.
Sigismund Forster, by Ida, Countess Hahn Hahn.
Silvanella.
Silver penny, *see* Adventures of a . . .
—— Swan, by Madame de Chatelain.
—— thimble, by Sarah Trimmer.
—— three-pence, *see* Adventures of a . . .

Silwood.
Simon the Rebel, by Rev. Caesar Henri Abraham Malan.
Simple facts, by Mrs. C. Mathews.
—— John and his twelve misfortunes, *see* Comical history of . . .
—— memorials of an Irish Family.
—— Narrative.
—— Simon's Misfortunes.
—— stories.
—— stories for children, by Mrs. W. C. Wilson.
—— stories for cottage children.
—— story, by Elizabeth Inchbald.
—— tales, by Amelia Opie.
—— tales for the young.
Sin and sorrow.
—— forgiven.
—— of M. Antoine, by A. L. A. D. Dudevant.
Sincerity : a tale.
Sinclair, by Mary Pilkington.
Sinful Sally, *see* Story of . . .
Singers of the Sanctuary.
Singleton Fontenoy, by James Hannay.
Singular adventures of Sir Gawin.
—— tale.
Singularity : a novel, by Jane Harvey.
——, patriotism and artifice.
Sinner's Redemption.
Sintram and his companions, by Friedrich Heinrich Karl Baron de la Motte Fouqué.
Sir Andrew Sagittarius.
—— Andrew Wylie, by John Galt.
—— Arthur Wilmot.
—— Bartholomew Sapskull, *see* Life and adventures of . . .
—— Bevis of Lancaster.
—— Bevis, of Southampton, *see* History of the life and death of that most noble Knight . . .
—— Charles Beaufort, *see* History of . . .
—— Charles Belville, *see* Memoirs of . . .
—— Charles Dormer and Miss Harriet Villers, *see* History of . . .
—— Charles Goodville, *see* Memoirs of . . .
—— Charles Grandison, *see* The history of . . .
—— Cosmo Digby, by James Augustus St. John.
—— Edward Graham, by Catherine Sinclair.
—— Edward Seaward's narrative of his shipwreck, by Jane Porter.
—— Elidoc, by Friedrich Heinrich Karl, Baron de la Motte Fouqué.
—— Ethelbert, by Catherine Cuthbertson.
—— Ferdinand of England, by James Norris Brewer.
—— Francis Darrell, by Robert Charles Dallas.
—— Frizzle Pumpkin, *see* Adventures of . . .

Sir Gawin, *see* Singular adventures of
. . .
—— Geoffrey Restless, *see* History of . . .
—— George Ellison, *see* History of . . .
—— George Warrington, *see* History of
. . .
—— Gilbert Easterling, by James Norris-
Brewer.
—— Guy de Lusignan, by Ellis Cornelia
Knight.
—— Harry Herald and Sir Edward
Haunch, *see* History of . . .
—— Henry Clarendon, *see* History of
. . .
—— Henry Longueville, *see* Confessions
of . . .
—— Henry Morgan, by Lieut. the
Honble. Edward Granville Howard.
—— John Chiverton, by William Harrison
Ainsworth.
—— John May Mead, by William
Urquhart.
—— Launcelot Greaves, *see* Adventures
of . . .
—— Michael Paulet, by Ellen Pickering.
—— Michael Scott, by Allan Cunning-
ham.
—— Owen Glendowr, by Anthony
Frederick Holstein.
—— Patrick Hume's daughter.
—— Philip Gasteneys, by Sir Roger
Gresley.
—— Ralph de Bigod, by Edward Moore.
—— Ralph Esher, by James Henry
Leigh Hunt.
—— Ralph Willoughby, by Sir Samuel
Egerton Brydges.
—— Richard Maltravers, *see* Life and
opinions of . . .
—— Roger and his son Joe, *see* History
of . . .
—— Roger de Clarendon, *see* Memoirs
of . . .
—— Roger de Coverley, by Robert
Folkestone Williams.
—— Roland, by Charles Robert
Forrester.
—— Roland Ashton, by Lady Catherine
Long.
—— Theodore Broughton, by George
Payne Rainsford James.
—— William Dorien, by Mrs. S. Sykes.
—— William Harrington, *see* History
of . . .
Sister Anne, by Charles Paul de Kock.
—— Mary's tales in natural history, by
Mary Roberts.
Sisters' Budget, by the Misses Corbett.
Sister's care.
Sisters : a domestic tale, by Barbara
Hofland.
Sister's gift.
Sisters, A Novel.
—— of Ashdale.
—— of Nansfield.
—— of St. Gothard, by Elizabeth Cullen
Brown.
——, or character exemplified.
——, or England and France.

Sisters : or the history of Lucy and
Caroline Sanson, by Dr. William Dodd.
——, or virtue triumphant.
—— : A pleasing domestic story, by
Clara Hall.
Sister's stories, by S. Martin.
—— stories for children, by Mrs. W. C.
Wilson.
Six pennyworth of wit, by T. Carnan.
—— Princesses of Babylon, *see* Adven-
tures of the . . .
—— stories for the nursery.
—— stories, in English and French.
—— weeks at Long's, by Eaton Stannard
Barrett.
—— weeks in Paris.
Sixty years hence, by Charles Frederick
Henningsen.
Sketch book, by George William
Macarthur Reynolds.
—— Book of Fashion, by Catherine
Grace Frances Gore.
—— Book of the South.
—— of her own circle, by Miss Russell.
—— of the life and transactions of Peter
Brown.
—— of the times.
Sketches by Boz, by Charles Dickens.
—— for youth, by Rev. Caesar Henri
Abraham Malan.
—— from Flemish life, by Hendrik
Conscience.
—— from Nature, by George Keate.
—— in London, by James Grant.
—— of Character.
—— of English character, by Catherine
Grace Frances Gore.
—— of human manners, by Priscilla
Wakefield.
—— of Irish character, by Anna Maria
Hall.
—— of life and character.
—— of little boys and girls, by Lady
Eleanor Fenn.
—— of married life, by Mrs. Follen.
—— of modern life, by William Frederic
Williams.
—— of Pumps, by Alfred Crowquill.
—— of a Sea Port Town, by Henry
Fothergill Chorley.
—— of Wales and the Welsh.
—— of young people, by Elizabeth
Sandham.
——, scenes and narratives.
——, three tales, by Elizabeth Missing
Sewell.
Skimmer, by Claude Prosper Jolyot de
Crebillon.
Skyrack.
Slave captain, by J. Dignan.
—— King, by Victor Hugo.
Slavery, or the Times, by Anna Maria
Mackenzie.
Sleeping Beauty in the Wood.
—— beauty in the wood, *see* History
of the . . .
Sloven.
Small-Talker.

Smiles and Tears.
—— and Tears : or the romance of life, by Charles Whitehead.
Smiths, a Novel, by Henrietta Camilla Jenkin.
Smuggler king, by Thomas Peckett Prest.
—— : a tale, by John Banim.
—— : a tale, by Edward Berens.
—— : a tale, by George Payne Rainsford James.
Smugglers, a chronicle of the Coast Guard, by Lieut. Francis Higginson.
Smuggler's son, by Agnes W. Mitchell.
—— son, or Sherwood Quarry.
Smugglers, a tale descriptive of the sea-coast manners of Scotland.
Snarleyyow, by Captain Frederick Marryat.
Snow-Storm, by Catherine Grace Frances Gore.
So much of the Diary of Lady Willoughby, by Hannah Mary Rathbone.
Social Distinction, by Sarah Stickney Ellis.
—— influences.
—— Tales for the Young, by Mary Martha Sherwood.
Society and Solitude, by Innes Hoole.
—— in India.
——, or the Spring in Town.
Socrates out of his senses, by Christoph Martin Wieland.
Soffrona and her cat Muff, by Mary Martha Sherwood.
Softness, by Captain Charles H. Knox.
Solar eclipse, by Rosina Maria Zornlin.
Soldier boy.
—— of Dierenstein, by Elizabeth Craven.
—— of fortune, by Capt. Thomas Ashe.
—— of Fortune, by Captain Henry Curling.
—— of Pennaflor.
Soldier's child, by Charlotte Caroline Richardson.
—— Cottage, by Dennis Lawler.
—— family, by Anne Ormsby.
Soldiers of Venezuela.
Soldier's Offspring, by Emma de Lisle.
—— Orphan, by Mrs. Costello.
—— tale.
Solemn injunction, by Agnes Musgrave.
Solicitudes of Absence.
Solitary castle, by Mr. Nicholson.
—— walks through many lands, by Henry David Inglis.
—— Wanderer, *see* Letters of a . . .
Solomon Seesaw, by J. P. Robertson.
Solyman and Almena, by John Langhorne.
—— and Fatima, by T. Wright.
Some Account of the Cunningham Family.
—— account of the life of the late Gilbert Earle, by Francis Barry Boyle St. Leger.
—— account of my cousin Nicholas, by Richard Harris Barham.
—— Account of myself, by Charles Monkton.

Some further portions of the diary of Lady Willoughby, by Hannah Mary Rathbone.
—— new thoughts for the New Year.
—— passages in the life of Adam Blair, by John Gibson Lockhart.
Somerset, by Henry Siddons.
Something new, by Richard Griffith.
—— new, by Anne Plumptre.
—— new from Aunt Mary, by Mary Hughes.
—— odd, by Mary Meeke.
—— strange.
Son and the nephew, by Catherine George Ward.
—— and the Ward, by Marianne Parrott.
—— of Duplicity.
—— of Ethelwolf, by Anne Fuller.
—— of a genius, by Barbara Hofland.
—— of O'Donnel, by Rosalia St. Clair.
—— of the storm, by Henry Siddons.
Sons of Altringham, by Alicia Tyndal Palmer.
—— of St. David, by Griffiths Ap Griffiths.
—— of the Viscount and the daughters of the Earl, by Selina Davenport.
Sopha : a novel, by Claude Prosper Jolyot de Crebillon.
Sophia, by Charlotte Lennox.
—— de Lissau.
—— : or the Dangerous Indiscretion.
—— : or the embarrassed wife.
—— Shakespear, *see* History of . . .
Sophron and Tigranes, *see* History of . . .
Sophronia.
Sorcerer, a tale, by Veit Weber.
Sorrowful Sam.
Sorrows of Caesar, by Mary S. Pilkington.
—— of Edith, by Mrs. Burke.
—— of Eliza, by R. B. Bayles.
—— of Gustavus.
—— of the Heart, by John Heriot.
—— of selfishness.
—— of Werter, by Johann Wolfgang Goethe.
Soubrette, *see* La . . .
Souriciere.
South Sea fortune.
Southennan, by John Galt.
Southern Euphrosyne, by Isaac Nathan.
—— Tower.
Southstone's Rock, by Mary Martha Sherwood.
Sowing and reaping, by Mary Howitt.
Spaewife, by John Galt.
Spanish Campaign, by Mary Meeke.
—— conscript, by Jane Strickland.
—— Daughter, by Rev. George Butt.
—— lady and the Norman knight, by Kate Montalbion.
—— Memoirs, by George Monck Berkeley.
—— Novelists, by Thomas Roscoe.
—— outlaw, by William Herbert.
—— Rogue, by Mateo Alemán.
—— Tales, by Alan Rene Le Sage.

Specimens of German Romance, by George Soane.

Spectre.

—— Mother.

—— of the mountain of Granada.

—— of the Turret, by Isaac Crookenden.

Spectres, by Sarah S. Wilkinson.

Speculation.

——, a Novel, by Julia S. H. Pardoe.

Spinster's Journal, by Medora Gordon Byron.

—— tale, by Ann Wingrove.

Spiridion, by A. L. A. D. Dudevant.

Spirit in armour.

—— of " The Book," by Captain Thomas Ashe.

—— of Buncle.

—— of Elbe.

—— of the Grotto, by Emilia Grosett.

Spirits of the past.

Spiritual Quixote, by Richard Graves.

Spitfire, by Frederick Chamier.

Splendid Follies.

—— Misery, by Thomas Skinner Surr.

Splendour of adversity, by J. H. James.

Spoiled child, by Mrs. Howell.

Sprite of the Nunnery, by Joseph Trapp.

Spy glass.

Squire, by Ellen Pickering.

—— Marcos de Obregon, *see* History of the Life of the . . .

Staff Officer, by Oliver Moore.

Stage Coach.

—— Coach, by John Mills.

Stanfield Hall, by John Frederick Smith.

Stanhope, a domestic novel, by Joseph Middleton.

Stanislaus of Cracow, by S. B. Gnorowski.

Stanley Buxton, by John Galt.

—— family, *see* Tales of the . . .

—— tales, by Ambrose Marten.

—— Thorn, by Henry Cockton.

Stanly, a Tale of the Fifteenth Century.

Stanmore, by Clara Reeve.

Stanton.

Star of the Court, by Selina Bunbury.

State prisoner, by Hon. Mary Louisa Boyle.

Statira, by Mrs. Showes.

Statue room, by Rossetta Ballin.

Steadfast ones, by Charlotte Lyndon.

Steam Packet, by George William Macarthur Reynolds.

Steam-Boat, by John Galt.

Steamers v. Stages.

Stella and Vanessa, by Armand François Léonde Wailly.

—— of the North, by Helen Craik.

——, a pastoral romance, by Jean Pierre Clavis de Florian.

Stellins.

Step-Brothers.

Stephen Dugard, by William Mudford.

Step-Mother: A domestic tale, by Helena Wells.

Step–Mother : or evil doings, by George Payne Rainsford James.

Stepmother, or good luck at last, by W. R. Chetwood.

Steward, by Henry Cockton.

Stingy farmer's dream.

Stoic, by Jane Kinderley Stanford.

Stokeshill Place, by Catherine Grace Frances Gore.

Stolen Boy, by Barbara Hofland.

—— child : A tale of the town, by John Galt.

Stonehenge : or the Romans in Britain, by Malachi Mouldy.

Stone-Pickers.

Stories about Alfred the Great, by Agnes M. Stewart.

—— about dogs, by Thomas Bingley.

—— about Greece, by Mary Howard Ballantyne.

—— about horses, by Thomas Bingley.

—— after Nature, by Charles Jeremiah Wells.

—— and sketches for the amusement of leisure moments.

—— and studies from the chronicles and history of England, by Anna Maria Hall and Mrs. Jonathan Foster.

—— by a mother for the use of her own children.

—— explanatory of the Church Catechism, by Mary Martha Sherwood.

—— for Calumniators, by John Bernard Trotter.

—— for children, by Annabella Plumptre.

—— for children, by Mrs. Leckie.

—— for Christmas week.

—— for the fireside, by Miss Rignall.

—— for summer days and winter nights.

—— for Sunday afternoons, by Susan F. Crompton.

—— for young children, by Jane Marcet.

—— from Fly Land.

—— from Froissart, by Francis Barry Boyle.

—— from Gladwin's Persian Moonshee, *see* Pleasant . . .

—— from Greek history, by Barthold Georg Niebuhr.

—— from Heathen Mythology, by John Mason Neale.

—— from the history of Italy, by Anne Manning.

—— from the History of Rome, by Lady Henrietta Cecilia Sandford.

—— from the History of Scotland, by Alexander Stewart.

—— from the History of Wales.

—— from old chroniclers.

—— from Roman history.

—— from Scripture, by Bourne Hall Draper.

—— illustrative of the instinct of animals, by Thomas Bingley.

—— of a Bride, by Jane C. Loudon.

—— of Chivalry and Romance.

—— of the Crusades, by John Mason Neale.

—— of Edward.

—— of the elements.

Stories of the Four Nations, by Mrs. S. Sykes.

—— of the head and heart.

—— of the Irish peasantry, by Anna Maria Hall.

—— of Old Daniel.

—— of school boys.

—— of the sea, by Captain Frederick Marryat.

—— of Senex, by Edward Augustus Kendall.

—— of the seven virtues, by Agnes M. Stewart.

—— of Spanish life, by V. A. Huber.

—— of the Study, by John Galt.

—— of Torres Vedras, by John Gideon Millingen.

—— of Waterloo, by William Hamilton Maxwell.

——, old and new.

—— Selected from the History of France.

—— selected from the history of Greece, by Sarah Laurence.

——, traditionary and romantic, of the two Rebellions in Scotland, by A. D. Fillans.

Story about a Christmas, by Mrs. Percy Sinnett.

—— Book of the Seasons, by Lydia Falconer Miller.

—— for Christmas.

—— of Al Raoui, by William Beckford.

—— of Anna.

—— of the caravan.

—— of Clarissa.

—— of Fatima.

—— of a feather, by William Douglas Jerrold.

—— of George Panton.

—— of the girl and her basket of eggs.

—— of Isobel, by Mary Ann Kelty.

—— of Lady Juliana Harley, by Elizabeth Griffith.

—— of La Roche, by Henry Mackenzie.

—— of a Life, by Col. Joseph Moyle Sherer.

—— of Lilly Dawson, by Catherine Crowe.

—— of the Methodist Lady.

—— of the Moor of Venice, by Giovanni Battista Giraldi.

—— of Mr. and Mrs. Wilson, by Edward Moore.

—— of Pigou, by William Gardiner.

—— of the rat with a bell.

—— of the Robins, *see* Fabulous Histories.

—— of a Royal favourite, by Catherine Grace Frances Gore.

—— of Sinful Sally.

—— of a wanderer, by Robert Dyer.

—— of which the new tragedy, call'd the Brothers.

—— on which the new tragedy, called Virginia.

—— without an end, by Friedrich Wilhelm Carové.

—— without a Name.

Story-book of wonders, by Mary Martha Sherwood.

Storys of the bewitched fiddler.

—— of Prince Lupin.

Story-Teller.

Stradella, by Walter Somers.

Strange adventures of Mons, de Jardin.

Stranger Chieftain.

——, or Llewellyn Family.

Stranger's grave, by Henry Villiers.

Strangers of the Glen, by Hannah Maria Lowndes.

—— of Lindenfeldt, by Mrs. Ross.

Stratagems defeated, by Mary Meeke.

Strathallan, by Alicia Lefanu.

Strathbogie, by Alicia M'Gennis.

Strathern : or life at home and abroad, by Marguerite, Countess of Blessington.

Stratton Hill, by John Carne.

Strawberries.

Strawberry Hill, by Robert Folkestone Williams.

Stray Child.

Strength and weakness, by Nora Bellairs.

Strife and Peace, by Frederika Bremer.

Striking likenesses, by Louisa Sidney Stanhope.

String of British pearls.

—— of Pearls, by Thomas Peckett Prest.

—— of Pearls, by George Payne Rainsford James.

Strive and thrive, by Mary Howitt.

Strolling player.

Struggles and adventures of Christopher Tadpole, by Albert Smith.

—— for Fame, by Eliza Meteyard.

Struwelpeter, *see* The English.

Student, by Edward Bulwer, Lord Lytton.

—— of Salamanca.

Stumble on the threshold, by Mary Molesworth.

Sturmer, by Isabella F. Romer.

Subaltern, by George Robert Gleig.

—— officer, by Captain George Wood.

Submission exemplified.

Submissions of dependence.

Substance and shadow.

Subterranean cavern, by Mary Pilkington.

Such follies are.

—— is the World.

Sufferings of Ouang.

Suffolk tale, by J. Hamilton Roche.

Suicide, or the progress of error, by John Corry.

——, a tale founded on facts, by William Maginn.

Sukey Shandy, *see* Life and opinions of Miss . . .

Summer at Brighton, by Mary Julia Young.

—— at De Courcy Lodge, by Mary Anne Bourne.

—— by the sea.

Summer's walk.

Sunday-School teacher, by Lucy Lyttelton Cameron.

Supplement to Baron Munchausen's travels.
—— to the life and opinions of Tristram Shandy.
—— to Lord Anson's Voyage, by Abbé Coyer.
Supposed daughter.
Supreme Bon Ton, by George Jones.
Surprises of Love.
Surprising adventures of Bigenio.
—— adventures of Captain Winterfield.
—— life and adventures of the gentleman-robber Redmond O'Hanlon.
—— life and adventures of M. Knowles, by William Fairbank.
—— life of Richard Turpin.
—— travels and adventures of Sylvester Tramper, by George Walker.
Susan and Magdalene.
—— Gray, see The History of . . .
—— Harvey.
—— Hopley, see Adventures of . . .
—— a novel.
—— Palmer.
Susanna ; or traits of a modern miss, by Mrs. Bullock.
Susannah, or the three guardians, by Mary Martha Sherwood.
Suspicion, or the benevolent recluse.
Suspicious lovers.
Suttee or the Hindoo Converts, by Mrs. M. Mainwaring.
Sutton Abbey.
Surry Cottage, by James Penn.
Suzette's dowry, by J. Fiévée.
—— Marriage Portion, by J. Fiévée.
Swallow, by Edward Augustus Kendall.
Swan's egg, by Anna Maria Hall.
Swedes in Prague, by Karoline von Geiner Pichler.
Swedish mysteries, by J. Kiddershaw.
—— Shepherd, by Rev. Christian Gottlob Barth.
Sweedish Countess de G***, see Life of the . . .
Sweep, Soot O !
Swiss emigrants, by Hugh Murray.
—— Family Robinson, by Johann David Rudolf Wyss.
—— Family Robinson. Second Series, by J. de Clinton Locke.
Sword, by Eliza Clarke.
Sybil Lennard, by Catherine Maria Grey.
——, a novel.
—— : or the two Nations, by Earl of Beaconsfield.
Syndenham, by W. Massie.
Sydney Beresford, by Louisa Sidney Stanhope.
—— Biddulph, see Memoirs of Miss . . .
—— Morcom.
—— St. Aubyn, by Mary Robinson.
Sylph, a novel, by Georgiana Cavendish, Duchess of Devonshire.
Sylvanella.
Sylvester Sound, by Henry Cockton.
—— Tramper, see Surprising travels and adventures of . . .
Sylvia Hughes, see Adventures of . . .

System and no system, by Maria Benson.
System : a tale of the West Indies, by Charlotte Elizabeth Tonna.

Tabart's Collection of Popular Stories for the Nursery, by Benjamin Tabart.
Tabby, see History of . . .
Table book, by Gilbert Abbott á Beckett.
Taciturna and Jocunda.
Talba, by Anna Eliza Bray.
Tale for Gentle and Simple.
—— of the Basyn.
—— of the Jewish captivity, by Henry John Betts.
—— of the last century.
—— of a looking glass.
—— of middle life.
—— of a modern genius, by John Fitzgerald Pennie.
—— of Mystery, by François Guillaume Ducray Dumenil.
—— of the Olden Time.
—— of the Rebellion.
—— of Rosamund Gray, by Charles Lamb.
—— of a sixpence.
—— of the times, by Jane West.
—— of warning, by Miss M. Woodland.
—— of the winds and the waves.
—— without an end.
—— without a title, by Eugenia de Acton.
Tales, by Eyre Evans Crowe.
——, by Thomas Colley Grattan.
——, by Jeanne Isabelle Bottens, Baroness de Montolieu.
—— about travellers, by Thomas Bingley.
—— about Wales, by Mrs. Campbell.
—— and Confessions, by Leitch Ritchie.
—— and Conversations, by Emily Cooper.
—— and conversations, by Elizabeth Penrose.
—— and dialogues : Prose and verse, by Jefferys Taylor.
—— and illustrations, by Charlotte Elizabeth Tonna.
—— and incidents of childhood.
—— and legends, by the Misses Corbett.
—— and legends of Ireland.
—— and legends of the Isle of Wight, by Abraham Elder.
—— and Poetry.
—— and popular fictions, by Thomas Keightley.
—— and romances of ancient and modern times, by Joseph Moser.
—— and romances of the Northern nations, see Popular . . .
—— and sketches, by William Carleton.
—— and sketches for fireside reading, by Charles Fleet.
—— and sketches of Christian life, by Mrs. E. Charles.
—— and sketches of the Scottish peasantry, by Alexander and John Bethune.

Tales and sketches of the West of Scotland, by Christopher Keelivine.

—— and stories from history, by Agnes Strickland.

—— and trifles from Blackwood's, by William Mudford.

——, Anecdotes and letters, by Jonathan Scott.

—— at the Fireside, by Emily Clarke.

—— by a Barrister.

—— by the O'Hara Family, by John and Michael Banim.

—— by an unwilling author.

—— characteristic, descriptive and allegorical, by Harriet Corp.

——, comprising the garden, by Mary Ann Bourne.

—— designed chiefly for the Young, by Johann Christoph von Schmid.

—— entertaining and sympathetic.

—— explanatory of the Sacraments, by Miss Eleanor C. Agnew.

—— for the amusement of young persons by John Corry.

—— for boys, by Mary Elliott.

—— for the British People.

—— for children, by Maria Joseph Crabb.

—— for cottages, by Mary Leadbetter and Elizabeth Shakleton.

—— for domestic instruction, by Harriet Ventum.

—— for Ellen, by Alicia Catherine Mant.

—— for an English home, by Miss G. M. Sterne.

—— for girls, by Mary Elliott.

—— for infant minds.

—— for mothers, by Jean Nicolas Bouilly.

—— for mothers and daughters, by Miss M. Woodland.

—— for my children, by E. C. Somers.

—— for my grandchildren.

—— for the times, *see* Young Protestant.

—— for the Young, by Hans Christian Andersen.

—— for Young Ladies, by Jane Alice Sargant.

—— for young people, by Agnes Loudon.

—— for young people, by Mary Russell Mitford.

—— for youth, by S. H. Piercy.

——, founded on facts, by Mrs. M. A. Grant.

—— from Chaucer, by Charles Cowden Clarke.

—— from Denmark, by Hans Christian Andersen.

—— from the Eastern land.

—— from the German.

—— from the German, by Johannes Heinrich Daniel Zschokke.

—— from the German, by John Oxenford and C. A. Feiling.

—— from the German, by Richard Holcroft.

—— from the mountains, by Mary Mister.

—— from the Parsonage, by A. Stevens.

Tales from the "Phantasus," by Ludwig Tieck.

—— from the Russian, by Nikolai Mikhailovich Karamzin.

—— from the scrap-book of a Country clergyman, by John Edward Nassau Molesworth.

—— from Shakespeare, by Charles and Mary Lamb.

—— in prose, by Mary Howitt.

——, moral and amusing.

—— : Mournful, mirthful and marvellous, by Sarah Wilmot Wells.

—— of the Academy.

—— of Adventure by Sea and Land.

—— of the Affections, by Mrs. Caddick.

—— of all Nations.

—— of an Antiquary, by Richard Thomson.

—— of Ardennes, by Henry David Inglis.

—— of a Briefless Barrister, by William Pitt Scargill.

—— of the bush, by Mrs. Francis Vidal.

—— of the Camp and Cabinet, by Colonel John Montmorency Tucker.

—— of the Caravanserai, by James Baillie Fraser.

—— of the Castle, by Comtesse de Genlis.

—— of the Century, by John Hay Allan and Charles Stuart.

—— of chivalry.

—— of the Classics.

—— of the Colonies, by John Howison.

—— of the Colonies, by Charles Rowcroft.

—— of the Cordelier Metamorphosed, by M. Colombo.

—— of the Cottage, by Mary S. Pilkington.

—— of the Covenanters, by Robert Pollok.

—— of the Crusaders, by Sir Walter Scott.

—— of the Cymry, by James Motley.

—— of the dead, by Mrs. Utterson.

—— of the Devil, by H. W. Bunbury.

—— of the Drama, by Elizabeth Wright Macauley.

—— of the early ages, by Horatio Smith.

—— of early piety.

—— of the East, by Henry Weber.

—— of Elam.

—— of the English, by Emily Taylor.

—— of an evening, by Jean François Marmontel.

—— of an exile, by W. F. Williams.

—— of the factories, by Caroline Southey.

—— of the fairies, *see* History of . . .

—— of Faith and Providence, by William Balmbro' Flower.

—— of Fancy, by Sarah Harriet Burney.

—— of the fancy.

—— of Fashion and Reality, by Caroline Frederica and Henrietta Mary Beauclerk.

—— of fashionable life, by Maria Edgeworth.

—— of Fault and feeling, by Mrs. Busk.

Tales of Field & Flood, by John Malcolm.
—— of the fire-side.
—— of the first French Revolution, by Anne Marsh.
—— of Flemish Life, by Hendrik Conscience.
—— of flood and field.
—— of former times, by Andrew St. John.
—— of Four Nations.
—— of the Genii, by James Ridley.
—— of the Glens, by Joseph Grant.
—— of good and great kings, by Margaret Fraser Tytler.
—— of a grandfather, by Sir Walter Scott.
—— of a Grandmother, by Mrs. A. C. Carmichael.
—— of the great and brave, by Margaret Fraser Tytler.
—— of the great St. Bernard, by Rev. George Croly.
—— of the Harem, by Mrs. Pickersgill.
—— of the Heart, by Amelia Opie.
—— of the heath, by Diana Bayley.
—— of the Hermitage, by Mary S. Pilkington.
—— of humble life.
—— of Humour, Gallantry, and Romance.
—— of the imagination.
—— of an Indian camp, by James Athearn Jones.
—— of instruction and amusement, by Mrs. Ives Hurry.
—— of Ireland, by William Carleton.
—— of Irish Life, by Michael James Whitty.
—— of a Jewess, by Madame Brendlah.
—— of Jewish history, by Misses C. and M. Moss.
—— of Kirkbeck, by W. J. E. Bennett.
—— of the late Revolutions, by Frederick William Naylor Bayley.
—— of Lay-brother.
—— of Lowanvale.
—— of the Manor, by Barbara Hofland.
—— of many lands, by Margaret Fraser Tytler.
—— of Military Life, by William Maginn.
—— of the minstrels, by Monsieur Le Grand.
—— of Modern days, by Elizabeth Baker.
—— of the Moor, by John Bradford.
—— of the Moors, by Caroline Southey.
—— of mothers and daughters, by Miss M. Woodland.
—— of the Munster Festivals, by Gerald Griffin.
—— of my Aunt Martha.
—— of my Country, by Selina Bunbury.
—— of my father.
—— of my grandfather, by Archibald Crawfurd.
—— of my landlady.
—— of my landlord, by Sir Walter Scott.
—— of my landlord. New series.

Tales of my neighbourhood, by Gerald Griffin.
—— of my time, by William Pitt Scargill.
—— of the North American Indians, by Barbara Hawes.
—— of old Mr. Jefferson.
—— of other days, by John Yonge Akerman.
—— of other realms.
—— of our Counties.
—— of a parrot, by B. Gerrans.
—— of Passion, by Francis Barry Boyle St. Leger.
—— of the passions, by George Moore.
—— of the Peerage and peasantry, by Mrs. Frederick Sullivan.
—— of the Pemberton family, by Amelia Opie.
—— of Perplexity.
—— of a physician, by W. H. Harrison.
—— of a pilgrim, by Lieut. Alexander Sutherland.
—— of the pirates.
—— of pity, by Anna Maria Porter.
—— of the Priory, by Barbara Hofland.
—— of the Ramad'han, by James Augustus St. John.
—— of a Rambler.
—— of real life, by Amelia Opie.
—— of the Rhenish chivalry, by Edward P. Turnerelli.
—— of the Saxons, by Emily Taylor.
—— of School life, by Agnes Loudon.
—— of the School-room, by Agnes Strickland.
—— of Shipwrecks, by James Lindridge.
—— of the Stanley family.
—— of Superstition and chivalry, by Anne Bannerman.
—— of Switzerland.
—— of a tar, by Captain William Nugent Glascock.
—— of terror, or more ghosts.
—— of today, by Mrs. Isaacs.
—— of the tombs.
—— of Ton, by Miss E. H. Macleod.
—— of a tourist, by Alicia Lefanu.
—— of the town, by Henry Walford Bellairs.
—— of the Trains, by Charles James Lever.
—— of Travel, by F. B. Miller.
—— of truth, by Mary Elliott.
—— of the twelfth and thirteenth centuries, by Le Grand.
—— of the vicarage, by A. Selwyn.
—— of the village, by Francis Edward Paget.
—— of the village children, by Francis Edward Paget.
—— of a voyager to the Arctic Ocean, by Robert Pierce Gillies.
—— of wars of Montrose, by James Hogg.
—— of the wars of our times, by Col. Joseph Moyle Sherer.
—— of Welsh society and scenery.

Tales of Welshland and Welsherie, by Edward Trevor Anwyl.

—— of the West, by John Carne.

—— of the wild and wonderful, by George Borrow.

—— of Woman, by Frederick Shoberl.

—— of Woman's trials, by Anna Maria Hall.

—— of Wonder, by Anne and Annabella Plumptre.

—— of the woods and fields, by Anne Marsh.

—— of yore.

—— original and translated from the Spanish.

——, Romances, Apologues, Anecdotes, and Novels.

—— round a Winter hearth, by Jane and Anna Maria Porter.

——, serious and instructive, by Ann Catherine Holbrook.

—— translated from the Persian [of Inatulla].

Talis Qualis, by Gerald Griffin.

Talisman.

Tame Robin, *see* History of a . . .

Tancred : or the new crusade, by Earl of Beaconsfield.

——, a tale of ancient times, by J. Fox.

Tarantula, by Eaton Stannard Barrett.

Tartarian Tales, by Thomas Simon Guellette.

Teachers tales.

Tears of Sensibility, by François Marie de Barnlard d'Arnaud.

Tell-tale, by Agnes Strickland.

—— Sophas, by John Battersby.

Temper and Temperament, by Sarah Stickney Ellis.

——, or domestic scenes, by Amelia Opie.

——, or the story of Susan and Betsy.

Temperance, or Edward Ashton, by Agnes M. Stewart.

Templar, by W. M. Cooke.

Templars. An Historical Novel, by Peter Leicester.

Temple beau.

—— of the fairies, by Marie-Catherine le Jumel de Berneville, Comtesse D'Aulnois.

—— of Gnidus, by Charles Secondat, Baron de Montesquieu.

—— of Melekartha, by Isaac Taylor.

Temptation and atonement, by Catherine Grace Frances Gore.

——, a Novel, by George Jones.

——, of wealth, by Emilie Carlén.

——, or the mysterious casket.

——, or the Watch Tower of Koat-Ven, by Marie Joseph Eugène Sue.

—— : or a wife's perils, by Mrs. M. A. Gascoigne.

Tempter and the tempted, by the Baroness de Calabrella.

—— : or domestic scenes, by Amelia Opie.

Temugin.

Ten Thousand a Year, by Samuel Warren.

Tenant of Wildfell Hall, by Anne Bronte.

Tenants of the wild.

Tender Father.

Tendrils cherished.

Tentamen, by Theodore Edward **Hook.**

Terentia : a novel.

Terrific Tales, by I. Lewis.

Terry Alt, by Stephen Joseph Meany.

Test of Filial duty, by Sarah Scott.

Tests of time, by Sara Wood.

Thaddeus of Warsaw, by Jane Porter.

Thatched cottage, by Sarah S. Wilkinson.

Theagenes and Chariclea, *see* Adventures of . . .

Theatre of love.

Theban and Carthaginian tales, by John Hifford.

Thelamont, or perfect generosity.

Themidore and Rozette.

Theodora, by Dorothea Du Bois.

Theodore and Blanche, by Sophie Cottin.

—— Cyphon, by George Walker.

——, a domestic tale, by Miss Street.

—— or the Crusaders, by Barbara Hofland.

——, or the enthusiast.

Theodosius and Arabella, by Mrs. Hampden Pye.

—— and Constantia, *see* Letters that passed between . . ., by John Langhorne.

—— de Zulvin, by George Moore.

Theopha.

Theophilus and Sophia, *see* History of . . .

There is poison in the packet.

—— is a secret, by Mary Meeke.

Theresa Marchmont, by Catherine **Grace** Frances Gore.

—— ; or the Wizard's fate.

Therese Dunoyer, by Marie Joseph Eugène Sue.

——, or the Orphan of Geneva, by M. Victor.

Things as they are, by William Godwin.

—— by their right names.

Thinks-I-to-myself, by Edward Nares.

Thiodolf the Icelander, by Friedrich Heinrich Karl, Baron de la Motte Fouqué.

Thirst for Gold, by Hannah D. Burdon.

Thirteenth, or the fatal number, by Pierce Egan, the younger.

Thomas Eustace, *see* Adventures of . . .

—— Fitzgerald, by Mac Erin O'Tara.

—— Hickathrift, *see* Pleasant **and** delightful history of . . .

—— Martin, *see* History of . . .

—— Shaw.

—— Steady and John Wild.

—— Two-shoes, *see* Adventures of . . .

Thornberry Abbey, by Mrs. G. Parsons.

Thoughtless ward, by Miss Furgess.

Thousand and one nights, by Edward William Lane.

—— Nights and one Night, translated by Henry Torrens.

Three Advices.

—— baskets, by Hannah D. Burdon.

—— birth-days.

Three brothers, by Joshua Pickersgill.
—— courses and a dessert, by William Clarke.
—— cousins, by Frances Trollope.
—— days, of the French Revolution, by Percy Bolingbroke St. John.
—— Eras of Woman's Life, by Elizabeth Elton Smith.
—— Germans.
—— ghosts of the forest.
—— Gil Blas, by Jean Henri Ferdinand La Marteliere.
—– histories, by Maria Jane Jewsbury.
—— little beggars.
—— monks, by Madame Guénard.
—— musketeers, by Alexandre Dumas.
—— nights in a lifetime.
—— old maids of the House of Penruddock.
—— Paths, by Julia Kavanagh.
—— Patriarchs.
—— Peers, by Catherine, Lady Stepney.
—— perils of man, by James Hogg.
—— perils of woman, by James Hogg.
—— Poets.
—— sisters, by Sir W. Domville.
—— sisters and their three pennies.
—— Spaniards, by George Walker.
—— springs of beauty, by Harriet Pigott.
—— Students, by William Hughes.
—— true and remarkable stories.
—— vows, by Robert Plumer Ward.
—— weeks at Fladong's.
—— whispers, by Rev. S. G. Cotton.
Thunderstorm, by Mary Martha Sherwood.
Thurlston Tales, by Robert Pierce Gillies.
Thy Kingdom come.
Times.
—— past.
Timon, but not of Athens.
—— of Athens, by Charles Lamb.
Timothy Ginnadrake, *see* Life and extraordinary adventures, the perils and critical escapes, of . . .
—— Grub.
Tippoo Sultan, by Colonel Philip Meadows Taylor.
'Tis an Old Tale, and often told, by Isabel Goldsmid.
Tithe Proctor, by William Carleton.
Titian: A romance of Venice, by R. Shelton Mackenzie.
Toads and diamonds.
Toby, *see* Life and adventures of . . .
To-day in Ireland, by Eyre Evans Crowe.
Toil and trial, by Mrs. Newton Crosland.
Token of Remembrance.
Tom Bowling, by Frederick Chamier.
—— Bragwell, *see* Affecting history of . . .
—— Burke of "Ours," by Charles James Lever.
—— Cringle's Log, by Michael Scott.
—— Fool, *see* History of . . .
—— Gay's comical jester.
—— Jones, *see* History of . . .

Tom Jones, the foundling in his married state, *see* History of . . . .
—— Long, *see* History of . . .
—— Racquet.
—— Rigby, *see* History of . . .
—— Spicer, *see* Adventures of . . .
—— Thumb.
—— Thumb, *see* Novel adventures of . . .
—— Tram, *see* Mad pranks of . . .
—— Weston, *see* History of . . .
—— White, *see* History of . . .
—— Wildman, *see* Rake, or adventures of . . .
Tombs of St. Denis, by Clemence Robert.
Tommy Playlove, *see* History of . . .
—— Titmouse, *see* History of . . .
To-morrow.
Tooti Nameh, by Lakshmana Mudaliyar.
Topsail-Sheet Blocks, by Mathew Henry Barker.
Tor Hill, by Horatio Smith.
Torini, a tale of Italy.
Torrenwald.
Torres Vedras, *see* Stories of . . .
Tory Baronet.
Tough Yarns, by Matthew Henry Barker.
Tour of Valentine, by Joseph Holden Pott.
Tourfications of Malachi Meldrum, by Dr. Robert Couper.
Tournament of Chalons, by P. J. Phillips.
Tournay, by James Wilson.
Tower of London, by William Harrison Ainsworth.
——, or the romance of Ruthyne by Sarah Lansdell.
Towers of Lothian.
—— of Ravenswold, by William Henry Hitchener.
Town and Country, by Frances Trollope.
Tracey, or the apparition, by Katharine Thomson.
—— the poet.
Tradition of the Castle, by Regina Maria Roche.
Traditional stories of old families, by Andrew Picken.
—— tales of the English and Scottish peasantry, by Allan Cunningham.
Traditionary stories of old families, by Andrew Picken
Traditions: a legendary tale, by Mary Martha Sherwood.
——, Legends, Superstitions and Sketches of Devonshire, by Anna Eliza Bray.
—— of Lancashire, by John Roby.
—— of Palestine, by Harriet Martineau.
—— of Western Germany, by Captain Charles H. Knox.
Traduced, by Nicholas Mitchell.
Tragical history of Walwyn and Avreola, by I. Ames.
Traits and stories of the Irish peasantry, by William Carleton.
—— and stories of the Welsh peasantry, by Anna Beale.

Traits and Traditions of Portugal, by Julia S. H. Pardoe.
—— and Trials.
—— and Trials of Early Life, by Letitia Elizabeth Landon.
—— of nature, by Sarah Harriet Burney.
—— of Scottish Life.
—— of travel, by Thomas Colley Grattan.
Transfusion, by William Godwin, Jun.
Transition.
Translation of the Fragment of an Arabic Manuscript.
—— of the Letters of a Hindoo Rajah, by Elizabeth Hamilton.
—— of Manon Lescaut, by Abbé Antoine François Prevost d'Exiles.
Trap, by Thomas Gilliland.
Trapper's bride, by Percy Bolingbroke St. John.
Traveller, or adventures on the Continent.
Travellers, by R. Shelton Mackenzie.
——, A Tale, by Tertius T. C. Kendrick.
Traveller's tale of the last Century, by Elizabeth Isabella Spence.
Travelling anecdotes through various parts of Europe, by J. Douglas.
Travels and adventures of Charles Durand, by Mrs. J. B. Webb.
—— and adventures of James Massey.
—— and adventures of Mdlle de Richelieu.
—— and surprising adventures of Mademoiselle De Leurich.
—— before the Flood.
—— for the heart, by Samuel Jackson Pratt.
—— in Phrenologasto, by John Trotter.
—— in town, by James Grant.
—— into France and Italy.
—— of Imagination, by John Murray.
—— of an Irish gentleman, by Thomas Moore.
—— of Mons. le Post Chaise.
—— of Polycletes.
—— of Rolando, by L. F. Jauffret.
—— of Zoroaster.
Tre giuli of Casti.
Treachery, by Mrs. Martin Lucas.
——, or the Grave of Antoinette, by Louisa Sidney Stanhope.
Treasure Trove, by Samuel Lover.
Trecothick Bower, by Regina Maria Roche.
Trelawney of Trelawne, by Anna Eliza Bray.
Tremaine : or the man of refinement, by Robert Plumer Ward.
Tremondyn Cliff, by Frances Trollope.
Trevanion, by Horatio Smith.
Trevelyan, by Lady Caroline Lucy Scott.
Trevethlan, by William Davy Watson.
Trevor.
—— Hastinges, by Nicholas Michel.
Trial and self-discipline, by Miss Savage.
—— of Betty.
—— of an ox.
——, or the history of Charles Horton.

Trials and Triumphs, by Daniel Richardson.
—— of domestic life, by Anna Eliza Bray.
—— of the Heart, by Anna Eliza Bray.
—— of the Human Heart, by Susanna Haswell Rowson.
—— of Life, by Hon. Mrs. Grey.
—— of love, by Hannah Maria Lowndes.
—— of Margaret Lyndsay, by John Wilson.
—— of strength, by Louisa Mary Barwell.
——, a tale, by Mary Ann Kelty.
Triflers, by Richard Graves.
Trinket.
Trip to London, by —— Jameson.
—— to Weymouth.
Tristram Shandy, *see* Life and opinions of . . .
Triumph of Benevolence, by Samuel Jackson Pratt.
—— of goodnature.
—— of truth, by Selina Bunbury.
—— of truth, by De la Villette.
—— of woman, by Charles Rowcroft.
Triumphs of Fortitude.
—— of Love, by Jean Pierre Camus.
—— of Time, by Anne Marsh.
Triumvirate, by Richard Griffith.
Troubles arising.
—— of a good husband.
—— of life.
Truant reclaimed, by Mary Elliott.
—— scholar.
Truckleborough Hall, by William Pitt Scargill.
True charity.
—— Cross, by Rev. Caesar Henri Abraham Malan.
—— delicacy.
—— heroism.
—— history of Henrietta de Bellgrave.
—— history of a litte old woman who found a silver penny.
—— history of Zoa.
—— stories for children, by Mrs. W. C. Wilson.
—— stories of cottagers.
—— Stories : or interesting anecdotes of children.
—— warnings.
Trustee, by George William Lovell.
Truth.
—— and falsehood, exemplified in the true history of Jane and Lucy.
—— and falsehood, a romance, by Elizabeth Thornton.
—— and falsehood, a tale, by Thomas Franklin.
—— and fashion.
—— and fiction, by Elizabeth Sarah Villa-Real Gooch.
—— and trust, by William Chambers.
—— in the garb of fiction.
——. A Novel, by William Pitt Scargill.
—— our best friend, by Mary Elliott.
Try again, by William Balmbro' Flower.
Tudor sisters.

Tuft-Hunter, by Lord William Pitt Lennox.
Tuileries : a tale, by Catherine Grace Frances Gore.
Turf : A satirical novel.
Turkish tales, by Joseph Moser.
Turn-out.
Tuscan vase, by Harriet Stewart.
Tutor of truth, by Samuel Jackson Pratt.
'Twas right to marry him.
—— wrong to marry him.
Twelve nights, by Baron Karl von Miltie.
—— nights entertainments.
—— years ago, by Sydney Warburton.
Twenty four tales of the English Church.
—— years after, by Alexandre Dumas.
—— years in retirement, by Blakiston.
—— -ninth of May, by William Henry Pyne.
Twin brothers.
—— sisters.
—— sisters, or Two girls of nineteen.
Twins, a domestic novel, by Martin Farquhar Tupper.
——, or the female traveller, by W. R. Chetwood.
Two apprentices, by Mary Howitt.
—— Baronesses, by Hans Christian Andersen.
—— Bogies.
—— brothers, a narrative.
—— brothers, or the family that lived in the first society, by Lady Emily Ponsonby.
—— Calmuck youths.
—— clerks of Oxenford.
—— cottagers.
—— cousins.
—— cousins, by Mrs. Pinchard.
—— death-beds, by Lucy Lyttelton Cameron.
—— delightful novels.
—— doves.
—— Edwards, by Mary Elliott.
—— farmers, by Sarah Rrimmer.
—— friends : a novel, by Marguerite, Countess of Blessington.
—— girls.
—— girls of eighteen.
—— heroes.
—— Hundred and Nine Days, by Thomas Jefferson Hogg.
—— lambs, by Lucy Lyttelton Cameron.
—— martyrs, by François René, Vicomte de Chateaubriand.
—— Mentors, by Clara Reeve.
—— modern adventurers, see History of . . .
—— mothers, by Lucy Lyttelton Cameron.
—— Novels in Letters, by Elizabeth and Richard Griffith.
—— old men of La Vosges, by Rev. Caesar Henri Abraham Malan.
—— old men's tales, by Anne Marsh.
—— orphans.
—— orphans, see History of . . .
—— pilgrims.
—— Princes of Persia, by Jane Porter.

Two Rectors, by George Wilkins.
—— Shoemakers, by Hannah More.
—— Sisters, by Mary Martha Sherwood.
—— Soldiers.
—— Sunday School boys.
—— wealthy farmers.
—— Wealthy farmers, see History of the . . .
—— widows, by W. H. Sweepstone.
—— young gentlewomen, see Affecting history of . . .
Tyburn Tree.
Tylney Hall, by Thomas Hood.
Tyranny of love.

Ulric and Gustavus.
—— and Ilvina.
Ulrica of Saxony, by Rosalia St. Clair.
Ulrich, by Ida, Countess Hahn Hahn.
Una and Arthur.
Unbaptised sceptic.
Unchanged, by Selina Davenport.
Uncle Barnaby.
—— Buncle's story book.
—— Horace, by Anna Maria Hall.
—— Oliver and his nephew.
—— Peregrine's heiress, by Ann Hatton.
—— Peter's fairy tales.
—— Tweazy.
Uncles, by Zara Wentworth.
Uncle's legacy, by J. Berry Torr.
Undine, by Friedrich Heinrich Karl, Baron de la Motte Fouqué.
—— by Rev. Thomas Tracey.
Unexpected Legacy, by Rachel Hunter.
—— Wedding.
Unfortunate and at last happy lady.
—— beauty.
—— Caledonian in England.
—— daughter, see Pleasant and delightful history of the . . .
—— Man, by Frederick Chamier.
—— officer.
—— Princess, by Eliza Haywood.
—— Russian.
—— Sensibility.
—— sisters.
—— Union.
—— young girl, see Short but **tragical** history of an . . .
—— young nobleman.
Unhappy bride.
—— Mistake.
United Irishman.
Unknown, by Francis Lathom.
—— Warrior.
Unloved One, by Barbara Hofland.
Unnatural mother.
—— mother and ungrateful wife.
—— uncle, by G. T. Morley.
Up the Rhine, by Thomas Hood.
Urbino, by T. R. Tuckett.
Usbeck and Fatima.
Uscoque, by A. L. A. D. Dudevant.
Use and abuse.
—— of sight.
Useful stories for children, by Mrs. W. C. Wilson.

Usong, by Albrecht von Haller.
Usurer's Daughter, by William Pitt Scargill.
Usurpation, by Thomas Pike Lathy.

Vaga, by Frances Peck.
Vagabond, by George Walker.
Vagaries, in quest of the wild and whimsical, by Pierce Shafton.
Vagras.
Vain cottager.
—— wishes, by Lucy Lyttelton Cameron.
Valaisane, by Rev. Caesar Henri Abraham Malan.
Vale of cedars, by Grace Aguilar.
—— of Clyde, by Honoria Scott.
—— of Glamorgan, by Charles Redwood.
Valentine and Orson, see History of . . .
—— de T., see Memoir of . . .
—— M'Clutchy, by William Carleton.
——, a novel.
—— Vaux, see Adventures of . . .
—— Vox, see Life and adventures of . . .
Valentine's Eve, by Amelia Opie.
Valerie, by Captain Frederick Marryat.
Valerius: a Roman story, by John Gibson Lockhart.
Valley of Collares, by Mrs. Yorke.
—— of St. Gothard, by Eliza Parsons.
Vallies, The, by Basil Tempest.
Valombroso.
Valperga, by Mary Wollstonecraft Shelley.
Value of money, by Louisa Mary Barwell.
—— of time, by Louisa Mary Barwell.
Vampyre: a tale, by John William Polidori.
Vancenza, by Mary Robinson.
Vandeleur, by Madame Pisani.
Vane of the Steeple, by Jerome Paturot.
Vanillo Gonzales, see History of . . .
Vanity Fair, by William Makepeace Thackeray.
Vargas, by Cornelius Villiers.
Varick, The Adventures of Anthony, by Charles Johnstone.
Varieties in Woman.
—— of life.
Variety: a novel, by Elizabeth Louisa Slater Princeps.
——, or stories for children.
Various recollections of Domestic scenes.
Varney the Vampire, by James Malcolm Rymer.
Vater Unser.
Vathek, see Arabian Tale.
Vaults of Lepanto, by T. R. Tucker.
Vaurien, by Isaac Disraeli.
Vavasour, De, by Earl of Blessington.
Vedàla Cadái, by Benjamin Guy Babington.
Veil lifted, by Mrs. Paxton.
Veiled Picture.
—— protectress, by Mary Meeke.
Velasco, by Cyrus Redding.
Velina, by Alexander Whyte.
Velvet cushion, by John W. Cunningham.

Vendee, see La . . .
Venetia, by Earl of Beaconsfield.
Veronica, or the Free Court of Aarau, by Johannes Heinrich Daniel Zschokke.
——, or the mysterious stranger.
Versenshon, by Harriet Butler.
Very little tales for very little children.
—— strange, but very true, by Francis Lathom.
Vesuvia.
Veteran, by Edward Harley.
Veterans of Chelsea Hospital, by George Robert Gleig.
Vicar of Bray.
—— of Lansdowne, by Regina Maria Roche.
—— of Wakefield, by Oliver Goldsmith.
—— of Wrexhill, by Frances Trollope.
Viceroy, by John Fisher Murray.
Vicissitudes abroad, by Agnes Maria Bennett.
—— in early life, by Dennis Lawler.
—— in genteel life.
—— of life, by Mrs. Cumming.
Victim of deception.
——, in five letters to Adolphus.
—— of intolerance, by Robert Torrens.
—— of Magical delusion, by Cajetan Tschink.
—— of passion.
—— of Prejudice, by Mary Hays.
Victims of Society, by Marguerite Countess of Blessington.
Victor Allen, see Adventures of . . .
——, or the Child of the forest, by François Guillaume Ducray Dumenil.
Victoria, by Martha Mary Sherwood.
—— Mortimer, see History of . . .
——. A novel, by Susanna Haswell Rowson.
—— : or the male coquette.
Victories of the Saints, by John Mason Neale.
Victorina, by J. C. Gorgy.
Victorious champion.
Victory, or ward-room Mess, by Matthew Henry Barker.
View of the Lancashire Dialect.
—— of Society and manners in high and low life, by G. Parker.
—— of the village of Hampton.
Vileroy, by Elizabeth Caroline Grey.
Villa Nova, by Catherine Selden.
—— Verocchio, by Diana Louisa Macdonald.
Village anecdotes, by Elizabeth Anne Le Noir.
—— annals, by Elizabeth Anne Le Noir.
—— annals, by Camilla Needham.
—— Association.
—— Belles, by Anne Manning.
—— Coquette.
—— curate.
—— Gentleman, by Mrs. John Duncombe.
—— incidents.
—— maid.
—— maid, by Elizabeth Somerville.

Village memoirs.

—— Nightingale, by Elizabeth Frances Dagley.

—— notary, by Baron Eötvös.

—— of Mariendorpt, by Anna Maria Porter.

—— of Martindale, by Mr. Nicholson

—— pastor, by George Wilkins.

——, by August Lafontaine.

—— rectory, by Robert William Dibdin.

—— Reminiscences, by Mrs. Monkland.

—— Romance, by Jane Elson.

—— scandal, by Hannah Maria Lowndes.

—— school, from " L'Ecole de Valdamont," by Rev. Caesar Henri Abraham Malan.

—— school, or memoirs of Mrs. Propriety and her little scholars.

—— school, a story for girls, by Mrs. Leckie.

—— school, with the history, by Julia Corner.

—— School-girls.

—— tale.

—— tales from Alsatia, by Alexandre Weill.

—— Tales from the Black Forest, by Berthold Auerbach.

—— tales, moral and religious.

—— walks.

Villars Family, *see* Memoirs of the . . .

Villasantelle, by Catherine Selden.

Villeroi.

Villeroy, by Henry Whitfield.

Villiers. A Tale of the last Century.

Vindictive spirit, by Mrs. Bridget.

Violet Hill, by E. Miles.

—— : or the Danseuse, by Lady Malet.

—— Vale, by Mary S. Pilkington.

Violina, by Friedrich Heinrich Karl, Baron de la Motte Fouqué.

Virgin bride.

—— widow, by W. R. Chetwood.

Virginia, or the peace of Amiens.

Virtue and vice, by W. H. Rayner.

—— and vice, or history of Charles Careful.

—— in a cottage.

—— rewarded.

—— Triumphant.

Virtue's friend.

Virtuous Orphan, by Pierre Carlet de Chamblain de Marivaux.

—— Poverty, by Henry Siddons.

—— villager, by Eliza Haywood.

—— villager, or, Virgin's Victory, by Charles de Fieux, Chevalier de Mouhy.

—— Villagers, by John Potter.

—— Wife, by Gervase C. Leverland.

Viscount Cherington, *see* Memoirs of the Right Honourable Lord . . .

Visit.

—— for a Week, by Lucy Peacock.

——, or mamma and the children, by Miss Grierson.

—— to the Castle of Truth.

—— to Clarina.

—— to Grove Cottage.

—— to London, by Barbara Hofland.

Visit to the Manor House.

—— to the Rectory of Passy, by John Witherington Peers.

Visiting day.

Visits and Sketches, by Anna Brownell Jameson.

—— of Tommy Lovebook.

Vittoria Colonna, by Charlotte Anne Eaton.

Vivian Grey, by the Earl of Beaconsfield.

Vivonio, by Sophia Frances.

Vizier's Son, by William Browne Hockley.

Vizirs, or the Labyrinth, by M. A. de Fauques.

Vladimir.

Voice of Conscience, by Mrs. Quintin Kennedy.

—— of Ida, by Charlotte Lyndon.

—— of many waters, by Fanny Osborne.

Voluntary exile, by Eliza Parsons.

Voluptuarian museum.

Voyage of Captain Popanilla, by Earl of Beaconsfield.

—— of Life, by Georgina C. Munro.

—— through Hell.

—— to Immanuel's Land.

—— to Lethe.

—— to Locuta, by E. S. Graham.

—— to the Moon.

—— to the Moon, by Samuel Derrick.

—— to the World in the Centre of the Earth.

Voyager to the Artic Ocean, *see* Tales of a . . .

Voyages and adventures of Edward Teach.

—— and travels of a Bible, by Rev. John Campbell.

Wagner : the wehr-wolf, by George William Macarthur Reynolds.

Waldeck Abbey.

Waldegrave, a novel.

Waldemar, by W. H. Harrison.

—— surnamed Seir, by Bernhard S. Ingemann.

Waldgrove.

Waldorf, by Sophia King.

Waldstein, by Karoline von Greiner Pichler.

Walks and talks.

Wallace, the hero of Scotland, by Gabriel Alexander.

Walladmor, by Thomas de Quincey.

Walsh Colville, by Regina Maria Roche.

Walsingham, by Mary Robinson.

—— the Gamester, by Frederick Chamier.

Walter Clayton, by M'Gauran.

—— Colyton, by Horatio Smith.

—— de Monbary, by Professor Kramer.

—— Deverell.

—— Fentor, by James Grant.

—— Hamilton, by Mrs. C. D. Burdett.

—— the Murderer, by C. A. Bolen.

—— O'Neil.

Waltham : a romance, by Andrew Picken.

Waltzburg.

Walwyn and Avreola, *see* Tragical History of . . .

Wanderer of the Alps.

—— : or female difficulties, by Madame d'Arblay.

—— : or the surprizing escape.

Wandering hermit, by Captain Felix Macdonough.

—— Islander, by Charles Henry Wilson.

—— Jew, by Marie Joseph Eugene Sue.

—— of fancy, by Mrs. Isaacs.

—— spirit.

Wanderings of Childe Harolde, by Lieut. John Harman Bedford.

—— of a goldfinch, by Mary Ann McMullan.

—— of the imagination, by Elizabeth Sarah Villa-Real Gooch.

—— of Warwick, by Charlotte Turner Smith.

Wang Keaou-Lwan Piu Nëen Han, by Robert Thom.

Waning church.

Wanley Penson.

Wanted ! a wife.

Wanton Tom.

Warbeck of Wolfstein, by Margaret Hodson.

——, a Pathetic Tale, by François Marie de Baculard D'Arnaud.

Warbroke legend.

Ward of the Crown, by Hannah D. Burdon.

—— of Delamere, by Mrs. Pinchard.

—— of Thorpe-Combe, by Frances Trollope.

Warden of Berkingholt, by Frances Edward Paget.

Warkfield Castle, by Jane Harvey.

Warleigh, or the Fatal Oath, by Anna Eliza Bray.

Warm Watch Coat, The history of a, *see* A Political Romance.

Warner Arundell, by E. L. Joseph.

Warning, a tale.

—— to wives, by Harriet Maria Yorick Smythies.

Warren family.

Wars of Montrose, *see* Tales of the . . .

Warwick Castle, an Historical Novel, by Miss Prickett.

Was it a dream, by Elizabeth Missing Sewell.

Wassail Bowl, by Albert Smith.

Waste not, want not, by Mary Martha Sherwood.

Wat Tyler, by Pierce Egan, the younger.

Watch Tower, by T. J. Horsley Curties.

Water Fairy's gift.

—— Queen, by H. J. Coates.

Waverley, or 'tis sixty years since, by Sir Walter Scott.

——, a tale.

Way of peace, by Eliza Paget.

—— of the World, by Hon. Mrs. Grey.

—— to be happy.

—— to lose him.

—— to make home comfortable.

—— to please him.

Way to Plenty.

Wayland Smith, by Adam Gottlob Oehlenschläger.

Ways of pleasantness.

Wayside Cross, by Edward Augustus Milman.

Wealth and poverty, by Susannah Frances Reynolds.

Wedded life in the upper ranks.

—— wanderer, by William Leman Rede.

Wedding Ring.

—— ring, by Hannah Maria Lowndes.

Wedlock, or Yesterday and to-day, by Henrietta Camilla Jenkin.

Week's amusement, by Maria Louisa Nicloux.

Weight of a feather.

Weird sisters.

—— Woman of the Wraagh, by H. J. Coates.

Welch mountaineer, by Arthur Mower.

—— peasant boy, by Frances Peck.

Well-Spent penny, by Rev. Caesar Henri Abraham Malan.

Welsh cottage, by Mary Martha Sherwood.

—— Legends, by William Earle, Jr.

—— Mountaineer, by Catharine Hutton.

—— Story, by Mary Barker.

Welshmen, by William Earle, Jr.

West Indian.

Westbrook village.

Western mail, by Anabella Plumptre.

Westerton.

Wharbroke Legend, by Albert Marmacopt.

What has been.

—— is liberty ? by Lucy Lyttelton Cameron.

—— may I learn.

—— shall be, shall be, by Mary Meeke.

—— will your neighbour Grinaway say ?

—— you please.

Wheel of fortune, by Eliza Lake.

Which is best.

—— is the Heroine.

—— is the Man ? by Mary Meeke.

—— is the wiser ? by Mary Howitt.

Whim, and its consequences, by George Payne Rainsford James.

——, or the mutual impressions.

Whisperer, by James Montgomery.

White boy, *see* Whiteboy.

—— bull, by François Marie Arouet de Voltaire.

—— cat, *see* History of the . . . *See* Renowned History of a . . .

—— Charger, by Lieut.-Col. J. J. Hort.

—— Cottage, by Arthur Mower.

—— Hoods, by Anna Eliza Bray.

—— lady, by Caroline von Voltmann.

—— Mask, by Katherine Thomson.

—— slave, or the Russian peasant girl, by Charles Frederick Henningsen.

——, slave a romance for the nineteenth century.

—— Stone Canoe, by Percy Bolingbroke St. John.

Whiteboy, by Anna Maria Hall.

Whitefriars, by Jane Robinson.

Whitehall or the Days of Charles I, by Jane Robinson.

—— : or the days of George IV, by William Maginn.

Whitlaw, Life and adventures of Jonathan Jefferson, by Frances Trollope.

Who can he be.

—— is the bridgegroom? by Sarah Green.

—— shall be heir? by Ellen Pickering.

Whole life and death of Long Meg.

—— pleasures of matrimony.

Who'll buy.

Who's the murderer? by Eleanor Sleath.

Whychcotte of St. John's by Erskine Neale.

Widow and the fatherless.

—— Barnaby, by Frances Trollope.

—— Married, by Frances Trollope.

—— Mortimer, by Thomas Peckett Prest.

—— of Calcutta, by A. V. Kirwan.

—— of Kent.

—— of the Wood, by Benjamin Victor.

—— of Zarephath.

—— O'Leary.

—— : or a picture of modern times, by Mary Robinson.

Widowed bride, by Sarah Ann Hook.

Widows and Widowers, by Katharine Thomson.

Widow's Daughter, by Rev. J. Allen.

—— Lodgings, by John Ballantyne.

—— walk, by Charles Rebou.

Wife and the lover, by Fanny Holcroft.

—— and the mistress, by Mary Charlton.

—— and Woman's Reward, by Honble. Caroline Elizabeth Sarah Norton.

——, by Mira, by Eliza Haywood.

—— Hunter, by John O'Brien Grant.

—— a model for women.

—— : a novel, by Maria Benson.

—— of Fitzalice, by Marianne Breton.

—— of two husbands, by Sarah S. Wilkinson.

——, or Caroline Herbert, by Maria Susanna Cooper.

——, or a model for women, by Mrs. Edgeworth.

Wife's duty : a tale, by Amelia Opie.

Wild Irish boy, by Charles Robert Maturin.

—— Irish girl, by Sydney, Lady Morgan.

—— Love, by Friedrich Heinrich Karl, Baron de la Motte-Fouqué.

—— roses.

—— Scenes in Forest and Prairie, by C. F. Hoffman.

—— sports of the West, by William Hamilton Maxwell.

Wilhelm Meister's Apprenticeship, by Johann Wolfgang Goethe.

Wilhelmina Susannah Dormer, *see* History of . . .

Will. Brown the poacher, *see* History of . . .

Will, or the half-brothers, by —— M'Gauran.

—— Ramble, *see* History of . . .

—— Watch, by William Johnson Neale.

—— Waver.

—— without wit.

William and Azubah.

—— and Charles.

—— and his uncle Ben, by Barbara Hofland.

—— Douglas, by Rev. Henry Duncan.

—— Langshawe, by Elizabeth Stone.

—— Montgomery, by Martha Blackford.

—— Ramble, *see* Life : or the adventures of . . .

—— Sedley.

—— Selwyn, *see* History of . . .

—— Tell, by J. H. Newton.

—— Tell, by Jean Pierre Clavis de Florian.

—— Thornborough, by The Misses Purbeck.

—— Wallace, by Henry Siddons.

—— Woodland, by Charlotte Adams.

William's Secret, by Mary Elliott.

Willie and Meggie's marriage, by James Leslie.

Willoughby: or Reformation, by Grace Kennedy.

Willy's grammar for boys, by Jane Marcet.

—— Holidays, by Jane Marcet.

Wilmingtons, by Anne Marsh.

Wilmot family, by Harriet Drummond.

—— or the pupil of folly..

—— Warwick, *see* Life and remains of . . .

Wiltshire beau.

Windsor Castle, by William Harrison Ainsworth.

—— tales.

Wine and Walnuts, by William Henry Pyne.

Winifred, a tale of wonder, by Rev. James Thomson.

Winter at De Courcy Lodge, by Mary Anne Bourne.

—— at St. James's, by Ann Hamilton.

—— Evening Stories, by Rev. Christian Gottlob Barth.

—— evening tales, by James Hogg.

—— evenings, by Maria Hack.

—— evenings companion.

—— in Bath, by J. H. James.

—— in Dublin, by Sir Charles Sedley.

—— in Edinburgh, by Honoria Scott.

—— in London, by Thomas Skinner Surr.

—— in Paris.

—— nights, by Calder Campbell.

—— tales, by Maria Scott.

—— -Scene, by Maria Hack.

Winter's Tale, by James Norris Brewer.

—— Tale, by Mary Lamb.

Winterton, a tale, by Mrs. Francis Vidal.

Wise men of Gosmanthorpe.

—— saws and modern instances, by Thomas Cooper.

—— -ones Bubbled.

Wish, or little Charles, by Mary Martha Sherwood.

Witch and the Maid of Honour.

—— of Aysgarth, by Miss C. D. Haynes.

—— of Ravensworth, by George Brewer.

—— of the Woodlands.

Witcheries of Craig Isaf by William Frederic Williams.

—— -Finder, by Thomas Gaspey.

Wit's miscellany.

Witty Parson and the Twelve Highwaymen, by James Alexander.

Wizard of Windshaw.

—— Priest, by Quintin Poynet.

—— wanderer of Jutland, by Honble. and very Rev. William Herbert.

Wolf of the Black Forest, by J. W. James.

Wolfe of Badenoch, by Sir Thomas Dick Lauder.

Wolfstein.

Woman and her master, by Sydney, Lady Morgan.

—— as she is, and as she should be.

—— as she should be, by Eliza Parsons.

—— of Fashion.

—— of feeling, by Samuel William Henry Ireland.

—— of Genius.

—— of Honor.

—— of quality.

—— of the World, by Catherine Grace Frances Gore.

—— : or Ida of Athens, by Sydney, Lady Morgan.

——, or Minor Maxims.

Woman's friendship, by Grace Aguilar.

—— Influence, by Mrs. Brereton.

—— Love, By George Herbert Rodwell.

—— Love, by Mary Leman Grimstone.

—— Revenge, or the tribunal of blood, by Veit Webber.

—— a riddle, by Ann Hatton.

—— wit and man's wisdom, by Henrietta Rouviere Mosse.

Women as they are, by Catherine Grace Frances Gore.

—— as they are, by Eliza Parsons.

—— : or Pour et Contre, by Charles Robert Maturin.

Wonder of the village, by Mary Meeke.

—— Seeker, by Margaret Fraser Tytler.

Wonderful adventures of Mr. O'Flynn.

—— Discovery Club, see Posthumous papers of the . . .

—— history of Peter Schlemihl, by Adelbert von Chamisso.

—— stories for children, by Hans Christian Andersen.

—— story teller, by Walley C. Oulton.

—— tour of little Peter Paganini.

—— travels of Prince Fan-Feredin, by Miss Watts.

Wonders of home.

Wondrous Tale of Alroy, by Benjamin Disraeli, Earl of Beaconsfield.

Wood Leighton, by Mary Howitt.

—— nymph.

Woodbury, or the memoirs of William Marchmont.

—— Papers.

Woodhouselee, by Charles Hooton.

Woodland cottage.

—— cousins, by Sarah S. Wilkinson.

—— family, by William Child Green.

Woodman, a romance of the times of Richard III, by Richard Payne Rainsford James.

Wood-Spirit, by Ernest Charles Jones.

Woodstock, by Sir Walter Scott.

Woodville.

Words of Truth.

Work and wages, by Mary Howitt.

—— -Box.

Works, by Jean Pierre Clavis de Florian.

——, by Francis Rabelais.

—— of the Caledonian bards, by John Clark.

Work-Table, by Miss E. A. Soutter.

World we live in, by William Frederic Williams.

—— without souls, by John William Cunningham.

Wreck ashore.

—— of the heart, by George Dibdin Pitt.

Wren, or the fairy of the green-house.

Writer's Clerk.

Wuthering Heights, by Emily and Anne Brontë.

Yamboo.

Yamhaska.

Year and a Day, by Frances Moore.

—— at Hartlebury.

—— of miracles, by Hendrik Conscience.

Yellow dwarf, see History of the . . .

—— shoe-string, by James Pedder.

Yes and no, by Constantine Henry Phipps, Marquis of Normanby.

Yesterday in Ireland, by Eyre Evans Crowe.

Yin Seaou Low.

Yorick's Sentimental Journey, see Continuation of . . .

—— Sentimental Journey, continued.

York dialogue.

—— House, by Barbara Hofland.

Yorkshire beauty.

Young Artist, by Martha Blackford.

—— authoress, by Rose Ellen Hendriks.

—— Baronet, by Robert Mackenzie Daniel.

—— baronet, or the broken leg.

—— Cadet, by Barbara Hofland.

—— child's moralist, by Madame Arblay.

—— cottager, by Legh Richmond.

—— Countess, or love and jealousy, by Frances Trollope.

—— countess, a tale for youth, by Mrs. Pinchard.

—— Crusoe, by Barbara Hofland.

—— drummer.

—— duellists.

—— Duke, by Earl of Beaconsfield.

Young Edwin, *see* History of . . .
—— emigrant, by Agnes Strickland.
—— enthusiast, by James Jolly.
—— exiles, by Comtesse de Genlis.
—— father, by William Frederic Williams.
—— fisherman's narrative.
—— forester.
—— French Emigrants, by W. Collins and A. Sears.
—— Grandison, by Maria Geertruida de Cambon.
—— Hearts.
—— hearts, by Jane Porter.
—— Hocus.
—— Infidel.
—— Islanders, by Jefferys Taylor.
—— James, by François Marie Arouet de Voltaire.
—— Jewess.
—— John Bull, by Francis Lathom.
—— Liar ! !, by William Francis Sullivan.
—— Lady of Distinction, *see* History of a . . .
—— Lady of Fortune, by Judith Alexander.
—— Lord and other tales, by Mrs. Newton Crosland.
—— love, by Frances Trollope.
—— man's home, by Rev. Richard Cobbold.
—— Milliner, by Elizabeth Stone.
—— mother, by Mary Martha Sherwood.
—— mother, or Albinia.
—— Muscovite, by Colin Mackenzie.
—— naturalist, by Alicia Catherine Mant.
—— philosopher, by Charlotte Turner Smith.
—— philosopher, or instructive entertainer.
—— physician, by Mrs. Paxton.
—— pilgrim, by Barbara Hofland.
—— Prima Donna, by Catherine Maria Grey.
—— Protestant.
—— Queen.
—— rifleman's comrade.
—— Robinson, by Madame Mallés de Beaulieu.
—— Rosiniere, by Frances Peck.
—— Scarron, by Thomas Mozeen.
—— Seer, by Elizabeth Frances Dagley.
—— servants.
—— South Country Weaver, by Rev. Henry Duncan.
—— student, by Elisabeth Charlotte Pauline de Guizot.

Young traveller, by George Richard Hoare.
—— Truants, by William Francis Sullivan.
—— Tyrolese, by Rev. Christian Gottlob Barth.
—— wanderer's cave.
—— Widow. A novel in Three Volumes, by Robert Mackenzie Daniel.
—— Widow, or the history of Cornelia Sedley, by William Hayley.
—— Wilfred, by William Francis Sullivan.
Younger brother.
—— brother, by Charles Dibdin.
—— sister, by Ann Dawe.
—— sister, by Mrs. Hubback.
Youth and manhood of Cyril Thornton, by Captain Thomas Hamilton.
—— of Shakspeare, by Robert Folkestone Williams.
Youthful Impostor, by George William Macarthur Reynolds.
—— jester.
Youth's mirror, by A. Selwyn.
—— monitor.
Yule log, by E. R. Chamerovzow.

Zadig, by François Marie Arouet de Voltaire.
Zanoni, by Edward Bulwer, Lord Lytton.
Zastrozzi, by Percy Bysshe Shelley.
Zayde, by M. de Segrais.
Zélie in the Desert.
Zeluca.
Zeluco, by Dr. John Moore.
Zenana, by William Browne Hockley.
Zenobia, by Adelaide O'Keefe.
——, Queen of the East, by Lucius Manlius Piso.
Zenon, by Rev. Richard Cobbold.
Zillah, by Horatio Smith.
Zoa, *see* True history of . . .
Zoë, an Athenian Tale, by John Campbell Colquhoun.
—— : the history of two lives, by Geraldine Endsor Jewsbury.
Zoflora, by J. B. Piguenard.
Zofloya, by Charlotte Dacre.
Zohrab the Hostage, by James Justinian Morier.
Zophiël, by Maria Brooks.
Zulma, by Madame A. L. G. Necker De Staël-Holstein.
Zulneida, by Arthur Mower.
Zuma, by Comtesse de Genlis.